Geometry:

A Fresh Approach

By Christy Walters

Table of Contents

Chapter 1 – Logical Thinking

Part I – Inductive and Deductive Reasoning

We will begin this section with two definitions.

<u>Inductive reasoning</u> is a type of reasoning where a person arrives at a conclusion by looking at several examples and noticing a pattern.

<u>Deductive reasoning</u> is a type of reasoning where a person arrives at a conclusion by realizing that it is a special case of a general principle that is known to be true.

Let's look at some examples that illustrate these definitions.

Example 1: You know that all fish have gills. You see a catfish, and you decide that it must have gills. Is this an example of inductive or deductive reasoning?

This is an example of deductive reasoning. You know that the general principle that all fish have gills is true. You also know that a catfish is a specific type of fish, and so you apply the general principle that all fish must have gills to this specific case.

Example 2: A two-year-old boy and his mother are walking through a park. The child's mother sees a hummingbird. She points to it and says, "bird." When they see a pigeon later on, the mother points to it and says "bird" again. A little bit later, a fly lands on the child's hand, and the child says "bird." Is this an example of inductive or deductive reasoning?

This is an example of inductive reasoning. The boy noticed that all the birds he saw had wings and could fly. The child used this information to conclude that, since the fly had wings and could fly, it had to be a bird also.

You should realize that you will always reach a correct conclusion using deductive reasoning *if you use it correctly*. When you use inductive reasoning, you will reach a correct conclusion some of the time, but not always (as shown by the last example).

Example 3: Find the next two numbers in the sequence 5, 7, 9, 11, 13, ... Did you use inductive or deductive reasoning?

If you look at the first couple of numbers in the sequence, you should see that, in order to get each successive number, you add two to the previous number. This tells us that the next two numbers in this sequence are probably 15 and 17. This is an example of inductive reasoning because we are looking at the first five numbers in the sequence and noticing a pattern. Now, notice that we said that the next two numbers are *probably* 15 and 17. This is because we do not know for sure that the next two numbers are 15 and 17. For instance, the sequence could start back over at 5 after the 13 (which would mean that the sequence is really 5, 7, 9, 11, 13, 5, 7, 9, 11, 13, 5, 7, 9, 11, 13, ...).

Since inductive reasoning can be wrong, it has no place in our discussion of logical reasoning. However, both inductive reasoning and deductive reasoning are important in mathematics. Many mathematical ideas have been discovered because a mathematician looked at several examples and noticed a pattern. For example, you may know that the measures of the angles in a triangle add up to 180°. However, you would probably never figure this out by starting with the properties of a triangle and aimlessly using deductive reasoning. You would be much more likely to discover this by studying lots of triangles and noticing the pattern.

Now, we need another definition.

A <u>conjecture</u> is a conclusion that a person reaches using inductive reasoning.

So, for example, we could say that, in Example 2, the two-year-old child made a conjecture that the fly that landed on his hand was a bird. In Example 3, we made a conjecture that the next two numbers in the sequence were 15 and 17.

Example 4: Mark draws five quadrilaterals (polygons with four sides) on his paper. He notices that, in each figure, the measures of the angles add up to 360°. What conjecture might he make based on this observation?

Mark might make the conjecture that the angles of any quadrilateral must add up to 360°.

Problems:

1-10. State whether inductive or deductive reasoning was used to reach each conclusion.

1. Stacey knows that anyone who lives in Orlando lives in Florida. She also knows that Jacqueline lives in Orlando, and so she concludes that Jacqueline must live in Florida.

2. Fido the dog has noticed that, every time his owner pulls out a leash, he is about to go for a walk. Fido sees his owner reaching for his leash, and so he concludes that he is about to go for a walk.

3. Bonnie has noticed that, every time she feeds her daughter peanuts, her daughter breaks out in hives. Bonnie concludes that her daughter must be allergic to peanuts.

4. Robert knows that his mother has fixed spaghetti for dinner every Saturday night for the past month. He also knows that today is Friday, and so he concludes that his mother will fix spaghetti for dinner tomorrow night.

5. Janet knows that all new patients of Dr. Taylor must fill out an information form and that she has her first appointment with him at 11:00 a.m. today. She concludes that she will have to fill out an information form when she goes in for her appointment.

6. Every time that Nadine has tried to order a certain camera from an online electronics store, the store has not had any in stock. She decides that, when she tries to order the camera from the store later today, the camera will probably be out of stock.

7. Helen knows that all odd numbers are not divisible by 2 and that 457 is an odd number. She concludes that 457 is not divisible by 2.

8. Chad wants to buy a chair. He sees a sign outside a furniture store that says, "All Chairs on Sale." When he finds a chair he likes, he concludes that the chair he wants to buy must be on sale.

9. Lori's Spanish teacher points to a blue spot on the wall and says, "*azul.*" She points to a blue book and says "*azul*" again. Lori concludes that the word "*azul*" must mean blue in Spanish.

10. Jack's teacher tells him that perpendicular lines form right angles when they intersect. He also knows that line m and line n are perpendicular, and so he concludes that line m and line n must form right angles when they intersect.

11-20. Make a conjecture based on the information given to you.

11. The first six numbers of a sequence are 12, 19, 26, 33, 40, and 47.

    Conjecture: The next two numbers of the sequence are _______ and _______.

12. The first six numbers of a sequence are 1, –1, 1, –1, 1, and –1.

    Conjecture: The next two numbers of the sequence are _______ and _______.

13. $7 + 2 = 9$ $51 + 42 = 93$ $33 + 54 = 87$

$5 + 12 = 17$ $75 + 10 = 85$ $67 + 84 = 151$

Conjecture: The sum of an odd number and an even number is an _________ number.

14. $5 + 0 = 5$ $-17 + 0 = -17$ $-62 + 0 = -62$

$12 + 0 = 12$ $43 + 0 = 43$ $-158 + 0 = -158$

Conjecture: ____

____

15. Adam has noticed that, for the past six weeks, the cafeteria at the college he is attending has served hamburgers every Friday. He also knows that today is Friday and that the cafeteria will be open today.

Conjecture: ____

____

16. Vanessa has noticed that it rains every day in the summer in the town she has just moved to. Today is a warm summer day.

Conjecture: ____

____

17. Suppose that you know that your local newspaper has correctly picked the winner of the election for your town's mayor for each of the past eighteen elections. Also suppose that the same newspaper has picked Pat Green to win the next election for the mayor of your town.

Conjecture: ____

____

18. For the past two weeks, Martha has heard a dog barking whenever she walks by the house at 123 Main Street, and she is about to walk by the house at 123 Main Street.

Conjecture: ____

____

19. Simon has noticed that, whenever he watches his favorite football team on television, they always lose. He knows that his favorite football team is playing at 7:00 tonight, and he plans to watch the game on television.

    Conjecture: ____

    ____

20. Carrie has just started a new job, and her boss has told paychecks will be issued every Friday. Today is Thursday.

    Conjecture: ____

    ____

21-22. Test some numbers and make a conjecture about each of the following.

21. The product of an odd number and an even number is an _________ number.

22. If a number is divisible by both 4 and 7, then it is also divisible by which of the following? (Circle all that apply.)

    (a) 2 (b) 14 (c) 6 (d) 28 (e) 56

Part II – Evaluating the Validity of Statements and Arguments

In this section, we will discuss how to tell if statements and arguments are true or false. Before we look some examples, we will note that statements that begin with the word "all" can often be rewritten as a statement with the word "if" at the beginning and the word "then" in the middle. For instance, the statement, "All triangles have three sides" can be rewritten as, "If a figure is a triangle, then it has three sides."

Example 1: Decide whether the following statement is true or false: *All squares are rectangles.*

We will begin by noting that a square is defined to be a polygon with four sides that have the same length and four right angles, and a rectangle is defined to be a polygon with four sides and four right angles. We will also note that this statement can be rewritten as, "If a figure is a square, then it is a rectangle." To figure out if this statement is true or false, we must start by thinking about a square – a polygon with four sides that have the same length and four right angles. Since this figure must have four sides and four right angles, we can say that our figure must also be a rectangle. This means that the statement, "All squares are rectangles" is true.

Example 2: Decide whether the following statement is true or false: *Some rectangles are squares.*

This question wants us to start by thinking about a rectangle, which is a figure with four sides and four right angles. Since this figure could have four sides that all have the same length, this figure could be a square. Hence, this statement is true.

Example 3: Suppose that a certain restaurant offers a buffet, and the prices for different age groups are listed at the right. In one of their advertisements, they say, "If you are a senior citizen, then your price to eat at the buffet is only \$5.99." Under what circumstances would this statement be false?

Buffet Prices	
Children (12 years old and younger)	\$5.99
Adults (ages 13-54)	\$6.99
Senior Citizens (55 years and older)	\$5.99

We will consider four different situations: (a) You are a senior citizen and you are charged \$5.99 to eat at the buffet, (b) You are a senior citizen and your price to eat at the buffet is not \$5.99, (c) You are not a senior citizen and you are charged \$5.99 to eat at the buffet, and (d) You are not a senior citizen and your price to eat at the buffet is not \$5.99.

(a) You are a senior citizen and your price to eat at the buffet is \$5.99.

If this happens, then the advertisement is true.

(b) You are a senior citizen and your price to eat at the buffet is not \$5.99.

If this happens, then the advertisement is false.

(c) *You are not a senior citizen and your price to eat at the buffet is $5.99.*

If this happens, then the advertisement is true. Notice that the advertisement makes no claim about what happens if you are not a senior citizen.

(d) *You are not a senior citizen and your price to eat at the buffet is not $5.99.*

If this happens, then the advertisement is true. Again, notice that the advertisement makes no claim about what happens if you are not a senior citizen.

This tells us that the only time this advertisement would be false is when a person is a senior citizen and is charged more or less than $5.99 to eat at the buffet.

This example gives rise to the following rule: Whenever the "if" part of a statement is false, it does not matter what the "then" part says – the original statement is true. Also, the only way that a statement in the form "if …, then …" can be false is if the "if" part of the statement is true and the "then" part of the statement is false.

Example 4: Tell whether the following statement is true or false: *If* $5 = -2$*, then 23 is divisible by 2.*

Since the "if" part of this statement is false, we can say that the entire statement must be true. The number 23 is obviously not divisible by 2, but this statement makes no claim about what happens when 5 is not equal to –2.

Now, we need two rules. The first is called the Law of Detachment, and the second is called the Law of Syllogism.

Let *p* and *q* represent two statements, and suppose that you know that the statement, "If *p*, then *q*" is true. Also suppose that you know that *p* is true. Then *q* must also be true.

Let *p*, *q*, and *r* represent three statements, and suppose that you know that the statements, "If *p*, then *q*" and "If *q*, then *r*" are both true. Then the statement, "If *p*, then *r*" is also true.

Example 5: Assume that the following statements are true: (a) If a figure is a rectangle, then its diagonals are congruent. (b) Polygon ABCD is a rectangle. Can you reach a conclusion that must be true based on these statements?

We can let *p* represent the statement, "A figure is a rectangle," and we can let *q* represent the statement, "The diagonals of the figure are congruent." This gives us a statement in the form "If *p*, then *q*" that we know is true. Also, we know that the statement *p* is true for polygon ABCD. Therefore, we can use the Law of Detachment to conclude that the statement *q* is also true for polygon ABCD. This tells us that we can say that the diagonals of polygon ABCD are congruent.

Example 6: Assume that the following statements are true: (a) If an animal is a rabbit, then it has fur. (b) Buster is not a rabbit. Can you reach a conclusion that must be true based on these statements?

We will let p represent the statement, "An animal is a rabbit," and we will let q represent the statement, "It has fur." This gives us a statement in the form "If p, then q" that we know is true. We also know that the statement p is not true for Buster. Note that neither the Law of Detachment nor the Law of Syllogism talks about what happens when p is not true, and so we cannot reach a conclusion that must be true based on these statements.

Example 7: Assume that the following statements are true: (a) If a figure is a rectangle, then its diagonals are congruent. (b) All squares are rectangles. Can you reach a conclusion that must be true based on these statements?

We will begin by noting that (b) can be rewritten as, "If a figure is a square, then it is a rectangle." Now, we will let p represent the statement, "A figure is a square," we will let q represent the statement, "A figure is a rectangle," and we will let r represent the statement, "The diagonals of the figure are congruent." This gives us a statement in the form "If p, then q" and a statement in the form, "If q, then r," as shown below.

If p, then q.
If a figure is a square, then it is a rectangle.

If q, then r.
If a figure is a rectangle, then its diagonals are congruent.

Since we know that both our "If p, then q" and our "If q, then r" statements are true, we can use the Law of Syllogism to conclude that "If p, then r" must also be true. This tells us that we can say that the statement, "If a figure is a square, then its diagonals are congruent" is true.

Example 8: Assume that the following statements are true: (a) If a figure is a square, then it is a rectangle. (b) If a figure is a square, then it is a rhombus. Can you reach a conclusion that must be true based on these statements?

We will let p represent the statement, "A figure is a square," we will let q represent the statement, "A figure is a rectangle," and we will let r represent the statement, "A figure is a rhombus." This gives us a statement in the form "If p, then q" and a statement in the form, "If p, then r," as shown below.

If p, then q.
If a figure is a square, then it is a rectangle.

If p, then r.
If a figure is a square, then it is a rhombus.

Neither the Law of Detachment nor the Law of Syllogism makes any claim about what happens when we know that two statements of the form "If *p*, then *q*," and "If *p*, then *r*," are true, and so we cannot make a conclusion from these two statements.

Now, we need one more definition.

A <u>counterexample</u> is an example that shows that a conjecture is false.

Example 9: Find a counterexample to the statement, "All mammals live on land."

We will begin by noting that this statement can be rewritten as, "If an animal is a mammal, then it lives on land." Now, to find a counterexample, we must find an example that proves that this statement is false. As we said after Example 3, the only way that a statement in the form "if …, then …" can be false is if the "if" part of the statement is true *and* the "then" part of the statement is false. So, in order to prove this statement false, we must find an example of an animal that is a mammal and does not live on land. Since a dolphin is a mammal that does not live on land, we can say that a dolphin is a counterexample to this statement.

Problems:

1-20. Decide whether each of following statements is *true* or *false*.

1. If $x = 8$, then $x - 5 = 3$.

2. If $x^2 = 9$, then $x = 3$.

3. If $x^2 = 9$, then x could equal 3.

4. Some triangles have three sides.

5. If $4 < 1$, then $5 = 2$.

6. If $3 = 4$, then $0 < 1$.

7. Some dogs have spots.

8. All unicorns on Saturn love pepperoni pizza.

9. There is a unicorn on Saturn that loves pepperoni pizza.

10. All numbers that are greater than 7 are greater than 10.

11. All numbers that are greater than 10 are greater than 7.

12. Some people who live in Chicago live in Illinois.

13. All people who live in Chicago live in Illinois.

14. All people who live in Illinois live in Chicago.

15. If $a = 10$, then $a - 4 = 6$.

16. If $7 < 8$, then pigs can fly.

17. If pigs can fly, then $7 < 8$.

18. If pigs can fly, then $7 > 8$.

19. All rectangles have four sides.

20. All figures with four sides are rectangles.

21-30. For each statement below, state or draw a counterexample that shows that the statement is false.

21. All prime numbers are odd.

22. All odd numbers are prime.

23. If x is a real number, then $x > \frac{1}{x}$.

24. If x is a real number, then $x^2 > x$.

25. All rational numbers are whole numbers. (Recall that rational numbers are numbers that can be written as either fractions or as decimals that either stop or repeat, and the whole numbers are 0, 1, 2, 3, 4, 5, 6, ….)

26. If a figure has four sides, then it is a square.

27. If a figure has four sides, then it is <u>not</u> a square.

28. If $x > 3$, then $x^2 > 15$.

29. If a number is divisible by 6, then it is also divisible by 12.

30. If a number is divisible by 6, then it is <u>not</u> divisible by 12.

31-42. Assume that each of the statements below are true, and then use either the Law of Detachment or the Law of Syllogism to write a conclusion that must be true *if possible*.

31. (a) If today is a holiday, then Calvin will not go to school today.
    (b) Today is not a holiday.

32. (a) If you do your homework, then you will get better grades.
    (b) If you get better grades, then you will get into a better college.

33. (a) If a figure is a rhombus, then it is a quadrilateral.
    (b) If a figure is a square, then it is a rhombus.

34. (a) If an animal is a bird, then it has feathers.
    (b) A cardinal is a type of bird.

35. (a) A number is said to be rational if it can be written as the ratio of two integers.
    (b) The number 3 can be written as the ratio $\frac{3}{1}$.

36. (a) If Tammy has school tomorrow, then she must be home by 8:30 p.m.
    (b) Tammy must be home by 8:30 p.m. tonight.

37. (a) If it is before 9 p.m., then the pharmacy is open.
    (b) If the pharmacy is open, then Helen will get her medicine.

38. (a) If a number is a natural number, then it is a whole number.

(b) All whole numbers are integers.

39. (a) Anyone who lives in Alabama lives in North America.

(b) Anyone who lives in Arkansas lives in North America.

40. (a) If $y = 3$, then $x = 4$.

(b) $x = 4$

41. (a) If point B is between points A and C, then $AB + BC = AC$.

(b) $AB + BC = AC$.

42. (a) If a number is less than 4, then it is less than 7.

(b) If a number is less than 4, then it is less than 12.

Part III – The Converse, Inverse, and Contrapositive of Statements

We will begin this section with a discussion of a concept called the negation of statements.

When you negate a statement, you say that the statement is false.

When you negate a statement correctly, either the original statement or the negation of the statement must be true. So, for example, we could not negate the statement, "The apple is red" by saying, "The apple is green" because this leaves out the possibility that the apple is yellow, brown, or some other color.

Example 1: Consider the following statement: *Everyone likes Sylvester.* Which of the following correctly negates this statement? (a) There is at least one person somewhere who does not like Sylvester. (b) No one likes Sylvester. (c) Everyone dislikes Sylvester. (d) It is false that everyone likes Sylvester.

To negate this statement, we must figure out how we can say, "It is not true that everyone likes Sylvester."

(a) This is a correct way of negating the original statement. If we look at the statements, "Everyone likes Sylvester" and "There is at least one person somewhere who does not like Sylvester," we see that we are not leaving out any possibilities.

(b) This is not a correct way of negating the original statement. If we look at the statements, "Everyone likes Sylvester" and "No one likes Sylvester," we see that these two statements leave out the possibility that some people like Sylvester and some people don't.

(c) This statement is equivalent to statement (b), and so it is not a correct way of negating the original statement.

(d) This is a correct way of negating the original statement. If we look at the statements, "Everyone likes Sylvester" and "It is false that everyone likes Sylvester," we see that we are not leaving out any possibilities.

Now, we need three more definitions.

The converse of a statement is formed by switching the "if" part and the "then" part.

The inverse of a statement is formed by negating both the "if" part and the "then" part.

The contrapositive of a statement is formed by switching the "if" part and the "then" part and negating both parts.

In the next two examples, we list two ways of writing the converse, inverse, and contrapositive of the statements, but these are not the only correct answers. There are many other ways to write these statements.

Example 2: Consider the following statement: *If a number is divisible by 4, then it is divisible by 3.* Write the converse, inverse, and contrapositive of this statement, and tell whether each is true or false.

We will begin by noting that, because the number 8 serves as a counterexample to the original statement, we can say that the original statement is false.

The converse of this statement can be written as *If a number is divisible by 3, then it is divisible by 4* or as *A number is divisible by 4 if it is divisible by 3.* The number 9 is a counterexample to either of these forms of the converse, and so we can say that the converse of this statement is false.

The inverse of this statement can be written as *If a number is not divisible by 4, then it is not divisible by 3* or as *A number is not divisible by 3 if it is not divisible by 4.* The number 9 is a counterexample to either of these forms of the inverse, and so we can say that the inverse of this statement is false.

The contrapositive of this statement can be written as *If a number is not divisible by 3, then it is not divisible by 4* or as *A number is not divisible by 4 if it is not divisible by 3.* The number 8 is a counterexample to either of these forms of the contrapositive, and so we can say that the contrapositive of the statement is false.

Example 3: Consider the following statement: *All numbers that are less than 5 are less than 8.* Write the converse, inverse, and contrapositive of this statement, and tell whether each is true or false.

We will begin by noting that this statement can be rewritten as *If a number is less than 5, then it is less than 8.* We will also note that this statement is true.

To find the converse of this statement, we must switch the "if" part of the statement with the "then" part of the statement. This tells us that the converse of this statement can be written as *If a number is less than 8, then it is less than 5* or as *All numbers that are less than 8 are also less than 5.* Since the number 7 serves as a counterexample to both of these forms of the converse, we can say that the converse is false.

To find the inverse of this statement, we must negate both the "if" part and the "then" part. This tells us that we can write the inverse of the statement as *If a number is not less than 5, then it is not less than 8* or as *If a number is greater than or equal to 5, then it is greater than or equal to 8.* Since the number 5 serves as a counterexample to both of these forms of the inverse, we can say that inverse is false.

To find the contrapositive of this statement, we must switch the "if" part with the "then" part and negate both of them. This tells us that we can write the contrapositive of this statement as *If a number is not less than 8, then it is not less than 5* or as *All numbers that are greater than or equal to 8 are also greater than or equal to 5.* Both of these statements are true. (To see why, think of a number that is greater than or equal to 8. This number must be greater than or equal to 5.)

Finally, we will note that, if the original statement is true, then the contrapositive of the statement must be true (and, if the original statement is false, then the contrapositive of the statement must be false). If the original statement is true, then the converse and inverse of the statement may or may not be true.

Example 4: Assume that the following statement is true: *All kowsers are green.* Which of the following statements **must** be true? (a) If an object is a kowser, then it must be green. (b) If an object is green, then it is a kowser. (c) If an object is green, then it could be a kowser. (d) If an object is not green, then it is not a kowser. (e) All green objects are kowsers. (f) If an object is not a kowser, then it is not green. (g) Kowsers exist. (h) Kowsers do not exist.

(a) We can use what we discussed in the last section to say that the original statement can be rewritten to say, "If an object is a kowser, then it is green." Thus, statement (a) must be true.

(b) This is the converse of the original statement, and we have no way of knowing whether it is true or not.

(c) The original statement tells us that, if we ever find a kowser, we know that it will be green. So, if we find a green object somewhere, it could be a kowser. Therefore, this statement is true.

(d) This is the contrapositive of the original statement. Since we were told that the original statement was true, we know that this statement must also be true.

(e) This statement is saying the same thing as statement (b), and so we have no way of knowing whether or not this statement is true.

(f) This is the inverse of the original statement, and we have no way of knowing whether it is true or not.

(g) The original statement tells us that, if we ever find a kowser, we know that it will be green. It does not tell us that kowsers exist, and it does not tell us that kowsers do not exist. Thus, we have no way of knowing whether or not this statement is true.*

(h) As we said in (g), the original statement tells us that, if we ever find a kowser, we know that it will be green. It does not tell us that kowsers exist, and it does not tell us that kowsers do not exist. Thus, we have no way of knowing whether or not this statement is true.*

This tells us that the only statements that must be true are (a), (c), and (d).

*If (g) and (h) confuse you, think about this statement: *All unicorns have one horn.* This is a true statement because anyone drawing a unicorn will draw the unicorn with one horn, but of course unicorns do not really exist.

Problems:

1-10. For each of the given statements, select all of the answer choices that negate the original statement correctly.

1. Benjamin has a dog.
   (a) Benjamin does not have a dog.
   (b) Benjamin has a cat.
   (c) It is not true that Benjamin has a dog.
   (d) Gavin has a dog.
   (e) Gavin does not have a dog.

2. $m \leq n$
   (a) $m > n$
   (b) It is false that $m \leq n$.
   (c) $m < n$
   (d) $m = n$
   (e) $m \neq n$
   (f) $m \geq n$

3. I am not going to the movies.
   (a) I am going shopping.
   (b) I am going to the movies.
   (c) Sam is not going to the movies.
   (d) Sam is going to the movies.

4. The light is bright.
   (a) The light is not bright.
   (b) The light is dim.
   (c) The light is off.
   (d) It is not true that the light is bright.
   (e) The sun is bright.

5. "I do not like green eggs and ham." –*Green Eggs and Ham* by Dr. Seuss
   (a) I like green eggs and ham.
   (b) I like yellow eggs and ham.
   (c) I do not like yellow eggs and ham.

6. This bell pepper is green.
   (a) This bell pepper is red.
   (b) This bell pepper is blue.
   (c) It is false to say that this bell pepper is green.
   (d) This bell pepper is not green.
   (e) This cucumber is green.

7. $x < 5$
   (a) $x = 8$
   (b) $x > 5$
   (c) $x \geq 6$
   (d) $x \geq 5$
   (e) x is not less than 5

8. The glass is half full.
   (a) The glass is half empty.
   (b) The glass is empty.
   (c) The glass is full.
   (d) The glass is not half full.
   (e) The glass is ¼ full.

9. Some taggles are not pink.
   (a) There exists a taggle that is pink.
   (b) Some taggles are red.
   (c) Some taggles are not red.
   (d) All taggles are pink.

10. All dogs are cute.
   (a) All dogs are ugly.
   (b) All cats are ugly.
   (c) All cats are cute.
   (d) There is at least one dog somewhere that is not cute.
   (e) Some dogs are cute.
   (f) It is false that all dogs are cute.

11-18. Write the converse, inverse, and contrapositive of each of the following statements, and then tell whether each is true or false.

11. If $x = 8$, then $x^2 - 7 \neq 9$.

    True or false?

    converse:

    True or false?

    inverse:

    True or false?

    contrapositive:

    True or false?

12. If $x = 3$, then $x > 5$.

    True or false?

    converse:

    True or false?

    inverse:

    True or false?

    contrapositive:

    True or false?

13. All positive numbers are natural numbers.

    (Recall that the natural numbers are the numbers 1, 2, 3, 4, 5, 6, … . They do not include fractions, decimals, negative numbers, or zero.)

    True or false?

    converse:

    True or false?

    inverse:

    True or false?

    contrapositive:

    True or false?

14. If $3 \cdot 4 = 25$, then $5 + 1 = 2$.

True or false?

converse:

True or false?

inverse:

True or false?

contrapositive:

True or false?

15. If $x = 7$, then $2x = 14$.

True or false?

converse:

True or false?

inverse:

True or false?

contrapositive:

True or false?

16. All squares have four sides.

True or false?

converse:

True or false?

inverse:

True or false?

contrapositive:

True or false?

17. All triangles have 12 sides.

    True or false?

    converse:

    True or false?

    inverse:

    True or false?

    contrapositive:

    True or false?

18. All numbers that are divisible by 2 are divisible by 4.

    True or false?

    converse:

    True or false?

    inverse:

    True or false?

    contrapositive:

    True or false?

19. Write the converse, inverse, and contrapositive of the following statement: *Call me at 1-800-555-1234 if you are interested in buying a house.*

    converse:

    inverse:

    contrapositive:

20. Write the converse, inverse, and contrapositive of the following statement, originally said by Mark Twain: *If you tell the truth, you don't have to remember anything.*

    converse:

    inverse:

    contrapositive:

21. Assume that the following statement is true: *All customers should exit the theater through the rear doors.* Select all of the following statements that must be true.

    (a) If you are a customer, then you should exit the theater through one of the rear doors.

    (b) If you are not a customer, then you should exit the theater through one of the rear doors.

    (c) If you are not a customer, then you could exit the theater through one of the rear doors.

    (d) If you work at the theater, then you should not exit the theater through one of the rear doors.

    (e) If you work at the theater, then you should exit the theater through one of the rear doors.

    (f) If you have to exit through the rear doors, then you must be a customer.

    (g) If you do not have to exit through the rear doors, then you are not a customer.

22. Assume that the following statement is true: *All pacadams are brackle.* Select all of the following statements that must be true.

    (a) If something is brackle, then it is a pacadam.

    (b) If something is not brackle, then it is not a pacadam.

    (c) There exists a pacadam somewhere that is brackle.

    (d) If something is a pacadam, then it is brackle.

    (e) If something is brackle, then it could be a pacadam.

    (f) If something is not a pacadam, then it is not brackle.

    (g) If something is not a pacadam, then it could be brackle.

23. Assume that the following statement is true: *If Victoria is wearing her black pants, then she is wearing her black shoes.* Select all of the statements below that must be true.

    (a) If Victoria is wearing her black shoes, then she is wearing her black pants.

    (b) If Victoria is not wearing her black shoes, then she is not wearing her black pants.

    (c) If Victoria is not wearing her black pants, then she is not wearing her black shoes.

    (d) Victoria is wearing her black pants.

    (e) Victoria is not wearing her black pants.

    (f) Victoria is wearing her black shoes.

    (g) Victoria is not wearing her black shoes.

24. Assume that the following statement is true: *If Samantha apologizes for her actions, then Allen will apologize for his actions*. Select all of the statements below that must be true.

    (a) If Allen apologizes for his actions, then Samantha apologized for her actions.

    (b) If Samantha does not apologize for her actions, then Allen will not apologize for his actions.

    (c) If Allen does not apologize for his actions, then Samantha did not apologize for her actions.

    (d) Allen will apologize for his actions.

    (e) Allen will not apologize for his actions.

25. Assume that the following statement is true: *If an object is queely, then it is either yellow or brown.* Select all of the statements below that must be true.

    (a) If an object is not queely, then it is not yellow or brown.

    (b) All objects that are queely are either yellow or brown.

    (c) If an object is not yellow or brown, then it is not queely.

    (d) If an object is either yellow or brown, then it is queely.

26. Assume that the following statement is true: *All molecules of water are made of hydrogen and oxygen*. Select all of the statements below that must be true.

    (a) If it is not a molecule of water, then it is not made of hydrogen and oxygen.

    (b) If it is not made of hydrogen and oxygen, then it is not a molecule of water.

    (c) If it is a molecule of water, then it is made of hydrogen and oxygen.

    (d) If it is made of hydrogen and oxygen, then it is a molecule of water.

27-28. Old Faithful is a geyser located in Yellowstone National Park in Wyoming.

27. If Frank is taking a picture of Old Faithful, then Frank _____________ (choose one: may be, is, is not) in Wyoming.

28. If Frank's cousin Billy is not taking a picture of Old Faithful, then Billy _____________ (choose one: may be, is, is not) in Wyoming.

29. Sabancaya is an active volcano is Peru, and Julio is visiting some family in Peru. Julio ___________ (choose one: may, will, will not) visit Sabancaya.

Part IV – Biconditional Statements and Definitions

We will begin this section with a definition.

> A biconditional statement is a statement that has two parts and is only true if both parts are true or both parts are false. Usually, a biconditional statement is written with the words "if and only if" in the middle.

When we want to give a definition of a word in this book, we will generally use biconditional statements.

Example 1: An angle is said to be a right angle *if and only if* its measure is 90°. What does this mean?

This statement means that we can make two statements: (1) If an angle is a right angle, then its measure is 90°, and (2) If the measure of an angle is 90°, then it is a right angle.

Example 2: Consider the statement "$x = 3$ if and only if $x < 7$." Is this statement true or false?

We will begin by noting that the statement "$x = 3$ if and only if $x < 7$" means two things: (1) If $x = 3$, then $x < 7$, and (2) If $x < 7$, then $x = 3$. In order for the original statement to be true, both of these statements must be true. The first statement is true, but the second is not. Thus, we can say that the original statement is false.

Example 3: Assume that the following statement is true: *Anyone who applies for a job at Nate's Trucking Company will be hired if and only if he or she has a perfect driving record.* Which of the following statements must be true? (a) Anyone who applies for a job at Nate's Trucking Company will be hired if he or she has a perfect driving record. (b) Anyone who applies for a job at Nate's Trucking Company will not be hired if he or she does not have a perfect driving record. (c) Some people who apply for a job at Nate's Trucking Company and who do not have perfect driving records will be hired. (d) If you apply for a job at Nate's Trucking Company and are hired, then you have a perfect driving record. (e) If you apply for a job at Nate's Trucking Company and are not hired, then you do not have a perfect driving record.

We will begin by noting that the original statement says two things: (1) If you apply for a job at Nate's Trucking Company and have a perfect driving record, then you will be hired, and (2) If you apply for a job at Nate's Trucking Company and are hired, then you have a perfect driving record.

(a) This statement is equivalent to statement (1) above, and so it must be true.

(b) This statement is equivalent to the contrapositive of statement (2) above, and, since the contrapositive of a statement is always true when the original statement is true, this statement must be true.

(c) This statement is not true because statement (2) above says that you must have a perfect driving record in order to be hired.

(d) This statement is true because it is the same as statement (2) on the previous page.

(e) This statement is equivalent to the contrapositive of statement (1) on the previous page, and, since the contrapositive of a statement is always true when the original statement is true, this statement must be true.

Problems:

1-11. Tell whether each statement below is *true* or *false*.

1. A number is positive if and only if it is greater than -3.

2. $x = y$ if and only if $x + 3 = y + 3$

3. $x^2 = 81$ if and only if $x = 9$

4. An insect is a mosquito if and only if it has wings.

5. $|-5| = 5$ if and only if $3 < 4$

6. $|-5| = 2$ if and only if $7 < 2$

7. In baseball, a team wins a game if and only if that team scores more runs than the other team.

8. $x = 3$ if and only if $x < 4$

9. A figure is a square if and only if it has four sides.

10. Today is Thursday if and only if tomorrow is Friday.

11. An animal is a snake if and only if it is a reptile.

12. Assume that the following statement is true: *Marlene will eat a piece of the pizza if and only if it has Italian sausage on it.* Select all of the statements below that must be true.

    (a) If Marlene eats a piece of the pizza, then the pizza has Italian sausage on it.

    (b) If the pizza has Italian sausage on it, then Marlene will eat a piece of the pizza.

    (c) If Marlene does not eat a piece of the pizza, then the pizza does not have Italian sausage on it.

    (d) If the pizza does not have Italian sausage on it, then Marlene will not eat a piece of it.

    (e) Marlene will eat a piece of the pizza.

    (f) The pizza has Italian sausage on it.

13. Assume that the following statement is true: *$x = 2$ if and only if $x = y$.* Select all of the answers below that must be true.

    (a) $x = 2$

    (b) $x = y$

    (c) $y = 2$

    (d) If $x = 2$, then $x = y$.

    (e) If $x = y$, then $x = 2$.

    (f) If $x \neq y$, then $x \neq 2$.

    (g) If $x \neq 2$, then $x \neq y$.

    (h) If $x < y$, then $x \neq 2$.

    (i) If $x \neq y$, then $x < 2$.

14. Assume that the following statement is true: *Jake will do the dishes if and only if his sister helps him.* Select all of the statements below that must be true.

    (a) Jake will do the dishes.

    (b) Jake will not do the dishes.

    (c) If Jake does the dishes, then his sister will help him.

    (d) If Jake does not do the dishes, then his sister will not help him.

    (e) If his sister helps him, then Jake will do the dishes.

    (f) If his sister does not help him, then Jake will not do the dishes.

15. Assume that the following statement is true: *Two lines are perpendicular if and only if they form right angles*. Select all of the statements below that must be true.

    (a) If two lines are perpendicular, then they form right angles.

    (b) If two lines are not perpendicular, then they do not form right angles.

    (c) If two lines do not form right angles, then they are not perpendicular.

    (d) Two lines are not perpendicular if they form right angles.

    (e) Two lines are not perpendicular if they do not form right angles.

16. Assume that the following statement is true: *A quadrilateral is a parallelogram if and only if its diagonals bisect each other*. Select all of the statements below that must be true.

    (a) If the diagonals of a quadrilateral bisect each other, then the quadrilateral is a parallelogram.

    (b) If the diagonals of a quadrilateral bisect each other, then the quadrilateral is not a parallelogram.

    (c) If the diagonals of a quadrilateral do not bisect each other, then the quadrilateral is not a parallelogram.

    (d) The diagonals of a quadrilateral will bisect each other if the quadrilateral is a parallelogram.

    (e) The diagonals of a quadrilateral will not bisect each other if the quadrilateral is not a parallelogram.

17. Assume that the following statement is true: *An object is a diblet if and only if it is jeppable*. Select all of the answers below that must be true.

    (a) All diblets are jeppable.

    (b) Some jeppable objects are not diblets.

    (c) All jeppable objects are diblets.

    (d) If an object is not a diblet, then it is not jeppable.

    (e) If an object is a diblet, then it is jeppable.

    (f) If an object is jeppable, then it might not be a diblet.

    (g) If an object is jeppable, then it is a diblet.

    (h) If an object is not jeppable, then it is not a diblet.

18. Assume that the following statement is true: *In Italian, an object is called a* matita *if and only if it is a pencil.* Select all of the answers below that must be true.

    (a) If an object is a pencil, then it is called a *matita* in Italian.

    (b) If an object is not a pencil, then it is not called a *matita* in Italian.

    (c) There is a pencil somewhere that is not called a *matita* in Italian.

    (d) If an object is called a *matita* in Italian, then it is a pencil.

    (e) If an object is not called a *matita* in Italian, then it is not a pencil.

    (f) There is an object called a *matita* in Italian that is not a pencil.

Part V – Direct and Indirect Proofs

In this section, we will discuss how to write two different kinds of proofs. A proof is a list of statements you know to be true and the reasons why you know these statements are true. In this section, we will only discuss algebraic proofs. The more complicated proofs that deal with geometric concepts will be discussed in later chapters. We will begin by reviewing some properties from Algebra. Also, you may find it helpful to review the sections on linear equations, linear inequalities, and solving systems of equations using substitution in Appendix A before you try to understand the examples in this section.

Let a, b, and c represent real numbers. Then:

- the Addition Property of Equality says that $a = b$ if and only if $a + c = b + c$.
- the Subtraction Property of Equality says that $a = b$ if and only if $a - c = b - c$.
- the Multiplication Property of Equality says that $a = b$ if and only if $ac = bc$ and $c \neq 0$.
- the Division Property of Equality says that $a = b$ if and only if $\frac{a}{c} = \frac{b}{c}$ and $c \neq 0$.
- the Addition Property of Inequality says that $a < b$ if and only if $a + c < b + c$.
- the Subtraction Property of Inequality says that $a < b$ if and only if $a - c < b - c$.
- the Multiplication Property of Inequality says that, if $a < b$ and $c > 0$, then $ac < bc$; if $a < b$ and $c < 0$, then $ac > bc$.
- the Division Property of Inequality says that, if $a < b$ and $c > 0$, then $\frac{a}{c} < \frac{b}{c}$; if $a < b$ and $c < 0$, then $\frac{a}{c} > \frac{b}{c}$.
- the Reflexive Property of Equality says that $a = a$.
- the Symmetric Property of Equality says that $a = b$ if and only if $b = a$.
- the Transitive Property of Equality says that, if $a = b$ and $b = c$, then $a = c$.
- the Substitution Property of Equality says that, if $a = b$, then a may be replaced by b in any equation or inequality.
- the Symmetric Property of Inequality says that $a < b$ if and only if $b > a$.
- the Transitive Property of Inequality says that, if $a < b$ and $b < c$, then $a < c$.
- the Distributive Property says that $a(b + c) = ab + ac$ and $a(b - c) = ab - ac$.

Example 1: Suppose that you know that $3x = 24$. Which property allows you to say that $x = 8$?

If we know that $3x = 24$, then we can divide both sides of this equation by 3 to find that $x = 8$. The Division Property of Equality allows us to do this, and so we can say that the Division Property of Equality tells us that $x = 8$.

The next four examples give you some examples of proofs. When you do the practice problems, you do not need to write the third column. We only included the third column so that you could understand what we were doing better.

Example 2: Solve for x in the equation $4x - 5 = 23$, and give a reason for each step. It turns out that $x = 7$, as shown in the proof below.

Statements	Reasons	Explanations
1. $4x - 5 = 23$	1. Given	We were told that $4x - 5 = 23$. When you are told that something is true at the beginning of the problem, you should write "Given" as your reason for knowing this statement.
2. $4x = 28$	2. Addition Property of Equality	We added 5 to both sides of the equation, and the Addition Property of Equality is the property that allows us to do this.
3. $x = 7$	3. Division Property of Equality	We divided both sides of the equation by 4, and the Division Property of Equality is the property that allows us to do this.

Example 3: Given that $4y - 5 < 7(y + 4) - 2$, prove that $y > -\frac{31}{3}$.

There are many different ways to work this problem, and one of them is shown below.

Statements	Reasons	Explanations
1. $4y - 5 < 7(y + 4) - 2$	1. Given	We were told that $4y - 5 < 7(y + 4) - 2$. When you are told that something is true at the beginning of the problem, you should write "Given" as your reason for knowing this statement.
2. $4y - 5 < 7y + 28 - 2$	2. Distributive Property	The Distributive Property tells us that $7(y + 4) = 7y + 28$.
3. $4y - 5 < 7y + 26$	3. Substitution Property of Equality	Note that $28 - 2 = 26$, and so we can substitute 26 for $28 - 2$.
4. $-5 < 3y + 26$	4. Subtraction Property of Inequality	We subtracted 4y from both sides of the inequality, and the Subtraction Property of Inequality is the property that allows us to do this.
5. $-31 < 3y$	5. Subtraction Property of Inequality	We subtracted 26 from both sides of the inequality, and the Subtraction Property of Inequality is the property that allows us to do this.
6. $-\frac{31}{3} < y$	6. Division Property of Inequality	We divided both sides of the inequality by 3, and the Division Property of Inequality is the property that allows us to do this.
7. $y > -\frac{31}{3}$	7. Symmetric Property of Inequality	The Symmetric Property of Inequality states that $a < b$ if and only if $b > a$.

Example 4: Given that $2x + 3y = 7$ and $x - y = 6$, prove that $x = 5$ and $y = -1$.

Once again, there are several ways of solving this problem, and one of them is shown below.

Statements	Reasons	Why did we choose the reason we did?
1. $2x + 3y = 7$ and $x - y = 6$	1. Given	We were told that $x - y = 6$. When you are told that something is true at the beginning of the problem, you should write "Given" as your reason for knowing this statement.
2. $x = 6 + y$	2. Addition Property of Equality	We added y to both sides of the second equation in Statement (1), and the Addition Property of Equality is the property that allows us to do this.
3. $2(6 + y) + 3y = 7$	3. Substitution Property of Equality	We said in Statement (2) that $x = 6 + y$, and so we can substitute $6 + y$ for x in the first equation in Statement (1).
4. $12 + 2y + 3y = 7$	4. Distributive Property	The Distributive Property tells us that $2(6 + y) = 12 + 2y$.
5. $12 + 5y = 7$	5. Distributive Property	When we combine like terms, we are using the Distributive Property. To see why this is true, note that $2y + 3y = y(2 + 3)$, or $5y$. (You could also use the Substitution Property of Equality as your reason here, but the Distributive Property is really a better reason.)
6. $5y = -5$	6. Subtraction Property of Equality	We subtracted 12 from both sides of the equation in Statement (5), and the Subtraction Property of Equality is the property that allows us to do this.
7. $y = -1$	7. Division Property of Equality	We divided both sides of the equation by 5, and the Division Property of Equality is the property that allows us to do this.
9. $x = 6 + (-1)$	9. Substitution Property of Equality	We already said that $y = -1$ and that $x = 6 + y$. So, we can substitute -1 for y in the equation $x = 6 + y$.
10. $x = 5$	10. Substitution Property of Equality	Since $6 + (-1) = 5$, we can substitute 5 for $6 + (-1)$.

All of the proofs that we have done up to this point have been what we call direct proofs. In the next example, we discuss the concept of indirect proofs. To write an indirect proof, you assume that the "given" part is true **and** the negation of the part that you want to prove is true. You work with both of these assumptions, and then you get a contradiction, which is a statement that cannot be true based on your assumptions.

Example 5: Given that $5x + 2 = -18$, prove that x must equal -4 using an indirect proof.

Once again, there are several ways to work this problem, and one of them is shown below.

Statements	Reasons	Why did we choose the reason we did?
1. $5x + 2 = -18$	1. Given	We were told that $5x + 2 = -18$. When you are told that something is true at the beginning of the problem, you should write "Given" as your reason for knowing this statement.
2. $x \neq -4$	2. Assumption	We are allowed to assume the negation of the statement that we are trying to prove.
3. $5x \neq -20$	3. Multiplication Property of Inequality	The Multiplication Property of Inequality tells us that we can multiply both sides of Statement (2) by 5.
4. $5x + 2 \neq -18$	4. Addition Property of Inequality	The Addition Property of Inequality tells us that we can add 2 to both sides of Statement (3).
5. x must equal -4	5. Contradiction	Our assumption must be false because Statement (4) is a contradiction to Statement (1).

When you are writing an indirect proof, make sure that you assume the "Given" **and the negation of the statement you are trying to prove**. If you don't do this, your answer will be wrong because you are not using correct logic.

Problems:

1-18. Prove each of the following statements using a direct proof.

1. Given that $5x = 3x - 14$, prove that $x = -7$.

2. Given that $7a - 2 = 3(2a - 4)$, prove that $a = -10$.

3. Given that $5y + 4 = 2 - 3y$, prove that $y = -\frac{1}{4}$.

4. Given that $\frac{p}{5} + 3 = 7$, prove that $p = 20$.

5. Given that $5 - \frac{3w}{4} = 15$, prove that $w = -\frac{40}{3}$.

6. Given that $2k + 3 = 5 - 2(k + 4)$, prove that $k = -\frac{3}{2}$.

7. Given that $2n - 5 = 3 - (n + 4)$, prove that $n = \frac{4}{3}$.

8. Given that $2(d - 3) + 1 = d - 5$, prove that $d = 0$.

9. Given that $3q + 4 \le 5$, prove that $q \le \frac{1}{3}$.

10. Given that $6 - 3m > 4$, prove that $m < \frac{2}{3}$.

11. Given that $x + 4(2x - 1) < 5$, prove that $x < 1$.

12. Given that $5 + 2(3 - c) \leq 4c$, prove that $c \geq \frac{11}{6}$.

13. Given that $3 - \frac{5y}{12} < \frac{1}{4}$, prove that $y > \frac{33}{5}$.

14. Given that $\frac{5}{6}+\frac{2u}{3} > \frac{1}{2}$, prove that $u > -\frac{1}{2}$.

15. Given that $5x + y = 36$ and $x - 5y = 2$, prove that $x = 7$ and $y = 1$.

16. Given that $2x + 3y = -17$ and $x - 4y = 8$, prove that $x = -4$ and $y = -3$.

17. Given that $2x + y = -4$ and $3x - y = -11$, prove that $x = -3$ and $y = 2$.

18. Given that $8x - y = 4$ and $5x + 2y = -8$, prove that $x = 0$ and $y = -4$.

19-25. Prove each of the following statements using an indirect proof.

19. Given that $5a - 4 = 31$, prove that $a = 7$.

20. Given that 2(b + 5) = 12, prove that b = 1.

21. Given that $\frac{5c}{8} + 1 = -9$, prove that c = –16.

22. Given that $\frac{2x}{3} - 4 = 1$, prove that $x = \frac{15}{2}$.

23. Given that $2 = 3 + 7y$, prove that $y = -\frac{1}{7}$.

24. Given that $3z + 1 < 5$, prove that $z < \frac{4}{3}$.

25. Given that $3 - 2n \geq 5$, prove that $n \leq -1$.

Chapter 2 – Points, Lines, Planes, and Angles

Part I – Points, Lines, and Planes

We will begin this chapter with a discussion of the terms *point*, *line*, and *plane*. We do not give these terms formal definitions; we call them undefined terms. To see why we do this, suppose that you look up *recherche* in the dictionary and it says that *recherche* means *pretentious*. You don't know what *pretentious* means, and so you look up *pretentious* in the dictionary. It tells you that *pretentious* means *recherche*. So, of course, you haven't learned anything. The same thing applies to the terms *point*, *line*, and *plane*. We have to have a starting point where we don't give certain terms formal definitions; everyone just knows what these terms mean.

A *point* is represented by a dot, and it has no length, width, or height. We label points by using a single capital letter. For example, we can call the points below "point A," "point B," and "point C."

A *line* is essentially a collection of points. Lines are straight (and not curved), and they continue infinitely in both directions. They have infinite length, but no width or height. We represent lines by drawing a part of the line and then putting arrows on both ends (the arrows show that the line continues infinitely in both directions). We talk about lines either by using a single lower-case cursive letter or by naming two points on the line. For example, the first line below could be called "line m," and the second line below could be called "line DE," "line ED," "line EF," "line FE," "line DF," or "line FD" (written $\overleftrightarrow{DE}$, $\overleftrightarrow{ED}$, $\overleftrightarrow{EF}$, $\overleftrightarrow{FE}$, $\overleftrightarrow{DF}$, or $\overleftrightarrow{FD}$).

Our last undefined term is *plane*. A *plane* is essentially a flat surface. It is a collection of lines, and, since lines extend infinitely in both directions, planes must extend infinitely in all directions in which they start. We draw planes by drawing a shape called a parallelogram, which looks like a slanted rectangle. We talk about planes by using either a cursive capital letter in a corner of the plane or by naming three points that are in the plane but not all on the same line. For example, the plane below could be called "plane $\mathcal{P}$" (note that $\mathcal{P}$ is not actually a point in the plane), "plane JKL," "plane JLK," "plane KLJ," "plane KJL," "plane LJK," or "plane LKJ."

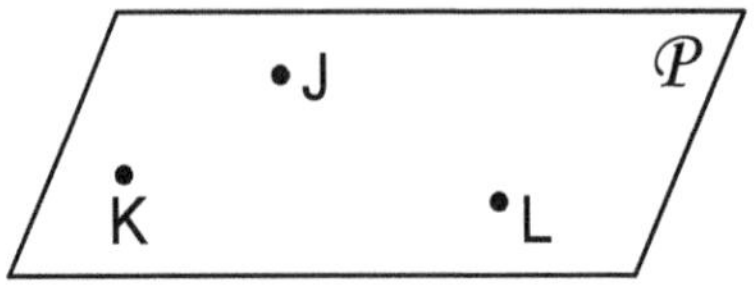

Now, we can state formal definitions for the terms *line segment* and *ray*.

A line segment (or just segment) consists of two points (called endpoints) and all the points between them.

A ray is a half line and half line segment, as it has one endpoint, but it continues infinitely in the other direction. A ray AB (written $\overrightarrow{AB}$) consists of the endpoint A, the point B, and all the points C such that either C is between A and B or B is between A and C.

We name line segments by naming their endpoints and putting a bar without arrows on the ends over the top of them. For instance, the line segment below could be called "segment OM" or "segment MO" (written $\overline{OM}$ or $\overline{MO}$), but **NOT** "segment MN" or "segment NO."

As we hinted in the definition above, we name rays by naming the endpoint first and then another point on the ray. This means that the only correct ways of naming the ray shown below are $\overrightarrow{RP}$ and $\overrightarrow{RQ}$.

Now, we need another definition.

The intersection of two figures is the set of points that the two figures have in common.

Example 1: Draw a picture to represent the following statement: $\overleftrightarrow{AB}$ intersects $\overline{CD}$ at point A.

There are many pictures we can draw to represent this statement, and one of them is shown below.* Notice that we did not put a dot at point A. This is because, when we want to label the point where two lines, segments, or rays cross, we do not need to put a dot there.

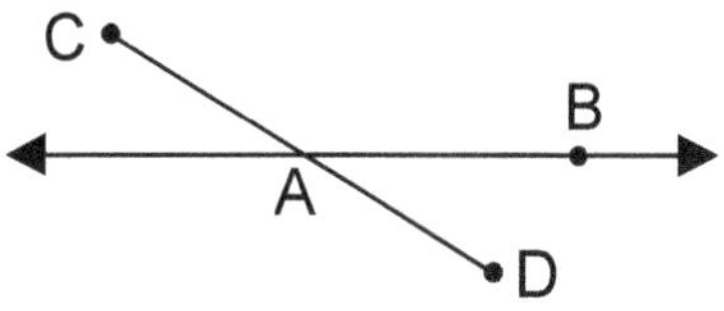

*Many students will try to draw a picture like the one below when they see this problem. However, you SHOULD NOT do this because this picture uses more than one point A, and we only want one point A in any picture. (Note that, if we were to try to talk about point A in the picture below, you would have no idea which point A we were talking about.)

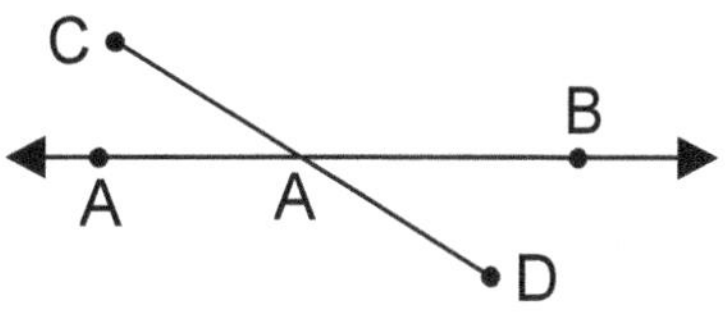

Example 2: Draw a picture to represent the following statement: Plane $\mathcal{R}$ contains line ℓ but not $\overleftrightarrow{XY}$.

Once again, there are several pictures that we can draw, and one of them is shown below.

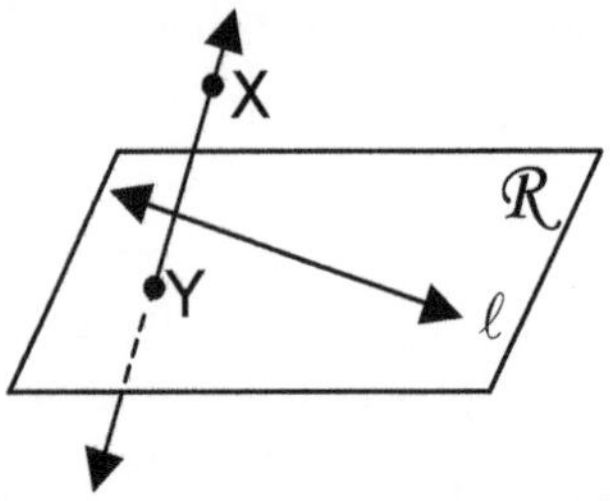

Let's talk about what this figure shows. We drew $\overleftrightarrow{XY}$ so that it kind of comes up out of the page. (The dashed part of $\overleftrightarrow{XY}$ represents the part that you don't see because it is hidden by plane $\mathcal{R}$ in our drawing. In reality, the entire bottom part of $\overleftrightarrow{XY}$ would be hidden by plane $\mathcal{R}$ since planes continue on forever in all directions. However, we can't draw a plane that continues on forever, and so we draw it as shown above.) We also drew $\overleftrightarrow{XY}$ so that it does not intersect line ℓ, but we did not have to draw it this way. Finally, the fact that the point Y separates the dashed part of $\overleftrightarrow{XY}$ from the solid part tells us that plane $\mathcal{R}$ contains the point Y. The question did not say that we had to draw it this way, and so we could have placed point Y at any other spot on the line.

Now, we need two more definitions.

A group of points is called collinear if and only if there exists a line that contains all of the points. A group of points is called noncollinear if and only if there is not a line that contains all of the points.

A group of points is called coplanar if and only if there exists a plane that contains all of the points. A group of points is called noncoplanar if and only if there is not a plane that contains all of the points.

Example 3: For each of the following statements, state whether each is *true* or *false* for the solid shown at the right. (a) Points K, B, and H are collinear. (b) Points K, L, and J are collinear. (c) Points G, Q, J, and K are coplanar. (d) Points K, H, B, and L are coplanar. (e) Points K, J, and G are coplanar.

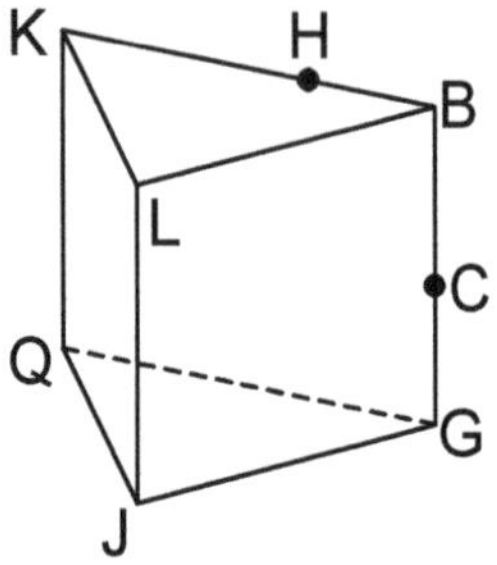

(a) This statement is true because $\overleftrightarrow{KB}$ passes through point K, point B, and point H.

(b) This statement is false because there is not a single line that passes through point K, point L, and point J. We can, however, say that points K, L, and J are *noncollinear*.

(c) This statement is false because there is not a single plane that contains point G, point Q, point J, and point K. This means that we can say that Points G, Q, J, and K are *noncoplanar.*

(d) This statement is true because plane KBL contains point K, point H, point B, and point L.

(e) This statement is true. The plane that contains points K, J, and G is difficult to see because it goes through the middle of the solid and is not drawn, but there is a plane that contains all three points.

Problems:

1-10. For each picture, state which of the answer choices below describe the picture. If more than one answer choice applies, state all that apply. Some of the answer choices will be used more than once.

(a) $\overline{MA}$	**(b)** $\overline{AM}$	**(c)** $\overline{AP}$	**(d)** $\overline{MP}$	**(e)** $\overrightarrow{AP}$	**(f)** $\overrightarrow{PA}$
(g) $\overrightarrow{PM}$	**(h)** $\overrightarrow{MP}$	**(i)** $\overleftrightarrow{PM}$	**(j)** $\overleftrightarrow{AM}$	**(k)** $\overleftrightarrow{PA}$	**(l)** $\overleftrightarrow{MA}$

1. ____________

2. ____________

3. ____________

4. ____________

5. ____________

6. ____________

7. ____________

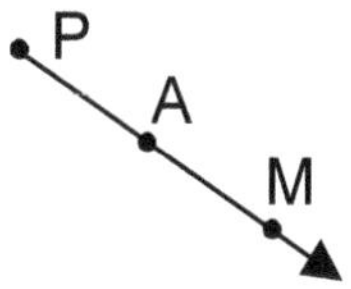

8. ____________

9. ____________

10. ____________

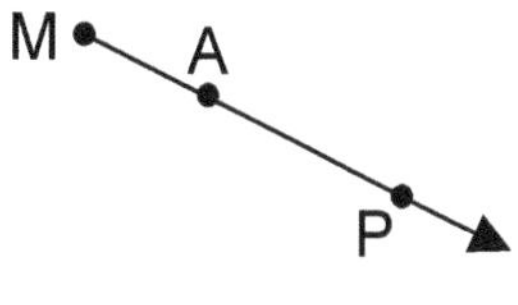

11-16. State all the possible ways of naming each picture shown.

11. ____________________

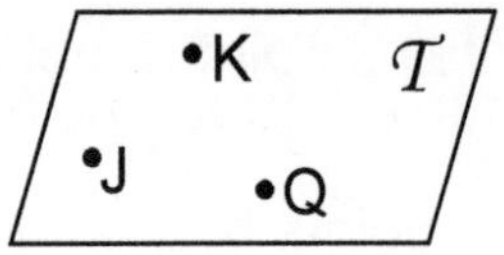

12. ____________________

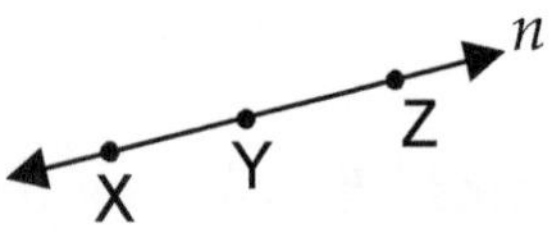

13. ____________________

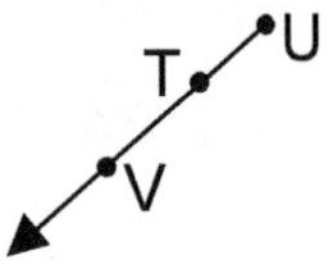

14. ____________________

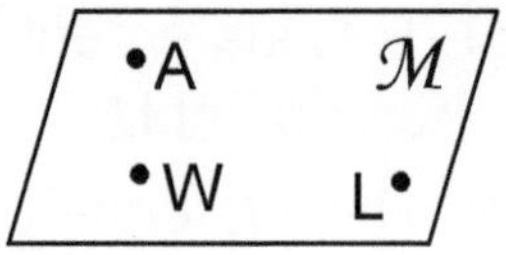

15. ____________________

16. ____________________

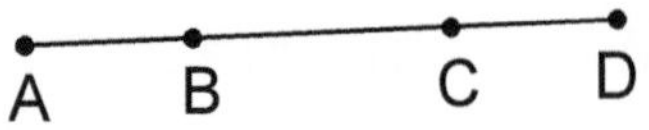

17-26. For each of the statements below, state whether each is *true* or *false* for the solid shown at the right.

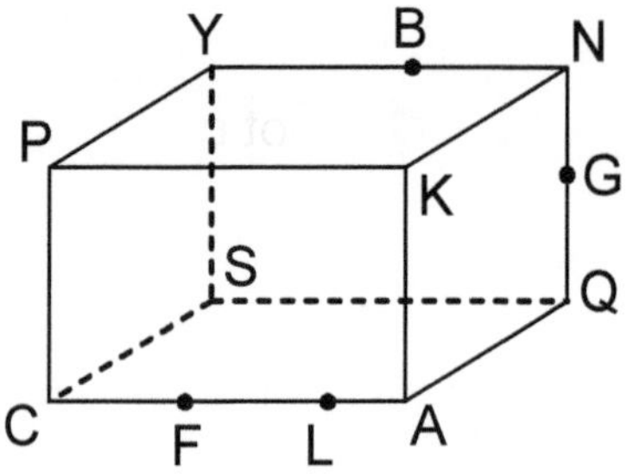

17. Points Y, B, and P are collinear. __________

18. Points P, B, and K are noncollinear. __________

19. Points N, Q, and G are noncollinear. __________

20. Points F, L, C, and A are collinear. __________

21. Points F, L, C, and A are coplanar. __________

22. Points S, C, A, and Q are coplanar. __________

23. Points Y, P, A, and Q are coplanar. __________

24. Points C, P, Q, and N are noncoplanar. __________

25. Points Y, B, N, G, and Q are noncoplanar. __________

26. Points C, L, K, and Y are noncoplanar. __________

27-40. Draw a picture to represent each of the following.

27. line ℓ intersects line m at point P

28. points A, B, and C are collinear

29. $\overrightarrow{DF}$ intersects $\overleftrightarrow{GE}$ at point H

30. D is not on $\overline{KM}$

31. line p is not in plane TUV

32. points E, F, G, and H are noncoplanar

33. plane $\mathcal{D}$ contains $\overrightarrow{LM}$ but does not contain $\overline{MO}$

34. plane ABC does not contain $\overleftrightarrow{BV}$

35. points W, X, Y, and Z are coplanar

36. line ℓ intersects $\overrightarrow{QS}$ at S

37. points M, P, and N are noncollinear

38. plane GCE intersects line n at point C and only C

39. $\overline{FG}$ and line m both lie in plane FGH, but line r does not lie in plane FGH

40. lines k and ℓ intersect $\overleftrightarrow{WX}$ at W

Part II – Postulates and Theorems About Points, Lines, and Planes

We will begin this section with two definitions.

A <u>postulate</u> is a statement that is accepted without proof.

A <u>theorem</u> is a statement that can be proven using definitions, undefined terms, postulates, and other theorems.

Now, we will state six postulates.

A line contains at least two points.

Through any two points there is exactly one line.

A plane contains at least three points that are not all on the same line.

Through any three noncollinear points there is exactly one plane.

If two distinct planes intersect, then they intersect in a line.

If two points lie in a plane, then the entire line containing those points lies in the plane.

Let's look at what each of these postulates tells us.

A line contains at least two points. This postulate tells us that, if we start out with a line, then we can find at least two points on this line. (In reality, we can find an infinite number of points on this line, but this postulate only promises us at least two.)

Through any two points there is exactly one line. This postulate tells us that, if we start out with two points, then we will be able to find one line, and only one line, that contains both points.

A plane contains at least three points that are not all on the same line. This postulate tells us that, if we start out with a plane, then we can find at least three points that are not all on the same line. (In reality, we can find an infinite number of noncollinear points in this plane, but this postulate only promises us at least three.)

Through any three noncollinear points there is exactly one plane. This postulate tells us that, if we start out with three noncollinear points, then we can find one plane, and only one plane, that contains all three points. (Notice that this postulate states the three points must be noncollinear. If the points are collinear, then there will be an infinite number of planes that contain all three points.)

If two distinct planes intersect, then they intersect in a line. This postulate tells us that, if we start with two distinct (or different) planes that intersect each other, then their intersection can be described as a line.

If two points lie in a plane, then the entire line containing those points lies in the plane. This postulate tells us that, if we start with two points in a plane, then the line that contains those two points also lies in the plane.

Example 1: State a conclusion that may be drawn from the following statement: Points A and B lie in plane $\mathcal{F}$. Also state a definition or postulate that supports this conclusion.

There are many different conclusions that one can draw from this statement, and two of them are discussed below.

The postulate *Through any two points there is exactly one line* tells us that there is one, and only one, line that contains both points A and B.

The postulate *If two points lie in a plane, then the entire line containing those points lies in the plane* tells us that all of $\overleftrightarrow{AB}$ lies in plane $\mathcal{F}$.

Example 2: Refer to the figure at the right. (a) Describe the intersection of plane QSP and plane NRS. (b) Which postulate(s), definition(s), and/or theorem(s) tell us that points R and S are collinear? (c) Are $\overleftrightarrow{SQ}$ and $\overleftrightarrow{SP}$ coplanar?

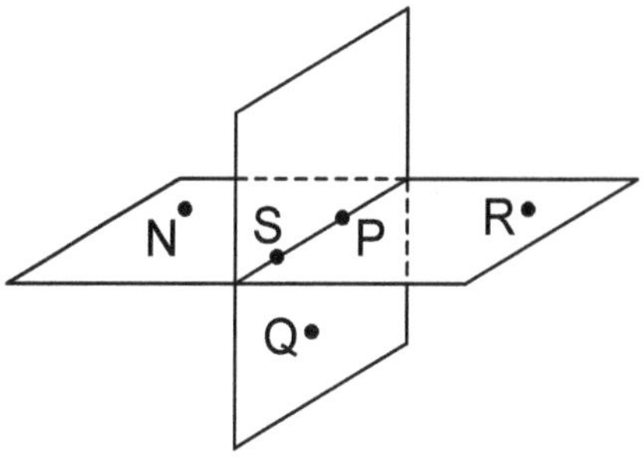

(a) The intersection of plane QSP and plane NRS can be described as $\overleftrightarrow{SP}$. Keep in mind that a plane extends infinitely in all directions in which it starts. Thus, even though the way the picture is drawn makes it looks as if the intersection is a line *segment* because it appears to stop in both directions, the intersection is actually a *line*.

(b) We can use the postulate *Through any two points there is exactly one line* to say that there is a line that passes through both point R and point S. Therefore, even though the line that passes through points R and S is not drawn, we can use the definition of collinear points to say that points R and S must be collinear.

(c) We will begin by noting that, even though $\overleftrightarrow{SQ}$ is not drawn, the postulate *Through any two points there is exactly one line* tells that there is a line, and only one line, that passes through both S and Q. Since plane SPQ contains both $\overleftrightarrow{SQ}$ and $\overleftrightarrow{SP}$, we can say that $\overleftrightarrow{SQ}$ and $\overleftrightarrow{SP}$ are coplanar.

Now, we can state a theorem.

If two distinct lines intersect, then they intersect in exactly one point.

As we said earlier in this section, a <u>theorem</u> is a statement that can be proven using definitions, undefined terms, postulate, and other theorems. Therefore, we will show how to prove that this statement is true in our next example.

Example 3: Prove that, if two distinct lines intersect, then they intersect in exactly one point.

Whenever we want to prove a property or theorem, the part of the property or theorem that follows the "if" is the information that is given to us, and the part that follows the "then" is what we are trying to prove. Hence, we can say that we are given two different lines that intersect, and we will call these lines ℓ and m. So, now we can draw the following picture.

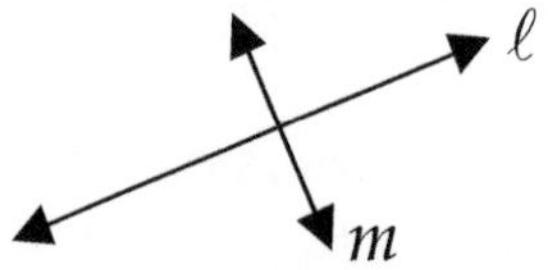

Whenever we draw a picture to go with a proof, we always try to draw the picture as generically (with nothing special about it) as possible. Also, we can tell that this theorem is obviously true by looking at the picture, but this does not *prove* the theorem. To *prove* that this theorem is true (and that it's always true, not just for the picture we drew), we must go through a set of statements and reasons like we discussed in the last chapter.

The definition of the intersection of two lines tells us that ℓ and m must intersect in *at least* one point, and so, in order to prove this theorem, we only need to show that ℓ and m cannot intersect in more than one point. We will use an indirect proof to do this. (As we said in the last section, you do not need to write the information in the third column when you do your proofs; we only do it here to explain what we are doing and why we are doing it.)

Statements	Reasons	Explanations
1. Lines ℓ and m are two different lines that intersect each other.	1. Given	As discussed above, when we want to prove a theorem, the information given to us is the part described by the "if" part of the theorem.
2. Assume that lines ℓ and m intersect in more than one point. Call these points A and B.	2. Assumption	Whenever we want to prove a statement with an indirect proof, we assume that the negation of the "then" part is true.
3. Lines ℓ and m both contain points A and B.	3. Definition of the intersection of two figures	We said in Statement (2) that lines ℓ and m intersect in both points A and B. Then, by the definition of the intersection of two figures discussed in the last section, lines ℓ and m must contain both point A and point B.
4. Lines ℓ and m must intersect in exactly one point.	4. Contradiction	We said in Step (3) that lines ℓ and m both contain points A and B. However, this cannot happen because there is only one line that passes through both A and B.

Problems:

1-20. Refer to the figure at the right.

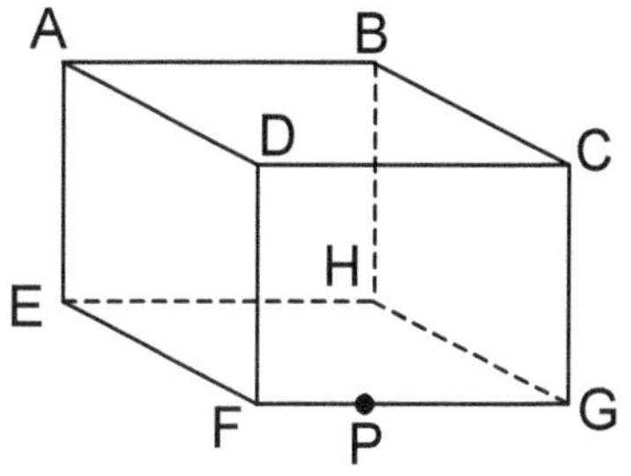

1. Are points D and E collinear? __________

2. Are points D, H, and F coplanar? __________

3. Are points F, G, A, and B coplanar? __________

4. Are points B, C, and D collinear? __________

5. Are $\overline{AB}$ and $\overline{DC}$ noncoplanar? __________

6. Are $\overline{HE}$ and $\overline{CG}$ noncoplanar? __________

7. Are $\overline{AE}$ and $\overline{FG}$ noncoplanar? __________

8. How many lines contain points E and G? Include any lines that are not drawn in the picture but could be drawn. __________

9. How many lines contain points A, P and G? Include any lines that are not drawn in the picture but could be drawn. __________

10. How many planes contain points F, P, and G? Include any planes that are not drawn in the picture but could be drawn. __________

11. How many planes contain points E, A, and C? Include any planes that are not drawn in the picture but could be drawn. __________

12. How many planes contain points B, D, F, and E? Include any planes that are not drawn in the picture but could be drawn. __________

13. Which postulate(s), definition(s), and/or theorem(s) tell us that points A and G are collinear? ____

____

14. Which definition discussed in the last section tells us that points A and B are collinear? ____

15. Which definition discussed in the last section tells us that points A, D, and C are coplanar? ____

16. Name a postulate and a definition that tell us that points A, B, and F are coplanar.

____

17. Describe the intersection of plane ABC and plane BCG. ____________________

18. Describe the intersection of plane DFG and plane CGH. ____________________

19. Describe the intersection of $\overleftrightarrow{AD}$ and $\overleftrightarrow{DF}$. ____________________

20. Describe the intersection of $\overleftrightarrow{BH}$ and $\overleftrightarrow{BC}$. ____________________

21. In the last section, we said that we can name planes by naming three noncollinear points in the plane. Why must the points be noncollinear? ____________________

____

____

Why do we name three points instead of two or four? ____________________

____

____

22. In the last section, we said that we can name lines by naming two points on the line. Why do we name two points instead of one or three? ____________________

____

____

23. Which postulate says that line m at the right must contain at least two points? ______________________________

____

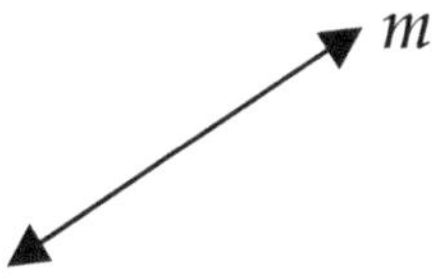

24. Which postulate says that plane $\mathcal{A}$ at the right must contain at least three noncollinear points? ______________________

____

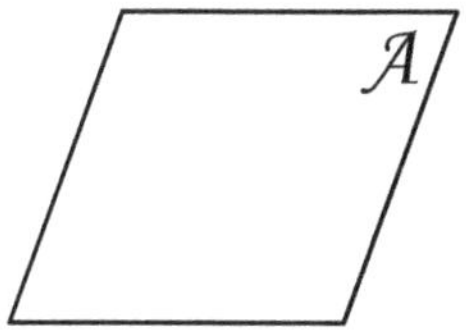

25. What does the postulate *A line contains at least two points* tell us about line n at the right? ______________________________

____

26. What does the postulate *A plane contains at least three points not all on the same line* tell us about plane $\mathcal{E}$ at the right? ______

____

____

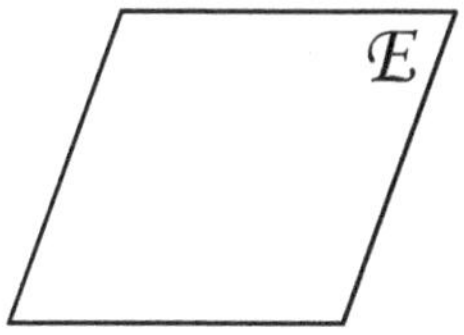

27-31. State a conclusion that may be drawn from each of the following given statements. Then state a definition, postulate or theorem that supports your conclusion for the problems where one is not already stated.

27. Given: Points L, M, and N are noncollinear.

    Conclusion: ____

    Definition, postulate or theorem used: definition of noncollinear points

28. Given: Points L, M, and N are noncollinear.

    Conclusion: ____

    Definition, postulate or theorem used: Through any three noncollinear points there is exactly one plane.

29. Given: There is a line that passes through points C, G, and U.

    Conclusion: ____

    Definition, postulate or theorem used: definition of collinear points

30. Given: $\overleftrightarrow{CD}$ and $\overleftrightarrow{JK}$ are two different lines that intersect each other.

Conclusion: ____

Definition, postulate or theorem used: ______________________________

____

31. Given: $\overleftrightarrow{DF}$ does not lie in plane $\mathcal{Y}$.

Conclusion: ____

Definition, postulate or theorem used: If two points lie in a plane, then the entire line containing them lies in the plane. (Use the contrapositive of this postulate.)

32-37. State the information that must be given to you before you can draw the stated conclusion. Then, for the problems where the definition, postulate, or theorem used is not stated, state the definition, postulate, or theorem used.

32. Given: ____

Conclusion: Plane $\mathcal{S}$ and plane $\mathcal{T}$ intersect in a line.

Definition, postulate or theorem used: ______________________________

____

33. Given: ____

Conclusion: Lines u and v intersect in exactly one point.

Definition, postulate or theorem used: ______________________________

____

34. Given: ____

Conclusion: Points X, Y, and Z are collinear.

Definition, postulate or theorem used: definition of collinear points

35. Given: ____

Conclusion: Points R, L, G, and I are noncoplanar.

Definition, postulate or theorem used: definition of noncoplanar points

36. Given: ______________________________

Conclusion: There is exactly one plane that contains points O, P, and Q.

Definition, postulate or theorem used: ______________________________

____

37. Given: ______________________________

Conclusion: The entire line containing points D and E lies in plane $\mathcal{H}$.

Definition, postulate or theorem used: ______________________________

____

38. Prove the following statement: If two lines intersect, then they are coplanar.

Given: Lines m and n intersect.

Prove: Lines m and n are coplanar.

Statements	Reasons
1.	1. Given
2. Lines m and n intersect in exactly one point. Call this point A.	2. If two lines intersect, then they intersect in exactly one point.
3. Lines m and n both contain point A.	3. Definition of point of intersection
4. Line m contains at least one more point. Call this point B. Line n contains at least one more point. Call this point C.	4.
5. There is exactly one plane that contains points A, B, and C.	5.
6. Plane ABC contains both line m and line n.	6.
7.	7. Definition of a set of coplanar points

Part III – Segments

We will begin this section with a postulate.

The Ruler Postulate

The points on a line can be paired with the real numbers so that, given two points A and B on the line, A corresponds with zero and B corresponds to a positive real number. If we pair two points A and B on a line in this way, then the positive real number is called the <u>length</u> of the segment, and it is equal to the distance between A and B.

If we want to talk about the length of a segment, we name the two endpoints and do not put a bar over the letters. For instance, if we wanted to talk about the length of the segment below, we could write either PR or RP. Either way, we would be talking about the distance between R and P.

Now, we need three definitions.

A point M is called a <u>midpoint</u> of $\overline{AB}$ if and only if it meets both of the following conditions:
(1) M is between A and B, and
(2) AM = MB

Two line segments are called <u>congruent</u> if and only if the two segments have the same length. The symbol "$\cong$" means "is congruent to."

A point, line, segment, ray, or plane is called a <u>bisector</u> of a line segment if and only if it intersects the line segment at its midpoint.

Example 1: In the picture below, DE = EF. Write three sentences, and use one of the terms above in each sentence.

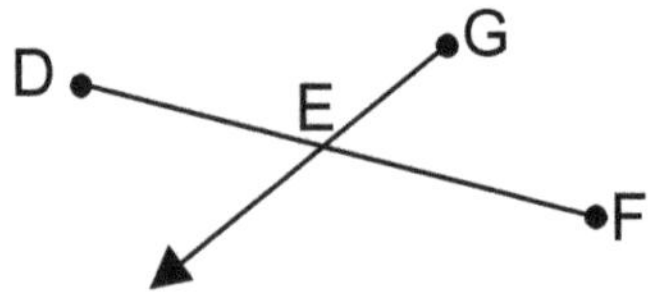

We can say that $\overline{DE}$ is congruent to $\overline{EF}$, and we can write this as "$\overline{DE} \cong \overline{EF}$."

We can say that E is the midpoint of $\overline{DF}$.

We can say that point E bisects $\overline{DF}$, or we can say that $\overrightarrow{GE}$ bisects $\overline{DF}$ at E.

We cannot say that $\overline{DE} = \overline{EF}$ or that DE $\cong$ EF. Whenever you want to talk about the length of the segment (in other words, when you want to use symbols like +, −, ×, ÷, =, ≠, or <), you cannot put a bar over the top of the endpoints.

When you want to talk about the *picture* of the segment (in other words, when you want to talk about congruence, a bisector, or something of the sort), you should put a bar over the top of the endpoints.

Now, we need a postulate and a theorem. You will prove the Midpoint Theorem in the exercises for this section.

A line segment has exactly one midpoint.

The Midpoint Theorem
If M is the midpoint of $\overline{AB}$, then $\overline{AM} \cong \overline{MB}$.

In the next example, we will discuss number lines and how these terms relate to them. On a number line, you can find the distance between two points by counting the spaces between the points or by subtracting the coordinates of the points and then taking the absolute value of the answer.

Example 1: Use the number line below to (a) find the length of $\overline{AC}$, (b) state whether or not $\overline{DB}$ is congruent to $\overline{CE}$, and (c) find the coordinate of the midpoint of $\overline{BF}$.

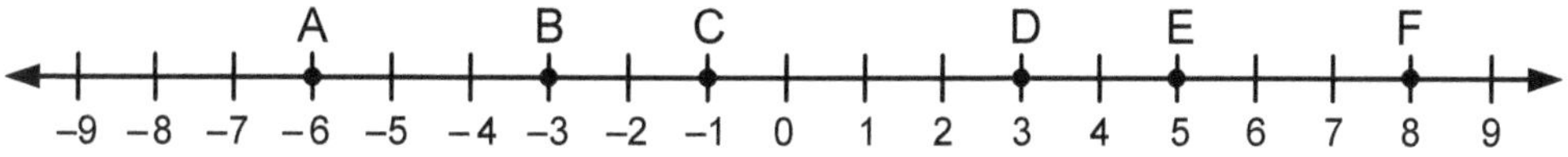

(a) We can say that $\overline{AC}$ is 5 units long. You can see this by counting the spaces between A and C. Or, if you prefer to use a formula instead, you can subtract the coordinates of A and C and then find the absolute value of the answer. If you want to work the problem this way, note that the coordinate of A is −6, the coordinate of C is −1, and both $|-1-(-6)|$ and $|-6-(-1)|$ equal 5.

(b) Using one of the methods discussed in part (a), we can say that DB = 6 units and CE = 6 units. Since these segments have the same length, we can say that $\overline{DB}$ is in fact congruent to $\overline{CE}$.

(c) You can probably answer this question by looking closely at the number line and finding the coordinate of the point that is halfway in the middle between B and F. However, if you prefer to use a formula instead, you can find the midpoint of a segment on a number line by averaging the coordinates of the endpoints. This tells us that the coordinate of the midpoint of $\overline{BF}$ is equal to $\frac{-3+8}{2}$, or 2.5. To make sure that answer this is correct, we can make sure that the distance from the point B (at the coordinate −3) to the point at the coordinate 2.5 is equal to the distance from the point F (at the coordinate 8) to the point at the coordinate 2.5. Since we can use one of the methods discussed in part (a) to say that both of these distances are 5.5, our answer that the coordinate of the midpoint of $\overline{BF}$ is 2.5 must be correct.

In the next example, we will discuss using a ruler to answer questions about segments. The numbers you get may be slightly different from the numbers we give, but they should be fairly close to the ones given.

Example 2: In the picture at the right, use a ruler to (a) find the length of $\overline{MO}$ in inches and in centimeters, (b) state the midpoint of $\overline{KN}$, and (c) state whether or not $\overline{KM} \cong \overline{KJ}$.

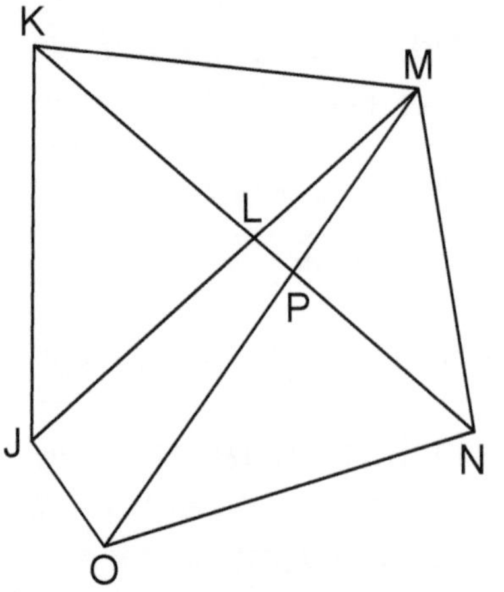

(a) The length of $\overline{MO}$ is about 2⅛ inches, or, equivalently, about 5.4 centimeters.

(b) We will begin by noting that $\overline{KN}$ is 2¼ inches (or, equivalently, about 5.7 centimeters) long. When we divide this by 2, we get 1⅛ inches (or, equivalently, about 2.86 centimeters). Since the point L is 1⅛ inches (or, equivalently, 2.86 centimeters) from both points K and L, we can say that L appears to be the midpoint of $\overline{KN}$.

(c) To answer this part of the question, we will begin by noting that $\overline{KM}$ has a length of 1½ inches (or, equivalently, about 3.8 centimeters), and $\overline{KJ}$ also has a length of 1½ inches (or, equivalently, about 3.8 centimeters). Therefore, based on our measurements, we can say that $\overline{KM} \cong \overline{KJ}$.

As we will discuss further in the next section, you should not use a ruler to answer any of the questions in this book unless you are specifically told to do so. The pictures in this book can and will be deceiving. However, even when they're not deceiving, your measurements may be off by a tiny bit. To see what we mean by this, look back at part (c) of the last example. Suppose that the correct length of $\overline{KM}$ is 3.81 centimeters, while the correct length of $\overline{KJ}$ is 3.80 centimeters. You would have no way of being able to tell this with a ruler, but $\overline{KM}$ would not be congruent to $\overline{KJ}$.

Problems:

1-5. In the figure below, AC = CE. Tell whether each of the following statements is *true* or *false*. Do not use a ruler to answer these questions.

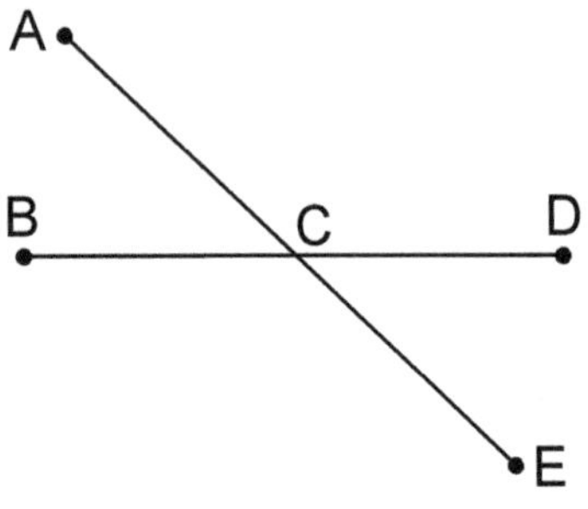

1. C is the midpoint of $\overline{AE}$
2. C is the midpoint of $\overline{BD}$
3. $\overline{AE}$ bisects $\overline{BD}$ at C
4. $\overline{BD}$ bisects $\overline{AE}$ at C
5. AE = EA

6-8. Fill in each of the following blanks with *always*, *sometimes*, or *never*.

6. $\overline{JK}$ is _______________ congruent to $\overline{KJ}$.

7. If $\overline{JK} \cong \overline{KL}$, then J is _______________ the midpoint of $\overline{JL}$.

8. If $\overline{JK} \cong \overline{KL}$, then K is _______________ the midpoint of $\overline{JL}$.

9-18. Use the number line below to answer these questions.

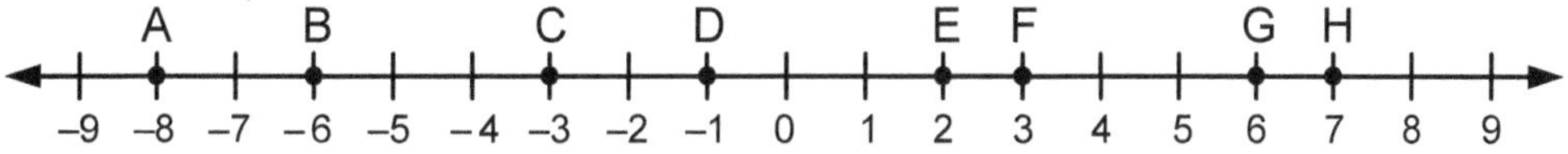

9. What is the length of $\overline{AE}$? ___________

10. What is the length of $\overline{HB}$? ___________

11. EG = ___________

12. AD = ___________

13. What is the coordinate of the midpoint of $\overline{GC}$? ___________

14. What is the coordinate of the midpoint of $\overline{AE}$? ___________

15. True or false: C is the midpoint of $\overline{BD}$. ___________

16. True or false: F is the midpoint of $\overline{DH}$. ___________

17. True or false: $\overline{GH} \cong \overline{FE}$ ___________

18. True or false: $\overline{AB} \cong \overline{BC}$ ___________

19-28. Use a ruler to answer the following questions about the figure at the right.

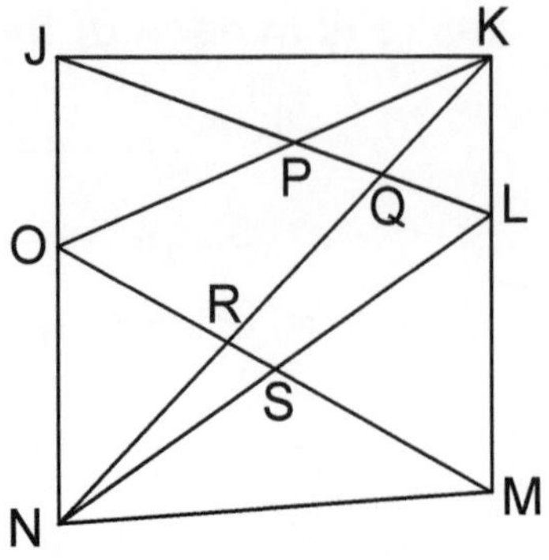

19. What is the length of $\overline{KM}$ in inches and in centimeters?

    ___________ inches

    ___________ centimeters

20. What is the length of $\overline{JL}$ in inches and in centimeters?

    ___________ inches

    ___________ centimeters

21. OK = ___________ millimeters

22. MN = ___________ millimeters

23. ON = ___________ inches

24. RK = ___________ inches

25. True or false: S is the midpoint of $\overline{NL}$. ___________

26. True or false: R is the midpoint of $\overline{OM}$. ___________

27. True or false: $\overline{OM} \cong \overline{KM}$ ___________

28. True or false: $\overline{OS} \cong \overline{SM}$ ___________

Part IV – More on Segments

We will begin this section with three more properties.

Reflexive Property of Segment Congruence: Any segment is congruent to itself.

Symmetric Property of Segment Congruence: If $\overline{AB} \cong \overline{CD}$, then $\overline{CD} \cong \overline{AB}$.

Transitive Property of Segment Congruence: If $\overline{AB} \cong \overline{CD}$ and $\overline{CD} \cong \overline{EF}$, then $\overline{AB} \cong \overline{EF}$.

Example 1: Prove the Transitive Property of Segment Congruence.

We can prove this property as shown below. (As we have said before, you do not need to write the statements in gray when you do your proofs; we only do this so that you can better understand what we are doing.)

Statements	Reasons	Explanations
1. $\overline{AB} \cong \overline{CD}$, $\overline{CD} \cong \overline{EF}$	1. Given	When you want to prove a property or theorem, the part of the property or theorem that follows the "if" is the information that is given to you, and the part that follows the "then" is what you are trying to prove.
2. AB = CD, CD = EF	2. Definition of congruent segments	The definition of congruent segments tells us that, if two segments are congruent, then their lengths are equal.
3. AB = EF	3. Transitive Property of Equality	The Transitive Property of Equality tells us that, if a = b and b = c, then a = c.
4. $\overline{AB} \cong \overline{EF}$	4. Definition of congruent segments	The definition of congruent segments tells us that, if the lengths of the two segments are equal, then the segments are congruent.

Next, we will discuss the Segment Addition Postulate.

The Segment Addition Postulate

If a point B is between points A and C, then AB + BC = AC.

Example 2: In the picture at the right, MN = 5 and MO = 12. What is the distance between N and O?

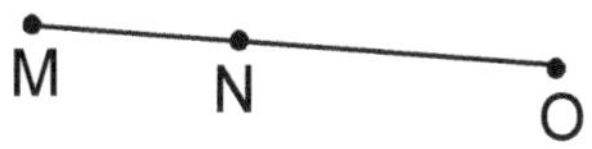

We will begin by noting that, since we can look at the picture and see that the point N is between points M and O, we can say that MN + NO = MO. So, since we were told that MN = 5 and MO = 12, we can say that 5 + NO = 12. When we subtract 5 from both sides of this equation, we find that NO must equal 7.

Example 3: In the picture at the right, PS = 20, PR = 11, and $\overline{QR} \cong \overline{RS}$. Find (a) RS, (b) QR, (c) PQ, and (d) QS.

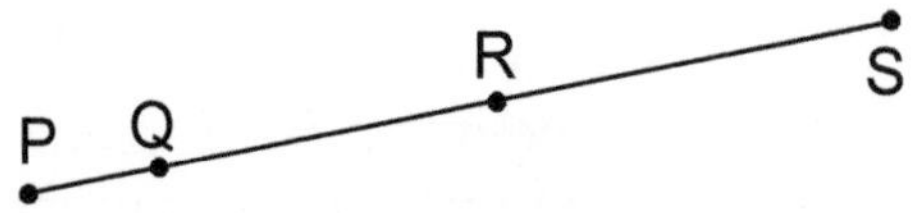

(a) We will begin by noting that PR + RS = PS. Since PR = 11 and PS = 20, we can say that 11 + RS = 20, and so RS must equal 9.

(b) Since we were told that $\overline{QR} \cong \overline{RS}$, we can say that QR must also equal 9.

(c) Next, to find PQ, we will note that PQ + QR = PR. Since we know that PR = 11 and that QR = 9, we can say that PQ + 9 = 11, and so PQ must equal 2.

(d) Note that QR + RS = QS. So, since we know that QR = 9 and RS = 9, we can say that QS = 18.

Example 4: In the figure at the right, V is the midpoint of $\overline{TU}$, TV = 4x – 3, and UV = x + 12. Find the value of x, and then find TU.

Since we know that V is the midpoint of $\overline{TU}$, we can say that TV = UV. So, since we also know that TV = 4x – 3 and UV = x + 12, we can say that 4x – 3 = x + 12. When we solve this equation for x, we find that x = 5.

Now, to find the length of $\overline{TU}$, we will note that TV = 4x – 3 and UV = x + 12. Since we just said that x = 5, we can say that TV = 4(5) – 3 and that UV = 5 + 12. Therefore, both TV and UV must equal 17. Now, we can use the Segment Addition Postulate to say that TU = 34.

Example 5: In the figure at the right, G is the midpoint of $\overline{FH}$, GF = 3y – 5, and FH = y + 17. Find the length of $\overline{GH}$.

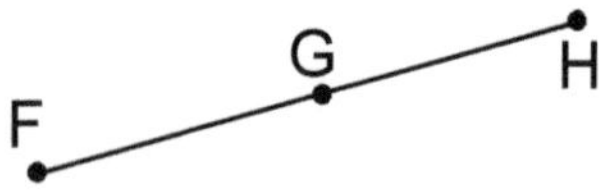

We will begin by noting that we can say that FG = GH since we were told that G is the midpoint of $\overline{FH}$. Hence, GH = 3y – 5. We will also note that the Segment Addition Postulate tells us that FG + GH = FH. This tells us that we can write 3y – 5 + 3y – 5 = y + 17. When we solve this equation for y, we find that $y = \frac{27}{5}$.

Now, to find GH, recall that we said that GH = 3y – 5. This means that GH must equal $3\left(\frac{27}{5}\right) - 5$, or $\frac{56}{5}$.

Finally, as we discussed in the last section, you should not use a ruler to answer any questions in this book unless the question specifically tells you to do so. Also, if two segments look like they are congruent, you should not assume that they are congruent unless you are told that they are congruent or you can prove that they are congruent. Furthermore, if two segments look like they are *not* congruent, you should not assume that they are not congruent unless you are told that they are not congruent or you can prove that they are not congruent. Many of the pictures in this book can and will be deceiving.

Problems:

1-4. In the figure at the right, O is the midpoint of $\overline{MQ}$, N is the midpoint of $\overline{MO}$, MQ = 24, and OP = 5. Find each of the following.

1. MN = _______________

2. PQ = _______________

3. NP = _______________

4. NQ = _______________

5-8. In the figure at the right, UW = 6, WY = 9, XZ = 8, and YZ = 3. Find each of the following.

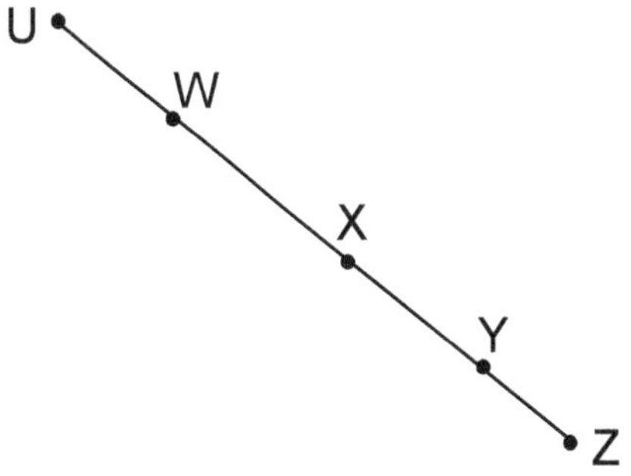

5. XW = _______________

6. XY = _______________

7. WZ = _______________

8. UX = _______________

9. In the figure at the right, EF = x + 4, FG = 2x – 7, and EG = 15. Then x = ____________ and EF = ____________.

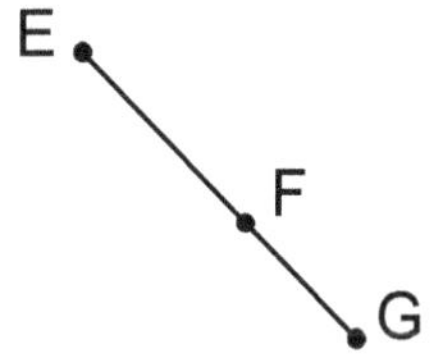

10. In the figure at the right, HI = 3x, IJ = x + 2, and HJ = 7x – 1. Then x = ____________ and HJ = ____________.

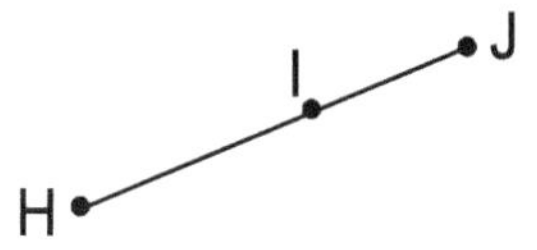

11. In the figure at the right, KL = 5y + 4, KM = 7y + 14, and $\overline{KL} \cong \overline{LM}$. Then LM = ____________ and KM = ____________.

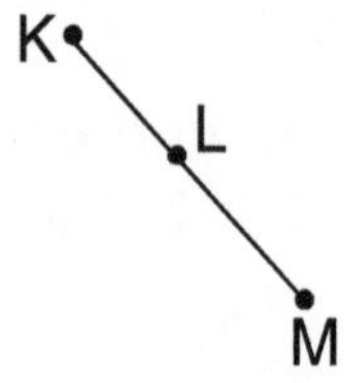

12. In the figure at the right, NO = x + 2, OP = 4x – 10, and $\overline{NO} \cong \overline{OP}$. Then NO = ____________ and NP = ____________.

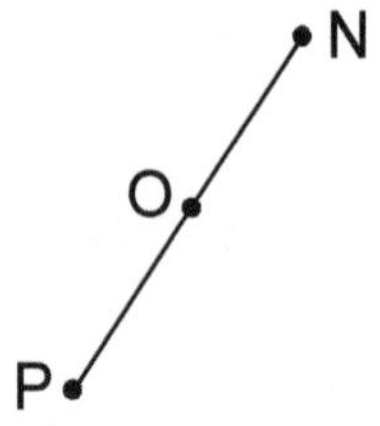

13. In the figure at the right, QR = 2n – 2, RS = n + 3, ST = 5n – 8, and QT = 41. Then QR = ____________ and QS = ____________.

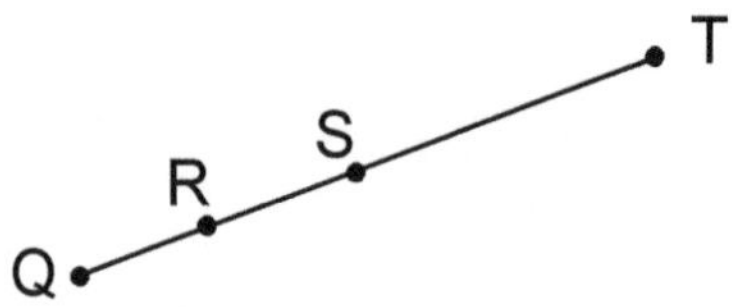

14. In the figure at the right, UV = k – 1, VW = k, WX = 2k, and UX = 7k – 16. Then VW = ____________ and VX = ____________.

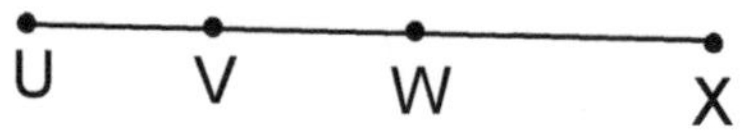

15. In the figure at the right, M is the midpoint of $\overline{AB}$, AM = 5y – 4, and MB = 3y + 1. Then AM = __________ and AB = __________.

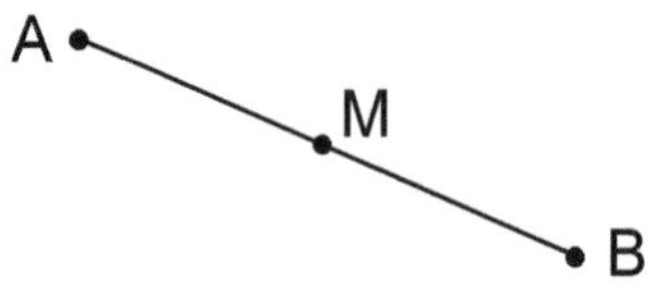

16. In the figure at the right, $\overline{DE} \cong \overline{DF}$, CD = 4n + 3, DE = 6n + 1, and CE = 84. Then n = __________ and DF = __________.

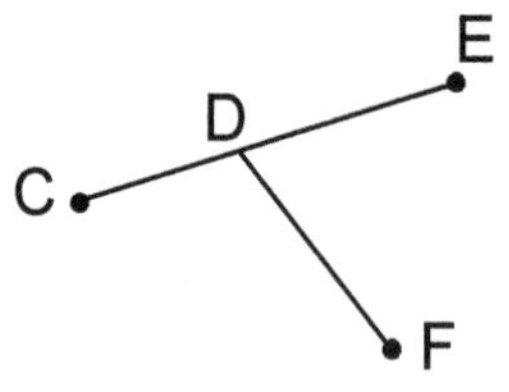

17. In the figure at the right, G bisects both $\overline{HK}$ and $\overline{JI}$, GJ = 2 + 2x, GI = 11 – y, GH = 5x, and GK = 27 + 2y. Then x = __________, y = __________, and GK = __________.

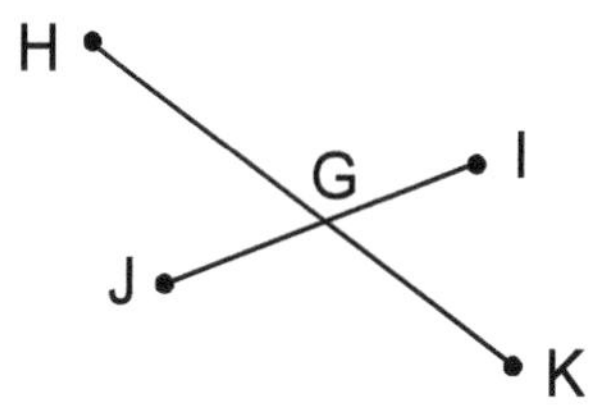

18. In the figure at the right, N bisects both $\overline{MP}$ and $\overline{LO}$, LN = 2x + 3y, LO = 3x + 15, MN = 2x, and MP = 6y. Then x = __________, y = __________, and MN = __________.

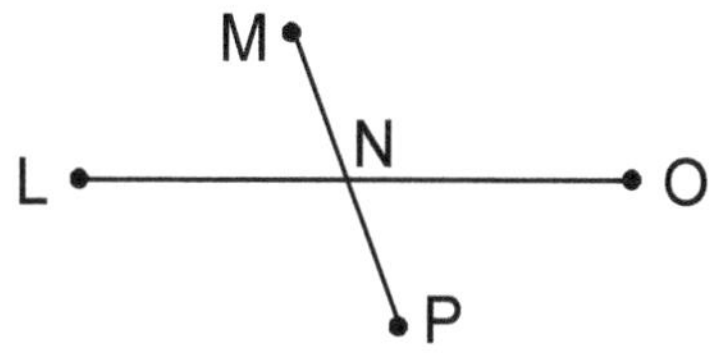

19-22. Complete each of the following proofs.

19. Complete the following proof of the Midpoint Theorem, which says this: If B is the midpoint of $\overline{AC}$, then $\overline{AB} \cong \overline{BC}$.

Given: B is the midpoint of $\overline{AC}$

Prove: ____________________

Statements	Reasons
1.	1. Given
2. AB = BC	2.
3.	3.

20. Write a proof of the Symmetric Property of Segment Congruence, which says this: If $\overline{AB} \cong \overline{CD}$, then $\overline{CD} \cong \overline{AB}$.

Given: ____________________

Prove: $\overline{CD} \cong \overline{AB}$

Statements	Reasons
1.	1.
2.	2.
3.	3.
4.	4.

21. Given that $\overline{AB} \cong \overline{CD}$ in the picture at the right, complete the proof that $\overline{AC} \cong \overline{BD}$.

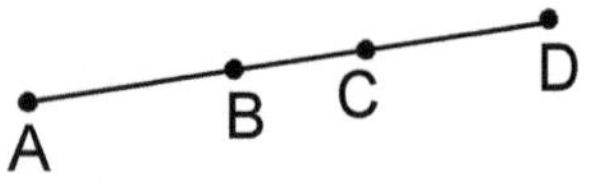

Statements	Reasons
1.	1.
2.	2. Definition of congruent segments
3. AB + BC = BC + CD	3.
4. AB + BC = AC and BC + CD = BD	4.
5.	5. Substitution Property of Equality
6.	6.

22. Given that $\overline{EG} \cong \overline{FH}$ in the picture at the right, prove that $\overline{EF} \cong \overline{GH}$.

Statements	Reasons
1.	1.
2.	2. Definition of congruent segments
3. EF + FG = EG and FG + GH = FH	3.
4. EF + FG = FG + GH	4.
5.	5. Subtraction Property of Equality
6.	6.

Part V – Angles

We will begin this section with some definitions.

> An angle is formed by two rays that have a common endpoint. The common endpoint is called the vertex of the angle, and the rays are called the sides of the angle.

We can name an angle in one of three ways:

- by naming a point on one of the sides, then the vertex, and then a point on the other side
- by naming the vertex if there is no possibility of ambiguity, or
- by placing a number inside the angle

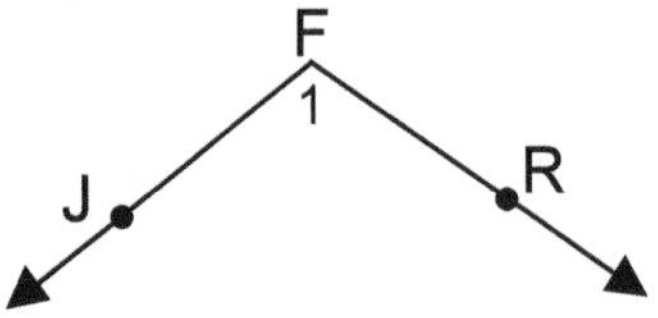

We place the symbol "∠" in front of the letters or number to denote that we are talking about an angle. For instance, we can name the angle at the right by writing "∠JFR," "∠F," or "∠1." We could also call it "∠RFJ," but we could not call it "∠FJR" or "∠JRF" because the vertex must be the middle letter.

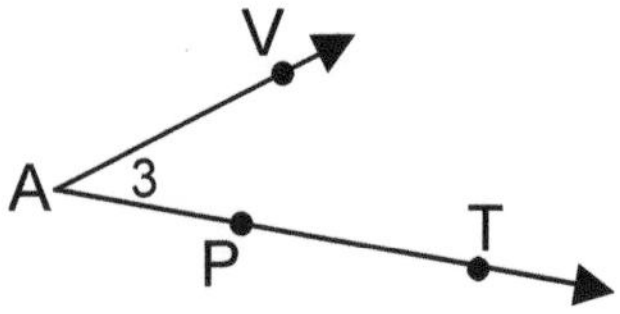

Example 1: State the vertex and sides of the angle drawn at the right, and then state six ways of naming the angle.

The vertex of this angle is the point A.

The sides are $\overrightarrow{AV}$ and $\overrightarrow{AP}$. (You could also say that the sides are $\overrightarrow{AV}$ and $\overrightarrow{AT}$. This is equally correct because you are still talking about the same two rays.)

We can name this angle by writing "∠VAP," "∠VAT," "∠TAV," "∠PAV," "∠A," or "∠3."

We said earlier that we can name an angle by naming the vertex *if there is no possibility of ambiguity*. To understand what we mean by this, look at the picture below.

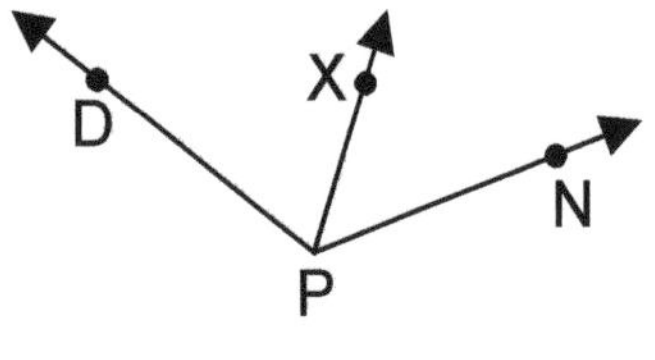

In this picture, we cannot talk about ∠P because you would have no idea if we were talking about ∠DPX, ∠XPN, or ∠NPD.

Now, we need a postulate. This postulate talks about the measure of an angle. We measure angles in units called degrees, and we find their measures by using a protractor. The video that came with this book shows you how to use a protractor.

The Protractor Postulate

Given $\overrightarrow{AB}$ and a number n between 0 and 180, there is exactly one $\overrightarrow{AC}$ on either side of AB such that the measure of $\angle$BAC is equal to n°.

When we find the measure of an angle, we are talking about how wide the opening is. We are NOT talking about the lengths of the sides that are drawn in the picture, as the next example illustrates.

Example 2: Find the measures of both of the angles shown below.

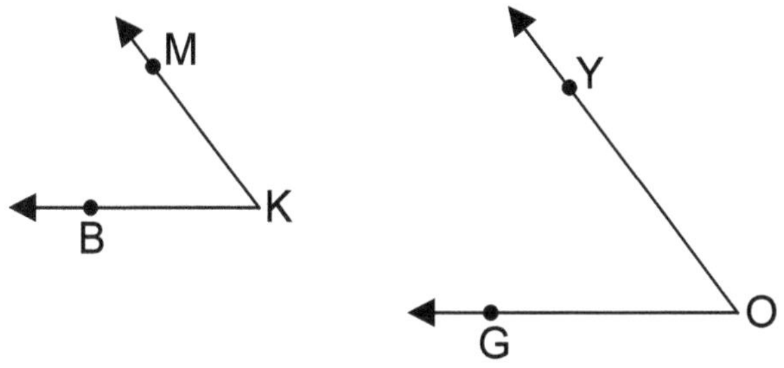

The measure of both of these angles is 52°, as the video that accompanies this book shows.

Now, let's look back at the Protractor Postulate and see what it tells us about the picture on the left. The Protractor Postulate tells us that there are exactly two rays (one above $\overrightarrow{BK}$ and one below $\overrightarrow{BK}$) with their endpoints at K such that the measure of the angle formed is 52°. It also tells us that there are exactly two rays (one on each side of $\overrightarrow{MK}$) with their endpoints at K such that the measure of the angle formed is 52°.

Now, we need four more definitions.

An angle is called an <u>acute angle</u> if and only if its measure is between 0° and 90°.

An angle is called a <u>right angle</u> if and only if its measure is 90°.

An angle is called an <u>obtuse angle</u> if and only if its measure is between 90° and 180°.

An angle is called a <u>straight angle</u> if and only if its measure is 180°.

Example 3: Find the measures of $\angle$ELZ, $\angle$LZQ, and $\angle$EQZ, and $\angle$QKZ, and classify each angle as *acute*, *right*, *obtuse*, or *straight*.

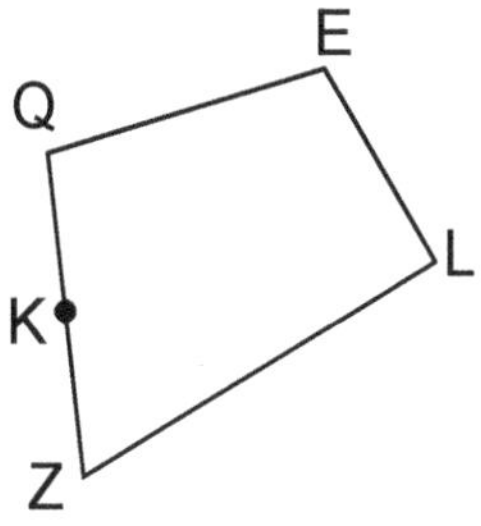

We will begin by noting that the sides of these angles are not drawn as rays, but that does not mean that these angles are not really angles. We could put arrows on the ends of the segments and make them into rays. Also, the answers you get for these questions may be slightly different from the answers we give here, but they should be fairly close to them.

The measure of $\angle$ELZ is 90°. This is a *right angle*.

The measure of $\angle$LZQ is 66°. Since this measure is between 0° and 90°, we can say that $\angle$LZQ is an *acute angle*.

The measure of $\angle$EQZ is 100°. Since this measure is between 90° and 180°, we can say that $\angle$EQZ is an *obtuse angle*.

The measure of $\angle$QKZ is 180°, and so we can say that $\angle$QKZ is a *straight angle*.

Whenever we want to talk about the measure of an angle, we put an "m" in front of the "$\angle$" symbol. For example, we can write $m\angle ELZ = 90°$, $m\angle LZQ = 66°$, $m\angle EQZ = 100°$, and $m\angle QKZ = 180°$. (We read these statements as, "the measure of angle ELZ is equal to 90°, the measure of angle LZQ is equal to 66°, the measure of angle EQZ is equal to 100°, and the measure of angle QKZ is equal to 180°.")

Now, we need two more definitions.

Two angles are called <u>congruent</u> if and only if their measures are equal.

A ray or segment is called a <u>bisector</u> of an angle if and only if it divides the angle into two congruent angles.

Example 4: In the picture at the right, $\overrightarrow{AB}$ bisects $\angle$CAD. What does this mean?

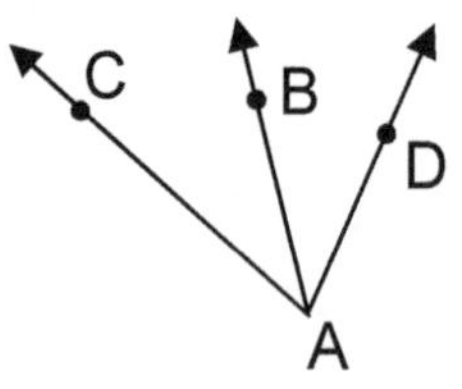

The definition of an angle bisector tells us that this means that $\angle CAB \cong \angle BAD$. We can use the definition of congruent angles to say that this means that $m\angle CAB = m\angle BAD$.

We **cannot** say that $\angle CAB = \angle BAD$ or that $m\angle CAB \cong m\angle BAD$. Whenever you want to talk about the measure of an angle (in other words, when you want to use symbols like +, −, ×, ÷, =, ≠, or <), you must put an "m" in front of the angle symbol. When you want to talk about the *picture* of the angle (in other words, when you want to talk about congruence, a bisector, or something of the sort), you should not put an "m" in front of the angle symbol.

Now, we need three more properties and another postulate. You will prove the properties in the exercises in the next section.

Reflexive Property of Angle Congruence: Any angle is congruent to itself. **Symmetric Property of Angle Congruence:** If $\angle ABC \cong \angle DEF$, then $\angle DEF \cong \angle ABC$. **Transitive Property of Angle Congruence:** If $\angle ABC \cong \angle DEF$ and $\angle DEF \cong \angle GHI$, then $\angle ABC \cong \angle GHI$.

The Angle Addition Postulate

If a point D is in the interior of $\angle ABC$, then m $\angle ABD$ + m $\angle DBC$ = m $\angle ABC$.

Example 5: In the picture at the right, m$\angle OPM = 42^\circ$ and m$\angle MPN = 83^\circ$. Find m$\angle OPN$.

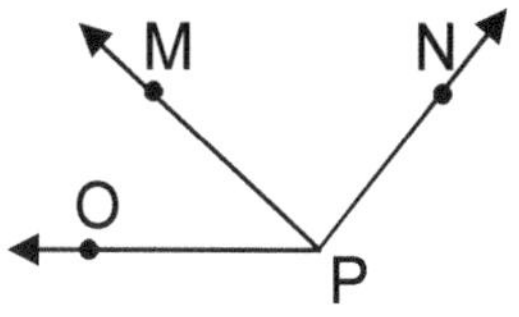

We will begin by noting that the Angle Addition Postulate tells us that m$\angle OPM$ + m$\angle MPN$ = m$\angle OPN$. This tells us that m$\angle OPN = 42^\circ + 83^\circ$, or 125°.

Example 6: Refer back to the picture from Example 4. Suppose that m$\angle CAD = 74^\circ$. Find m$\angle CAB$ and m$\angle BAD$.

Since we know that $\overrightarrow{AB}$ divides $\angle CAD$ into two congruent angles, we can say that $74^\circ \div 2 = 37^\circ$. This tells us that m$\angle CAB = 37^\circ$, and m$\angle BAD$ is also equal to 37°.

Problems:

1-7. For each angle shown, name the vertex and sides of the angle. Then name each angle in as many different ways as possible.

1. Vertex: ______________

   Sides: ______________

   Name the angle in four different ways. _________,

   _________, _________, _________

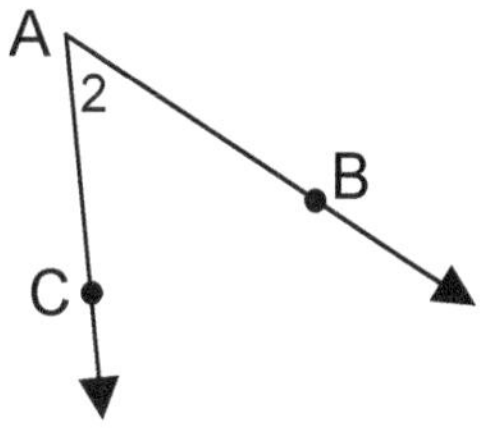

2. Vertex: ______________

   Sides: ______________

   Name the angle in four different ways. _________,

   _________, _________, _________

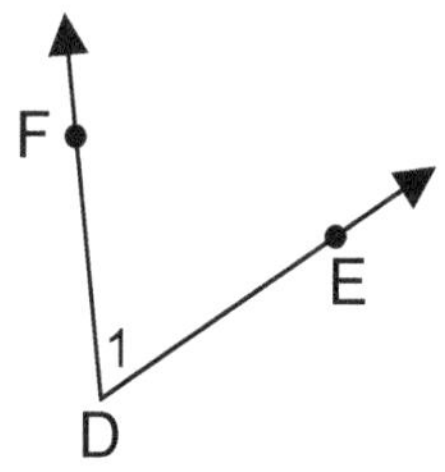

3. Vertex: ______________

   Sides: ______________

   Name the angle in four different ways. _________,

   _________, _________, _________

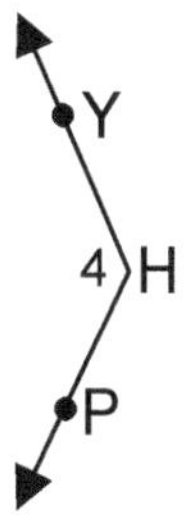

4. Vertex: ______________

Sides: ______________

Name the angle in six different ways. _________,

_________, _________, _________, _________,

____

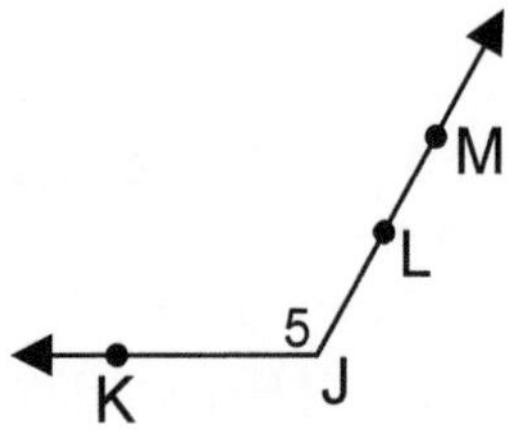

5. Vertex: ______________

Sides: ______________

Name the angle in six different ways. _________,

_________, _________, _________, _________,

____

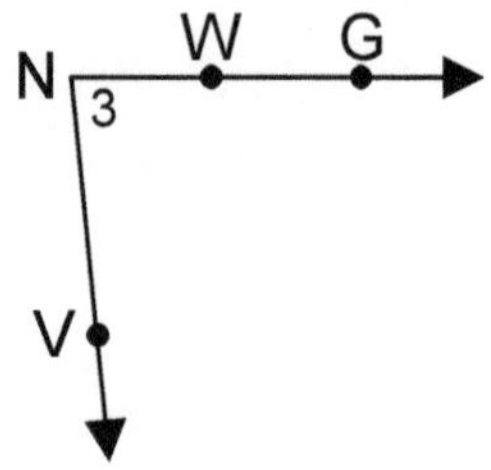

6. Vertex: ______________

Sides: ______________

Name the angle in ten different ways. _________,

_________, _________, _________, _________,

_________, _________, _________, _________, _________

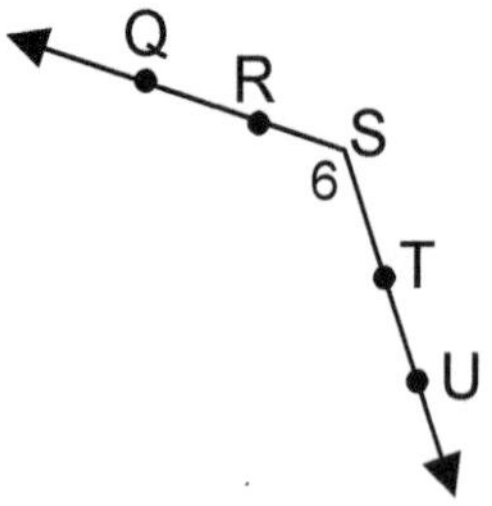

7. Vertex: ______________

Sides: ______________

Name the angle in ten different ways. _________,

_________, _________, _________, _________,

_________, _________, _________, _________, _________

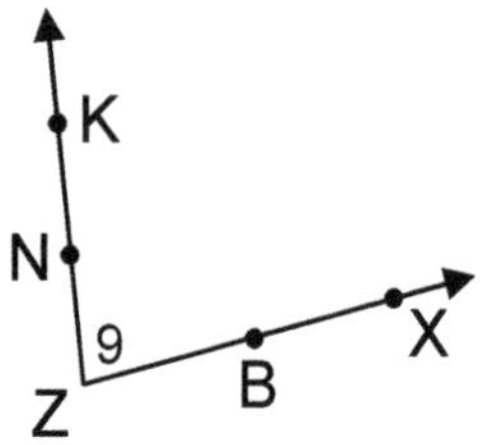

8-10. Name all of the angles shown in each picture.

8. ___________, ___________, ___________

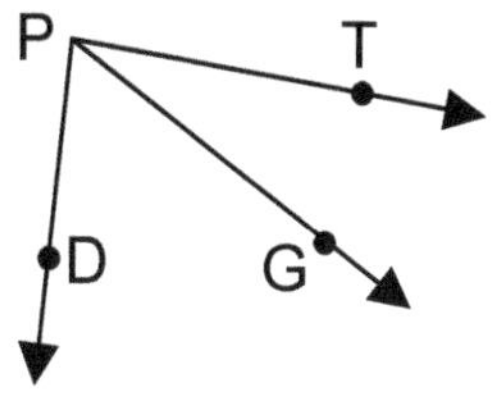

9. ___________, ___________, ___________

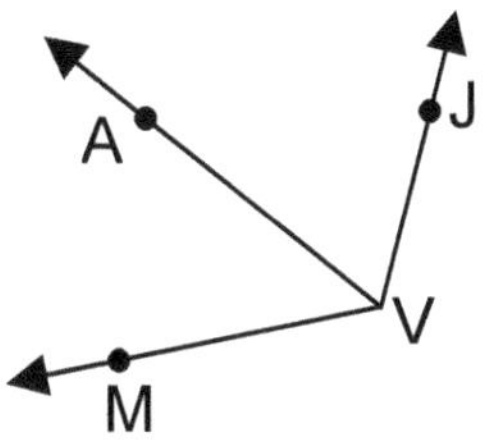

10. ___________, ___________, ___________, ___________, ___________, ___________

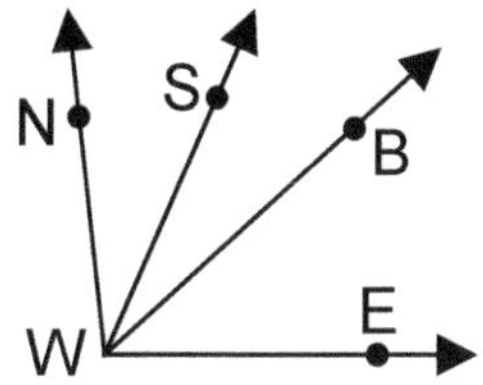

11-14. Use a protractor to find the measures of each of the stated angles in the figure at the right. Then tell whether the angle is *acute*, *right*, *obtuse*, or *straight*.

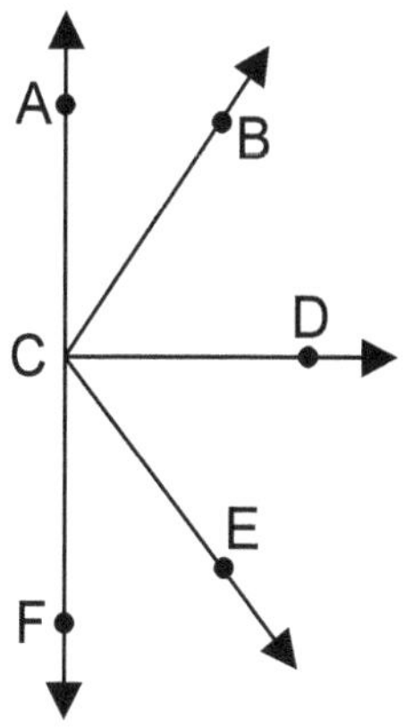

11. m∠ACE = _____________

Is this an *acute*, *right*, *obtuse*, or *straight* angle? _____________

12. m∠ACF = _____________

Is this an *acute*, *right*, *obtuse*, or *straight* angle? _____________

13. m∠ACD = _____________

Is this an *acute*, *right*, *obtuse*, or *straight* angle? _____________

14. m∠BCE = _____________

Is this an *acute*, *right*, *obtuse*, or *straight* angle? _____________

15-26. Use a protractor to answer each of the following questions about the figure at the right.

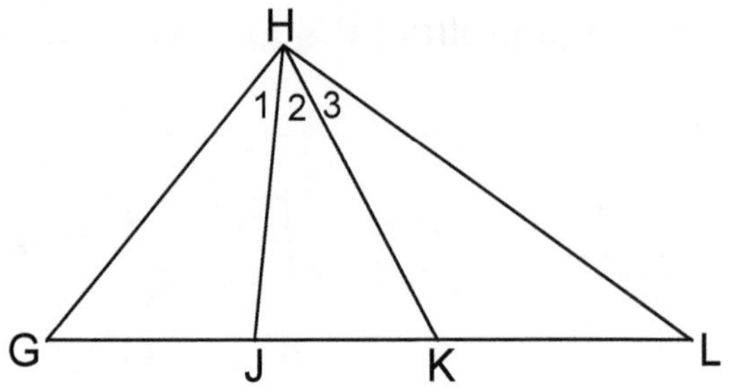

15. m$\angle$1 = ______________

    Is this an *acute*, *right*, *obtuse*, or *straight* angle? ______________

16. m$\angle$G = ______________

    Is this an *acute*, *right*, *obtuse*, or *straight* angle? ______________

17. m$\angle$3 = ______________

    Is this an *acute*, *right*, *obtuse*, or *straight* angle? ______________

18. m$\angle$JHL = ______________

    Is this an *acute*, *right*, *obtuse*, or *straight* angle? ______________

19. m$\angle$GKL = ______________

    Is this an *acute*, *right*, *obtuse*, or *straight* angle? ______________

20. True or false: $\angle G \cong \angle JHL$ ______________

21. True or false: $\angle 1 \cong \angle 2$ ______________

22. True or false: m$\angle$GHL – m$\angle$1 = m$\angle$JHL ______________

23. True or false: m$\angle$GJH + m$\angle$HJL = 180° ______________

24. True or false: m$\angle$JHL = m$\angle$2 + m$\angle$3 ______________

25. True or false: $\overrightarrow{HJ}$ bisects $\angle$GHK ______________

26. True or false: $\overrightarrow{HK}$ bisects $\angle$JHL ______________

27. Use a protractor to draw an angle with a measure of 73°.

28. Use a protractor to draw an angle with a measure of 127°.

29. Use a protractor to draw an angle with a measure of 49°.

30. Use a protractor to draw an angle with a measure of 32°.

31. Use a protractor to draw an angle with a measure of 98°.

32. Use a protractor to draw an angle with a measure of 154°.

33-38. Refer to the picture at the right, and do not use a protractor to answer these questions.

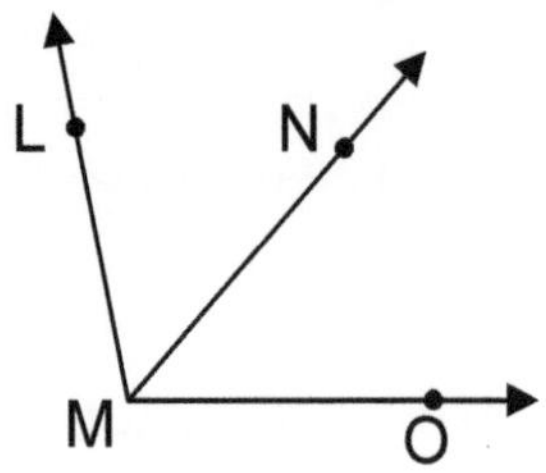

33. $m\angle LMN + m\angle NMO = m\angle$ ____________

34. If $m\angle LMO = 110°$ and $m\angle OMN = 49°$, then $m\angle LMN =$ ____________.

35. If $m\angle LMN = 51°$ and $m\angle OMN = 42°$, then $m\angle LMO =$ ____________.

36. If $\overrightarrow{MN}$ bisects $\angle LMO$ and $m\angle LMN = 53°$, then $m\angle NMO =$ ____________ and $m\angle LMO =$ ____________.

37. If $\overrightarrow{MN}$ bisects $\angle LMO$ and $m\angle LMO = 126°$, then $m\angle LMN =$ ____________ and $m\angle NMO =$ ____________.

38. If $\overrightarrow{MN}$ bisects $\angle LMO$, then $\angle$ ____________ $\cong \angle$ ____________.

Part VI – More on Angles

We will begin this section with another definition.

> Two lines, segments, or rays are called <u>perpendicular</u> if and only if they intersect to form a right angle.

We use the symbol "⊥" to say "is perpendicular to."

Example 1: In the figure at the right, $\overrightarrow{ML} \perp \overrightarrow{MJ}$, $m\angle 1 = (5x + 2)^0$, and $m\angle 2 = (7x + 4)^0$. Find the value of x.

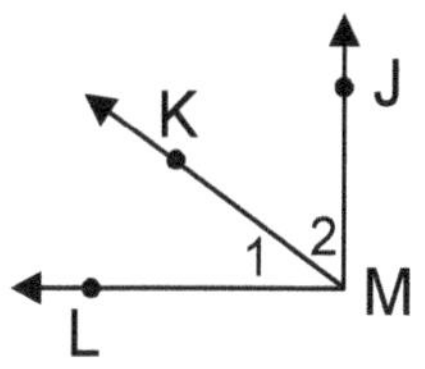

We will begin by noting that, since we know that $\overrightarrow{ML} \perp \overrightarrow{MJ}$, we can say that $m\angle 1 + m\angle 2 = 90°$. This tells us that we can write $5x + 2 + 7x + 4 = 90$. When we solve this equation for x, we find that $x = 7$.

Now, we need two more definitions.

> Two angles are called <u>complementary</u> if and only if the sum of their measures is 90°.

> Two angles are called <u>supplementary</u> if and only if the sum of their measures is 180°.

So, in the pictures below, we can say that ∠A is complementary to ∠B, and we can say that ∠A is supplementary to ∠C.

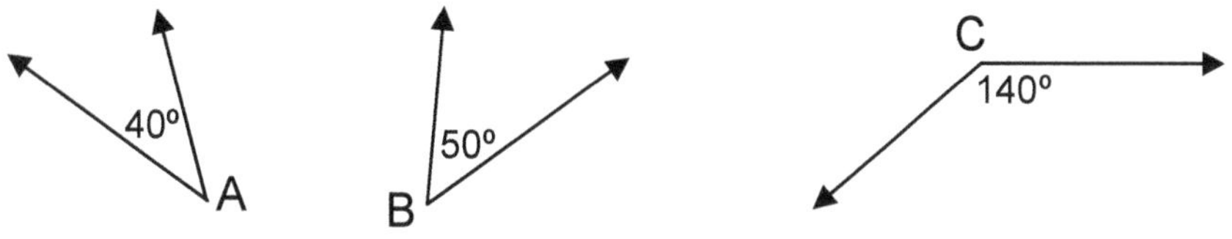

Now, we need two more theorems.

> **Congruent Complements Theorem**
> If two angles are complementary to the same angle, then they are congruent.

> **Congruent Supplements Theorem**
> If two angles are supplementary to the same angle, then they are congruent.

Example 2: Prove the Congruent Complements Theorem.

As we have said before, when we want to prove a theorem, we start by assuming that the "if" part is true, and then we prove that the "then" part must be true. So, we will start by drawing two generic-looking angles that are both complementary to the same angle. (We want to draw generic-looking angles because we want to show that this theorem is true for *all* pictures where two angles are complementary to the same angle, and not just some of them.)

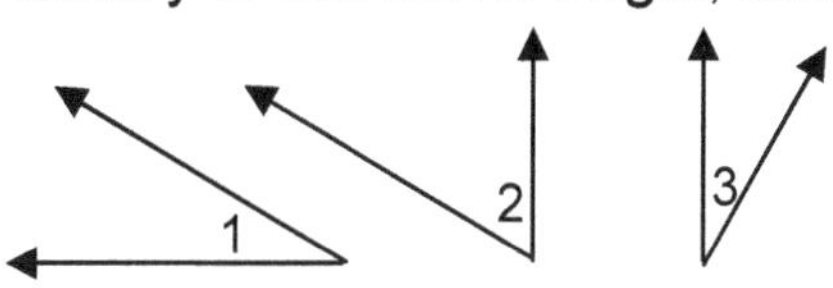

Now, we can write the information that is given to us as "$\angle 1$ is complementary to $\angle 2$, and $\angle 3$ is complementary to $\angle 2$," and we want to prove that $\angle 1 \cong \angle 3$. This tells us that we can prove this theorem as shown below.

Statements	Reasons	Explanations
1. $\angle 1$ is complementary to $\angle 2$ $\angle 3$ is complementary to $\angle 2$	1. Given	This information was given to us.
2. $m\angle 1 + m\angle 2 = 90°$ $m\angle 3 + m\angle 2 = 90°$	2. Definition of complementary angles	The definition of complementary angles tells us that, if two angles are complementary, then the sum of the measures of the angles is 90°.
3. $m\angle 1 + m\angle 2 = m\angle 3 + m\angle 2$	3. Substitution Property of Equality	We already said that $m\angle 3 + m\angle 2 = 90°$, and so we can take the statement $m\angle 1 + m\angle 2 = 90°$ and change the 90° to $m\angle 3 + m\angle 2$.
4. $m\angle 1 = m\angle 3$	4. Subtraction Property of Equality	The Subtraction Property of Equality tells us that we can subtract $m\angle 2$ from both sides.
5. $\angle 1 \cong \angle 3$	5. Definition of congruent angles	The definition of congruent angles tells us that, if the measures of two angles are equal, then the angles are congruent.

By the way, a lot of students try to write "Congruent Complements Theorem" as their reason for knowing that statement (5) is true. However, you **cannot** do this because the question wants us to *prove* that the Congruent Complements Theorem is true, and, when you are proving that a theorem is true, you cannot use it as one of your reasons.

Before we look at the next definition, we will review one concept. Recall that you can form an angle that measures 180° by drawing a pair of opposite rays, as shown in the picture below.

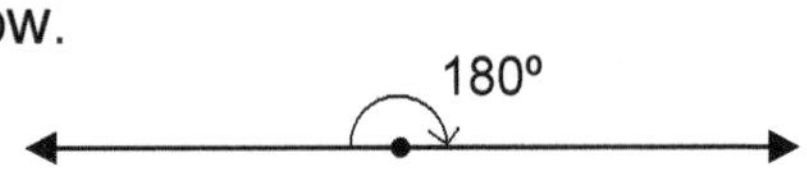

Now, we need another definition.

Two angles form a <u>linear pair</u> if and only if they meet both of the following conditions.
(1) They are adjacent angles (meaning that the angles share a common side, but the angles do not have any interior points in common), and
(2) The sides that the angles do not have in common are opposite rays.

Example 3: In the picture at the right, which angle forms a linear pair with $\angle DHE$?

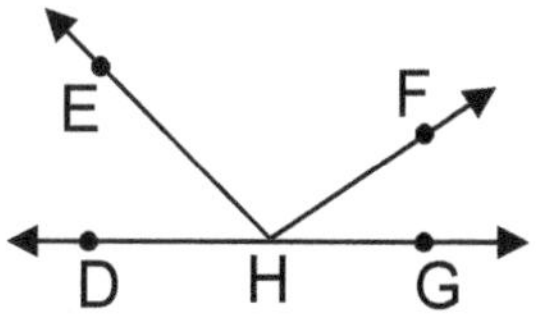

Note that we can say that $\angle EHG$ is adjacent to $\angle DHE$ because they share $\overrightarrow{HE}$, but they do not have any interior points in common. Also notice that the sides they do not share ($\overrightarrow{HD}$ and $\overrightarrow{HG}$) are opposite rays. Therefore, we can say that $\angle EHG$ forms a linear pair with $\angle DHE$.

Now, if you think about what we said about 180^0 on the previous page, you should realize that the postulate stated below is true.

Linear Pair Postulate
If two angles form a linear pair, then they are supplementary.

Example 4: In the picture at the right, $m\angle IKJ = 142°$. Find $m\angle JKL$, $m\angle LKM$, and $m\angle IKM$.

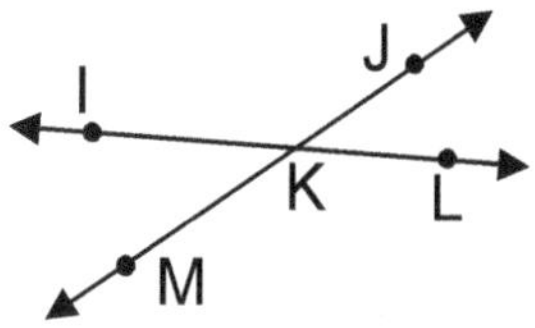

We will begin by noting that $\angle IKJ$ and $\angle JKL$ form a linear pair, and so we can say that $m\angle IKJ + m\angle JKL = 180°$. Since we were told that $m\angle IKJ = 142°$, this means that $m\angle JKL = 38°$. Next, we will note that $\angle JKL$ and $\angle LKM$ also form a linear pair, and so we can say that $m\angle JKL + m\angle LKM = 180°$. Since we already said that $m\angle JKL = 38°$, this means that $m\angle LKM = 142°$. Now, to find $m\angle IKM$, we will note that $\angle IKM$ forms a linear pair with $\angle IKJ$, and so $m\angle IKM + m\angle IKJ = 180°$. This means that $m\angle IKM = 38°$. (You could also note that $\angle IKM$ forms a linear pair with $\angle LKM$, and so $m\angle IKM + m\angle LKM = 180°$. Notice that you would still get the same answer.)

Now, we need one more definition.

Two angles are called <u>vertical angles</u> if and only if they are formed by two pairs of opposite rays.

To understand this definition, look back at the picture from Example 4. We can say that $\angle IKJ$ and $\angle LKM$ are vertical angles. To see why, notice that $\angle IKJ$ is formed by $\overrightarrow{KI}$ and $\overrightarrow{KJ}$ and that $\angle LKM$ is formed by $\overrightarrow{KL}$ and $\overrightarrow{KM}$. Also notice that $\overrightarrow{KI}$ is opposite $\overrightarrow{KL}$ and $\overrightarrow{KJ}$ is opposite $\overrightarrow{KM}$. You might also note that $\angle IKM$ and $\angle JKL$ are vertical angles because $\overrightarrow{KI}$ is opposite $\overrightarrow{KL}$, $\overrightarrow{KM}$ is opposite $\overrightarrow{KJ}$, and $\angle IKM$ and $\angle JKL$ are formed by these two sets of rays.

Now, notice that the measure of $\angle IKJ$ was equal to the measure of $\angle LKM$ and that the measure of $\angle IKM$ was equal to the measure of $\angle LKJ$. This gives rise to the following theorem, which you will prove in Problem #30.

Vertical Angles Theorem

If two angles are vertical angles, then they are congruent to each other.

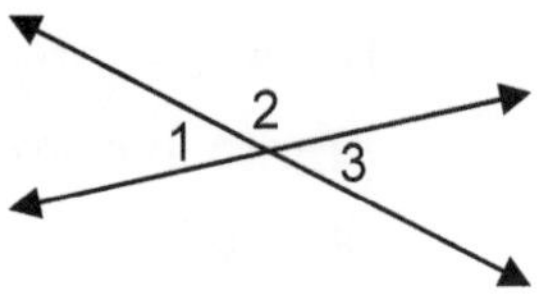

Example 5: In the figure at the right, $m\angle 1 = (y + 20)^\circ$, $m\angle 2 = (2x + 3y)^\circ$, and $m\angle 3 = (2x - 15)^\circ$. Find the values of x and y, and then find $m\angle 2$.

We can use the information that is given to us to write the following three equations: $y + 20 = 2x - 15$ (note that $\angle 1$ and $\angle 3$ are vertical angles, and so we know that their measures are equal), $y + 20 + 2x + 3y = 180$ (because $\angle 1$ and $\angle 2$ form a linear pair), and $2x + 3y + 2x - 15 = 180$ (because $\angle 2$ and $\angle 3$ form a linear pair). Now, we can pick two of these equations and solve this system of equations using either the substitution method or the elimination method. (If you have forgotten how to use the elimination method to solve a system of equations, there is a section in Appendix A that discusses this concept.) When we do this, we find that $x = 30$ and $y = 25$. To find $m\angle 2$, we will note that we were told that $m\angle 2 = (2x + 3y)^\circ$, and so we can say that $m\angle 2 = (2 \cdot 30 + 3 \cdot 25)^\circ$, or $m\angle 2 = 135^\circ$.

Next, we will state three more theorems. You will prove these theorems in the exercises for this section.

If two congruent angles form a linear pair, then the angles are right angles.

If two lines are perpendicular, then they intersect to form *four* right angles.

If two angles are right angles, then they are congruent.

Finally, we will state that, if two angles look like they are congruent, you should not assume that they are congruent unless you are told that they are congruent or you can prove that they are congruent. Also, if two angles look like they are *not* congruent, you should not assume that they are not congruent unless you are told that they are not congruent or you can prove that they are not congruent. Additionally, you should not assume that an angle is acute, right, or obtuse based solely on what it looks like, and you should not use a protractor to work any of the problems in this book unless the question specifically says to do so. Many of the pictures in this book can and will be deceiving.

Problems:

1-15. In the picture at the right, $\overleftrightarrow{AE} \perp \overleftrightarrow{GC}$.

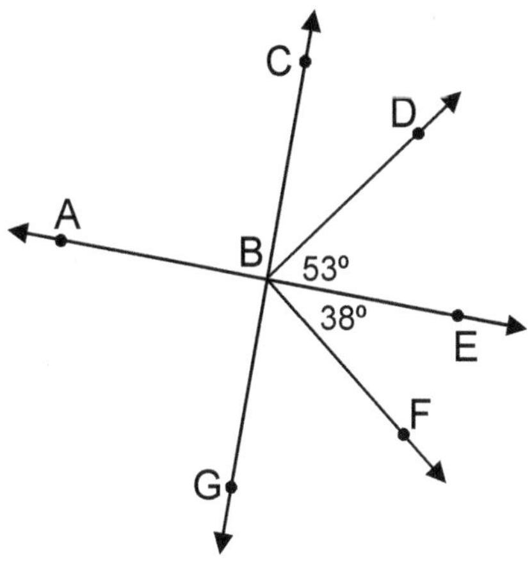

1. m∠CBE = _______________

2. m∠CBF = _______________

3. m∠CBD = _______________

4. m∠GBF = _______________

5. m∠FBA = _______________

6. m∠DBA = _______________

7. True or false: $\overrightarrow{BD} \perp \overrightarrow{BF}$

8. Which angle forms a linear pair with ∠FBG?

9. Which angle forms a linear pair with ∠DBE?

10. Name two pairs of complementary angles.

11. Name a pair of supplementary angles.

12. Name a pair of congruent angles.

13. Which angle is vertical to ∠ABC?

14. Find the measure of an angle complementary to ∠EBF.

15. Name all the right angles shown in the picture.

16. In the picture below, $m\angle 1 = (x + 1)^\circ$ and $m\angle 2 = 3x^\circ$, and $m\angle 3 = (2x - 7)^\circ$.

x = ______________

$m\angle 1$ = __________

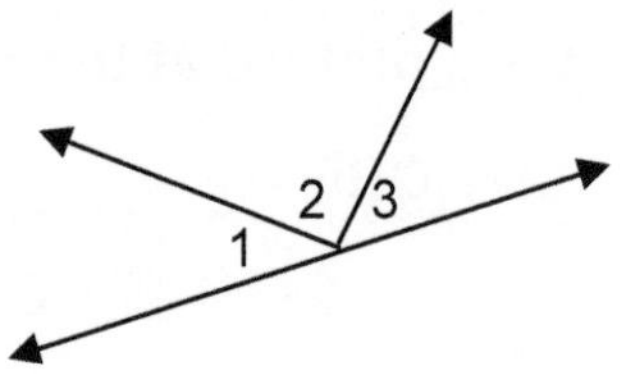

17. In the picture below, $m\angle 4 = (2x + 1)^\circ$ and $m\angle 6 = (3x - 21)^\circ$.

x = ______________

$m\angle 5$ = __________

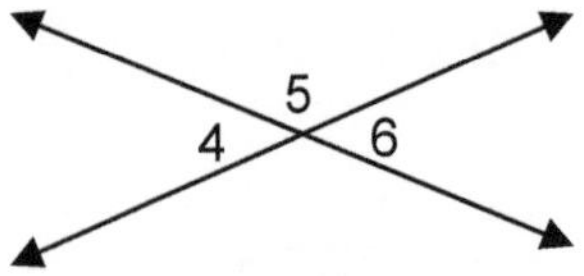

18. In the picture below, $m\angle 7 = (3x - 5)^\circ$, $m\angle 8 = (x + 23)^\circ$, and $m\angle HKJ = 78^\circ$.

x = ______________

$m\angle 8$ = __________

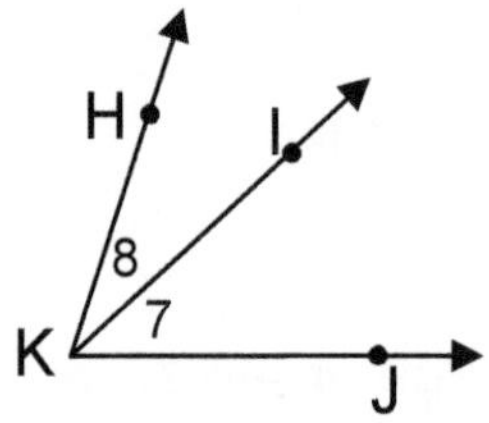

19. In the picture below, $\overrightarrow{ON} \perp \overrightarrow{OM}$, $m\angle NOL = (3x + 1)^\circ$, and $m\angle LOM = (2x - 6)^\circ$.

x = ______________

$m\angle LOM$ = ________

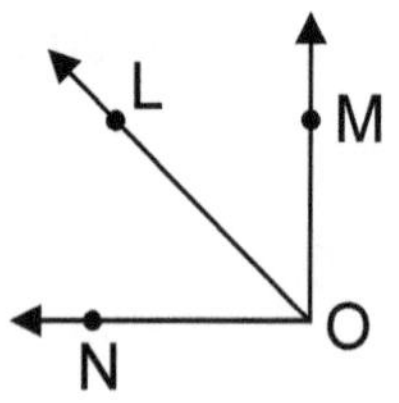

20. In the picture below, $m\angle 1 = (2x + 7)^\circ$, $m\angle 2 = (7y + 6)^\circ$, and $m\angle 3 = (58 - x)^\circ$.

x = ______________

$m\angle 2$ = __________

y = ______________

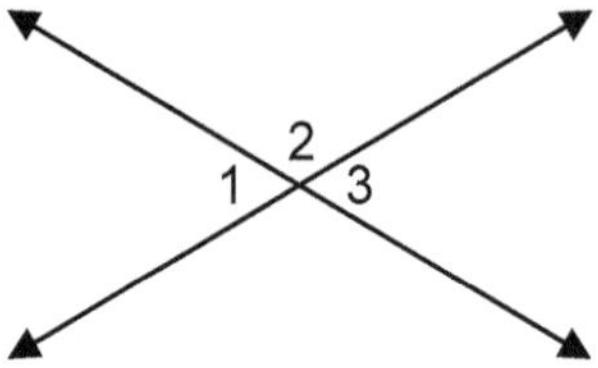

21. In the picture below, $m\angle RSP = 3x^\circ$, $m\angle PSQ = (3x + 15)^\circ$, and $m\angle QST = 63^\circ$.

x = ______________

$m\angle RSQ$ = ________

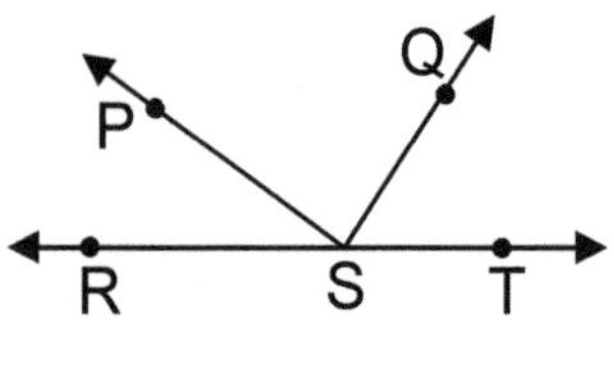

22. In the picture below, $\overrightarrow{XU} \perp \overrightarrow{XW}$, $m\angle UXV = (90 - n)^\circ$, and $m\angle VXW = (2n - 10)^\circ$.

n = ______________

$m\angle UXV$ = ________

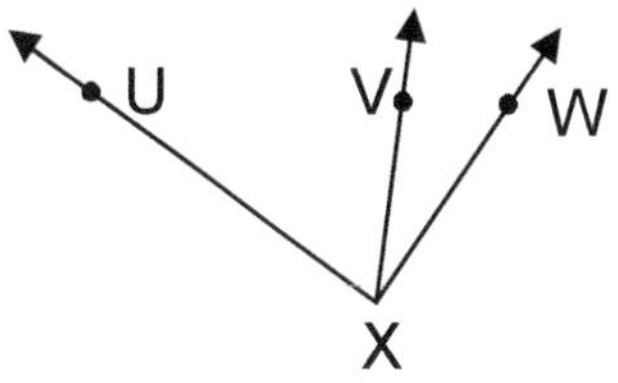

23. In the picture below, $m\angle 1 = (4x - 7)^\circ$, $m\angle 2 = (12x - y)^\circ$, and $m\angle 3 = (8x - 11y)^\circ$.

x = ______________

y = ______________

$m\angle 2$ = __________

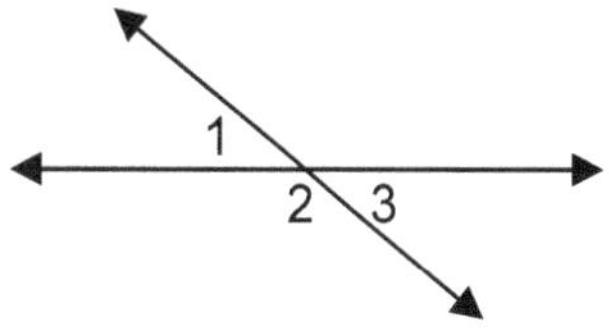

24. In the picture below, $m\angle ACB = 2y^\circ$, $m\angle BCD = (y + 1)^\circ$, and $m\angle DCE = (3y - 1)^\circ$.

y = ______________

$m\angle DCE$ = ________

$m\angle BCE$ = ________

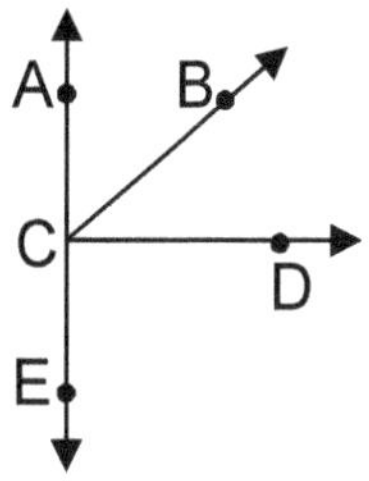

25. In the picture below, $\overrightarrow{IG}$ bisects $\angle FIH$, $m\angle FIG = (x + 17)^\circ$, and $m\angle GIH = (3x - 5)^\circ$.

x = ______________

$m\angle FIG$ = ________

$m\angle FIH$ = ________

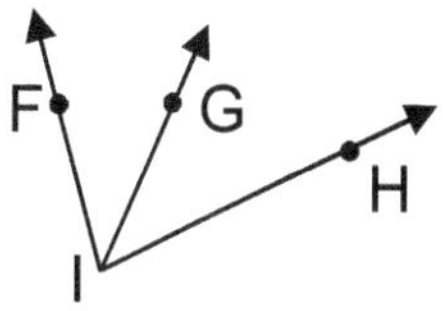

26. In the picture below, $\overrightarrow{LK}$ bisects $\angle JLM$, $m\angle 4 = (3x + 17)^\circ$, and $m\angle JLM = (9x - 20)^\circ$.

x = ______________

$m\angle 4$ = _________

$m\angle 5$ = _________

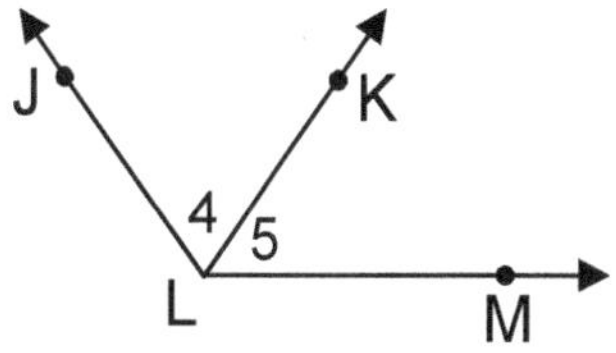

27. Prove the Symmetric Property of Angle Congruence, which says this: If $\angle ABC \cong \angle DEF$, then $\angle DEF \cong \angle ABC$.

Statements	Reasons
1. $\angle ABC \cong \angle DEF$	1.
2.	2. Definition of congruent angles
3.	3.
4.	4.

28. Prove the Transitive Property of Angle Congruence, which says this: If $\angle ABC \cong \angle DEF$ and $\angle DEF \cong \angle GHI$, then $\angle ABC \cong \angle GHI$.

Statements	Reasons
1.	1.
2.	2. Definition of congruent angles
3.	3.
4.	4.

29. Prove the Congruent Supplements Theorem.

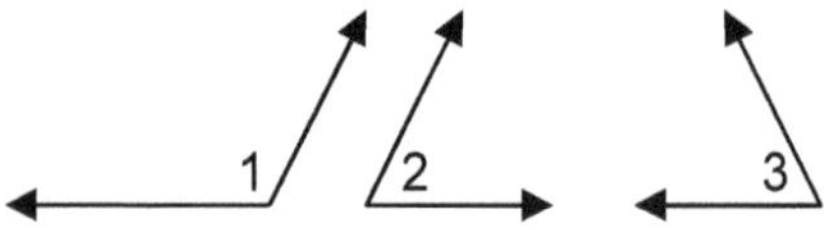

Given: $\angle 1$ is supplementary to $\angle 2$
$\angle 1$ is supplementary to $\angle 3$

Prove: $\angle 2 \cong \angle 3$

Statements	Reasons
1.	1.
2.	2.
3.	3.
4.	4.
5.	5.

30. Prove the Vertical Angles Theorem.

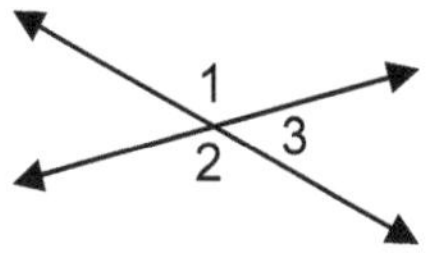

Given: $\angle 1$ and $\angle 2$ are vertical angles

Prove: $\angle 1 \cong \angle 2$

Statements	Reasons
1.	1. Given
2. $\angle 1$ and $\angle 3$ form a linear pair, and $\angle 2$ and $\angle 3$ form a linear pair	2. Definition of a linear pair
3.	3.
4.	4. Congruent Supplements Theorem

31. Prove the following theorem: If two congruent angles form a linear pair, then the angles are right angles.

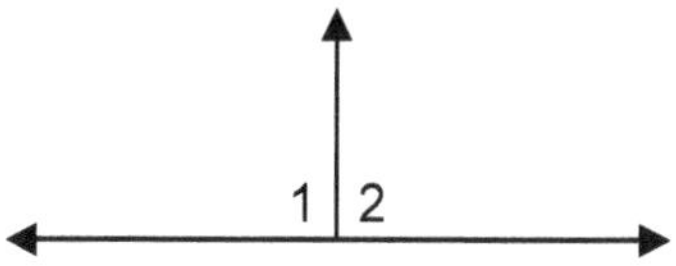

Given: $\angle 1$ and $\angle 2$ form a linear pair and $\angle 1 \cong \angle 2$

Prove: $\angle 1$ and $\angle 2$ are both right angles

Statements	Reasons
1. $\angle 1$ and $\angle 2$ form a linear pair	1.
2.	2. Linear Pair Postulate
3.	3. Definition of supplementary angles
4. $\angle 1 \cong \angle 2$	4.
5.	5. Definition of congruent angles
6. $m\angle 2 + m\angle 2 = 180°$	6.
7. $2(m\angle 2) = 180°$	7. Distributive Property
8.	8. Division Property of Equality
9. $m\angle 1 = 90°$	9.
10.	10. Definition of a right angle

32. Given that $\angle 2 \cong \angle 3$ in the picture at the right, prove that $\angle 1 \cong \angle 4$.

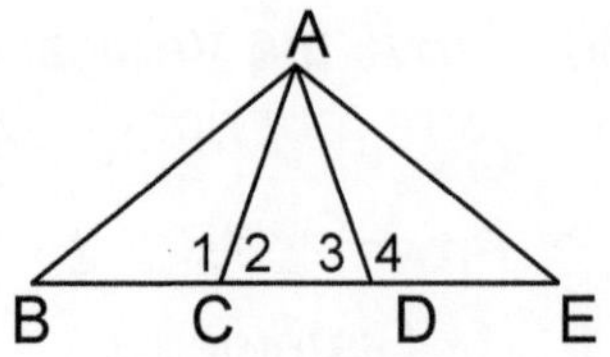

Statements	Reasons
1.	1. Given
2.	2.
3. $\angle 1$ and $\angle 2$ form a linear pair, and $\angle 3$ and $\angle 4$ form a linear pair	3.
4.	4.
5.	5.
6. $m\angle 1 + m\angle 2 = m\angle 3 + m\angle 4$	6.
7. $m\angle 1 + m\angle 2 = m\angle 2 + m\angle 4$	7.
8.	8.
9.	9.

33. Prove the following theorem: If two lines are perpendicular, then they intersect to form *four* right angles.

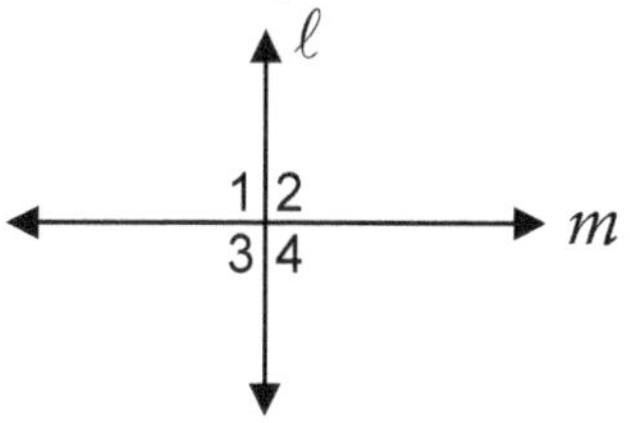

Given: $\ell \perp m$, making $\angle 1$ a right angle

Prove: $\angle 2$, $\angle 3$, and $\angle 4$ are all right angles

Statements	Reasons
1. $\ell \perp m$, making $\angle 1$ a right angle	1.
2.	2. Definition of right angle
3. $\angle 1$ and $\angle 2$ form a linear pair $\angle 1$ and $\angle 3$ form a linear pair	3. Definition of a linear pair
4. $\angle 1$ and $\angle 2$ are supplementary $\angle 1$ and $\angle 3$ are supplementary	4.
5.	5.
6. $90° + m\angle 2 = 180°$ $90° + m\angle 3 = 180°$	6.
7.	7. Subtraction Property of Equality
8. $\angle 2$ is a right angle $\angle 3$ is a right angle	8.
9.	9. Vertical Angles Theorem
10.	10.
11.	11.
12. $\angle 4$ is a right angle	12.

34. Given that $\overleftrightarrow{AE} \perp \overrightarrow{FC}$ and that $\angle 1 \cong \angle 3$ in the figure at the right, prove that $\angle 2 \cong \angle 4$.

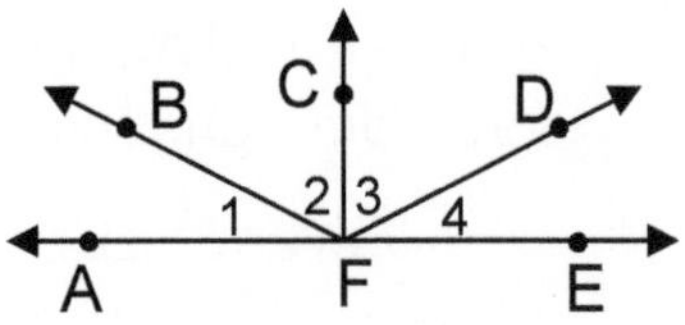

Statements	Reasons
1. $\overleftrightarrow{AE} \perp \overrightarrow{FC}$	1.
2.	2. If two lines are perpendicular, then they intersect to form four right angles.
3.	3.
4. $m\angle 1 + m\angle 2 = m\angle AFC$ and $m\angle 3 + m\angle 4 = m\angle CFE$	4.
5. $m\angle 1 + m\angle 2 = 90°$ and $m\angle 3 + m\angle 4 = 90°$	5.
6. $m\angle 1 + m\angle 2 = m\angle 3 + m\angle 4$	6.
7. $\angle 1 \cong \angle 3$	7.
8.	8. Definition of congruent angles
9. $m\angle 1 + m\angle 2 = m\angle 1 + m\angle 4$	9.
10.	10.
11.	11.

35. Prove the following theorem: If two angles are right angles, then they are congruent.

Given: $\angle 1$ and $\angle 2$ are right angles

Prove: $\angle 1 \cong \angle 2$

Statements	Reasons
1.	1.
2.	2.
3.	3.
4.	4.

Part VII – Mixed Review

1. Nadine buys a dishwasher, and then it begins to leak two weeks after she installs it. She goes back to the store and exchanges it for another model that is made by the same company. This dishwasher begins to leak four days after she installs it. Nadine concludes that all dishwashers made by this company are defective. Is this an example of inductive or deductive reasoning? ________________

2. David's teacher tells him that all right angles have measures of 90°. He also knows that $\angle ABC$ is a right angle, and so he concludes that $\angle ABC$ must have a measure of 90°. Is this an example of inductive or deductive reasoning? ________________

3. Write the converse, inverse, and contrapositive of the following statement, and then tell whether each is *true* or *false*: *All obtuse angles have measures of 133°.*

   True or false?

   converse:

   True or false?

   inverse:

   True or false?

   contrapositive:

   True or false?

4. True or false: An angle is an acute angle if and only if its measure is 75°. __________

5. Prove the following statement: If $2x - 8 = 11x - 35$, then $x = 3$.

6. Prove the following statement: If $3y + 4(y - 2) = y + 2$, then $y = \frac{5}{3}$.

7. Prove the following statement using an indirect proof: If $3k - 10 = 11$, then $k = 7$.

8. Prove the following statement using an indirect proof: If $n = 4$, then $5(n - 3) = n + 1$.

9. Draw point T between points U and V. Then tell which of the following statements are true. Circle all that apply.

(A) $\overleftrightarrow{TU}$ is the same as $\overleftrightarrow{UV}$.

(B) $\overleftrightarrow{UV}$ is the same as $\overleftrightarrow{VU}$.

(C) $\overrightarrow{TU}$ is the same as $\overrightarrow{UV}$.

(D) $\overrightarrow{VT}$ is the same as $\overrightarrow{VU}$.

(E) $\overrightarrow{VT}$ is the same as $\overrightarrow{TV}$.

(F) $\overline{VT}$ is the same as $\overline{TV}$.

(G) $\overline{UV}$ is the same as $\overline{UT}$.

10. Use a protractor to find the measures of the angles in the triangle at the right.

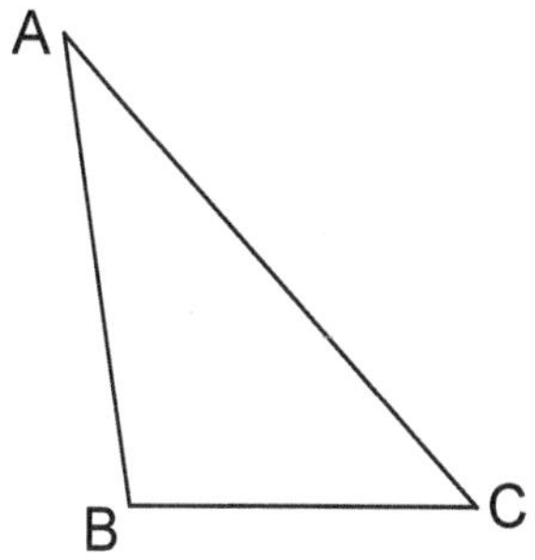

$m\angle ABC =$ ________________

$m\angle BAC =$ ________________

$m\angle BCA =$ ________________

11-20. In the figure at the right, $m\angle LAK = 51^\circ$ and $m\angle MAR = 32^\circ$. (Do not use a ruler or protractor to answer these questions.)

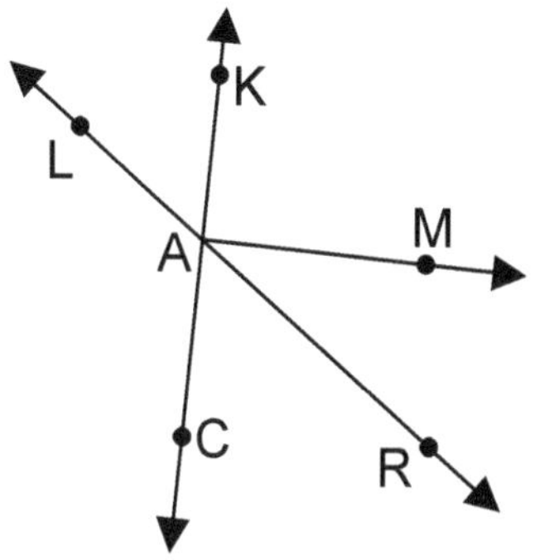

11. Are the points L, A, and K collinear? __________

12. Are the points L, A, and K coplanar? __________

13. $m\angle KAM =$ ____________

14. $m\angle RAC =$ ____________

15. $m\angle MAC =$ ____________

16. Is $\overleftrightarrow{KA} \perp \overrightarrow{AM}$? ____________ Why or why not? ____________________

____

17. Does $\overrightarrow{RA}$ bisect $\angle MAC$? ____________ Why or why not? ______________

____

18. Which angle forms a linear pair with $\angle MAR$? ____________

19. If LA = 8, LR = 19, and $\overline{LA} \cong \overline{AM}$, then AR = _________ and AM = _________.

20. If A is the midpoint of $\overline{KC}$ and KC = 10, then AC = _________ and AK = _________.

21. In the figure at the right, $m\angle 1 = (2x - 5)°$, $m\angle 2 = 2y°$, and $m\angle 3 = (x + 18)°$. Then x = _________, y = _________, $m\angle 1$ = _________, and $m\angle 2$ = _________. (Do not use a protractor.)

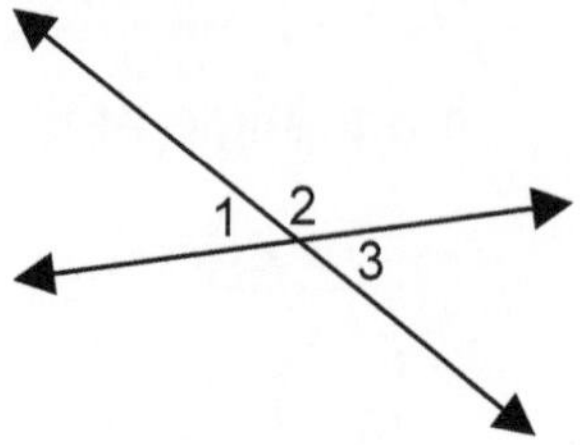

22. In the figure at the right, $m\angle 4 = (5a + 4)°$, $m\angle 5 = 3a°$, and $\angle 5 \cong \angle 6$. Then a = _________ and $m\angle 4$ = _________. (Do not use a protractor.)

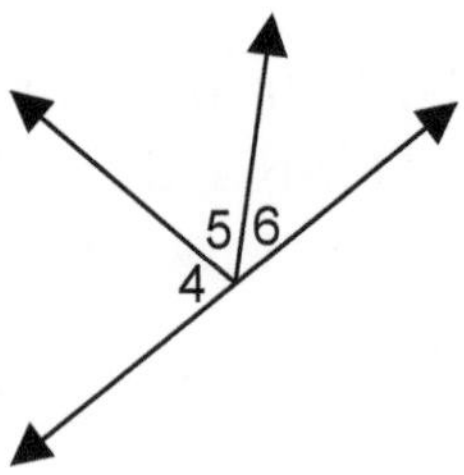

23. In the figure at the right, ST = 6 – 5b, SW = 3b + 50, and TW = b + 30. Then b = _________ and SW = _________. (Do not use a ruler.)

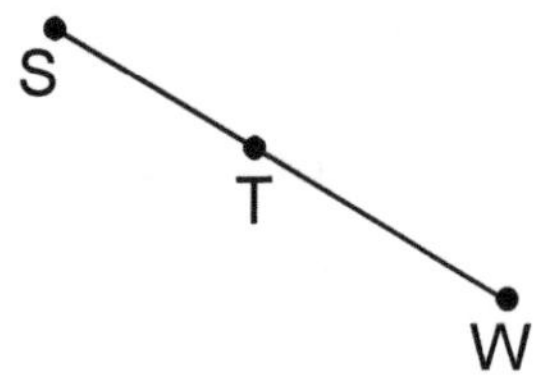

24. Draw a picture to represent the following statement: The intersection of plane $\mathcal{X}$ and plane $\mathcal{W}$ is $\overleftrightarrow{LN}$.

25. Draw a picture to represent the following statement: Plane PQR contains point Z but not line m.

26. Draw a picture to represent the following statement: $\angle$ABC and $\angle$DBE are vertical angles.

27. Draw a picture to represent the following statement: ∠FGH and ∠JKL are complementary angles.

28. We can only talk about the midpoint of a line segment, and not a ray or a line.

Why? ____

____

29. A table with four or more legs may wobble, but a table with three legs will not wobble. Which postulate or theorem proves this fact? ____________________

____

30. State a conclusion that may be drawn from the following statement: Points F, G, and H are collinear. ______________________________

Which definition, postulate, or theorem supports your conclusion? __________

____

31. What does the postulate *A line contains at least two points* tell you about the figure at the right? ____________________

____

32. Name the vertex and the sides of the angle at the right. Then name this angle in six different ways.

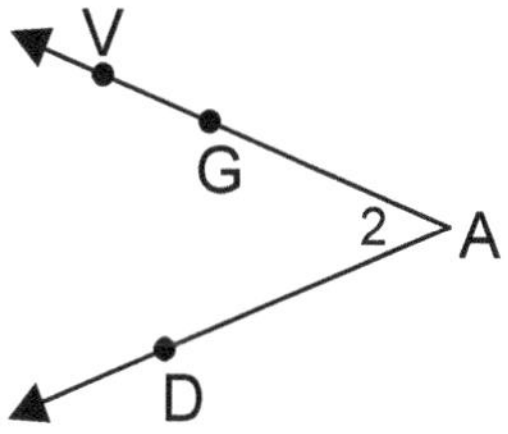

Vertex: ____________

Sides: ____________

Name the angle in six different ways. ________, ________,

________, ________, ________, ________

33. State all the possible ways of naming the figure at the right.

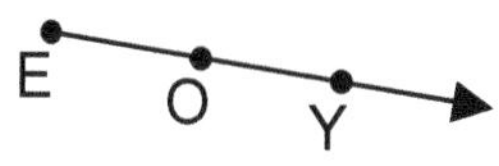

____

Chapter 3 – Parallel Lines and Planes

Part I – Parallel Lines and Planes

We will begin this section with four definitions.

Two lines are called intersecting if and only if they have at least one point in common.

Two lines are called parallel if and only if they meet both of the following conditions.
(1) They have no points in common, and
(2) There is a plane that contains both lines.

Two segments or rays are called parallel if and only if they are part of two lines that are parallel.

Two lines are called skew if and only if they meet both of the following conditions.
(1) They have no points in common, and
(2) There is not a plane that contains both lines.

Example 1: The picture at the right shows a rectangular prism (or a rectangular box) with various points labeled. Describe each of the following sets of lines as *intersecting*, *parallel*, or *skew*: (a) $\overleftrightarrow{AB}$ and $\overleftrightarrow{CD}$, (b) $\overleftrightarrow{AE}$ and $\overleftrightarrow{CA}$, (c) $\overleftrightarrow{EF}$ and $\overleftrightarrow{DH}$, (d) $\overleftrightarrow{CG}$ and $\overleftrightarrow{BF}$, (e) $\overleftrightarrow{FH}$ and $\overleftrightarrow{CD}$

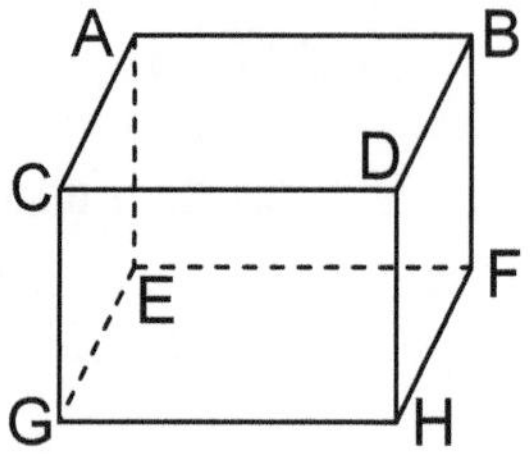

We will begin by stating that the dotted segments represent the edges of the prism that you can't see. This picture shows that we are looking at the top, front, and the right side of the prism. (If you have trouble seeing this, feel free to make yourself a model.) Also, you should note that, even though the lines that the question asks about are actually drawn as *segments*, we can extend the segments past the endpoints and make the segments into lines.

(a) We can say that $\overleftrightarrow{AB}$ and $\overleftrightarrow{CD}$ are *parallel* to each other. If you extend them out forever in both directions, they will never intersect each other, and there is a plane (plane ACD) that contains both lines.

(b) We can say that $\overleftrightarrow{AE}$ and $\overleftrightarrow{CA}$ *intersect* each other because they have point A in common.

(c) $\overleftrightarrow{EF}$ and $\overleftrightarrow{DH}$ are *skew* to each other. If you extend them out forever in both directions, they will never cross each other, and you cannot find a plane that entirely contains both lines.

(d) $\overleftrightarrow{CG}$ and $\overleftrightarrow{BF}$ are *parallel* to each other. If you extend them out forever in both directions, they will never cross each other, and there is a plane that entirely contains both lines. This plane is difficult to see because it is not drawn, but you should be able to imagine sliding a flat piece of paper through the middle of the prism so that the piece of paper represents a plane that entirely contains both lines.

(e) $\overleftrightarrow{FH}$ and $\overleftrightarrow{CD}$ are *skew* to each other. If you extend them out forever in both directions, they will never cross each other, and you cannot find a plane that entirely contains both lines.

Now, we need a postulate.

The Parallel Postulate
Given a line ℓ and a point P not on the line, there is exactly one line parallel to ℓ that passes through P.

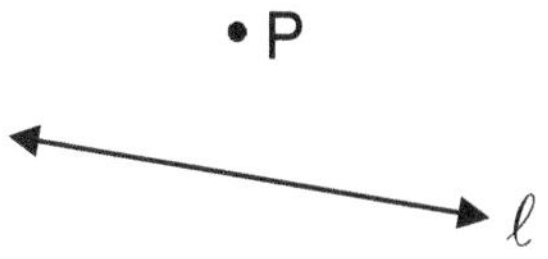

To understand this postulate, look at the figure at the right. The Parallel Postulate states that there is a line that passes through P and is parallel to ℓ. It also states that there is *only one* line that passes through P and is parallel to ℓ.

This postulate is sometimes called Euclid's Fifth Postulate because it was the fifth in a series of postulates that the ancient Greek mathematician Euclid proposed. It has been a subject of much discussion among mathematicians since it was proposed, and entire books have been written that discuss what happens when one assumes that the postulate is false. However, we are concerned only with *Euclidean* geometry in this course, and so we will assume that the postulate is true.

Now, we need two more definitions. Note that these definitions talk about planes instead of lines, but the definitions are similar to the definitions we discussed earlier.

Two planes are called parallel if and only if they have no points in common.

Two planes are called intersecting if and only if they have at least one point in common.

Example 2: Refer back to the picture from Example 1. (a) Which plane(s) are parallel to plane ECG? (b) Which plane(s) intersect plane ECG?

Before we begin discussing this problem, we will note that we always name planes by naming three points that are in the plane but not all on the same line.

(a) The only plane that is parallel to plane ECG is plane BDH. (You could also describe this plane as plane DBH, plane FHD, plane HFB, or one of several other similar names.)

(b) There are four planes that intersect plane ECG: plane ACD, plane ABF, plane EFG, and plane CGH. (Again, there are many other equally correct ways of naming each of these planes.)

Finally, we will note that, technically, you should never assume that two lines or planes are parallel or that they are not parallel based solely upon the way the picture is drawn. However, as you are working the problems in this section (but not the rest of the chapter), you may assume that the pictures are not deceiving.

Problems:

1-6. State which of the terms *parallel lines*, *intersecting lines*, *skew lines*, *parallel planes*, or *intersecting planes* best describes each of the following.

1. a floor and a ceiling of a room
2. a floor and a wall of a room
3. a set of railroad tracks
4. two roads that cross each other at a traffic light
5. the flight paths of two airplanes (Note: Two answers are possible for this question. Name them both.)
6. the shelves of a bookshelf

7-16. Refer to the triangular prism drawn at the right.

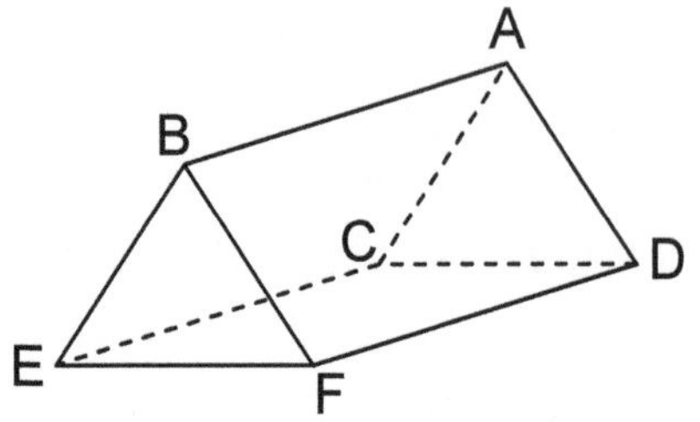

7. Can $\overleftrightarrow{BF}$ and $\overleftrightarrow{AC}$ be described as *intersecting*, *parallel*, or *skew*?
8. Can $\overleftrightarrow{AB}$ and $\overleftrightarrow{FD}$ be described as *intersecting*, *parallel*, or *skew*?
9. Can $\overleftrightarrow{AD}$ and $\overleftrightarrow{AC}$ be described as *intersecting*, *parallel*, or *skew*?
10. Can $\overleftrightarrow{BE}$ and $\overleftrightarrow{CD}$ be described as *intersecting*, *parallel*, or *skew*?
11. Can $\overleftrightarrow{EF}$ and $\overleftrightarrow{CD}$ be described as *intersecting*, *parallel*, or *skew*?
12. Can $\overleftrightarrow{CE}$ and $\overleftrightarrow{AC}$ be described as *intersecting*, *parallel*, or *skew*?
13. Can plane BEF and plane ADC be described as *intersecting* or *parallel*?
14. Can plane CEB and plane DEF be described as *intersecting* or *parallel*?
15. Which plane(s) intersect plane BFD?
16. Which plane(s) intersect plane ACD?

17-27. Refer to the hexagonal prism drawn at the right.

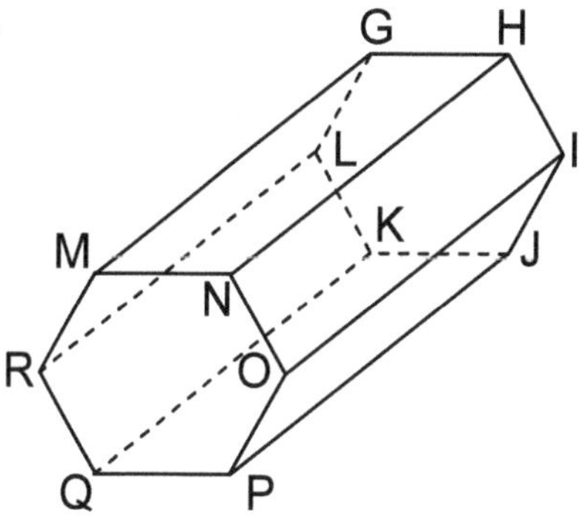

17. Which lines appear to be parallel to $\overleftrightarrow{MN}$?

18. Which lines appear to be skew to $\overleftrightarrow{MN}$? (There are eight of them.)

19. Which lines appear to intersect $\overleftrightarrow{MN}$? (There are six of them, and remember that a line extends forever in both directions.)

20. Which lines appear to be parallel to $\overleftrightarrow{LR}$?

21. Which lines appear to be skew to $\overleftrightarrow{LR}$? (There are eight of them.)

22. Which lines intersect $\overleftrightarrow{LK}$? (There are six of them, and remember that a line extends forever in both directions.)

23. Which lines appear to be parallel to $\overleftrightarrow{NO}$?

24. Which plane(s) appear to be parallel to plane GJL?

25. Which plane(s) appear to be parallel to plane MNH?

26. Which plane(s) intersect plane GJL?

27. Which plane(s) intersect plane MNH?

28-37. Fill in each blank with *always*, *sometimes*, or *never*.

28. If two distinct lines intersect, then they will _____________ intersect in more than one point.

29. If two distinct lines intersect, then they will _____________ intersect in exactly one point.

30. If two distinct planes intersect, then they will _____________ intersect in exactly one point.

31. If two distinct planes intersect, then they will _____________ intersect in more than one point.

32. If two lines are parallel, then they will _____________ intersect.

33. Two skew lines will _____________ intersect.

34. If two lines are parallel, then there will _____________ be a plane that contains both lines.

35. If a plane contains two lines, then the lines will _____________ be parallel.

36. If line ℓ is contained in plane ABC, line m is contained in plane DEF, and plane ABC is parallel to plane DEF, then line ℓ is _____________ parallel to line m.

37. If plane $\mathcal{N}$ contains line t, and plane $\mathcal{P}$ intersects plane $\mathcal{N}$ in line v, then line t is _____________ skew to line v.

Part II – Angles and Parallel Lines

We will begin this section with a definition.

In a plane, a line, line segment, or ray is called a transversal if and only if it intersects two other lines in different points. The other lines may or may not be parallel.

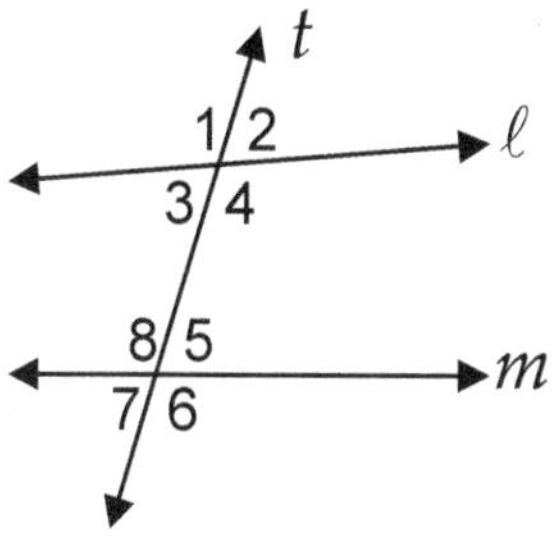

To understand this definition, look at the picture at the right, and notice that line t intersects line ℓ and line m in different points. This means that we can say that line t is a transversal that intersects (or cuts) line ℓ and line m.

As this picture shows, eight angles are formed when a transversal intersects two lines. We use different names for various sets of these angles.

The interior angles are the angles that are found between the two lines. In the picture above, the interior angles are $\angle 3$, $\angle 4$, $\angle 5$, and $\angle 8$.

The exterior angles are the angles that are found outside the two lines. In the picture above, the exterior angles are $\angle 1$, $\angle 2$, $\angle 6$, and $\angle 7$.

Corresponding angles are angles that have the same position. When a transversal intersects two lines, four sets of corresponding angles are formed. In the picture above, these sets of angles are $\angle 1$ and $\angle 8$, $\angle 2$ and $\angle 5$, $\angle 4$ and $\angle 6$, and $\angle 3$ and $\angle 7$.

Alternate interior angles are interior angles that are on opposite sides of the transversal. When a transversal intersects two lines, two sets of alternate interior angles are formed. In the picture above, $\angle 3$ and $\angle 5$ are alternate interior angles, and so are $\angle 4$ and $\angle 8$.

Alternate exterior angles are exterior angles that are on opposite sides of the transversal. When a transversal intersects two lines, two sets of alternate exterior angles are formed. In the picture above, $\angle 1$ and $\angle 6$ are alternate exterior angles, and so are $\angle 2$ and $\angle 7$.

Same-side interior angles are interior angles that are on the same side of the transversal. When a transversal intersects two lines, two sets of same-side interior angles are formed. In the picture above, $\angle 3$ and $\angle 8$ are same-side interior angles, and so are $\angle 4$ and $\angle 5$.

Same-side exterior angles are exterior angles that are on the same side of the transversal. When a transversal intersects two lines, two sets of same-side exterior angles are formed. In the picture above, $\angle 1$ and $\angle 7$ are same-side exterior angles, and so are $\angle 2$ and $\angle 6$.

Now, we need a postulate and some theorems. A proof of the Alternate Interior Angles Theorem is shown in Example 4, and you will be asked to prove the other four theorems in the exercises for this section.

Corresponding Angles Postulate

If two corresponding angles are formed by two parallel lines and a transversal, then they are congruent.

Alternate Interior Angles Theorem

If two alternate interior angles are formed by two parallel lines and a transversal, then they are congruent.

Alternate Exterior Angles Theorem

If two alternate exterior angles are formed by two parallel lines and a transversal, then they are congruent.

Same-Side Interior Angles Theorem

If two same-side interior angles are formed by two parallel lines and a transversal, then they are supplementary.

Same-Side Exterior Angles Theorem

If two same-side exterior angles are formed by two parallel lines and a transversal, then they are supplementary.

Perpendicular Transversal Theorem

If a line is perpendicular to one of two parallel lines, then it is perpendicular to the other line also.

Example 1: In the picture at the right, m∠8 = 62°, and $\ell \parallel m$. (We read this as, "ℓ is parallel to m.") Find m∠1, m∠2, m∠3, m∠4, m∠5, m∠6, and m∠7.

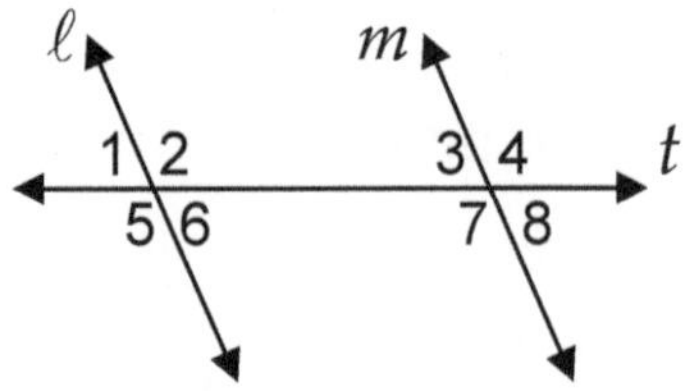

You do not have to find the measures of these angles in any particular order. (For instance, you could find m∠7 before you find m∠2.) This means that there are several ways of finding the correct answers for the measures of each of the angles. We describe some of these ways below.

We can say that m∠1 = 62° because ∠1 and ∠8 are alternate exterior angles formed by two parallel lines and a transversal.

We can say that m∠2 = 118° because ∠1 and ∠2 form a linear pair, and we just noted that m∠1 = 62°.

Since ∠3 and ∠8 are vertical angles, we can say that m∠3 = 62°. (You could also find this by noting one of the following: (1) ∠1 and ∠3 are corresponding angles formed by two parallel lines and a transversal, and so they must be congruent, or (2) ∠2 and ∠3 are same-side interior angles formed by two parallel lines and a transversal, and so they must be supplementary.)

We can say that m$\angle$4 = 118° because $\angle$4 and $\angle$8 form a linear pair. (You could also find this by noting one of the following: (1) $\angle$1 and $\angle$4 are same-side exterior angles formed by two parallel lines and a transversal, and so they must be supplementary, (2) $\angle$2 and $\angle$4 are corresponding angles formed by two parallel lines and a transversal, and so they must be congruent, or (3) $\angle$3 and $\angle$4 form a linear pair, and so they must be supplementary.)

We can say that m$\angle$5 = 118° because $\angle$5 and $\angle$8 are same-side exterior angles, and so they must be supplementary. (You could also find this by noting one of the following: (1) $\angle$1 and $\angle$5 form a linear pair, meaning that they must be supplementary, (2) $\angle$2 and $\angle$5 are vertical angles, meaning that they must be congruent, or (3) $\angle$4 and $\angle$5 are alternate exterior angles formed by two parallel lines and a transversal, meaning that they must be congruent.)

We can say that m$\angle$6 = 62° because $\angle$6 and $\angle$8 are corresponding angles formed by two parallel lines and a transversal, and so they must be congruent. (You could also find this by noting one of the following: (1) $\angle$5 and $\angle$6 form a linear pair, meaning that they must be supplementary, (2) $\angle$2 and $\angle$6 form a linear pair, meaning that they must be supplementary, (3) $\angle$1 and $\angle$6 are vertical angles, meaning that they must be congruent, or (4) $\angle$3 and $\angle$6 are alternate interior angles formed by two parallel lines and a transversal, meaning that they must be congruent.)

We can say that m$\angle$7 = 118° because $\angle$7 and $\angle$8 form a linear pair, and so they must be supplementary. (You could also find this by noting one of the following: (1) $\angle$3 and $\angle$7 form a linear pair, meaning that they must be supplementary, (2) $\angle$4 and $\angle$7 are vertical angles, meaning that they must be congruent, (3) $\angle$2 and $\angle$7 are alternate interior angles formed by two parallel lines and a transversal, meaning that they must be congruent, (4) $\angle$6 and $\angle$7 are same-side interior angles formed by two parallel lines and a transversal, meaning that they must be supplementary, or (5) $\angle$5 and $\angle$7 are corresponding angles formed by two parallel lines and a transversal, meaning that they must be congruent.)

Example 2: In the figure at the right, $b \parallel c$, m$\angle$1 = (4x – 5)°, m$\angle$2 = 3y°, and m$\angle$3 = (3x + 15)°. Find the values of x and y.

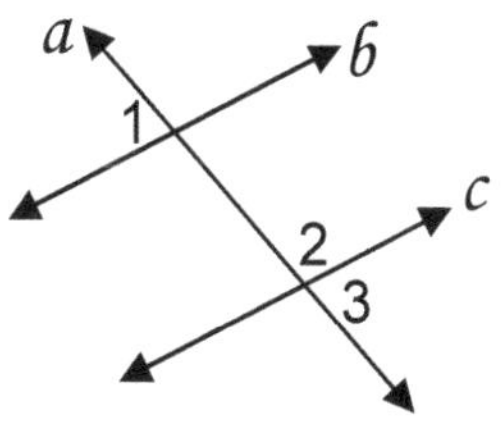

We will begin by noting that $\angle$1 and $\angle$3 are alternate exterior angles, and so they must be congruent. Since this means that their measures are equal, we can write 4x – 5 = 3x + 15. When we solve this equation for x, we find that x = 20.

To find the value of y, we will note that this tells us that m$\angle$3 = (3 • 20 + 15)°, or 75°. Since $\angle$2 and $\angle$3 form a linear pair (which tells us that their measures must add up to 180°), we can write 75 + 3y = 180. When we solve this equation for y, we find that y = 35.

Example 3: In the figure at the right, $\overline{AB} \parallel \overline{CD}$, $\overline{AD} \parallel \overline{BC}$, $m\angle ABD = (5x - 4)^\circ$, $m\angle BDC = (3x + 10)^\circ$, $m\angle ADB = 5y^\circ$, and $m\angle BCD = (5y + 3)^\circ$. Find the values of x and y.

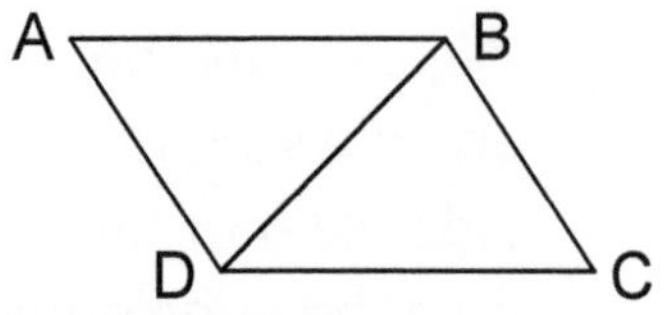

We will begin by noting that $\angle ABD$ and $\angle BDC$ are alternate interior angles formed by $\overleftrightarrow{AB}$ and $\overleftrightarrow{CD}$ (which are parallel) and the transversal $\overleftrightarrow{BD}$. To see why this is true, look at the picture below. We have redrawn part of the original picture, and we have extended these lines.

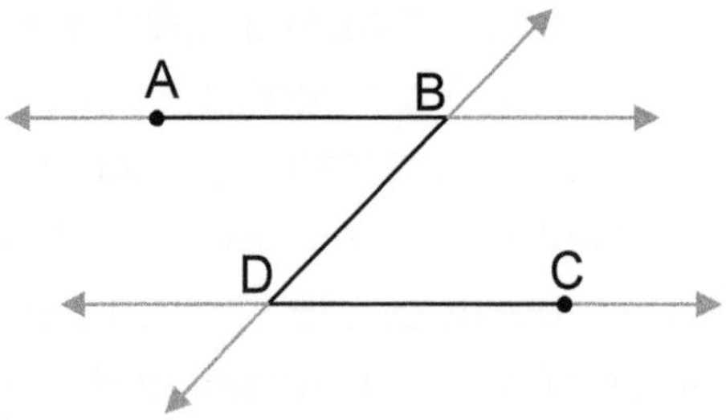

This means that we can say that $\angle ABD \cong \angle BDC$, and so we can write $5x - 4 = 3x + 10$. This tells us that $x = 7$.

Now, to find the value of y, we will note that $\angle ADC$ and $\angle DCB$ are same-side interior angles formed by $\overleftrightarrow{AD}$ and $\overleftrightarrow{BC}$ (which are parallel) and the transversal $\overleftrightarrow{CD}$. To see why this is true, look at the picture below. We have redrawn part of the original picture, and we have extended these lines.

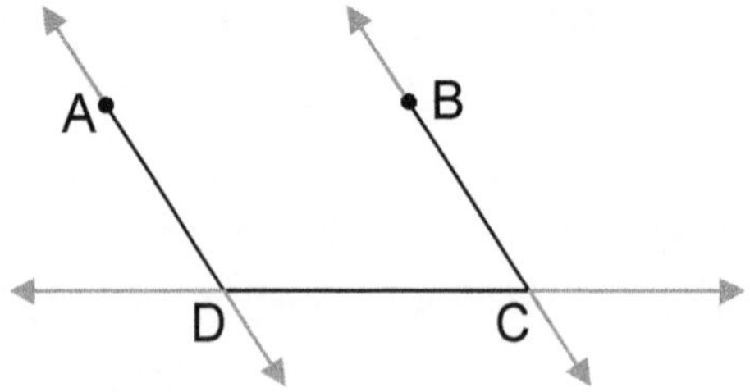

Next, we will note that $m\angle BDC = (3 \cdot 7 + 10)^\circ$, or 31°. We will also note that $m\angle ADC = m\angle ADB + m\angle BDC$, and so we can say that $m\angle ADC = 5y^\circ + 31^\circ$. Now, since $\angle ADC$ and $\angle BCD$ are same-side interior angles formed by two parallel lines and a transversal, we know that the sum of their measures is 180°. This tells us that we can say that $5y + 31 + 5y + 3 = 180$. When we solve this equation for y, we find that $y = \frac{73}{5}$.

Example 4: Prove the Alternate Interior Angles Theorem.

We will begin by drawing a generic-looking picture. As we said in the last section, we want to draw a generic-looking picture so that we can say that this theorem is true for *all* pairs of alternate interior angles formed by two parallel lines and a transversal, and not just some of them.

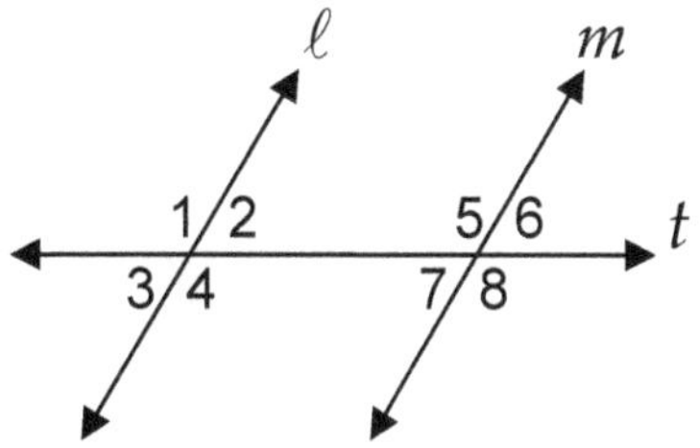

Now, remember that, when we are trying to prove a theorem, we start by assuming that the part of the theorem that follows the "if" is true, and we want to show that the part that follows the "then" is also true. This means that we can write the information that is given to us as "$\ell \parallel m$, and the transversal t intersects both line ℓ and line m," and we want to prove that $\angle 2 \cong \angle 7$ and $\angle 4 \cong \angle 5$.

Statements	Reasons	Explanations
1. $\ell \parallel m$, and the transversal t intersects both line ℓ and line m	1. Given	This information was given to us.
2. $\angle 2 \cong \angle 6$ $\angle 4 \cong \angle 8$	2. Corresponding Angles Postulate	Since we were given that $\ell \parallel m$, and that the transversal t intersects both line ℓ and line m, we can use the Corresponding Angles Postulate to say that the corresponding angles must be congruent.
3. $\angle 6 \cong \angle 7$ $\angle 8 \cong \angle 5$	3. Vertical Angles Theorem	We can look at the picture and see that $\angle 6$ and $\angle 7$ are vertical angles, and so we can use the Vertical Angles Theorem to say that they are congruent. Similarly, we can look at the picture and see that $\angle 8$ and $\angle 5$ are vertical angles, and so we can use the Vertical Angles Theorem to say that they are congruent.
4. $\angle 2 \cong \angle 7$ $\angle 4 \cong \angle 5$	4. Transitive Property of Angle Congruence	We said that $\angle 2 \cong \angle 6$ and $\angle 6 \cong \angle 7$, and so we can use the Transitive Property of Angle Congruence to say that $\angle 2 \cong \angle 7$. Similarly, we said that $\angle 4 \cong \angle 8$ and $\angle 8 \cong \angle 5$, and so we can use the Transitive Property of Angle Congruence to say that $\angle 4 \cong \angle 5$.

Problems:

1-6. In the figure at the right, m∠1 = 84º, m∠16 = 60º, line ℓ is parallel to line m, and line n is *not* parallel to line p. Find the measures of each of the following angles.

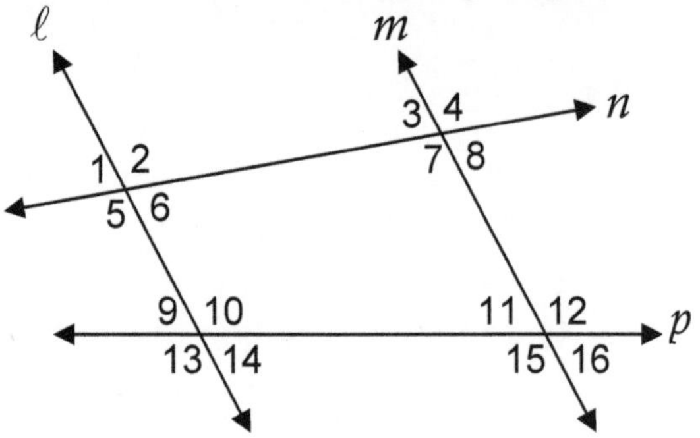

1. m∠3 = __________

2. m∠9 = __________

3. m∠4 = __________

4. m∠7 = __________

5. m∠10 = __________

6. m∠13 = __________

7-17. In the figure at the right, $\overline{AC} \parallel \overline{DF}$, $\overline{AD} \parallel \overline{BE}$, $\overline{BD} \parallel \overline{CE}$, $\overline{CF} \perp \overline{DF}$, $\overrightarrow{BE}$ bisects ∠DBC, and m∠DBC = 128º. Find the measures of each of the following angles. (The little square in ∠F says that ∠F is a right angle, and the arrows tell which lines are parallel. For instance, $\overline{AC} \parallel \overline{DF}$, and both $\overline{AC}$ and $\overline{DF}$ are marked with one arrow each.)

Hint: Do not answer the questions in which they are asked. For instance, you may answer #11 before you answer #8.

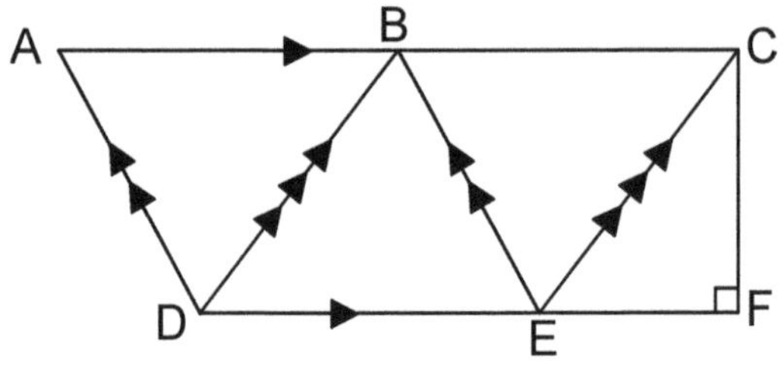

7. m∠DBA = __________

8. m∠DAB = __________

9. m∠DBE = __________

10. m∠EBC = __________

11. m∠ECB = __________

12. m∠ECF = __________

13. m∠ADB = __________

14. m∠BDE = __________

15. m∠BED = __________

16. m∠BEC = __________

17. m∠CEF = __________

18. In the picture at the right, $\overline{AB} \parallel \overline{CD}$ and $\overline{AC} \parallel \overline{BD}$. Find the values of each of the variables.

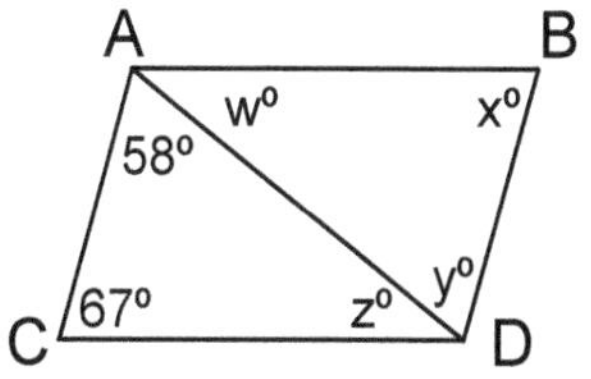

w = __________

x = __________

y = __________

z = __________

19. In the picture at the right, $\overleftrightarrow{EF} \parallel \overleftrightarrow{GH}$ and $\overleftrightarrow{EG} \parallel \overleftrightarrow{FH}$. Find the values of each of the variables.

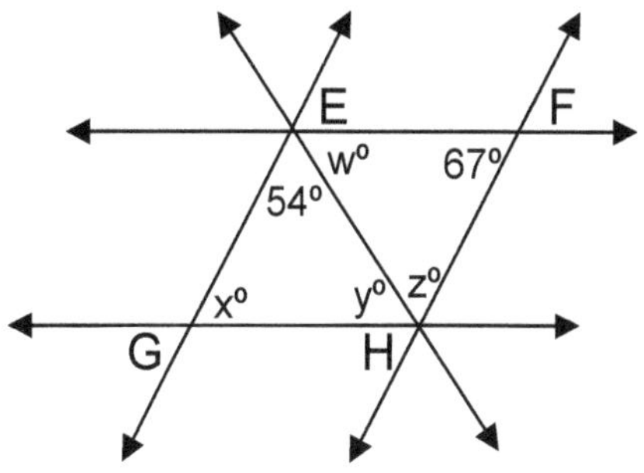

w = __________

x = __________

y = __________

z = __________

20. In the picture at the right, $\overline{IJ} \parallel \overline{KL}$ and $\overline{JL} \perp \overline{KL}$. Find the values of each of the variables.

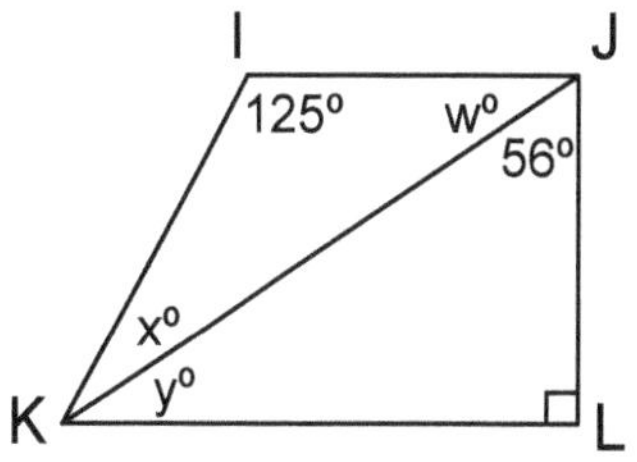

w = __________

x = __________

y = __________

21. In the picture at the right, $\ell \parallel m$. Find the values of x and y.

x = __________

y = __________

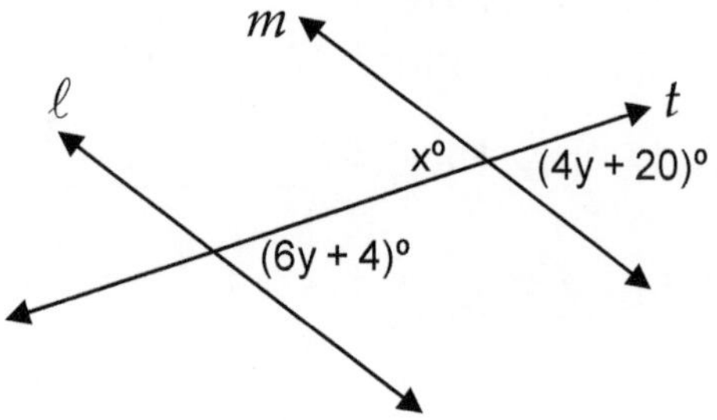

22. In the picture at the right, $\ell \parallel m$. Find the values of x and y.

x = __________

y = __________

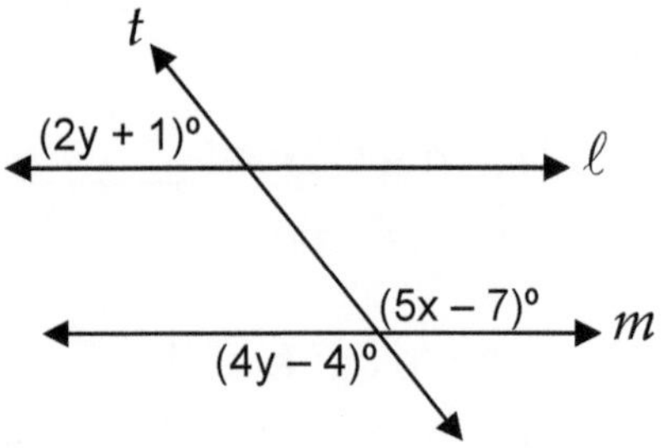

23. In the picture at the right, $\ell \parallel m$. Find the values of x and y.

x = __________

y = __________

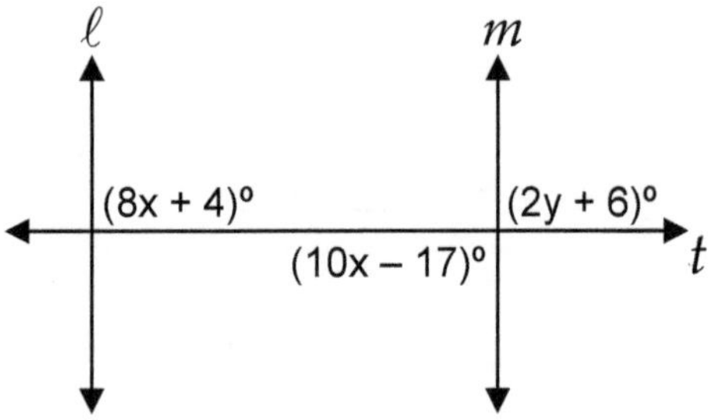

24. In the picture at the right, $\overrightarrow{DA} \parallel \overline{BC}$, $m\angle EDA = (5x - 3)°$, $m\angle ADB = (y + 14)°$, $m\angle BDC = (2y - 3)°$, and $m\angle BCD = (x + 33)°$. Find the values of x and y.

x = __________

y = __________

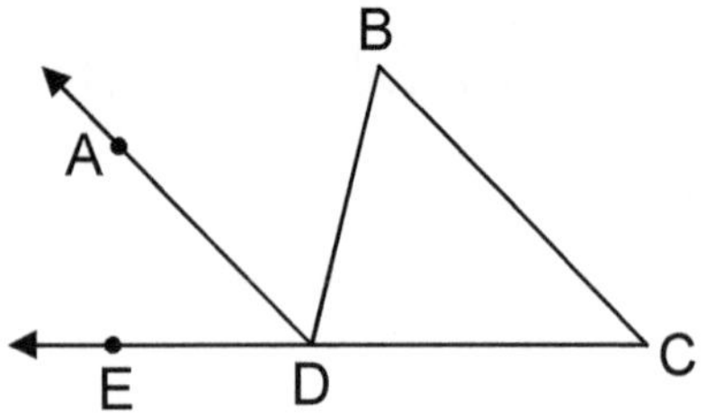

25. In the picture at the right, $\overline{FI} \parallel \overline{GJ}$ and $\overline{FG} \parallel \overline{IJ}$. Find the values of x and y.

x = __________

y = __________

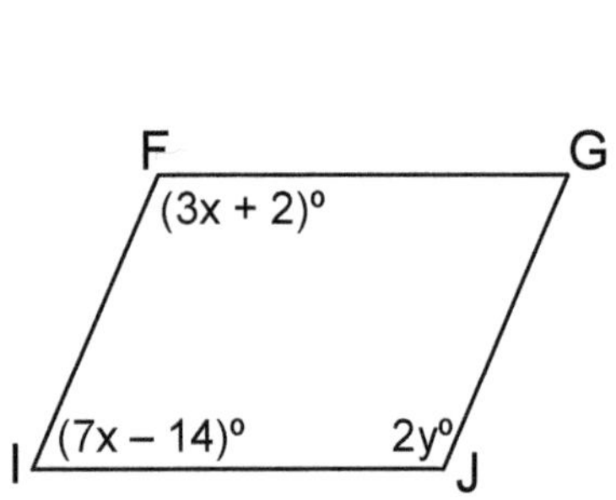

26. In the picture at the right, $\ell \parallel m$ and $\ell \perp t$. Find the values of x and y.

x = __________

y = __________

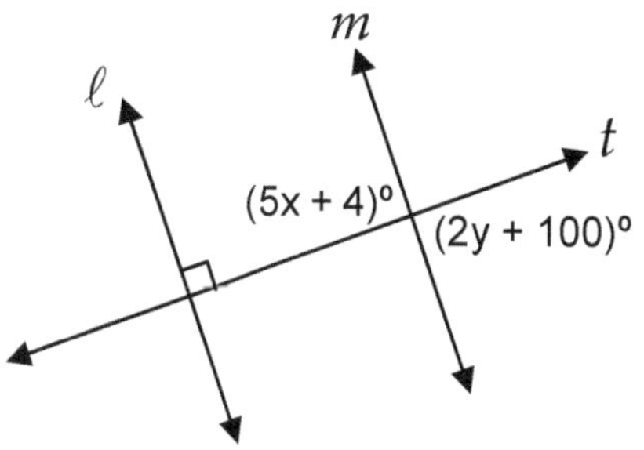

27. In the picture at the right, $\overleftrightarrow{MN} \parallel \overleftrightarrow{OQ}$, $\overleftrightarrow{PQ} \perp \overleftrightarrow{MQ}$, $m\angle KML = 2x°$, $m\angle LMN = 3x°$, and $m\angle OPR = 4y°$. Find the values of x and y.

x = __________

y = __________

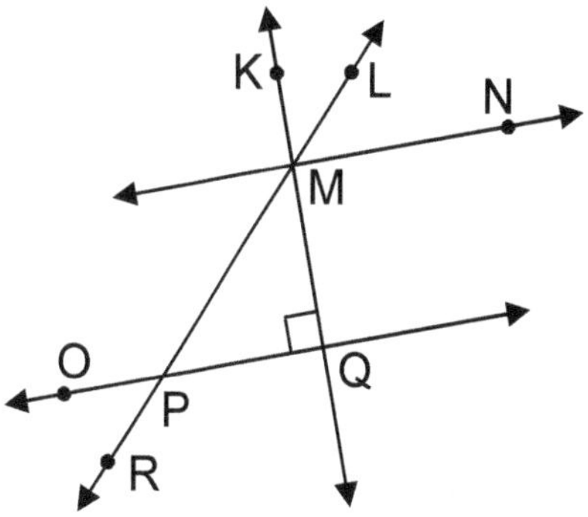

28. In the picture at the right, $\ell \parallel m$. Find the values of x and y.

x = __________

y = __________

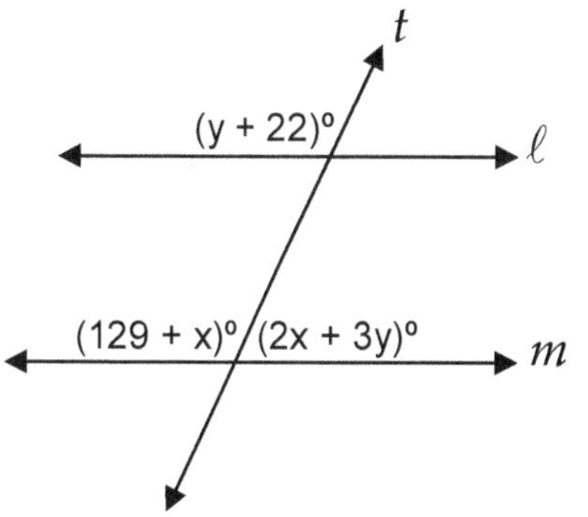

29. In the picture at the right, $\ell \parallel m$. Find the values of x and y.

x = __________

y = __________

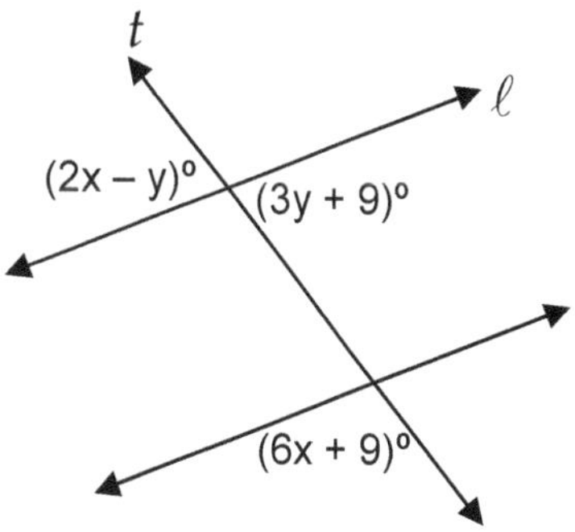

30. Prove the Alternate Exterior Angles Theorem. Hint: You may use the Corresponding Angles Postulate (because postulates are accepted without proof), and you may use the Alternate Interior Angles Theorem (because we have already proven it). You may not, however, use any of the other theorems discussed in this section because you have not proven them yet.

Given: $\ell \parallel m$, and the transversal t intersects both line ℓ and line m

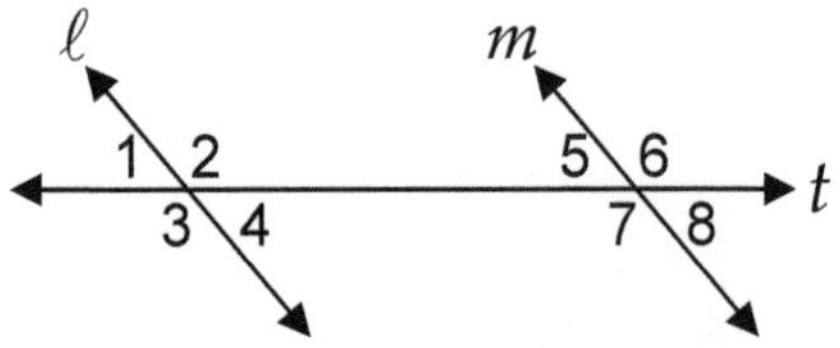

Prove: $\angle 1 \cong \angle 8$

$\angle 3 \cong \angle 6$

Statements	Reasons

31. Prove the Same-Side Interior Angles Theorem. Hint: You may use the Corresponding Angles Postulate (because postulates are accepted without proof), the Alternate Interior Angles Theorem (because it was proven in the examples for this section), and the Alternate Exterior Angles Theorem (because you proved it in #30). You may not, however, use any of the other theorems discussed in this section because you have not proven them yet.

Given: $\ell \parallel m$, and the transversal t intersects both line ℓ and line m

Prove: $\angle 2$ is supplementary to $\angle 5$
$\angle 4$ is supplementary to $\angle 7$

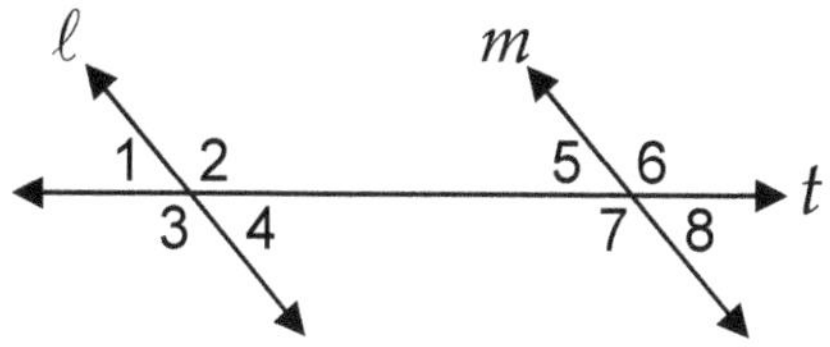

Statements	Reasons
1.	1. Given
2.	2.
3.	3.
4.	4. Definition of a linear pair
5.	5.
6.	6. Definition of supplementary angles
7.	7. Substitution Property of Equality
8.	8.

32. Prove the Same-Side Exterior Angles Theorem. Hint: You may use the Corresponding Angles Postulate, the Alternate Interior Angles Theorem, the Alternate Exterior Angles Theorem (because you proved it in #30), and the Same-Side Interior Angles Theorem (because you proved it in #31). You may not, however, use any of the other theorems discussed in this section because you have not proven them yet.

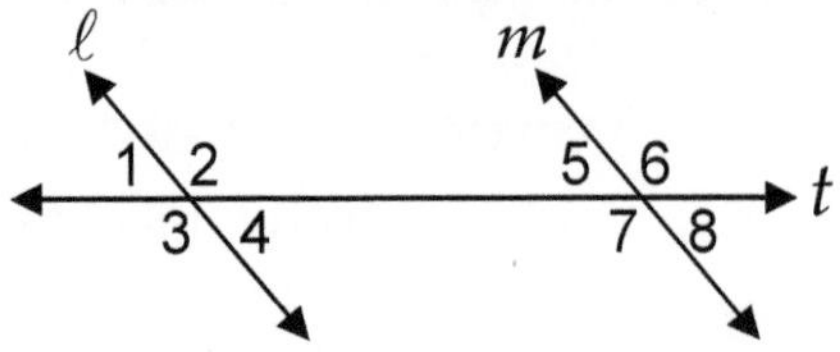

Given: $\ell \parallel m$, and the transversal t intersects both line ℓ and line m

Prove: $\angle 1$ is supplementary to $\angle 6$
$\angle 3$ is supplementary to $\angle 8$

Statements	Reasons
1.	1. Given
2.	2.
3.	3. Definition of congruent angles
4.	4. Definition of a linear pair
5.	5.
6.	6.
7.	7. Substitution Property of Equality
8.	8.

33. Complete the proof of the Perpendicular Transversal Theorem.

Given: $\ell \parallel m$ and $\ell \perp t$

Prove: $m \perp t$

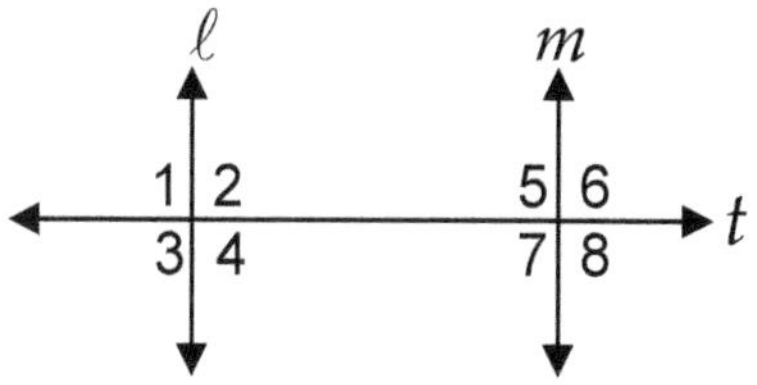

Statements	Reasons
1.	1. Given
2.	2.
3.	3. Definition of a right angle
4.	4.
5.	5. Definition of congruent angles
6.	6.
7.	7. Definition of a right angle
8.	8.

34. Given that $\overline{AB} \parallel \overline{CD}$ and $\overline{AC} \parallel \overline{BD}$ in the figure at the right, prove that $\angle A \cong \angle D$ and $\angle C \cong \angle B$.

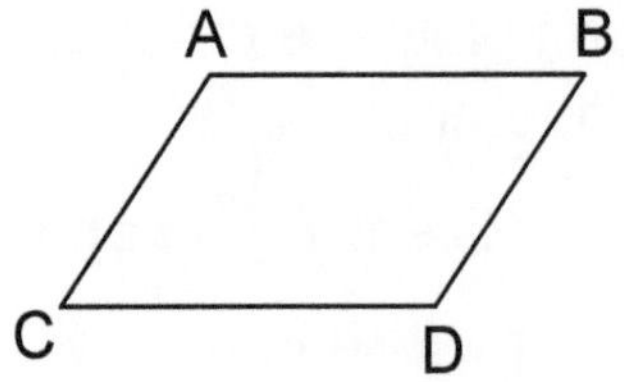

Statements	Reasons

35. Given that $\overline{IJ} \parallel \overline{KL}$ in the figure at the right, prove that $m\angle 1 + m\angle 2 + m\angle 3 = 180^\circ$.

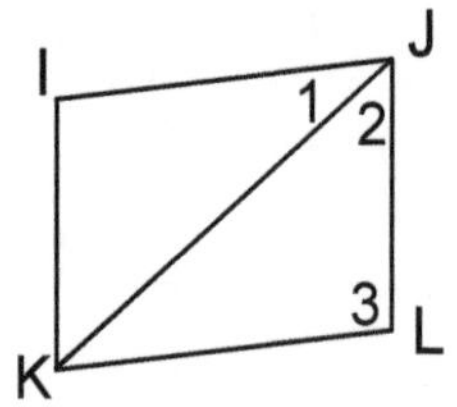

Statements	Reasons

36. Given that $\overline{MN} \parallel \overline{OP}$ and $\overline{MP} \parallel \overline{NO}$ in the figure at the right, prove that $m\angle 1 + m\angle 2 = m\angle 4 + m\angle 3$.

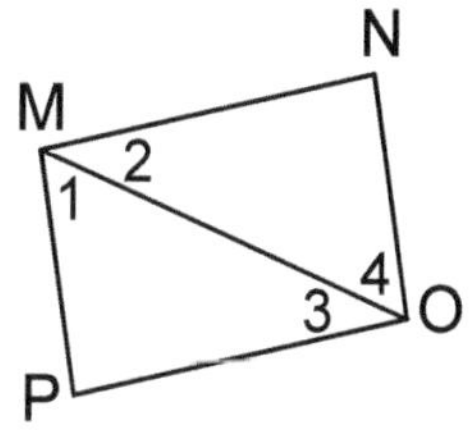

Statements	Reasons

37. Given that $\overleftrightarrow{EF} \parallel \overleftrightarrow{GH}$ and $\angle EFH \cong \angle GHF$ in the figure at the right, prove that $\overleftrightarrow{EF} \perp \overleftrightarrow{FH}$ and $\overleftrightarrow{GH} \perp \overleftrightarrow{FH}$.

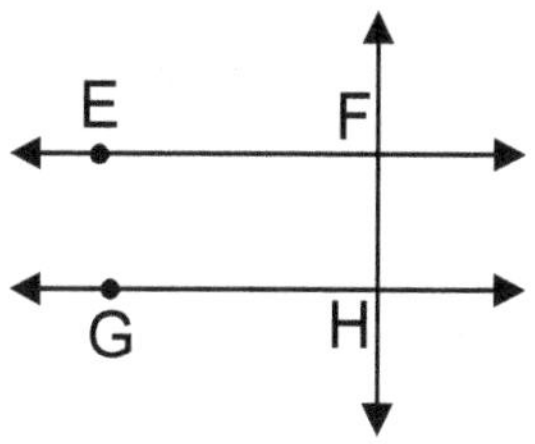

Statements	Reasons
1.	1.
2.	2. Definition of congruent angles
3.	3.
4.	4.
5.	5.
6. $2(m\angle EFH) = 180°$	6. Distributive Property
7.	7.
8. $\angle EFH$ is a right angle	8.
9.	9.
10.	10. Perpendicular Transversal Theorem

Part III – Proving Lines Parallel

We will begin this section with a postulate and six theorems.

Corresponding Angles Converse Postulate
In a plane, if two lines ℓ and m and a transversal t form a pair of congruent corresponding angles, then $\ell \parallel m$.

Alternate Interior Angles Converse Theorem
In a plane, if two lines ℓ and m and a transversal t form a pair of congruent alternate interior angles, then $\ell \parallel m$.

Alternate Exterior Angles Converse Theorem
In a plane, if two lines ℓ and m and a transversal t form a pair of congruent alternate exterior angles, then $\ell \parallel m$.

Same-Side Interior Angles Converse Theorem
In a plane, if two lines ℓ and m and a transversal t form a pair of supplementary same-side interior angles, then $\ell \parallel m$.

Same-Side Exterior Angles Converse Theorem
In a plane, if two lines ℓ and m and a transversal t form a pair of supplementary same-side exterior angles, then $\ell \parallel m$.

In a plane, if two different lines are perpendicular to a third line, then the first two lines are parallel.

Transitive Property of Parallel Lines
If two lines are both parallel to a third line, then the first two lines are also parallel.

(The Corresponding Angles Converse Postulate can actually be proven indirectly using the Exterior Angle of a Triangle Inequality Theorem that will be discussed in Chapter 4. However, we have not proven this theorem yet, and so we will call this statement a postulate for now.)

Many students have a tendency to get this postulate and these theorems confused with the Corresponding Angles Postulate and the theorems that we discussed in the last section. Notice that the Corresponding Angles Postulate and the theorems that we discussed in the last section told us what we could say about various relationships among angles when we started out knowing that we had two parallel lines and a transversal. The postulate, theorems, and property stated above discuss different ways of showing that the lines are parallel. In other words, with the exception of the Transitive Property of Parallel Lines, we start out knowing that we have the different relationships among the angles, and then we use this information to show that the lines are parallel.

We will prove the Same-Side Interior Angles Converse Theorem and the Transitive Property of Parallel Lines in Examples 1 and 2, and you will be asked to prove the other theorems in the exercises for this section.

Example 1: Prove the Same-Side Interior Angles Converse Theorem.

Recall that, when we want to prove a theorem, we start by drawing a generic picture that illustrates the part of the statement that follows the "if." So, we will start by drawing the following picture.

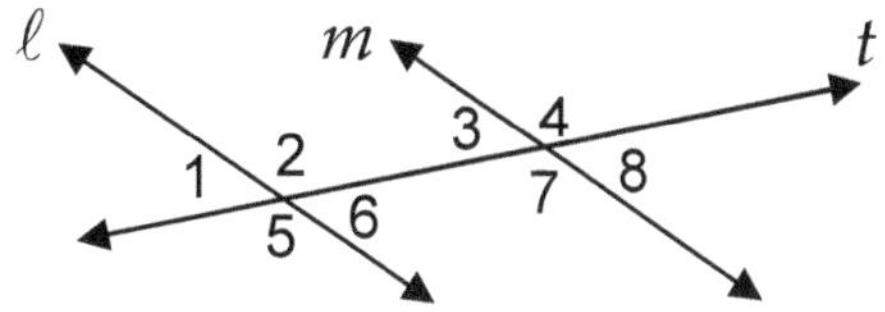

This tells us that we can write the information that is given to us as, "$\angle 2$ and $\angle 3$ are supplementary, and the transversal t intersects lines ℓ and m," and we want to prove that line ℓ must be parallel to line m. (You could also write the information that is given to you as, "$\angle 6$ and $\angle 7$ are supplementary, and the transversal t intersects lines ℓ and m." Your proof would look similar to the one below, but it would not be identical.)

Statements	Reasons	Explanations
1. $\angle 2$ and $\angle 3$ are supplementary, and the transversal t intersects both line ℓ and line m	1. Given	This information was given to us.
2. $\angle 3$ and $\angle 4$ form a linear pair	2. Definition of a linear pair	We can look at the picture and use the definition of a linear pair to say that $\angle 3$ and $\angle 4$ form a linear pair.
3. $\angle 3$ and $\angle 4$ are supplementary	3. Linear Pair Postulate	Since we said that $\angle 3$ and $\angle 4$ form a linear pair, we can now use the Linear Pair Postulate to say that $\angle 3$ and $\angle 4$ are supplementary.
4. $\angle 2 \cong \angle 4$	4. Congruent Supplements Theorem	Since we said that $\angle 3$ is supplementary to both $\angle 2$ and $\angle 4$, we can use the Congruent Supplements Theorem to say that $\angle 2 \cong \angle 4$.
5. $\ell \parallel m$	5. Corresponding Angles Converse Postulate	Since we said in Statement (4) that $\angle 2 \cong \angle 4$, and since we can look at the picture and see that these two angles are corresponding angles, we can use the Corresponding Angles Converse Postulate to say that line ℓ must be parallel to line m.

Example 2: Prove the Transitive Property of Parallel Lines.

Once again, we will begin by drawing a generic-looking picture to describe the part of the statement that follows the "if."

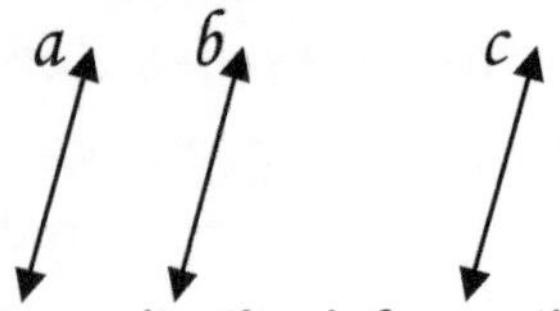

Using this picture, we can write the information that is given to us as, "$a \parallel b$ and $b \parallel c$," and we want to prove that $a \parallel c$.

We will use an indirect proof to prove this theorem. Recall that, in an indirect proof, you assume that the part of the statement that follows the "if" *and* the negation of the part of the statement that follows the "then."

Statements	Reasons	Explanations
1. $a \parallel b$ and $b \parallel c$	1. Given	This information was given to us.
2. Assume that line a is not parallel to line c.	2. Assumption	In an indirect proof, we are allowed to assume the negation of the part of the statement that follows the "then."
3. Lines a and c intersect in exactly one point. We will call this point P.	3. If two lines intersect, then they intersect in exactly one point.	Since we said in Statement (2) that line a is not parallel to line c, and since the definition of parallel lines tells us that lines a, b, and c are coplanar, we can say that lines a and c must intersect. The theorem *If two lines intersect, then they intersect in exactly one point* tells us that this will happen in exactly one point.
4. Point P is not on line b	4. Definition of parallel lines	Since we were told that $a \parallel b$, we can use the definition of parallel lines to say that the point P is not on line b.
5. Point P is on line a and on line c	5. Definition of intersecting lines	The definition of intersecting lines tells us that the point P must lie somewhere on line a, and it must also lie somewhere on line c.
6. Line a is parallel to line c	6. Contradiction	In Statements (1), (4), and (5) we said that we had two different lines that are parallel to line b and pass through a point P that is not on line b. However, the Parallel Postulate says that this cannot happen, and so our assumption must be false.

Example 3: Given that $\angle DBA \cong \angle CDB$ and that $\overline{AB} \perp \overline{BD}$ in the figure at the right, prove that $\overline{AB} \parallel \overline{CD}$.

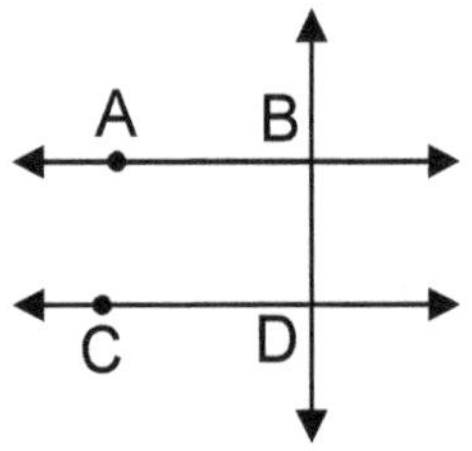

There are several different versions of this proof, and one of them is shown on the next page.

Statements	Reasons	Explanations
1. $\angle DBA \cong \angle CDB$	1. Given	This information was given to us.
2. $m\angle DBA = m\angle CDB$	2. Definition of congruent angles	The definition of congruent angles tells us that, if two angles are congruent, then their measures are equal.
3. $\overline{AB} \perp \overline{BD}$	3. Given	This information was given to us. (Yes, we could have put this up in Statement (1), but the proof flows a little better if we do it in this order.)
4. $\angle DBA$ is a right angle	4. If two lines are perpendicular, then they intersect to form four right angles.	We were told that $\overline{AB} \perp \overline{BD}$, and so we know that all the angles formed by the intersection of $\overline{AB}$ and $\overline{BD}$ are right angles. (We could state that the other angles are right angles as well, but we only need this one.)
5. $m\angle DBA = 90°$	5. Definition of a right angle	The definition of right angle says that, if an angle is a right angle, then its measure is 90°.
6. $m\angle CDB = 90°$	6. Substitution Property of Equality	We said in Statement (2) that $m\angle DBA = m\angle CDB$, and so we can use the Substitution Property of Equality to replace $m\angle DBA$ in Statement (5) with $m\angle CDB$.
7. $\angle CDB$ is a right angle	7. Definition of a right angle	The definition of right angle says that, if an angle measures 90°, then it is a right angle. (By the way, we cannot say that $\overline{DC} \perp \overline{BD}$ yet because the definition of perpendicular lines says that, *if two lines form a right angle*, then they are perpendicular. Thus, we must state that we have a right angle before we can say that the lines are perpendicular.)
8. $\overline{DC} \perp \overline{BD}$	8. Definition of perpendicular lines	Since we just said that $\angle CDB$ is a right angle, we can now use the definition of perpendicular lines to say that $\overline{DC} \perp \overline{BD}$.
9. $\overline{AB} \parallel \overline{CD}$	9. In a plane, if two different lines are perpendicular to a third line, then the first two lines are parallel.	We said in Statements (3) and (8) that both $\overline{AB}$ and $\overline{DC}$ are perpendicular to $\overline{BD}$, and so now we can say that $\overline{AB} \parallel \overline{CD}$.

Example 4: Which, if any, of the segments in the figure at the right *must* be parallel? State a postulate or theorem that supports each answer.

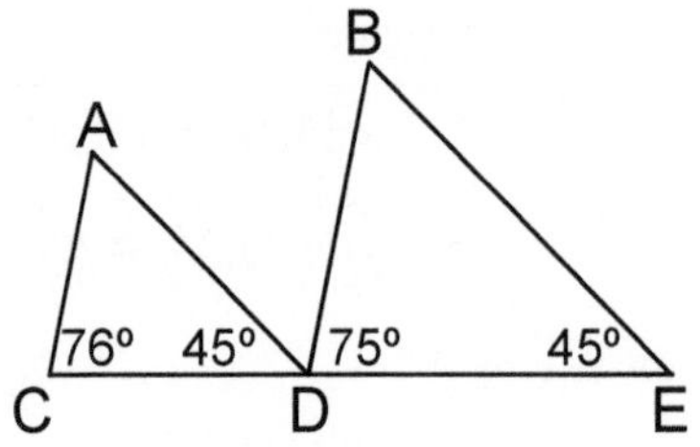

We will begin by noting that $\angle ADC$ and $\angle BED$ are two corresponding angles formed by $\overline{AD}$, $\overline{BE}$, and the transversal $\overline{CE}$. To see this, look at the picture below. We have redrawn the parts of the picture that form $\angle ADC$ and $\angle BED$, and we have extended the lines.

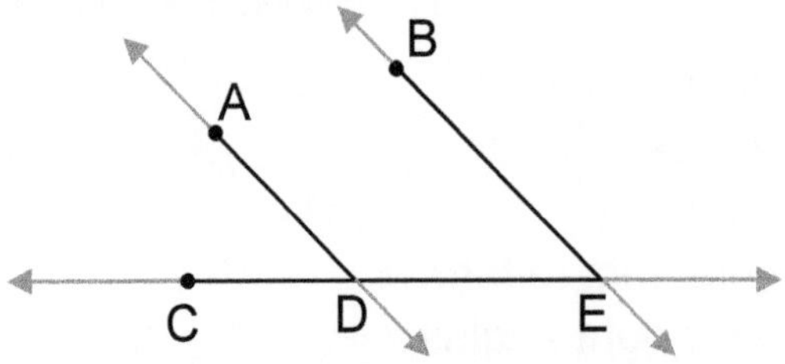

Now, since we were told that both $\angle ADC$ and $\angle BED$ have measures of 45°, we can conclude that $\overline{AD}$ must be parallel to $\overline{BE}$, and the Corresponding Angles Converse Postulate supports this answer.

Now, to find out if $\overline{AC}$ is parallel to $\overline{BD}$, we will note that $\angle ACD$ and $\angle BDE$ are two corresponding angles formed by $\overline{AC}$, $\overline{BD}$, and the transversal $\overline{CE}$. To see this, look at the picture below. We have redrawn the parts of the picture that form $\angle ACD$ and $\angle BDE$, and we have extended the lines.

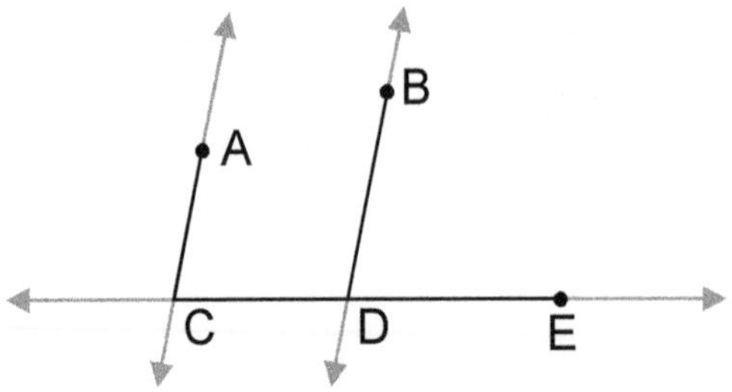

Now, since we were told that $\angle ACD$ and $\angle BDE$ have different measures, we can conclude that $\overline{AC}$ is *not* parallel to $\overline{BD}$, and the contrapositive of the Corresponding Angles Postulate supports this statement. (Recall that, when a theorem is true, the contrapositive of the statement is also true.)

(Alternatively, you could also note that $\angle ACD$ and $\angle BDC$ are same-side interior angles that are not supplementary. To see why, you would need to note that $m\angle BDC + m\angle BDE = 180°$, and so $m\angle BDC$ must equal 105°. Note that this still tells us that $\overline{AC}$ is not parallel to $\overline{BD}$.)

Example 5: In the picture at the right, $m\angle 1 = (5y + 4)°$, $m\angle 2 = (3y + 28)°$, and $m\angle 3 = (2x + 30)°$. Find the values of x and y that make lines ℓ, m, and n parallel to each other.

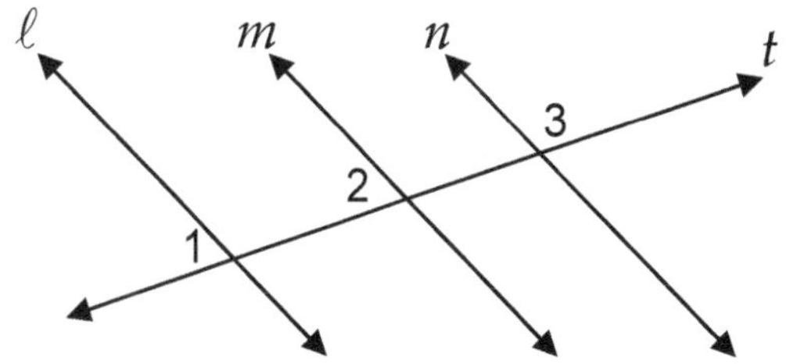

We will begin by noting that $\angle 1$ and $\angle 2$ are corresponding angles, and so, since we want lines ℓ and m to be parallel to each other, we can say that they must be congruent. This means that we can write 5y + 4 = 3y + 28. When we solve this equation for y, we find that y = 12.

Now, to find x, we will first note that $m\angle 2 = (3 \cdot 12 + 28)°$, or 64°. Since $\angle 2$ and $\angle 3$ are same-side exterior angles, and since we want lines m and n to be parallel to each other, $\angle 2$ and $\angle 3$ must be supplementary. This means that we can write 64 + 2x + 30 = 180. When we solve this equation for x, we find that x = 43. (You could also note that $\angle 1$ and $\angle 3$ are same-side exterior angles, and since we want lines ℓ and n to be parallel to each other, $\angle 1$ and $\angle 3$ must be supplementary to each other. You would still find that x must equal 43.)

Finally, when you are working the problems in this section, remember that some of the pictures can and will be deceiving.

Problems:

1-6. Given the following information, state which, if any, of the segments in the picture at the right must be parallel. Do not assume that the information in a problem applies to a later problem. For instance, when you are working #2, do not assume that $\angle$CAB is supplementary to $\angle$DBA.

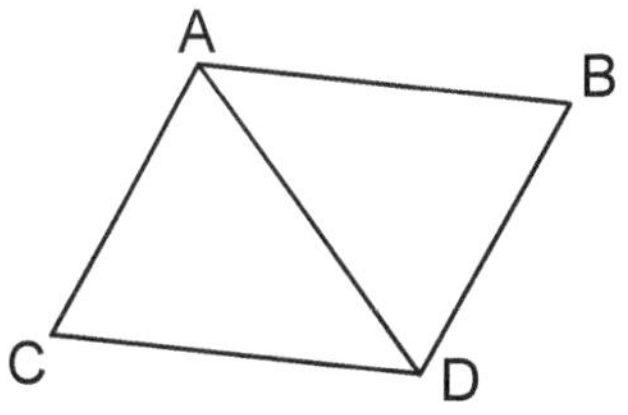

1. $\angle$CAB is supplementary to $\angle$DBA

2. $\angle$CAB $\cong$ $\angle$CDB

3. $\angle$CAD $\cong$ $\angle$ADC and $\angle$BAD $\cong$ $\angle$ADB

4. $\angle$ABD is supplementary to $\angle$BDC

5. $\angle$CAD $\cong$ $\angle$DAB

6. $\angle$CDA $\cong$ $\angle$DAB

7-15. For each of the figures drawn below, state which pairs of lines, segments, or rays must be parallel, and state a postulate or theorem from this section to support each answer.

7. Which segments and rays, if any, must be parallel in the figure at the right?

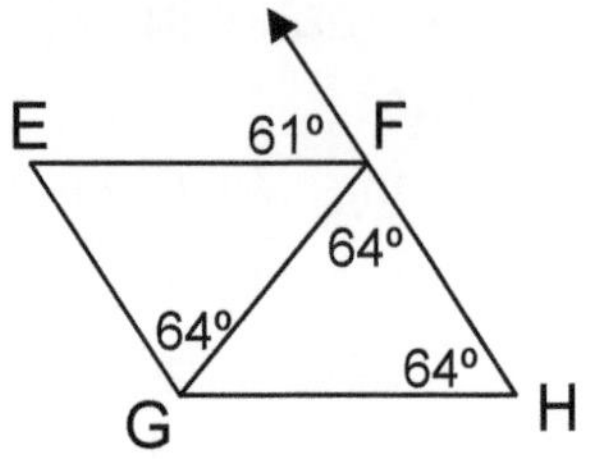

8. Which segments, if any, must be parallel in the figure at the right?

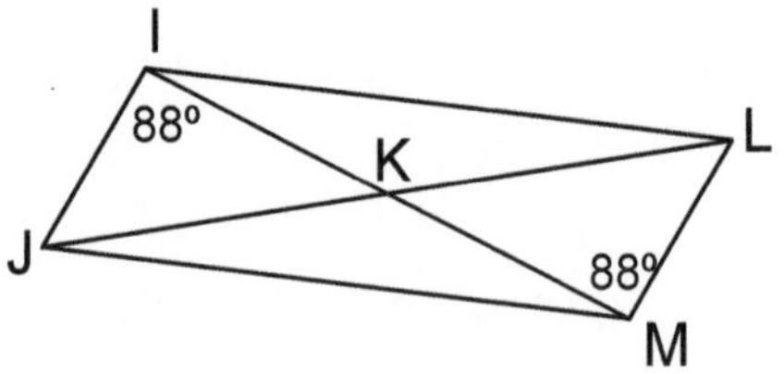

9. In the figure at the right, $\angle 1 \cong \angle 2$ and $\angle 1 \cong \angle 3$. Which lines, if any, must be parallel?

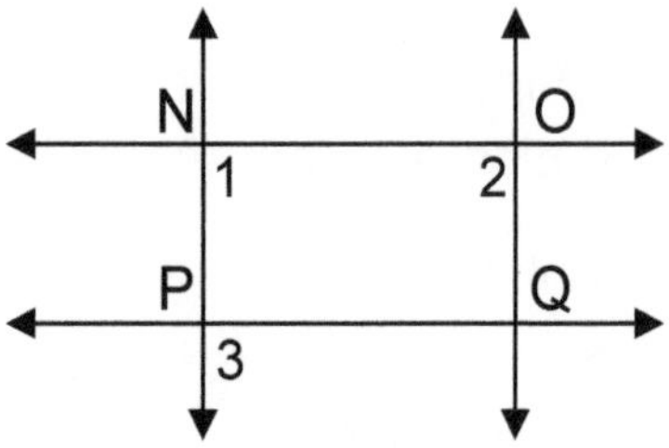

10. Which lines, if any, must be parallel in the figure at the right?

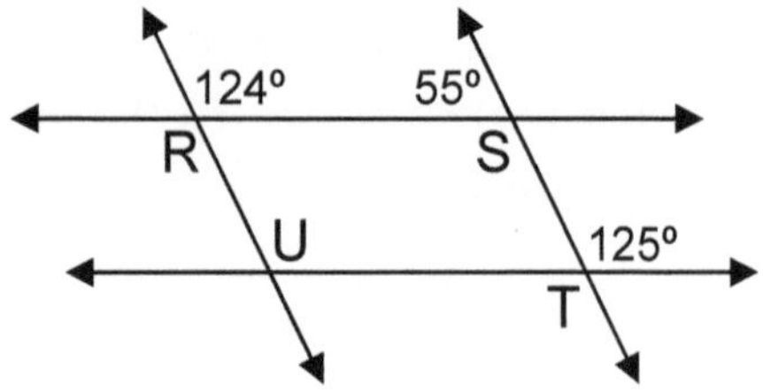

11. In the figure at the right, $\angle VWX \cong \angle YZX$. Which segments, if any, must be parallel?

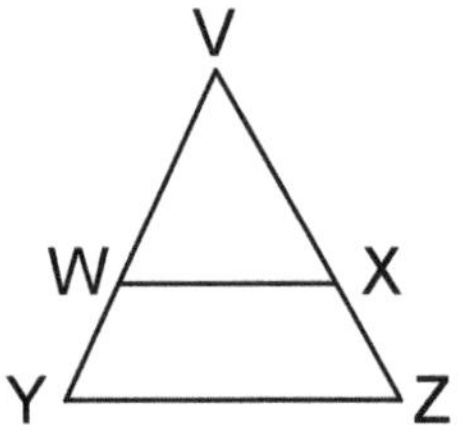

12. In the figure at the right, $\angle ABD \cong \angle BDE$, $\angle BDE \cong \angle BCE$, and $\angle EBA$ is supplementary to $\angle DAB$. Which segments, if any, must be parallel?

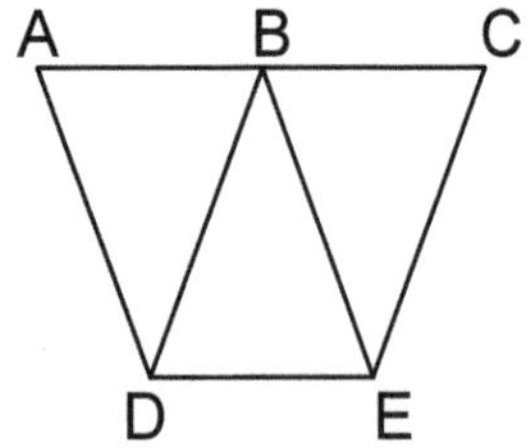

13. In the figure at the right, m∠HFG = 119°, m∠FGI = 62°, m∠IGJ = 28°, and $\overline{GJ} \perp \overline{HJ}$. Which segments, if any, must be parallel?

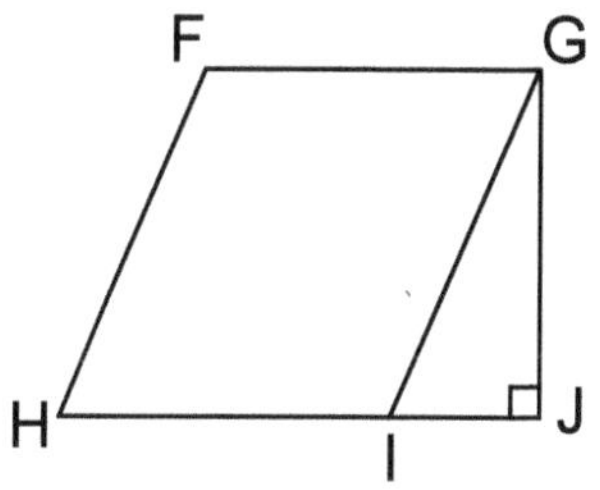

14. Which lines, if any, must be parallel in the figure at the right?

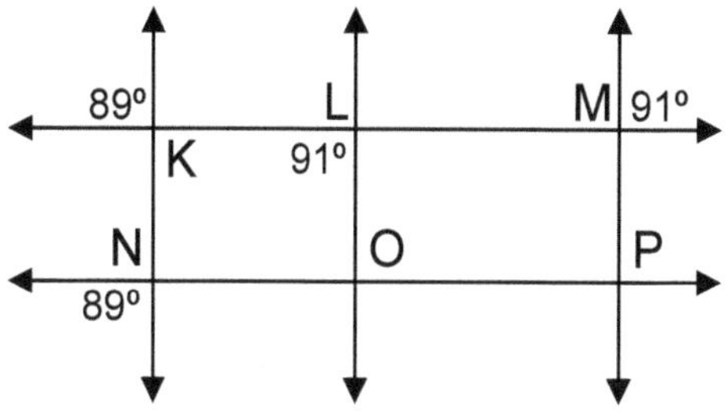

15. Which lines, if any, must be parallel in the figure at the right?

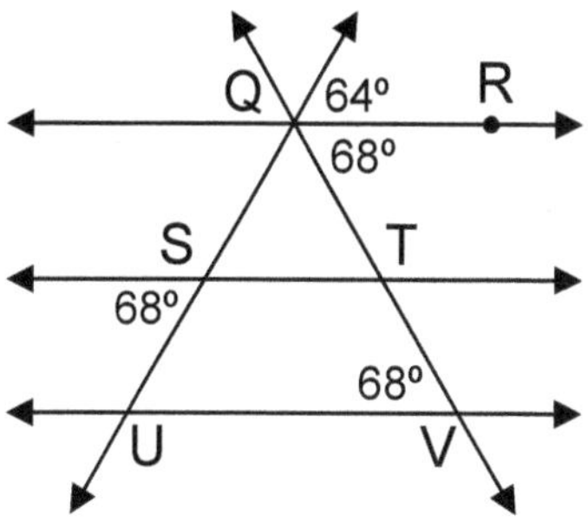

16-24. For each of the figures below, find the values of x and y that make line ℓ parallel to line m.

16. x = ________________

y = ________________

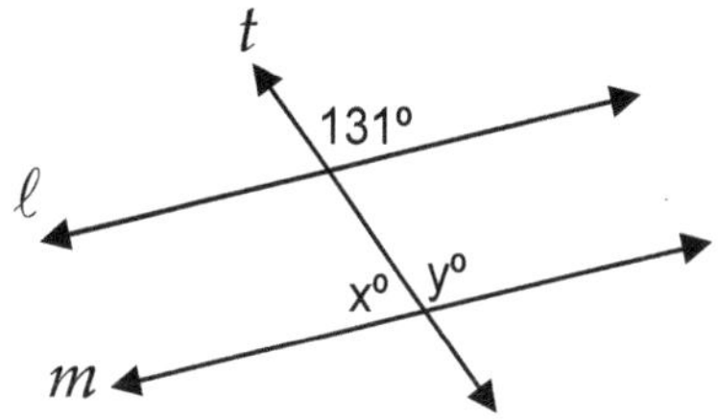

17. x = ________________

y = ________________

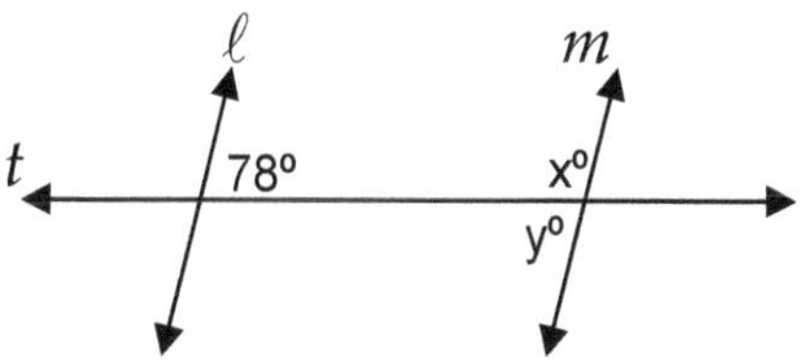

18. x = ________________

y = ________________

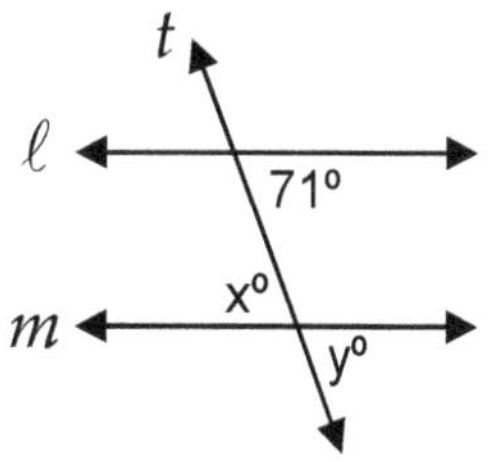

19. x = ______________

y = ______________

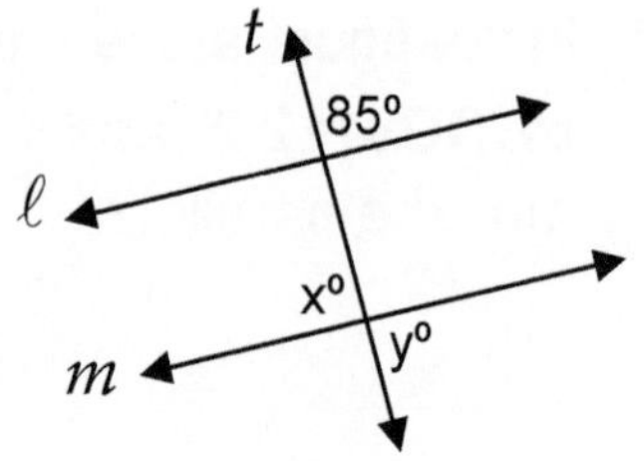

20. x = ______________

y = ______________

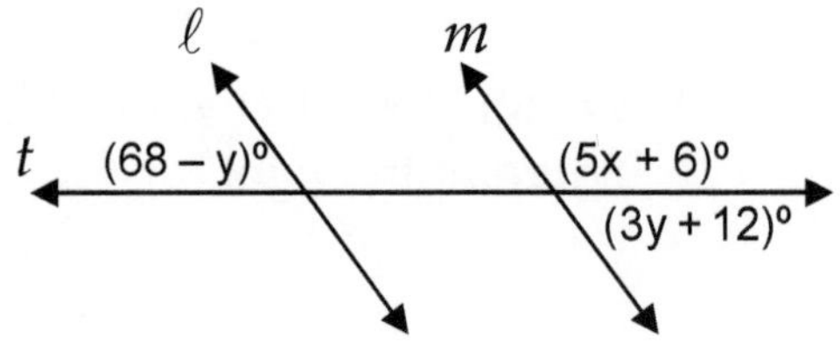

21. x = ______________

y = ______________

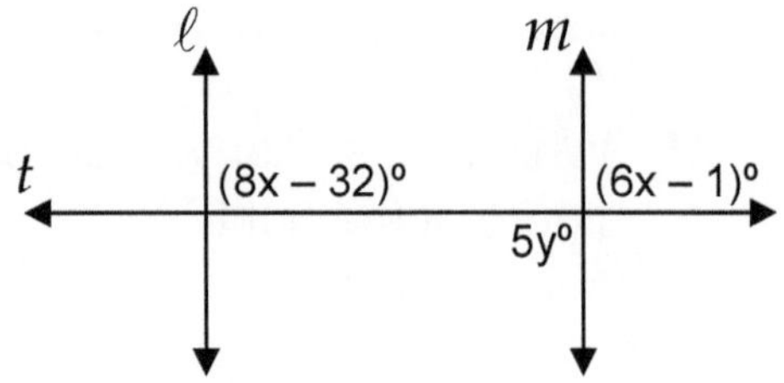

22. $m \perp t$

x = ______________

y = ______________

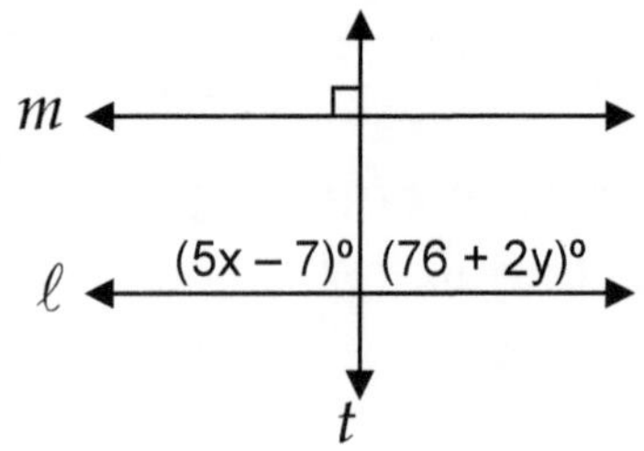

23. x = ______________

y = ______________

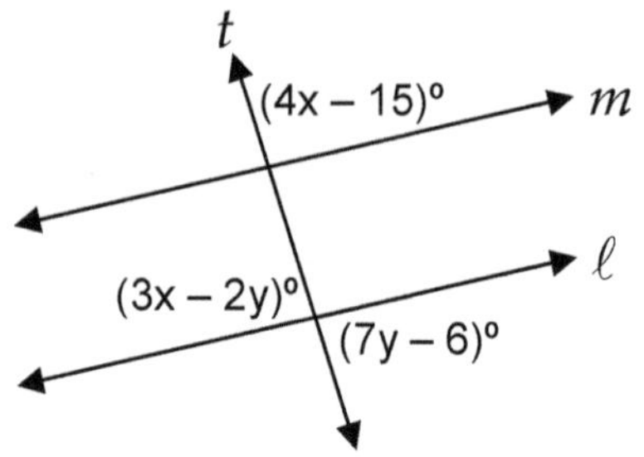

24. x = ______________

y = ______________

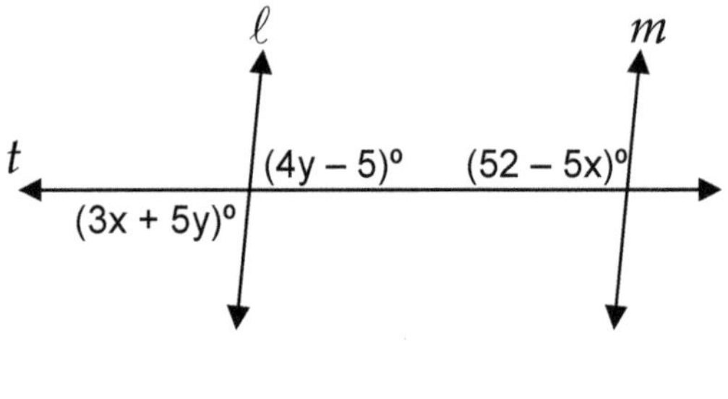

25-26. For each of the figures below, find the values of x and y that make $\overline{AB}$ parallel to $\overline{CD}$.

25. x = ______________

y = ______________

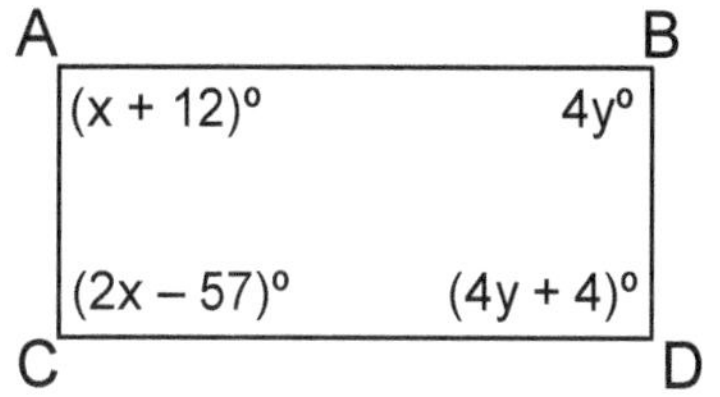

26. x = ______________

y = ______________

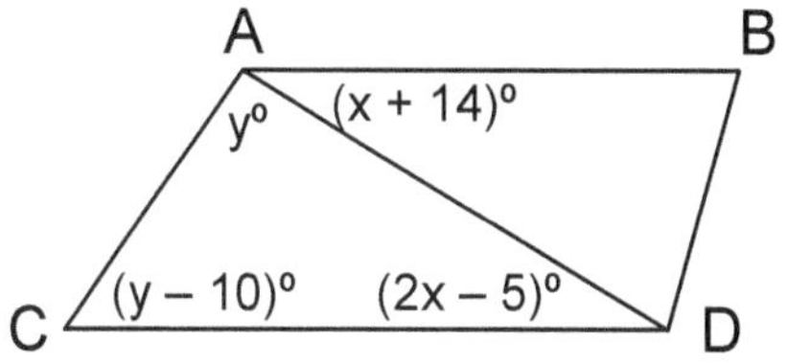

27. Prove the Alternate Interior Angles Converse Theorem. Hint: You may use the Corresponding Angles Converse Postulate (because postulates are accepted without proof), the Same-Side Interior Angles Converse Theorem (because we proved it in Example 1), and the Transitive Property of Parallel Lines (because we proved it in Example 2). You may not, however, use any of the other theorems that we discussed in this section because you have not proven them yet.

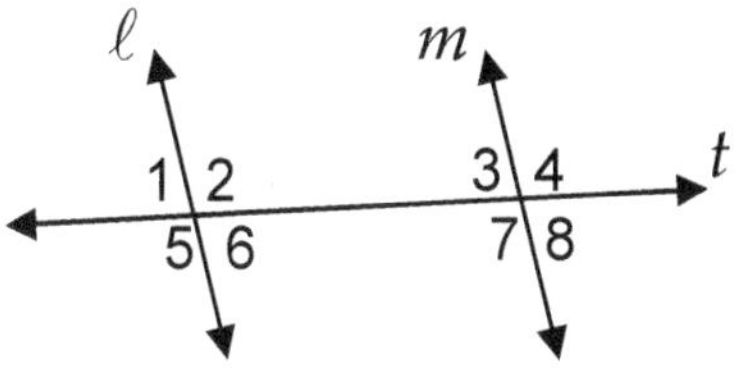

Given: $\angle 2 \cong \angle 7$

Prove: $\ell \parallel m$

Statements	Reasons

28. Prove the Alternate Exterior Angles Converse Theorem.

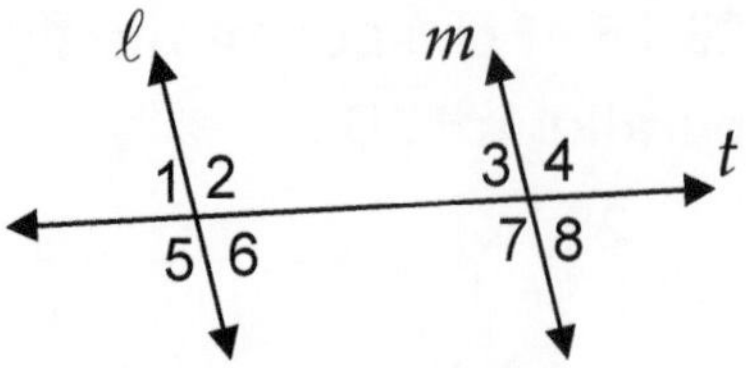

Given: $\angle 1 \cong \angle 8$

Prove: $\ell \parallel m$

Statements	Reasons

29. Prove the Same-Side Exterior Angles Converse Theorem.

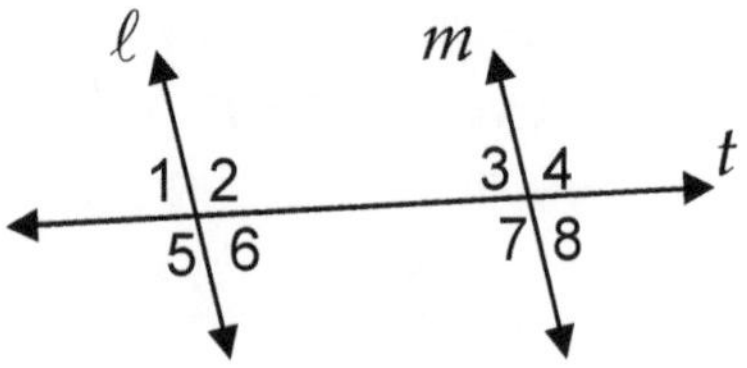

Given: $\angle 1$ is supplementary to $\angle 4$

Prove: $\ell \parallel m$

Statements	Reasons

30. Prove the following theorem: In a plane, if two different lines are perpendicular to a third line, then the first two lines are parallel.

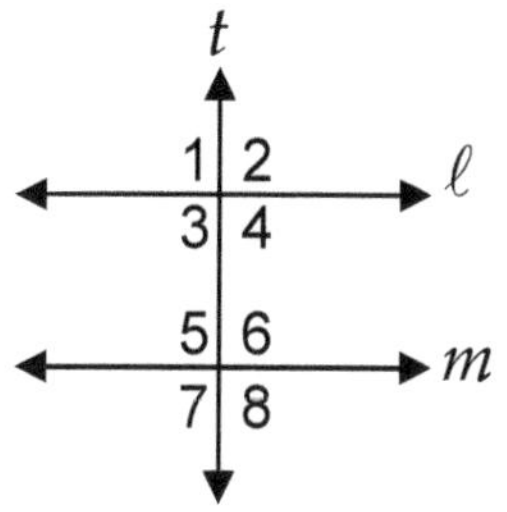

Given: ______________________________

Prove: ______________________________

Statements	Reasons
1.	1.
2.	2. If two lines are perpendicular, then they intersect to form four right angles.
3. $m\angle 1 = 90°$ $m\angle 5 = 90°$	3.
4.	4. Substitution Property of Equality
5.	5.
6.	6.

31. Given that $\angle 2$ is supplementary to $\angle 8$ and that $\angle 8 \cong \angle 9$ in the figure at the right, prove that $\angle 2 \cong \angle 11$.

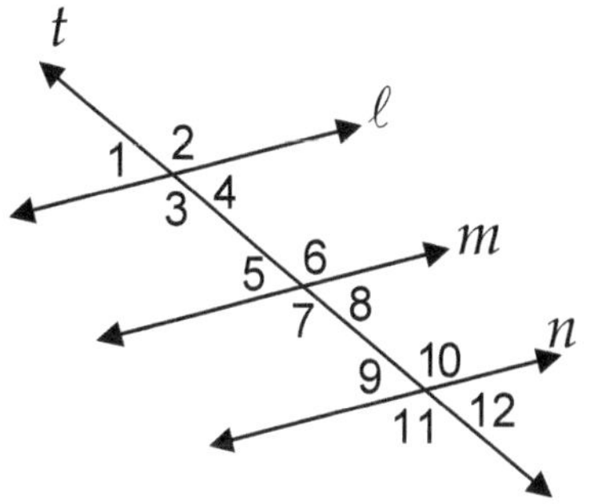

Statements	Reasons

32. Given that $\angle A \cong \angle E$ in the figure at the right, prove that $\angle B \cong \angle D$.

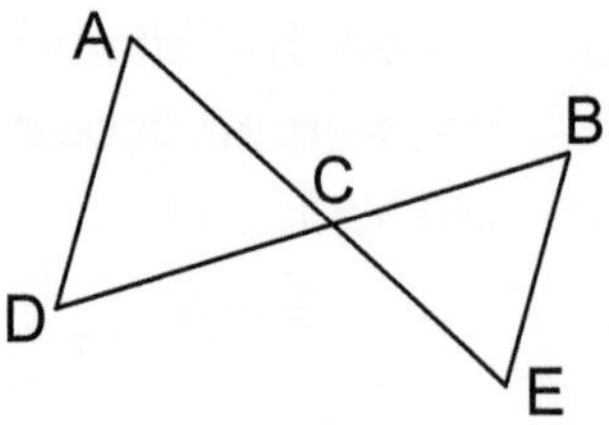

Statements	Reasons

33. Given that line ℓ is not parallel to line m in the figure at the right, prove that $\angle 1$ is not congruent to $\angle 2$ using an indirect proof.

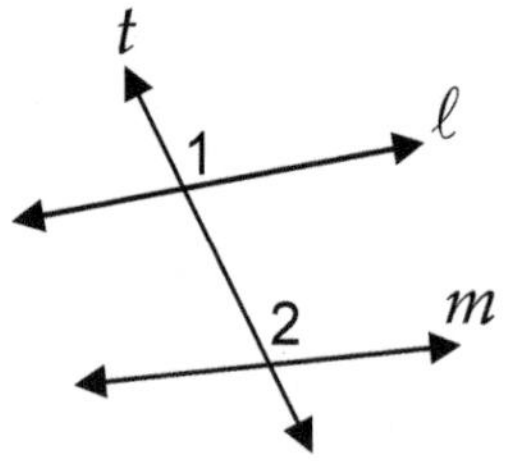

Statements	Reasons
1.	1. Given
2.	2. Assumption
3.	3. Corresponding Angles Converse Postulate
4.	4. Contradiction

34. Given that line ℓ is not parallel to line m in the figure at the right, prove that $\angle 3$ is not congruent to $\angle 4$ using an indirect proof.

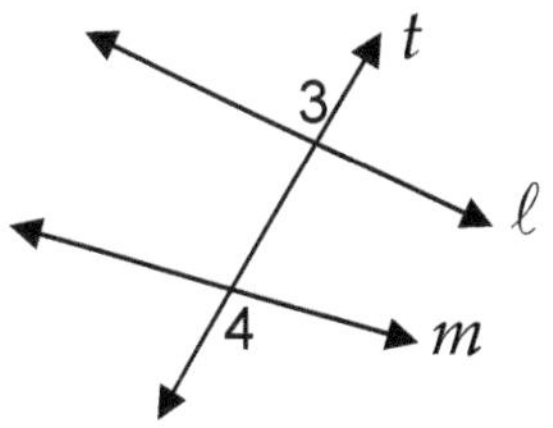

Statements	Reasons
1.	1. Given
2.	2. Assumption
3.	3.
4.	4. Contradiction

Part IV – Mixed Review

1. True or false: In a plane, two lines ℓ and m and a transversal t form a pair of supplementary same-side interior angles if and only if lines ℓ and m are parallel.

   ____

2-6. Fill in each blank with *are*, *are not*, or *may be*.

2. In a plane, if two lines ℓ and m and a transversal t form a pair of congruent alternate interior angles, then lines ℓ and m _______________ parallel.

3. In a plane, if two lines ℓ and m and a transversal t form a pair of congruent same-side exterior angles, then lines ℓ and m _______________ parallel.

4. In a plane, if two lines ℓ and m and a transversal t form a pair of supplementary alternate interior angles, then lines ℓ and m _______________ parallel.

5. In a plane, if two lines ℓ and m and a transversal t form a pair of supplementary angles, then lines ℓ and m _______________ parallel.

6. In a plane, if two lines ℓ and m and a transversal t form a set of alternate exterior angles that are not congruent, then lines ℓ and m _______________ parallel.

7. Draw a picture of a counterexample of the following statement: If two angles are supplementary, then they form a linear pair.

8. If MN = 7 and NO = 3, which of the following could be the distance between M and O? Circle all that apply.

   (A) 2 (B) 4 (C) 5 (D) 10 (E) 12

9-11. In the figure at the right, $\overleftrightarrow{ZV} \perp \overrightarrow{PH}$ and m∠RPV = 131°.

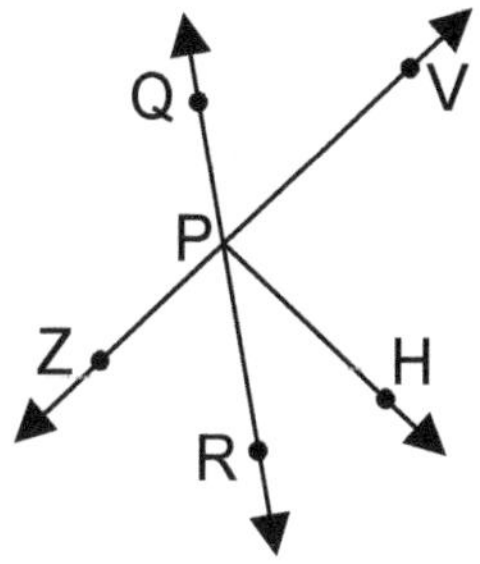

9. m∠RPH = _______________

10. m∠RPZ = _______________

11. m∠ZPQ = _______________

12-19. Classify each pair of angles as *corresponding*, *alternate interior*, *alternate exterior*, *same-side interior*, *vertical*, *linear pair*, or *none of these*.

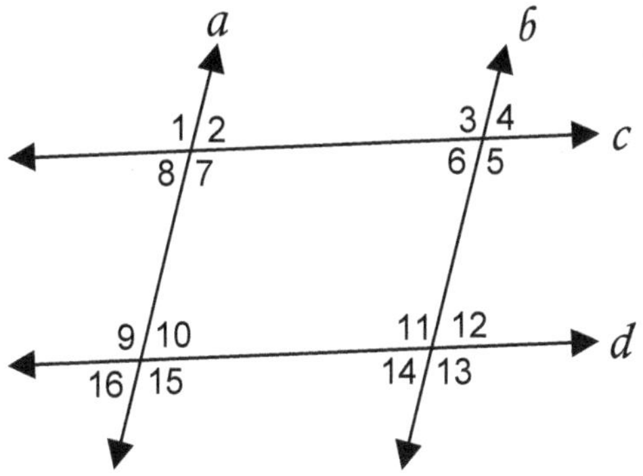

12. ∠2 and ∠3

13. ∠1 and ∠15

14. ∠7 and ∠11

15. ∠4 and ∠6

16. ∠14 and ∠6

17. ∠2 and ∠9

18. ∠11 and ∠14

19. ∠7 and ∠9

20-22. In the figure at the right, $\overline{JK} \parallel \overline{LM}$ and $\overrightarrow{LJ} \parallel \overline{MK}$.

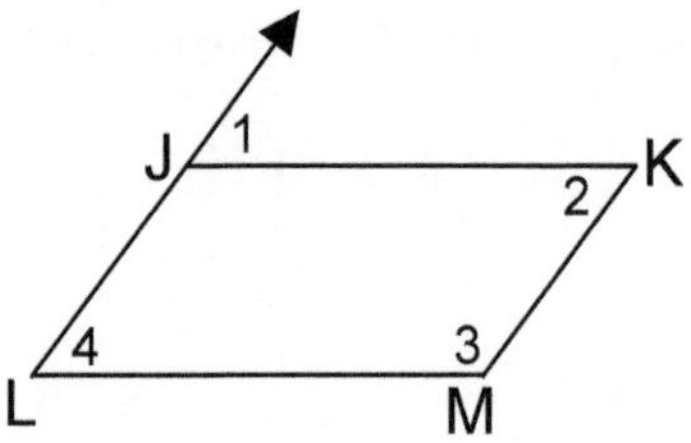

20. If $m\angle 1 = (3x - 5)^\circ$ and $m\angle 2 = (x + 31)^\circ$, then

    x = __________ and $m\angle 1$ = __________.

21. If $m\angle 1 = (4y - 20)^\circ$ and $m\angle 2 = (3y + 1)^\circ$, then y = __________,

    $m\angle 2$ = __________, and $m\angle 3$ = __________.

22. If $m\angle 4 = (7n - 10)^\circ$ and $m\angle 3 = 3n^\circ$, then n = __________, $m\angle 2$ = __________,

    and $m\angle 4$ = __________.

23-28. In the figure at the right, $m\angle 3 = 109^\circ$, $m\angle 10 = 82^\circ$, $p \parallel q$, and r is not parallel to s.

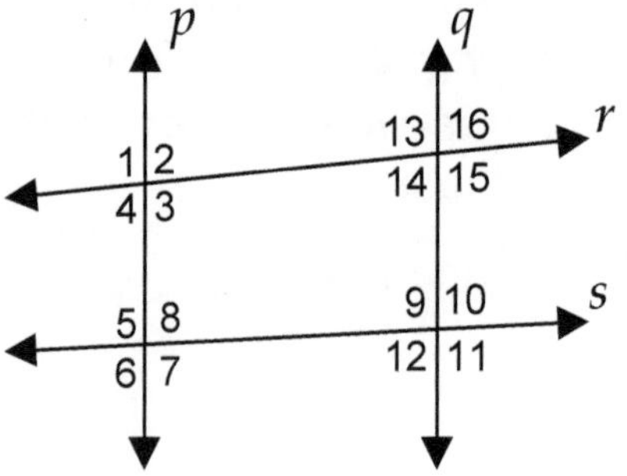

23. $m\angle 1$ = ______________

24. $m\angle 11$ = ______________

25. $m\angle 6$ = ______________

26. $m\angle 8$ = ______________

27. $m\angle 12$ = ______________

28. $m\angle 7$ = ______________

29. In the figure at the right, $\angle 1$, $\angle 2$, $\angle 3$, and $\angle 4$ are all congruent to each other. Which lines, if any, must be parallel? State a postulate or theorem from this chapter that supports each answer.

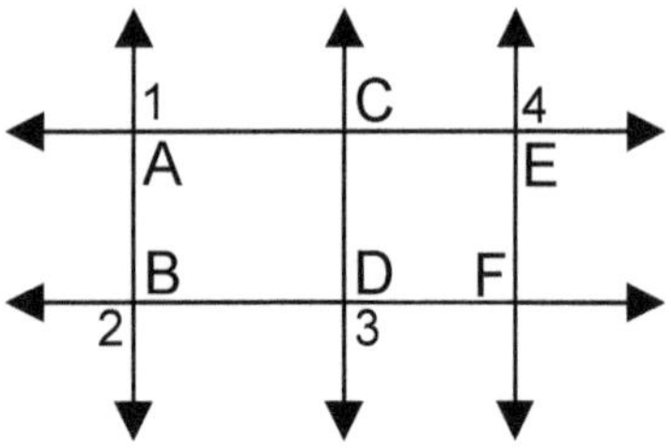

30. In the figure at the right, $m\angle S = 125°$, $m\angle STV = 25°$, and $m\angle UTV = 30°$. Which segments, if any, must be parallel? State a postulate or theorem from this chapter that supports each answer.

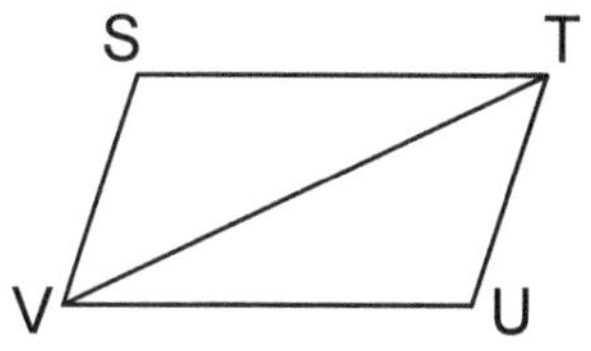

31. In the figure at the right, which segments, if any, must be parallel? State a postulate or theorem from this chapter that supports each answer.

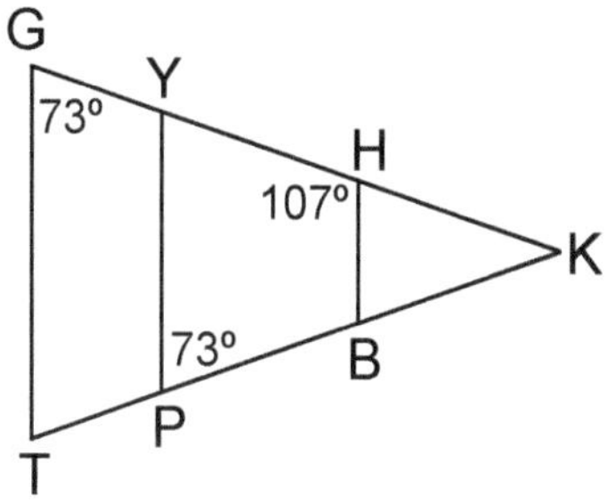

32. In the figure at the right, $\angle 1 \cong \angle 2$, and $\angle 3$ is supplementary to both $\angle 2$ and $\angle 4$. Which lines, if any, must be parallel? State a postulate or theorem from this chapter that supports each answer.

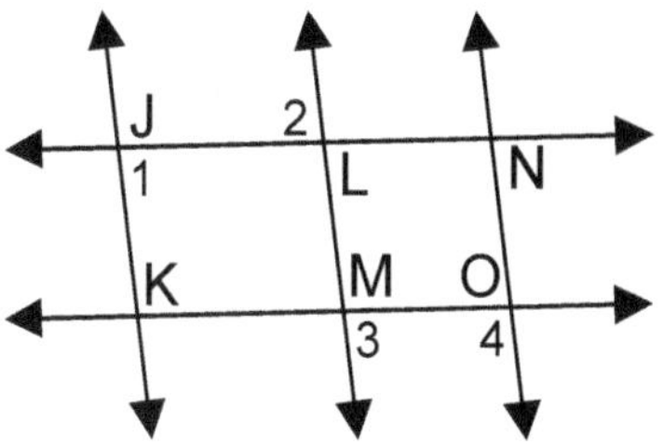

33. Given that $\overleftrightarrow{WX} \perp \overleftrightarrow{XY}$ and that $\overleftrightarrow{XY} \perp \overleftrightarrow{ZY}$ in the figure at the right, prove that $\angle WXZ \cong \angle YZX$.

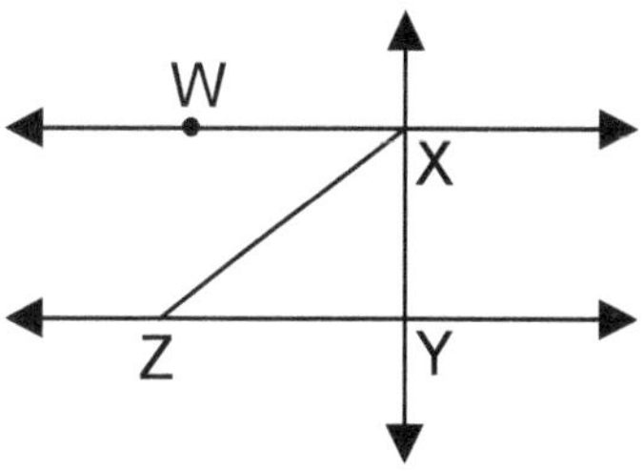

Statements	Reasons

Chapter 4 – Triangles

Part I – The Sum of the Measures of the Angles in a Triangle Theorem

We will begin this section with a theorem.

Sum of the Measures of the Angles in a Triangle Theorem
The sum of the measures of the interior angles of a triangle is 180°.

In our next example, we will prove the Sum of Measures of the Angles in a Triangle Theorem. Before we can do this, however, we need a definition.

An auxiliary line is a line or segment added to a diagram to help in a proof.

Example 1: Prove the Sum of the Measures of the Angles in a Triangle Theorem.

As usual, we will begin by drawing a generic-looking picture.

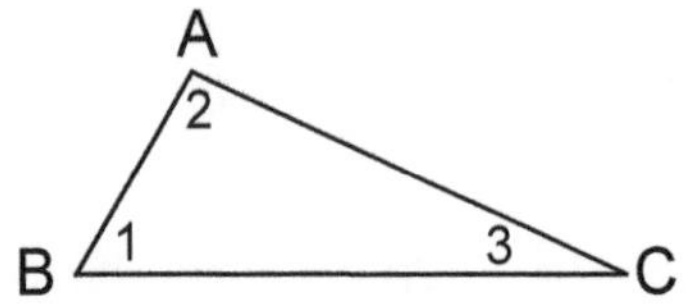

We will begin by stating that we name triangles by naming the vertices, or corners, of the triangle. This means that we can say that we are given ΔABC, and we want to prove that $m\angle 1 + m\angle 2 + m\angle 3 = 180°$. Now, in order to prove this theorem, we will need to draw an auxiliary line. We need to draw the line that is parallel to $\overline{BC}$ that goes through the point A. We know that we can do this because the Parallel Postulate (which we discussed in the last chapter) tells us that there is a line, and only one line, that passes through the point A and is parallel to $\overline{BC}$. We will also label a point D on the new line and the new angles that are formed as shown below.

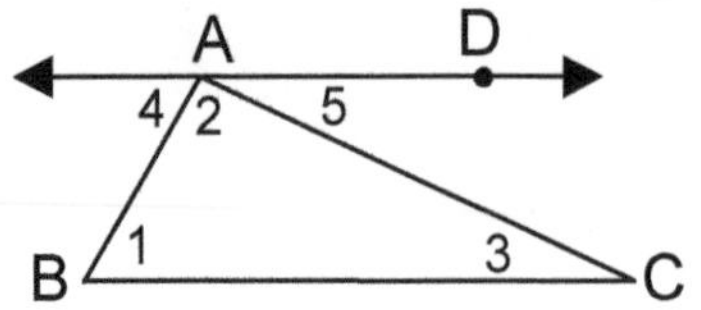

Now, we can prove this theorem. As we have said in the last two chapters, you do not need to write the explanations in gray when you are working your problems; we just put them there to help you better understand what we are doing.

Statements	Reasons	Explanations
1. We have Δ ABC shown above.	1. Given	This was given to us.
2. Draw the line that passes through point A and is parallel to $\overline{BC}$. Label point D and the new angles that are formed $\angle 4$ and $\angle 5$ as shown in the picture above.	2. Parallel Postulate	The Parallel Postulate tells us that there is a line, and only one line, that passes through A and is parallel to $\overline{BC}$.

Statements continued	Reasons continued	Explanations continued
3. $\angle 1 \cong \angle 4$ $\angle 3 \cong \angle 5$	3. Alternate Interior Angles Theorem	Since we know that line $\overleftrightarrow{DA}$ is parallel to $\overline{BC}$, we can use the Alternate Interior Angles Theorem to say that the alternate interior angles that are formed are congruent.
4. $m\angle 1 = m\angle 4$ $m\angle 3 = m\angle 5$	4. Definition of congruent angles	We said in Statement (3) that we had two sets of congruent angles, and so now we can say that their measures are equal.
5. $\angle 4$ and $\angle DAB$ are a linear pair	5. Definition of linear pair	We can look at the picture and use the definition of linear pair to say that $\angle 4$ and $\angle DAB$ form a linear pair.
6. $\angle 4$ and $\angle DAB$ and are supplementary	6. Linear Pair Postulate	Since we already said that $\angle 4$ and $\angle DAB$ form a linear pair, we can use the Linear Pair Postulate to say that they are supplementary.
7. $m\angle 4 + m\angle DAB = 180°$	7. Definition of supplementary angles	Since we just said that $\angle 4$ and $\angle DAB$ are supplementary, we can now use the definition of supplementary angles to say that the sum of their measures is 180°.
8. $m\angle DAB = m\angle 2 + m\angle 5$	8. Angle Addition Postulate	The Angle Addition Postulate tells us that the sum of the measures of two adjacent angles is equal to the measure of the big angle.
9. $m\angle 4 + m\angle 2 + m\angle 5 = 180°$	9. Substitution Property of Equality	Since we said in Statement (8) that $m\angle DAB = m\angle 2 + m\angle 5$, we can go back to Statement (7) and substitute $m\angle 2 + m\angle 5$ for $m\angle DAB$.
10. $m\angle 1 + m\angle 2 + m\angle 3 = 180°$	10. Substitution Property of Equality	Since we said in Statement (4) that $m\angle 1 = m\angle 4$ and $m\angle 3 = m\angle 5$, we can go back to Statement (9) and substitute $m\angle 1$ for $m\angle 4$ and $m\angle 3$ for $m\angle 5$.

Example 2: In the figure at the right, $\overline{AB} \parallel \overline{CD}$. (The arrowheads say that those segments are parallel.) Find the values of w, x, y, and z.

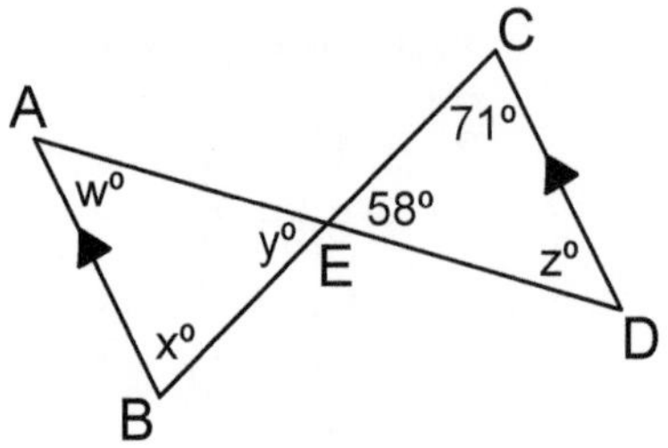

We will begin by noting that we have two triangles, and the Sum of the Measures of the Angles in a Triangle Theorem tells us that the sum of the measures of the interior angles for *each* triangle is 180°. Thus, we can say that $w + x + y = 180$ and that $71 + 58 + z = 180$. Since we know that $71 + 58 + z = 180$, we can say that $z = 51$. Next, since $\angle AEB$ and $\angle CED$ are vertical angles, and since we know that vertical angles are congruent, we can say that $y = 58$. Finally, we can use the Alternate Interior Angles Theorem to say that $\angle A \cong \angle D$ and $\angle B \cong \angle C$, which tells us that $w = 51$ and $x = 71$. (Or, we could have used the Alternate Interior Angles Theorem to find one of the measures and then used the Sum of the Measures of the Angles in a Triangle Theorem to find the measure of the other angle.)

Now, we need another theorem. We will prove part of this theorem in Example 3.

> A triangle cannot have more than one right or obtuse angle, and it cannot have both a right angle and an obtuse angle.

Example 3: Prove the following theorem: A triangle can have no more than one right angle.

We will start by drawing a generic-looking triangle.

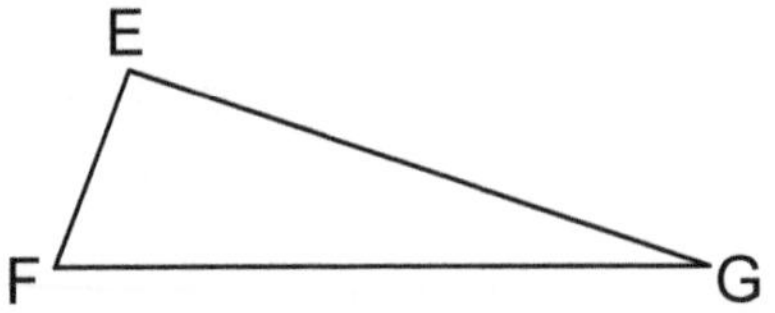

We are given $\triangle EFG$, and we want to prove that this triangle cannot have more than one right angle. The easiest way to prove this theorem is with an indirect proof, as shown on the next page. (As we said in the theorem above, it is also true that a triangle can have no more than one obtuse angle, and it cannot have both a right angle and an obtuse angle. You should be able to verbally convince someone that this is true in an informal way, but, since it is more difficult to prove these statements using the formal reasons that we have discussed, we will not prove these parts of the theorem here.)

Statements	Reasons	Explanations
1. We have ΔEFG shown on the previous page.	1. Given	This was given to us.
2. Assume that $\angle E$ and $\angle F$ are both right angles.	2. Assumption	When we want to prove a statement using an indirect proof, we start by assuming the information we are given and the negation of what we want to prove.
3. $m\angle E = 90°$ $m\angle F = 90°$	3. Definition of a right angle	Since we said in Statement (2) that $\angle E$ and $\angle F$ are both right angles, we can use the definition of right angles to say that they both have measures of 90°.
4. $m\angle E + m\angle F + m\angle G = 180°$	4. Sum of the Measures of the Angles in a Triangle Theorem	The Sum of the Measures of the Angles in a Triangle Theorem tells us that the sum of the measures of the interior angles of a triangle must equal 180°.
5. $90° + 90° + m\angle G = 180°$	5. Substitution Property of Equality	Since we said in Statement (3) that $m\angle E = 90°$ and that $m\angle F = 90°$, we can substitute 90° for $m\angle E$, and we can also substitute 90° for $m\angle F$ in Statement (4).
6. $m\angle G = 0°$	6. Subtraction Property of Equality	We can use the Subtraction Property of Equality to subtract 90° from both sides of the equation in Statement (5) twice.
7. $\angle E$ and $\angle F$ cannot both be right angles.	7. Contradiction	Since we cannot have a triangle in which one of the angles measures 0°, we can conclude that our assumption must be false.

Now, we need another definition.

An exterior angle of a polygon is an angle that is formed by extending one (and only one) of the sides of the polygon.

Example 4: Name the exterior angles of ΔJMN drawn in the figure at the right.

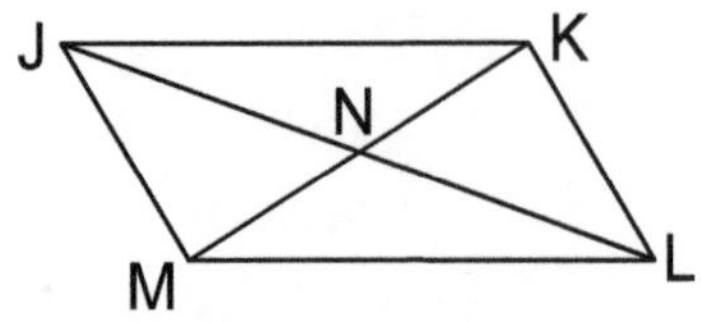

If we start off with a picture of *only* ΔJMN, we can form $\angle JNK$ by extending $\overline{MN}$, and we can form $\angle MNL$ by extending $\overline{JN}$. Therefore, we can say that both $\angle JNK$ and $\angle MNL$ are exterior angles of ΔJMN. These two angles are the only exterior angles of ΔJMN drawn in the picture because all of the other angles drawn in the picture cannot be formed by extending one, and only one, of the sides of ΔJMN.

Now, we need another theorem.

Exterior Angle of a Triangle Theorem

The measure of an exterior angle of a triangle is equal to the sum of the measures of the two interior angles of the triangle that are not adjacent to the exterior angle.

Example 5: Find the value of x in the figure at the right.

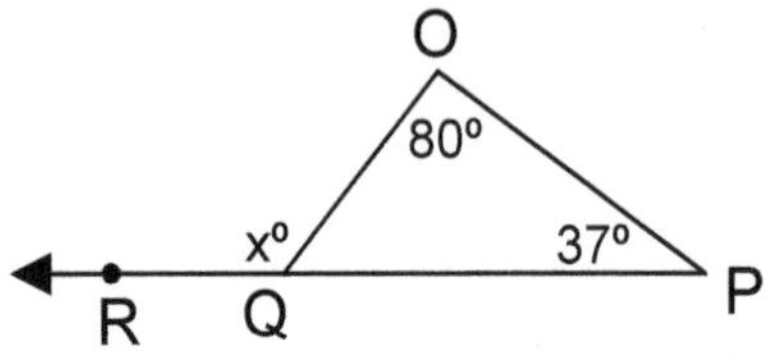

We can use the Exterior Angle of a Triangle Theorem to say that $m\angle OQR = m\angle O + m\angle P$. This tells us that $m\angle OQR = 80° + 37°$, or 117°. Thus, x must equal 117.

(Alternatively, we could have noted that $m\angle OQP$ must equal 63° because $m\angle OQP + m\angle O + m\angle P = 180°$, and so $m\angle OQR$ must equal 117° because $\angle OQR$ and $\angle OQP$ are supplementary. You will prove the Exterior Angle of a Triangle Theorem in Problem #21, and you should keep this idea in mind when you do.)

Example 6: Find the value of y and $m\angle STV$ in the figure at the right.

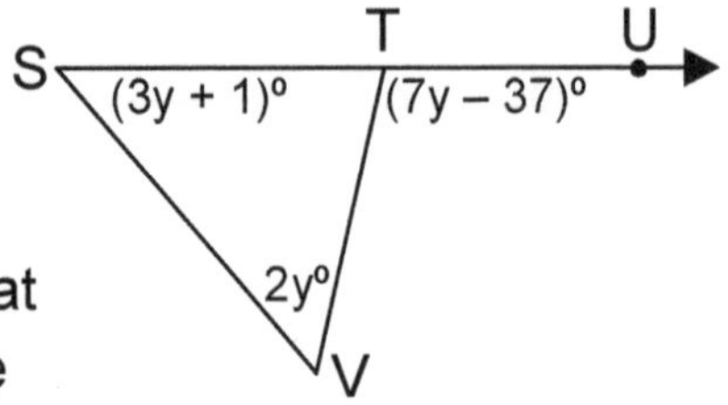

Note that the Exterior Angle of a Triangle Theorem tells us that $m\angle S + m\angle V = m\angle VTU$. This tells that we can write $3y + 1 + 2y = 7y - 37$. When we solve this equation for y, we find that $y = 19$.

To find $m\angle VTS$, we will note that $m\angle VTU = (7 \cdot 19 - 37)°$, or 96°. Since $\angle VTU$ and $\angle VTS$ form a linear pair, we can say that $m\angle VTS = 180° - 96°$, or 84°.

Now, we need one more definition and another theorem.

Definition of Inequality

For all real numbers a and b,

(1) $a < b$ if and only if there is a real number $c > 0$ such that $a + c = b$, and

(2) $a > b$ if and only if there is a real number $c > 0$ such that $a = b + c$

Exterior Angle of a Triangle Inequality Theorem
The measure of an exterior angle of a triangle is greater than either of the measures of the two interior angles of the triangle that are not adjacent to the exterior angle.

Example 7: Given the figure at the right, use the Exterior Angle of a Triangle Inequality Theorem to write two inequalities.

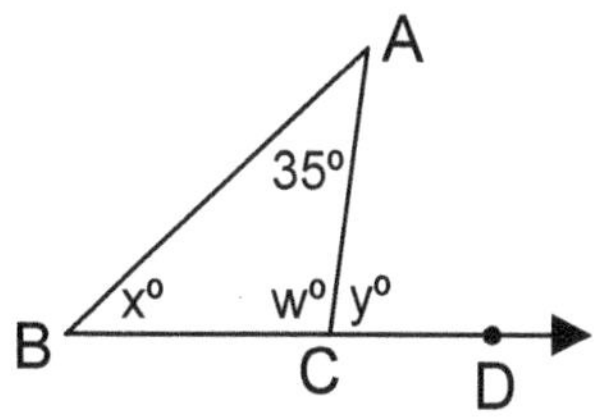

Notice that the Exterior Angle of a Triangle Inequality Theorem tells us that m∠ACD is larger than m∠B, and that m∠ACD is also larger than m∠A. This tells us that we can write y > x and y > 35 (or, equivalently, x < y and 35 < y). We cannot say anything about the relationship between w and y because, even though the picture makes it look as though w > y, pictures can be deceiving.

Finally, we will state three more theorems. You will prove the first two theorems and part of the third theorem in the Problems 23, 25, 27, and 28 of this section. (The other part of the third theorem is intuitive but difficult to prove.)

The sum of the measures of the interior angles of a quadrilateral is 360°. (The definition of a quadrilateral says that a polygon is a quadrilateral if and only if it has four sides.)

If two angles of a triangle are congruent to two angles of another triangle, then the third angles are also congruent.

Through a point P not on a line, there is exactly one line perpendicular to the given line.

Problems:

1. In the figure at the right, $\overline{AC} \perp \overline{BC}$. Then x = ________.

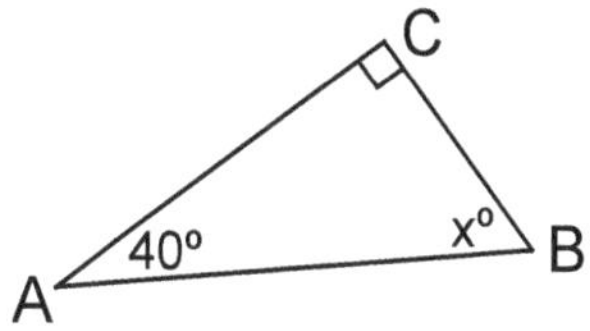

2. In the figure at the right, ∠1 ≅ ∠2. Then m∠1 = ________.

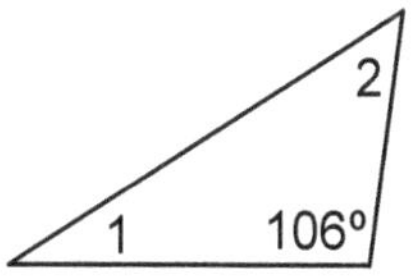

3. In the figure at the right, ∠D ≅ ∠F. Then m∠E = ________.

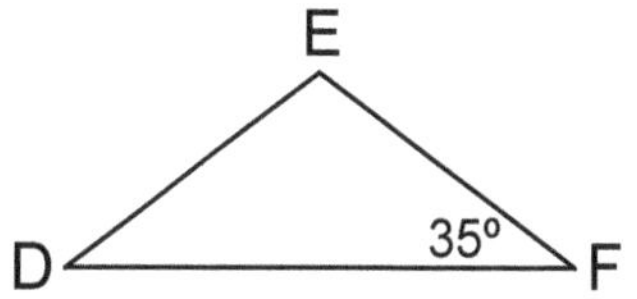

4. In the figure at the right, $\overline{HI} \perp \overline{IJ}$. Then w = ________, x = ________, and y = ________.

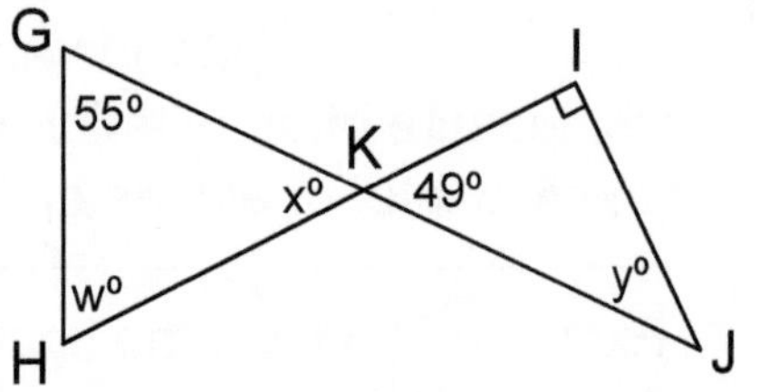

5. In the figure at the right, $\angle LMN \cong \angle NLO$. Then w = ________, x = ________, y = ________, and z = ________.

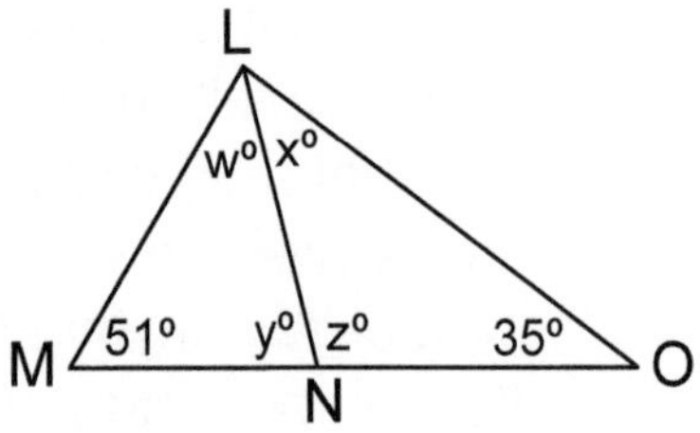

6. In the figure at the right, w = ________, x = ________, y = ________, and z = ________.

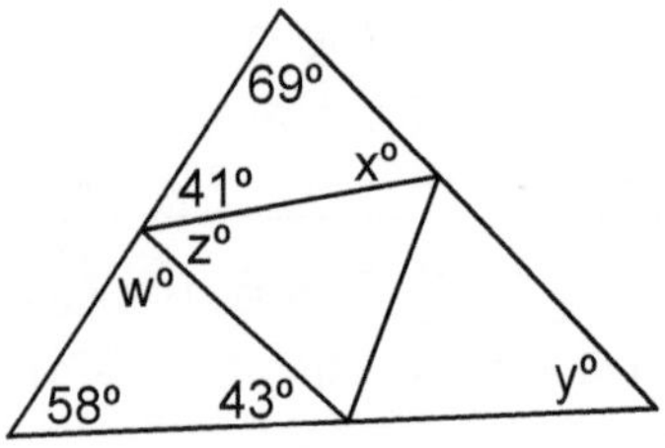

7. In the figure at the right, w = ________, x = ________, y = ________, and z = ________.

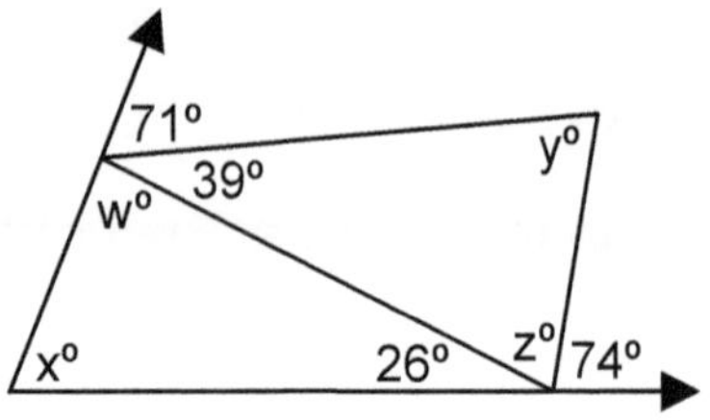

8. In the figure at the right, $\overline{PR} \parallel \overline{ST}$ and $\overline{PR} \perp \overline{SP}$. Then $m\angle 1$ = ________, $m\angle 2$ = ________, $m\angle 3$ = ________, $m\angle 4$ = ________, and $m\angle 5$ = ________.

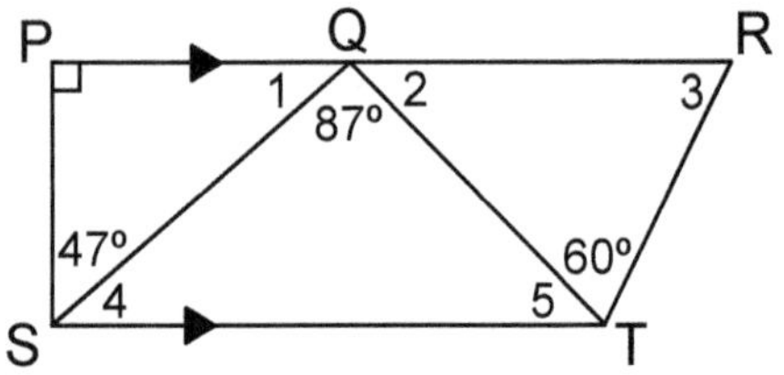

9. In the figure at the right,

$m\angle DAB + m\angle B + m\angle BCD + m\angle D =$ ________.

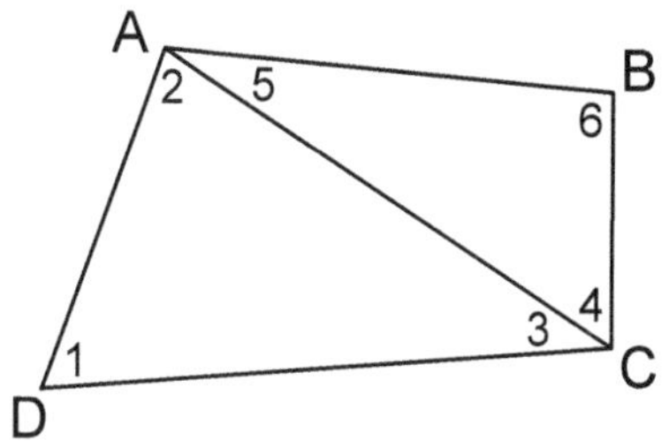

10. In the figure at the right, $w + x + y + z =$ ________.

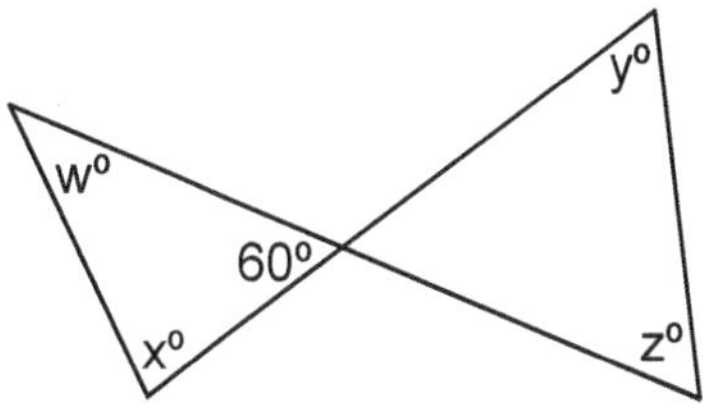

11. In the figure at the right, $m\angle 1 = (2x + 12)°$, $m\angle 2 = (3x - 5)°$,

$m\angle 3 = (x + 17)°$. Then x = ________ and $m\angle 1 =$ ________.

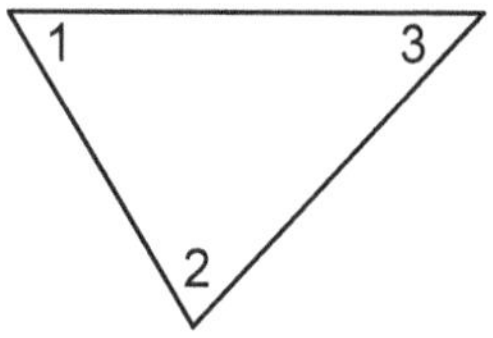

12. In the figure at the right, $\overline{EF} \perp \overline{FG}$, $m\angle 1 = (7x - 2)°$, and

$m\angle 2 = (5x - 4)°$. Then x = ________ and $m\angle 1 =$ ________.

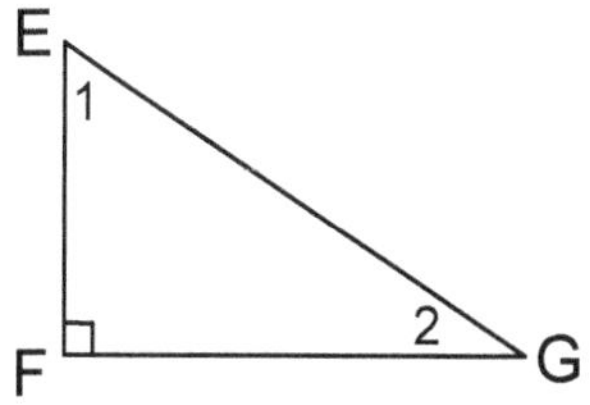

13. In the figure at the right, $\angle 1 \cong \angle 2$, $m\angle 1 = (x - 5)°$, and

$m\angle 3 = (4x + 22)°$. Then x = ________ and

$m\angle 1 =$ ________.

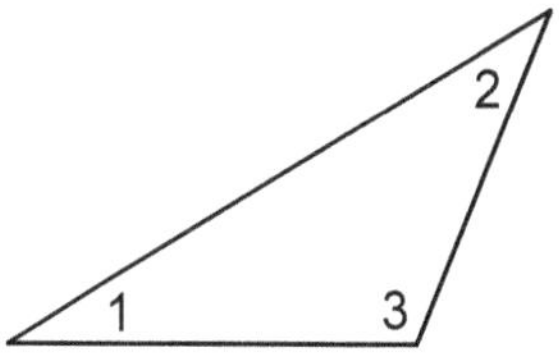

14. In the figure at the right, $m\angle 1 = (3x - 1)^\circ$, $m\angle 2 = (2x + 2)^\circ$, and $m\angle 4 = (4x + 17)^\circ$. Then x = ________ and $m\angle 3$ = ________.

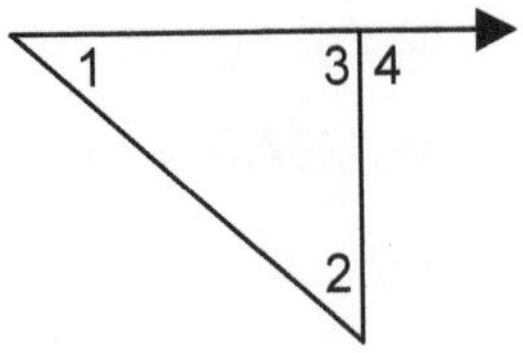

15. In the figure at the right, $m\angle 1 = (120 + x)^\circ$, $m\angle 2 = (14 - 2x)^\circ$, and $m\angle 4 = (10 - 5x)^\circ$. Then x = ________ and $m\angle 3$ = ________.

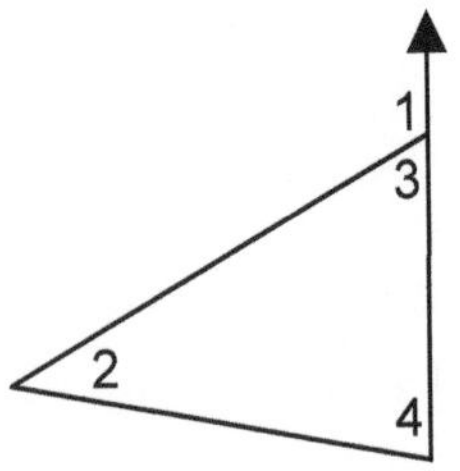

16. In the figure at the right, $m\angle 1 = w^\circ$, $m\angle 2 = (5x - 23)^\circ$, $m\angle 3 = (4x - 1)^\circ$, $m\angle 4 = 3x^\circ$, and $m\angle 5 = (7y + 3)^\circ$. Then x = ________, $m\angle 2$ = ________, $m\angle 5$ = ________, w = ________, and y = ________.

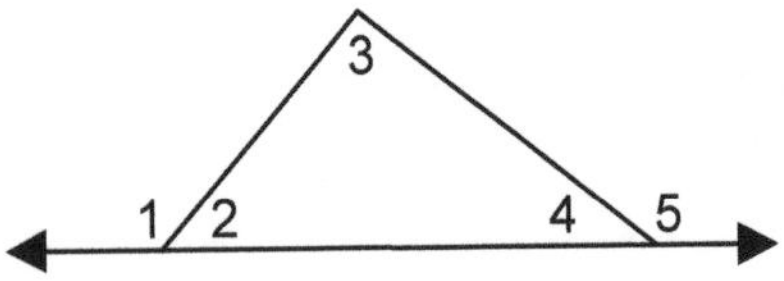

17. In the figure at the right, $m\angle 1 = (4w + 22)^\circ$, $m\angle 3 = (3w + 3)^\circ$, $m\angle 4 = (2w - 12)^\circ$, and $m\angle 5 = (7x - 10)^\circ$. Then w = ________, $m\angle 1$ = ________, $m\angle 2$ = ________, $m\angle 5$ = ________, and x = ________.

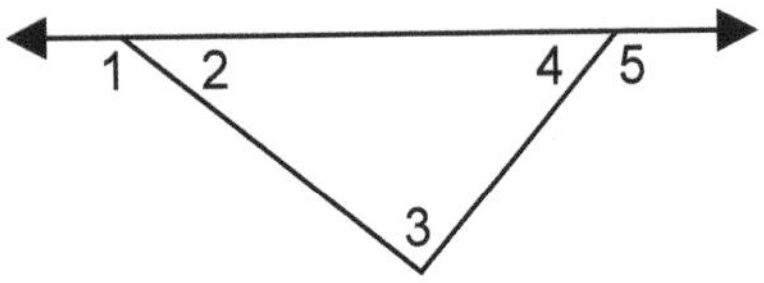

18. In the figure at the right, $\angle JIH \cong \angle IHJ$. Then

x = ________, m$\angle$HJK = ________,

y = ________, m$\angle$JHK = ________, and

m$\angle$2 = ________.

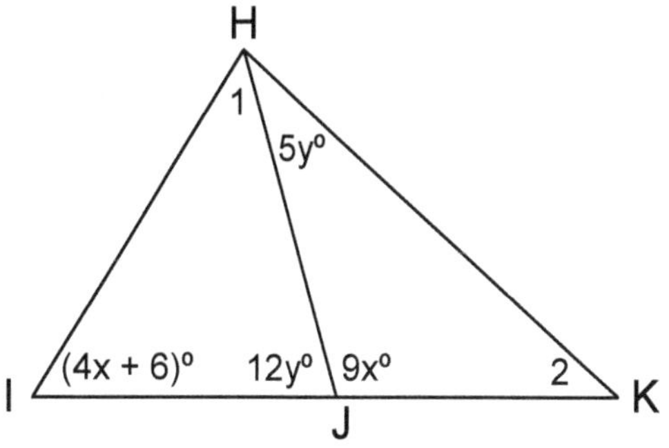

19. In the figure at the right, m$\angle$1 = (x + 15)°, m$\angle$2 = (3y + 4)°,

m$\angle$3 = (5y + 11)°, and m$\angle$4 = (3x + 4)°. Then x = ________,

y = ________, and m$\angle$1 = ________.

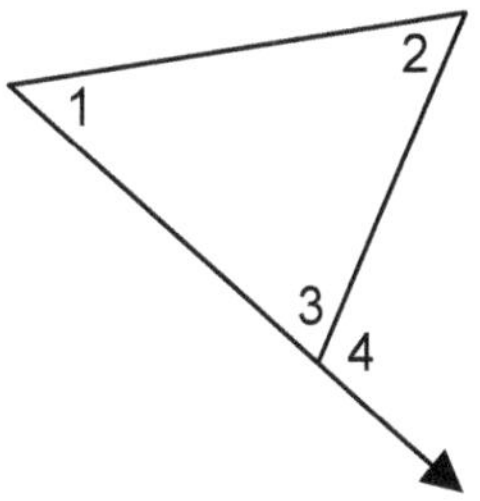

20. In the figure at the right, x = ________, y = ________,

m$\angle$L = ________, and w = ________.

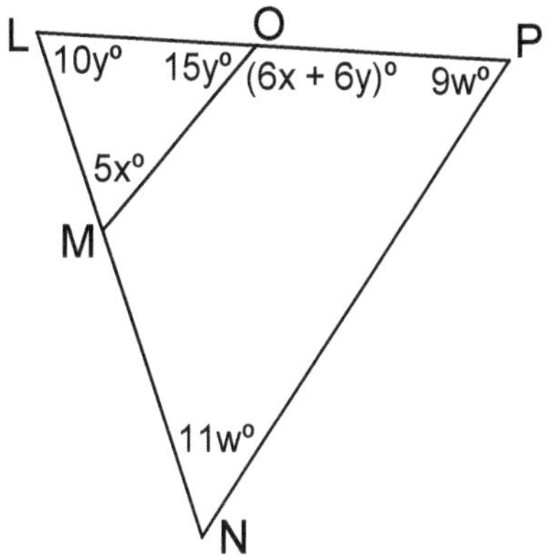

21. Prove the Exterior Angle of a Triangle Theorem, which says this: The measure of an exterior angle of a triangle is equal to the sum of the measures of the two interior angles of the triangle that are not adjacent to the exterior angle.

Given: $\triangle ABC$ with $\angle BCD$ as an exterior angle

Prove: $m\angle BCD = m\angle A + m\angle B$

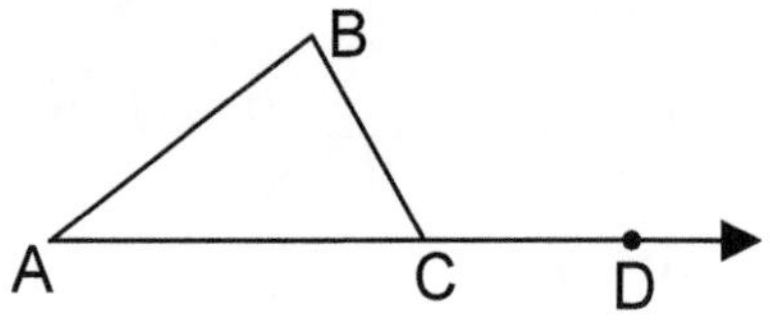

Statements	Reasons
1.	1. Given
2.	2.
3.	3. Linear Pair Postulate
4.	4.
5.	5. Sum of the Measures of the Angles in a Triangle Theorem
6.	6. Substitution Property of Equality
7.	7.

22. Prove the Exterior Angle of a Triangle Inequality Theorem, which says this: The measure of an exterior angle of a triangle is greater than either of the measures of the two interior angles of the triangle that are not adjacent to the exterior angle.

Given: $\triangle ABC$ with $\angle BCD$ as an exterior angle

Prove: $m\angle BCD > m\angle A$

$m\angle BCD > m\angle B$

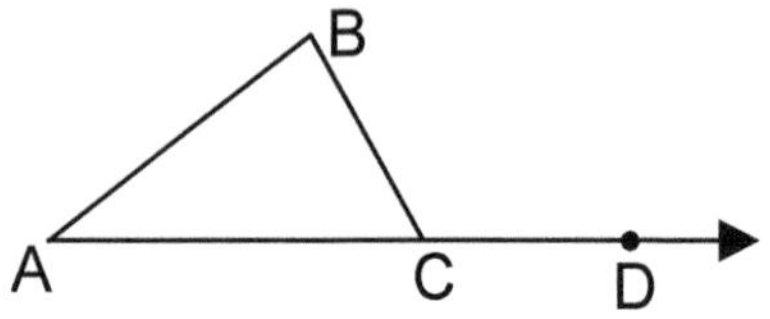

Statements	Reasons
1.	1. Given
2.	2.
3.	3.

23. Prove the following theorem: The sum of the measures of the interior angles of a quadrilateral is 360°. (The definition of a quadrilateral says that a polygon is a quadrilateral if and only if it has four sides.)

Given: quadrilateral HIJK

Prove: $m\angle J + m\angle HIJ + m\angle H + m\angle JKH = 360°$

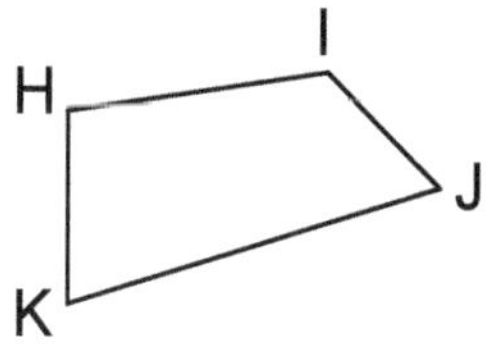

Statements	Reasons
1.	1. Given
2. Draw $\overline{IK}$.	2. Through any two points, there is exactly one line.
3. $m\angle J + m\angle KIJ + m\angle JKI = 180°$ $m\angle H + m\angle IKH + m\angle HIK = 180°$	3.
4. $m\angle J + m\angle KIJ + m\angle JKI + 180° = 360°$	4.
5.	5.
6. $m\angle HIK + m\angle KIJ = m\angle HIJ$ $m\angle JKI + m\angle IKH = m\angle JKH$	6.
7.	7.

24. We said in the last chapter that the Corresponding Angles Converse Postulate could be proven with an indirect proof that uses the Exterior Angle of a Triangle Inequality Theorem. Prove the Corresponding Angles Postulate, which says this: In a plane, if two lines and a transversal form a set of congruent corresponding angles, then the lines are parallel.

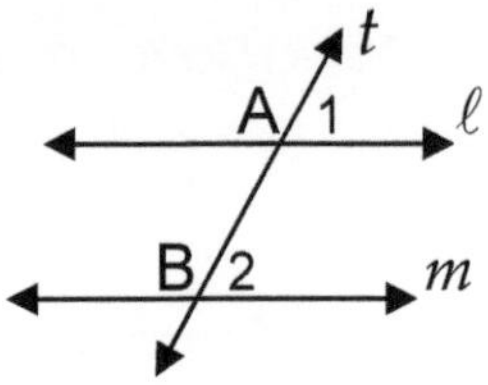

Given: $\angle 1 \cong \angle 2$

Prove: $\ell \parallel m$

Statements	Reasons
1.	1. Given
2.	2.
3. Lines ℓ and m must intersect at a point, and assume it happens on the left side of the transversal t. (Note that, because $\angle 1 \cong \angle 2$, the Exterior Angle of a Triangle Inequality Theorem says they cannot intersect on the right side of the transversal t.) Call this point P.	3. Definition of parallel lines
4. $\angle PAB \cong \angle 1$	4.
5. $\angle PAB \cong \angle 2$	5.
6. $m\angle PAB = m\angle 2$	6.
7.	7. Exterior Angle of a Triangle Inequality Theorem
8.	8.

25. Prove the following theorem: If two angles of a triangle are congruent to two angles of another triangle, then the third angles are also congruent.

Given: $\angle L \cong \angle O$ and $\angle M \cong \angle P$

Prove: $\angle N \cong \angle Q$

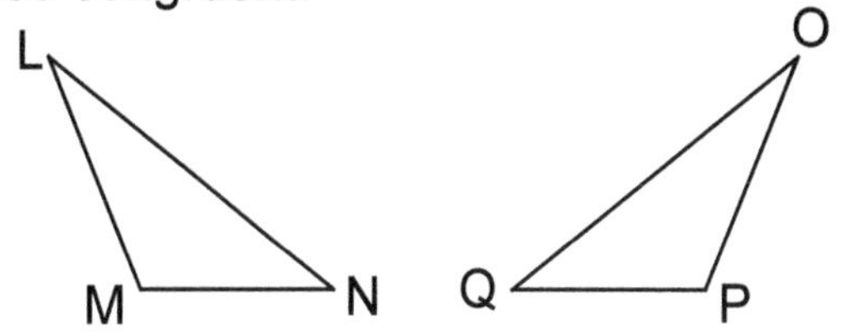

Statements	Reasons

26. Given that $\angle 1$ is not congruent to $\angle 5$ in the figure at the right, prove that $\angle 2$ is not congruent to $\angle 6$ using an indirect proof.

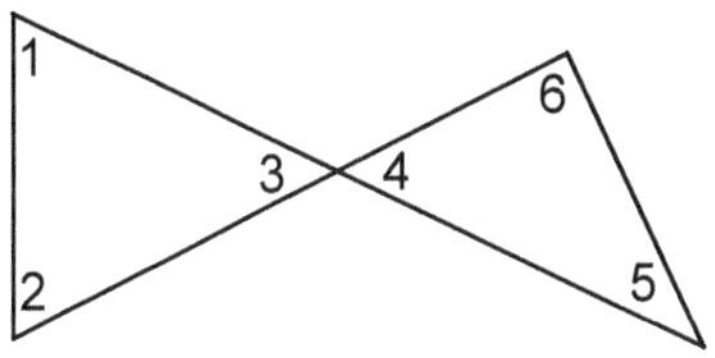

Statements	Reasons

27. Use an indirect proof to prove the following theorem: Through a point P not on a line, you cannot draw more than one line perpendicular to the given line.

Given: line ℓ and point P not on line ℓ

Prove: You cannot draw more than one line through P that is perpendicular to ℓ

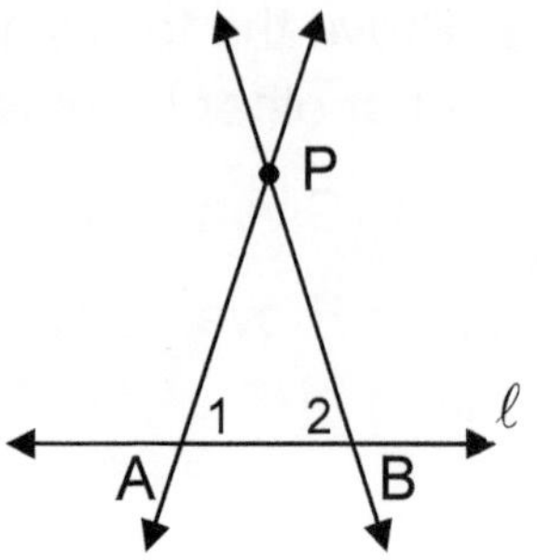

Statements	Reasons
1.	1. Given
2. Assume that you can draw two lines that pass through P and are perpendicular to line ℓ. Draw these lines, and call the points of intersection A and B as shown in the figure above. Also label $\angle 1$, and $\angle 2$ as shown in the figure above.	2.
3. $\angle 1$ and $\angle 2$ are right angles	3.
4. $m\angle 1 = 90°$ and $m\angle 2 = 90°$	4.
5.	5. Sum of the Measures of the Angles in a Triangle Theorem
6.	6. Substitution Property of Equality
7. $m\angle APB = 0°$	7.
8.	8.

28. Prove the theorem stated in #27 with an indirect proof that uses the Exterior Angle of a Triangle Inequality Theorem instead of the Sum of the Measures of the Angles in a Triangle Theorem.

Given: line ℓ and point P not on line ℓ

Prove: You cannot draw more than one line through P that is perpendicular to ℓ

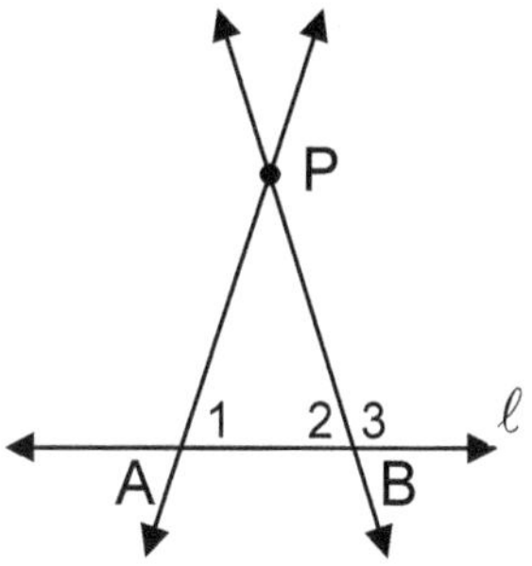

Statements	Reasons
1.	1.
2. Assume that you can draw two lines that pass through P and are perpendicular to line ℓ. Draw these lines, and call the points of intersection A and B as shown in the figure above. Also label $\angle 1$ and $\angle 3$ as shown in the figure above.	2.
3.	3.
4.	4.
5.	5.
6.	6.
7.	7.

Part II – Classifying Triangles

We will begin this section with seven definitions.

A triangle is called a <u>scalene triangle</u> if and only if all three of its sides have different lengths.

A triangle is called an <u>isosceles triangle</u> if and only if at least two of its sides are congruent to each other.

A triangle is called an <u>equilateral triangle</u> if and only if all three of its sides are congruent to each other.

A triangle is called an <u>acute triangle</u> if and only if all of its angles are acute.

A triangle is called a <u>right triangle</u> if and only if one of its angles is a right angle.

A triangle is called an <u>obtuse triangle</u> if and only if one of its angles is an obtuse angle.

A triangle is called an <u>equiangular triangle</u> if and only if all three of its angles are congruent to each other.

Note that, in an acute triangle, <u>all</u> of the angles must be acute; in right triangles and obtuse triangles, only <u>one</u> of the angles must be obtuse or right. (And, in fact, as we discussed in the last section, we *cannot* have more than one obtuse or right angle in a triangle.)

Example 1: Classify each of the triangles below according to their sides and angles. For each triangle, name all of the terms that apply.

(a)

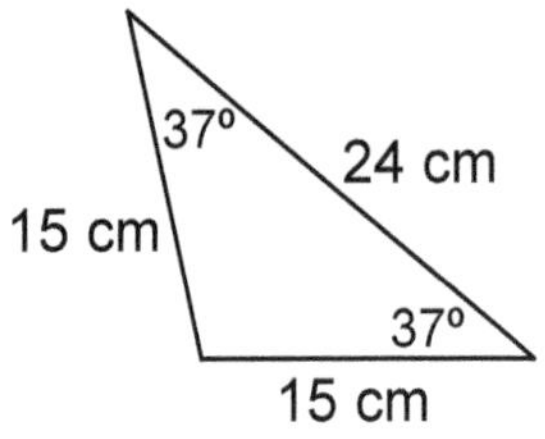

(b)

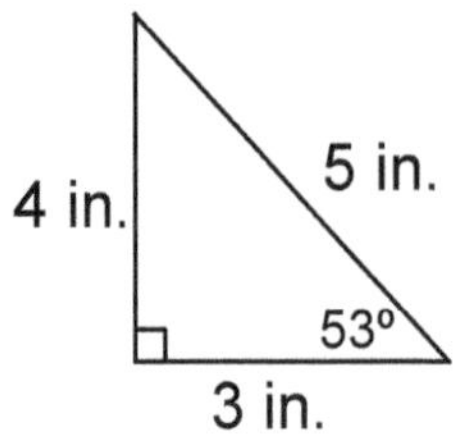

(c)

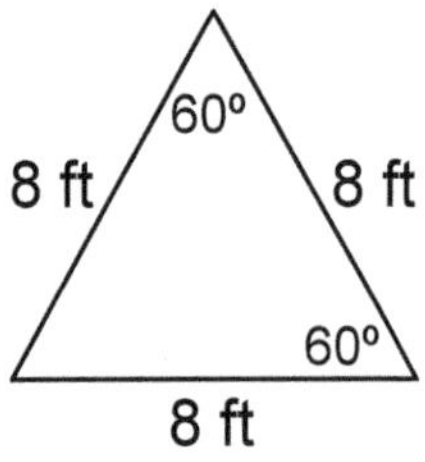

(d)

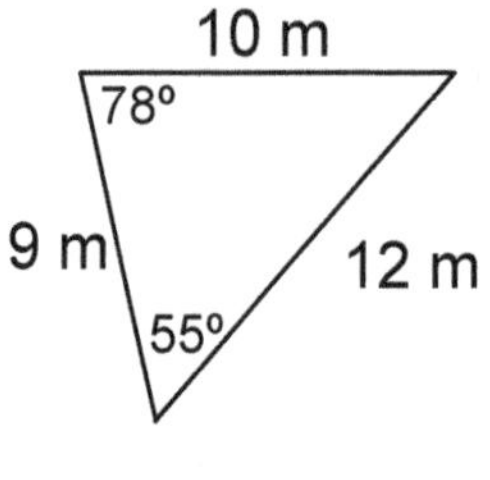

(a) This is an *obtuse isosceles* triangle. It is an isosceles triangle because two of its sides are congruent to each other, and it is an obtuse triangle because it has one obtuse angle. (Note that the third angle must have a measure of 106° because the sum of the measures of all the angles in the triangle must equal 180°.)

(b) This is a *right scalene* triangle. It is a scalene triangle because all three of its sides have different lengths, and it is a right triangle because it has a right angle.

(c) We will begin by noting that, since the measures of the angles in a triangle must add up to 180°, the third angle in this triangle must have a measure of 60°. This tells us that all of the following terms apply to this triangle: *equilateral* (because all three sides of this triangle are congruent to each other), *acute* (because all three of the angles of this triangle have measures that are less than 90°), *isosceles* (because at least two sides of the sides of this triangle are congruent to each other), and *equiangular* (because all of the angles in this triangle are congruent to each other).

(d) We will begin by noting that the Sum of the Measures of the Angles in a Triangle Theorem tells us that the third angle of this triangle has a measure of 47°. This tells us that this triangle is an acute scalene triangle. It is an acute triangle because all three of its angles are acute, and it is a scalene triangle because all three of its sides have different lengths.

Finally, we will state two theorems. You will prove these theorems in the exercises for this section.

If a triangle is equiangular, then each angle of the triangle measures 60°.

The acute angles of a right triangle are complementary.

Problems:

1-16. Classify each of the triangles below according to their sides and angles. For each triangle, name all of the terms that apply.

1. ____________________________

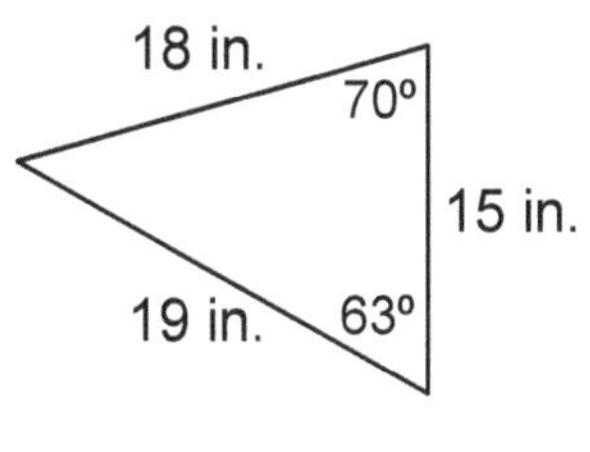

2. ____________________________

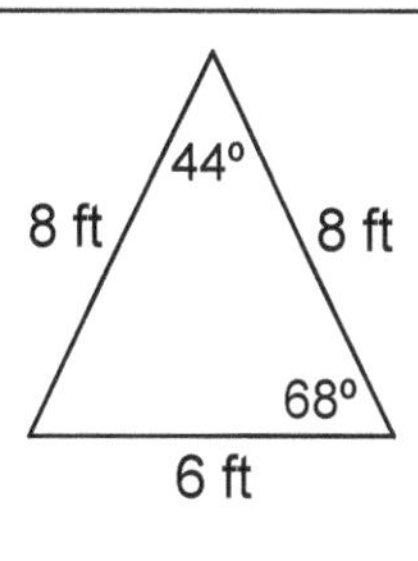

3. ____________________

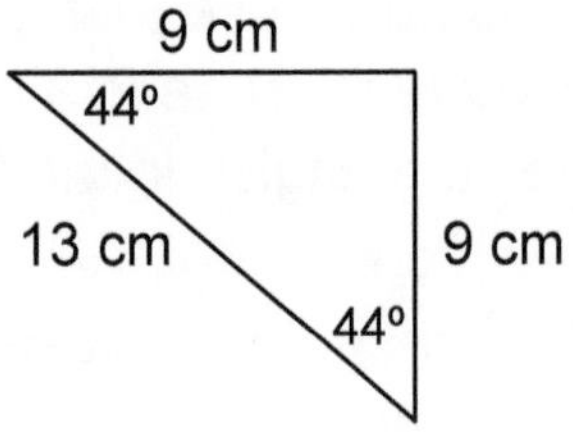

4. ____________________

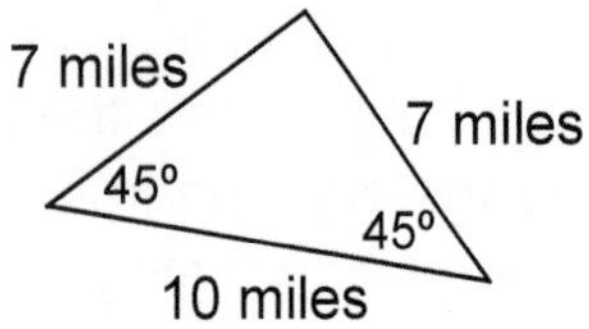

5. ____________________

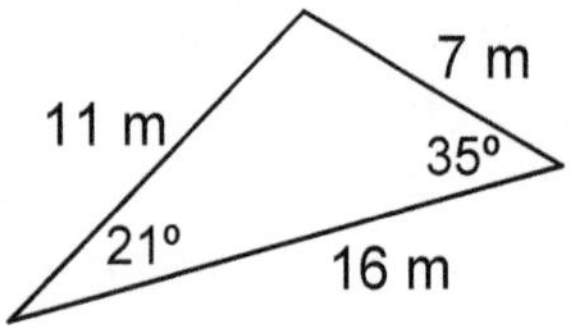

6. ____________________

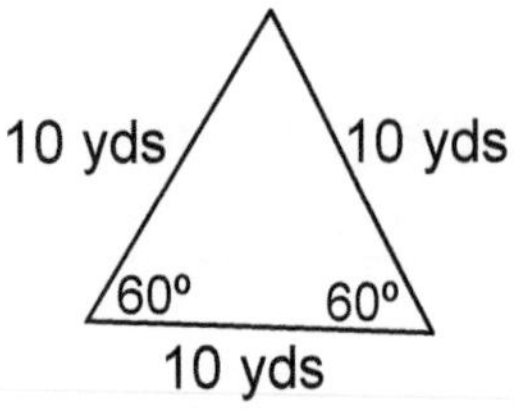

7. ____________________

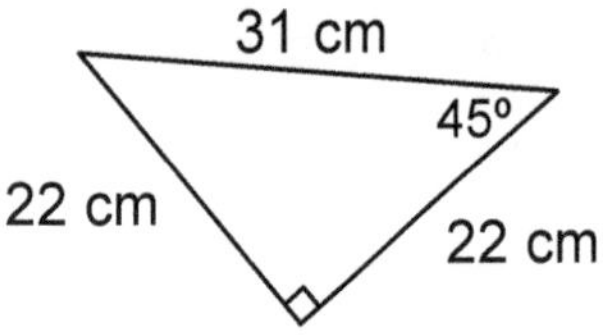

8. ____________________

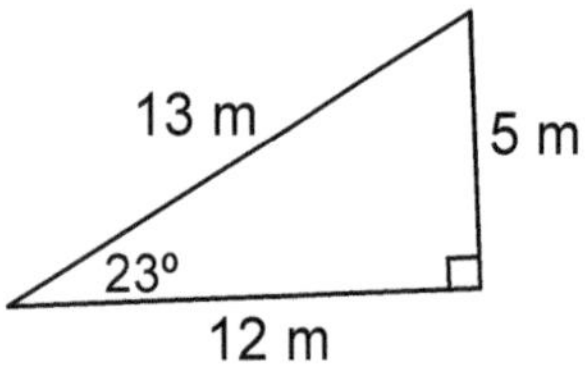

9. ____________________

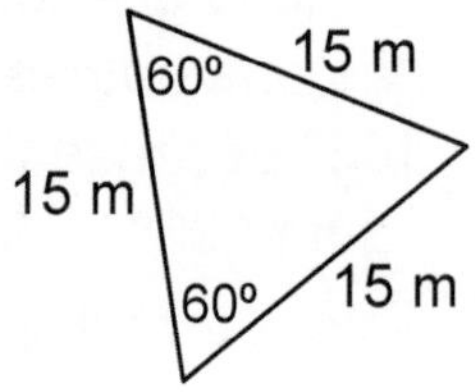

10. ____________________

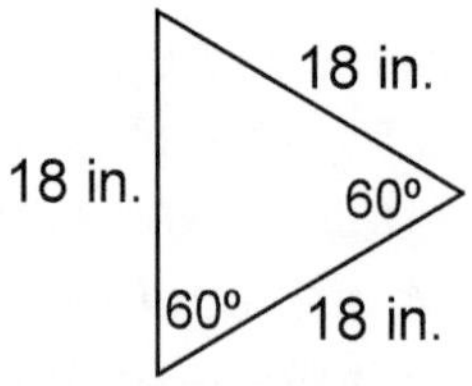

11. ____________________

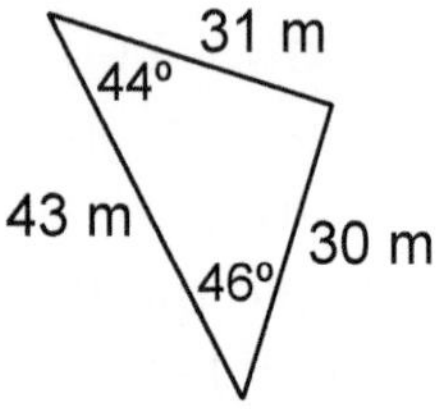

12. ____________________

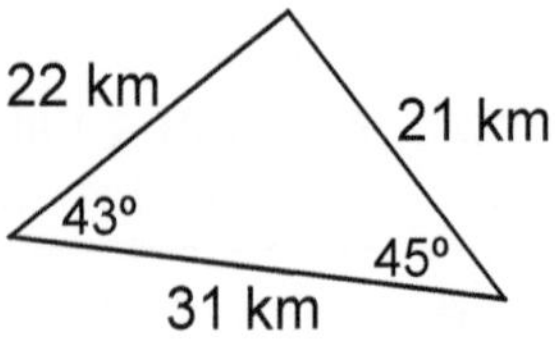

13. ____________________

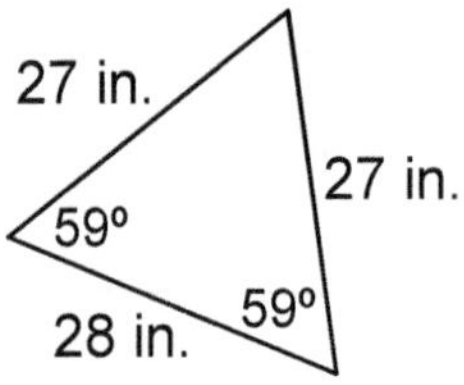

14. ____________________

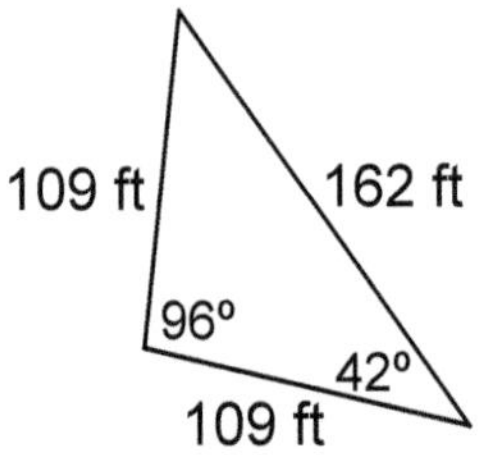

15. ___________________________

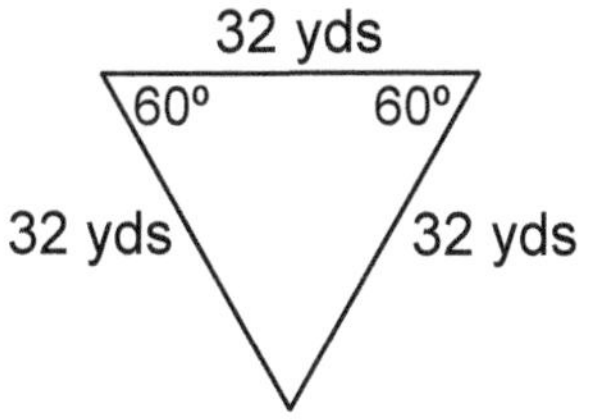

16. ___________________________

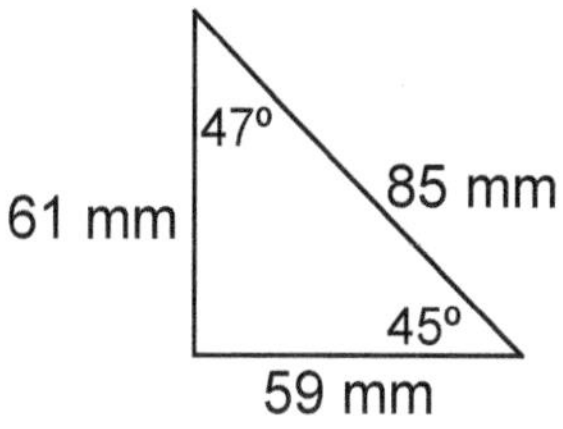

17-25. Draw a triangle that appears to fit each description *if possible*. You may use a ruler and a protractor to work these problems.

17. a scalene acute triangle

18. a right isosceles triangle

19. an acute equilateral triangle

20. a scalene obtuse triangle

21. a right equiangular triangle

22. an acute isosceles triangle

23. a right scalene triangle

24. an obtuse equilateral triangle

25. an obtuse isosceles triangle

26. Prove the following theorem: If a triangle is equiangular, then each angle of the triangle measures 60º.

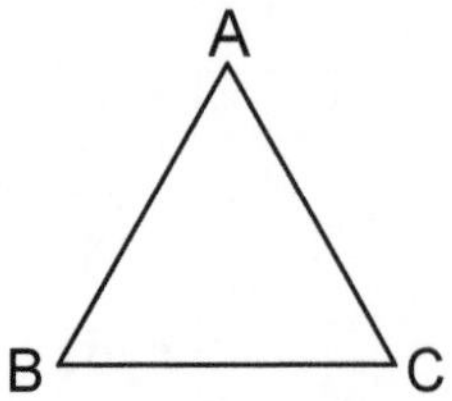

Given: ΔABC is an equiangular triangle

Prove: $m\angle A = 60^\circ$, $m\angle B = 60^\circ$, and $m\angle C = 60^\circ$

Statements	Reasons
1.	1.
2.	2. Definition of an equiangular triangle
3.	3. Definition of congruent angles
4. $m\angle A + m\angle B + m\angle C = 180^\circ$	4.
5.	5.
6. $3(m\angle A) = 180^\circ$	6. Distributive Property
7.	7.
8.	8.

27. Prove the following theorem: The acute angles of a right triangle are complementary.

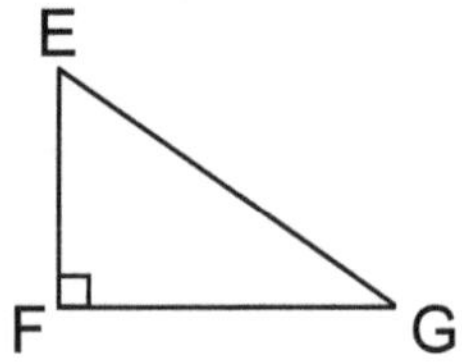

Given: ΔEFG is a right triangle with $\angle F$ as the right angle

Prove: $\angle E$ and $\angle G$ are complementary

Statements	Reasons

28. Given that m∠U = 42° and m∠W = 48° in the figure at the right, use an indirect proof to show that △UVW is not an acute triangle.

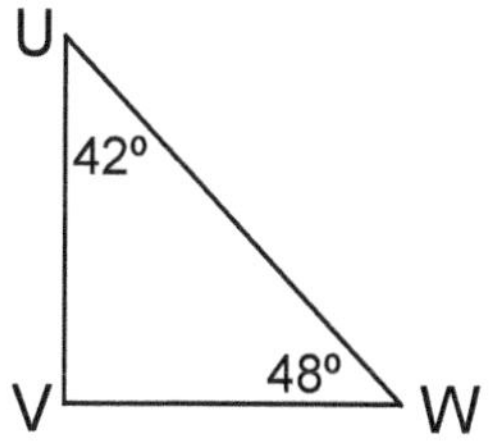

Statements	Reasons

29. Given that m∠R = 30° and m∠T = 41° in the figure at the right, prove that △RST is an obtuse triangle.

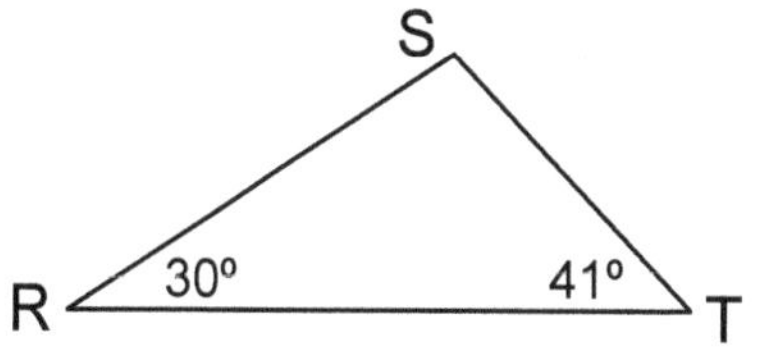

Statements	Reasons
1.	1.
2.	2.
3. 30° + 41° + m∠S = 180°	3.
4. m∠S = 109°	4.
5. ∠S is an obtuse angle	5.
6.	6.

Part III – Congruent Triangles

We will begin this section with a definition.

Two triangles are called <u>congruent</u> if and only if their corresponding parts are congruent.

Notice that we used the word *corresponding* in this definition. We will talk more about what this means in the next two examples, but please do not think that this use of the word has anything to do with our discussion of corresponding angles from the last chapter.

Example 1: You are told that $\Delta ABC \cong \Delta DEF$. What does this mean?

The order in which we name the vertices of each of the triangles is very important. Since we named A first in the first triangle, and since we named D first in the second triangle, we know that point A corresponds to (or coincides with) point D. This tells us that $\angle A \cong \angle D$. Similarly, we can say that $\angle B \cong \angle E$ and that $\angle C \cong \angle F$. We can also say that $\overline{AB} \cong \overline{DE}$ (because the points A and B were named first and second in the first triangle, and points D and E were named first and second in the second triangle). Similarly, we can say that $\overline{BC} \cong \overline{EF}$ and that $\overline{AC} \cong \overline{DF}$. This means that the picture below shows what ΔABC and ΔDEF could look like. There are many other pictures that we could draw, but this is one of them.

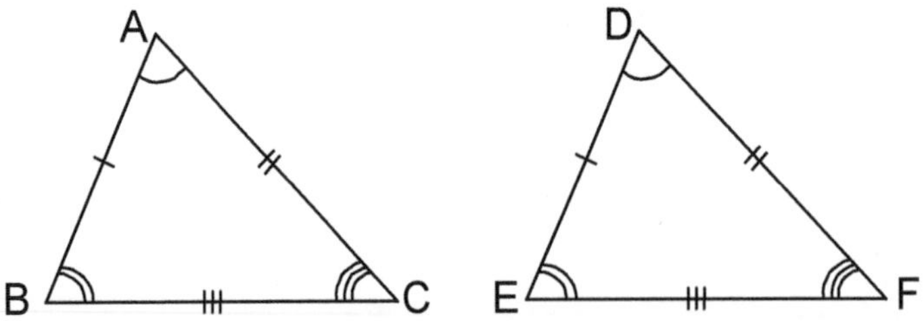

In this picture, the short straight marks show that those segments are congruent to each other, and the arcs show that those angles are congruent to each other. For instance, we can look at the picture and see that it says that $\overline{AB}$ and $\overline{DE}$ are congruent because they both have one mark through them. We would not, however, be able to say that $\overline{AB}$ and $\overline{AC}$ are congruent because they have different numbers of marks through them. We can also look at the picture and see that $\angle C$ and $\angle F$ are congruent because they are both marked with three arcs, but we cannot say that $\angle A$ and $\angle E$ are congruent because they are marked with different numbers of arcs.

Example 2: In the figure at the right, $\Delta KML \cong \Delta NPO$. Find the values of w, x, and y.

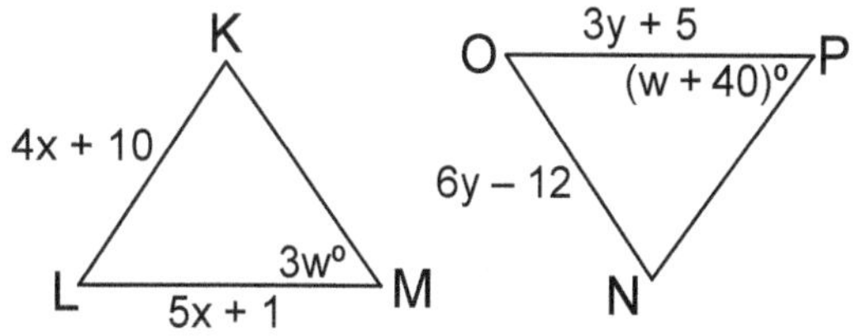

We will begin by noting we can say that $\angle M \cong \angle P$ because, when we say that $\Delta KML \cong \Delta NPO$, both M and P are named second. This means that we can say that 3w = w + 40, which tells us that w = 20. Next, we will note that $\overline{LM} \cong \overline{OP}$ (note that L and M we were second and third in the statement $\Delta KML \cong \Delta NPO$, and so were O and P) and that $\overline{KL} \cong \overline{NO}$. This means that we can write 5x + 1 = 3y + 5 and 4x + 10 = 6y – 12. This is a system of equations with two variables that you should be able to solve using either the substitution method or the elimination method. When you do this, you should find that x = 5 and y = 7.

If you want to use the definition of congruent triangles to say that two triangles are congruent, you must know that you have three sets of congruent sides *and* three sets of congruent angles. However, as the postulates and the theorem below show, we can know that two triangles are congruent without having to know that we have three sets of congruent sides *and* three sets of congruent angles.

Side-Side-Side (SSS) Congruence Postulate

If the sides of a triangle are congruent to the sides of another triangle, then the two triangles are congruent.

Side-Angle-Side (SAS) Congruence Postulate

If two sides of a triangle are congruent to two sides of another triangle and the angles between these are congruent to each other, then the triangles are congruent.

Angle-Side-Angle (ASA) Congruence Postulate

If two angles of a triangle are congruent to two angles of another triangle and the sides between these angles are also congruent, then the triangles are congruent.

Hypotenuse-Leg (HL) Congruence Postulate

If a leg and the hypotenuse of a right triangle are congruent to a leg and the hypotenuse of another right triangle, then the triangles are congruent. (We will talk more about this in later chapters, but the legs of a right triangle are the sides of the triangle that form the right angle, and the hypotenuse of a right triangle is the side that is opposite the right angle.)

Angle-Angle-Side (AAS) Congruence Theorem

If two angles and a nonincluded side of one triangle are congruent to two angles and the corresponding nonincluded side of another triangle, then the triangles are congruent.

Example 3: For each pair of triangles below, (a) determine whether or not the triangles are congruent, and (b) if your answer to part (a) was *yes*, complete the congruence statement and state a postulate or theorem to support your conclusion. (As we said in Example 1, the straight marks through the different pairs of segments show pairs of segments that are congruent to each other, and the arcs in the angles show different pairs of angles that are congruent to each other.)

(i) $\Delta ABC \cong \Delta$________

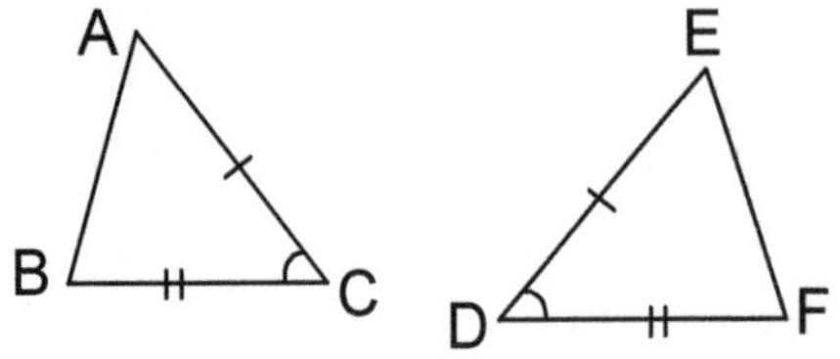

(ii) $\Delta GIH \cong \Delta$________

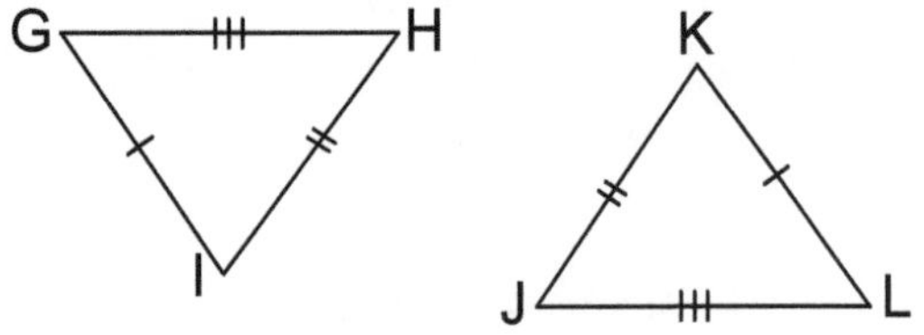

(iii) $\Delta MNP \cong \Delta$________

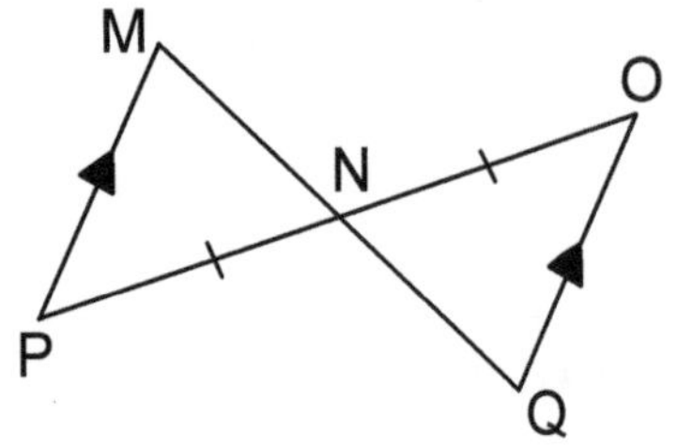

(iv) Δ________$\cong \Delta RST$

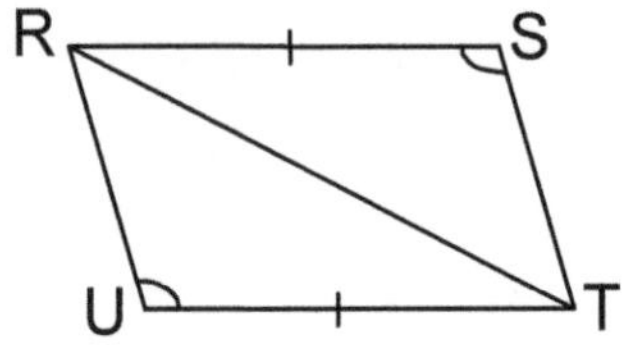

(v) Δ________$\cong \Delta WXY$

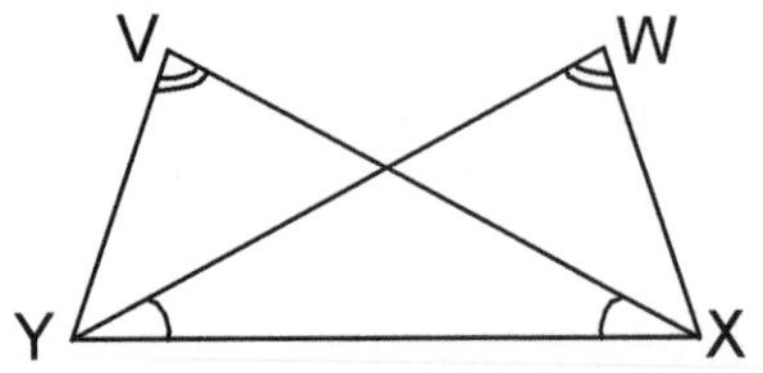

(vi) Δ________$\cong \Delta ABC$

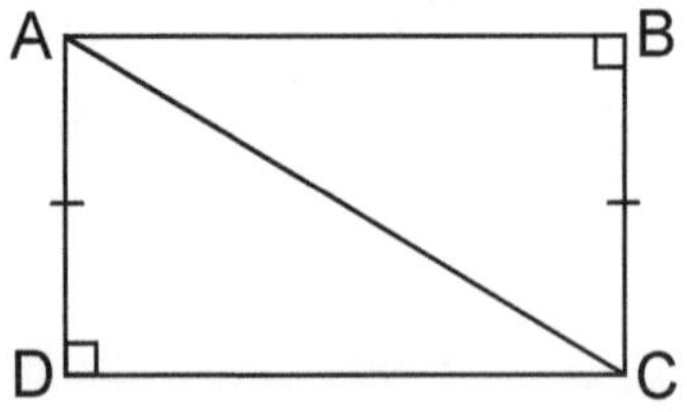

(i) Since the information in the picture tells us that we have two sets of congruent sides ($\overline{AC} \cong \overline{DE}$ and $\overline{BC} \cong \overline{DF}$) AND that the angles between the sides are congruent ($\angle C \cong \angle D$), we can use the SAS Congruence Postulate to say that $\Delta ABC \cong \Delta EFD$.

(ii) Since the information in the picture tells us that we have three sets of congruent sides, we can use the SSS Congruence Postulate to say that $\Delta GIH \cong \Delta LKJ$.

(iii) We will begin by noting that we can use the Vertical Angles Theorem to say that $\angle MNP \cong \angle QNO$. Next, we will note that the picture tells us that $\overline{MP} \parallel \overline{OQ}$, and so we can use the Alternate Interior Angles Theorem to say that $\angle P \cong \angle O$. Since we now have two sets of congruent angles, and since the picture tells us that the sides between these angles are congruent, we can use the ASA Congruence Postulate to say that $\Delta MNP \cong \Delta QNO$.

(Alternatively, we could have noted that the Alternate Interior Angles Theorem tells us that $\angle P \cong \angle O$ and $\angle M \cong \angle Q$. This would have given us two sets of congruent angles and a set of congruent corresponding sides not between these angles, and so we could have used the AAS Congruence Theorem to say that $\Delta MNP \cong \Delta QNO$. Or, we could have said that $\angle M \cong \angle Q$ and $\angle MNP \cong \angle QNO$. This also would have also given us two sets of congruent angles and a set of congruent corresponding sides not between these angles, and so the AAS Congruence Theorem again tells us that $\Delta MNP \cong \Delta QNO$.)

(iv) We will begin by noting that, whether we are talking about $\overline{RT}$ as part of ΔRST or as part of ΔTUR, the length of $\overline{RT}$ is the same. Formally, we say that $\overline{RT} \cong \overline{RT}$ because of the Reflexive Property of Segment Congruence. Now, we will draw two separate triangles to show what we know so far.

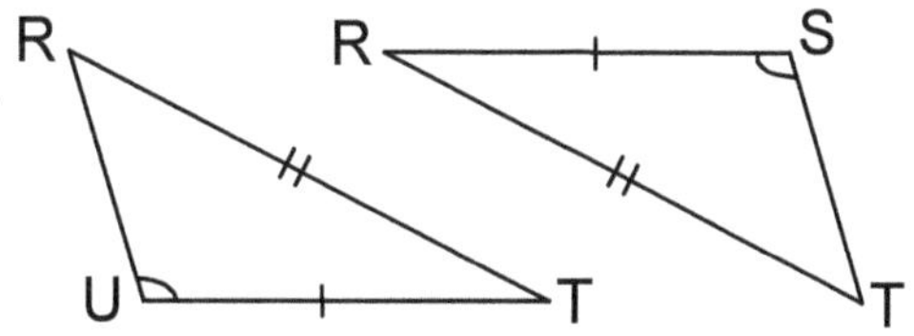

This tells us that we have two sets of congruent sides and a set of congruent corresponding angles that are not included between the two sides. However, there is no such thing as a SSA (or ASS) Congruence Postulate or Theorem, and so we cannot say that these two triangles must be congruent.

(v) We can use the Reflexive Property of Segment Congruence to say that $\overline{XY} \cong \overline{XY}$, and so we can draw the two separate triangles shown below.

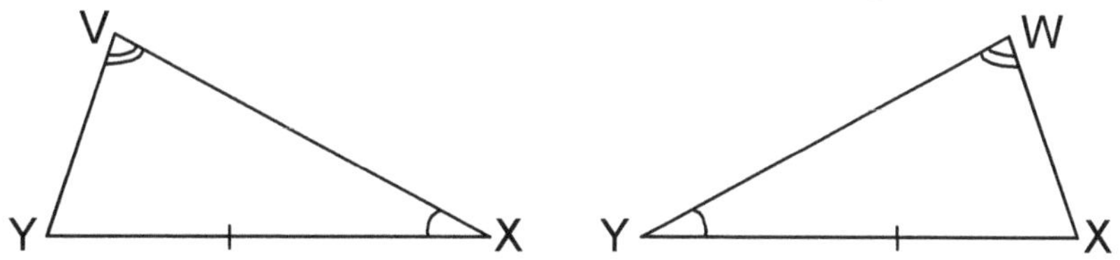

This tells us that we have two sets of congruent angles and a set of congruent corresponding sides that are not in between the angles, and so we can use the AAS Congruence Theorem to say that $\Delta VYX \cong \Delta WXY$.

(vi) We will begin by noting that the little squares in $\angle B$ and $\angle D$ tell us that $\angle B$ and $\angle D$ are right angles, and so we can say that $\angle B \cong \angle D$. We can also use the Reflexive Property of Segment Congruence to say that $\overline{AC} \cong \overline{AC}$. This gives us two sets of congruent sides and a set of congruent angles not in between the two sets of sides, but, as we said in part (iv), there is no such thing as a SSA Congruence Theorem or Postulate. We can, however, use the HL Congruence Postulate to say that these triangles are congruent. We know that we have two right triangles, and we know that $\overline{AD}$ (one of the legs of ΔCDA) is congruent to $\overline{BC}$ (one of the legs of ΔABC). We also know that the hypotenuse of ΔCDA, $\overline{AC}$, is congruent to the hypotenuse of ΔABC, $\overline{AC}$, by the Reflexive Property of Segment Congruence. Therefore, we can use the HL Congruence Postulate to say that $\Delta CDA \cong \Delta ABC$.

Finally, we will note that you should make sure you understand the order in which we name the vertices of congruent triangles. For example, if you had said in (vi) that $\Delta ADC \cong \Delta ABC$, your answer would have been wrong because, for instance, A and D were named first and second in the first triangle, and A and B were named first and second in the second triangle, but $\overline{AD}$ does not correspond to $\overline{AB}$.

Example 4: Given that $\overline{FG} \cong \overline{GH}$ and $\overline{EG} \perp \overline{FH}$ in the figure at the right, prove that $\Delta EFG \cong \Delta EHG$.

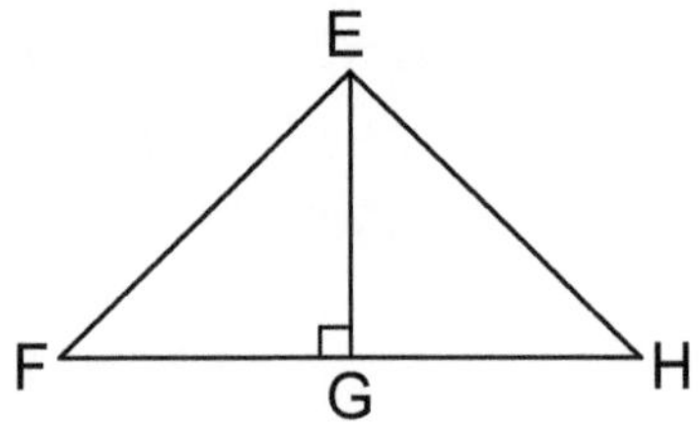

We can prove this statement as shown below.

Statements	Reasons	Explanations
1. $\overline{FG} \cong \overline{GH}$ $\overline{EG} \perp \overline{FH}$	1. Given	This was given to us.
2. $\angle EGH$ and $\angle EGF$ are right angles	2. If two lines are perpendicular, then they form four right angles.	Since we know that $\overline{EG} \perp \overline{FH}$, we can use the theorem *If two lines are perpendicular, then they form four right angles* to say that $\angle EGH$ and $\angle EGF$ are both right angles.
3. $\angle EGH \cong \angle EGF$	3. If two angles are right angles, then they are congruent.	Since we said in Statement (2) that $\angle EGH$ and $\angle EGF$ are both right angles, we can use the theorem *If two angles are right angles, then they are congruent* to say that $\angle EGH \cong \angle EGF$.
4. $\overline{EG} \cong \overline{EG}$	4. Reflexive Property of Segment Congruence	The Reflexive Property of Segment Congruence says that a segment is congruent to itself.
5. $\Delta EFG \cong \Delta EHG$	5. SAS Congruence Postulate	Since we have said that we have two sets of congruent sides and a set of congruent angles between these sides, we can use the SAS Congruence Postulate to say that $\Delta EFG \cong \Delta EHG$.

Problems:

1-7. Use the figure at the right to answer *true* or *false* to each of the statements below.

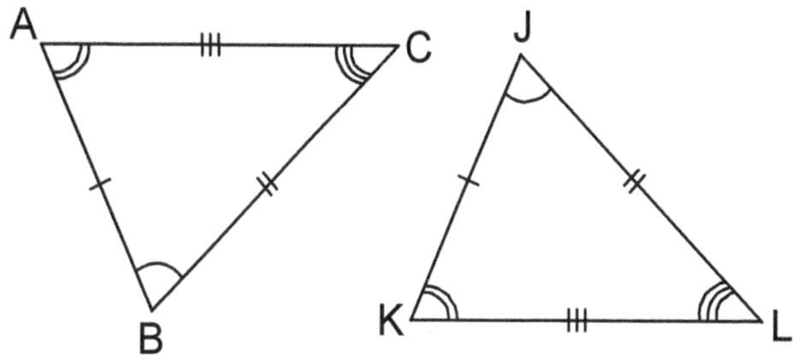

1. $\triangle CBA \cong \triangle LKJ$

2. $\triangle ABC \cong \triangle JKL$

3. $\triangle BCA \cong \triangle KJL$

4. $\triangle CAB \cong \triangle LKJ$

5. $\triangle ABC \cong \triangle KJL$

6. $\triangle BAC \cong \triangle JKL$

7. $\triangle ACB \cong \triangle JLK$

8. In the figure at the right, $\triangle QRS \cong \triangle UVT$. Find the values of w, x and y.

   w = ________

   x = ________

   y = ________

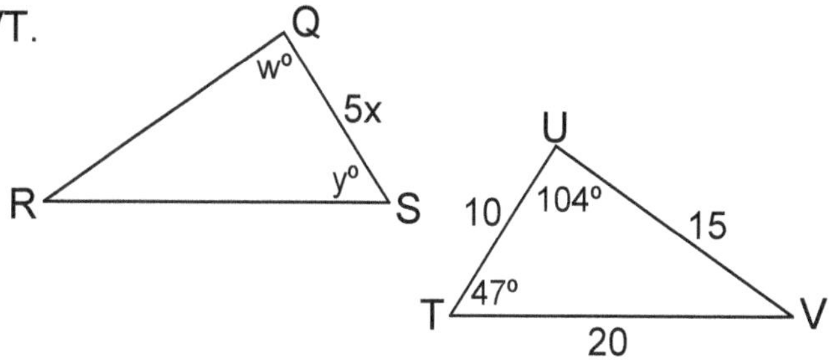

9. In the figure at the right, $\triangle ADB \cong \triangle FCE$, AD = y + 14, AB = 3y + 19, BD = 6 – 2y, and CF = 4y + 20. Find the values of w, x, and y.

   w = ________

   x = ________

   y = ________

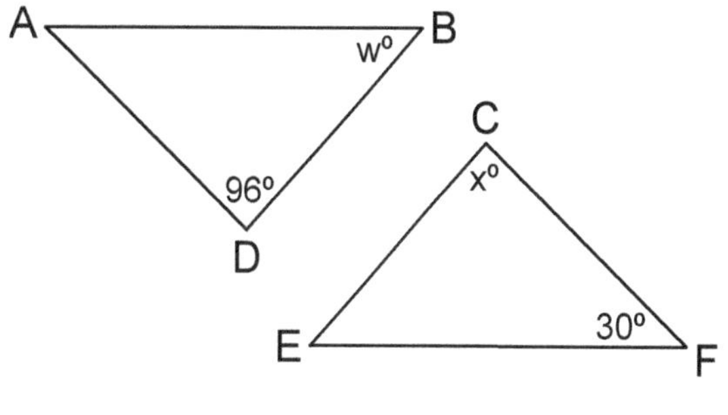

10. In the figure at the right, $\triangle GJH \cong \triangle IJH$, GH = 6y, GJ = 10y + 2, and JI = 7y + 11. Find the values of x and y, and then find the length of $\overline{GI}$.

   x = ________

   y = ________

   GI = ________

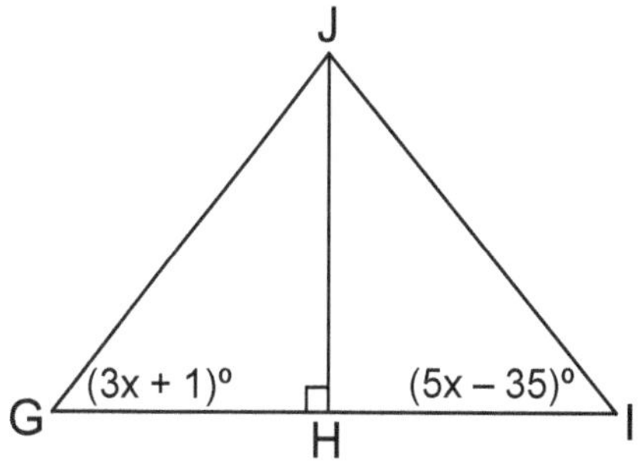

11. In the figure at the right, $\Delta LMP \cong \Delta NOP$ and $\Delta MPN \cong \Delta OPL$. If OP = 7x + 2, LP = 3y, PN = 4x + 10, and MP = 3x + y, find the values of x and y.

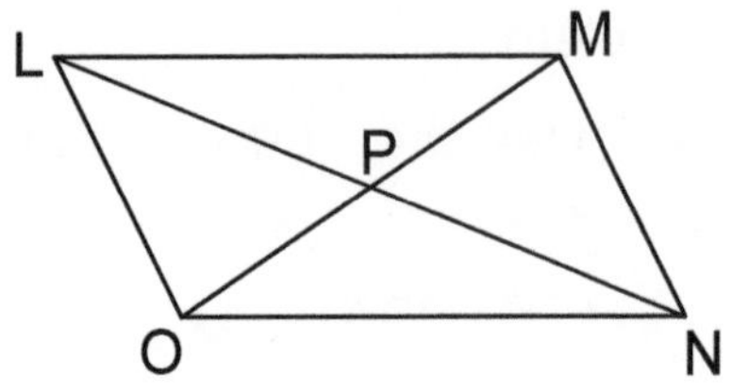

x = ________

y = ________

12-26. For each pair of triangles below, (a) determine whether or not the triangles are congruent, and (b) if your answer to part (a) was *yes*, complete the congruence statement and then state a postulate or theorem from this section to support your conclusion.

12. (a) Are the triangles congruent? ________

(b) If your answer to part (a) was yes, then $\Delta ABC \cong \Delta$________.

Postulate or theorem: ____________

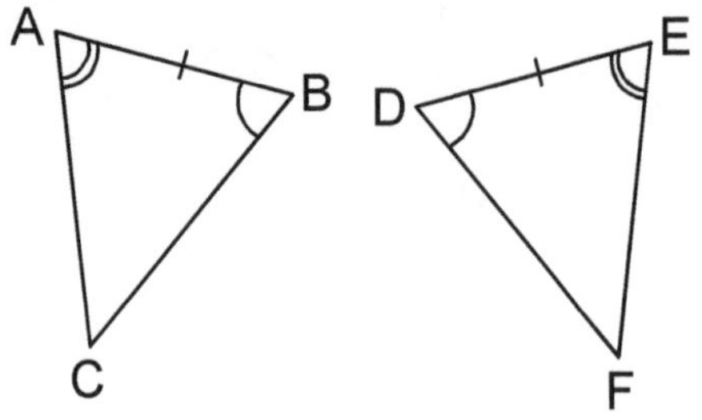

13. (a) Are the triangles congruent? ________

(b) If your answer to part (a) was yes, then $\Delta GIH \cong \Delta$________.

Postulate or theorem: ____________

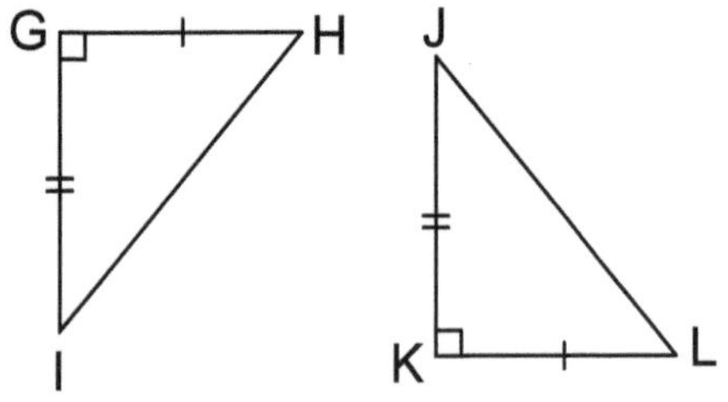

14. (a) Are the triangles congruent? ________

(b) If your answer to part (a) was yes, then $\Delta MNO \cong \Delta$________.

Postulate or theorem: ____________

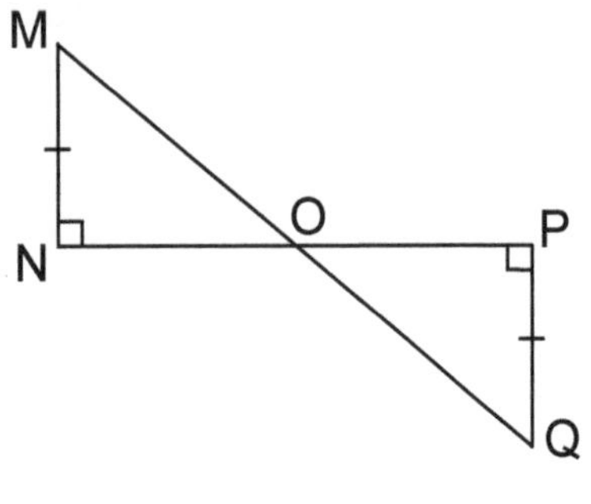

15. (a) Are the triangles congruent? ________

(b) If your answer to part (a) was yes, then $\Delta ABE \cong \Delta$________.

Postulate or theorem: ____________

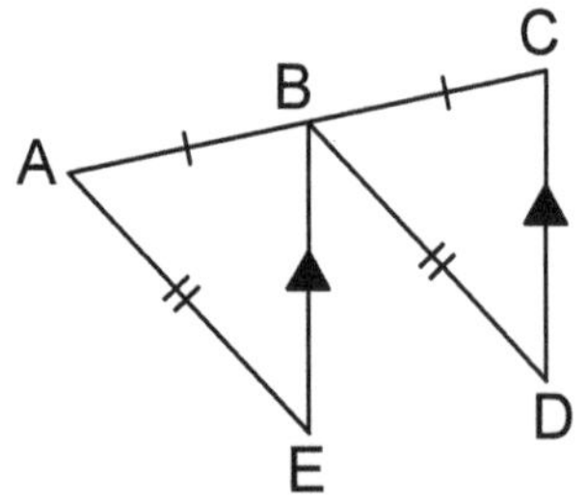

16. (a) Are the triangles congruent? ________

(b) If your answer to part (a) was yes, then $\Delta BAC \cong \Delta$________.

Postulate or theorem: ______________

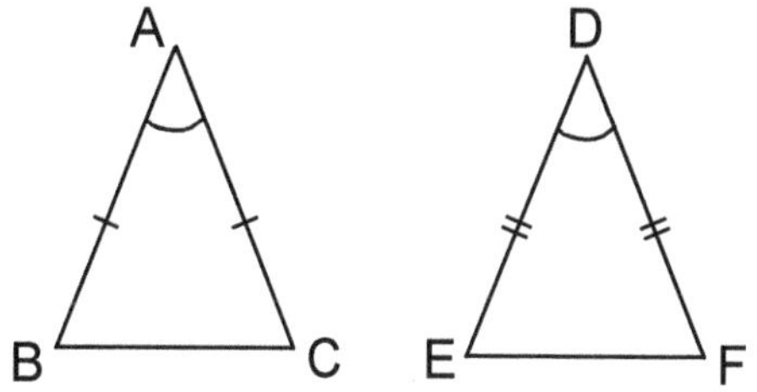

17. (a) Are the triangles congruent? ________

(b) If your answer to part (a) was yes, then $\Delta ZYG \cong \Delta$________.

Postulate or theorem: ______________

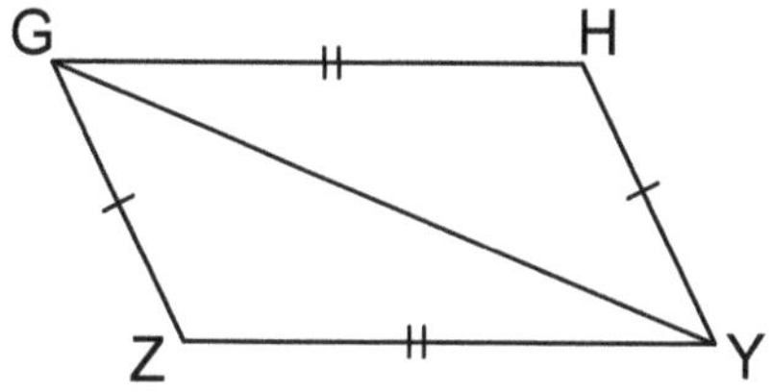

18. (a) Are the triangles congruent? ________

(b) If your answer to part (a) was yes, then $\Delta KLM \cong \Delta$________.

Postulate or theorem: ______________

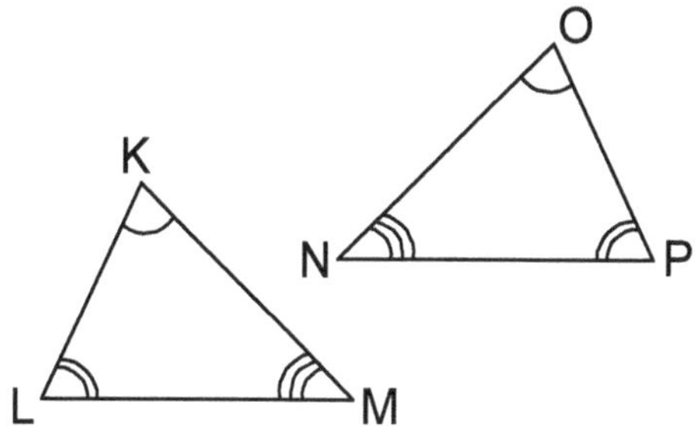

19. (a) Are the triangles congruent? ________

(b) If your answer to part (a) was yes, then $\Delta QRS \cong \Delta$________.

Postulate or theorem: ______________

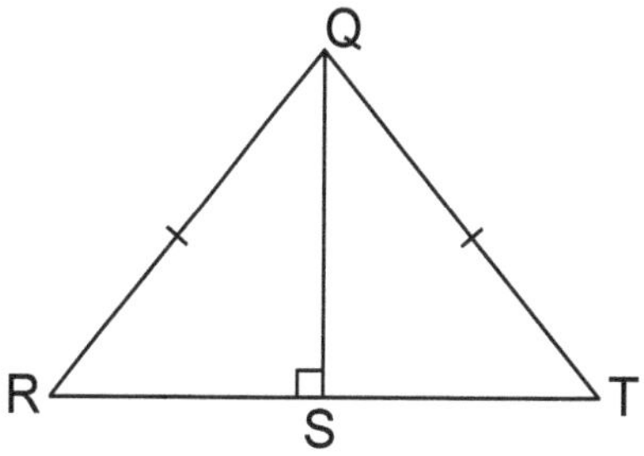

20. (a) Are the triangles congruent? ________

(b) If your answer to part (a) was yes, then $\Delta UVX \cong \Delta$________.

Postulate or theorem: ______________

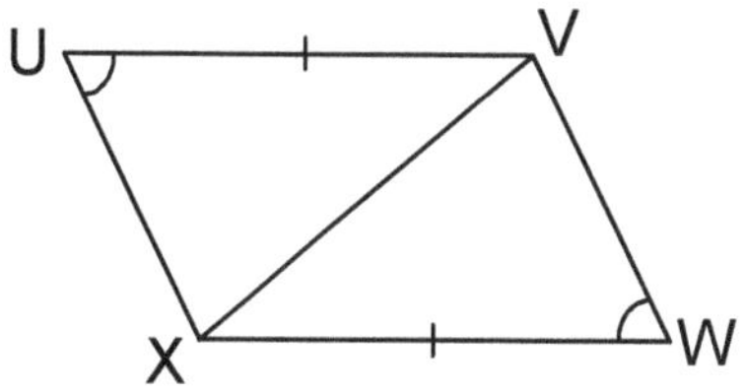

21. (a) Are the triangles congruent? ________

(b) If your answer to part (a) was yes,

then Δ________ ≅ ΔABC.

Postulate or theorem: ______________

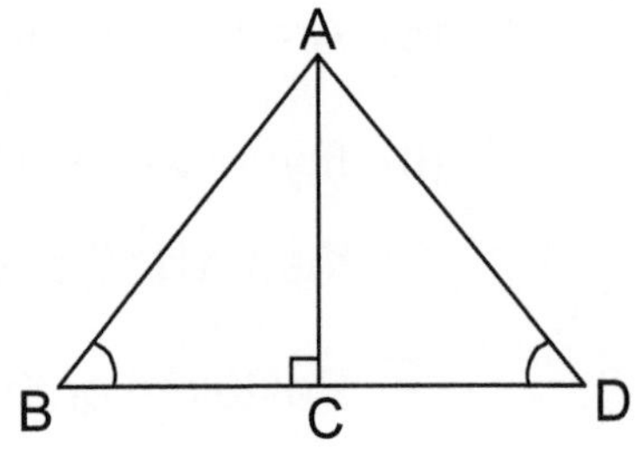

22. (a) Are the triangles congruent? ________

(b) If your answer to part (a) was yes,

then Δ________ ≅ ΔGHF.

Postulate or theorem: ______________

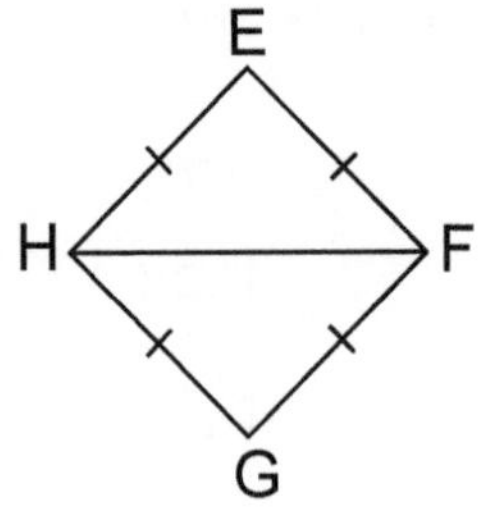

23. (a) Are the triangles congruent? ________

(b) If your answer to part (a) was yes,

then Δ________ ≅ ΔIML.

Postulate or theorem: ______________

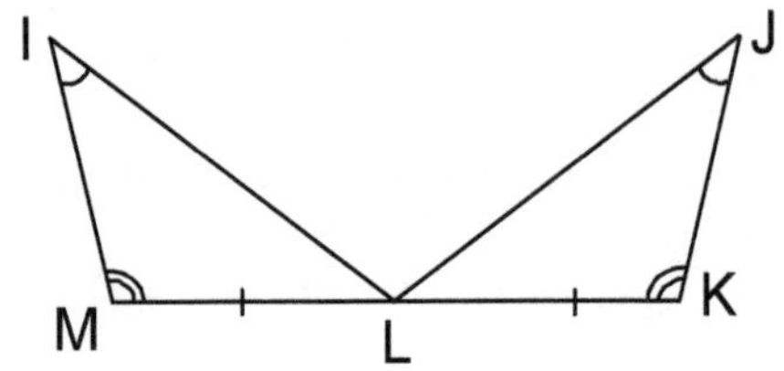

24. (a) Are the triangles congruent? ________

(b) If your answer to part (a) was yes,

then Δ________ ≅ ΔRST.

Postulate or theorem: ______________

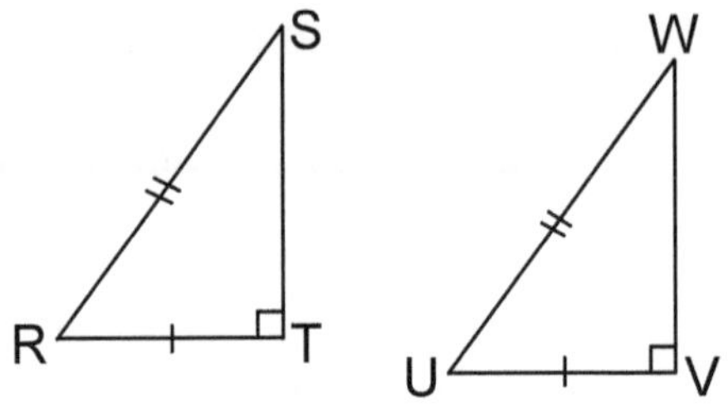

25. (a) Are the triangles congruent? ________

(b) If your answer to part (a) was yes,

then Δ________ ≅ ΔORN.

Postulate or theorem: ______________

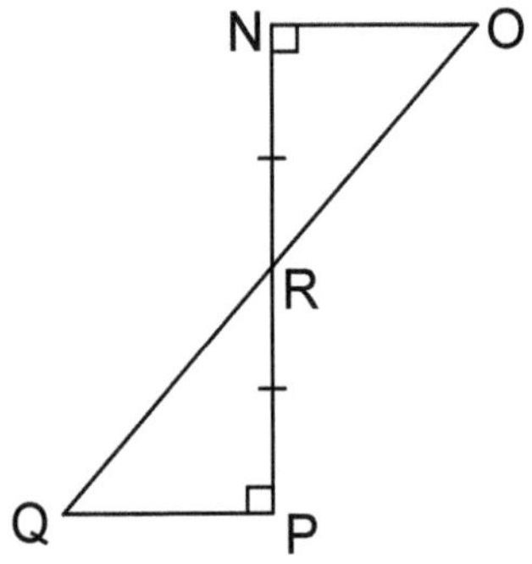

26. (a) Are the triangles congruent? ________

(b) If your answer to part (a) was yes,

then Δ________ $\cong \Delta DFE$.

Postulate or theorem: _______________

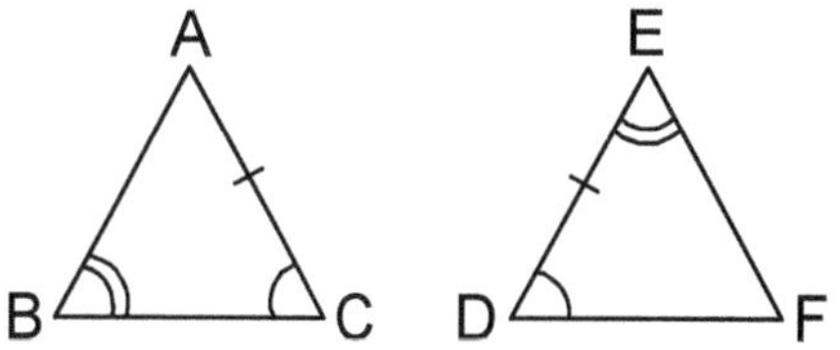

27. Prove the AAS Theorem.

Given: $\overline{MO} \cong \overline{PQ}$, $\angle M \cong \angle P$, and $\angle N \cong \angle R$

Prove: $\Delta MON \cong \Delta PQR$

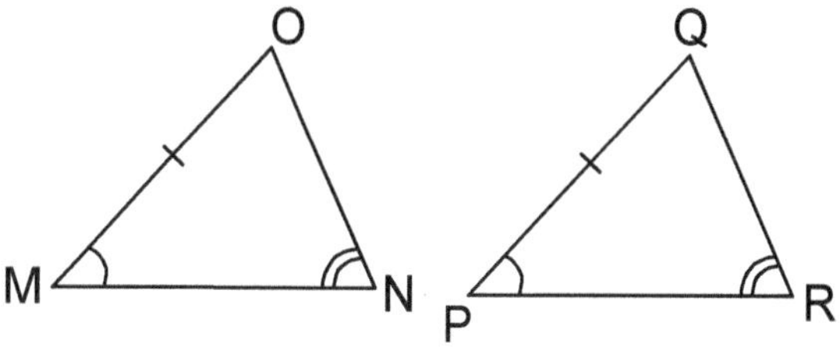

Statements	Reasons

28-29. Use the figure below to complete the proofs in #28 and #29.

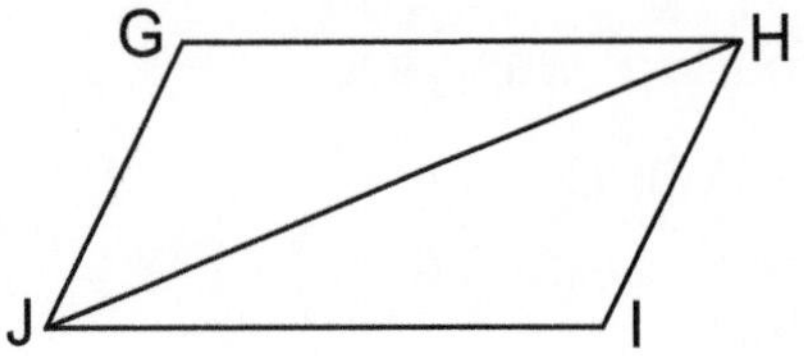

28. Given: $\overline{GH} \parallel \overline{IJ}$ and $\overline{GJ} \parallel \overline{HI}$

Prove: $\Delta GHJ \cong \Delta IJH$

Statements	Reasons

29. Given: $\overline{GH} \cong \overline{IJ}$ and $\overline{GJ} \cong \overline{HI}$

Prove: $\Delta GHJ \cong \Delta IJH$

Statements	Reasons

30-31. Use the figure below to complete the proofs in #30 and #31.

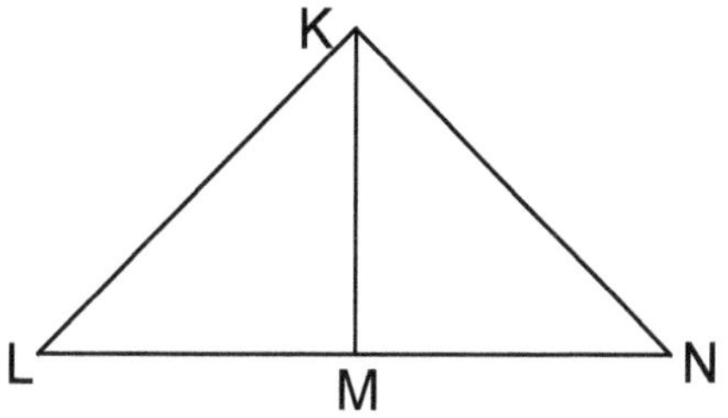

30. Given: $\overline{KL} \cong \overline{KN}$ and M is the midpoint of $\overline{LN}$

Prove: $\Delta KLM \cong \Delta KNM$

Statements	Reasons

31. Given: $\overline{KL} \cong \overline{KN}$ and $\overline{KM}$ bisects $\angle LKN$

Prove: $\Delta KLM \cong \Delta KNM$

Statements	Reasons

32-33. Use the figure below to complete the proofs in #32 and #33.

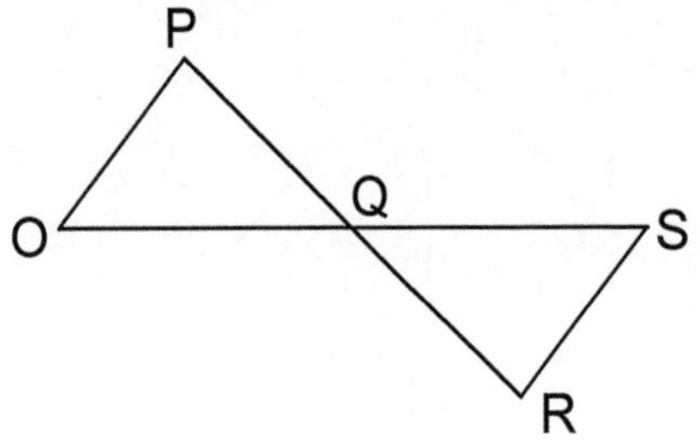

32. Given: Q is the midpoint of both $\overline{OS}$ and $\overline{PR}$

Prove: $\Delta OPQ \cong \Delta SRQ$

Statements	Reasons

33. Given: $\overline{OP} \parallel \overline{SR}$ and Q is the midpoint of $\overline{OS}$

Prove: $\Delta OPQ \cong \Delta SRQ$

Statements	Reasons

34-35. Use the figure below to complete the proofs in #34 and #35.

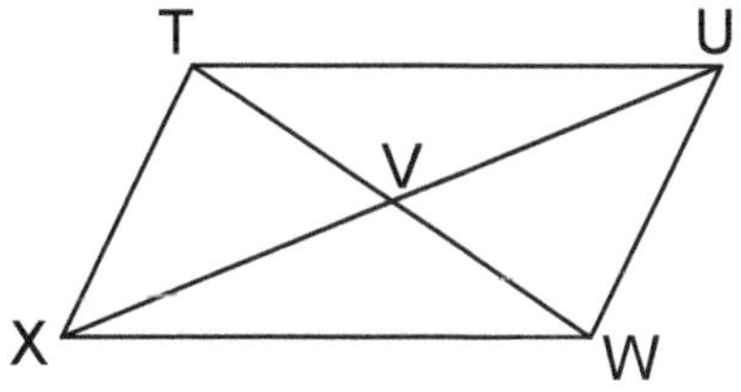

34. Given: $\overline{TX} \cong \overline{WU}$ and $\overline{TX} \parallel \overline{WU}$

Prove: $\Delta TXV \cong \Delta WUV$

Statements	Reasons

35. Given: $\overline{TX} \cong \overline{TU}$ and $\overline{TV} \perp \overline{XU}$

Prove: $\Delta VXT \cong \Delta VUT$

Statements	Reasons

36-37. Use the figure below to complete the proofs in #36 and #37.

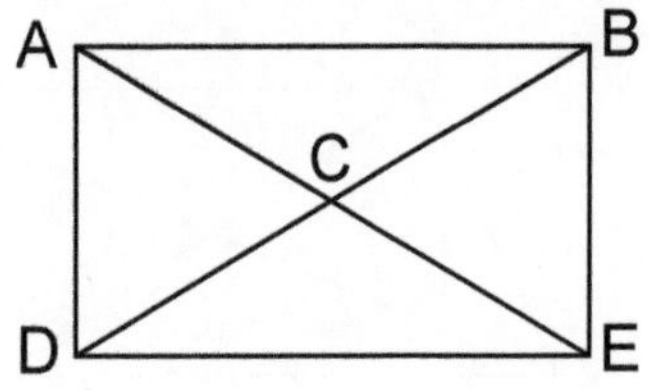

36. Given: $\overline{AE} \cong \overline{BD}$, $\overline{AD} \perp \overline{DE}$, and $\overline{BE} \perp \overline{DE}$

Prove: $\Delta ADE \cong \Delta BED$

Statements	Reasons

37. Given: $\overline{AD} \perp \overline{DE}$, $\overline{BE} \perp \overline{DE}$, and $\angle DBE \cong \angle DAE$

Prove: $\Delta ADE \cong \Delta BED$

Statements	Reasons

Part IV – More on Congruent Triangles

We will begin this section with the following observation.

Corresponding parts of congruent triangles are congruent.

This observation is often abbreviated CPCTC (**C**orresponding **P**arts of **C**ongruent **T**riangles are **C**ongruent), and it is really just a way of rephrasing the definition of congruent triangles. It tells us that, when we know that two triangles are congruent, we can say that the corresponding angles are congruent and that the corresponding sides are congruent.

Now, let's look at some examples that use this concept.

Example 1: Given that $\Delta ACB \cong \Delta ECD$ in the figure at the right, prove that $\overline{AD} \cong \overline{BE}$.

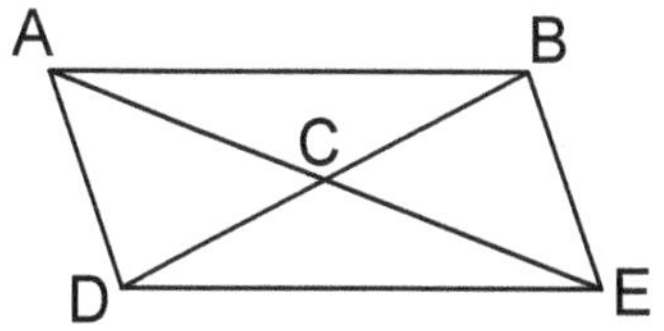

There are actually several different ways that we can prove that $\overline{AD} \cong \overline{BE}$. One of them is shown below, and another is shown on the next page. Both proofs are equally correct.

Statements	Reasons	Explanations
1. $\Delta ACB \cong \Delta ECD$	1. Given	This was given to us.
2. $\overline{AC} \cong \overline{EC}$ $\overline{BC} \cong \overline{DC}$	2. CPCTC	Since we were told that $\Delta ACB \cong \Delta ECD$, we can use CPCTC to say that $\overline{AC} \cong \overline{EC}$ and that $\overline{BC} \cong \overline{DC}$. We could have also used CPCTC to say that $\overline{AB} \cong \overline{ED}$, $\angle BAC \cong \angle DEC$, $\angle ABC \cong \angle EDC$, and $\angle ACB \cong \angle ECD$. However, these statements do not help us with this particular proof, and so we will not write them in our statements column.
3. $\angle ACD \cong \angle BCE$	3. Vertical Angles Theorem	We can look at the picture and see that $\angle ACD$ and $\angle BCE$ are vertical angles, and so we can use the Vertical Angles Theorem to say that they are congruent.
4. $\Delta ACD \cong \Delta ECB$	4. SAS Congruence Postulate	We have said that we have two sets of congruent sides ($\overline{AC} \cong \overline{EC}$ and $\overline{BC} \cong \overline{DC}$) and a set of congruent angles between them ($\angle ACD \cong \angle BCE$), and so now we can use the SAS Postulate to say that $\Delta ACD \cong \Delta ECB$.
5. $\overline{AD} \cong \overline{BE}$	5. CPCTC	Since we said in Statement (4) that $\Delta ACD \cong \Delta ECB$, we can say that the corresponding parts of these triangles are congruent.

We can also prove this statement as shown below.

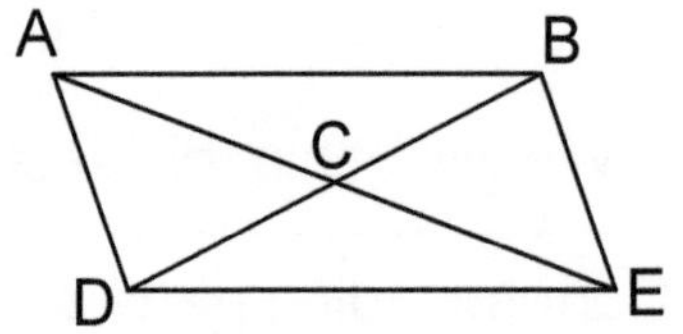

Statements	Reasons	Explanations
1. $\triangle ACB \cong \triangle ECD$	1. Given	This was given to us.
2. $\overline{AB} \cong \overline{DE}$ $\angle ABC \cong \angle EDC$	2. CPCTC	Since we were told that $\triangle ACB \cong \triangle ECD$, we can use CPCTC to say that $\overline{AB} \cong \overline{DE}$ and that $\angle ABC \cong \angle EDC$. We could have also used CPCTC to say that $\overline{AC} \cong \overline{EC}$, $\overline{BC} \cong \overline{DC}$, $\angle BAC \cong \angle DEC$, and $\angle ACB \cong \angle ECD$. However, these statements do not help us with this particular proof, and so we will not write them in our statements column.
3. $\overline{BD} \cong \overline{BD}$	3. Reflexive Property of Segment Congruence	The Reflexive Property of Segment Congruence tells us that a segment is congruent to itself.
4. $\triangle ADB \cong \triangle EBD$	4. SAS Congruence Postulate	We have said that we have two sets of congruent sides ($\overline{AB} \cong \overline{DE}$ and $\overline{BD} \cong \overline{BD}$) and a set of congruent angles between them ($\angle ABC \cong \angle EDC$), and so now we can use the SAS Congruence Postulate to say that $\triangle ADB \cong \triangle EBD$.
5. $\overline{AD} \cong \overline{BE}$	5. CPCTC	Since we said in Statement (4) that $\triangle ADB \cong \triangle EBD$, we know that the corresponding parts of these triangles are congruent.

Example 2: Given that $\overline{FH} \cong \overline{IH}$ and $\overline{GH} \cong \overline{JH}$ in the figure at the right, prove that $\overline{FG} \parallel \overline{JI}$.

We can prove that $\overline{FG} \parallel \overline{JI}$ as shown on the next page.

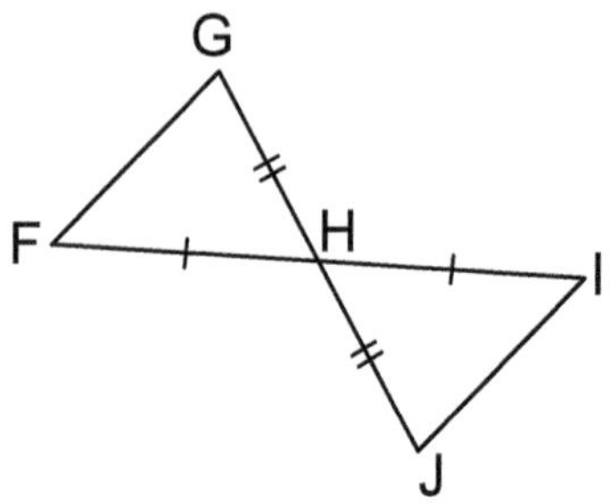

Statements	Reasons	Explanations
1. $\overline{FH} \cong \overline{IH}$ $\overline{GH} \cong \overline{JH}$	1. Given	This was given to us.
2. $\angle GHF \cong \angle JHI$	2. Vertical Angles Theorem	We can look at the picture and see that $\angle GHF$ and $\angle JHI$ are vertical angles, and so we can use the Vertical Angles Theorem to say that they are congruent.
3. $\Delta HGF \cong \Delta HJI$	3. SAS Congruence Postulate	We have said that we have two sets of congruent sides ($\overline{FH} \cong \overline{IH}$ and $\overline{GH} \cong \overline{JH}$) and a set of congruent angles between them ($\angle GHF \cong \angle JHI$), and so now we can use the SAS Congruence Postulate to say that $\Delta HGF \cong \Delta HJI$.
4. $\angle F \cong \angle I$	4. CPCTC	Since we said in Statement (3) that $\Delta HGF \cong \Delta HJI$, we can say that the corresponding parts of these triangles are congruent.
5. $\overline{FG} \parallel \overline{JI}$	5. Alternate Interior Angles Converse Theorem	We can look at the picture and see that $\angle F$ and $\angle I$ are alternate interior angles. Since we said in Statement (4) that they are congruent, we can use the Alternate Interior Angles Converse Theorem to say that $\overline{FG}$ must be parallel to $\overline{JI}$.

Finally, we will note that, even though the proofs we looked at here only used the SAS Congruence Postulate, you are still allowed to use the SSS Congruence Postulate, the ASA Congruence Postulate, the HL Congruence Postulate, and the AAS Congruence Theorem in your proofs.

Problems:

1. Prove the following theorem: Congruence of triangles is reflexive.

   Given: ΔABC

   Prove: $\Delta ABC \cong \Delta ABC$

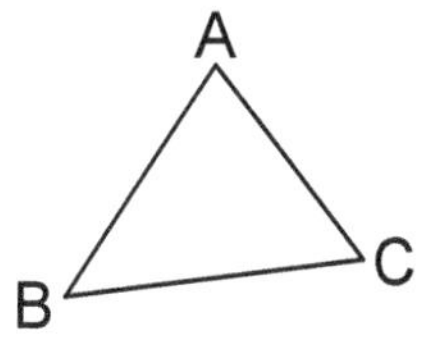

Statements	Reasons

2. Prove the following theorem: Congruence of triangles is symmetric.

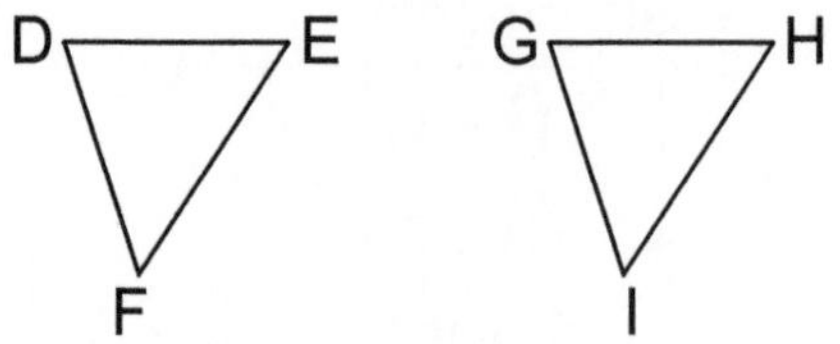

Given: $\Delta DEF \cong \Delta GHI$

Prove: $\Delta GHI \cong \Delta DEF$

Statements	Reasons

3. Prove the following theorem: Congruence of triangles is transitive.

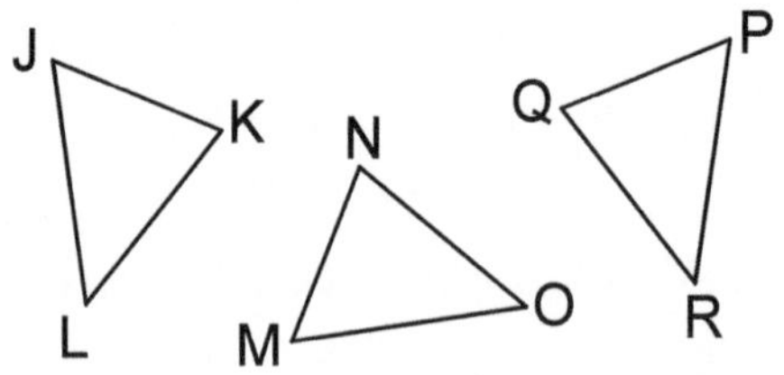

Given: $\Delta JKL \cong \Delta MNO$ and $\Delta MNO \cong \Delta PQR$

Prove: $\Delta JKL \cong \Delta PQR$

Statements	Reasons

4. Given that $\overline{AB} \cong \overline{DE}$, $\overline{AC} \cong \overline{DF}$, $\angle C$ is a right angle, and $\angle F$ is a right angle in the figure at the right, prove that $\angle B \cong \angle E$.

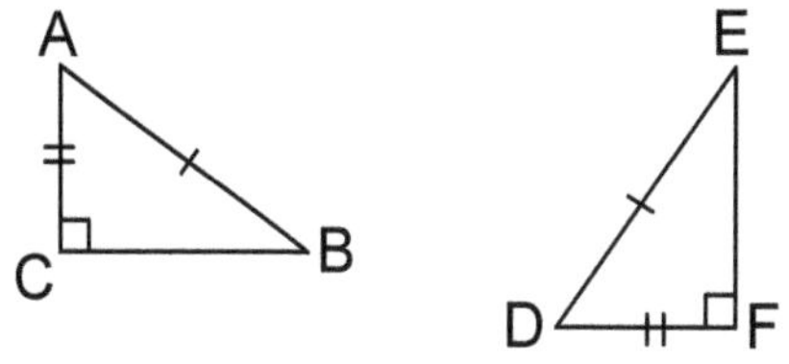

Statements	Reasons

5. Given that $\overline{GH} \cong \overline{JL}$, $\angle G \cong \angle L$, and $\angle H \cong \angle J$ in the figure at the right, prove that $\overline{GI} \cong \overline{LK}$.

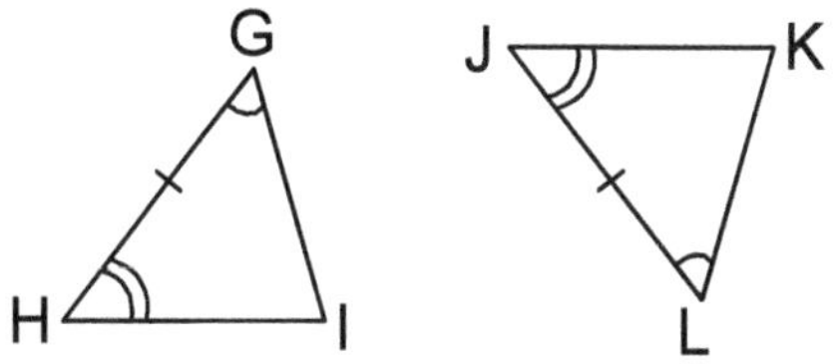

Statements	Reasons

6-9. Use the figure below to complete #6-#9.

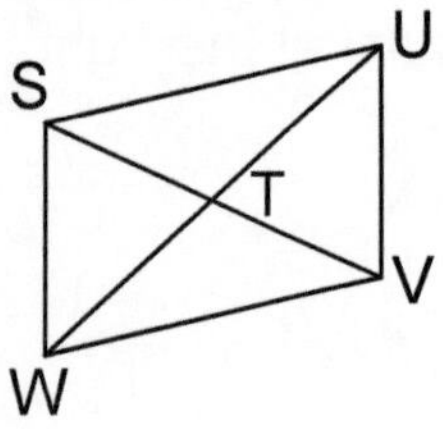

6. Given: $\overline{SW} \parallel \overline{UV}$ and $\overline{SU} \parallel \overline{VW}$

   Prove: $\overline{SU} \cong \overline{VW}$ and $\overline{SW} \cong \overline{VU}$

   Hint: First prove that $\triangle WSU \cong \triangle UVW$.

Statements	Reasons

7. Given: $\overline{SW} \cong \overline{UV}$ and $\overline{SW} \parallel \overline{UV}$

   Prove: $\overline{ST} \cong \overline{VT}$

Statements	Reasons

8. Given: $\overline{UT} \perp \overline{SV}$ and $\overline{SU} \cong \overline{UV}$

Prove: $\overline{UT}$ bisects $\angle SUV$

Statements	Reasons

9. Given: $\overline{SW} \cong \overline{SU}$ and $\overline{ST}$ bisects $\angle USW$

Prove: $\angle SWT \cong \angle SUT$

Statements	Reasons

10-11. Use the figure below to complete #10 and #11.

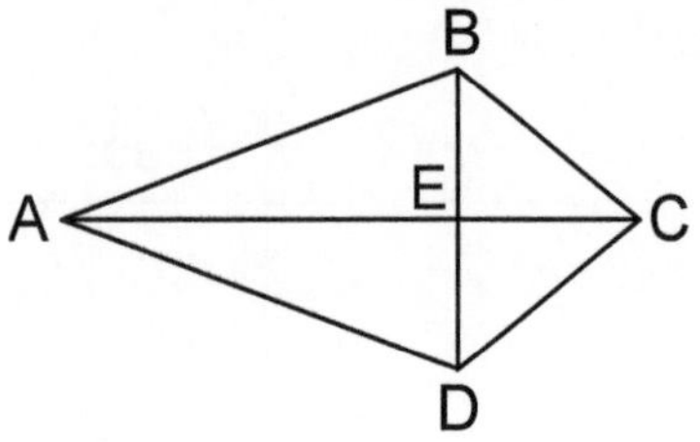

10. Given: $\overline{BD} \perp \overline{EC}$ and $\overline{BE} \cong \overline{DE}$

Prove: $\angle EBC \cong \angle EDC$

Statements	Reasons

11. Given: $\Delta ABE \cong \Delta ADE$

Prove: $\overline{BC} \cong \overline{CD}$

Statements	Reasons

12-13. Use the figure below to complete #12 and #13.

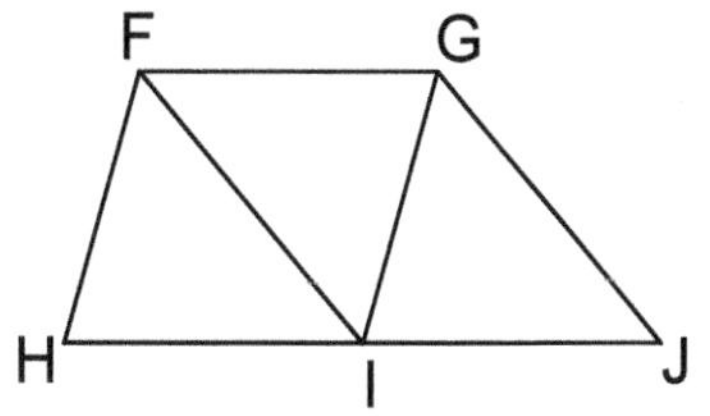

12. Given: $\overline{FG} \cong \overline{HI}$ and $\overline{FH} \cong \overline{GI}$

    Prove: $\overline{FG} \parallel \overline{HI}$

Statements	Reasons

13. Given: $\overline{FH} \cong \overline{GI}$, $\overline{HI} \cong \overline{IJ}$, and $\overline{FH} \parallel \overline{GI}$

    Prove: $\overline{FI} \parallel \overline{GJ}$

Statements	Reasons

14-16. Use the figure below to complete #14-#16.

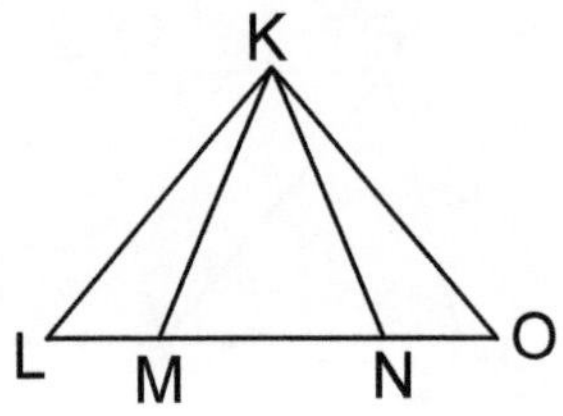

14. Given: $\Delta LKN \cong \Delta OKM$
    Prove: $\overline{LM} \cong \overline{ON}$

Statements	Reasons
1.	1.
2.	2.
3. LN = OM	3.
4. LN = LM + MN and OM = ON + MN	4.
5.	5.
6.	6.
7.	7.

15. Given: $\angle L \cong \angle O$, $\overline{LM} \cong \overline{NO}$, and $\angle LKM \cong \angle OKN$
    Prove: ΔMKN is an isosceles triangle

Statements	Reasons

16. Given: $\overline{LM} \cong \overline{ON}$, $\overline{LK} \cong \overline{OK}$, and $\angle L \cong \angle O$

Prove: $\angle LKN \cong \angle OKM$

Statements	Reasons
1.	1.
2.	2. SAS Congruence Postulate
3.	3.
4. $m\angle LKM = m\angle OKN$	4.
5. $m\angle LKM + m\angle MKN = m\angle OKN + m\angle MKN$	5.
6. $m\angle LKN = m\angle LKM + m\angle MKN$ $m\angle OKM = m\angle OKN + m\angle MKN$	6.
7.	7.
8.	8.

17-18. Use the figure below to complete #17 and #18.

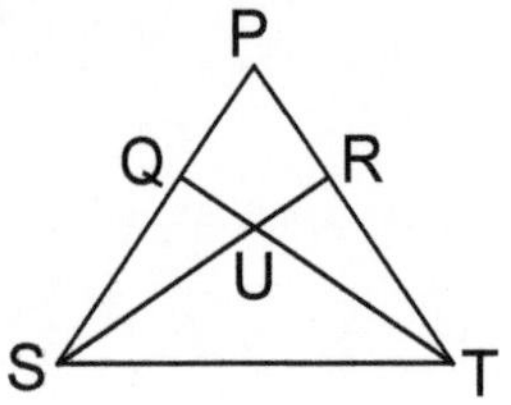

17. Given: $\Delta SQU \cong \Delta TRU$
Prove: $\Delta RST \cong \Delta QTS$

Statements	Reasons
1.	1.
2. $\overline{QS} \cong \overline{RT}$, $\overline{SU} \cong \overline{TU}$, and $\overline{UQ} \cong \overline{UR}$	2.
3. SU = TU and UQ = UR	3.
4. SR = SU + UR and TQ = TU + UQ	4.
5. TQ = SU + UR	5.
6. TQ = SR	6.
7.	7.
8.	8.
9.	9.

18. Given: $\overline{PQ} \cong \overline{PR}$ and $\angle PTQ \cong \angle PSR$
Prove: ΔSTP is an isosceles triangle

Statements	Reasons

19-20. Use the figure below to complete #19 and #20.

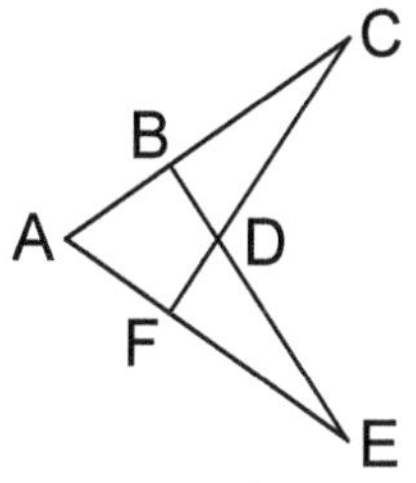

19. Given: $\overline{AB} \cong \overline{AF}$, $\angle EBA$ is a right angle, and $\angle CFA$ is a right angle
Prove: $\angle E \cong \angle C$

Statements	Reasons

20. Given: $\triangle AEB \cong \triangle ACF$
Prove: $\triangle FDE \cong \triangle BDC$

Statements	Reasons
1.	1.
2. $\angle E \cong \angle C$, $\overline{AB} \cong \overline{AF}$, and $\overline{AE} \cong \overline{AC}$	2.
3.	3. Definition of congruent segments
4.	4. Segment Addition Postulate
5. AF + FE = AB + BC	5.
6.	6.
7.	7.
8.	8.
9.	9.
10.	10.

21. Given that $\angle 1 \cong \angle 2$ and that $\overline{LN}$ is not congruent to $\overline{ON}$ in the figure at the right, prove that $\overline{LM}$ is not congruent to $\overline{OM}$ using an indirect proof.

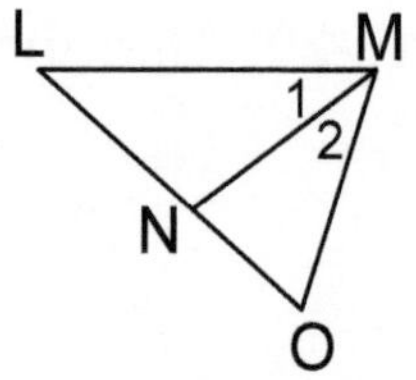

Statements	Reasons

22. Given that $\overline{TQ} \cong \overline{RQ}$ and that $\overline{PQ}$ is not congruent to $\overline{SQ}$ in the figure at the right, prove that $\overline{TP}$ is not parallel to $\overline{RS}$ using an indirect proof.

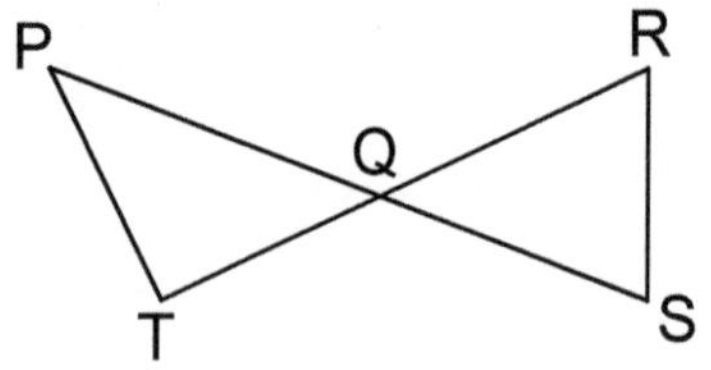

Statements	Reasons

23. Given that $\overline{GI}$ is not parallel to $\overline{HJ}$ in the figure at the right, prove that $\triangle GKH$ is not congruent to $\triangle JKI$ using an indirect proof.

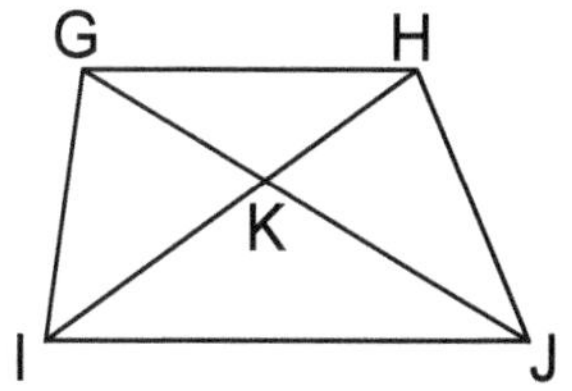

Statements	Reasons
1.	1.
2.	2.
3. $\overline{GK} \cong \overline{JK}$ and $\overline{HK} \cong \overline{IK}$	3
4.	4.
5. $\triangle IKG \cong \triangle HKJ$	5.
6.	6.
7.	7
8.	8. Contradiction

Part V – Isosceles Triangles

We will begin this section by discussing some definitions. Recall that a triangle is called an isosceles triangle if and only if it has at least two congruent sides. The two congruent sides are called the legs, and the third side is called the base. The angle formed by the two legs is called the vertex angle, and the other two angles are called the base angles. This tells that we can make the following statements about the figure at the right:

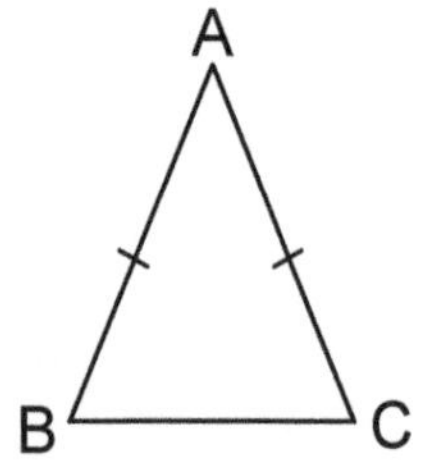

- $\triangle ABC$ is an isosceles triangle with legs $\overline{AB}$ and $\overline{AC}$. The base is $\overline{BC}$.
- The base angles are $\angle B$ and $\angle C$, and the vertex angle is $\angle A$.

Now, we need a theorem.

> **Isosceles Triangle Theorem**
> If two sides of a triangle are congruent, then the angles opposite those sides are congruent.

You will be asked to prove this theorem in the problems for this section. Now, let's look at some examples that use this theorem.

Example 1: In the figure at the right, $\triangle DEF$ is an isosceles triangle with base $\overline{DE}$. Find the values of w, x, and y.

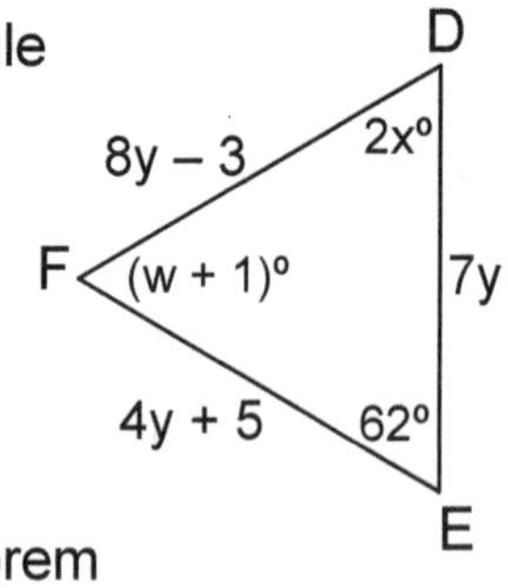

We will begin by noting that, since the question tells us that $\triangle DEF$ is an isosceles triangle with base $\overline{DE}$, we can say that $\overline{DF} \cong \overline{EF}$. This tells us that we can write $8y - 3 = 4y + 5$. When we solve this equation for y, we find that $y = 2$.

Next, since $\overline{DF} \cong \overline{EF}$, we can use the Isosceles Triangle Theorem to say that $\angle E \cong \angle D$. This tells us that we can write $62 = 2x$. When we solve this equation for x, we find that $x = 31$.

Finally, to solve for w, we will note that $m\angle D + m\angle E + m\angle F = 180°$ and that $m\angle D = m\angle E = 62°$. This tells us that we can write $62 + 62 + w + 1 = 180$, and so w must equal 55.

The next theorem tells us that the converse of the Isosceles Triangle Theorem is also true. You will prove this theorem in the problems for this section as well.

> **Isosceles Triangle Converse Theorem**
> If two angles of a triangle are congruent, then the sides opposite those angles are also congruent.

Example 2: Given that $\angle HIJ \cong \angle HJI$ and that $\angle GHJ \cong \angle GHI$ in the figure at the right, prove that $\angle GJI \cong \angle GIJ$.

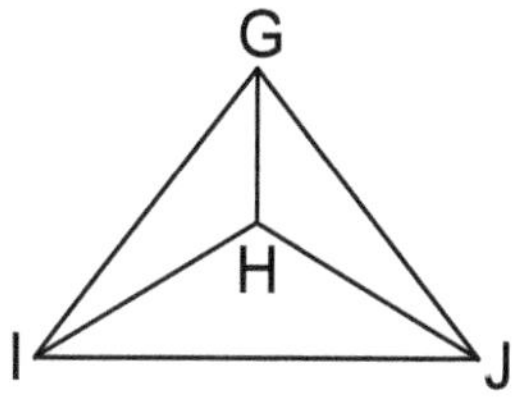

We can prove this statement as shown below.

Statements	Reasons	Explanations
1. $\angle HIJ \cong \angle HJI$	1. Given	This was given to us.
2. $\overline{HJ} \cong \overline{HI}$	2. Isosceles Triangle Converse Theorem	We were told that two angles of ΔHIJ are congruent to each other, and so we can say that the sides opposite those angles must also be congruent.
3. $\angle GHJ \cong \angle GHI$	3. Given	This was given to us. We could have stated this up in Statement (1), but the proof flows a little better if we state it here.
4. $\overline{HG} \cong \overline{HG}$	4. Reflexive Property of Segment Congruence	The Reflexive Property of Segment Congruence tells us that a segment is congruent to itself.
5. $\Delta GIH \cong \Delta GJH$	5. SAS Congruence Postulate	We have said that we have two sets of congruent sides ($\overline{HJ} \cong \overline{HI}$ and $\overline{HG} \cong \overline{HG}$) and a set of congruent angles between them ($\angle GHJ \cong \angle GHI$), and so now we can use the SAS Congruence Postulate to say that $\Delta GIH \cong \Delta GJH$.
6. $\overline{GI} \cong \overline{GJ}$	6. CPCTC	Since we said in Statement (5) that $\Delta GIH \cong \Delta GJH$, we can say that the corresponding parts of these triangles are congruent.
7. $\angle GJI \cong \angle GIJ$	7. Isosceles Triangle Theorem	Since we said in Statement (6) that two sides of ΔGIJ are congruent, we can use the Isosceles Triangle Theorem to say that the angles opposite those sides are congruent.

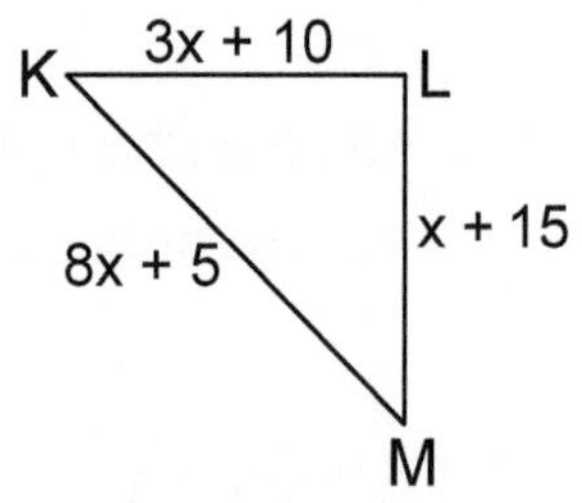

Example 3: In the figure at the right, $\angle K \cong \angle M$. Find the perimeter of ΔKLM.

We will begin by noting that, since the question tells us that $\angle K \cong \angle M$, we can use the Isosceles Triangle Converse Theorem to say that $\overline{KL} \cong \overline{LM}$. Hence, we can say that 3x + 10 = x + 15. This tells us that $x = \frac{5}{2}$.

Next, we will note that we find the perimeter of a triangle by adding the lengths of all the sides of the triangle together. So, in order to find the perimeter, we must first find the lengths of the sides. Since we now know that $x = \frac{5}{2}$, we can say that $KL = 3\left(\frac{5}{2}\right) + 10$, or $\frac{35}{2}$. We can also say that $LM = \frac{35}{2}$ and that $KM = 8\left(\frac{5}{2}\right) + 5$, or 25. This tells us that the perimeter of ΔKLM is equal to $\frac{35}{2} + \frac{35}{2} + 25$, or 60, units.

Lastly, we will state that the Isosceles Triangle Theorem and its converse give rise to the following theorem. In order to understand this theorem, you should recall that the definition of an equilateral triangle says that a triangle is called an <u>equilateral triangle</u> if and only if all the sides are congruent to each other.

A triangle is an equilateral triangle if and only if each interior angle measures 60º.

You will prove this theorem in Problem numbers 19 and 20.

Problems:

1-11. Find the values of each of the variables in each of the triangles below.

1. x = ___________

   y = ___________

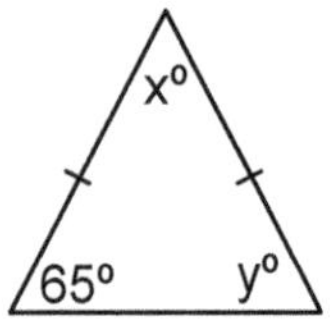

2. x = ___________

   y = ___________

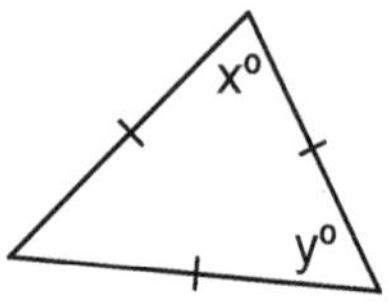

3. x = ___________

y = ___________

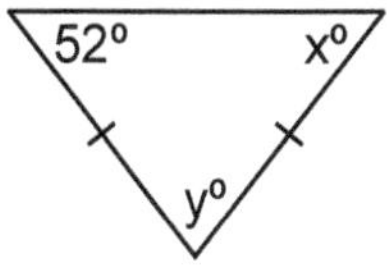

4. x = ___________

y = ___________

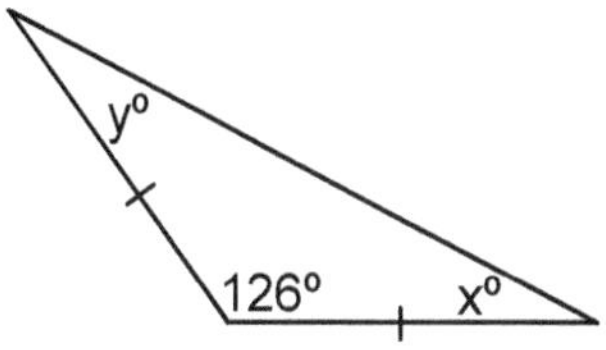

5. x = ___________

y = ___________

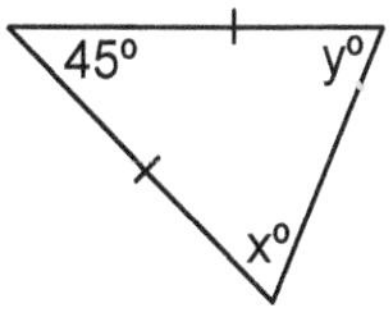

6. w = ___________

x = ___________

y = ___________

z = ___________

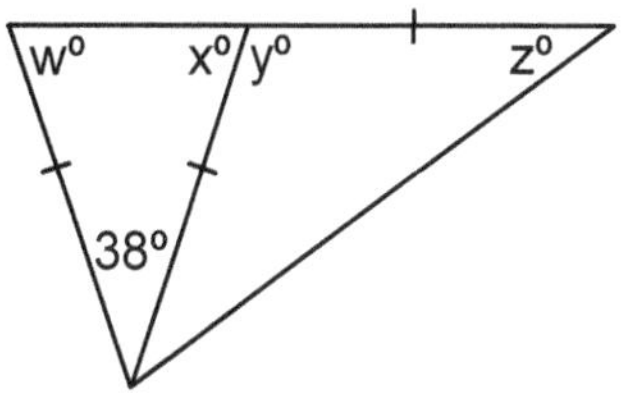

7. w = ___________

x = ___________

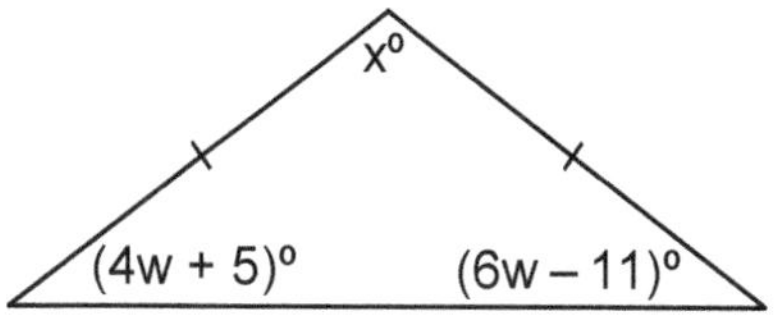

8. x = ___________

y = ___________

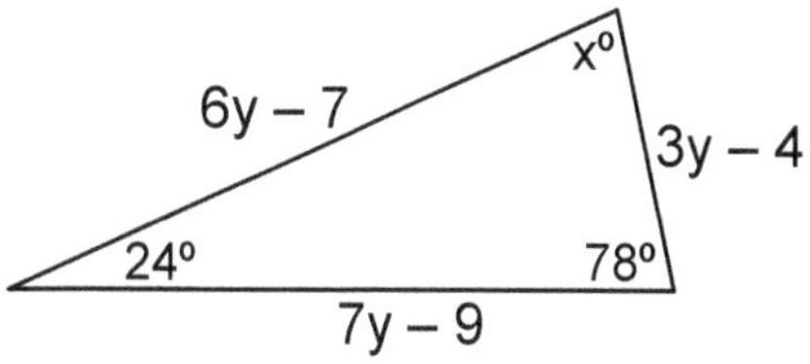

9. In the figure below, $\triangle ABC$ is an isosceles triangle with $\angle B$ as its vertex angle.

w = ___________

x = ___________

y = ___________

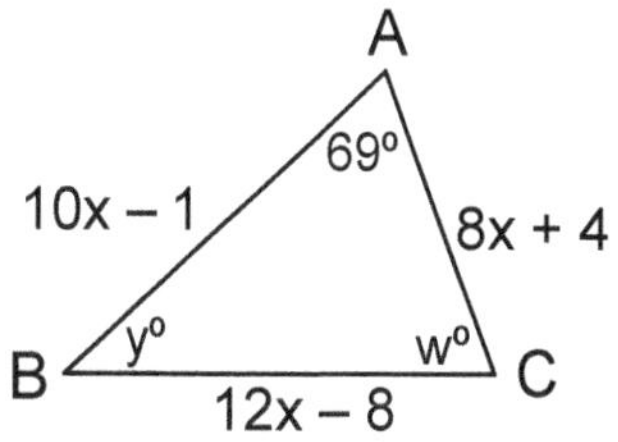

10. In the figure below, ΔDEF is an isosceles triangle with base $\overline{DF}$.

n = ___________

x = ___________

y = ___________

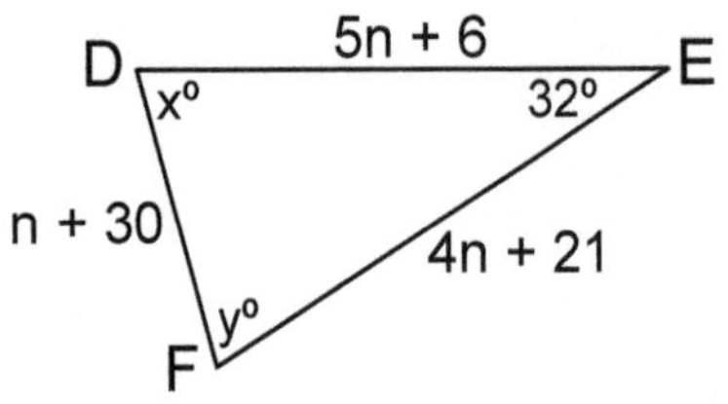

11. In the figure below, HI = 8w + 2, HG = 4w + 6, GJ = 4w + 22, and HJ = 7y.

w = ___________

x = ___________

y = ___________

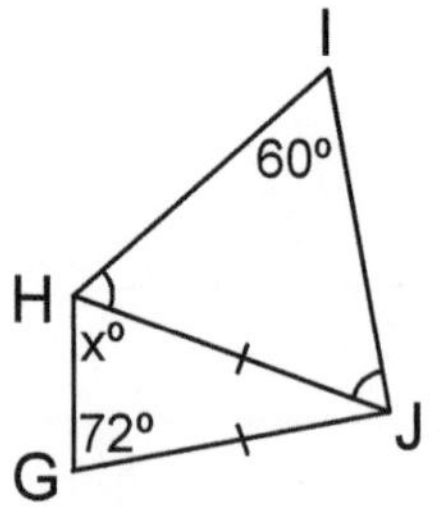

12-16. In each of the triangles below, find the value of x, and then find the perimeter of the triangle.

12. x = _______________

Perimeter = ________

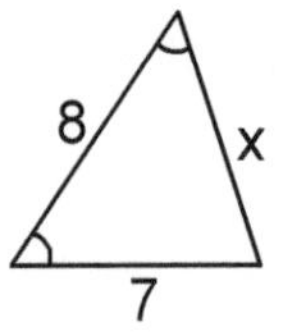

13. x = _______________

Perimeter = ________

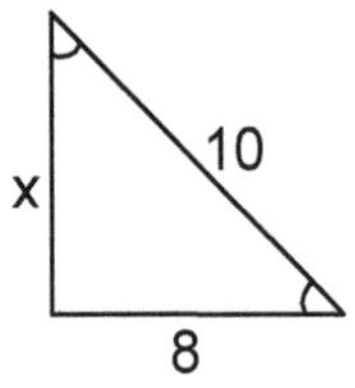

14. x = _______________

Perimeter = ________

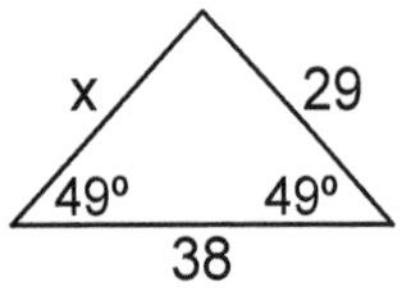

15. x = _______________

Perimeter = ________

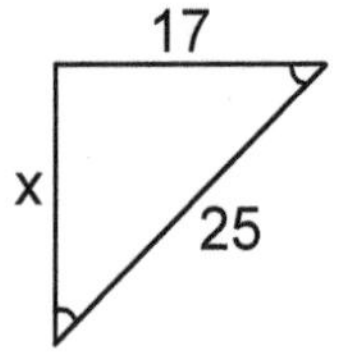

16. x = _______________

Perimeter = ________

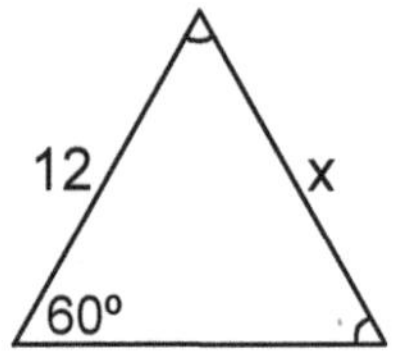

17. Prove the Isosceles Triangle Theorem.

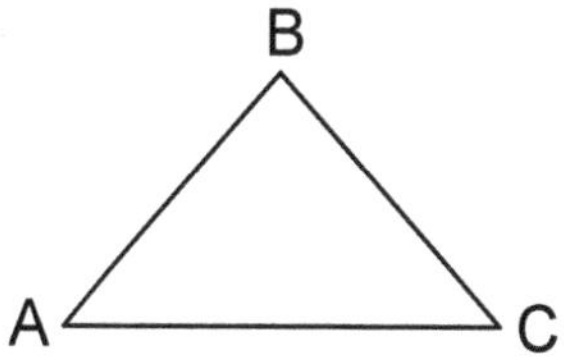

Given: ΔABC is an isosceles triangle with $\overline{AB} \cong \overline{BC}$
Prove: $\angle A \cong \angle C$

Statements	Reasons
1.	1.
2. Let M be the midpoint of $\overline{AC}$.	2. A segment has exactly one midpoint.
3. Draw $\overline{BM}$.	3. Through any two points there is exactly one line.
4.	4. Midpoint Theorem
5.	5.
6.	6.
7.	7.

18. Prove the Isosceles Triangle Converse Theorem.

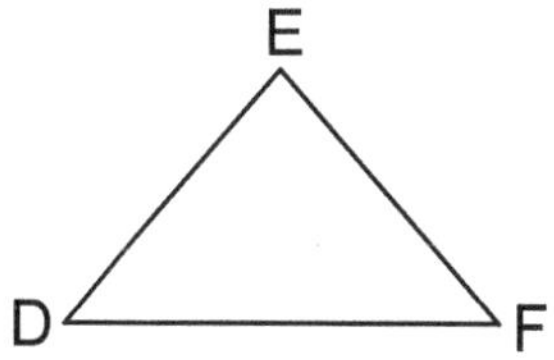

Given: $\angle D \cong \angle F$
Prove: $\overline{DE} \cong \overline{EF}$

Statements	Reasons
1.	1.
2. Draw $\overline{EQ}$ such that Q is on $\overline{DF}$ and $\overline{EQ} \perp \overline{DF}$.	2. Through a point P not on a line, there is exactly one line perpendicular to the given line.
3.	3.
4.	4.
5.	5.
6.	6.
7.	7.

19. Prove the following theorem: If a triangle is an equilateral triangle, then each interior angle measures 60°.

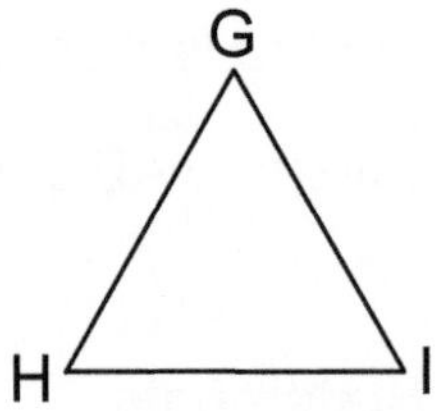

Given: $\triangle GHI$ is an equilateral triangle

Prove: $m\angle G = 60°$, $m\angle H = 60°$, $m\angle I = 60°$

Statements	Reasons
1.	1.
2.	2. Definition of an equilateral triangle
3. $\angle G \cong \angle H$ and $\angle G \cong \angle I$	3.
4. $\angle G \cong \angle H \cong \angle I$	4. Transitive Property of Angle Congruence
5. $\triangle GHI$ is an equiangular triangle	5.
6.	6.

20. Prove the following theorem: If each interior angle of a triangle measures 60°, then the triangle is an equilateral triangle.

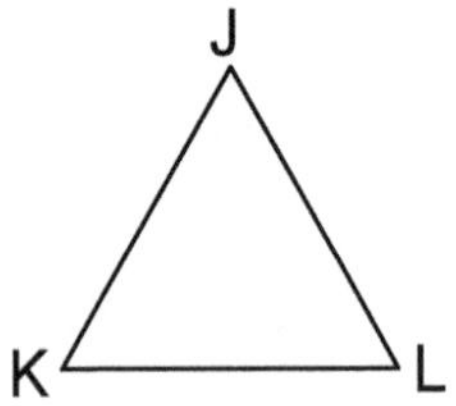

Given: $m\angle J = 60°$, $m\angle K = 60°$, $m\angle L = 60°$

Prove: $\triangle JKL$ is an equilateral triangle

Statements	Reasons

21. Given that $\angle 1 \cong \angle 4$ in the figure at the right, prove that $\overline{AB} \cong \overline{BC}$.

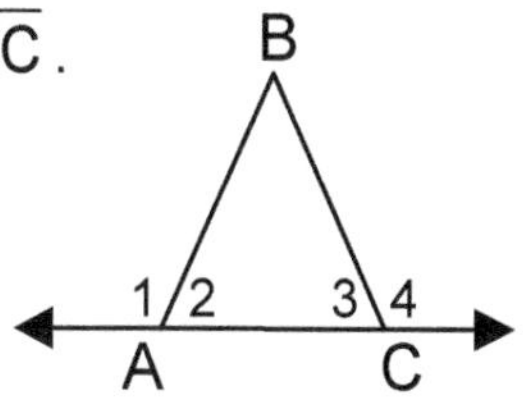

Statements	Reasons

22. Given that $\overline{AC} \cong \overline{BC}$ in the figure at the right, prove that $\angle 1 \cong \angle 4$.

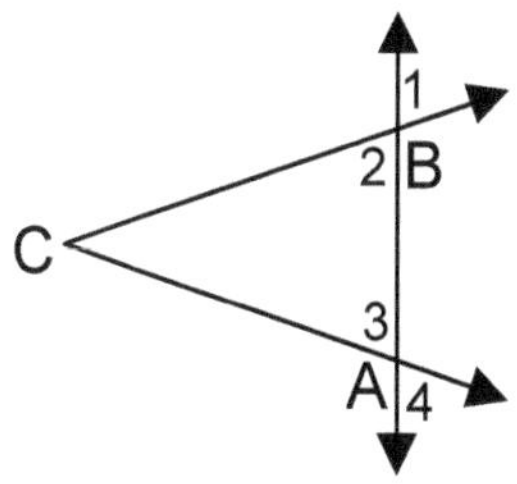

Statements	Reasons

23-24. Use the picture below to complete #23 and #24.

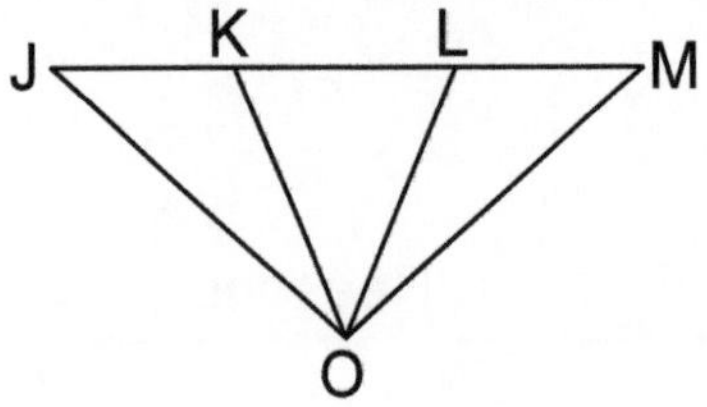

23. Given: $\overline{JK} \cong \overline{ML}$ and $\angle LKO \cong \angle KLO$

Prove: $\triangle JOM$ is an isosceles triangle

Statements	Reasons

24. Given: $\angle JOK \cong \angle MOL$ and $\overline{JO} \cong \overline{MO}$

Prove: ΔKOL is an isosceles triangle

Statements	Reasons

Part VI – Mixed Review

1. If the measure of an angle is x°, how can you represent the measure of its supplement? ______________

2. You know that ∠H and ∠P are complementary, and you know that the measure of ∠H is six degrees more than twice the measure of ∠P. Find the measures of both angles.

   m∠H = ___________

   m∠P = ___________

3. A triangle has one obtuse angle and two acute angles. The measure of one of the acute angles is 2° more than the measure of the other acute angle, and the measure of the obtuse angle is 7° less than three times the measure of the smaller acute angle. Find the measures of the angles of the triangle. ________, ________, ________

4. In ΔABC, the measure of ∠A is twice the measure of ∠B, and the measure of ∠C is twelve degrees fewer than three times the measure of ∠B. Find the measures of each of the angles of ΔABC.

   m ∠A = ___________

   m ∠B = ___________

   m ∠C = ___________

5. True or false: Every equilateral triangle is isosceles.

6. True or false: Every isosceles triangle is equilateral.

7. True or false: Every equilateral triangle is equiangular.

8. True or false: Every isosceles triangle is equiangular.

9. True or false: No scalene triangle is equiangular.

10. True or false: Some acute triangles are scalene.

11. In the figure at the right, m∠J = 30°, m∠L = 4x°, and m∠MKL = (7x – 21)°. Then x = __________, m∠MKL = __________, and m∠LKJ = __________.

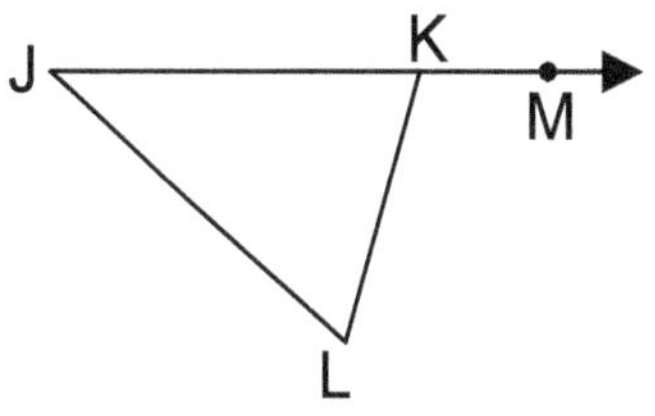

12. In the figure at the right, m∠E = (3x – 2y)°, m∠F = 30°, m∠EGF = (3x + 8y)°, and m∠FGH = (5x + 2y)°. Then x = __________, y = __________, m∠E = __________, and m∠FGH = __________.

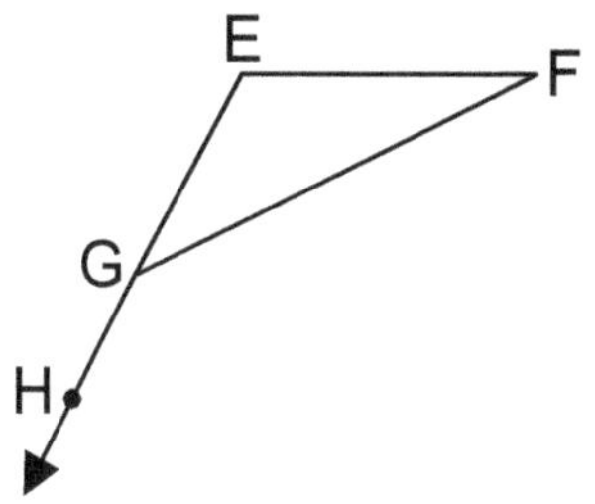

13-14. Use the picture below to answer #13 and #14.

13. Which of the following statements MUST be true? Circle all that apply.

(I) AB + BC + CD = AD (II) BD – CD = BC (III) AB + CD = AD

(IV) AB = BC (V) AC + CD = AD (VI) AD – BD = AC – BC

14. Which of the following statements CANNOT be true? Circle all that apply.

(I) AB + BC + CD = AD (II) BD – CD = BC (III) AB + CD = AD

(IV) AB = BC (V) AC + CD = AD (VI) AD – BD = AC – BC

15. In the figure at the right, ΔSTU is an isosceles triangle with $\overline{TU}$ as its base. Then w = __________, x = __________, and y = __________.

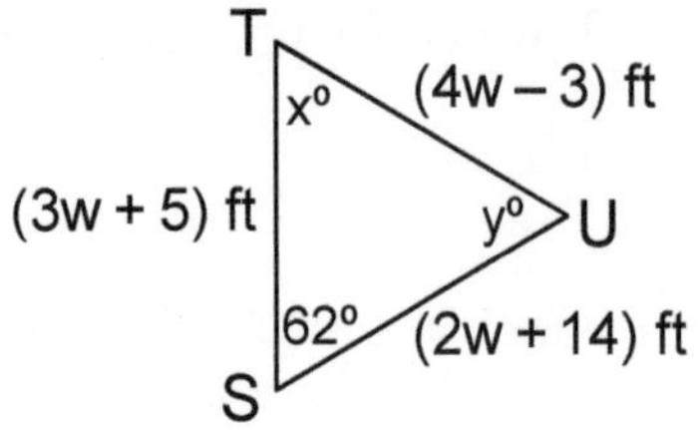

16. In the figure at the right, ΔAZV is an isosceles triangle with $\angle A$ as its vertex angle. Then w = __________, x = __________, and y = __________.

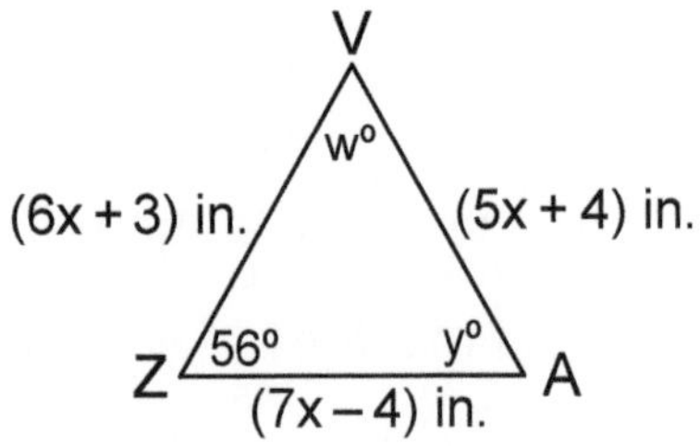

17-19. For each pair of triangles below, (a) determine whether or not the triangles are congruent, and (b) if your answer to part (a) was *yes*, complete the congruence statement and then state a postulate or theorem to support your conclusion.

17. (a) Are the triangles congruent? _________

(b) If your answer to part (a) was yes, then $\Delta DEF \cong \Delta$_________.

Postulate or theorem: ________________

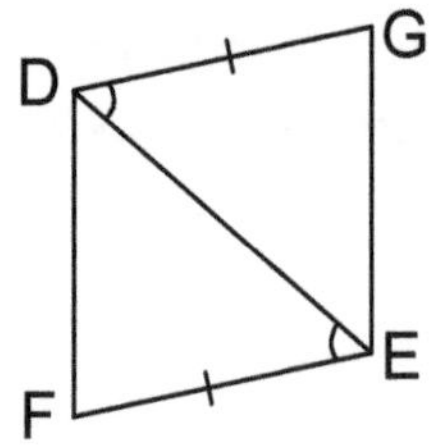

18. (a) Are the triangles congruent? _________

(b) If your answer to part (a) was yes, then $\Delta IHJ \cong \Delta$_________.

Postulate or theorem: ________________

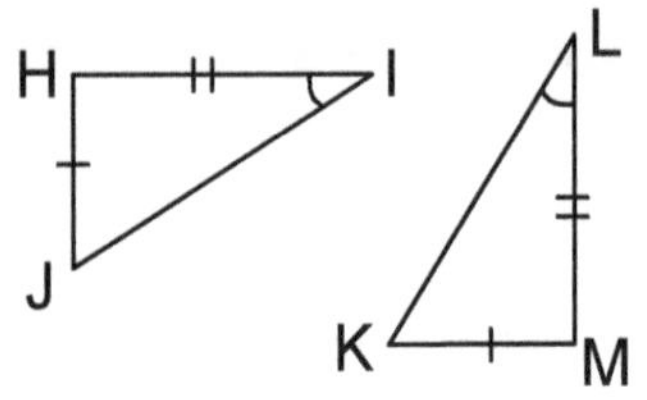

19. (a) Are the triangles congruent? _________

(b) If your answer to part (a) was yes, then $\Delta NOP \cong \Delta$_________.

Postulate or theorem: ________________

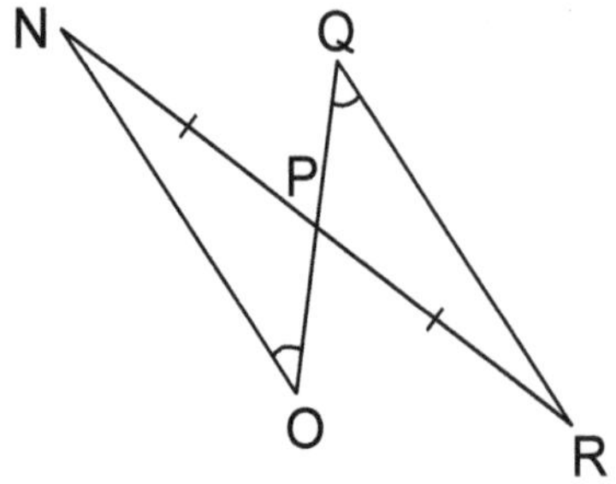

20-21. Use the figure below to complete the proofs in #20 and #21.

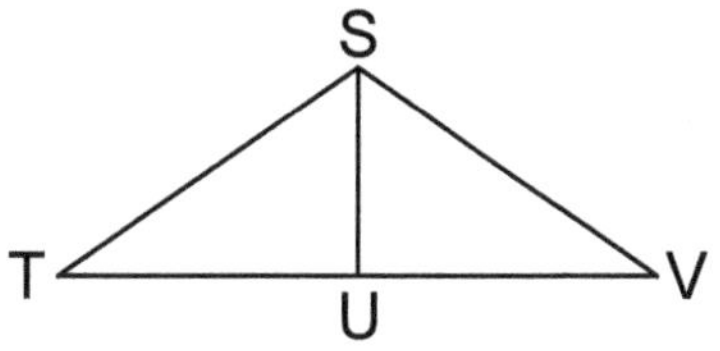

20. Given: $\overline{TV} \perp \overline{SU}$ and $\overline{ST} \cong \overline{SV}$

Prove: $\angle UST \cong \angle USV$

Statements	Reasons

21. Given: $\overline{ST} \cong \overline{SV}$ and U is the midpoint of $\overline{TV}$

Prove: $\overline{TV} \perp \overline{SU}$

Statements	Reasons

22. Classify each of the triangles according to their sides and angles. Be sure to name all of the terms that apply.

(a) ______________________ (b) ______________________

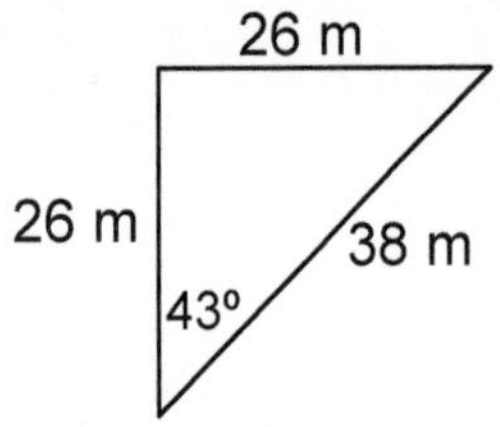

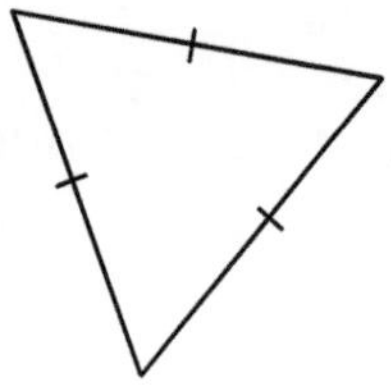

23-28. In the figure at the right, $\overleftrightarrow{CK} \parallel \overleftrightarrow{NP}$.

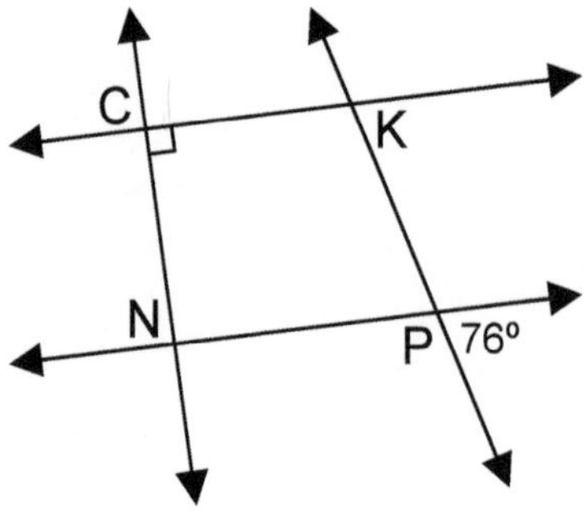

23. $m\angle CKP$ = ___________

24. Is $\angle CNP$ is supplementary to $\angle NPK$?

____

25. Is $\overleftrightarrow{NC} \perp \overleftrightarrow{NP}$? ___________

26. Are the points C, N, and P collinear? ___________

27. Is $\angle KCN$ an *acute angle*, a *right angle*, an *obtuse angle*, or a *straight angle*?

____

28. Is $\angle CKP$ an *acute angle*, a *right angle*, an *obtuse angle*, or a *straight angle*?

____

29. In the figure at the right, must line ℓ be parallel to line m? If your answer is *yes*, state a postulate or theorem to support your answer.

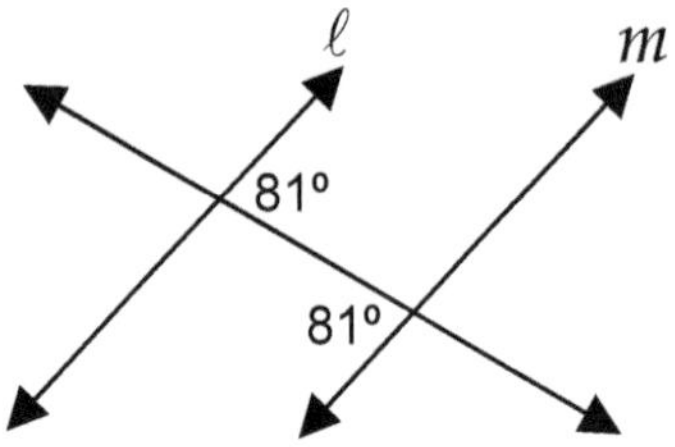

30. Find the values of x and y that will make line ℓ parallel to line m in the figure at the right.

x = ___________

y = ___________

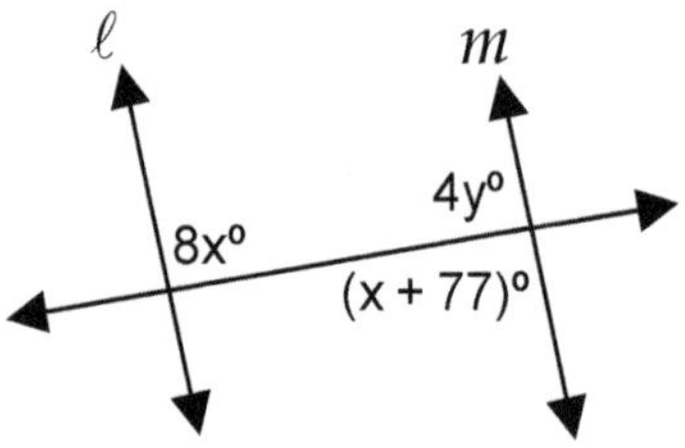

31. If $\ell \parallel m$ in the figure at the right, then x = ___________

and y = ___________.

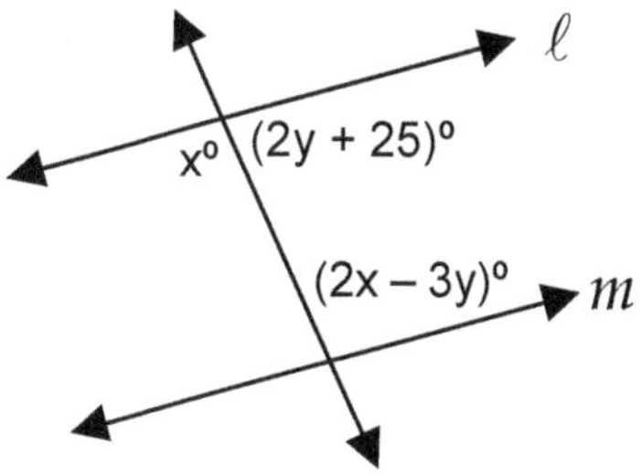

32. Use a ruler and a protractor to draw a picture to represent the following statement: *ΔXYZ is an acute isosceles triangle.*

33. Draw a picture to represent the following statement: *$\angle 1$ is an exterior angle of ΔTUV.*

34. Draw a picture to represent the following statement: *$\overleftrightarrow{AB}$ is skew to $\overleftrightarrow{CD}$.*

35. Draw a counterexample to show that the following statement is false: *No scalene triangle is also an acute triangle.*

Chapter 5 – More on Triangles

Part I – Inequalities in Triangles

We will begin this section with two theorems.

Opposite Angles of a Triangle Theorem
If the lengths of two sides of a triangle are unequal, then the angle opposite the longer side has a measure that is larger than the measure of the angle opposite the shorter side.

Opposite Sides of a Triangle Theorem
If the measures of two angles of a triangle are unequal, then the side opposite the angle with the larger measure is longer than the side opposite the angle with the smaller measure.

In the example below, we will prove the Opposite Angles of a Triangle Theorem using a paragraph proof, or a proof written in the form of one or more paragraphs instead of the two-column format we have been using. You will prove the Opposite Sides of a Triangle Theorem in Problem #33.

Example 1: Prove the Opposite Angles of a Triangle Theorem.

As usual, we will begin by drawing a generic-looking triangle.

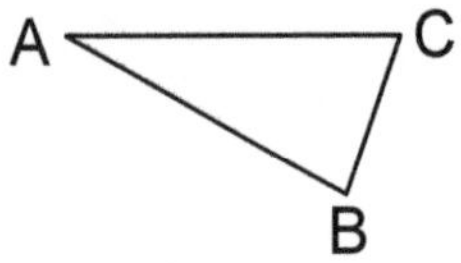

We can use this picture to say that we are given that AC > BC, and we want to prove that $m\angle ABC > m\angle A$.

We will begin by drawing an auxiliary segment, $\overline{BD}$ shown in gray below, so that D is between A and C and $\overline{CD} \cong \overline{CB}$.

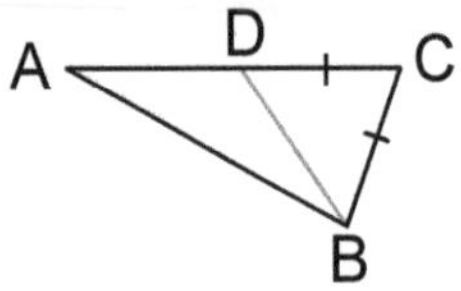

Now, we can use the Exterior Angle of a Triangle Inequality Theorem to say that $m\angle BDC > m\angle A$.

Next, we can use the Isosceles Triangle Theorem to say that $\angle CBD \cong \angle BDC$. By the definition of congruent angles, this tells us that $m\angle CBD = m\angle BDC$. Since we already said that $m\angle BDC > m\angle A$, we can use the Substitution Property of Equality to say that $m\angle CBD > m\angle A$.

Now, the Angle Addition Postulate tells us that $m\angle ABC = m\angle DBA + m\angle CBD$, and so we can use the definition of inequality to say that $m\angle ABC > m\angle CBD$. Since we already said that $m\angle CBD > m\angle A$, we can use the Transitive Property of Inequality to say that $m\angle ABC > m\angle A$.

Example 2: List the sides of the triangle at the right in order from shortest to longest.

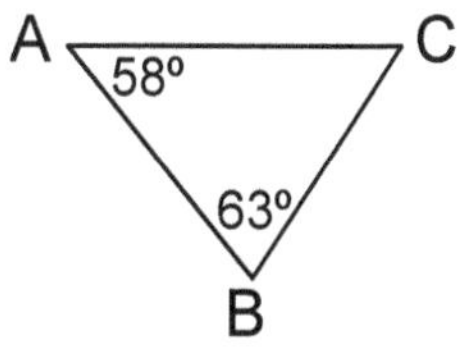

We will begin by noting that, since the sum of the measures of the angles in a triangle is 180º, we can say that m$\angle$C = 59º. Now, since the smallest angle in this triangle is $\angle$A, we can use the Opposite Sides of a Triangle Theorem to say that the shortest side in this triangle is $\overline{BC}$. Since the angle with the next smallest measure is $\angle$C in this triangle, we can say that the next shortest side is $\overline{AB}$. Finally, the angle with the largest measure in this triangle is $\angle$B, and so $\overline{AC}$ must be the longest side of this triangle. All of this tells us that the correct answer to this question is $\overline{BC}$, $\overline{AB}$, and $\overline{AC}$.

Example 3: List the angles of the triangle at the right in order from the smallest measure to the largest measure.

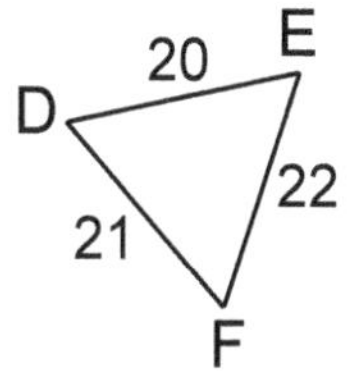

We can use the Opposite Angles of a Triangle Theorem to say that the angle with the smallest measure is $\angle$F (because it is the angle opposite $\overline{DE}$, the shortest side). The next shortest side is $\overline{DF}$, and so the angle with the next smallest measure is $\angle$E. The longest side of this triangle is $\overline{EF}$, and so the angle with the largest measure is $\angle$D. This tells us that we can list the angles of this triangle in order from smallest measure to largest measure as follows: $\angle$F, $\angle$E, and $\angle$D.

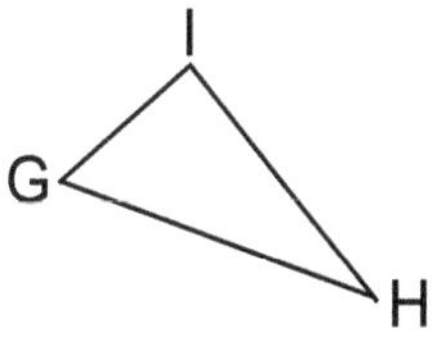

Before we discuss the next theorem, let's talk about the picture at the right. Suppose that your home is at point H, and you are going with a friend to a movie theater located at point G. You are allowed to go on the condition that "you will come straight home after the movie is finished." After the movie is finished, should you follow $\overline{GH}$ to get home, or could you take a detour and go by your friend's house at point I? The answer, of course, is that you should follow $\overline{GH}$. You were told that you should come *straight home* after the movie was finished, but following $\overline{GI}$ and then $\overline{IH}$ is longer than following $\overline{GH}$. Or, in mathematical terms, GI + IH > GH.

Now, we need another theorem.

Triangle Inequality Theorem
The sum of the lengths of two sides of a triangle is always greater than the length of the third side.

Example 4: Prove the Triangle Inequality Theorem using a paragraph proof.

Of course, we will begin by drawing a generic triangle.

We can use this picture to say that we are given ΔJKL, and we want to prove all of the following statements: LK + KJ > JL, JK + JL > KL, and KL + JL > JK. We will actually only show the proof that LK + KJ > JL here, but the other statements can be proven similarly.

Next, we will extend $\overline{LK}$ to point M so that $\overline{KJ} \cong \overline{KM}$, as shown in the picture below.

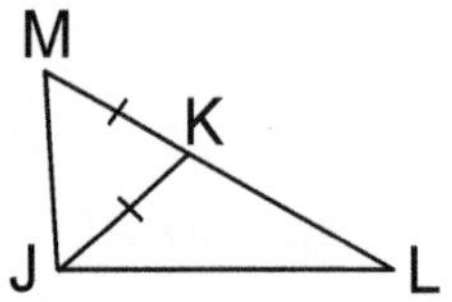

The definition of congruent segments tells us that KJ = KM, and the Segment Addition Postulate tells us that LM = LK + KM. So, now we can use the Substitution Property of Equality to say that LM = LK + KJ.

Next, we can use the Angle Addition Postulate to state that $m\angle LJM = m\angle LJK + m\angle KJM$. Using the definition of inequality discussed in Part I of Chapter 4, we can say that this means that $m\angle LJM > m\angle KJM$.

Now, we will use the Isosceles Triangle Theorem to say that $\angle KJM \cong \angle M$. We can use the definition of congruent angles to say that this tells us that $m\angle KJM = m\angle M$. So, since we said earlier that $m\angle LJM > m\angle KJM$, we can use the Substitution Property of Equality to say that $m\angle LJM > m\angle M$. This tells us that we can use the Opposite Sides of a Triangle Theorem to say that LM > JL.

Now, since we said earlier that LM = LK + KJ, we can use the Substitution Property of Equality to say that LK + KJ > JL.

Example 5: State whether or not you can form a triangle with sides of the given lengths. (a) 17 feet, 12 feet, and 10 feet; (b) 3 meters, 9 meters, and 5 meters; (c) 12 yards, 7 yards, and 5 yards

(a) In order to see if we can form a triangle with sides that have lengths of 17 feet, 12 feet, and 10 feet, we must check and make sure that the sum of *each pair* of lengths is greater than the third length, as shown below.

Is 17 ft + 12 ft > 10 ft? yes

Is 17 ft + 10 ft > 12 ft? yes

Is 12 ft + 10 ft > 17 ft? yes

Since the answer to all three of these questions was *yes*, we can say that it is possible to draw a triangle with sides of lengths 17 feet, 12 feet, and 10 feet.

(b) Again, we must make sure that the sum of *each pair* of side lengths is greater than the third length.

Is 3 m + 9 m > 5 m? yes

Is 3 m + 5 m > 9 m? no

Is 9 m + 5 m > 3 m? yes

Since the answer to one of these questions was *no*, we can say that it is not possible to draw a triangle that has sides of lengths 3 meters, 9 meters, and 5 meters.

(c) Once again, we must make sure that the sum of *each pair* of side lengths is greater than the third length.

Is 12 yds + 7 yds > 5 yds? yes

Is 12 yds + 5 yds > 7 yds? yes

Is 7 yds + 5 yds > 12 yds? no

Since the answer to one of these questions was *no*, we can say that it is not possible to draw a triangle that has sides of lengths 12 yards, 7 yards, and 5 yards.

Example 6: In $\triangle NOP$ at the right, $m\angle N > m\angle P$. Describe all possible values of x.

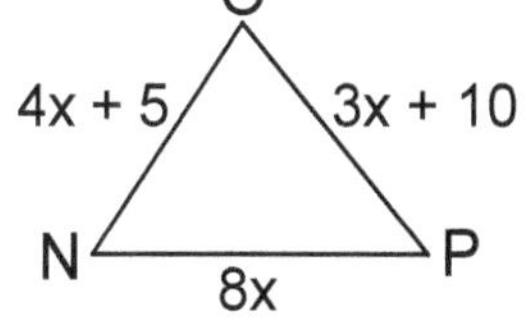

We will begin by noting that we can use the Opposite Sides of a Triangle Theorem to say that OP > ON. Thus, we can say that $3x + 10 > 4x + 5$. When we solve this inequality for x, we find that $x < 5$.

Next, we can use the Triangle Inequality Theorem to make each of the following statements.

$NO + OP > NP$	$NO + NP > OP$	$OP + NP > NO$
$4x + 5 + 3x + 10 > 8x$	$4x + 5 + 8x > 3x + 10$	$3x + 10 + 8x > 4x + 5$
$15 > x$	$x > \frac{5}{9}$	$x > -\frac{5}{7}$

We can summarize these three statements along with the statement of $x < 5$ that we found earlier by writing $\frac{5}{9} < x < 5$. (Note that all numbers that are greater than $\frac{5}{9}$ are also greater than $-\frac{5}{7}$ and that all numbers that are less than 5 are also less than 15.)

Finally, we will note that all sides of the triangle must have lengths that are greater than zero, and so we can also make each of the following statements.

$NO > 0$	$OP > 0$	$NP > 0$
$4x + 5 > 0$	$3x + 10 > 0$	$8x > 0$
$x > -\frac{5}{4}$	$x > -\frac{10}{3}$	$x > 0$

Each of these statements were taken care of when we said that x must be larger than $\frac{5}{9}$, and so we can say that the final answer to this question is $\frac{5}{9} < x < 5$.

Now, we need two more theorems.

SAS Inequality Theorem

If two sides of one triangle are congruent to two sides of another triangle, and if the included angle between the two sides of the first triangle has a measure that is greater than the measure of the included angle between the two sides of the second triangle, then the third side of the first triangle is longer than the third side of the second triangle.

SSS Inequality Theorem

If two sides of one triangle are congruent to two sides of another triangle, and if the third side of the first triangle is longer than the third side of the second triangle, then the included angle between the two sides of the first triangle has a measure that is greater than the measure of the included angle between the two sides of the second triangle.

We will prove the SAS Inequality Theorem in Example 7, and you will prove the SSS Inequality Theorem in the exercises for this section.

Example 7: Prove the SAS Inequality Theorem using a paragraph proof.

We will begin by drawing a picture to describe the part of the theorem that follows the "if" in the statement of this theorem.

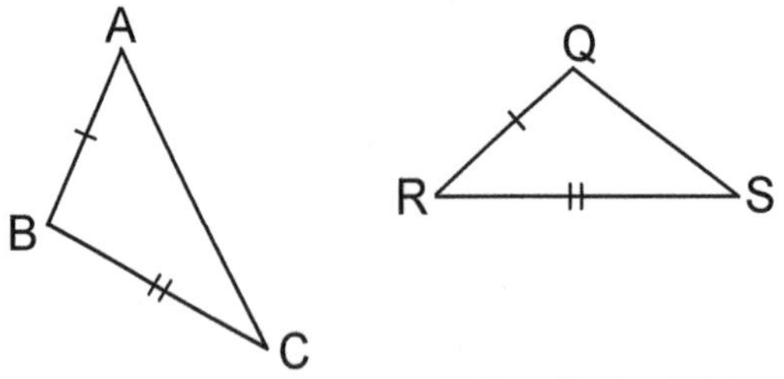

We can say that we are given that $\overline{AB} \cong \overline{QR}$, $\overline{BC} \cong \overline{RS}$, and $m\angle ABC > m\angle QRS$. We want to prove that AC > QS.

Now, we will draw $\overline{BD}$ so that $\angle DBC \cong \angle QRS$ and $\overline{BD} \cong \overline{AB}$ (and so, by the Transitive Property of Segment Congruence, $\overline{BD}$ will also be congruent to $\overline{QR}$). There are two possibilities for the location of D: either D is on $\overline{AC}$, or D is not on $\overline{AC}$ but is in the interior of $\angle ABC$.

Case 1: D is on $\overline{AC}$.

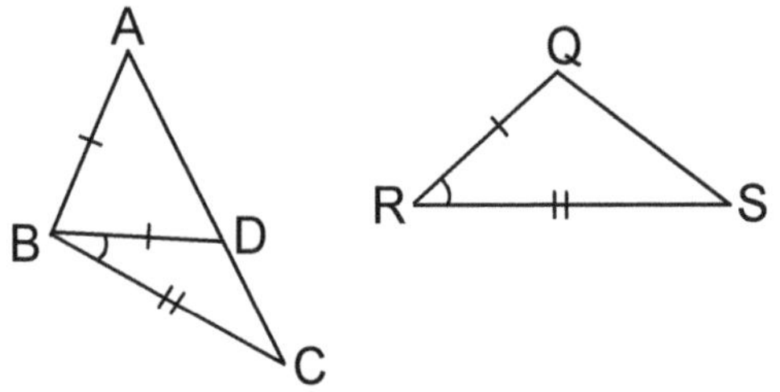

If D is on $\overline{AC}$, then we can use the SAS Congruence Postulate to say that $\triangle CBD \cong \triangle SRQ$. Then $\overline{DC} \cong \overline{QS}$ by CPCTC. The definition of congruent segments tells us that this means that DC = QS.

Since the Segment Addition Postulate tells us that AC = AD + DC, we can now use the definition of an inequality discussed in Part I of Chapter 4 to say that AC > DC. Since we already said that DC = QS, we can use the Substitution Property of Equality to say that this means that AC > QS.

Case 2: D is not on $\overline{AC}$ but is in the interior of $\angle ABC$.

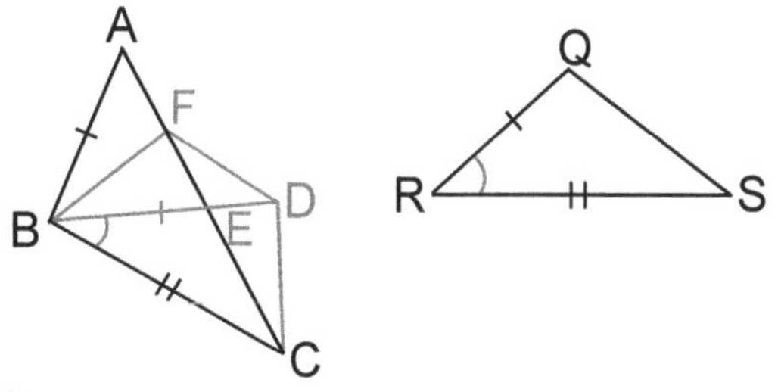

We will assume that D lies on the exterior of $\triangle ABC$. (If it lies on the interior of $\triangle ABC$, the proof is exactly the same; only the picture would change.) We will call the point where $\overrightarrow{BD}$ intersects $\overline{AC}$ point E.

Next, we will draw $\overline{BF}$ so that F is on $\overline{AE}$ and $\angle ABF \cong \angle DBF$. We will also draw $\overline{FD}$ and $\overline{DC}$. (We know that we can do this because there is one, and only one, line between any two given points.) We will also note that $\overline{BF} \cong \overline{BF}$ by the Reflexive Property of Segment Congruence. Then $\triangle ABF \cong \triangle DBF$ by the SAS Congruence Postulate, and so we can say that $\overline{AF} \cong \overline{DF}$ by CPCTC. The definition of congruent segments tells us that this means that AF = DF.

Next, we will note that the Triangle Inequality Theorem tells us that DF + FC > DC. Since we already said that AF = DF, we can use the Substitution Property of Equality to say that AF + FC > DC. The Segment Addition Postulate tells us that AC = AF + FC, and so we can use the Substitution Property of Equality again to say that AC > DC.

Next, we will note that the SAS Congruence Postulate tells us that $\triangle DBC \cong \triangle QRS$, and so $\overline{DC}$ must be congruent to $\overline{QS}$ by CPCTC. So, by the definition of congruent segments, DC = QS.

Since we said earlier that AC > DC, we can now use the Substitution Property of Equality to say that AC > QS.

Example 8: Use the figures below to fill in each of the blanks with <, >, or =, and then state the postulates, properties, definitions, and/or theorems used.

(a) QS _______ ST

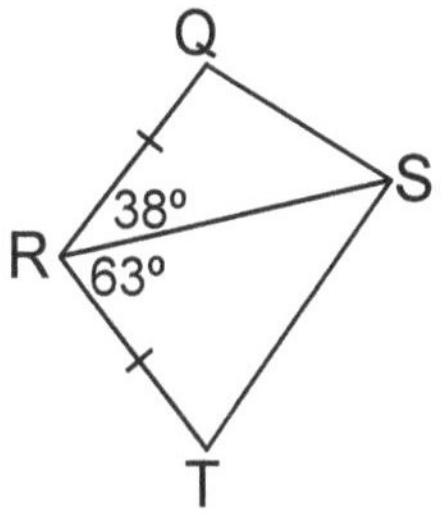

(b) $m\angle VUW$ _______ $m\angle XUW$

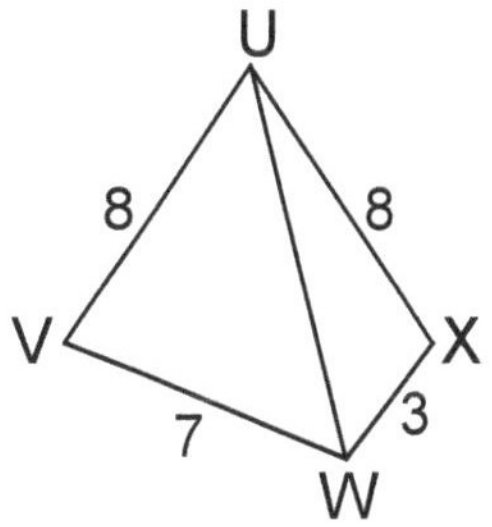

(c) AB _______ BC

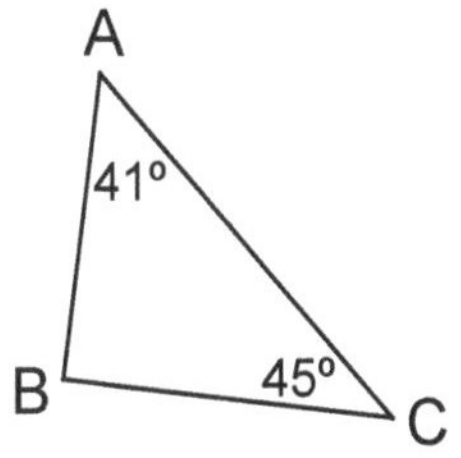

(d) EF + FG _______ DE + DG

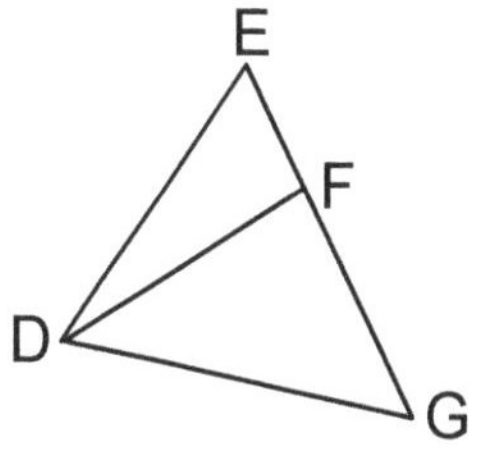

(a) Notice that we have two triangles in this picture, ΔQRS and ΔTRS, and that the Reflexive Property of Segment Congruence tells us that $\overline{RS} \cong \overline{RS}$. So, we have two sets of congruent sides ($\overline{TR} \cong \overline{QR}$ and $\overline{RS} \cong \overline{RS}$) and, of the angles between these sides, $m\angle SRT > m\angle SRQ$. Thus, we can use the SAS Inequality Theorem to say that the side opposite $\angle SRT$ is longer than the side opposite $\angle SRQ$. Or, in other words, QS < ST, and the theorems that support this statement are the Reflexive Property of Segment Congruence and the SAS Inequality Theorem.

(b) We have two triangles in this picture, ΔVUW and ΔXUW. The Reflexive Property of Segment Congruence tells us that $\overline{UW} \cong \overline{UW}$. The information in the picture tells us that $\overline{UV} \cong \overline{UX}$ and that VW > WX. This tells us that we can use the SSS Inequality Theorem to say that the angle opposite $\overline{VW}$ must have a greater measure than the angle opposite $\overline{WX}$. Or, in other words, $m\angle VUW > m\angle XUW$, and the theorems that support this statement are the Reflexive Property of Segment Congruence and the SSS Inequality Theorem.

(c) We can use the Opposite Sides of a Triangle Theorem to say that AB > BC.

(d) The Triangle Inequality Theorem tells us that EG < DE + DG. Since the Segment Addition Postulate tells us that EG = EF + FG, we can use the Substitution Property of Equality to say that EF + FG < DE + DG.

Problems:

1-3. List the angles of each triangle below in order from smallest measure to largest measure.

1. ________, ________, ________

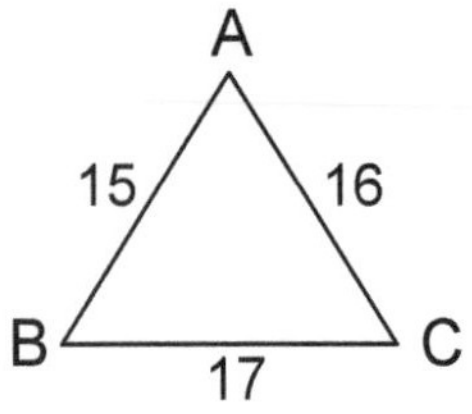

3. ________, ________, ________

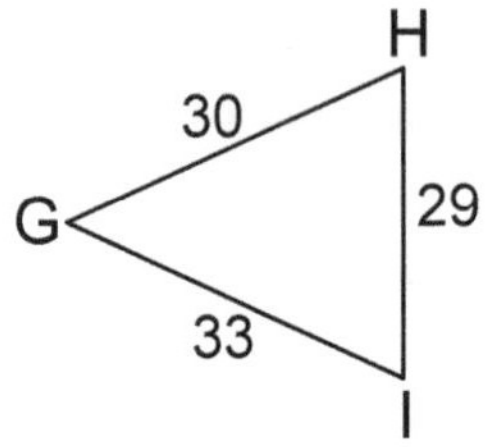

2. ________, ________, ________

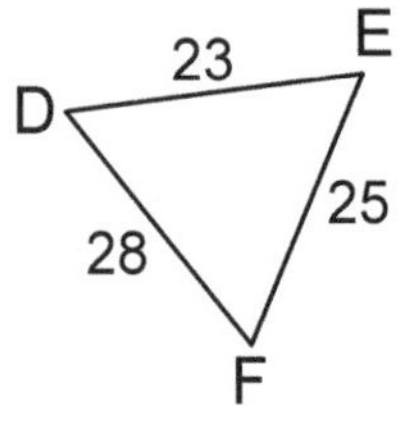

4-6. List the sides of each triangle below in order from shortest to longest.

4. ________, ________, ________

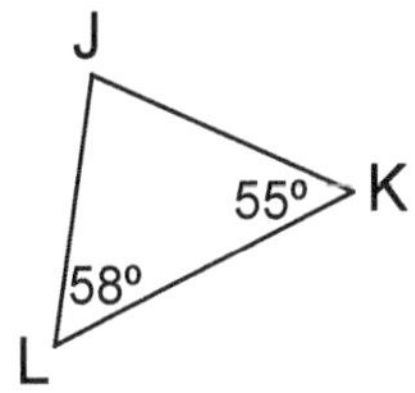

6. ________, ________, ________

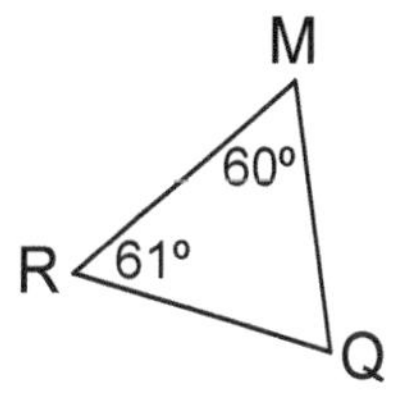

5. ________, ________, ________

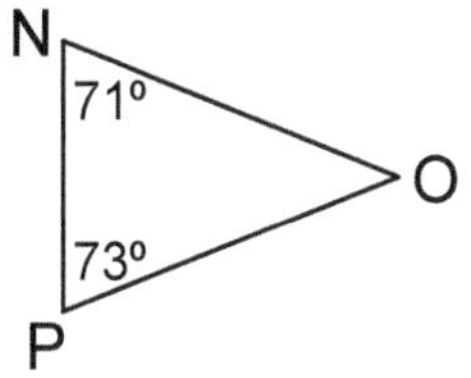

7-18. Fill in each blank with <, >, or =, and then state the postulates, properties, definitions, and/or theorems used.

7. $m\angle T$ ________ $m\angle U$

Postulates, properties, definitions, and/or theorems used:

____

____

____

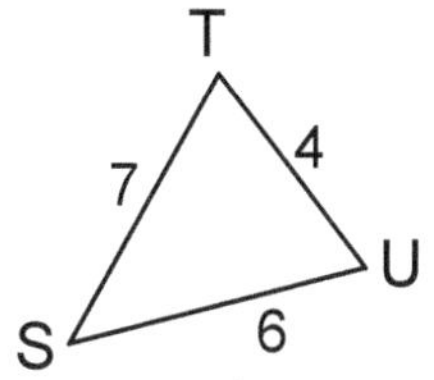

8. In the figure at the right, $\overline{WV} \cong \overline{WY}$ and $VX < XY$. Then $m\angle VWX$ ________ $m\angle YWX$.

Postulates, properties, definitions, and/or theorems used:

____

____

____

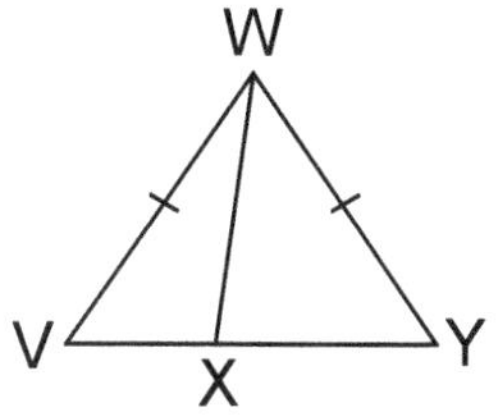

9. $m\angle ABD$ ________ $m\angle CBD$

Postulates, properties, definitions, and/or theorems used:

____

____

____

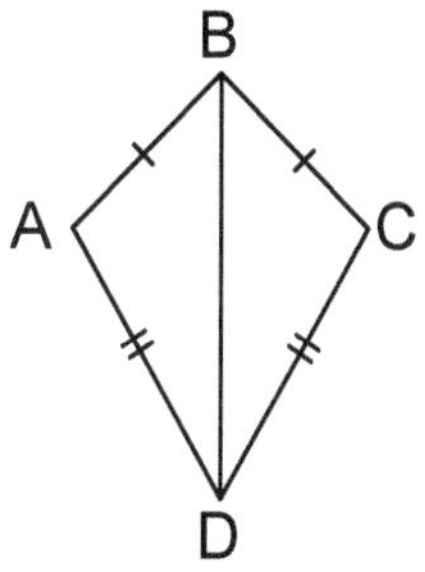

10. In the figure at the right, $m\angle E < m\angle F$. Then DE _______ DF.

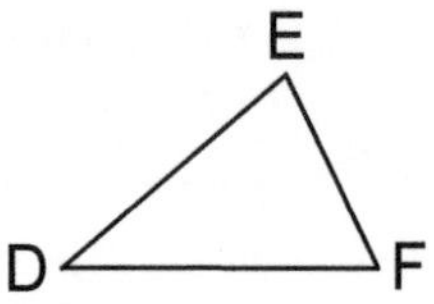

Postulates, properties, definitions, and/or theorems used:

____

____

____

11. In the figure at the right, $\overline{GH} \cong \overline{IJ}$, $m\angle HGI = 25°$, and $m\angle GIJ = 98°$. Then HI _______ GJ.

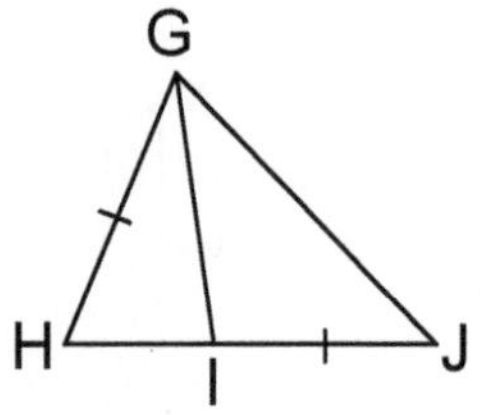

Postulates, properties, definitions, and/or theorems used:

____

____

____

12. $m\angle K$ _______ $m\angle L$

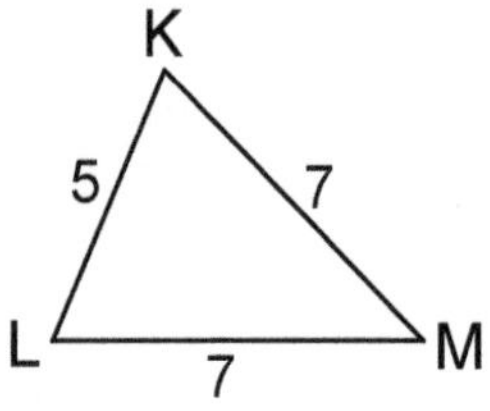

Postulates, properties, definitions, and/or theorems used:

____

____

____

13. $m\angle Q + m\angle P$ _______ $m\angle NOP$

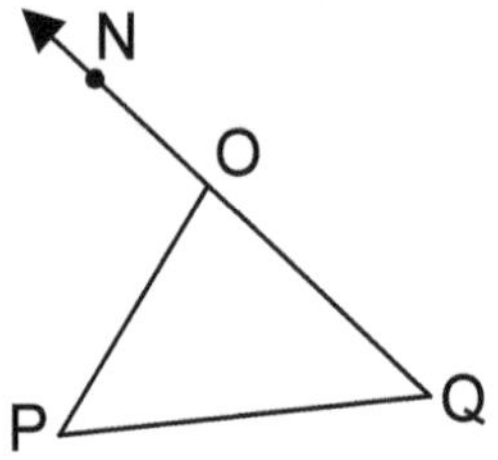

Postulates, properties, definitions, and/or theorems used:

____

____

____

14. RS + SU _______ RV + VU

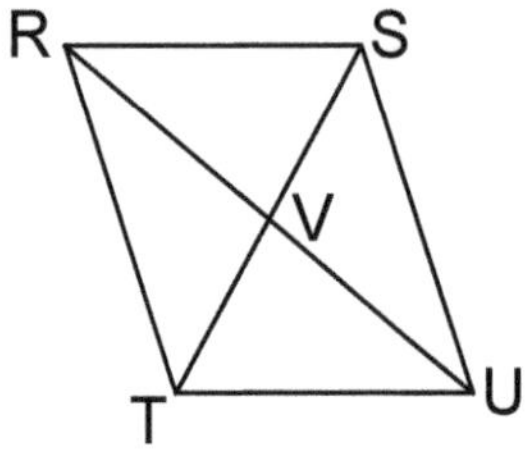

Postulates, properties, definitions, and/or theorems used:

____

____

____

15. In the figure at the right, $m\angle ZXW < m\angle YWX$ and $\overline{WY} \cong \overline{XZ}$. Then XY _______ WZ.

Postulates, properties, definitions, and/or theorems used:

____

____

____

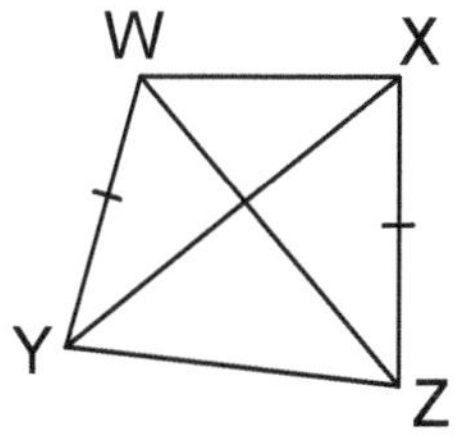

16. In the figure at the right, $m\angle BAC > m\angle DAC$ and $\overline{AB} \cong \overline{AD}$. Then BC _______ CD.

Postulates, properties, definitions, and/or theorems used:

____

____

____

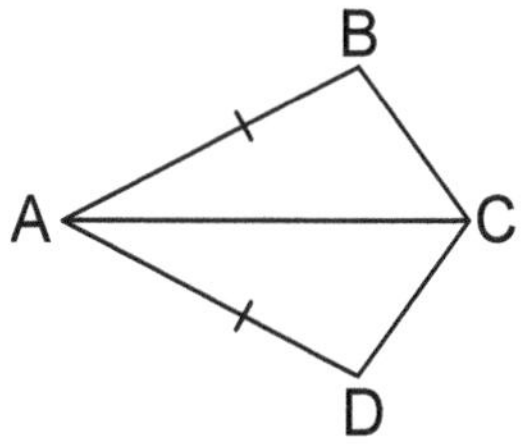

17. EF + EG _______ FG

Postulates, properties, definitions, and/or theorems used:

____

____

____

18. In the figure at the right, $\overline{HJ} \cong \overline{LJ}$ and $\overline{JI} \cong \overline{JK}$. Then HI _______ KL.

Postulates, properties, definitions, and/or theorems used:

____

____

____

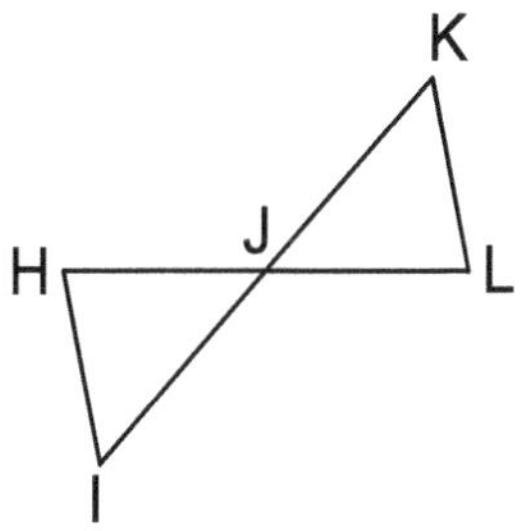

19-24. State whether or not you can form a triangle with sides of the given lengths.

19. 3 centimeters, 8 centimeters, 3 centimeters _________________

20. 4 inches, 5 inches, 2 inches _________________

21. 11 meters, 15 meters, 7 meters _________________

22. 4 feet, 3 feet, 7 feet _________________

23. 28 yards, 12 yards, 14 yards _________________

24. 23 millimeters, 15 millimeters, 4 millimeters _________________

25. In $\triangle ABC$ at the right, $m\angle B > m\angle C$. Describe all possible values of x.

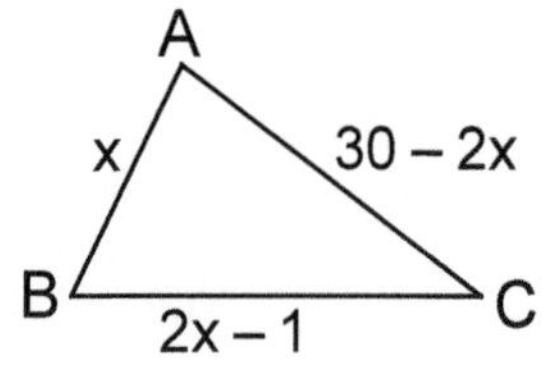

26. In $\triangle DEF$ at the right, $m\angle F > m\angle E$. Describe all possible values of x.

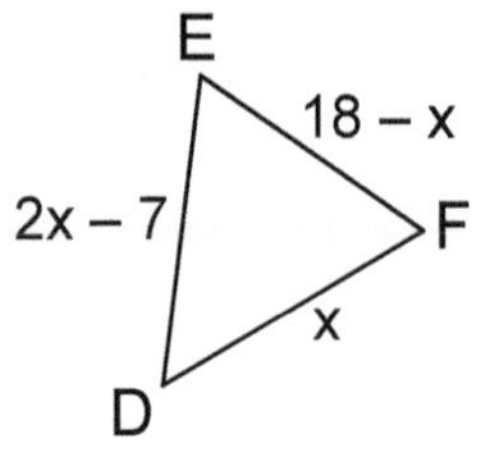

27. In $\triangle GHI$ at the right, GH < HI. Describe all possible values of x and y.

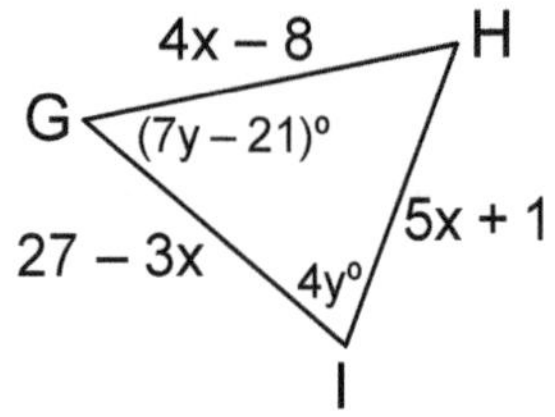

28. In $\triangle JKL$ at the right, JK < KL, $m\angle L = (78 - y)°$, and $m\angle J = (y + 32)°$. Describe all possible values of x and y.

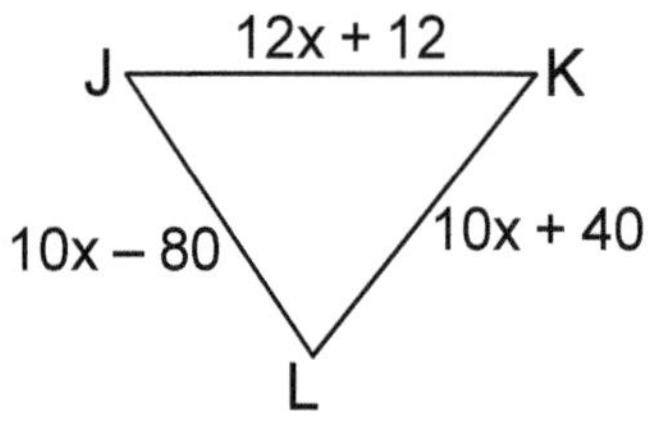

29. If a triangle has one side that has a length of 8 inches and another side that has a length of 3 inches, then the third side must have a length greater than __________ inches and less than __________ inches.

30. If a triangle has one side that has a length of 23 meters and another side that has a length of 31 meters, then the third side must have a length greater than _________ meters and less than __________ meters.

31. If one side of a triangle has a length of 12 feet, then the perimeter of the triangle must be greater than __________ feet.

32. When a football player is returning a punt, he will get to the goal line quicker if he follows a straight line to the goal line instead of cutting across the field and then heading toward the goal line. Which theorem from this section proves this fact?

____

33. Prove the Opposite Sides of a Triangle Theorem using an indirect paragraph proof.

Given: $m\angle K > m\angle J$

Prove: $JL > KL$

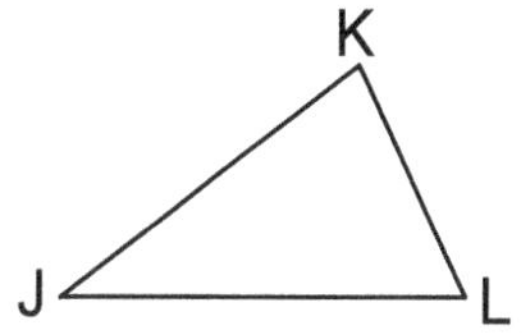

We are given that $m\angle K > m\angle J$. Assume that JL is NOT greater than KL. Then either $JL = KL$ or $JL < KL$.

Case 1: $JL = KL$

Then, by the Isosceles Triangle Theorem, ____________________, which contradicts what we were given. Therefore, this is impossible.

Case 2: $JL < KL$

Then ____________________ because of the __________________________ Theorem. This contradicts what we were given, and so this is also impossible.

Hence, JK must be larger than KL.

34. Prove the SSS Inequality Theorem using an indirect paragraph proof.

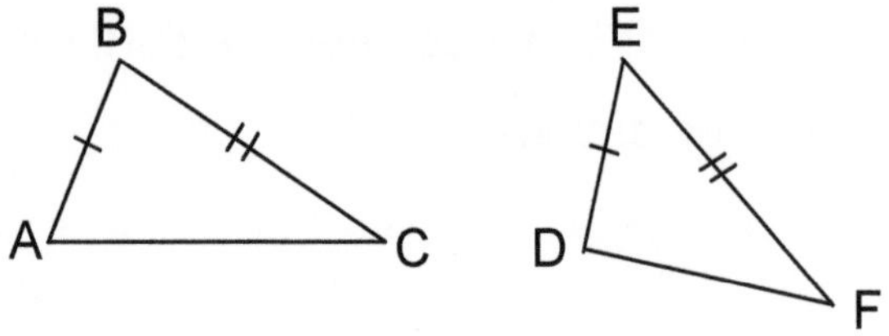

Given: $\overline{AB} \cong \overline{DE}$, $\overline{BC} \cong \overline{EF}$, and AC > DF

Prove: $m\angle B > m\angle E$

We are given that $\overline{AB} \cong \overline{DE}$, $\overline{BC} \cong \overline{EF}$, and AC > DF. Assume that $m\angle B$ is NOT greater than $m\angle E$. Then either $m\angle B = m\angle E$ or $m\angle B < m\angle E$.

Case 1: $m\angle B = m\angle E$

Then, by the ______________________________, $\angle B \cong \angle E$. Then, by the ______________________________, $\Delta ABC \cong \Delta DEF$. This means that ___________________________ by CPCTC. This contradicts what we were given, and so this is impossible.

Case 2: $m\angle B < m\angle E$

Then ____________________ because of the ___________________________ Theorem. This contradicts what we were given, and so this is also impossible.

Hence, $m\angle B$ must be larger than $m\angle E$.

35-41. To complete each of these proofs, you may use either a paragraph proof or the two-column format that we have used in previous chapters.

35. Prove the following theorem: In a right triangle, the longest side is the side opposite the right angle.

Given: ΔGHI is a right triangle with $\angle H$ as its right angle

Prove: GI > GH and GI > HI

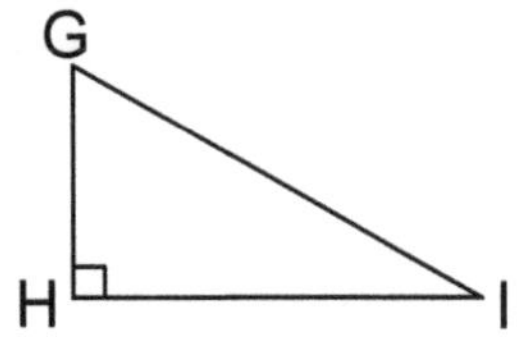

36. Prove the following theorem using an indirect proof: Given a line and a point not on the line, the shortest segment from the point to the line is the perpendicular segment.

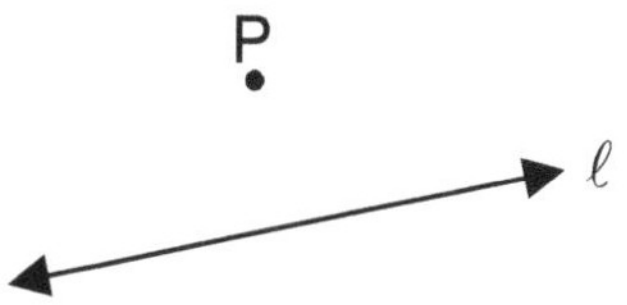

Given: Point P is not on line ℓ

Prove: The shortest segment from P to line ℓ is the perpendicular segment.

Hint: Begin by using the theorem *Through a point P not on a line, there is exactly one line perpendicular to the given line* to note that there is a line that passes through P and is perpendicular to ℓ. Also, you may use the theorem that you proved in #35.

37. In the figure at the right, $\overline{TU} \cong \overline{VW}$, $\overline{TV} \cong \overline{UW}$, and $m\angle TUV < m\angle TVU$. Prove that UW < VW.

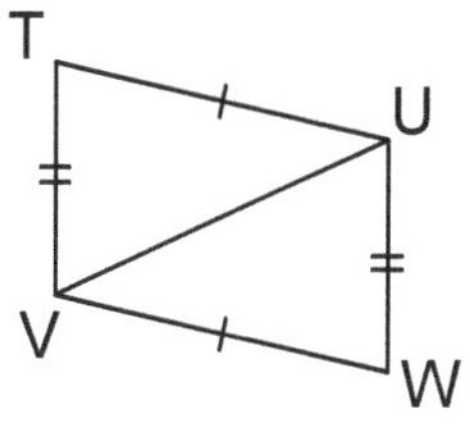

38. Given that BC > CD in the figure at the right, prove that m∠ABC > m∠CBD.

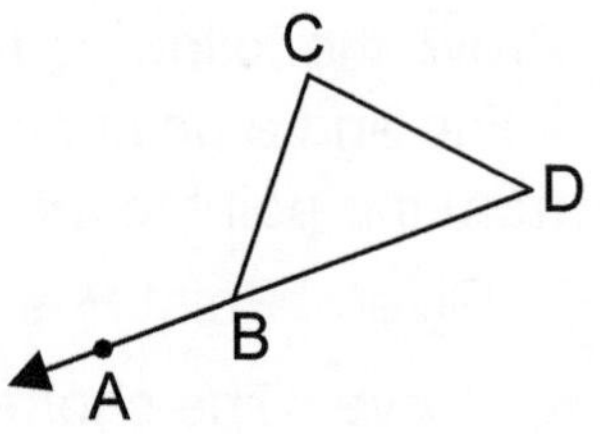

39. In the figure at the right, ∠FIH ≅ ∠FHI, $\overline{EF} \cong \overline{FG}$, and EI > GH. Prove that m∠EFI > m∠GFH.

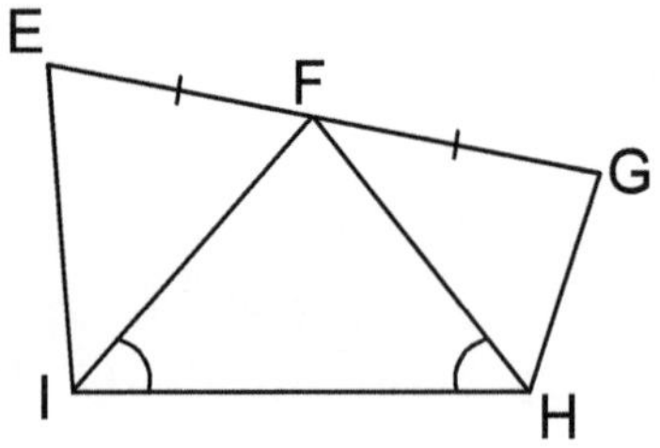

40. In the figure at the right, $\angle J \cong \angle LTJ$. Prove that $LM + MT > LJ$.

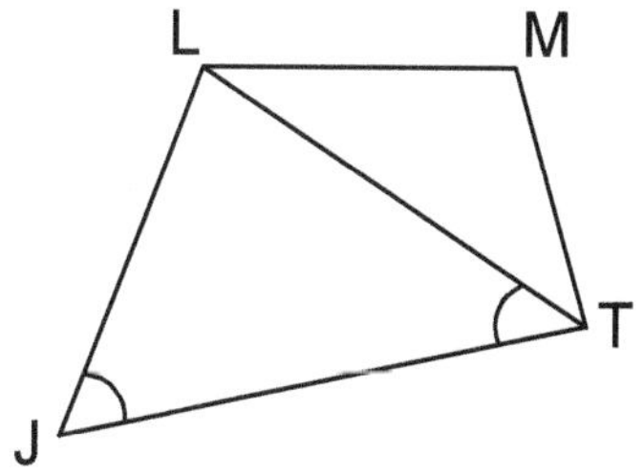

41. In the figure at the right, $\overline{NP} \cong \overline{PQ}$. Prove that $m\angle ONQ > m\angle Q$.

Hint: Note that $OP + NP > ON$.

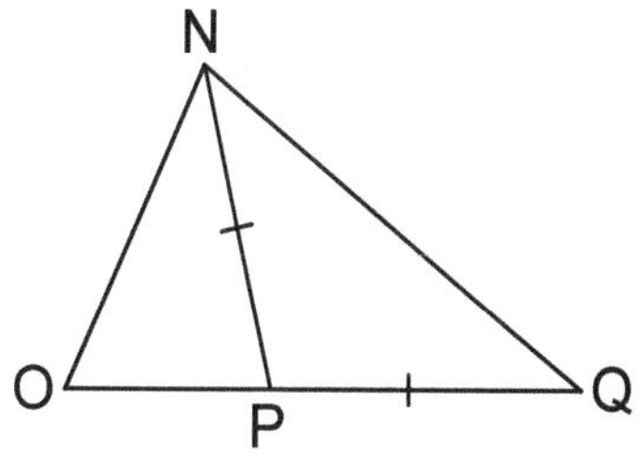

Part II – The Pythagorean Theorem

Before you try to understand the examples in this section, you may find it helpful to look at the sections on solving quadratic equations and simplifying square roots found in Appendix A.

We will begin this section by reviewing the parts of a right triangle. The legs of a right triangle are the sides of the triangle that help form the right angle, and the hypotenuse of a right triangle is the side opposite the right angle.

So, for example, in the figure at the right, we can say that the legs are $\overline{JK}$ and $\overline{KL}$, and we can say that the hypotenuse is $\overline{JL}$.

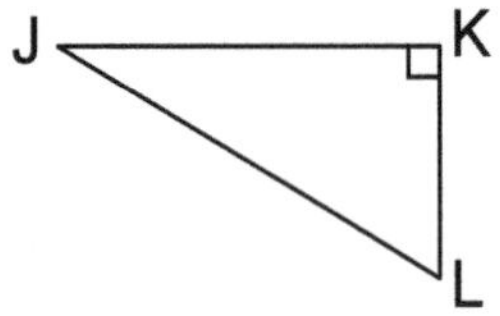

Now, we can discuss one of the most famous theorems in Geometry, the Pythagorean Theorem.

The Pythagorean Theorem

Let a and b represent the lengths of the legs of a right triangle, and let c represent the length of the hypotenuse of the triangle. Then $a^2 + b^2 = c^2$.

There are literally hundreds of ways that this theorem can be proven, and one of them is shown below in the form of a paragraph proof.

Example 1: Prove the Pythagorean Theorem using a paragraph proof.

We will begin by drawing a generic-looking right triangle. We will label the legs a and b, and we will label the hypotenuse c, just as the statement of the Pythagorean Theorem above says we should do.

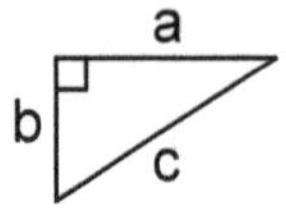

Now, we will draw the following picture.

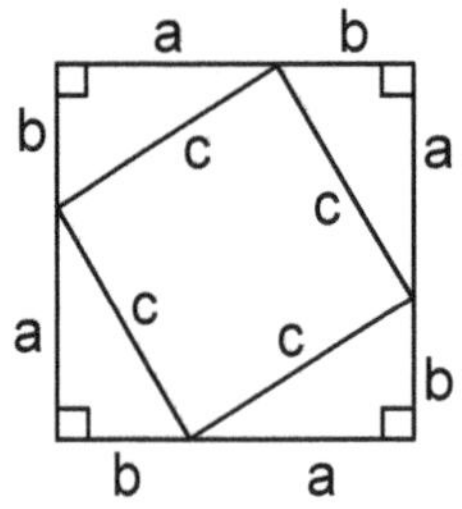

Now, we can say that both the large figure with four sides and the small figure with four sides are squares because each of these figures have four congruent sides and four angles that must measure 90° each. (To see why the smaller figure must have four angles that measure 90° each, recall that the acute angles of a right triangle are complementary.)

Now, we can calculate the area of the big square by noting that it has sides of length (a + b), and so we can say the following.

Area of the big square* = $(a + b)^2$

$= a^2 + 2ab + b^2$

We can also calculate the area of the big square by finding the areas of each of the triangles* and adding the result to the area of the small square.

Area of the big square = $4\left(\frac{1}{2}ab\right) + c^2$

$= 2ab + c^2$

Since both of these calculations were talking about the area of the same square, we can say that they are equal to each other.

$a^2 + 2ab + b^2 = 2ab + c^2$

When we subtract 2ab from both sides of this equation, we find that $a^2 + b^2 = c^2$.

Example 2: Find the value of x in the figure at the right.

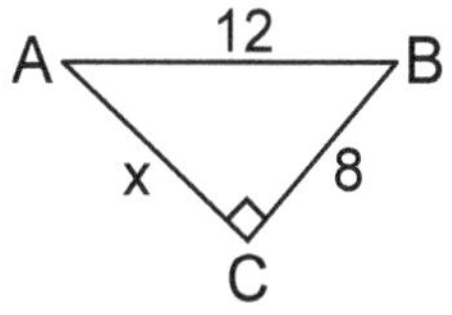

We will begin by noting that the legs of $\triangle ABC$ are $\overline{AC}$ and $\overline{BC}$, and the hypotenuse is $\overline{AB}$. Thus, we can solve this problem by following the steps shown below.

$8^2 + x^2 = 12^2$ Use the Pythagorean Theorem. (We could have written $x^2 + 8^2 = 12^2$ instead; in the end, we would have still come up with the same answer. We could **NOT**, however, have written $8^2 + 12^2 = x^2$ or $12^2 + x^2 = 8^2$.)

$64 + x^2 = 144$

$x^2 = 80$ Subtract 64 from both sides.

$x = \pm 4\sqrt{5}$ Take the square root of both sides.

Since x represents the length of a side of a triangle, and since the lengths of sides of a triangle cannot be negative, x must equal $4\sqrt{5}$.

Example 3: The length of a leg of a right triangle is 4 inches more than four times the length of the other leg, and the length of the hypotenuse is 4 inches shorter than the five times the length of the first leg. Find the length of each side of the triangle.

We can use the information given to us in the problem to draw the following picture.

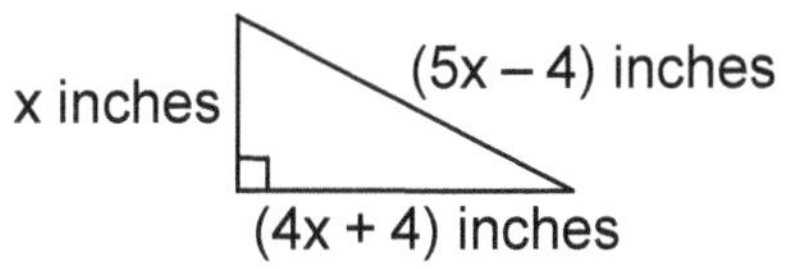

Now, we can use the Pythagorean Theorem to finish solving this problem as shown below. (We will leave off the units for this part of the problem because they only make the problem more confusing.)

$$x^2 + (4x + 4)^2 = (5x - 4)^2$$
$$x^2 + 16x^2 + 32x + 16 = 25x^2 - 40x + 16$$
$$0 = 8x^2 - 72x$$

*Recall that we can use the formula area = (length)(width) to find the area of a square or rectangle, and we can use the formula area = $\frac{1}{2}$(base)(height) to find the area of a triangle.

When we solve this equation using one of the methods discussed in the section on solving quadratic equations in Appendix A, we find that x can equal 0 or 9. However, since x represents the lengths of one of the sides of the triangle, we can say that x cannot equal 0, and so x must equal 9.

Now, recall that we represented the lengths of the sides of the triangle by x inches, (4x + 4) inches, and (5x – 4) inches. This tells us that the lengths of the sides of this triangle are 9 inches, 40 inches, and 41 inches.

Example 5: At 1:00 p.m., Warren leaves a coffee shop and drives due north at an average speed of 42 miles per hour. At the same time, his sister Veronica leaves the same coffee shop and drives due east at an average rate of 56 miles per hour. How far apart are they at 3:00 p.m.?

We will begin by noting that the formula distance = (rate)(time) tells us that Warren will have driven 42 • 2, or 84, miles at 3:00 p.m., and Veronica will have driven 56 • 2, or 112, miles at 3:00 p.m. This means that we can draw the following picture.

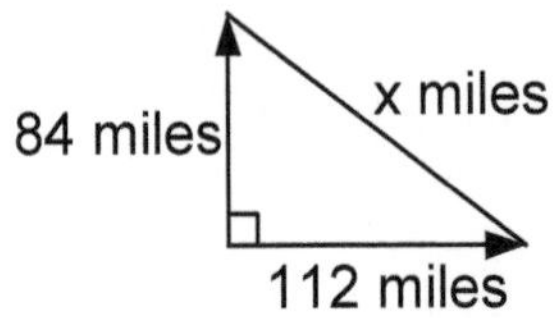

Now, of course, we can use the Pythagorean Theorem as shown below. (Once again, we will leave off our units in this next step because they only make the problem confusing.)

$$84^2 + 112^2 = x^2$$
$$7{,}056 + 12{,}544 = x^2$$
$$19{,}600 = x^2$$
$$\pm 140 = x \quad \text{(by taking the square root of both sides)}$$

Since x represents a distance, and since distances cannot be negative, we can now say that x must equal 140. Therefore, Warren and Veronica must be 140 miles apart at 3:00 p.m.

Now, we need one more theorem. We will not prove it here because the proof is quite complicated.

> Suppose that c represents the length of the longest side of a triangle, and suppose that a and b represent the lengths of the other two sides. Then:
> - If $a^2 + b^2 > c^2$, the triangle is an acute triangle.
> - If $a^2 + b^2 = c^2$, the triangle is a right triangle.
> - If $a^2 + b^2 < c^2$, the triangle is an obtuse triangle.

Example 6: Determine if you can form an *acute triangle*, a *right triangle*, an *obtuse triangle*, or *no triangle* from each set of lengths. (a) 3 feet, 5 feet, and 4 feet; (b) 1 foot, 9 inches, and 8 inches; (c) 7 yards, 7 yards, and 33 feet; (d) 10 meters, 6 meters, and 4 meters

(a) We will begin by noting that, since the longest length must be represented by c, c must equal 5 feet for this part of the problem. Now, we must decide which of the symbols <, >, or = we should put in the blanks below.

$a^2 + b^2$ ____ c^2

$3^2 + 4^2$ ____ 5^2

$9 + 16$ ____ 25

Since an equals symbol belongs in the blank above, we can say that a triangle that has sides with lengths of 3 feet, 5 feet, and 4 feet must be a right triangle.

(b) We will begin by noting that 1 foot = 12 inches. So, to answer this question, we must decide which of the symbols <, >, or = belongs in the blanks below.

$a^2 + b^2$ ____ c^2

$9^2 + 8^2$ ____ 12^2

$81 + 64$ ____ 144

Since a ">" symbol belongs in the blank above, we can say that a triangle that has sides with lengths of 1 foot, 9 inches, and 8 inches must be an acute triangle.

(c) We will begin by noting that 3 feet = 1 yard, and so 33 feet = 11 yards. This tells us that, in order to answer this question, we must decide which of the symbols <, >, or = belongs in the blanks below.

$a^2 + b^2$ ____ c^2

$7^2 + 7^2$ ____ 11^2

$49 + 49$ ____ 121

Since a "<" symbol belongs in the blank above, we will say *for now* that a triangle that has sides with lengths of 7 yards, 7 yards, and 33 feet must be an obtuse triangle.

However, when you are working these problems and you decide that the triangle is an obtuse triangle, you should always check and make sure that the Triangle Inequality Theorem does not tell you that it is impossible to form a triangle with the given lengths. So, before we say that our final answer is an obtuse triangle, we must answer the following questions.

Is $7 + 7 > 11$? yes

Is $11 + 7 > 7$? yes

Is $7 + 11 > 7$? yes

Since the answer to each of these questions was *yes*, we can say that our final answer is that a triangle that has sides with lengths of 7 yards, 7 yards, and 33 feet must be an obtuse triangle.

(d) In order to answer this question, we must decide which of the symbols <, >, or = belongs in the blanks below.

$a^2 + b^2$ ____ c^2

$6^2 + 4^2$ ____ 10^2

$36 + 16$ ____ 100

Since a "<" symbol belongs in the blanks above, we will say *for now* that a triangle that has sides with lengths of 10 meters, 6 meters, and 4 meters must be an obtuse triangle.

However, as we said in part (c) of this example, when you are working these problems and you decide that the triangle is an obtuse triangle, you should always check and make sure that the Triangle Inequality Theorem does not tell you that it is impossible to form a triangle with the given lengths. So, before we say that our final answer is an obtuse triangle, we must answer the following questions.

Is $10 + 6 > 4$? yes

Is $10 + 4 > 6$? yes

Is $6 + 4 > 10$? no

Since the answer to one of these questions was *no*, we can say that our final answer is that there is *no triangle* that has sides with lengths of 10 meters, 6 meters, and 4 meters.

Problems:

1-14. Find the value of x in each of the pictures below. Leave your answers in simplified radical form where necessary.

1. x = ____________

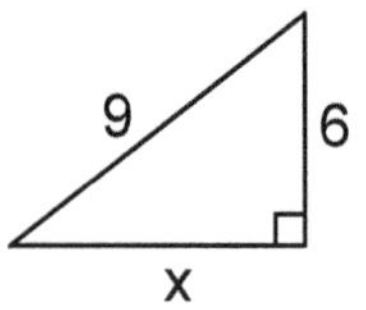

2. x = ____________

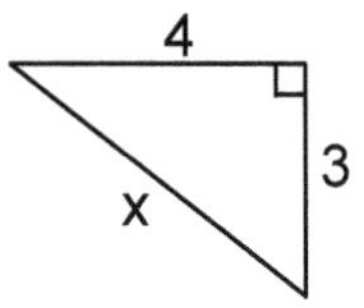

3. x = ____________

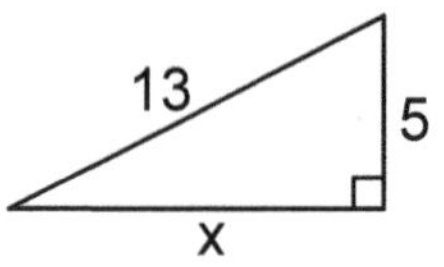

4. x = ____________

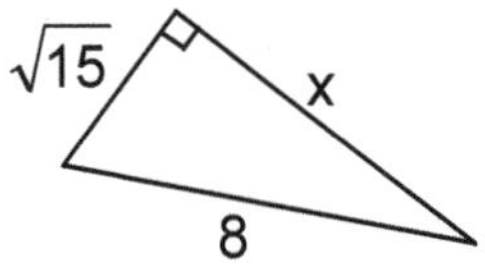

5. x = ___________

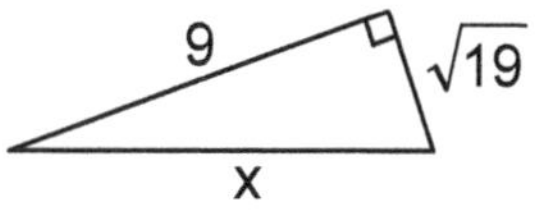

6. x = ___________

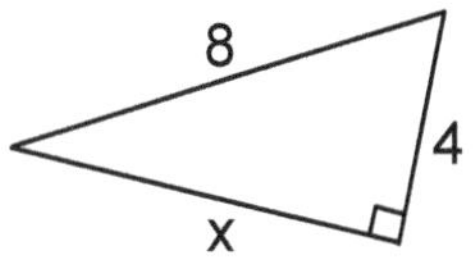

7. x = ___________

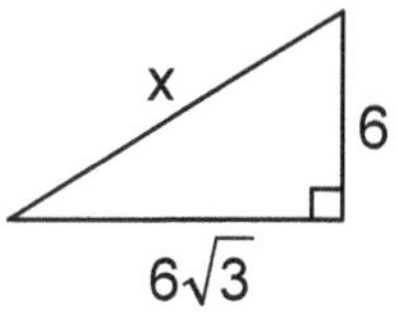

8. x = ___________

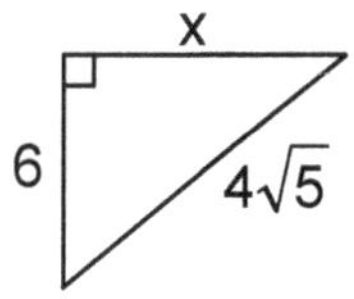

9. x = ___________

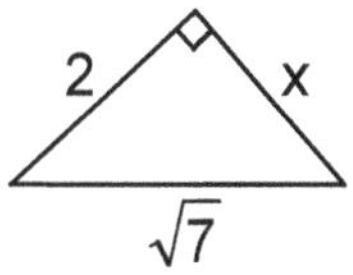

10. x = ___________

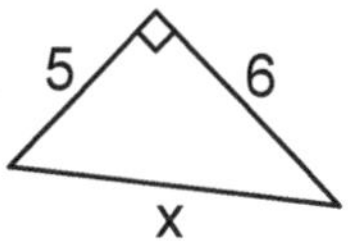

11. x = ___________

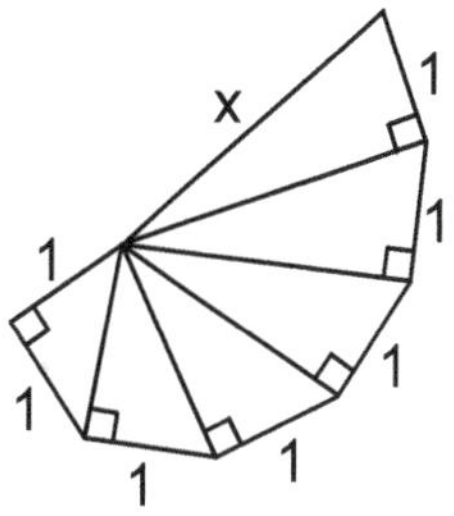

12. x = ___________

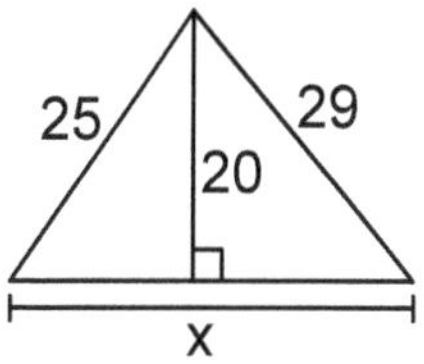

13. x = ___________

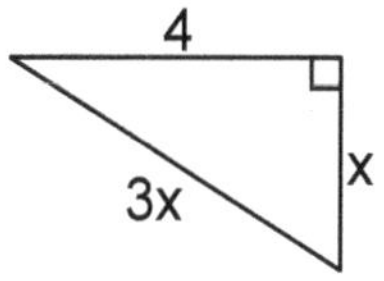

14. x = ___________

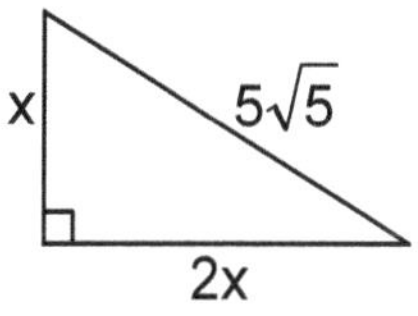

15-24. Determine whether a triangle with each set of given side lengths must be an *acute triangle*, a *right triangle*, an *obtuse triangle*, or *no triangle*.

15. 8 feet, 15 feet, 17 feet ___________

16. 9 inches, 9 inches, 4 inches ___________

17. 5 meters, 6 meters, 7 meters ___________

18. 1 kilometer, 2 kilometers, 3 kilometers ___________

19. 4 miles, 8 miles, 9 miles ___________

20. 1 foot, 1 foot, 17 inches ___________

21. 45 inches, 21 inches, 17 inches ___________

22. $3\sqrt{5}$ centimeters, $4\sqrt{5}$ centimeters, $5\sqrt{5}$ centimeters ___________

23. $6\sqrt{3}$ yards, 15 yards, 10 yards ___________

24. 3 feet, 3 feet, $3\sqrt{2}$ feet ___________

25-44. For each of these problems, round your answers to the nearest tenth where necessary.

25. A rectangle has a length of 7 inches and a width of 12 inches. What is the length of a diagonal? (A diagonal starts at one corner of the rectangle and goes to the opposite corner.) ___________

26. The length of a diagonal of a square is 12 meters. What is the length of one side? ___________

27. In a rectangular prism (such as the one shown at the right), the diagonal of the prism starts at one corner of the prism and goes to the opposite corner. For instance, the diagonals of the prism at the right are $\overline{AG}$, $\overline{BH}$, $\overline{CE}$, and $\overline{DF}$.

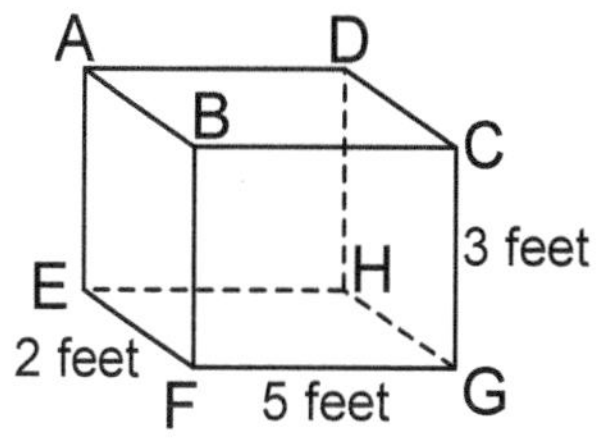

a. Find the distance from H to B. ___________
Hint: Begin by drawing $\overline{HF}$.

b. Find the distance from C to E. ___________

28. Find the length of a diagonal of the rectangular prism at the right. ___________

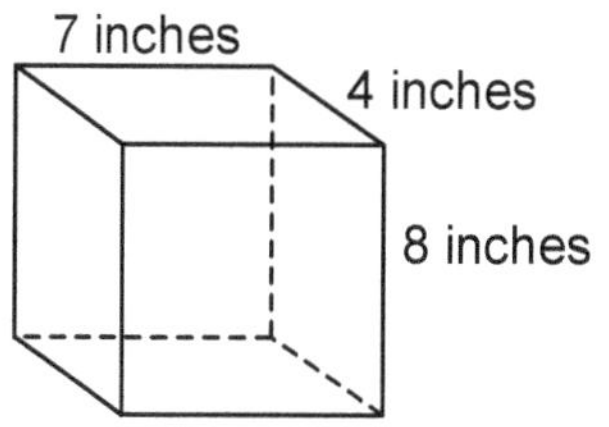

29. Find the length of a diagonal of a rectangular prism that has a length of 6 meters, a width of 2 meters, and a height of 9 meters. ___________

30. A rectangular prism at the right has a length of L meters, a width of W meters, and a height of H meters. What is the length of a diagonal of the prism?

____

31. The sides of a right triangle have lengths that are consecutive even integers. How long are the sides of the triangle? _________, __________, and __________

32. In a certain right triangle, the length of the longer leg is five inches more than the length of the shorter leg. If the length of the hypotenuse is five inches less than twice the length of the shorter leg, what are the lengths of the sides of the triangle? ________ inches, ________ inches, and ________ inches

33. Televisions are measured in terms of the length of the diagonal from a top corner to the opposite bottom corner. Owen is considering buying a new television. He knows that his current television is a 27-inch television, and he knows that the length-to-width ratio of his current television is 4 : 3. He also knows that this television barely fits in his entertainment cabinet. Will a 26-inch television that has a length-to-width ratio of 16 : 9 fit in his entertainment cabinet? _________

Current Television

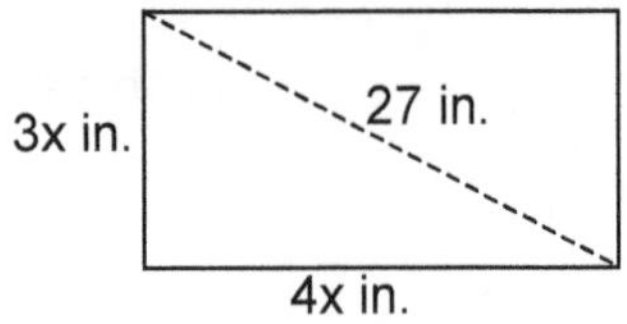

New Television

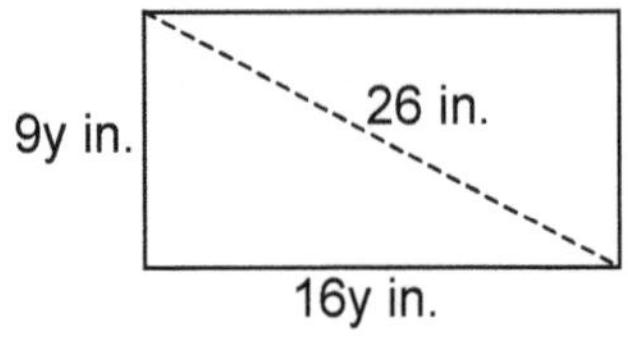

34. A ladder that is 30 feet long needs to reach the roof of a house that is 20 feet high. If the tip of the ladder needs to just barely reach the roof of the house, how far from the base of the house should the base of the ladder be placed?

____

35. A ladder that is 25 feet long is leaning against a house so that it just barely reaches a second story window of the house. If the base of the ladder is 10 feet away from the wall, how high above the ground is the bottom of the window? ___________

36. Refer back to #35. If the base of the ladder slides backward 4 feet, how far down the side of the house will the tip of the ladder slide? Hint: The correct answer is not 4 feet. ___________

37. A plane leaves an airport and flies due north at a speed of 400 kilometers per hour. At the same time, another jet leaves the same airport and flies due west at a speed of 420 kilometers per hour. How far apart are the jets after one hour and thirty minutes? ___________

38. Refer back to #37. How long will it be before the two planes are 2320 kilometers apart? ___________

39. Caleb left a restaurant at 5:00 p.m. and drove due east at an average speed of 48 miles per hour. Two hours later, Dwayne left the same restaurant and drove due north at an average speed of 60 miles per hour. At what time were they exactly 300 miles apart? ___________

40. Juan drives due north at an average speed of j kilometers per hour, and Kathryn drives due west at an average speed of k kilometers per hour. After 3 hours, they are 250 kilometers apart.

a. Find a formula for j. j = ____________

b. Find a set of values for j and k. (There are many correct answers.)

j = ____________ and k = ____________

41. At 11:00 a.m., Al leaves a port in his sailboat and travels due south at an average speed of 9 miles per hour. At the same time, Carl leaves the same port and travels due east at an average speed of 12 miles per hour.

a. How far apart are they at 1:00 p.m.? ____________

b. At 1:00 p.m., Carl realizes he left his dinner in Al's boat. How fast must Carl travel if he wants to meet up with Al at 4:00 p.m.? ____________ About how fast must Carl travel if he wants to meet up with Al at 6:00 p.m.? ____________ (Keep in mind that Al will continue heading south at an average speed of 9 miles per hour.)

42. What is the longest pole that can fit in a box that is 5 meters long, 2 meters high, and 4 meters wide? ____________

43. At practice every day, each player on the Central High School varsity basketball team normally runs 16 laps from one corner of their court to the opposite corner of the court and back (in the diagram at the right, from point A to point B and back). However, the junior varsity basketball team has shown up today, and now the varsity team cannot use part of the court to run laps. If the coach decides to have each player on the team run from point A to point C and back, how many laps should the coach have his players run in order to equal the distance that the players normally run? ___________ If the coach decides to have each player on the team run from point A to point D and back, how many laps should the coach have his players run in order to equal the distance that the players normally run? ___________

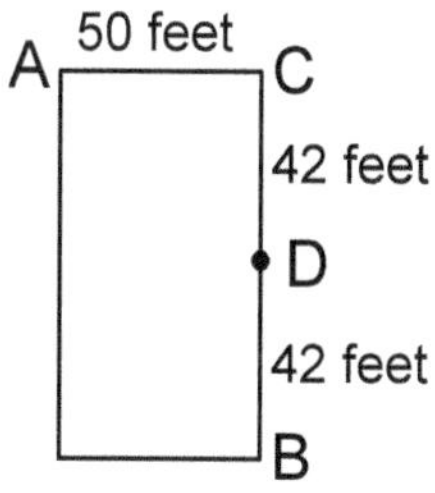

44. The figure at the right shows a part of the town of Uma. The city's library is located at point A, and the town hall is located at point B. Currently, if a person wants to travel from the town hall to the library, the person must travel 4.2 miles west along Main Street and then 2.8 miles north along Highway 20. If the town cuts a road directly from the town hall to the library (shown by the dotted lines in the picture), how much distance would this save a person traveling from the town hall to the library? _________

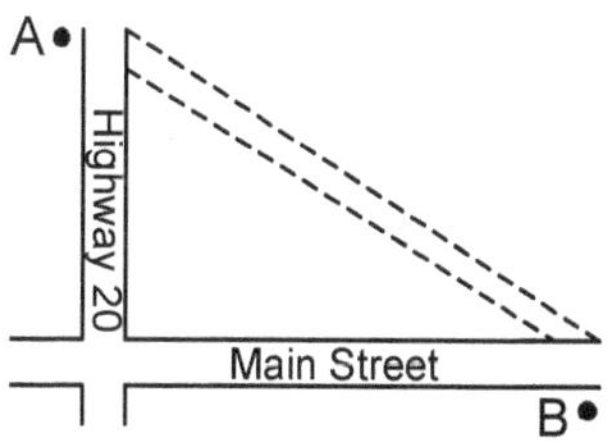

45. In the figure at the right, x = _________ and y = _________. (Leave your answers in simplified radical form where necessary.)

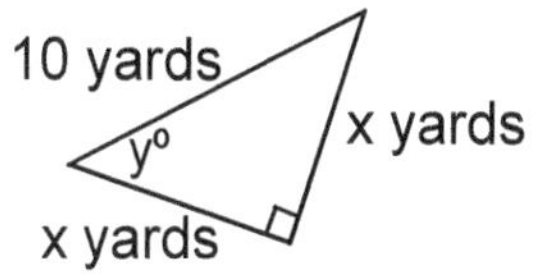

Part III – Special Segments in Triangles

We will begin this section with a definition.

> A line, segment or ray is called a perpendicular bisector of a triangle if and only if it passes through the midpoint of one of the sides and is perpendicular to that side of the triangle.

Example 1: Draw the perpendicular bisectors of each of the triangles below.

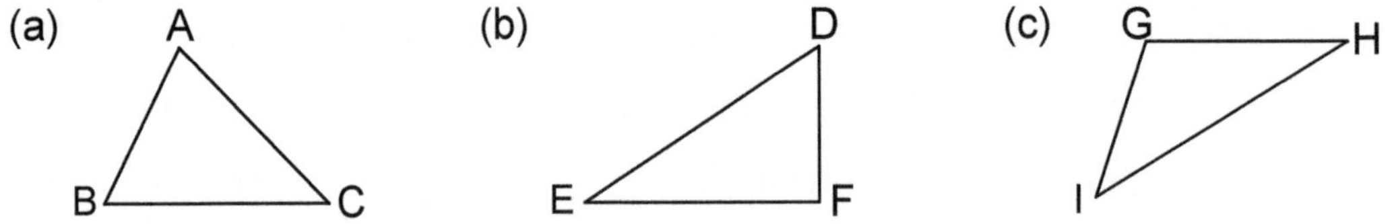

We will begin by noting that, as you will see in these examples, there are three perpendicular bisectors in any triangle.

(a) We will begin by finding the midpoint of $\overline{BC}$ and labeling it point J. We will also draw a segment that passes through J and is perpendicular to $\overline{BC}$.

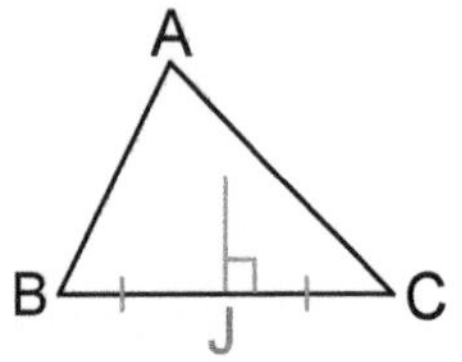

For the next perpendicular bisector, we will find the midpoint of $\overline{AC}$ and label it point K. We will draw a segment through point K that is perpendicular to $\overline{AC}$.

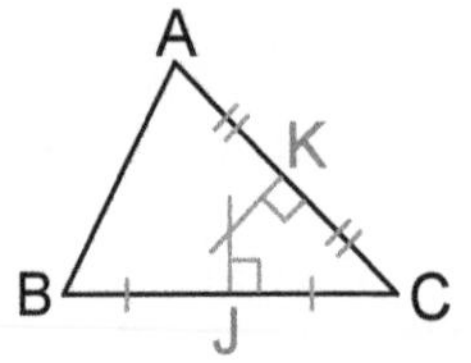

For the third and final perpendicular bisector, we will find the midpoint of $\overline{AB}$, and we will label it point L. We will also draw a segment perpendicular to $\overline{AB}$ that passes through L.

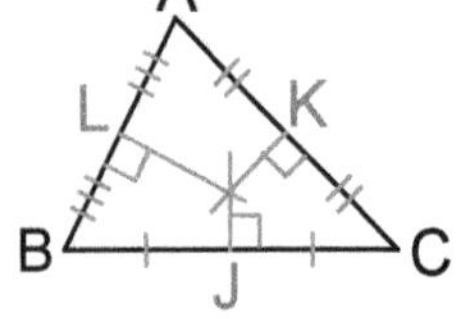

(b) We can draw the perpendicular bisectors of this triangle as shown on the next page. In this figure, the gray segments are the perpendicular bisectors.

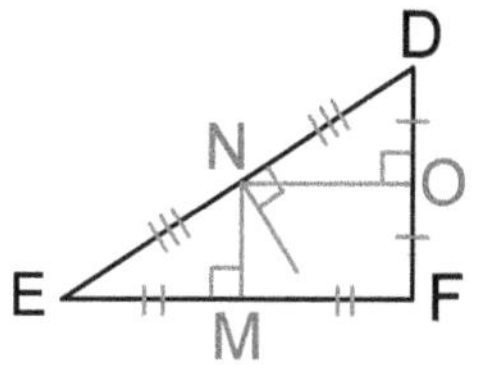

(c) We can draw the perpendicular bisectors of ΔGHI as shown in the figure below. In this figure, the gray segments are the perpendicular bisectors.

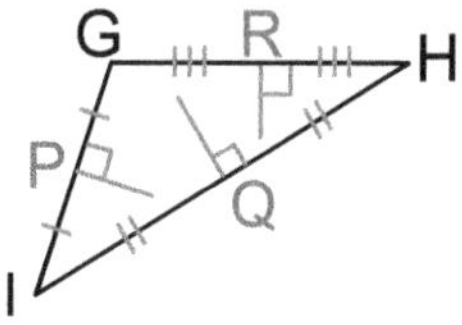

Notice how, in each of these pictures, the perpendicular bisectors all cross each other in one point. (In part (c), you need to extend the segments to a point outside the triangle, but they will, in fact, cross each other at a single point.) We say that this means that they are concurrent. These examples suggest that the three perpendicular bisectors of any triangle are concurrent, and, in fact, they are, as the next theorem tells us.

Concurrency of the Perpendicular Bisectors of a Triangle
The three perpendicular bisectors of a triangle will always cross each other in a single point, called the circumcenter of the triangle.

This theorem is difficult to prove, and so we will not worry about it here. We will, however, state another theorem that this idea leads to. You will prove this theorem in the problems for this section.

The distance from the circumcenter of a triangle to a vertex of the triangle is the same as the distance from the circumcenter to either of the other two vertices.

To understand what this theorem is telling you, let's look back at the final figure we drew for part (a) of Example 1. We will draw it again here, and we will label the circumcenter point S.

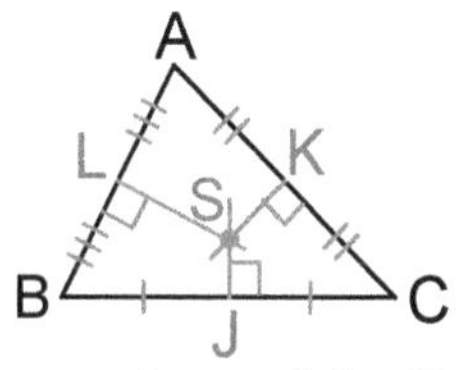

This theorem tells us that the distance from A to S is equal to the distance from B to S, and both distances are equal to the distance from C to S.

By the way, this theorem leads to a discussion of why we call the point where the perpendicular bisectors intersect the *circumcenter*. This theorem tells us that we can draw a *circumscribed* circle around a triangle with the circumcenter as the center of the circle. (A circle circumscribed around a triangle is a circle where all of the vertices of the triangle are on the circle.)

Now, we need another definition.

> A line, segment, or ray is called an <u>angle bisector</u> of a triangle if and only if it bisects one of the angles of the triangle.

Example 2: Draw the angle bisectors of each of the triangles below.

(a) 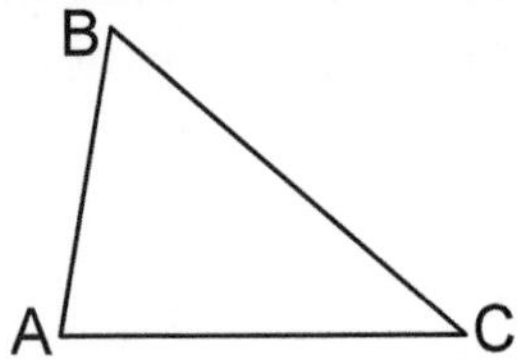

(b) 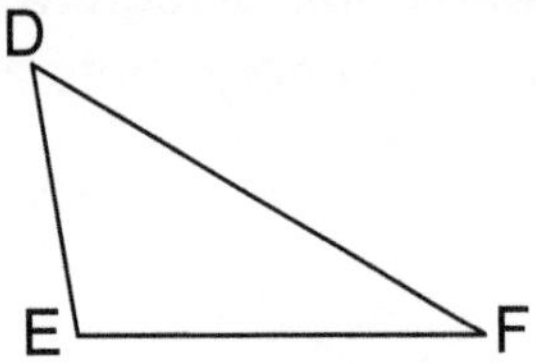

(a) Since each angle bisector of a triangle must bisect an angle of the triangle, the gray segments in the figure below represent the angle bisectors of the triangle.

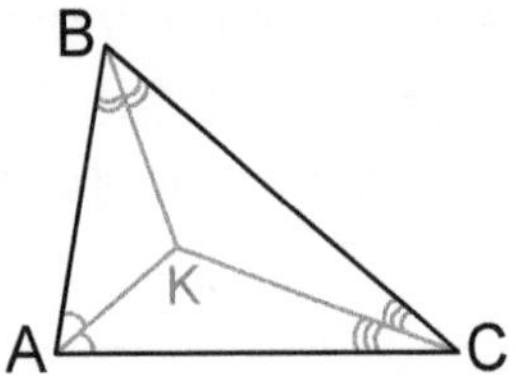

(b) The gray segments in the figure below represent the angle bisectors of $\triangle DEF$.

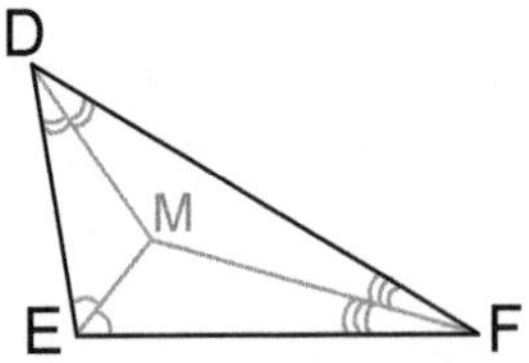

You might notice that, just like the perpendicular bisectors of a triangle are concurrent, the angle bisectors of a triangle are also concurrent. This gives rise to another theorem.

> **Concurrency of the Angle Bisectors of a Triangle**
> The three angle bisectors of a triangle will always cross each other in a single point, called the <u>incenter</u> of the triangle.

This theorem is also very difficult to prove, and so we will not worry about it here. We will, however, state another theorem that this leads to. Before we can do this, however, we need to define what we mean when we talk about the distance from a point to a line.

> To find the distance from a point P to a line $\overleftrightarrow{AB}$, you must first draw $\overline{PQ}$, where the point Q is on $\overleftrightarrow{AB}$ and $\overline{PQ} \perp \overleftrightarrow{AB}$. The distance from P to $\overleftrightarrow{AB}$ is equal to the length of $\overline{PQ}$.

For example, look at the figure at the right. In order to find the distance from point T to line ℓ, we must first draw $\overline{TQ}$ as shown below.

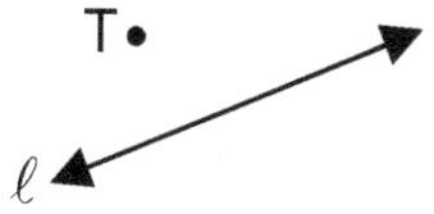

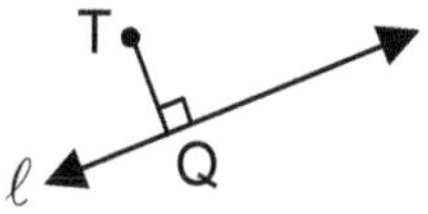

In this figure, the distance from the point T to line ℓ is equal to the length of $\overline{TQ}$.

Now, we need one more theorem. You will prove this theorem in the exercises for this section.

> The distance from the incenter of a triangle to a side of the triangle is the same as the distance from the incenter to either of the other two sides of the triangle.

To understand what this theorem is telling us, we have redrawn the figure from part (a) of Example 2 below. We have also drawn $\overline{KX}$, $\overline{KW}$, and $\overline{KY}$ to represent the distance from the incenter (point K) to the sides of the triangle.

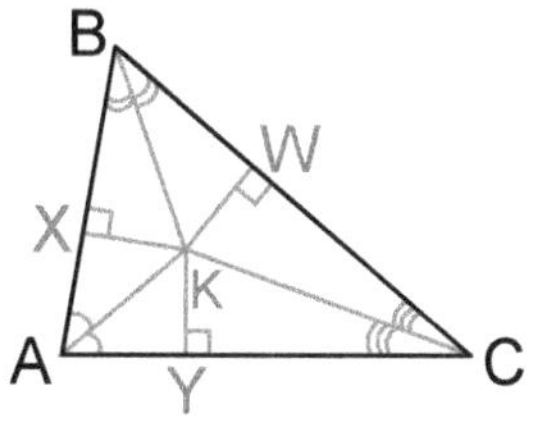

The theorem above tells us that KY = KX = KW in this picture.

Problems:

1. Draw the perpendicular bisectors in the triangle below.

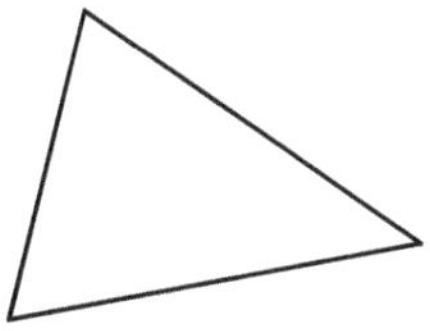

2. Draw the perpendicular bisectors in the triangle below.

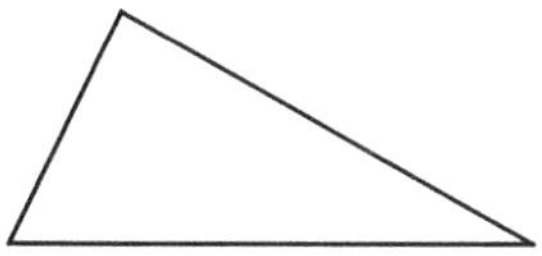

3. Draw the perpendicular bisectors in the triangle below.

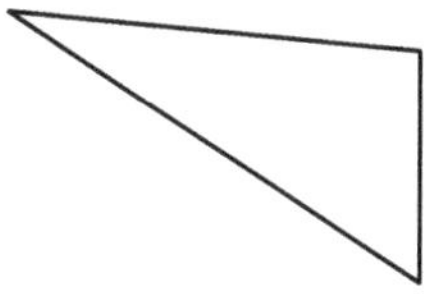

4. Draw the angle bisectors in the triangle below.

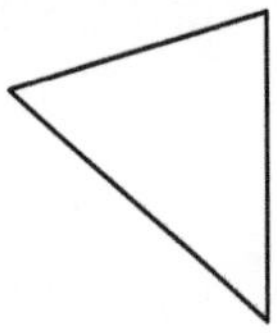

5. Draw the angle bisectors in the triangle below.

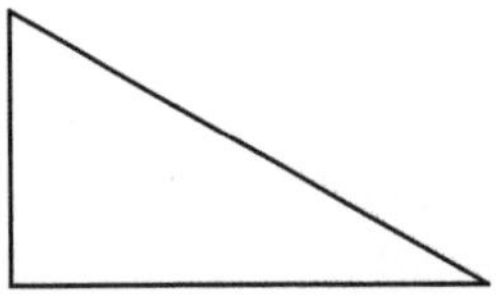

6. Draw the angle bisectors in the triangle below.

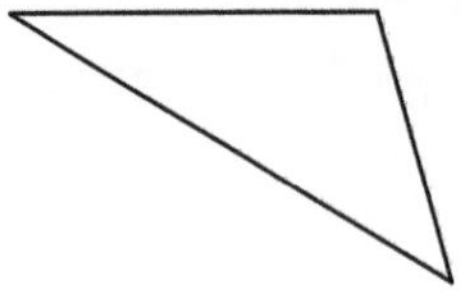

7-12. In the figure at the right, $\overline{AB} \perp \overline{BD}$, $\overline{AE} \perp \overline{CD}$, and $\overline{BC} \perp \overline{CD}$. Name the segment whose length represents the distance from the given point to the given segment.

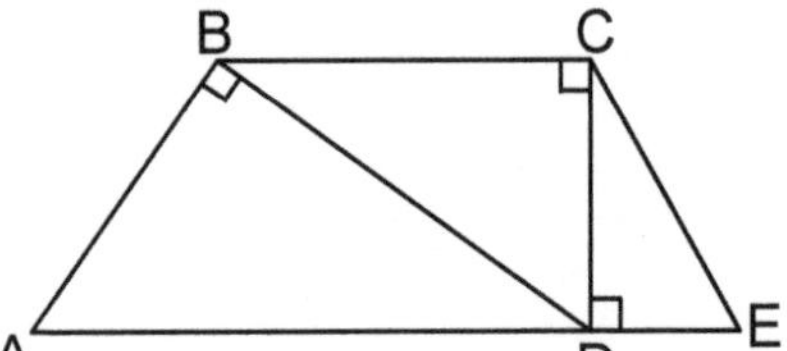

7. A to $\overline{CD}$ ____________

8. C to $\overline{AE}$ ____________

9. D to $\overline{AB}$ ____________

10. B to $\overline{CD}$ ____________

11. E to $\overline{CD}$ ____________

12. D to $\overline{BC}$ ____________

13-24. Fill in each of the following blanks with *always*, *sometimes*, or *never*.

13. If a segment is a perpendicular bisector of a triangle, then it is ____________ an angle bisector of the triangle.

14. If a segment is an angle bisector of a triangle, then it is ____________ a perpendicular bisector of the triangle.

15. If a segment is an angle bisector of a triangle, then it _____________ divides one of the angles of the triangle into two congruent angles.

16. If a segment is a perpendicular bisector of a triangle, then it _____________ divides one of the sides of the triangle into two congruent segments.

17. If a segment is a perpendicular bisector of a triangle, then it _____________ forms a right angle with one of the sides of the triangle.

18. If a segment is a perpendicular bisector of a triangle, then it _____________ forms a right angle with two sides of the triangle.

19. If a segment is an angle bisector of a triangle, then it _____________ forms a right angle with one of the sides of the triangle.

20. If a segment is an angle bisector of a triangle, then it _____________ divides one of the sides of the triangle into two congruent segments.

21. If a point P is the circumcenter of $\triangle ABC$, then PA _____________ equals PB.

22. If a point P is the incenter of $\triangle ABC$, then PA _____________ equals PB.

23. If a line is an angle bisector of a triangle, then it _____________ passes through a vertex (or corner) of the triangle.

24. If a line is a perpendicular bisector of a triangle, then it _____________ passes through a vertex (or corner) of the triangle.

25-30. In the figure at the right, $\overline{JD}$, $\overline{HD}$, and $\overline{LD}$ are perpendicular bisectors of ΔABC.

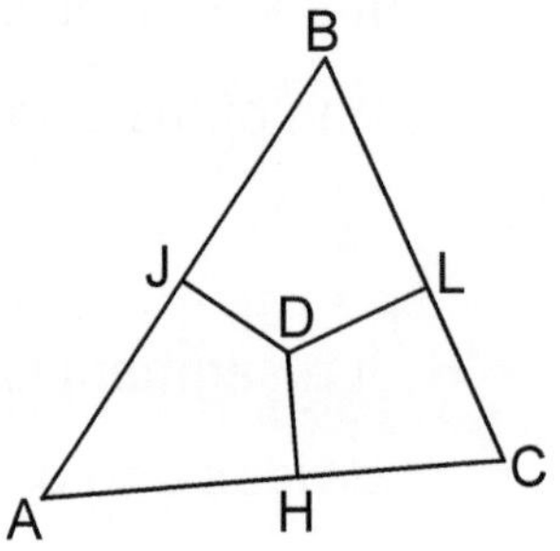

25. $m\angle CLD$ = __________

26. If $m\angle DJA = (7x + 6)^\circ$, then x = __________.

27. If JA = 19 inches, then AB = ________ inches and JB = ________ inches.

28. If AH = 5y – 2 and HC = 4y + 12, then y = ________ and AC = ________.

29. If AD = 15 feet, then BD = ________ feet and DC = ________ feet.

30. If AD = 15 inches and AH = 12 inches, then HD = ________ inches.

31-35. In the figure at the right, $\overline{PS}$, $\overline{SQ}$, and $\overline{RS}$ are angle bisectors of ΔPQR.

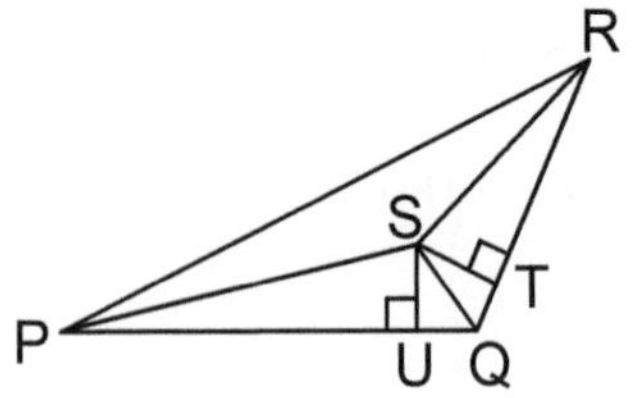

31. If $m\angle RPQ = 30^\circ$, then $m\angle RPS$ = ________ and $m\angle SPQ$ = ________.

32. If $m\angle PRS = 18^\circ$, then $m\angle PRQ$ = ________ and $m\angle QRS$ = ________.

33. If $m\angle PQS = (4x - 3)^\circ$ and $m\angle SQR = (2x + 27)^\circ$, then x = ________ and $m\angle PQR$ = ________.

34. If $m\angle PRQ = (3y + 1)^\circ$ and $m\angle PRS = (2y - 4)^\circ$, then y = ________ and $m\angle SRT$ = ________.

35. If SU = 8 centimeters, then ST = ________ centimeters.

36. Prove the following theorem: The distance from the circumcenter of a triangle to a vertex of the triangle is the same as the distance from the circumcenter to either of the other two vertices. (We assume here that the circumcenter is inside the triangle. If it is not, only the picture will change.)

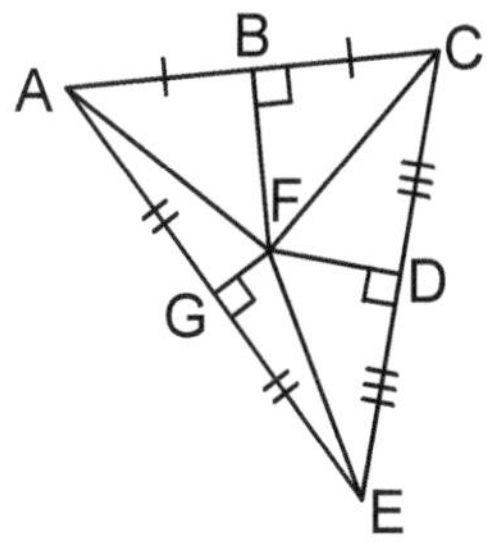

Given: $\overline{GF}$, $\overline{BF}$, and $\overline{DF}$ are perpendicular bisectors of $\triangle ACE$

Prove: AF = EF = CF

37. Prove the following theorem: The distance from the incenter of a triangle to a side of the triangle is the same as the distance from the incenter to either of the other two sides of the triangle.

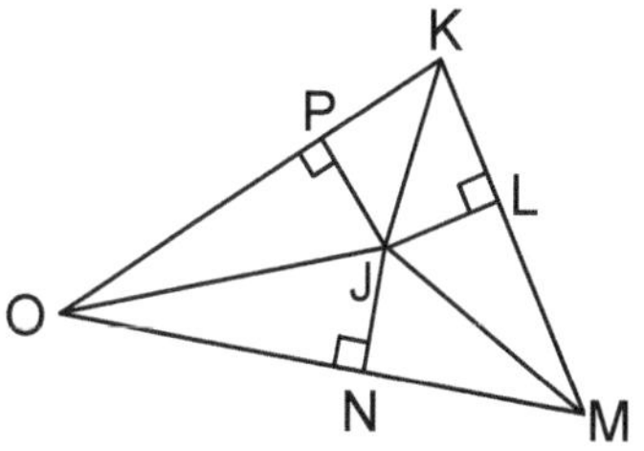

Given: Point J is the incenter of $\triangle KOM$, $\overline{JP} \perp \overline{KO}$, $\overline{JL} \perp \overline{KM}$, and $\overline{JN} \perp \overline{OM}$

Prove: JN = JP = JL

Part IV – More Special Segments in Triangles

We will begin this section with another definition.

> A segment is a <u>median</u> of a triangle if and only if it connects a vertex of the triangle and the midpoint of the opposite side.

Example 1: Draw the medians in each of the triangles below.

(a)

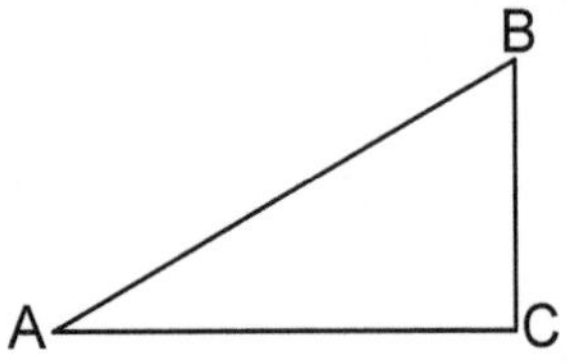

(b)

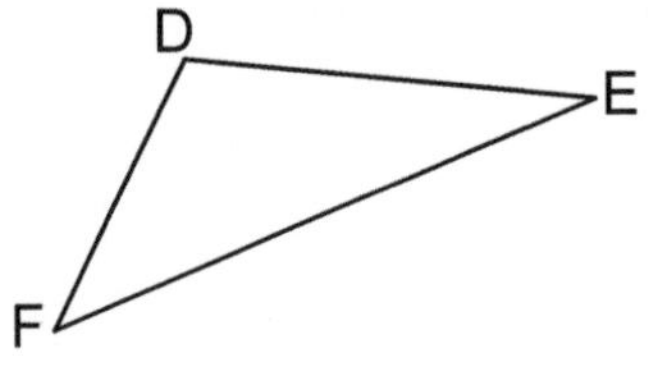

(a) To draw the first median of this triangle, we will begin by finding the midpoint of $\overline{AB}$. We will label it point P and then draw $\overline{CP}$.

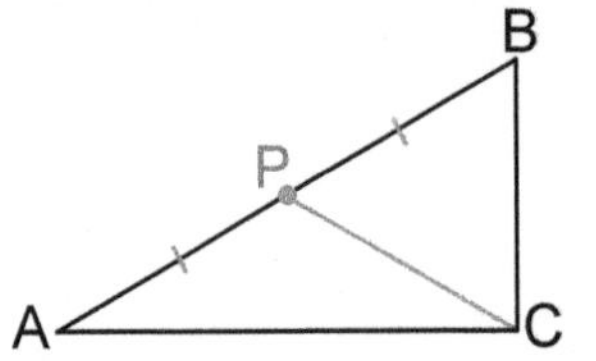

To draw the second median, we will find the midpoint of $\overline{AC}$, label it point Q, and then draw $\overline{BQ}$. To draw the third and final median, we will find the midpoint of $\overline{BC}$, label it point R, and then draw $\overline{AR}$.

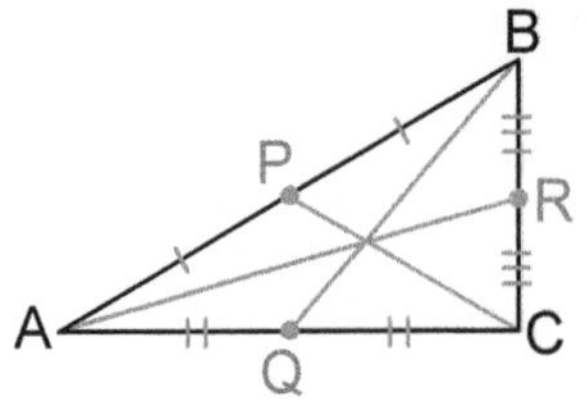

(b) The medians of this triangle are $\overline{EJ}$, $\overline{DK}$, and $\overline{FL}$ shown in the figure below.

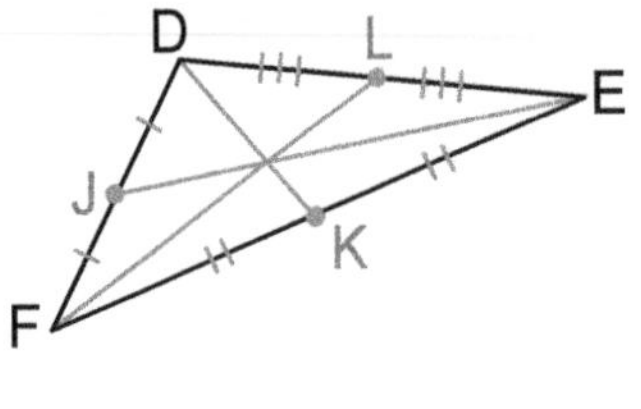

As you can see from these examples, the medians of a triangle all cross each other in a single point (just like we said for the perpendicular bisectors and the angle bisectors of a triangle).

> **Concurrency of the Medians of a Triangle**
>
> The three angle medians of a triangle will always cross each other in a single point, called the <u>centroid</u> of the triangle.

The centroid is also called the <u>center of mass</u> or the <u>balance point</u> of the triangle because you can balance a triangle on the tip of a pencil (or something similar) by placing the tip of the pencil at the centroid.

Now, we need another theorem about the medians of a triangle. This theorem is also difficult to prove, and so we will not worry about the proof here.

> The centroid of a triangle divides each median into two segments. For each median, the distance from the vertex to the centroid is equal to $\frac{2}{3}$ of the length of the entire median.

Example 2: In the figure at the right, $\overline{HU}$, $\overline{IN}$, and $\overline{GS}$ are medians of ΔGHI. (a) Suppose that $HN = 5x$, $GN = x + 28$, and $GU = 45 - x$. Find the length of $\overline{GI}$. (b) Suppose that $HT = 12$. Find the length of $\overline{TU}$. (c) Suppose that $TI = y + 32$ and $NT = 2y + 25$. Find the length of $\overline{IN}$.

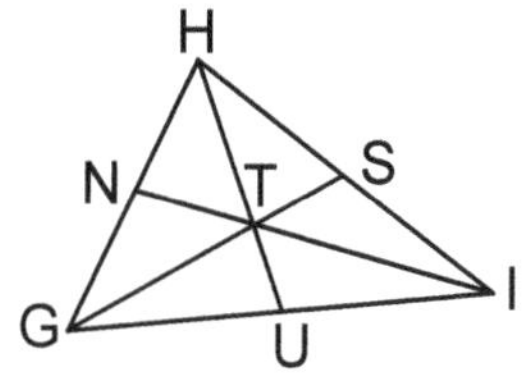

(a) Since $\overline{IN}$ is a median of ΔGHI, we can say that $\overline{GN} \cong \overline{HN}$. This means that we can say that $x + 28 = 5x$, and so x must equal 7. This tells us that $GU = 45 - 7$, or 38. Since $\overline{HU}$ is a median of ΔGHI, we know that $\overline{GU} \cong \overline{UI}$, and so UI must also equal 38. Hence, the length of $\overline{GI}$ must equal 38 + 38, or 74, units.

(b) We can use the theorem above to say that $HT = \frac{2}{3} \cdot HU$. Since we were told that $HT = 12$, we can say that $12 = \frac{2}{3} \cdot HU$. When we divide both sides of this equation by $\frac{2}{3}$, we find that HU must equal 18. Since $TU = HU - HT$, $\overline{TU}$ must be 6 units long.

(c) We can use the theorem above to say that $TI = \frac{2}{3} \cdot NI$. This means that $NT = \frac{1}{3} \cdot NI$, and so $\overline{TI}$ must be twice as long as $\overline{NT}$. This means that we can say that $y + 32 = 2(2y + 25)$. When we solve this equation for y, we find that $y = -6$. Therefore, $TI = -6 + 32$ (or 26), and $NT = 2 \cdot -6 + 25$ (or 13). Since $IN = TI + NT$, $\overline{IN}$ must be 39 units long.

Now, we need another definition.

> A segment is an <u>altitude</u> of a triangle if and only if it has an endpoint at a vertex and is perpendicular to the side of the triangle opposite that vertex (or the line that contains the side of the triangle opposite that vertex).

Example 3: Draw the altitudes of each of the triangles below.

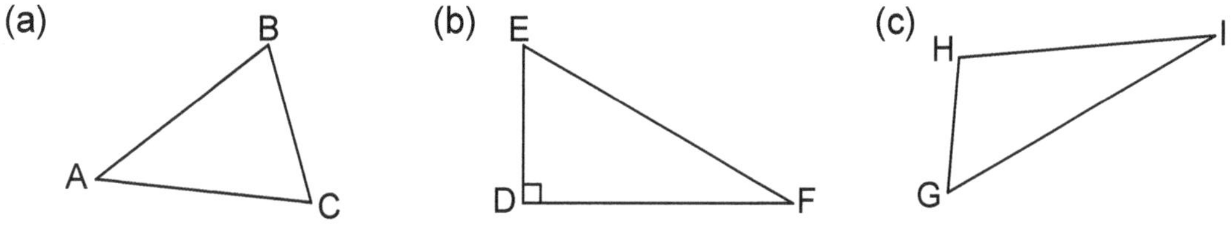

(a) To draw the first altitude of this triangle, we will start at point B and draw a segment perpendicular to $\overline{AC}$.

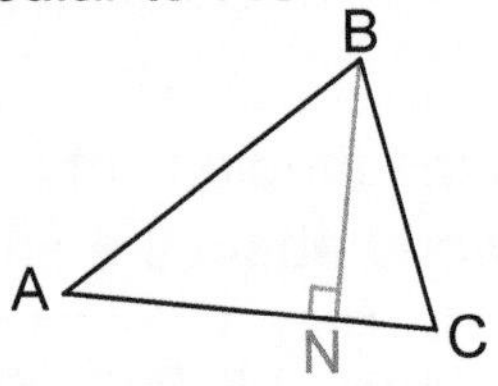

Now, to draw the next altitude, we will start at C and draw a segment perpendicular to $\overline{AB}$. To draw the third altitude, we will start at A and draw a segment perpendicular to $\overline{BC}$. This gives us the picture below.

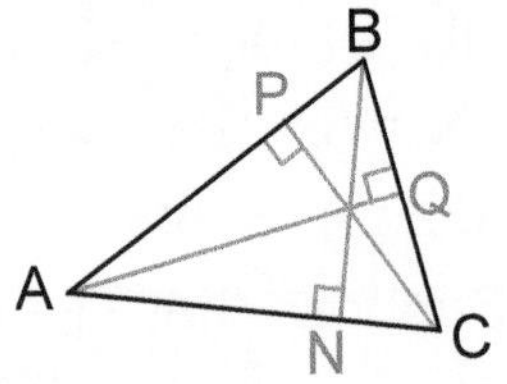

(b) To draw our first altitude for this triangle, we will start at D and draw a segment perpendicular to $\overline{EF}$, as shown below.

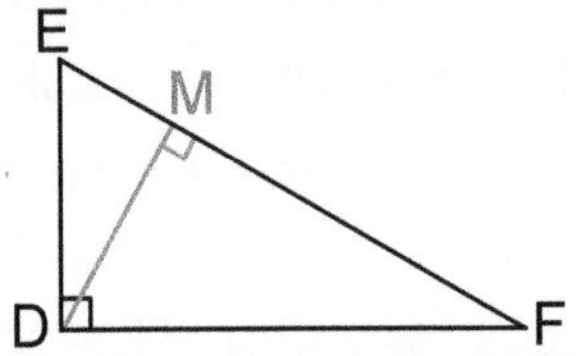

The other two altitudes are a little difficult to see. To start at E and draw a segment perpendicular to $\overline{DF}$, we must follow $\overline{ED}$. To start at F and draw a segment perpendicular to $\overline{ED}$, we must follow $\overline{FD}$. This tells us that the altitudes of this triangle are shown in gray in the picture below.

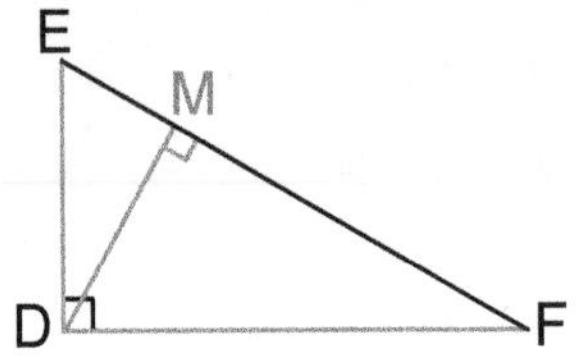

(c) To draw the altitude of $\triangle GHI$ that starts at H, we will start at H and draw a segment perpendicular to $\overline{GI}$.

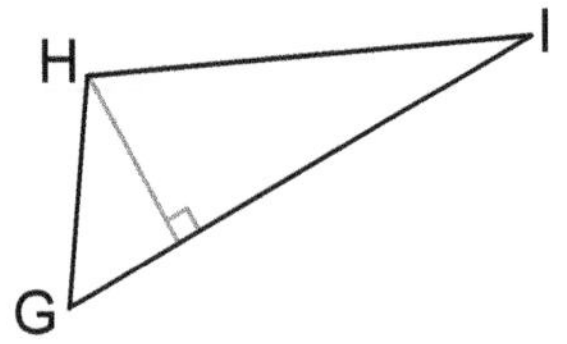

To draw the altitude of this triangle that starts at G, we must first extend $\overline{HI}$.

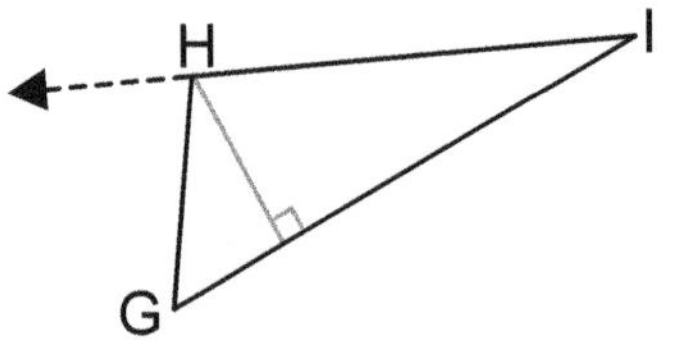

Now, we can draw the altitude of this triangle that starts at G as shown below.

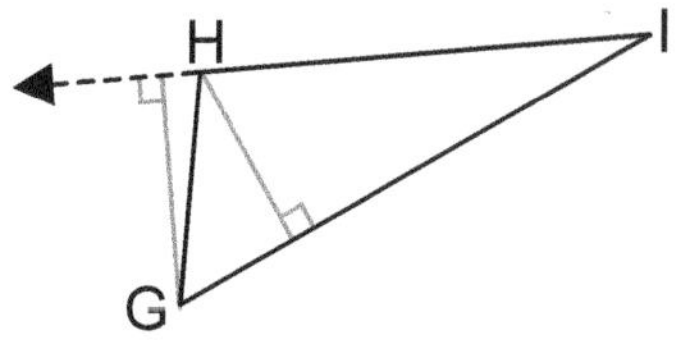

To draw the altitude of ΔGHI that starts at I, we must first extend $\overline{HG}$, and then we can draw the final altitude of this triangle.

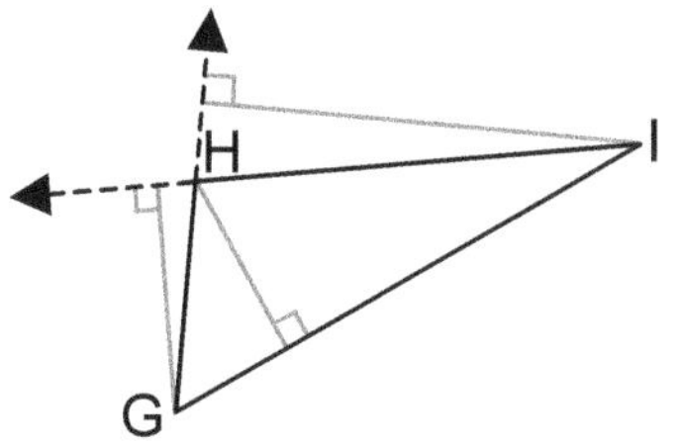

Notice that, in each of these examples, the altitudes all intersect each other in a single point, just as they did when we discussed the perpendicular bisectors, angle bisectors, and medians of triangles. (To see the point where the altitudes of ΔGHI cross each other, you have to extend the altitudes out further, but they will all cross each other in a single point.) This gives rise to the following theorem.

Concurrency of the Altitudes of a Triangle

The three angle altitudes of a triangle will always cross each other in a single point, called the orthocenter of the triangle.

Now, we need one more definition.

A segment is a midsegment of a triangle if and only if its endpoints are the midpoints of two sides of the triangle.

Example 4: Draw the midsegments of each of the triangles below.

(a)

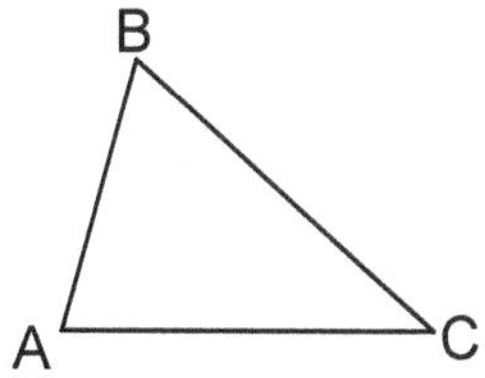

(b)

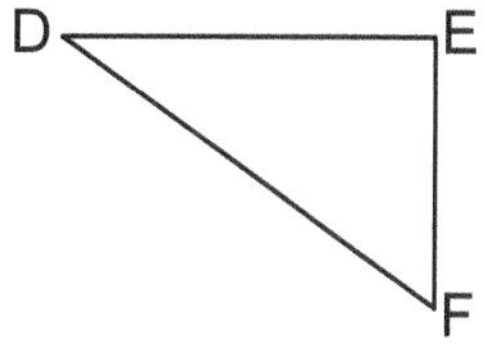

(a) We will begin by labeling the midpoints of the sides of this triangle.

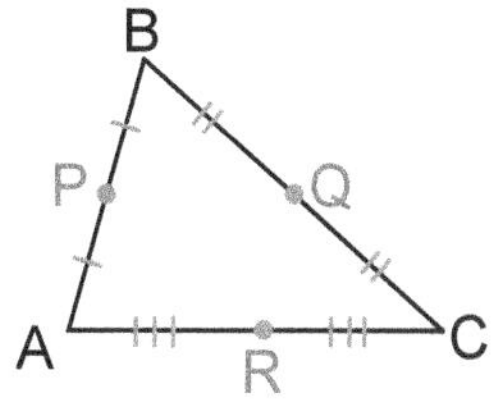

Next, we will draw segments connecting these midpoints. The midsegments of this triangle are shown in gray on the next page.

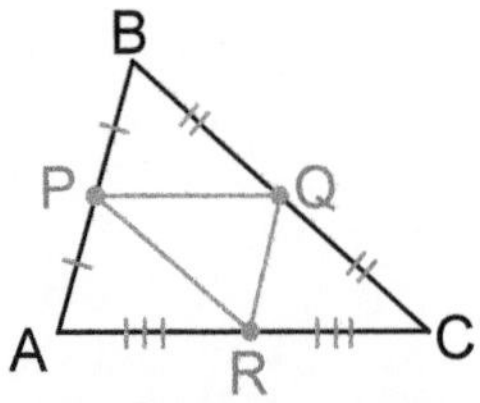

(b) As we did in part (a) of this example, we will begin by labeling the midpoints of the sides of this triangle, and then we will connect these midpoints. The midsegments of this triangle are shown in gray in the figure below.

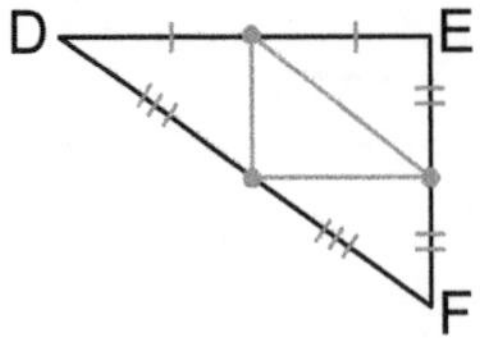

Now, we need one more theorem. You will prove this theorem in Chapter 7.

Midsegment of a Triangle Theorem

If a segment is a midsegment of a triangle, then it is parallel to a side of a triangle, and the length of this side of the triangle is equal to twice the length of the midsegment.

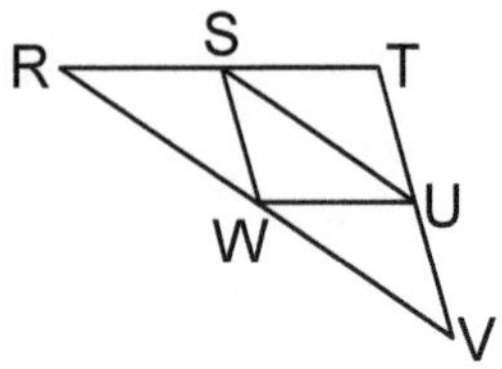

Example 5: In the figure at the right, $\overline{SW}$, $\overline{SU}$, and $\overline{UW}$ are midsegments of ΔTRV. (a) If UW = 3x – 5 and RT = 4x + 6, then what is the length of $\overline{RT}$? (b) If $m\angle R = (7y + 28)^\circ$ and $m\angle TSU = (10y + 22)^\circ$, then what is $m\angle RSU$?

(a) We will begin by noting that the Midsegment of a Triangle Theorem tells us that RT = 2 • UW. This tells us that we can say that 4x + 6 = 2(3x – 5). When we solve this equation for x, we find that x = 8. This means that $\overline{RT}$ must be 4 • 8 + 6, or 38, units long.

(b) We will begin by noting that the Midsegment of a Triangle Theorem tells us that $\overline{SU} \parallel \overline{RV}$. This means that $\angle R$ and $\angle TSU$ are corresponding angles formed by two parallel lines and a transversal, and so they must be congruent. Therefore, we can say that 7y + 28 = 10y + 22. When we solve this equation for y, we find that y = 2. Now, to find $m\angle RSU$, we will note that $m\angle TSU = (10 \cdot 2 + 22)^\circ$, or 42°. Since $\angle RSU$ and $\angle TSU$ form a linear pair and are therefore supplementary, we can now say that $m\angle RSU = 138^\circ$. (You could have also found this by noting that $m\angle R = 42^\circ$ and that $\angle RSU$ and $\angle R$ are supplementary because they are same-side interior angles formed by two parallel lines and a transversal.)

Problems:

1. Draw the medians in the triangle below.

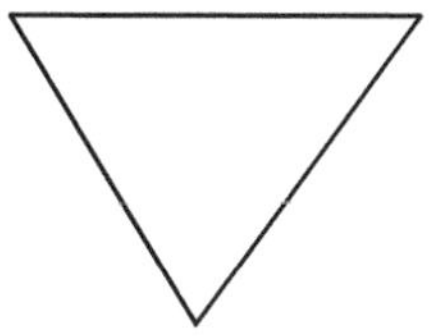

2. Draw the medians in the triangle below.

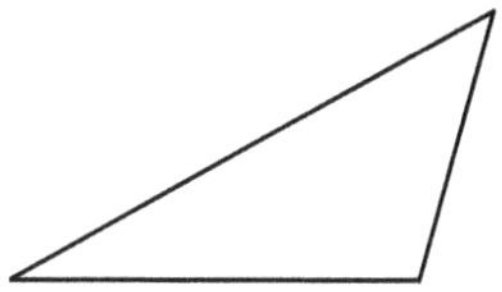

3. Draw the medians in the triangle below.

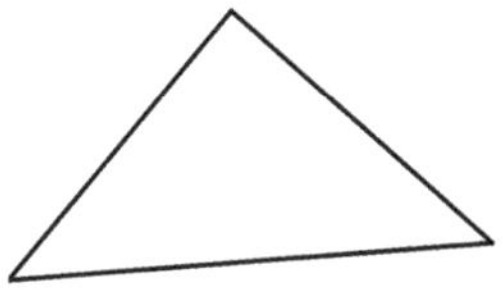

4. Draw the altitudes in the triangle below.

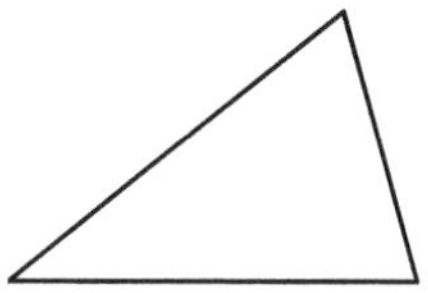

5. Draw the altitudes in the triangle below.

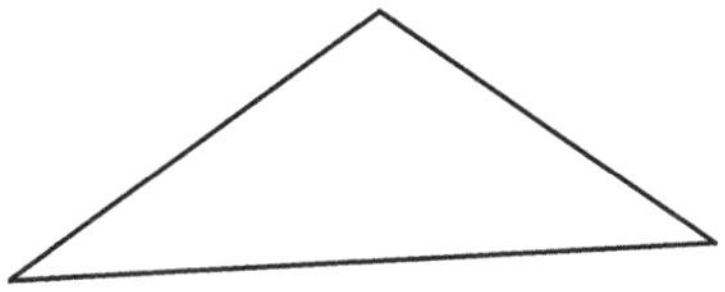

6. Draw the altitudes in the triangle below.

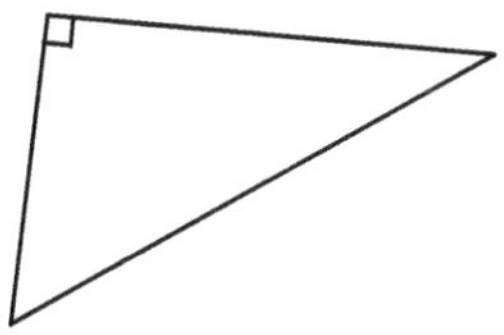

7. Draw the midsegments in the triangle below.

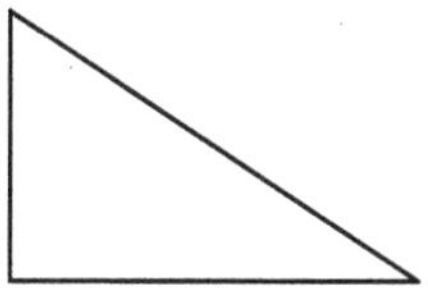

8. Draw the midsegments in the triangle below.

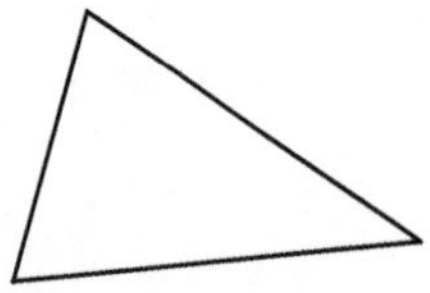

9. Draw the midsegments in the triangle below.

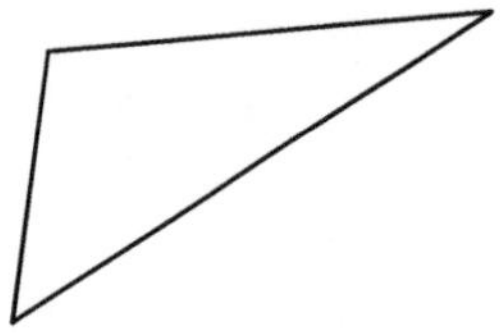

10-15. In the figure at the right, $\overline{AD}$, $\overline{CF}$, and $\overline{BE}$ are medians of ΔACE.

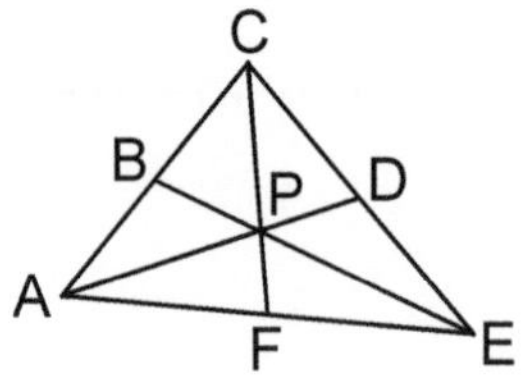

10. If AB = 5x + 7, BC = 3x + 15, and CD = 6x – 1, then AB = __________ and CD = __________.

11. If PF = 18, then CP = __________ and CF = __________.

12. If AP = 48, then AD = __________ and PD = __________.

13. If BP = 2w + 1 and BE = 3w + 18, then w = __________ and BE = __________.

14. If PF = x + 12 and CP = 6x + 4, then x = __________ and CF = __________.

15. If CD = 3y + 12 and CE = 8y – 14, then y = __________ and DE = __________.

16-18. In the figure at the right, $\overline{TQ}$ is an altitude of ΔQUS, and $\overline{SV}$ is a median of ΔQUS.

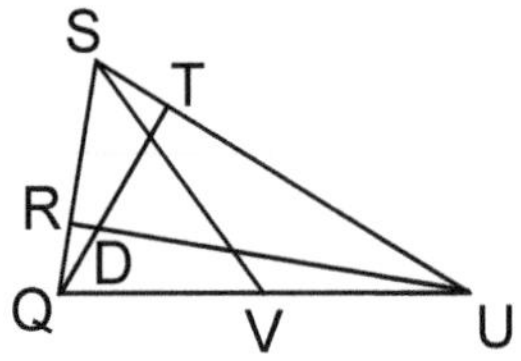

16. $m\angle QTS$ = ____________

17. If $m\angle QTU = (4x + 6)^\circ$, then x = ____________.

18. If QV = 4y, VU = 7y – 18, and $m\angle QRU = (14y + 3)^\circ$, is $\overline{RU}$ an altitude of ΔQUS? ____________ Why or why not? ________________________

19-27. In the figure at the right, $\overline{KM}$, $\overline{MO}$, and $\overline{KO}$ are midsegments of ΔLJN.

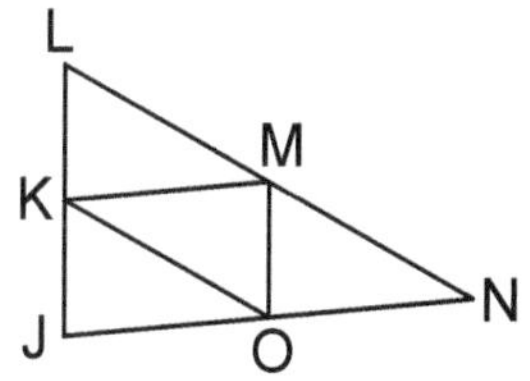

19. If $m\angle MKO = 42°$ and $m\angle KJO = 71°$, then $m\angle OKJ =$ _________.

20. If $m\angle LMK = (7x + 2)°$ and $m\angle N = (50 - x)°$, then $m\angle N =$ _________

21. If KM = 12, then JN = _________, JO = _________, and ON = _________.

22. If LJ = 46, then MO = _________, LK = _________, and KJ = _________.

23. If OK = 7w and LN = 12w + 8, then w = _________ and LN = _________.

24. If MO = x and JL = 10x – 2, then x = _________ and JK = _________.

25. If LM = 2y + 9 and MN = 3y – 1, then LM = _________ and LN = _________.

26. If JN = 5z – 4 and JO = z + 10, then z = _________ and JO = _________.

27. If MK = 8a – 1, JN = 6a + 38, and LN = 18a + 5, then LN = _________.

Part V – Mixed Review

1. In the figure at the right, $\overline{LT}$ is an angle bisector of $\triangle NLR$. If $m\angle NLT = (w + 30)°$ and $m\angle NLR = (8w - 24)°$, then $w =$ _________ and $m\angle RLT =$ _________.

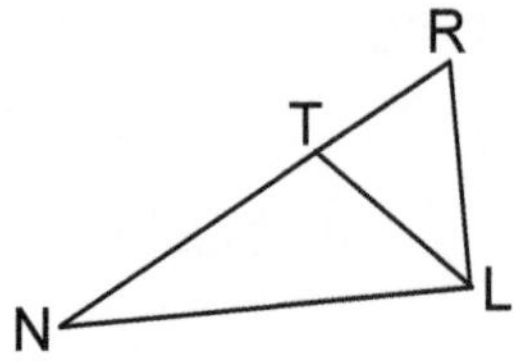

2. In the figure at the right, $\overline{CD}$ is an altitude of $\triangle ABC$. If $m\angle CDB = (6x + 12)°$, then $x =$ _________.

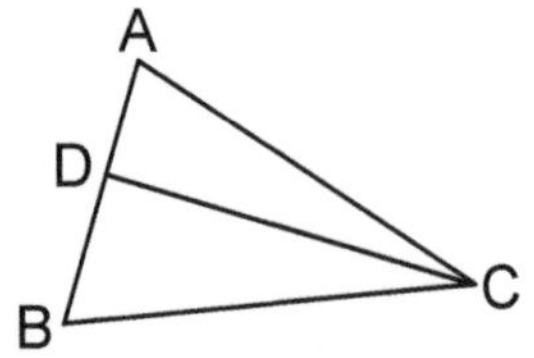

3. In the figure at the right, the point J is the centroid of $\triangle EGI$. If HJ = y centimeters, then EJ = _________ centimeters and EH = _________ centimeters.

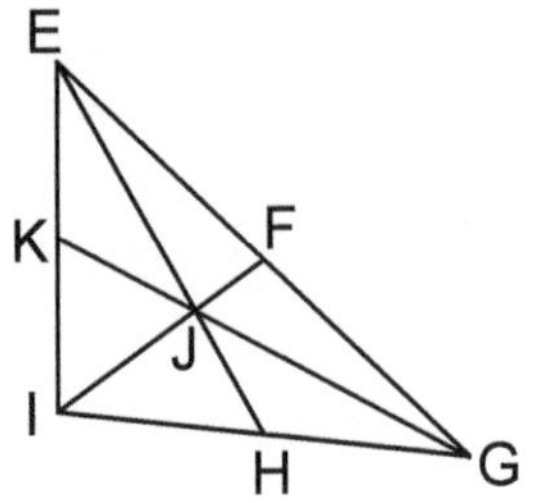

4. In the figure at the right, $\overline{LN}$ is a midsegment of $\triangle MOP$. If $LN = 3x + 8$ and $OP = 4x + 22$, then $x =$ _________ and $OP =$ _________.

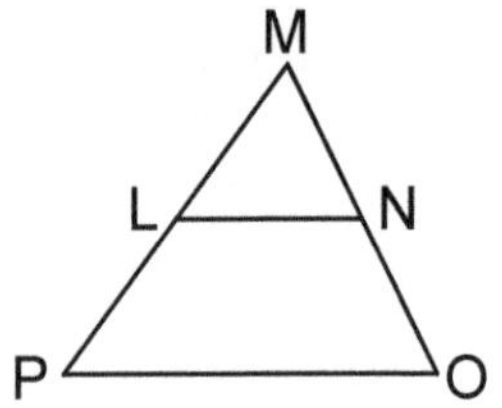

5. In the figure at the right, which of the following terms apply to $\overline{QS}$? Circle all that apply.

   altitude of $\triangle QRT$ perpendicular bisector of $\triangle QRT$

   median of $\triangle QRT$ angle bisector of $\triangle QRT$

   midsegment of $\triangle QRT$

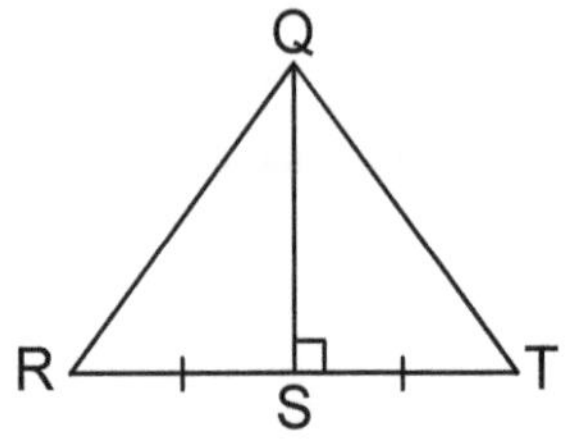

6. In the figure at the right, which of the following terms apply to $\overline{XV}$? Circle all that apply.

   altitude of $\triangle UWY$ perpendicular bisector of $\triangle UWY$

   median of $\triangle UWY$ angle bisector of $\triangle UWY$

   midsegment of $\triangle UWY$

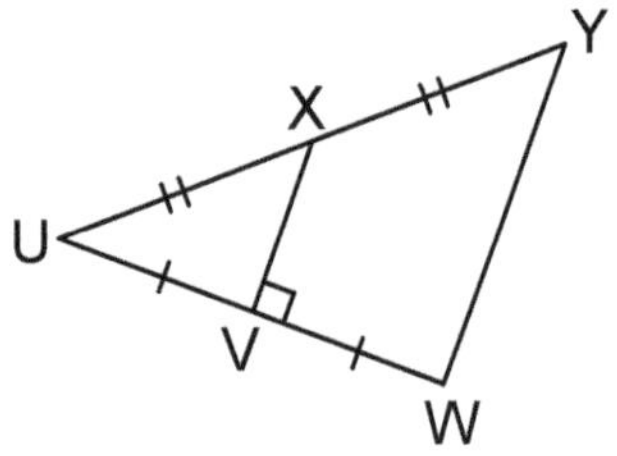

7. Use a ruler and a protractor to draw an obtuse scalene triangle and its three altitudes.

8. Use a ruler and a protractor to draw a right scalene triangle and its three perpendicular bisectors.

9. Use a ruler and a protractor to draw an acute isosceles triangle and its three midsegments.

10. Draw a picture to represent the following statement: $\overline{AB}$ *is a median of* $\triangle BCD$.

11. Draw a picture to represent the following statement: The angle bisectors of $\triangle EFG$ *are* $\overline{EH}$, $\overline{FH}$, *and* $\overline{GH}$.

12. Draw a counterexample to show that the statement *The three altitudes of a triangle always intersect inside the triangle* is false.

13. In the figure at the right, x = __________.

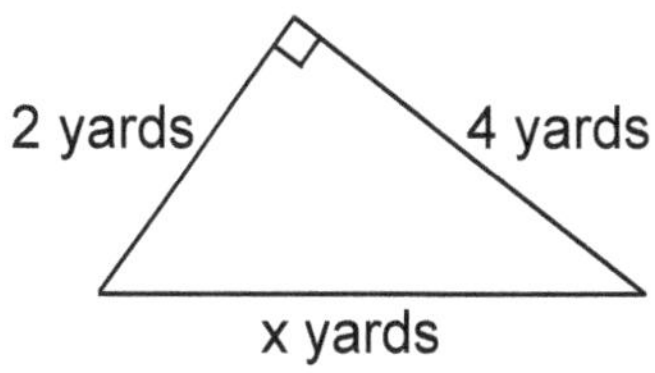

14. In the figure at the right, x = __________.

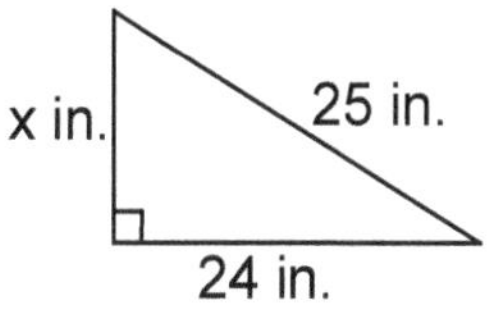

15-17. Refer to the figure at the right, and fill in each blank with <, >, or =, and then state the postulates, properties, and/or theorems used.

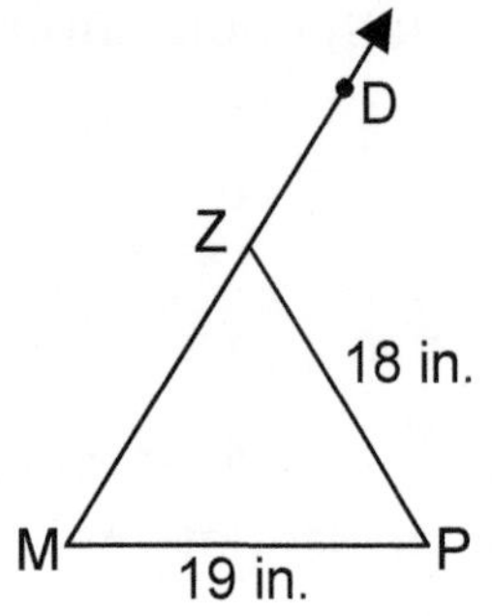

15. $m\angle MZP$ ________ $m\angle M$

Postulates, properties, and/or theorems used:

____

____

____

16. $m\angle P$ ________ $m\angle DZP$

Postulates, properties, and/or theorems used:

____

____

17. MP + PZ ________ MZ

Postulates, properties, and/or theorems used:

____

____

18. In the figure at the right, $\overline{LG} \cong \overline{CL}$. Then x = __________ and y = __________.

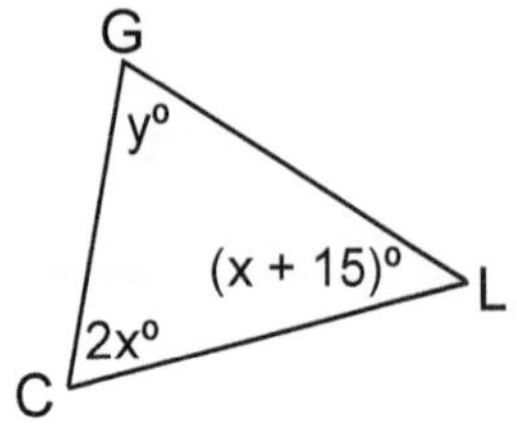

19. In the figure at the right, which segments, if any, must be parallel? Name a postulate or theorem to support each answer.

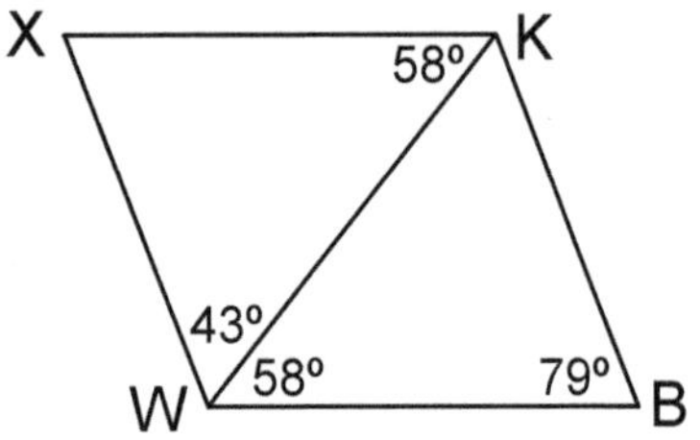

20. In the figure below, x = ____________ and $m\angle VBJ$ = ____________.

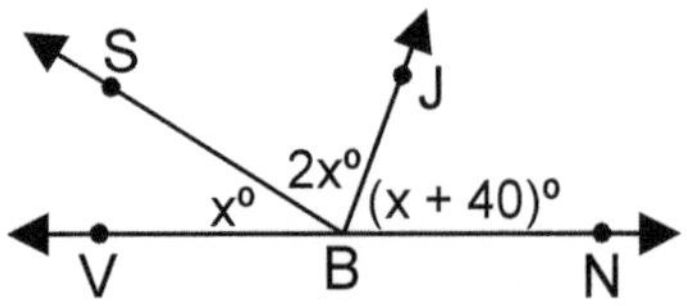

21. The length of the longer leg of a right triangle is 1 foot less than twice the length of the shorter leg, and the length of the hypotenuse is 1 foot more than twice the length of the shorter leg. Find the lengths of the sides of the triangle.

____________, ____________, ____________

22. In the figure at the right, m∠C > m∠T. Describe all the possible values of x.

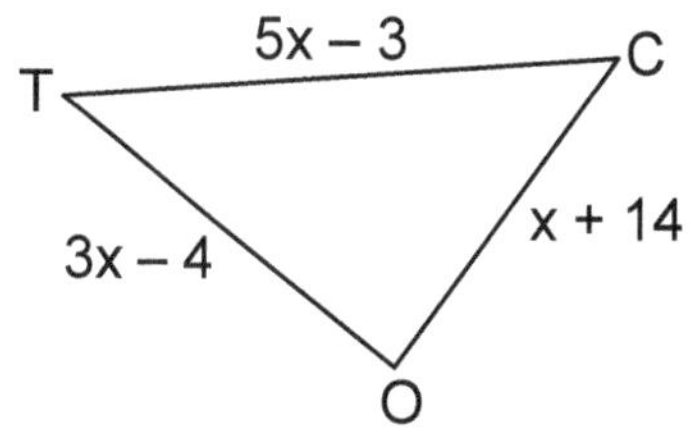

23. In the figure at the right, $\ell \parallel m$. Which of the numbered angles must measure 77°? Name all that apply.

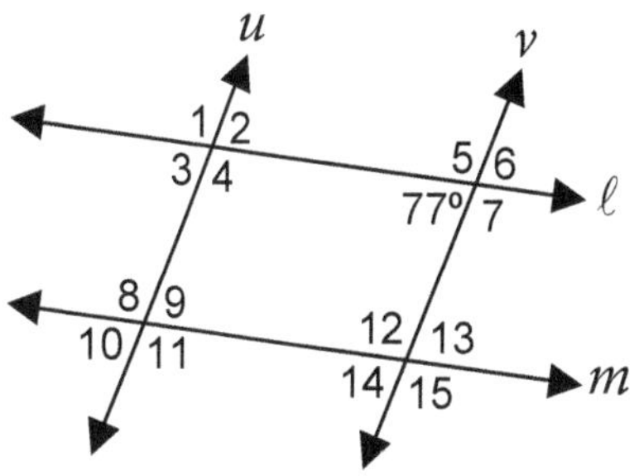

24-28. In the figure at the right, SV = 6 cm, KV = 15 cm, AV = 10 cm, VJ = 4 cm, and VQ = 5 cm.

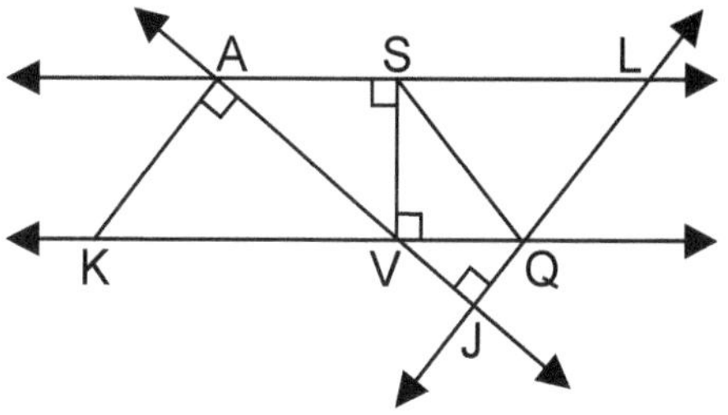

24. What is the distance between V and $\overleftrightarrow{QJ}$? ________

25. What is the distance between Q and $\overleftrightarrow{VJ}$? ________

26. What is the distance between S and $\overleftrightarrow{KQ}$? ________

27. What is the distance between V and $\overleftrightarrow{AL}$? ________

28. What is the distance between A and $\overleftrightarrow{LJ}$? ________

29-32. A baseball diamond is laid out so that the distance between first base and home plate is 90 feet, and the distance from first base to second base is also 90 feet. The distance from home plate to the pitcher's mound is 60.5 feet. For each of these questions, round your answers to two decimal places where necessary. Hint: For some of these problems, you will need to use the formula distance = (rate)(time).

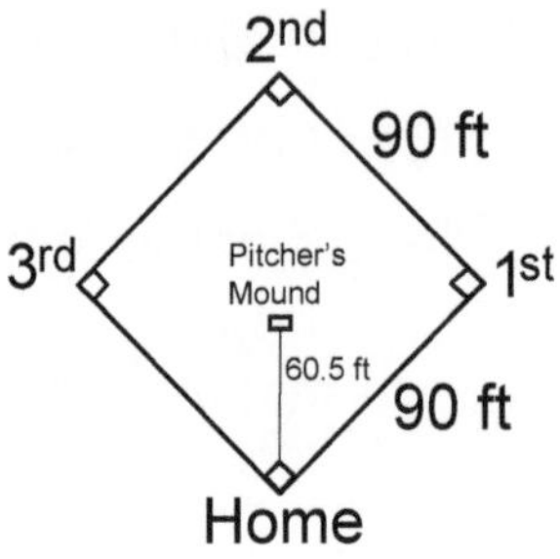

29. What is the distance from home plate to second base? ___________

30. A pitcher throws a ball from the pitcher's mound to home plate. If it travels horizontally at an average speed of 118 feet per second, how long does it take the ball to reach home plate? ___________

31. At the instant that the ball leaves the pitcher's hand, a runner leaves first base headed for second base at an average speed of 27 feet per second. How long does it take the runner to get to second base? ___________

32. The catcher catches the ball at home plate. After ¾ of a second more, the ball leaves the catcher's hand traveling horizontally at an average speed of 105 feet per second. Which arrives at second base first: the runner trying to steal second base or the ball? ___________

33. Last week while working at a department store, Robert made more sales than Henry but fewer sales than Sally. Let r represents the number of sales that Robert made, let h represent the number of sales that Henry made, and let s represent the number of sales that Sally made. Which of the following must be true?

(A) $r < h < s$ (B) $r < s < h$ (C) $s < r < h$ (D) $h < r < s$

34. Prove the following theorem: If a point is equidistant from the endpoints of a segment, then it lies on the perpendicular bisector of the segment.

Given: PA = PB

Prove: Point P is on the perpendicular bisector of $\overline{AB}$

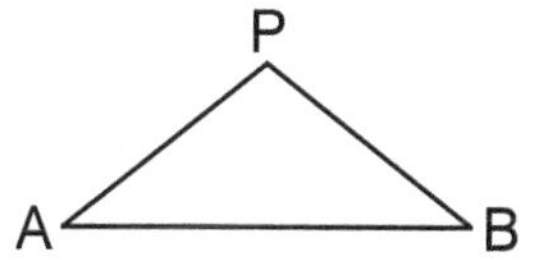

Hint: Use the postulate *A segment has exactly one midpoint* to make the statement, "Let M be the midpoint of $\overline{AB}$."

35. Prove the following theorem: The altitude from the vertex angle of an isosceles triangle is also a perpendicular bisector, a median, and an angle bisector of the triangle.

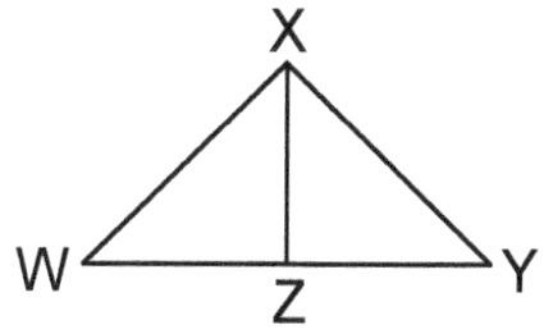

Given: ______________________________

Prove: ______________________________

Chapter 6 – Polygons

Part I – Interior and Exterior Angles of Polygons

We will begin this section with some definitions.

> A figure is a <u>polygon</u> if and only if it is a closed figure made up of three or more segments (called <u>sides</u>) that meet the following conditions.
> 1. The segments all lie in a single plane, and
> 2. Each side intersects exactly two other sides, but only at the endpoints of the sides.

> A polygon is called a <u>concave polygon</u> if and only if a side of the polygon can be extended to intersect another side of the polygon.

> A polygon is called a <u>convex polygon</u> if and only if it is not a concave polygon.

> A polygon is called a <u>regular polygon</u> if and only if it is equilateral and equiangular.

To understand these definitions, look at the following figures.

(a)
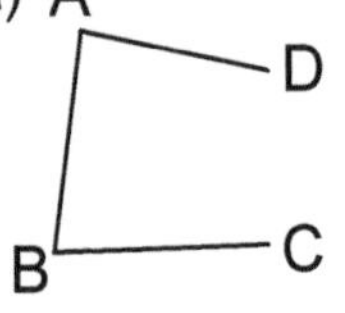

(b)
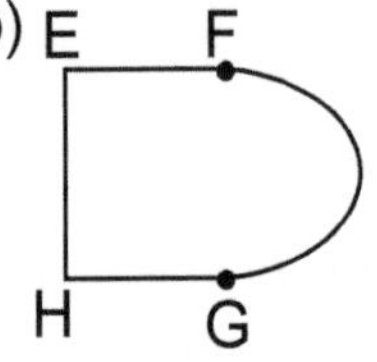

(c)
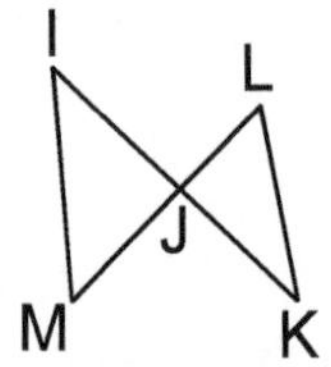

(d)
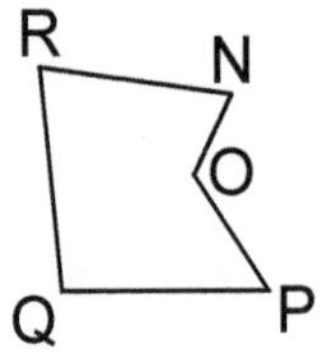

(e)
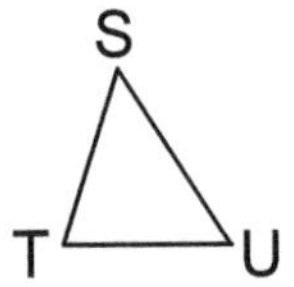

(f)
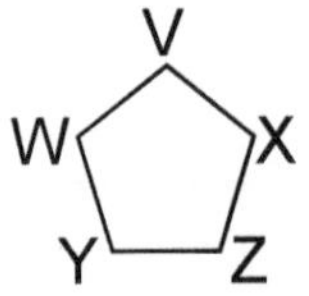

(g)
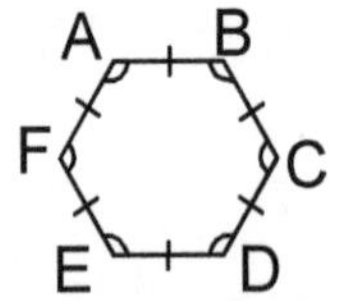

Figure (a) is not a polygon because it is not a closed figure.

Figure (b) is not a polygon because it is not made up entirely of straight segments.

Figure (c) is not a polygon because $\overline{IK}$ and $\overline{LM}$ both intersect more than two segments and because $\overline{IK}$ and $\overline{LM}$ intersect at a point other than their endpoints.

Figure (d) is a polygon. It is a concave polygon because, if you extend $\overline{NO}$ as shown below, it will intersect $\overline{QP}$. (You could also say that figure (d) is a concave polygon because, if you extend $\overline{OP}$ in both directions, it will intersect $\overline{RN}$.)

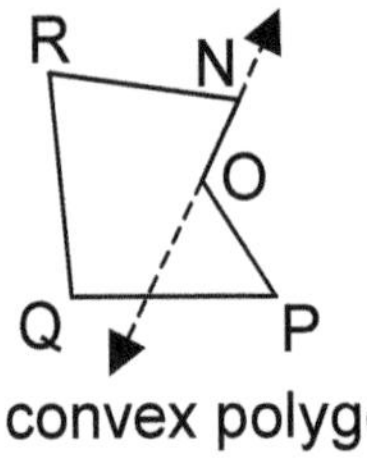

Figures (e), (f), and (g) are all convex polygons. Figure (g) is a regular polygon because all the angles are congruent to each other and all the sides are congruent to each other.

Now, let's talk about how we name polygons. We classify polygons according to the number of sides that the polygon has. To do this, we use the following chart.

Number of sides	Name of polygon
3	triangle
4	quadrilateral
5	pentagon
6	hexagon
7	heptagon

Number of sides	Name of polygon
8	octagon
9	nonagon
10	decagon
12	dodecagon
n (if n > 12)	n-gon

For example, figures (d) and (f) on the previous page are *pentagons*, figure (g) on the previous page is a *hexagon*, and any polygon with 19 sides would be called a *19-gon*.

To name polygons, we often state the name for the polygon according to its number of sides, and then we name the vertices (or corners) in consecutive order. For example, to refer to the figure below on the left, we could say *quadrilateral ABDC* or *quadrilateral CDBA*, but we could not say *quadrilateral ABCD* (because the vertex B is not next to the vertex C). To refer to the figure below on the right, we could say *heptagon FEHJKIG* or *heptagon EFGIKJH*, but we could not say *heptagon EFGHIKJ* (because the vertex H is not next to either the vertex G or the vertex I).

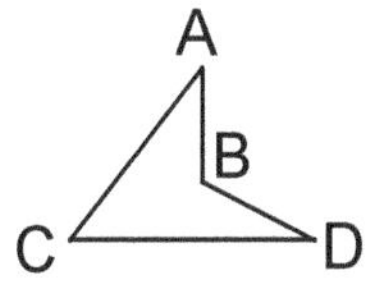

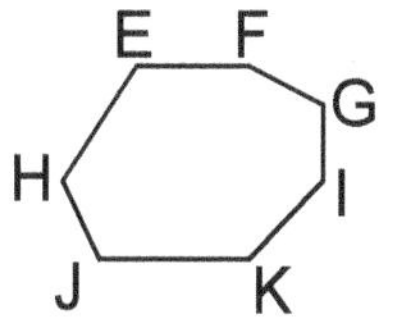

Now, we need another definition.

> A segment is a <u>diagonal</u> of a polygon if and only if its endpoints are two nonconsecutive vertices of the polygon.

Example 1: Draw all of the diagonals from point P in each of the polygons below.

(a)
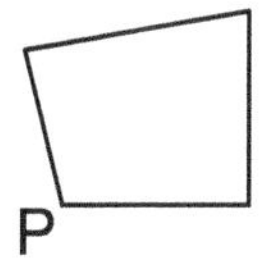

(b)
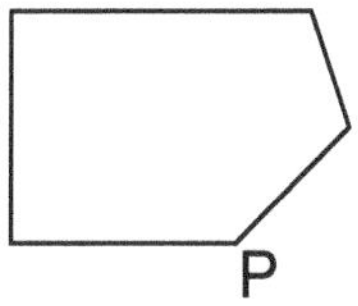

(c)
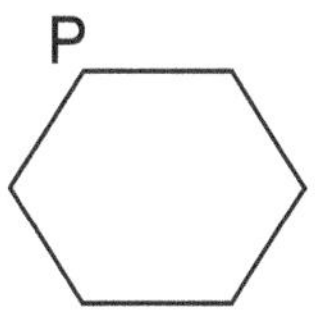

(d)
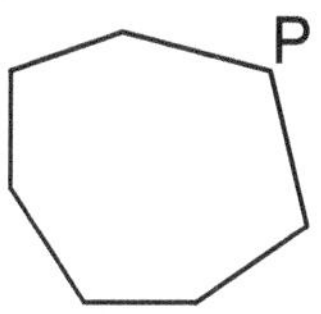

For each of these figures, the diagonals from point P are the gray segments shown below.

(a)
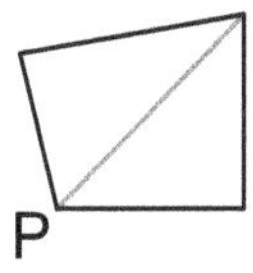

(b)
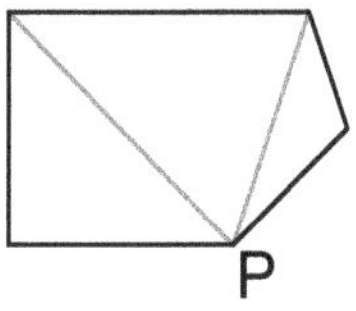

(c)
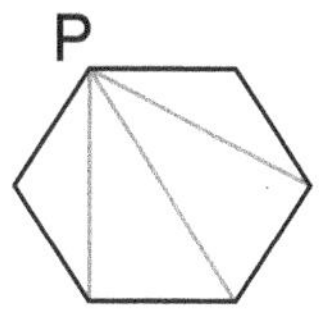

(d)
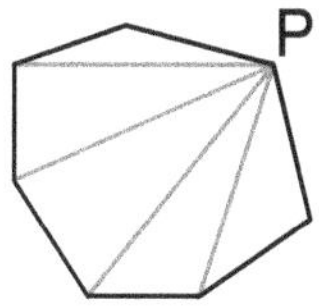

Notice that, when there were four sides, we could draw one diagonal from a given vertex, and this formed two triangles. When there were five sides, we could draw two diagonals from a given vertex, and this formed three triangles. When there were six sides, we could draw three diagonals from a given vertex, and this formed four triangles. When there were seven sides, we could draw four diagonals from a given vertex, and this formed five triangles. These examples and the thought process behind them tell us that, if a convex polygon has n sides, then you can draw exactly n – 3 diagonals from a given vertex, and this will form exactly n – 2 triangles. This gives rise to the following theorem.

> If a convex polygon has n sides, then the sum of the measures of the interior angles is equal to 180°(n – 2).

To see why this theorem is true, look back at the figures from Example 1 on the previous page, and recall that the sum of the measures of the interior angles of a triangle is always 180°. In each figure, the sum of the measures of the angles that make up the triangles is equal to the sum of the measures of the angles in the original figure. So, to find the sum of the measures of the interior angles, we need to multiply 180° by the number of triangles that are formed by drawing all the diagonals from a given vertex.

Example 2: What is the value of x in the figure at the right?

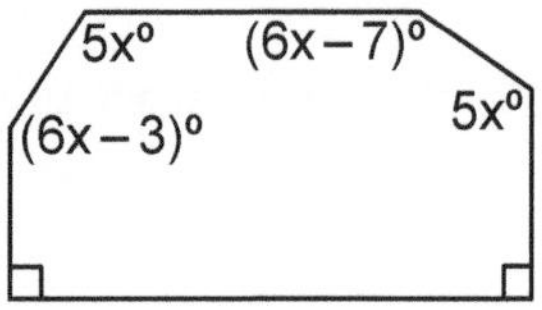

We will begin by noting that this figure has six sides, and thus the sum of the measures of the interior angles must equal 180° • 4, or 720°. This tells us we can say that $6x - 3 + 5x + 6x - 7 + 5x + 90 + 90 = 720$. When we solve this equation for x, we find that x = 25.

Example 3: What is the measure of one interior angle of a regular decagon?

We will begin by noting that a decagon has 10 sides, and so the sum of the measures of the interior angles of a decagon must equal 180° • 8, or 1440°. Since the question asks for the measure of one interior angle of a *regular* decagon, we know that all the interior angles are congruent to each other. This means that the measure of one interior angle of a regular decagon must equal 1440° ÷ 10, or 144^0.

Now, let's review a definition that we saw back in Chapter 4.

> An <u>exterior angle</u> of a polygon is an angle that is formed by extending one (and only one) of the sides of the polygon.

So, for instance, in the figure at the right, ∠1, ∠2, ∠4, and ∠5 are all exterior angles of the hexagon, but ∠3 is not an exterior angle of the pentagon.

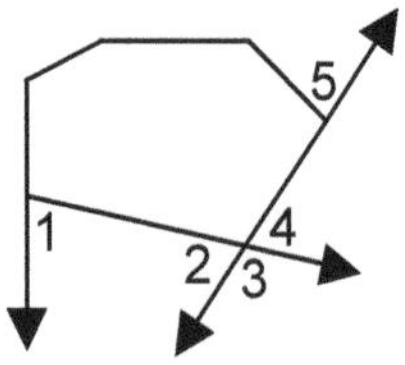

Now, we need another theorem.

For any convex polygon, if one exterior angle is drawn at each vertex, then the sum of the measures of these angles will be 360°.

To understand what this theorem is saying, look at the figures below. We can look at the figure on the left and say that $m\angle 1 + m\angle 2 + m\angle 3 + m\angle 4 + m\angle 5 = 360°$. Also, we can look at the figure on the right and say that $m\angle 6 + m\angle 7 + m\angle 8 + m\angle 9 = 360°$.

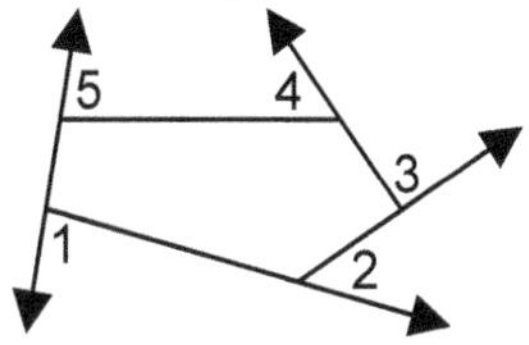

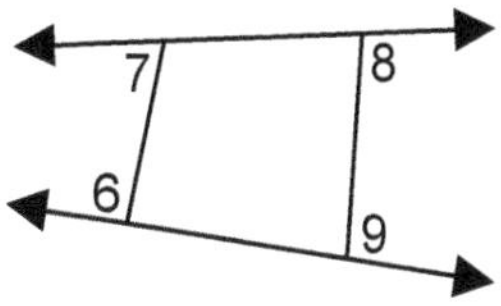

Example 4: Given a polygon with n sides and one exterior angle drawn at each vertex, prove that the sum of the measures of the exterior angles (one angle at each vertex) is 360°.

We will begin by noting that each exterior angle forms a linear pair with an interior angle (and each interior angle forms a linear pair with an exterior angle). Since we have n sides, then we n interior angles and n exterior angles. The Linear Pair Postulate tells us that the sum of the measures of each pair of interior and exterior angles is 180°. This tells us that the measures of all the interior angles and exterior angles (with only one exterior angle at each vertex) is 180n°.* Now, if we subtract the sum of the measures of the interior angles from 180n°, it will leave us with the sum of the measures of the exterior angles. Since the sum of the measures of the interior angles is 180°(n – 2), we can say the following.

$$\begin{aligned}\text{the sum of the measures of the exterior angles} &= 180n° - 180°(n-2)\\ &= 180n° - 180n° + 360°\\ &= 360°\end{aligned}$$

Example 5: Find the measure of an exterior angle of a regular 15-gon.

There are two different methods we can use to solve this problem, and we will discuss both of them.

Method 1: Use the fact that the sum of the measures of the exterior angles equals 360°.

Since we are talking about a *regular* 15-gon (a polygon with 15 congruent sides and 15 congruent interior angles), each of the exterior angles must be congruent to each other. Therefore, the measure of one exterior angle of a 15-gon must equal 360° ÷ 15, or 24°.

*If you have trouble understanding what we are saying here, look at the figure at the right. In this figure, n = 5 and all of the numbered angle add up to 180(5)°.

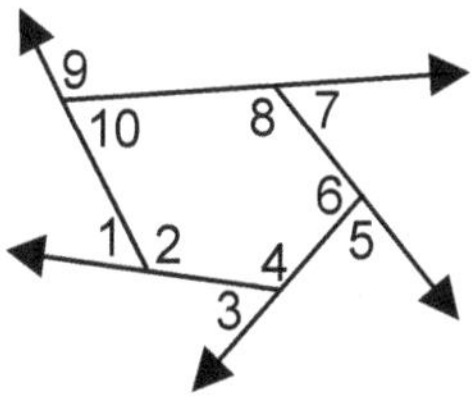

Method 2: Use the fact that the sum of the measures of the interior angles equals 180°(n – 2).

Since the measures of the interior angles of a 15-gon add up to 180° • 13, or 2340°, the measure of one angle of a regular 15-gon must equal 2340° ÷ 15, or 156°. (Recall that, since this is a *regular* 15-gon, the angles must all be congruent to each other.) Since each interior angle forms a linear pair with an exterior angle, each exterior angle must measure 180° – 156°, or 24°.

Problems:

1. Which of the following figures are polygons? Circle all that apply.

(a) 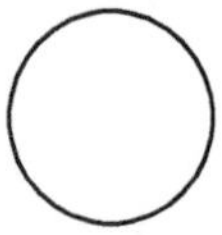 (b)  (c) 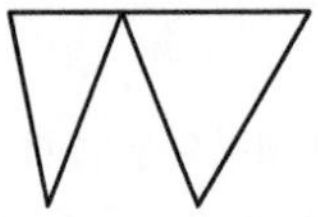 (d) 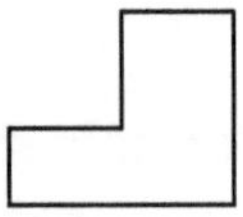

2. Which of the following figures are concave polygons? Circle all that apply.

(a)  (b)  (c) 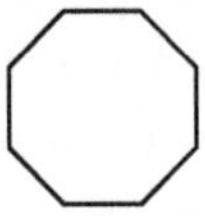 (d) 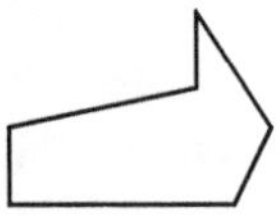

3. Which of the following figures are convex polygons? Circle all that apply.

(a) 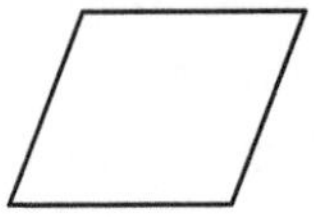 (b) 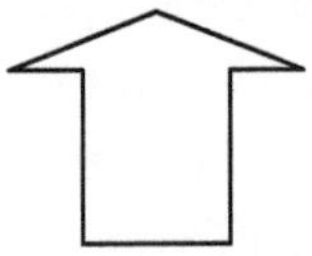 (c)  (d) 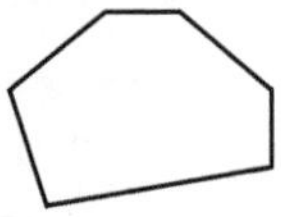

4. Name the figure below by classifying it according to how many sides it has and then naming the vertices in consecutive order (as we discussed on page 250).

____

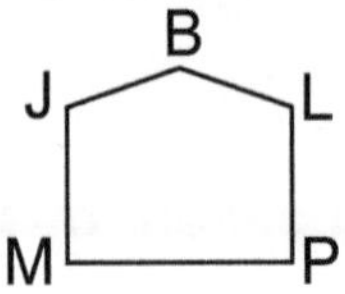

5. Name the figure below by classifying it according to how many sides it has and then naming the vertices in consecutive order (as we discussed on page 250).

____

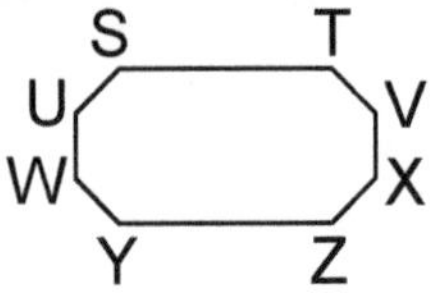

6. What does a regular nonagon look like? ________________________________

____

7. What does a regular 24-gon look like? ________________________________

____

8. What is the sum of the measures of the interior angles of a convex quadrilateral?

____

9. What is the sum of the measures of the interior angles of a convex heptagon?

____

10. What is the value of x in the figure at the right?

x = ________

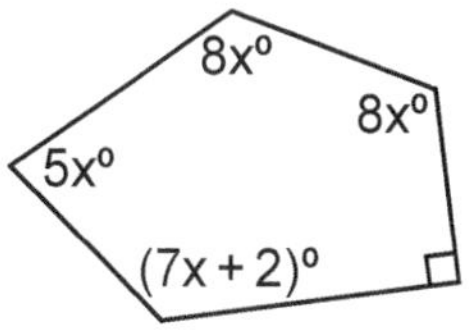

11. What is the value of y in the figure at the right?

y = ________

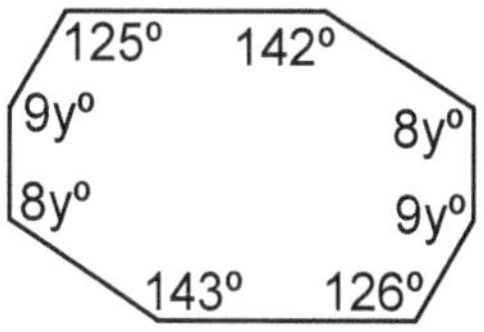

12. What is the value of b in the figure at the right?

b = ________

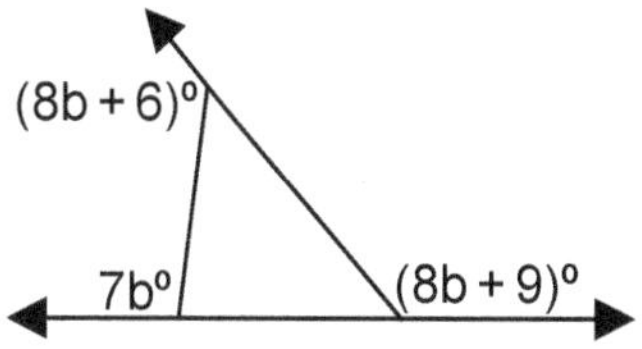

13. What are the values of c and d in the figure at the right?

c = ________

d = ________

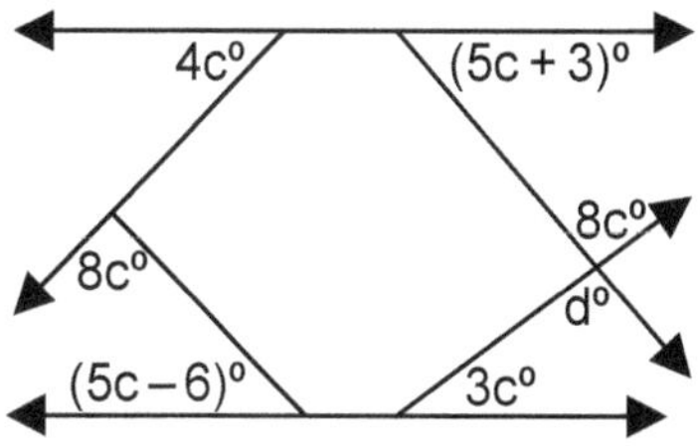

14. What is the measure of one interior angle of a regular hexagon? ________

15. What is the measure of one interior angle of a regular 18-gon? ________

16. What is the measure of one interior angle of a regular 30-gon? ________

17. What is the measure of one interior angle of a regular octagon? ________

18. What is the measure of one interior angle of a regular n-gon? ________

19. What is the measure of one exterior angle of a regular octagon? ________

20. What is the measure of one exterior angle of a regular dodecagon? ________

21. What is the measure of one exterior angle of a regular pentagon? ________

22. What is the measure of one exterior angle of a regular 20-gon? ________

23. What is the measure of one exterior angle of a regular n-gon? ________

24. If the interior angles of a regular polygon all measure 90º, how many sides does the polygon have? ________

    Hint: Use the formula you found in #18.

25. If the interior angles of a regular polygon all measure 140º, how many sides does the polygon have? ________

26. If the interior angles of a regular polygon all measure 157.5°, how many sides does the polygon have? ________

27. If the interior angles of a regular polygon all measure 171°, how many sides does the polygon have? ________

28. If the interior angles of a regular polygon all measure x°, how many sides does the polygon have? ________

29. If the exterior angles of a regular polygon all measure 2°, how many sides does the polygon have? ________

    Hint: Use the formula you found in #23.

30. If the exterior angles of a regular polygon all measure 15°, how many sides does the polygon have? ________

31. If the exterior angles of a regular polygon all measure 60°, how many sides does the polygon have? ________

32. If the exterior angles of a regular polygon all measure 120°, how many sides does the polygon have? ________

33. If the exterior angles of a regular polygon all measure y°, how many sides does the polygon have? ________

34. What happens to the measures of the interior angles of a regular polygon as the number of sides increases? ____

____

35. What happens to the measures of the exterior angles of a regular polygon as the number of sides increases? ____

____

Part II – Parallelograms

We will begin this section with a definition and some theorems.

A figure is a <u>parallelogram</u> if and only if it is a quadrilateral with two sets of parallel sides.

Opposite Sides of a Parallelogram Theorem
If a quadrilateral is a parallelogram, then the opposite sides are congruent to each other.

Opposite Angles of a Parallelogram Theorem
If a quadrilateral is a parallelogram, then the opposite angles are congruent to each other.

Consecutive Angles of a Parallelogram Theorem
If a quadrilateral is a parallelogram, then each pair of consecutive interior angles is supplementary. (The term *consecutive* means that the angles are next to each other.)

Diagonals of a Parallelogram Theorem
If a quadrilateral is a parallelogram, then the diagonals bisect each other.

Example 1: Quadrilateral ABCD at the right is a parallelogram. What do the definition and theorems above tell us about quadrilateral ABCD?

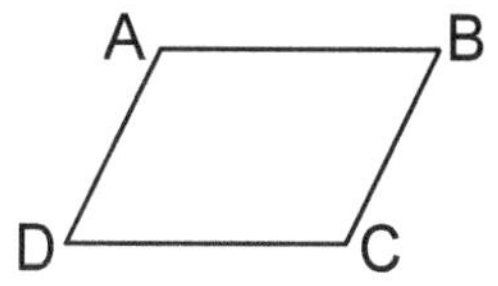

The definition of a parallelogram tells us that $\overline{AD} \parallel \overline{BC}$ and $\overline{AB} \parallel \overline{DC}$.

The Opposite Sides of a Parallelogram Theorem tells us that $\overline{AD} \cong \overline{BC}$ and $\overline{AB} \cong \overline{DC}$.

The Opposite Angles of a Parallelogram Theorem tells us that $\angle A \cong \angle C$ and $\angle B \cong \angle D$.

The Consecutive Angles of a Parallelogram Theorem tells us that $\angle A$ and $\angle B$ are supplementary, $\angle B$ and $\angle C$ are supplementary, $\angle C$ and $\angle D$ are supplementary, and $\angle A$ and $\angle D$ are supplementary.

To state what the Diagonals of a Parallelogram Theorem tells us, we first need to draw the diagonals of the parallelogram and label the point where they intersect, as shown at the right. After we do this, we can say that the Diagonals of a Parallelogram Theorem tells us that $\overline{DB}$ bisects $\overline{AC}$ and $\overline{AC}$ bisects $\overline{DB}$.

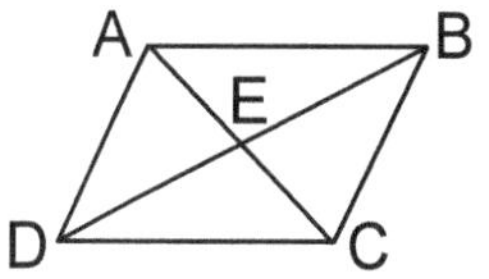

Example 2: Prove the Opposite Sides of a Parallelogram Theorem.

We will prove this theorem using the two-column format that we used in Chapters 1-4, but you may use paragraph proofs in the exercises for this section if you wish to do so.

To prove this theorem, we must start by drawing a generic picture that represents the part of the theorem that follows the "if."

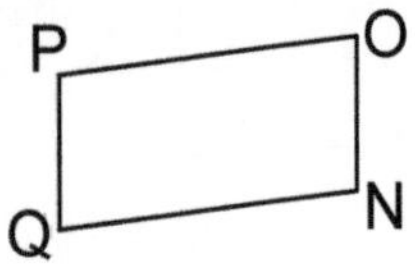

This tells us that we are given that quadrilateral NOPQ is a parallelogram, and we want to prove that $\overline{PQ} \cong \overline{ON}$ and $\overline{PO} \cong \overline{QN}$.

One of the first things we will do in our proof is draw $\overline{PN}$, and so we will go ahead and do that below so that you can understand this proof better as you read it.

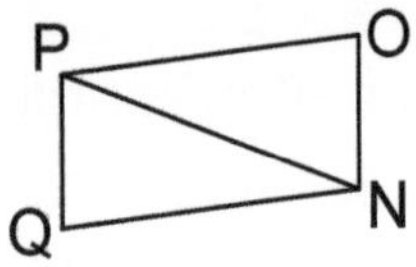

Statements	Reasons	Explanations
1. Quadrilateral NOPQ is a parallelogram.	1. Given	This was given to us.
2. $\overline{PQ} \parallel \overline{ON}$ and $\overline{PO} \parallel \overline{QN}$	2. Definition of a parallelogram	The definition of a parallelogram tells us that, if a figure is a parallelogram, then the opposite sides must be parallel.
3. Draw $\overline{PN}$.	3. Through any two points there is exactly one line.	There is one (and only one) line that passes through both points P and N, and so there is one (and only one) segment that has its endpoints at points P and N.
4. $\angle OPN \cong \angle QNP$ and $\angle QPN \cong \angle ONP$	4. Alternate Interior Angles Theorem	$\angle OPN$ and $\angle QNP$ are alternate interior angles formed by the parallel segments $\overline{OP}$ and $\overline{QN}$ and the transversal $\overline{PN}$, and so we can use the Alternate Interior Angles Theorem to say that $\angle OPN \cong \angle QNP$. Similarly, $\angle QPN$ and $\angle ONP$ are alternate interior angles formed by the parallel segments $\overline{PQ}$ and $\overline{ON}$ and the transversal $\overline{PN}$, and so we can use the Alternate Interior Angles Theorem to say that $\angle QPN \cong \angle ONP$.

Statements continued	Reasons continued	Explanations continued
5. $\overline{PN} \cong \overline{PN}$	5. Reflexive Property of Segment Congruence	The Reflexive Property of Segment Congruence tells us that a segment is congruent to itself.
6. $\triangle OPN \cong \triangle QNP$	6. ASA Congruence Postulate	We have proven that we have two sets of congruent angles ($\angle OPN \cong \angle QNP$ and $\angle QPN \cong \angle ONP$) and that the sides between these angles are congruent ($\overline{PN} \cong \overline{PN}$). This tells us that we can use the ASA Congruence Postulate to say that the triangles are congruent.
7. $\overline{PQ} \cong \overline{ON}$ and $\overline{PO} \cong \overline{QN}$	7. CPCTC	We said in Statement (6) that we had two congruent triangles, and so now we can say that the corresponding parts of these triangles must be congruent to each other.

Example 3: Quadrilateral HIJK is a parallelogram, KL = 5w – 1, LJ = 4w + 7, KI = 8w + 9, KJ = 2x + 5, HI = 3x – 6, m$\angle$HKJ = (7y – 1)°, and m$\angle$HIJ = (5y + 29)°. Find the values of w, x, and y. Then find the length of $\overline{LJ}$, the length of $\overline{KJ}$, and m$\angle$KHI.

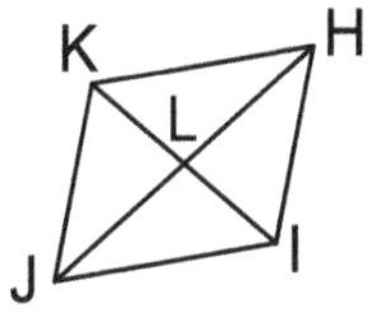

To find the value of w, we will begin by noting that the Diagonals of a Parallelogram Theorem tells us that $\overline{HJ}$ bisects $\overline{KI}$, and so $\overline{KL} \cong \overline{LI}$. This tells us that the length of $\overline{KI}$ is equal to twice the length of $\overline{KL}$, and so we can say that 8w + 9 = 2(5w – 1). When we solve this equation for w, we find that w = 5.5.

Now, to find the value of x, we will note that the Opposite Sides of a Parallelogram Theorem tells us that $\overline{KJ} \cong \overline{HI}$, and so we can say that 2x + 5 = 3x – 6. When we solve this equation for x, we find that x = 11.

To find the value of y, we will note that the Opposite Angles of a Parallelogram Theorem tells us that $\angle$HKJ $\cong$ $\angle$HIJ, and so we can say that 7y – 1 = 5y + 29. This tells us that y = 15.

To find the length of $\overline{LJ}$, we will note that we were told that LJ = 4w + 7, and we already said that w = 5.5. Therefore, we can say that LJ = 4 • 5.5 + 7, or 29.

To find the length of $\overline{KJ}$, we will note that we were told that KJ = 2x + 5, and we already said that x = 11. Thus, KJ = 2 • 11 + 5, or 27.

To find m$\angle$KHI, we will note that we were told that m$\angle$HKJ = (7y – 1)°, and we already said that y = 15. Hence, m$\angle$HKJ = (7 • 15 – 1)°, or 104°. Since the Consecutive Interior Angles of a Parallelogram Theorem tells us that $\angle$HKJ and $\angle$KHI are supplementary, we know that m$\angle$KHI = 180° – 104°, or 76°.

Problems:

1-12. Quadrilateral STVU at the right is a parallelogram.

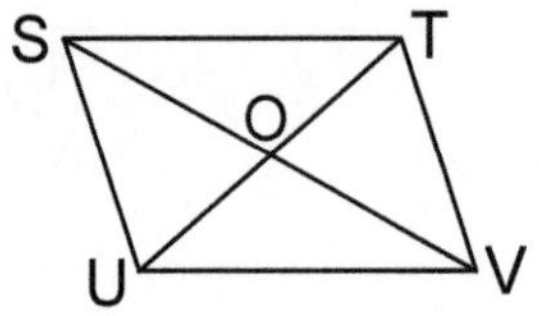

1. If $OU = 35$, then $OT =$ ________ and $UT =$ ________.

2. If $SO = 17$, then $OV =$ ________ and $SV =$ ________.

3. If $SU = 6$ and $ST = 8$, then $UV =$ ________ and $TV =$ ________.

4. If $m\angle TSU = 81^\circ$, then $m\angle SUV =$ ________ and $m\angle STV =$ ________.

5. If $m\angle STV = 114^\circ$, then $m\angle SUV =$ ________ and $m\angle UVT =$ ________.

6. If $m\angle SUV = 103^\circ$ and $m\angle SUT = 61^\circ$, then $m\angle TUV =$ ________ and $m\angle UTV =$ ________.

7. If $m\angle SVT = 44^\circ$ and $m\angle SVU = 32^\circ$, then $m\angle UVT =$ ________, $m\angle VSU =$ ________, and $m\angle UST =$ ________.

8. If $UV = 11$ and $TV = 7$, then $ST =$ ________ and $SU =$ ________.

9. If $UT = 15$, then $OU =$ ________ and $OT =$ ________.

10. If $m\angle TUS = 58^\circ$ and $m\angle UTS = 40^\circ$, then $m\angle TSU =$ ________ and $m\angle TVU =$ ________.

11. $\Delta OUS \cong \Delta$____________

12. $\Delta VST \cong \Delta$____________

13-21. Quadrilateral EZLR at the right is a parallelogram.

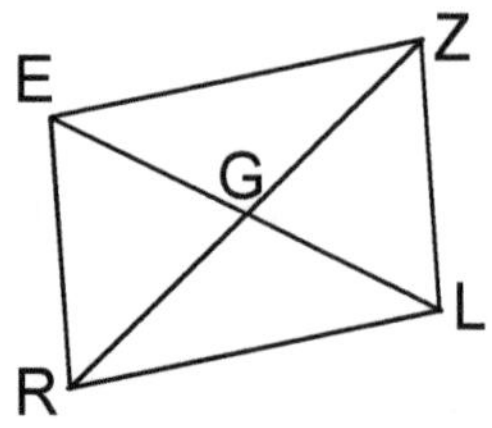

13. If $m\angle REZ = (6n + 19)^\circ$ and $m\angle RLZ = (8n - 9)^\circ$, then $n =$ ________ and $m\angle REZ =$ ________.

14. If ER = 2x, EZ = 4x – 8, and RL = 3x, then x = ________ and RL = ________.

15. If EG = 4a + 11 and GL = 7a + 14, then a = ________ and EG = ________.

16. If RZ = 9b + 10 and ZG = 6b – 4, then b = ________ and RG = ________.

17. If $m\angle ZLR = (2p - 8)^\circ$ and $m\angle ERL = (p + 35)^\circ$, then p = ________ and $m\angle ERL$ = ________.

18. If $m\angle ZEL = (4y + 35)^\circ$ and $m\angle ELR = (20 - 2y)^\circ$, then y = ________ and $m\angle ZEL$ = ________.

19. If $m\angle ZEL = (7w - 6)^\circ$, $m\angle RLE = 43^\circ$, and $m\angle LER = (2w + 34)^\circ$, then w = ________, $m\angle LER$ = ________, and $m\angle ZER$ = ________.

20. If $m\angle ERL = x^\circ$, $m\angle REZ = (x - 4y)^\circ$, and $m\angle ZLR = (2x + 6y)^\circ$, then x = ________, y = ________, and $m\angle REZ$ = ________.

21. If EZ = 7c + 18, RL = 4c + 21, EG = 5c + 14, and EL = 5c + d, then d = ________ and EL = ________.

22. Prove the Opposite Angles of a Parallelogram Theorem.

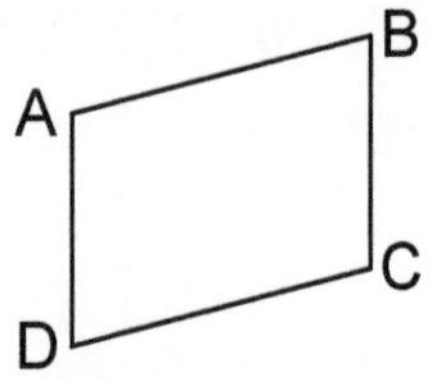

Given: Quadrilateral ABCD is a parallelogram

Prove: ______________________

Note: You may use the Opposite Sides of a Parallelogram Theorem (because we proved it in Example 2), but you may not use any of the other theorems in this section because you have not proven them yet.

23. Prove the Diagonals of a Parallelogram Theorem.

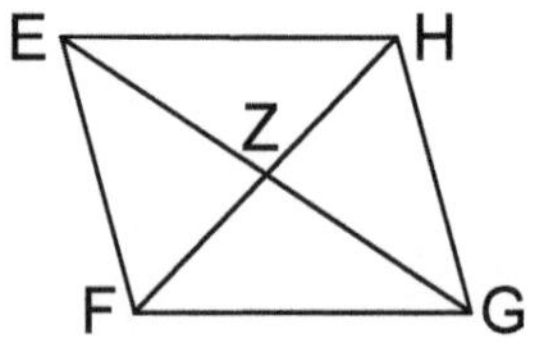

Given: Quadrilateral EFGH is a parallelogram

Prove: $\overline{EG}$ bisects $\overline{HF}$ and $\overline{HF}$ bisects $\overline{EG}$

24. Prove the Consecutive Angles of a Parallelogram Theorem.

Given: Quadrilateral JKLM is a parallelogram

Prove: ______________________________________

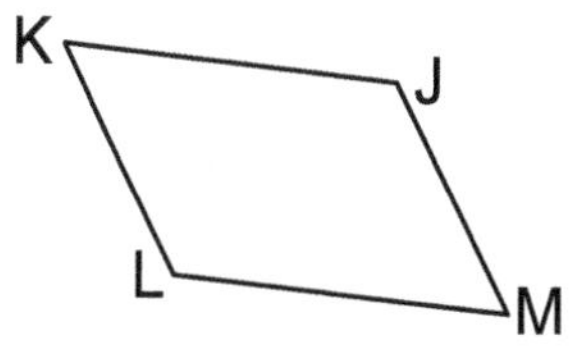

25. In the figure at the right, quadrilaterals NOQR and NOPQ are both parallelograms. Prove that $\Delta RNQ \cong \Delta QOP$.

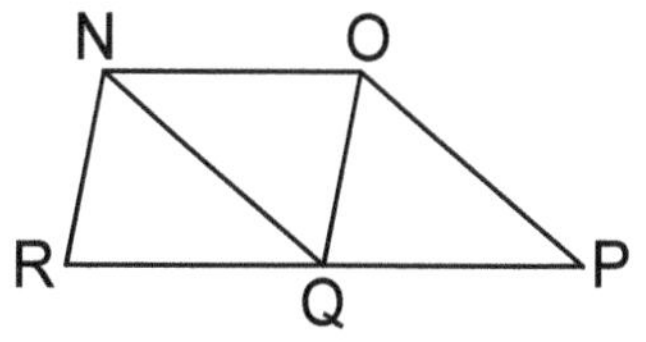

26. In the figure at the right, quadrilateral UVXY is a parallelogram, $\overline{YW} \perp \overline{XV}$, and $\overline{VZ} \perp \overline{UY}$. Prove that $\overline{WY} \cong \overline{ZV}$.

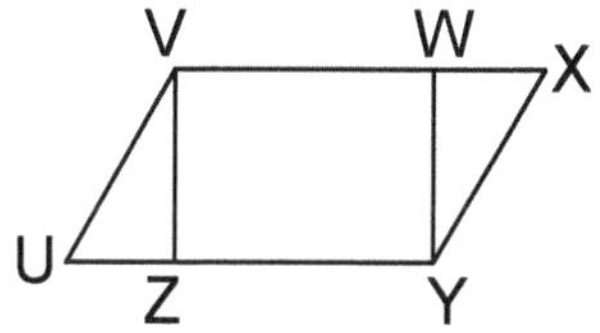

Part III – Tests for Parallelograms

In this section, we will discuss different ways that we can prove that a quadrilateral is a parallelogram. We will begin with some theorems.

Opposite Sides of a Parallelogram Converse Theorem
If both pairs of opposite sides of a quadrilateral are congruent, then the quadrilateral is a parallelogram.

Opposite Angles of a Parallelogram Converse Theorem
If both pairs of opposite angles of a quadrilateral are congruent, then the quadrilateral is a parallelogram.

Consecutive Angles of a Parallelogram Converse Theorem
If an angle of a quadrilateral is supplementary to both of its consecutive angles, then the quadrilateral is a parallelogram.

Diagonals of a Parallelogram Converse Theorem
If the diagonals of a quadrilateral bisect each other, then the quadrilateral is a parallelogram.

If one pair of opposite sides of a quadrilateral is both parallel and congruent, then the quadrilateral is a parallelogram.

Notice that the first four theorems are very similar to the ones that we discussed in the last section. The difference is that, in the theorems we used in the last section, we started out knowing that the quadrilaterals were parallelograms, and then we were able to say various things about the figures. With the theorems in this section, we do not start out knowing that the quadrilaterals are parallelograms; instead, we use the theorems to *prove* that the quadrilaterals are parallelograms.

We will prove the Opposite Angles of a Parallelogram Converse Theorem in Example 3. First, however, we will look at two examples that illustrate what these theorems tell us.

Example 1: Make a list of the different ways that you could show that quadrilateral EWGM is a parallelogram.

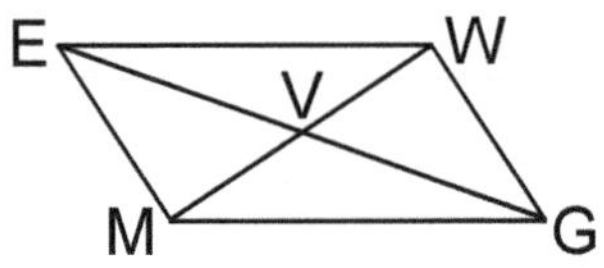

To use the definition of a parallelogram to show that quadrilateral EWGM is a parallelogram, you would need to prove that $\overline{EM} \parallel \overline{WG}$ AND that $\overline{EW} \parallel \overline{MG}$.

To use the Opposite Sides of a Parallelogram Converse Theorem to show that quadrilateral EWGM is a parallelogram, you would need to prove that $\overline{EW} \cong \overline{MG}$ AND that $\overline{EM} \cong \overline{WG}$.

To use the Opposite Angles of a Parallelogram Converse Theorem to show that quadrilateral EWGM is a parallelogram, you would need to prove that $\angle EMG \cong \angle EWG$ AND that $\angle MEW \cong \angle MGW$.

To use the Consecutive Angles of a Parallelogram Converse Theorem to show that quadrilateral EWGM is a parallelogram, you would need to prove one of the following: (1) $\angle EMG$ is supplementary to both $\angle MGW$ and $\angle MEW$, (2) $\angle MGW$ is supplementary to both $\angle GWE$ and $\angle GME$, (3) $\angle GWE$ is supplementary to both $\angle MGW$ and $\angle MEW$, or (4) $\angle WEM$ is supplementary to both $\angle EWG$ and $\angle EMG$.

To use the Diagonals of a Parallelogram Converse Theorem to show that quadrilateral EWGM is a parallelogram, you would need to prove that $\overline{EG}$ bisects $\overline{MW}$ AND that $\overline{MW}$ bisects $\overline{EG}$.

Finally, we could show that quadrilateral EWGM is a parallelogram by proving that either (1) $\overline{EW} \parallel \overline{MG}$ AND $\overline{EW} \cong \overline{MG}$, or (2) $\overline{EM} \parallel \overline{WG}$ AND $\overline{EM} \cong \overline{WG}$.

Example 2: In the figure at the right, KP = 5x + 1, UP = x + 18, SG = 6y – 24, and SP = 3y – 12. Find all the values of x and y that ensure that quadrilateral KSUG is a parallelogram.

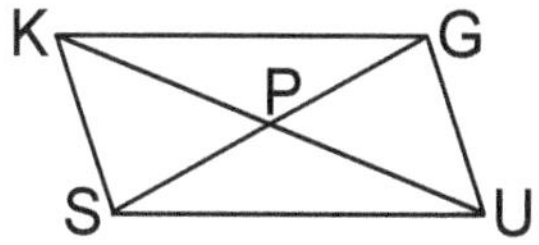

We can use the Diagonals of a Parallelogram Converse Theorem to say that, if $\overline{KP} \cong \overline{UP}$ and $\overline{SP} \cong \overline{GP}$ (or, equivalently, if KP = UP and 2 • SP = SG), then quadrilateral KSUG must be a parallelogram. This tells us that, if 5x + 1 = x + 18 and 2(3y – 12) = 6y – 24, then quadrilateral KSUG must be a parallelogram. When we solve these equations, we find that x = 4.25 and y can be any real number. (Recall that, if you are solving an equation and you get an obviously true statement such as 0 = 0, –24 = –24, or 3 = 3, then the equation has an infinite number of solutions.) However, y cannot be just any number in this particular problem. If, for instance, y = 1, then SG would have to equal 6 • 1 – 24, or –18. Since the lengths of all segments must be positive, we must note that 6y – 24 > 0 and 3y – 12 > 0. When we solve these inequalities, we find that y > 4. This tells us that, if x = 4.25 and y equals any real number greater than 4, then quadrilateral KSUG must be a parallelogram.

Example 3: Prove the Opposite Angles of a Parallelogram Converse Theorem.

We will prove this theorem using the two-column format that we discussed in Chapters 1-4, but you can write paragraph proofs when you work the exercises in this section if you want to.

As usual, we will begin by drawing a generic-looking picture to describe the "if" part of the theorem.

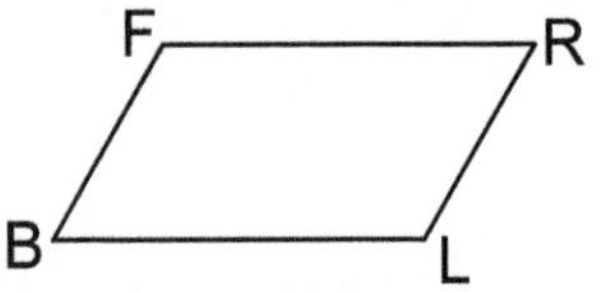

Now, we can say that we are given that $\angle B \cong \angle R$ and $\angle F \cong \angle L$, and we want to prove that quadrilateral FRLB is a parallelogram.

Statements	Reasons	Explanations
1. $\angle B \cong \angle R$ and $\angle F \cong \angle L$	1. Given	This was given to us.
2. $m\angle B = m\angle R$ and $m\angle F = m\angle L$	2. Definition of congruent angles	The definition of congruent angles tells us that, if two angles are congruent, then their measures are equal.
3. $m\angle B + m\angle F = m\angle R + m\angle F$	3. Addition Property of Equality	The Addition Property of Equality tells us that we can add $m\angle F$ to both sides of the equation $m\angle B = m\angle R$.
4. $m\angle B + m\angle F = m\angle R + m\angle L$	4. Substitution Property of Equality	We said in Statement (2) that $m\angle F = m\angle L$, and so we can change $m\angle R + m\angle F$ to $m\angle R + m\angle L$.
5. $m\angle B + m\angle F + m\angle R + m\angle L = 360^o$	5. The sum of the measures of the interior angles of a quadrilateral is 360°.	In Chapter 4, you proved that the sum of the measures of the interior angles of a quadrilateral is 360°. (We could have used the theorem that the sum of the interior angles of a convex polygon with n sides must equal $180^o(n-2)$ instead. This would have been equally correct.)
6. $m\angle B + m\angle F + m\angle B + m\angle F = 360^o$	6. Substitution Property of Equality	We said in Statement (4) that $m\angle B + m\angle F = m\angle R + m\angle L$, and so we can change $m\angle R + m\angle L$ to $m\angle B + m\angle F$.
7. $2(m\angle B + m\angle F) = 360^o$	7. Distributive Property	When we combine like terms, we are using the Distributive Property.

Statements continued	Reasons continued	Explanations continued
8. $m\angle B + m\angle F = 180°$	8. Division Property of Equality	The Division Property of Equality tells us that we can divide both sides of the equation in Statement (7) by 2.
9. $\angle B$ and $\angle F$ are supplementary	9. Definition of supplementary angles	We said in Statement (8) that $m\angle B + m\angle F = 180°$, and so $\angle B$ and $\angle F$ must be supplementary.
10. $\overline{BL} \parallel \overline{FR}$	10. Consecutive Interior Angles Converse Theorem	$\angle B$ and $\angle F$ are supplementary consecutive interior angles formed by $\overline{FR}$ and $\overline{BL}$ and the transversal $\overline{FB}$, and so we can use the Consecutive Interior Angles Converse Theorem to say that $\overline{BL} \parallel \overline{FR}$.
11. $m\angle B + m\angle L = 180°$	11. Substitution Property of Equality	We said in Statement (2) that $m\angle F = m\angle L$, and so we can change the $m\angle F$ in Statement (8) to $m\angle L$.
12. $\angle B$ and $\angle L$ are supplementary	12. Definition of supplementary angles	We said in Statement (11) that $m\angle B + m\angle L = 180°$, and so $\angle B$ and $\angle L$ must be supplementary.
13. $\overline{FB} \parallel \overline{RL}$	13. Consecutive Interior Angles Converse Theorem	$\angle B$ and $\angle L$ are supplementary consecutive interior angles formed by $\overline{FB}$ and $\overline{LR}$ and the transversal $\overline{BL}$, and so we can use the Consecutive Interior Angles Converse Theorem to say that $\overline{FB} \parallel \overline{RL}$.
14. Quadrilateral FRLB is a parallelogram	14. Definition of a parallelogram	We said in Statements (10) and (13) that $\overline{BL} \parallel \overline{FR}$ and $\overline{FB} \parallel \overline{RL}$, and so we can use the definition of a parallelogram to say that quadrilateral FRLB must be a parallelogram.

Problems:

1-10. For each of the figures below, (a) state whether or not quadrilateral ABCD must be a parallelogram, and (b) if your answer to part (a) is *yes*, state one or more theorems, definitions, or postulates to support your answer.

1a. Must quadrilateral ABCD be a parallelogram? ________

b. Theorems, definitions, and/or postulates used: ________

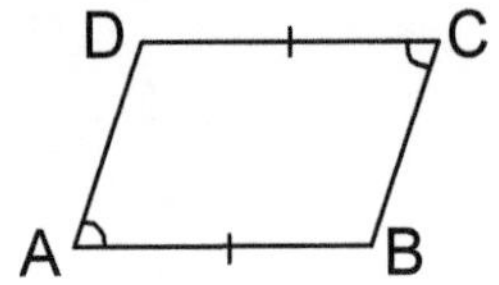

____

____

2a. Must quadrilateral ABCD be a parallelogram? ________

b. Theorems, definitions, and/or postulates used: ________

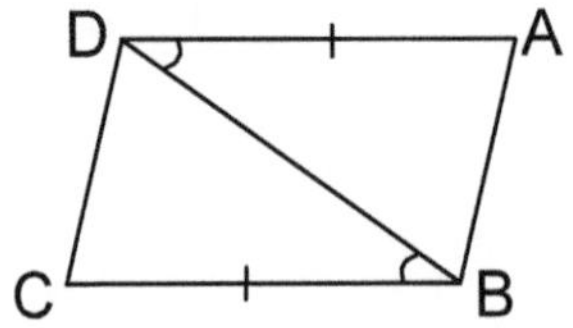

____

____

3a. Must quadrilateral ABCD be a parallelogram? ________

b. Theorems, definitions, and/or postulates used: ________

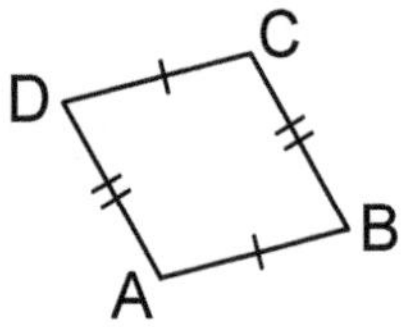

____

____

4a. Must quadrilateral ABCD be a parallelogram? ________

b. Theorems, definitions, and/or postulates used: ________

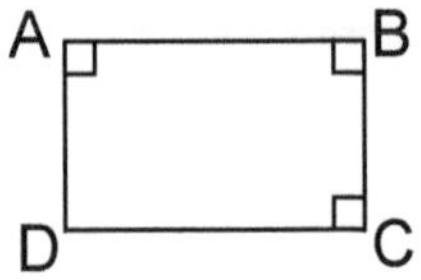

____

____

5a. Must quadrilateral ABCD be a parallelogram? ________

b. Theorems, definitions, and/or postulates used: ________

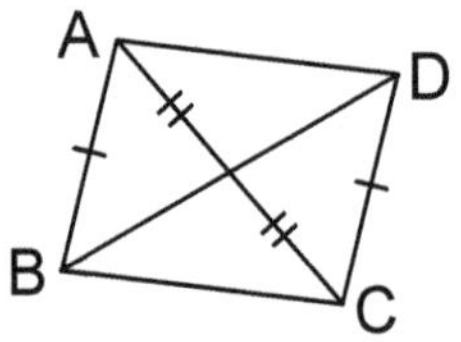

____

____

6a. Must quadrilateral ABCD be a parallelogram? ________

b. Theorems, definitions, and/or postulates used: _______

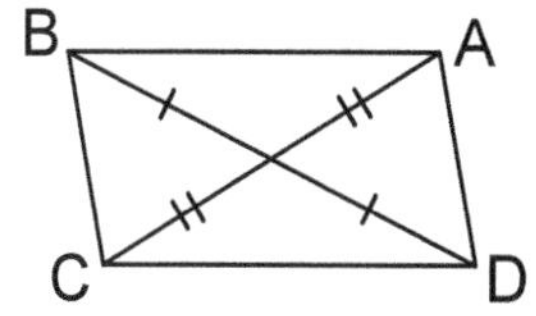

____

____

7a. Must quadrilateral ABCD be a parallelogram? ________

b. Theorems, definitions, and/or postulates used: _______

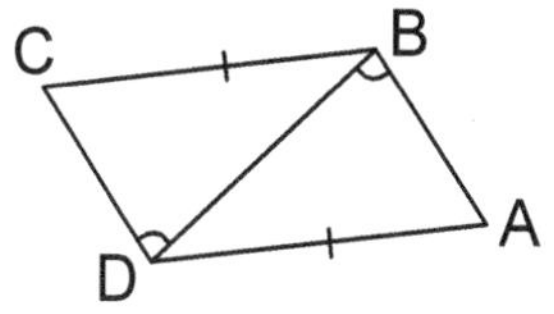

____

____

8a. Must quadrilateral ABCD be a parallelogram? ________

b. Theorems, definitions, and/or postulates used: _______

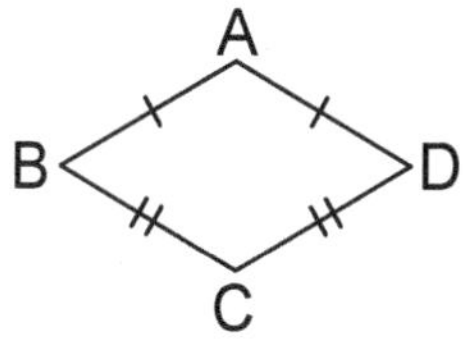

____

____

9a. Must quadrilateral ABCD be a parallelogram? ________

b. Theorems, definitions, and/or postulates used: _______

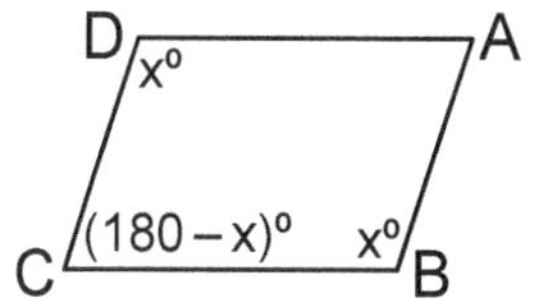

____

____

10a. Must quadrilateral ABCD be a parallelogram? ________

b. Theorems, definitions, and/or postulates used: _______

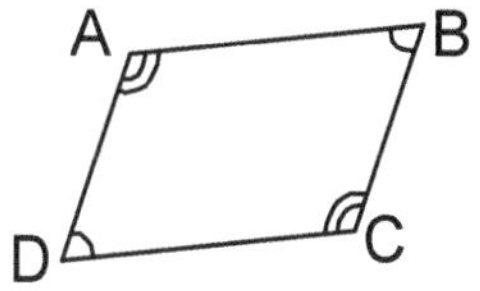

____

____

11-20. Find the values of x and y that will ensure that quadrilateral EFGH is a parallelogram.

11. x = ___________

y = ___________

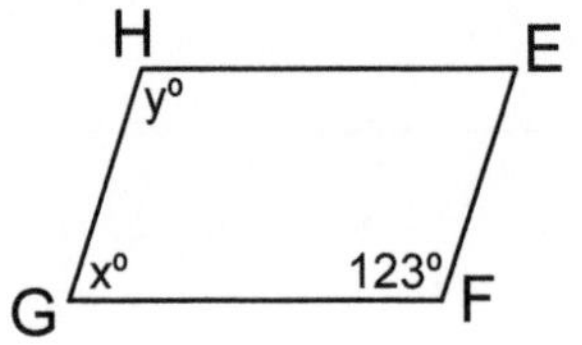

12. x = ___________

y = ___________

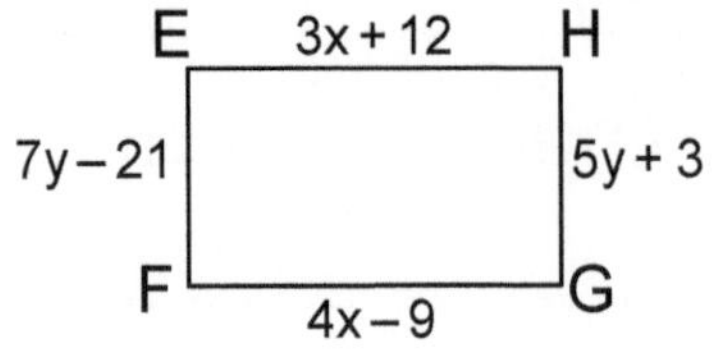

13. x = ___________

y = ___________

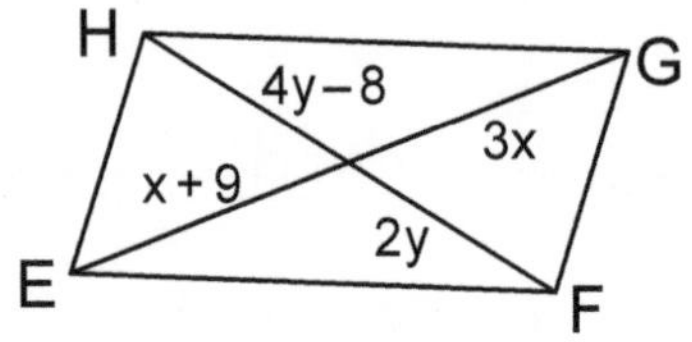

14. x = ___________

y = ___________

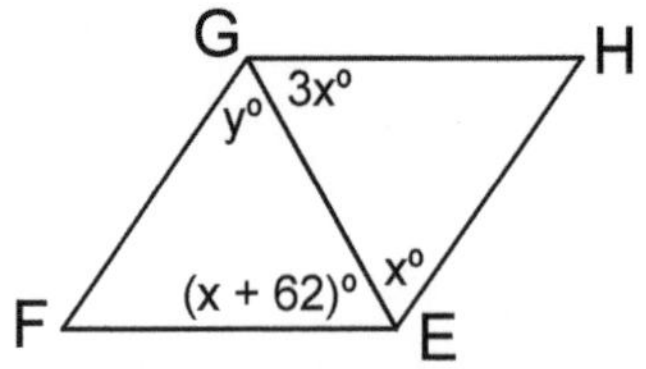

15. x = ___________

y = ___________

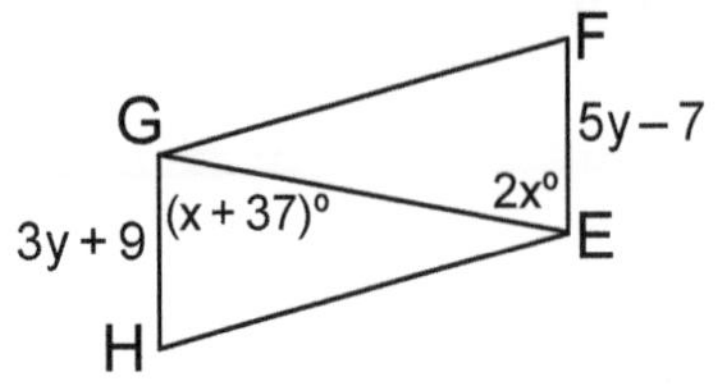

16. x = ___________

y = ___________

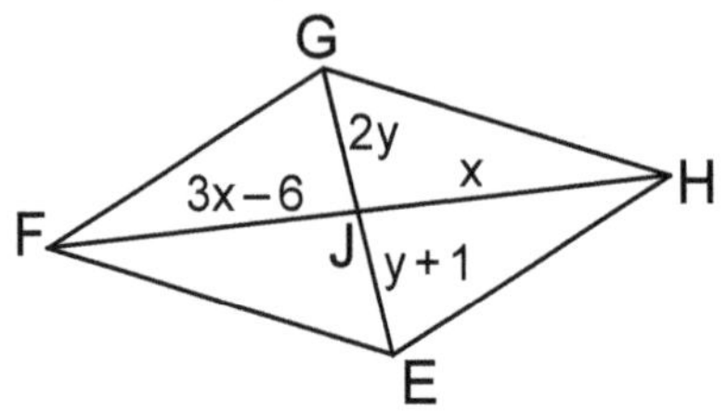

17. x = ___________

y = ___________

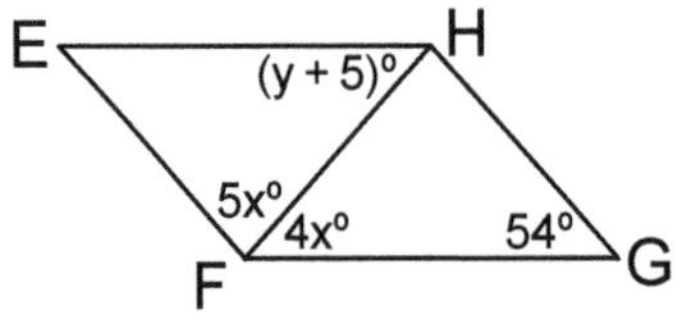

18. $x =$ ____________

$y =$ ____________

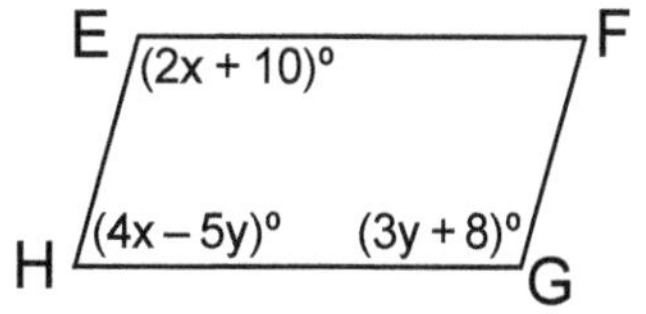

19. $x =$ ____________

$y =$ ____________

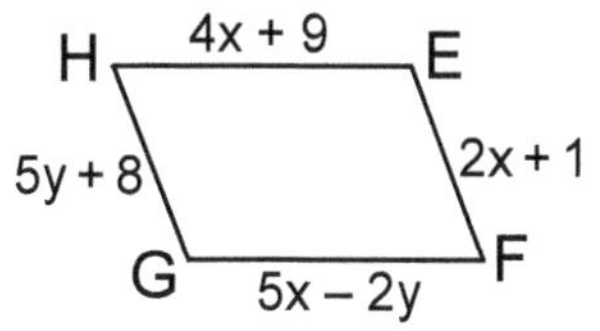

20. $x =$ ____________

$y =$ ____________

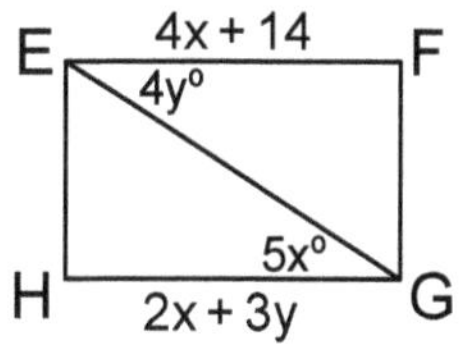

21. Prove the Opposite Sides of a Parallelogram Converse Theorem.

Given: $\overline{AD} \cong \overline{BC}$ and $\overline{AB} \cong \overline{DC}$

Prove: ________________________________

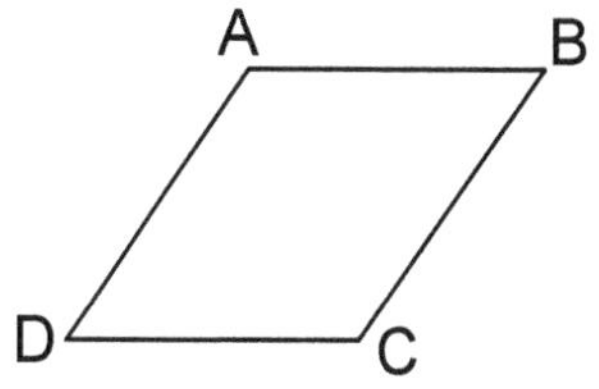

22. Prove the Diagonals of a Parallelogram Converse Theorem.

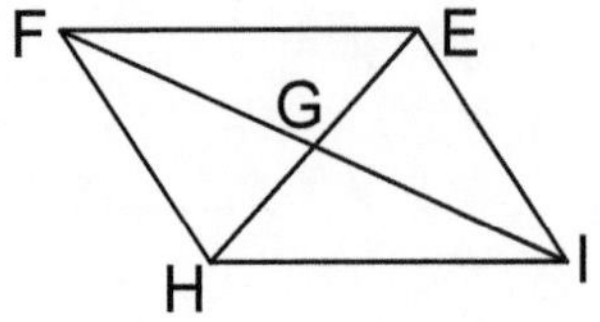

Given: $\overline{FI}$ bisects $\overline{HE}$ and $\overline{HE}$ bisects $\overline{FI}$

Prove: ______________________________

23. Prove that, if one pair of opposite sides of a quadrilateral is both parallel and congruent, then the quadrilateral must be a parallelogram.

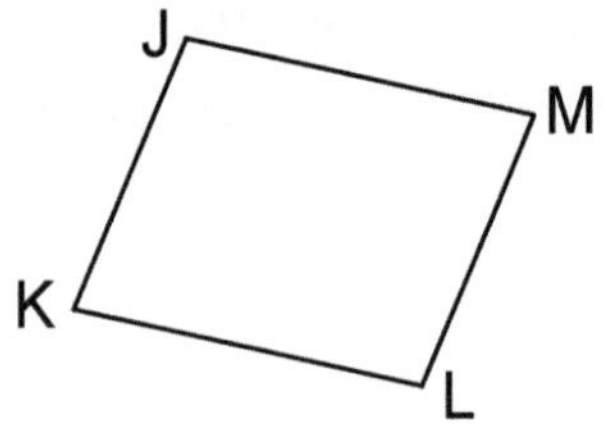

Given: ______________________________

Prove: ______________________________

24. Prove the Consecutive Angles of a Parallelogram Converse Theorem.

Given: $\angle P$ is supplementary to both $\angle N$ and $\angle Q$.

Prove: ______________________________

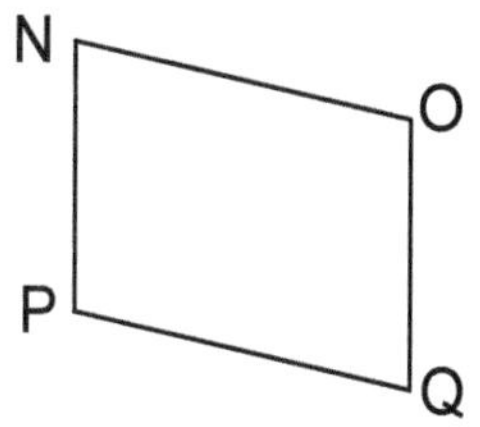

25. Given that $\overline{GH}$ bisects both $\angle FGI$ and $\angle FHI$ and that $\angle FGI \cong \angle FHI$ in the figure at the right, prove that quadrilateral FGIH is a parallelogram.

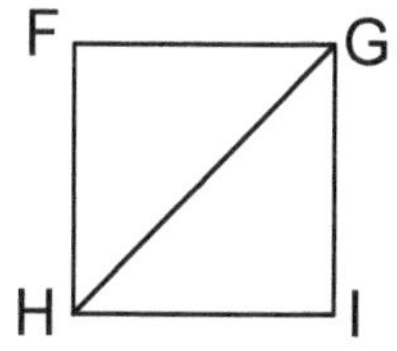

26. Given that $\overline{AE} \cong \overline{ED}$ and that $\overline{AB} \parallel \overline{CD}$ in the figure at the right, prove that quadrilateral ABDC is a parallelogram.

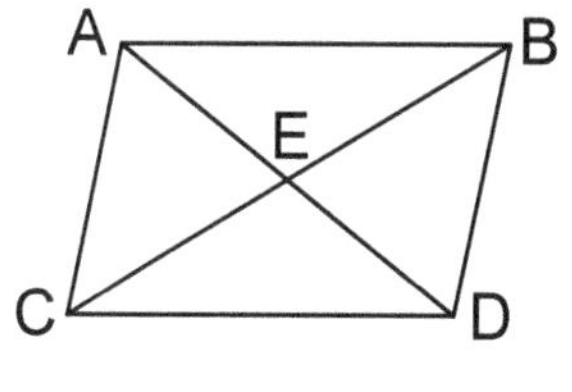

27. Given that quadrilaterals RSVU, STWV, UVYX, and VWZY are all parallelograms in the figure at the right, prove that quadrilateral RTZX is a parallelogram.

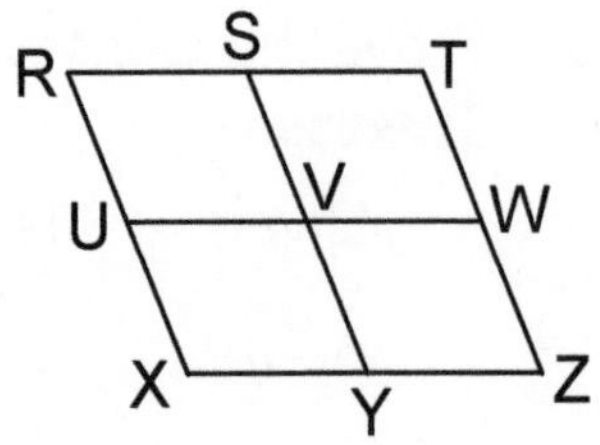

28. Given that $\angle M \cong \angle T$ and that $\angle MHA \cong \angle TAH$ in the figure at the right, prove that quadrilateral MATH is a parallelogram.

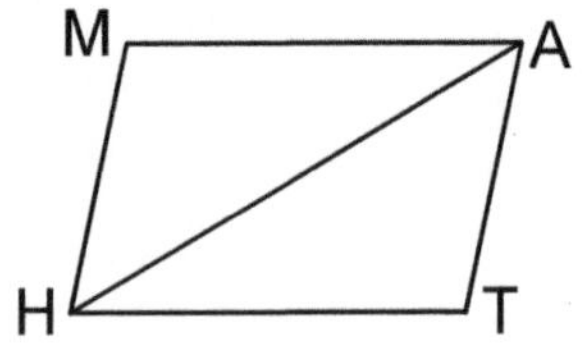

Part IV – Rectangles, Rhombi, and Squares

We will begin this section with a definition followed by three theorems. You will prove the theorems in the exercises for this section.

A quadrilateral is a rectangle if and only if all four angles are right angles.

If a quadrilateral is a rectangle, then it is a parallelogram.

If a quadrilateral is a rectangle, then its diagonals are congruent.

If the diagonals of a parallelogram are congruent, then it is a rectangle.

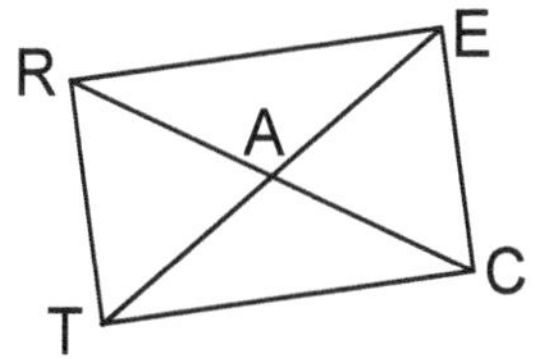

Example 1: Richard has just drawn quadrilateral RECT at the right. (a) If he knows that quadrilateral RECT is a rectangle, what should this tell him? (b) If he wants to *prove* that quadrilateral RECT is a rectangle, what are the ways in which he could do this?

(a) If Richard knows that quadrilateral RECT is a rectangle, the definition of a rectangle should tell him that $\angle ERT$, $\angle RTC$, $\angle TCE$, and $\angle CER$ are all right angles. Also, the first theorem above tells us that quadrilateral RECT must be a parallelogram. This means that all the properties of parallelograms that we discussed in Part II of this chapter hold true for quadrilateral RECT. Finally, the fact that the diagonals of a rectangle are congruent to each other should tell Richard that $\overline{RC} \cong \overline{ET}$.

(b) If Richard wants to *prove* that quadrilateral RECT is a rectangle, he would have to do one of two things.

He would have to find a way of proving that $\angle ERT$, $\angle RTC$, $\angle TCE$, and $\angle CER$ are all right angles. Then, by the definition of a rectangle, quadrilateral RECT would have to be a rectangle.

OR

He would have to find a way of showing that quadrilateral RECT is a parallelogram and that $\overline{RC} \cong \overline{ET}$. Then he could use the theorem *If the diagonals of a parallelogram are congruent, then it is a rectangle.* to say that quadrilateral RECT must be a rectangle.

Now, we need another definition and five more theorems. You will prove the theorems in the exercises for this section.

A quadrilateral is a rhombus if and only if all four sides are congruent to each other.

If a quadrilateral is a rhombus, then it is a parallelogram.

If a quadrilateral is a rhombus, then each diagonal bisects a pair of opposite angles.

If a quadrilateral is a rhombus, then its diagonals are perpendicular.

If a diagonal of a parallelogram bisects an angle of the parallelogram, then it is a rhombus.

If the diagonals of a parallelogram are perpendicular, then it is a rhombus.

Example 2: Juan has just drawn quadrilateral RHOM at the right. (a) If he knows that quadrilateral RHOM is a rhombus, what should this tell him? (b) If he wants to *prove* that quadrilateral RHOM is a rhombus, what are the ways in which he could do this?

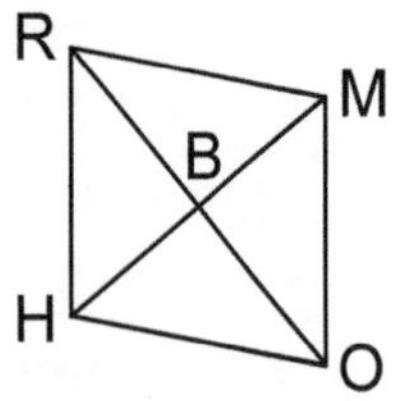

(a) If Juan knows that quadrilateral RHOM is a rhombus, then, by the definition of a rhombus, he should know that $\overline{RH}$, $\overline{RM}$, $\overline{MO}$, and $\overline{HO}$ are all congruent to each other. Also, as the first theorem above tells us, all rhombi are also parallelograms. This means that Juan should know that all the properties of parallelograms that we discussed in Part II of this chapter hold true for quadrilateral RHOM. Additionally, the second theorem above should tell Juan that $\overline{RO}$ bisects both $\angle MRH$ and $\angle MOH$ and that $\overline{HM}$ bisects both $\angle RMO$ and $\angle RHO$. Finally, the theorem *If a quadrilateral is a rhombus, then its diagonals are perpendicular* should tell Juan that $\overline{RO} \perp \overline{HM}$.

(b) If Juan wants to *prove* that quadrilateral RHOM is a rhombus, he would have to do one of four things.

He would have to find a way of proving that $\overline{RH}$, $\overline{RM}$, $\overline{MO}$, and $\overline{HO}$ are all congruent to each other. Then, by the definition of a rhombus, quadrilateral RHOM would have to be a rhombus.

OR

He would have to find a way of showing that quadrilateral RHOM is a parallelogram and that $\overline{RO}$ bisects either $\angle MRH$ or $\angle MOH$. Then he could use the theorem *If a diagonal of a parallelogram bisects an angle of the parallelogram, then it is a rhombus* to say that quadrilateral RHOM must be a rhombus.

OR

He would have to find a way of showing that quadrilateral RHOM is a parallelogram and that $\overline{HM}$ bisects either $\angle RMO$ or $\angle RHO$. Then he could use the theorem *If a diagonal of a parallelogram bisects an angle of the parallelogram, then it is a rhombus* to say that quadrilateral RHOM must be a rhombus.

OR

He would have to find a way of showing that quadrilateral RHOM is a parallelogram and that $\overline{RO} \perp \overline{HM}$. Then he could use the last theorem on the previous page to say that quadrilateral RHOM must be a rhombus.

Now, we need one more definition.

A quadrilateral is a <u>square</u> if and only if it is both a rhombus and a rectangle.

Example 3: Becky has just drawn quadrilateral SQUA at the right. (a) If she knows that quadrilateral SQUA is a square, what should this tell her? (b) If she wants to *prove* that quadrilateral SQUA is a square, what are the ways in which she could do this?

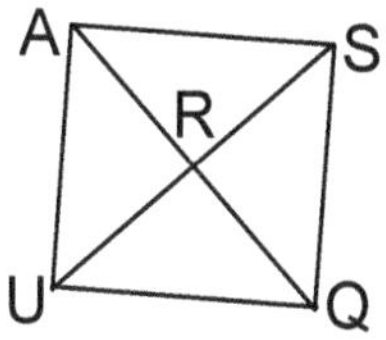

(a) If Becky know that quadrilateral SQUA is a square, then she should know that it is both a rhombus and a rectangle. This means that she should know that quadrilateral SQUA has all the properties of rectangles and rhombi that we just discussed.

(b) If Becky wants to *prove* that quadrilateral SQUA is a square, then she needs to find a way to prove that it is a rectangle, and then she must find a way to prove that it is a rhombus.

Problems:

1-4. Quadrilateral ABDE at the right is a rhombus.

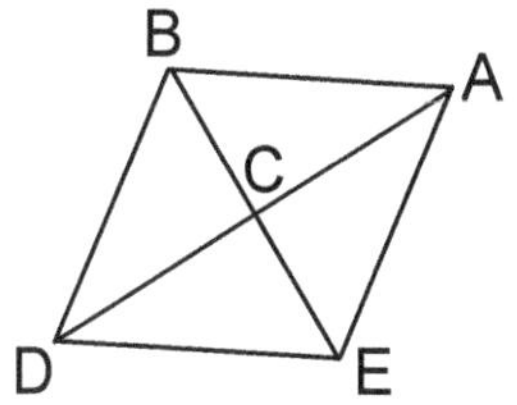

1. If BC = 3 and AB = 5, then AC = _________,

   AD = _________, and BD = _________.

2. If m∠DBC = 38°, then m∠DBA = _________, m∠BAE = _________, and

   m∠BAD = _________.

3. If m∠ACE = (7x – 8)° and m∠BDE = 5x°, then x = _________,

   m∠BDE = _________, and m∠BDA = _________.

4. If AC = 7y + 9 and CD = 10y – 12, then y = _________ and AD = _________.

5-8. Quadrilateral FGHI at the right is a rectangle.

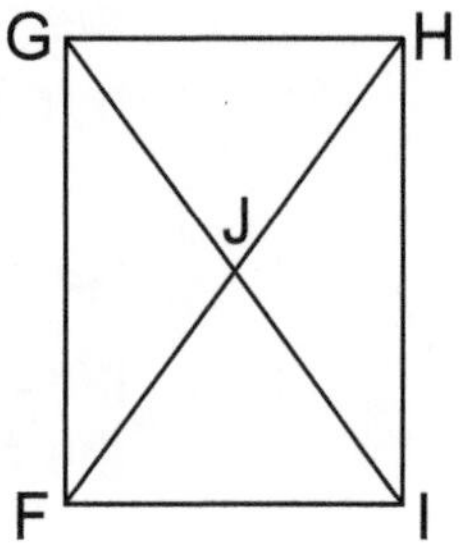

5. If $m\angle GFH = 54°$, then $m\angle HFI =$ _________ and $m\angle GHF =$ _________.

6. If HJ = 7, then HF = _________ and GI = _________.

7. If HF = 28 – 2n and GJ = n + 8, then n = _________ and GI = _________.

8. If $m\angle IHF = (3p + 8)°$ and $m\angle HFI = (5p + 2)°$, then p = _________ and $m\angle IHF =$ _________.

9-12. Quadrilateral KLMN at the right is a square.

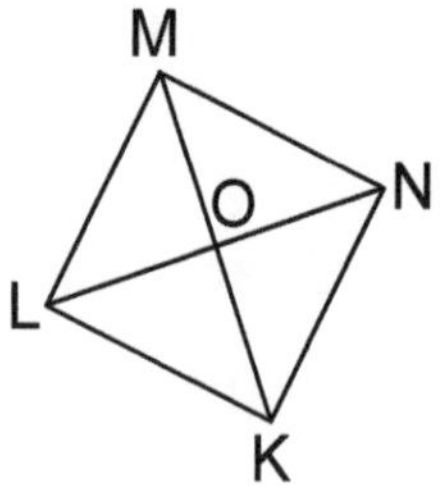

9. $m\angle NOK =$ _________, $m\angle MNK =$ _________, and $m\angle NMK =$ _________

10. If MN = 8, then NK = _________ and MK = _________.

11. If OL = 3w + 20 and LN = 12w – 2, then w = _________ and MK = _________.

12. If $m\angle NLK = 5q°$ and $m\angle LOK = 3v°$, then q = _________ and v = _________.

13-29. Fill in each of the following blanks with *might be*, *must be*, or *cannot be*.

13. If a figure is a square, then its diagonals _______________ perpendicular.

14. If a figure is a rectangle, then its diagonals ________________ perpendicular.

15. If a quadrilateral is a parallelogram, then it ________________ a rhombus.

16. If a quadrilateral is a square, then it ________________ a rhombus.

17. If a quadrilateral is a rectangle, then it ________________ a square.

18. If a quadrilateral is not a square, then it ________________ a rectangle.

19. If a quadrilateral is not a square, then it ________________ a rhombus.

20. If a quadrilateral is not a parallelogram, then it ________________ a rectangle.

21. If a quadrilateral is not a rhombus, then it ________________ a parallelogram.

22. In the figure at the right, $\overline{AB} \parallel \overline{CD}$ but $\overline{AD}$ is not parallel to $\overline{BC}$.

Then quadrilateral ABCD ________________ a rhombus.

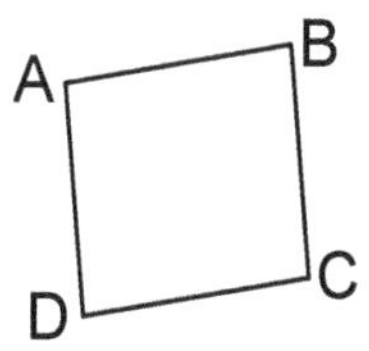

23. In the figure at the right, EP = 18, GP = 19, FP = 18, and HP = 19. Then quadrilateral EFGH ________________ a rectangle.

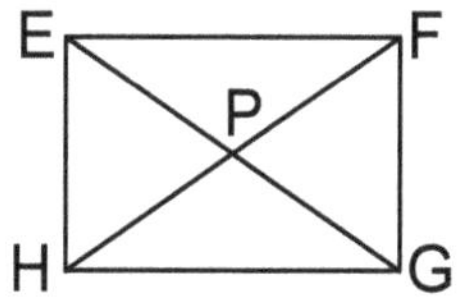

24. In the figure at the right, $\overline{JN}$, $\overline{LN}$, $\overline{MN}$, and $\overline{KN}$ are all congruent to each other. Then quadrilateral JKLM _______________ a rectangle.

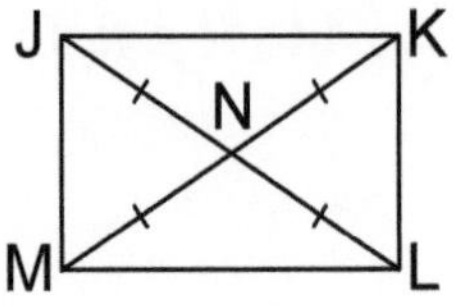

25. In the figure at the right, quadrilateral TUVW is a parallelogram and $\angle U$ is a right angle. Then quadrilateral TUVW _______________ a rectangle.

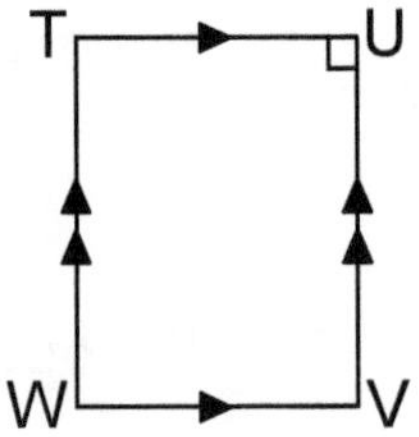

26. In quadrilateral ABCD, $\overline{AC} \cong \overline{BD}$ and $\overline{AC} \perp \overline{BD}$. Then quadrilateral ABCD _______________ a square.

Hint: Draw a picture.

27. In quadrilateral EFGH, EF = 14, FG = 15, GH = 14, and EH = 15. Then quadrilateral EFGH _______________ a parallelogram, _______________ a rhombus, _______________ a rectangle, and _______________ a square.

28. In quadrilateral IJKL, $\angle IKJ$ is a right angle. Then quadrilateral IJKL _______________ a rectangle.

29. In quadrilateral MNOP, $\overline{MO}$ bisects both $\angle NMP$ and $\angle NOP$, $\angle MNO \cong \angle MPO$, and $\angle MNP$ is a right angle. Then quadrilateral MNOP _______________ a square.

30. Prove the following theorem: If a quadrilateral is a rectangle, then it must be a parallelogram.

Given: Quadrilateral ABCD is a rectangle

Prove: ______________________________

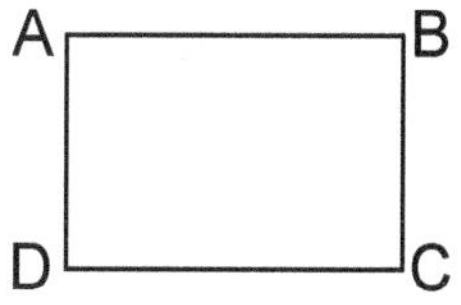

31. Prove the following theorem: If a quadrilateral is a rhombus, then it must be a parallelogram.

Given: Quadrilateral EFGH is a rhombus

Prove: ______________________________

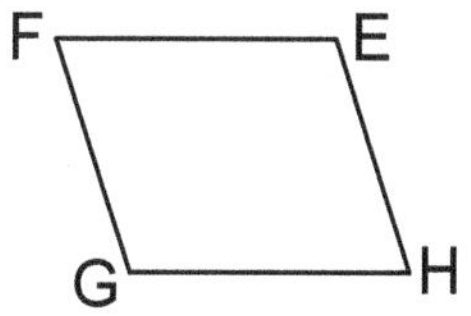

32. Prove the following theorem: If a quadrilateral is a square, then it must be a parallelogram.

Given: ______________________________

Prove: ______________________________

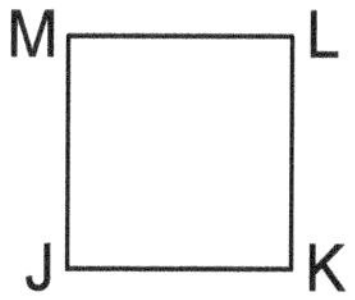

33. Prove the following theorem: If a quadrilateral is a rectangle, then its diagonals are congruent.

Given: Quadrilateral NORQ is a rectangle

Prove: ______________________

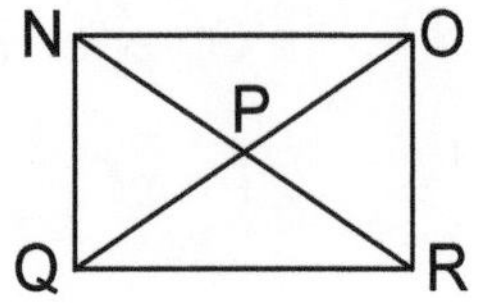

34. Prove the following theorem: If the diagonals of a parallelogram are congruent, then it is a rectangle.

Given: Quadrilateral STUV is a parallelogram and $\overline{TV} \cong \overline{SU}$

Prove: ____

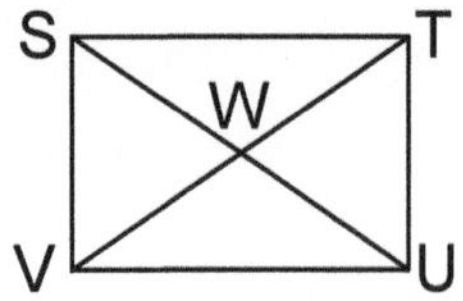

35. Prove the following theorem: If a quadrilateral is a rhombus, then each diagonal bisects a pair of opposite angles.

Given: ______________________________

Prove: ______________________________

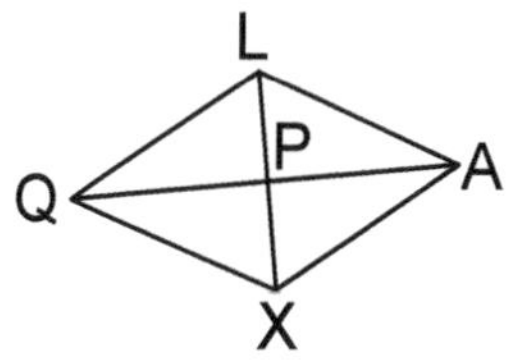

36. Prove the following theorem: If a quadrilateral is a rhombus, then its diagonals are perpendicular.

Given: ______________________________

Prove: ______________________________

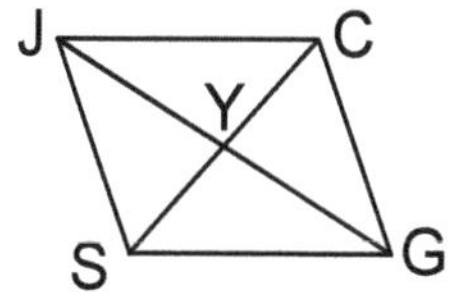

37. Prove the following theorem: If a diagonal of a parallelogram bisects an angle of the parallelogram, then it is a rhombus.

Given: ____

Prove: ____

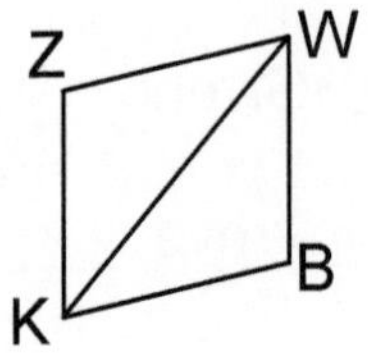

Hint: You will use the Isosceles Triangle Converse Theorem.

38. Prove the following theorem: If the diagonals of a parallelogram are perpendicular, then it is a rhombus.

Given: ____

Prove: ____

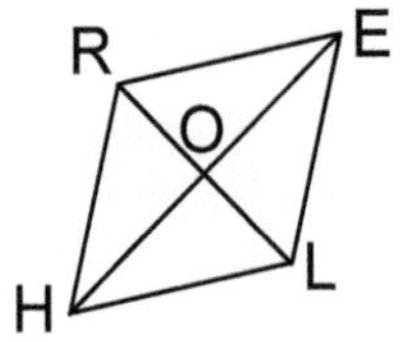

39. Given that quadrilateral RSTU at the right is a rhombus, prove that $\angle TSU \cong \angle TUS$.

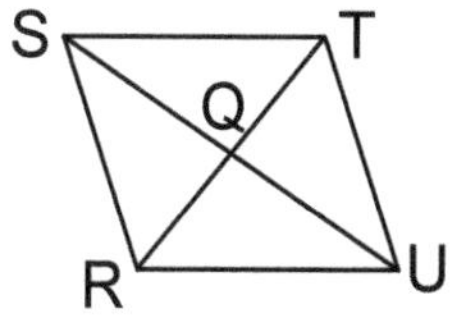

40. In the figure at the right, quadrilateral DHGC is a rhombus, and points D, H, and G are the midpoints of $\overline{AC}$, $\overline{AB}$, and $\overline{BC}$. Prove that ΔABC is an isosceles triangle.

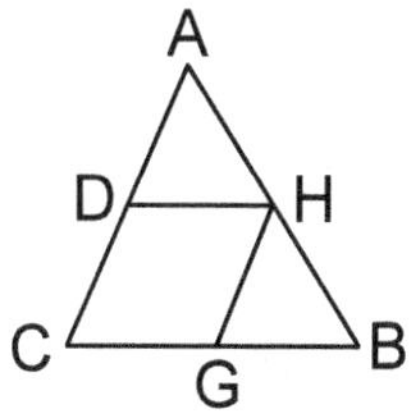

41. Given that quadrilateral EAKR is a rectangle, prove that $\overline{RN} \cong \overline{KN}$.

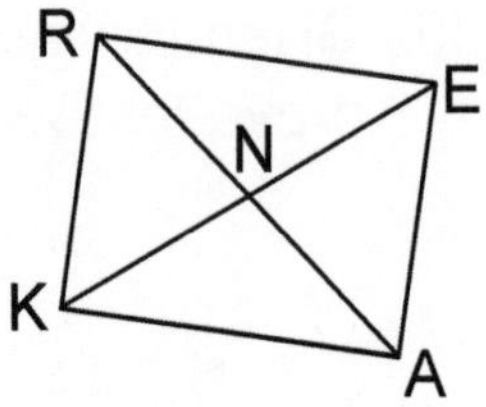

Part V – Kites and Trapezoids

We will begin this section with some definitions.

A quadrilateral is a trapezoid if and only if it has *exactly* one set of parallel sides. In a trapezoid, the sides that are parallel to each other are called the bases, and the sides that are not parallel to each other are called the legs. The two adjacent angles that share a base as a common side are called the base angles.

This tells us that the figures below are all trapezoids. In quadrilateral ABCD, the bases are $\overline{AB}$ and $\overline{CD}$, the legs are $\overline{AD}$ and $\overline{BC}$, $\angle A$ and $\angle B$ make up one pair of base angles, and $\angle D$ and $\angle C$ make up the other pair of base angles. In quadrilateral EFGH, the bases are $\overline{EH}$ and $\overline{FG}$, the legs are $\overline{EF}$ and $\overline{HG}$, $\angle E$ and $\angle H$ make up one pair of base angles, and $\angle F$ and $\angle G$ make up the other pair of base angles. In quadrilateral IJKL, the bases are $\overline{LI}$ and $\overline{JK}$, the legs are $\overline{IJ}$ and $\overline{LK}$, $\angle I$ and $\angle L$ make up one pair of base angles, and $\angle J$ and $\angle K$ make up the other pair of base angles.

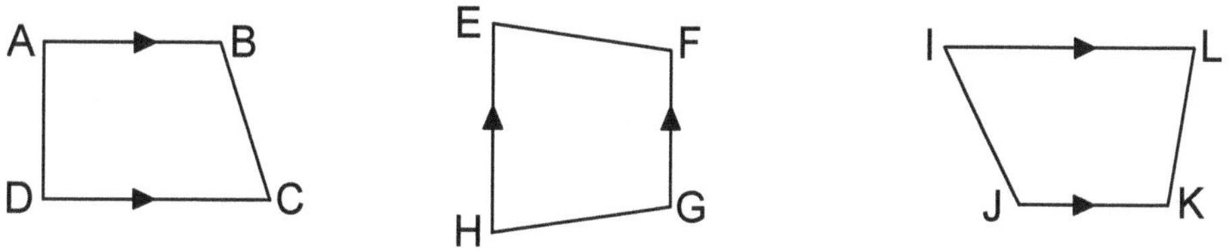

Now, we need another definition and another theorem. We will prove this theorem in the next chapter.

A segment is a midsegment of a trapezoid if and only if it connects the midpoints of the two legs of the trapezoid.

Midsegment of a Trapezoid Theorem

The midsegment of a trapezoid is parallel to the bases, and its length is equal to the average of the lengths of the two bases of the trapezoid.

We will illustrate this definition and theorem with an example.

Example 1: If NO = 8 + x, RS = 4 – x, and QP = 15 + 2x in the trapezoid at the right, what is the length of $\overline{RS}$?

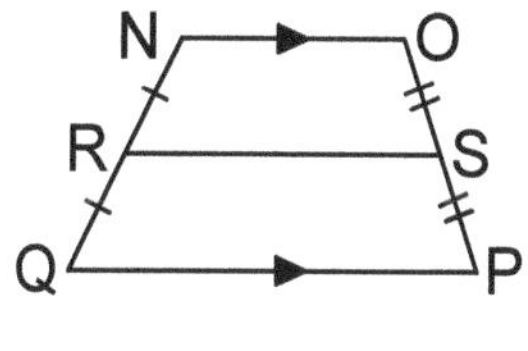

We will begin by noting that R is the midpoint of $\overline{NQ}$, S is the midpoint of $\overline{OP}$, and $\overline{RS}$ connects R and S. Therefore, $\overline{RS}$ is the midsegment of trapezoid NOPQ. By the Midsegment of Trapezoid Theorem, this means that $\overline{RS}$ is parallel to both $\overline{NO}$ and $\overline{QP}$ and that $RS = \frac{NO + QP}{2}$. Thus, we can find the value of x by writing $4 - x = \frac{8 + x + 15 + 2x}{2}$ and then solving this equation as shown on the next page.

$$4 - x = \frac{8 + x + 15 + 2x}{2}$$

$$4 - x = \frac{23 + 3x}{2}$$

$$8 - 2x = 23 + 3x \quad \text{(by multiplying both sides by 2)}$$

$$-3 = x$$

This tells us that RS = 4 – (–3), or 7.

Now, we need another definition and four more theorems. You will prove these theorems in the exercises for this section.

> A trapezoid is an <u>isosceles trapezoid</u> if and only if its legs are congruent to each other.

> **Base Angles of an Isosceles Trapezoid Theorem**
> The base angles of an isosceles trapezoid are congruent.

> **Diagonals of an Isosceles Trapezoid Theorem**
> If a quadrilateral is an isosceles trapezoid, then its diagonals are congruent.

> **Base Angles of an Isosceles Trapezoid Converse Theorem**
> If a pair of base angles of a trapezoid are congruent to each other, then the trapezoid is an isosceles trapezoid.

> **Diagonals of an Isosceles Trapezoid Converse Theorem**
> If the diagonals of a trapezoid are congruent, then it is an isosceles trapezoid.

Example 2: Caroline has just drawn the quadrilateral at the right. (a) If she knows that this is an isosceles trapezoid with bases $\overline{TU}$ and $\overline{VM}$, what should this tell her? (b) If Caroline wants to *prove* that quadrilateral TUMV is an isosceles trapezoid, what are the ways in which she can do this?

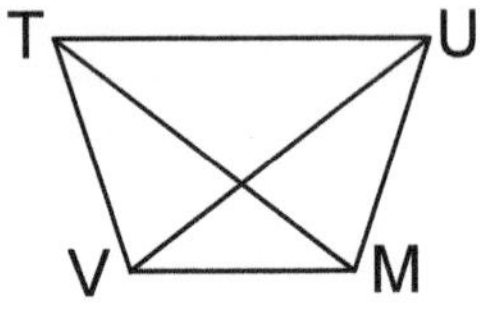

(a) If Caroline knows that quadrilateral TUMV is an isosceles trapezoid with bases $\overline{TU}$ and $\overline{VM}$, the definition of an isosceles trapezoid should tell her that quadrilateral TUMV is a trapezoid (which means that $\overline{TU} \parallel \overline{VM}$ and that $\overline{TV}$ is not parallel to $\overline{UM}$) and that $\overline{TV} \cong \overline{UM}$. The Base Angles of an Isosceles Trapezoid Theorem should tell her that $\angle UTV \cong \angle TUM$ and that $\angle TVM \cong \angle UMV$, and the Diagonals of an Isosceles Trapezoid Theorem should tell her that $\overline{TM} \cong \overline{UV}$.

(b) If Caroline wants to *prove* that quadrilateral TUMV is an isosceles trapezoid, she must first prove that it is a trapezoid (which means she must find a way of proving that $\overline{TU} \parallel \overline{VM}$ and that $\overline{TV}$ is not parallel to $\overline{UM}$), and then she must find a way of proving one of the following.

She could find a way of showing that $\overline{TV} \cong \overline{UM}$. Then, by the definition of an isosceles trapezoid, quadrilateral TUMV would have to be an isosceles trapezoid.

OR

She could find a way of showing that $\angle UTV \cong \angle TUM$. Then, by the Base Angles of an Isosceles Trapezoid Converse Theorem, quadrilateral TUMV would have to be an isosceles trapezoid.

OR

She could find a way of showing that $\angle TVM \cong \angle UMV$. Then, by the Base Angles of an Isosceles Trapezoid Converse Theorem, quadrilateral TUMV would have to be an isosceles trapezoid.

OR

She could find a way of showing that $\overline{TM} \cong \overline{UV}$. Then, by the Diagonals of an Isosceles Trapezoid Converse Theorem, quadrilateral TUMV would have to be an isosceles trapezoid.

Now, we need one more definition.

A quadrilateral is a <u>kite</u> if and only if it has two pairs of disjoint consecutive sides that are congruent.

Before we talk about any theorems for kites, let's look at what this definition is saying. The figures below are both examples of kites. In quadrilateral AREY, $\overline{AR}$ and $\overline{AY}$ are consecutive sides that are congruent to each other, and $\overline{RE}$ and $\overline{EY}$ are consecutive sides that are congruent to each other. In quadrilateral PKSN, $\overline{PN}$ and $\overline{PK}$ are consecutive sides that are congruent to each other, and $\overline{NS}$ and $\overline{KS}$ are consecutive sides that are congruent to each other.

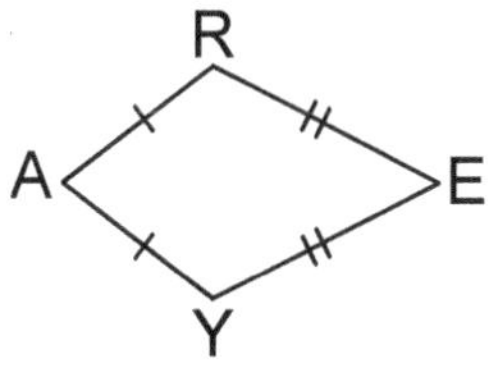

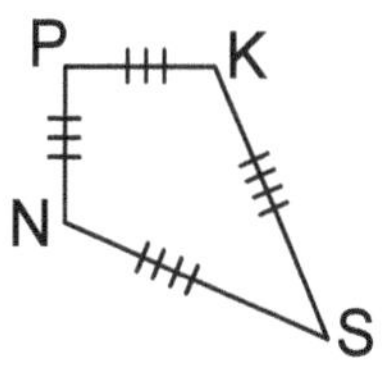

Now, look back at the definition of a kite and notice that the word *disjoint* is part of the definition. This means that we cannot have all four sides of the quadrilateral congruent to each other. For instance, in order for quadrilateral AREY above to be a kite, $\overline{AR}$ and $\overline{AY}$ cannot be congruent to $\overline{RE}$ and $\overline{EY}$.

Now, we need one more theorem. You will prove this theorem in the exercises for this section.

The diagonals of a kite are perpendicular to each other.

Example 3: In the figure at the right, $m\angle TIK = 124°$, $IA = 8$, and $KI = 17$. Find $m\angle EIK$, KA, and KT.

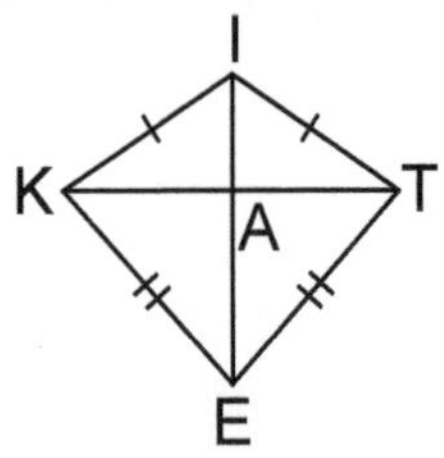

We will begin by noting that the Reflexive Property of Segment Congruence and the SSS Congruence Postulate tell us that $\Delta IKE \cong \Delta ITE$. One of the things that this tells us is that $\angle EIK \cong \angle EIT$. This means that $m\angle EIK = m\angle TIK \div 2$, and so $m\angle EIK$ must equal 62°.

To find the length of $\overline{KA}$, we will begin by noting that the theorem above tells us that $\overline{IA} \perp \overline{KT}$. This tells us that ΔIKA is a right triangle, and so we can find the length of $\overline{KA}$ by using the Pythagorean Theorem, as shown below.

$$(IA)^2 + (KA)^2 = (KI)^2$$
$$8^2 + (KA)^2 = 17^2$$
$$64 + (KA)^2 = 289$$
$$(KA)^2 = 225$$
$$KA = 15$$

To find the length of $\overline{KT}$, we will note that the SAS Congruence Postulate tells us that $\Delta IKA \cong \Delta ITA$ (note that we were given that $\overline{KI} \cong \overline{TI}$, the Reflexive Property of Segment Congruence tells us that $\overline{IA} \cong \overline{IA}$, and we already said that $\angle EIK \cong \angle EIT$). Among other things, this tells us that $\overline{KA} \cong \overline{AT}$, and so we can say that AT = 15. This means that KT = 15 + 15, or 30.

Problems:

1. In the figure at the right, $\overline{MN}$ is parallel to ________ and ________. Which theorem proves this? ______________

____

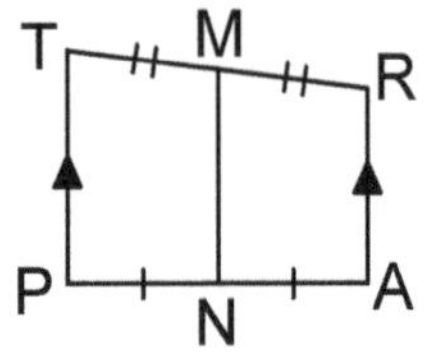

2-7. Quadrilateral ABCD is a trapezoid, and $\overline{JK}$ is the midsegment of trapezoid ABCD.

2. If AB = 12 and CD = 8, then JK = __________.

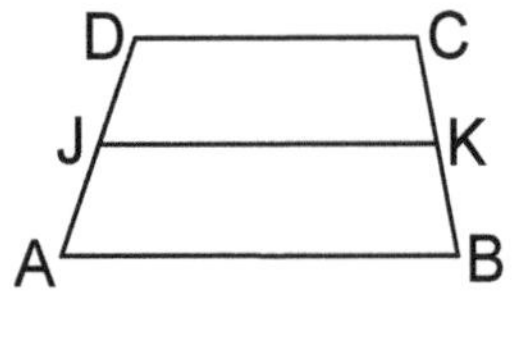

3. If AB = 22 and CD = 32, then JK = __________.

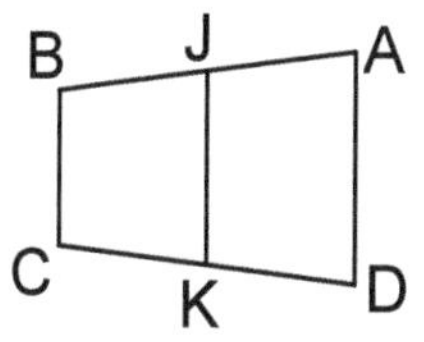

4. If AD = 27 and JK = 22, then BC = __________.

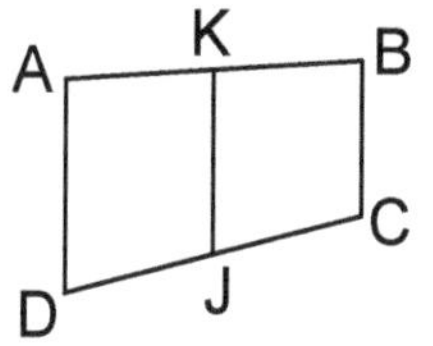

5. If BC = 12 and JK = 8, then AD = __________.

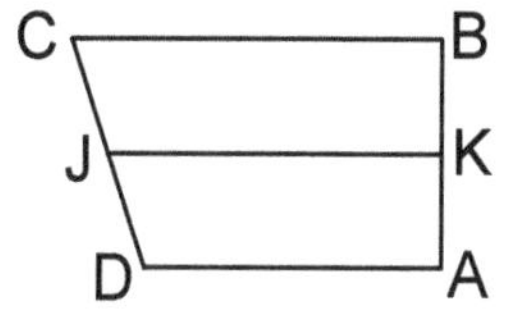

6. If AB = 4x + 5, JK = 3x + 5, and CD = 4x + 7, then

x = __________ and JK = __________.

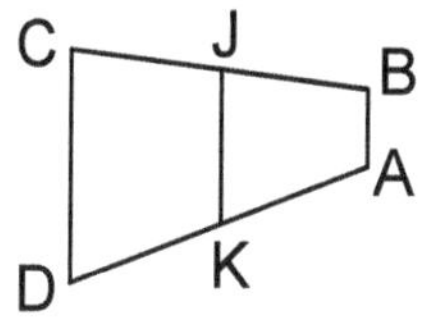

7. If AD = 5y – 16, BC = 14 – y, and JK = 3y – 5, then

AD =__________ and JK = __________.

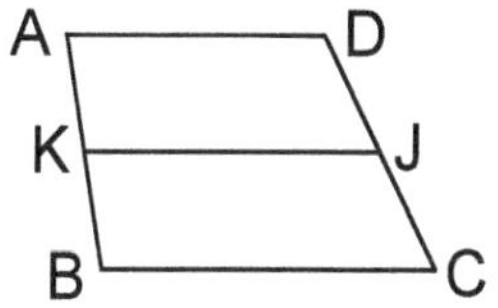

8-11. Quadrilateral EFGH at the right is a trapezoid with $\overline{FG}$ and $\overline{EH}$ as its bases, and ∠E is a right angle.

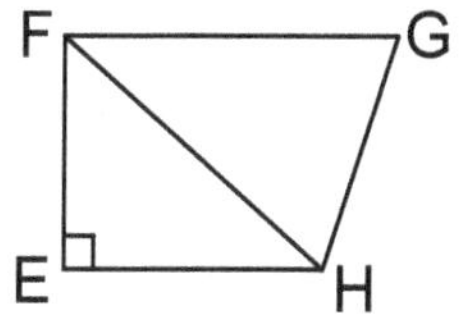

8. m∠EFG = __________

9. If m∠EHG = 112°, then m∠G = __________.

10. If m∠GFH = 37°, then m∠HFE = __________ and m∠FHE = __________.

11. If m∠EFH = 48°, then m∠HFG = __________ and m∠FHE = __________.

12-17. Quadrilateral STWV is an isosceles trapezoid with legs $\overline{SV}$ and $\overline{TW}$.

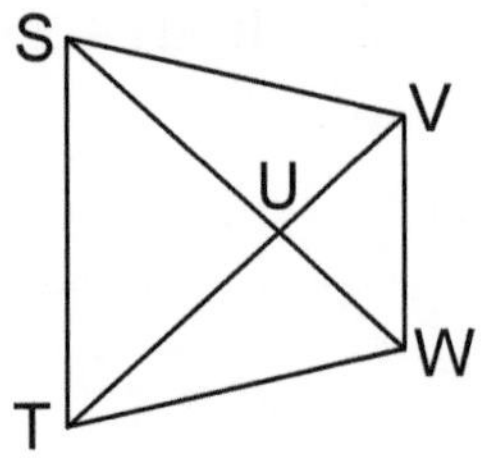

12. If SW = 8, then VT = _________. Which definition(s), postulate(s), and/or theorem(s) from this section support your answer? ________________________________

____

13. If m∠TSV = 71°, then m∠STW = _________. Which definition(s), postulate(s), and/or theorem(s) from this section support your answer? _________________

____

14. If m∠STW = 75°, then m∠VWT = _________. Which definition(s), postulate(s), and/or theorem(s) from this section support your answer? _________________

____

15. If SV = 5, then TW = _________. Which definition(s), postulate(s), and/or theorem(s) from this section support your answer? _______________________

____

16. If SU = 6, UW = 4, and TV = x + 1, then x = _________.

17. If SV = 5y + 7 and TW = 4 – y, then y = _________ and TW = _________.

18-25. Quadrilateral RSTL is a kite, LY = 5, YR = 3, m∠LTY = 30°, and m∠LRS = 118°.

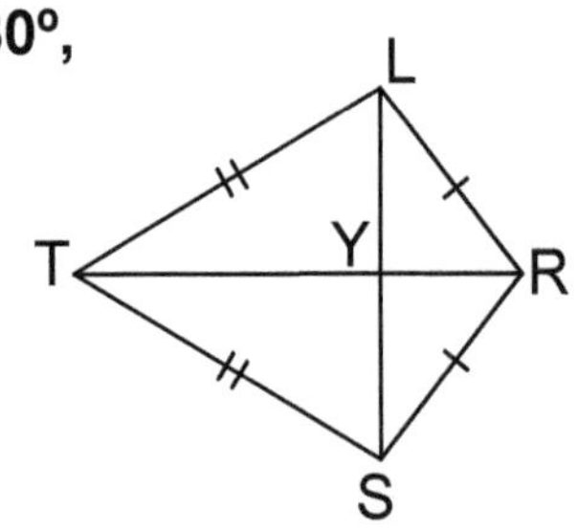

18. ΔLYT ≅ Δ_________, ΔRLT ≅ Δ_________, and ΔRSY ≅ Δ_________

19. m∠LYT = _________

20. m∠LTS = _________, m∠TLY = _________, and m∠TSL = _________

21. m∠LRT = _________, m∠RLS = _________, and m∠RSL = _________

22. m∠RLT = _________ and m∠RST = _________

23. LR = _________ and RS = _________.

24. LS = _________

25. YS = _________

26. Prove the Base Angles of an Isosceles Trapezoid Theorem.

Given: ____________________________________

Prove: ____________________________________

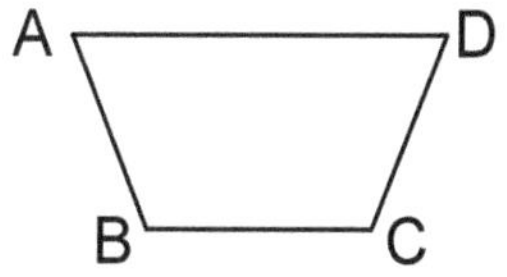

Hint: After you state the information given to you and what it tells you, use the theorem *Through a point P not on a line, there is exactly one line perpendicular to the given line* to draw $\overline{BE}$ so that $\overline{BE} \perp \overline{AD}$ and E is on $\overline{AD}$. Also draw $\overline{CF}$ so that $\overline{CF} \perp \overline{AD}$ and F is on $\overline{AD}$. Then use the following theorem: *If two lines are parallel, then they are everywhere equidistant*. After you have said that $\overline{AD} \parallel \overline{BC}$, you can use this theorem to say that BE = CF.

27. Prove the Diagonals of an Isosceles Trapezoid Theorem.

Given: ______________________________

Prove: ______________________________

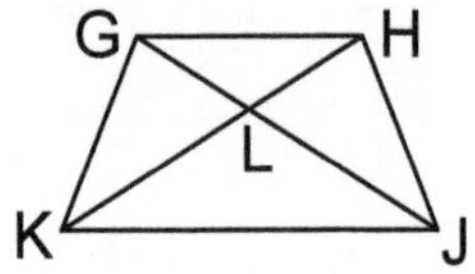

Hint: Since you proved the Base Angles of an Isosceles Trapezoid Theorem in the last problem, you may use it to work this problem.

28. Prove the Base Angles of an Isosceles Trapezoid Converse Theorem. (Here, we will assume that the congruent base angles are formed by the longer base. If the congruent base angles were formed by the shorter base, then the proof would be very similar.)

Hint: Begin by extending $\overline{NQ}$ and $\overline{OP}$ until they intersect each other, and call the point where they intersect point R. Then prove that ΔNRO and ΔQRP are both isosceles triangles. Or, if you wish, you can go in a completely different direction and look back at the hint for #26.

Given: Quadrilateral NOPQ is a trapezoid with $\overline{NQ}$ and $\overline{OP}$ as its legs and $\angle N \cong \angle O$

Prove: ______________________________

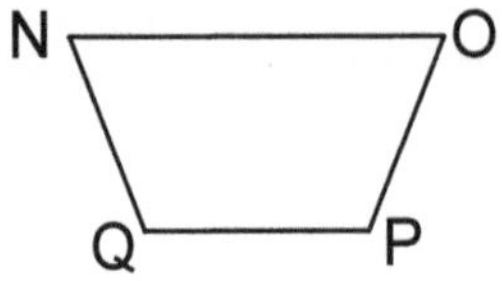

29. Prove the Diagonals of a Trapezoid Converse Theorem.

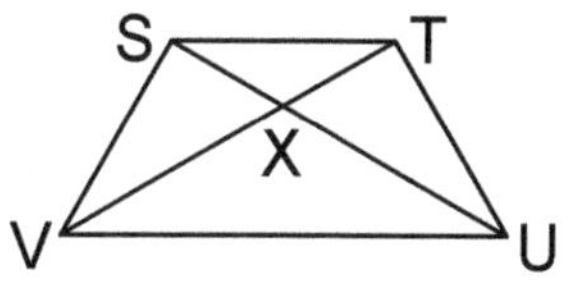

Given: ______________________________

Prove: ______________________________

Hint: Draw $\overline{VY}$ so that Y is on $\overleftrightarrow{ST}$ and $\overline{VY} \perp \overleftrightarrow{ST}$. Also draw $\overline{UZ}$ so that Z is on $\overleftrightarrow{ST}$ and $\overline{UZ} \perp \overleftrightarrow{ST}$. Then look back at the hint for #26.

30. Prove that the diagonals of a kite are perpendicular to each other.

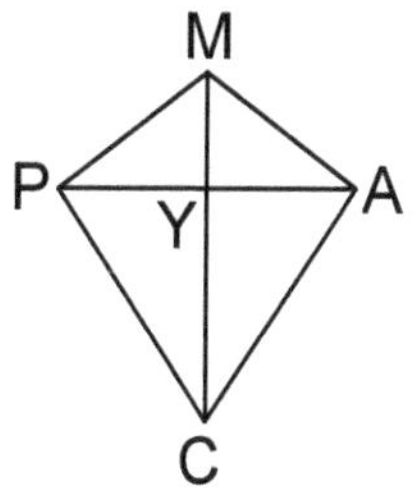

Given: Quadrilateral MACP is a kite with $\overline{MP} \cong \overline{MA}$ and $\overline{PC} \cong \overline{AC}$

Prove: ______________________________

Hint: First prove that $\triangle MCP \cong \triangle MCA$, and then prove that $\triangle MPY \cong \triangle MAY$.

31. Given that $\angle CBD \cong \angle ADB$ and that $\overline{AB}$ is not parallel to $\overline{CD}$, prove that quadrilateral ABCD is a trapezoid.

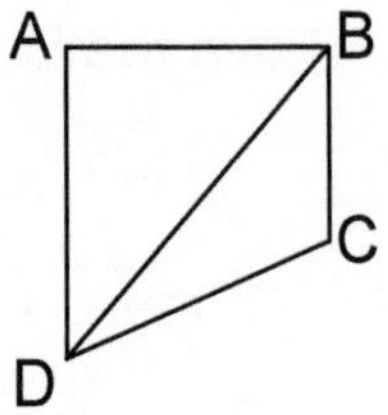

32. Given that $\triangle EFH$ at the right is an isosceles triangle and that $\overline{EF} \parallel \overline{GI}$, prove that quadrilateral EFGI is an isosceles trapezoid.

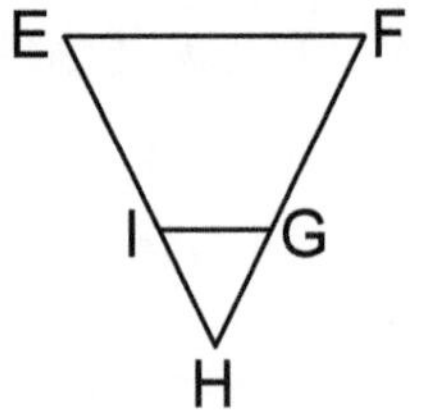

33. Given that $\Delta KNJ \cong \Delta MNJ$ and that $\overline{KJ}$ is not congruent to $\overline{KL}$, prove that quadrilateral JMLK is a kite.

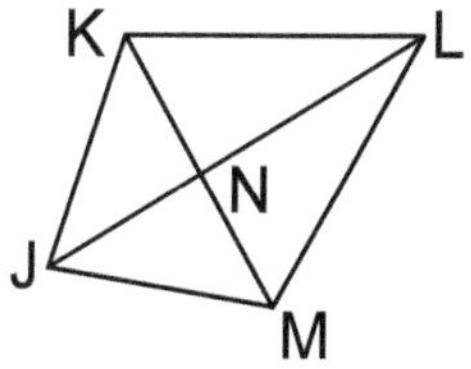

34. Given that $\overline{QR}$ is not congruent to $\overline{PQ}$ and that $\overline{PR}$ bisects both $\angle SPQ$ and $\angle SRQ$, prove that quadrilateral PQRS is a kite.

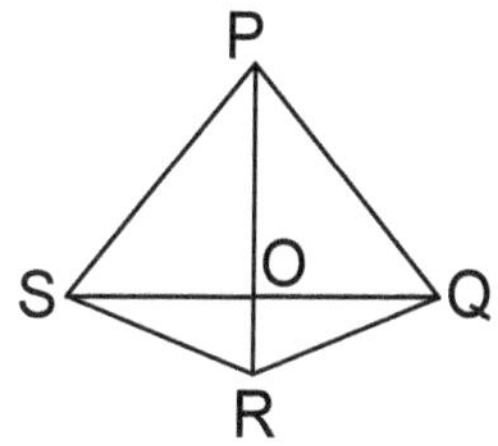

Part VI – Mixed Review

1. If quadrilateral ABCD is a parallelogram and $m\angle A = 78°$, then $m\angle B$ = ________, $m\angle C$ = ________, and $m\angle D$ = ________.

2. In the figure at the right, F is the midpoint of $\overline{EH}$, EF = 3x + 9, EH = 10x + 2, and FG = 2x + 2. Then x = ________ and FG = ________.

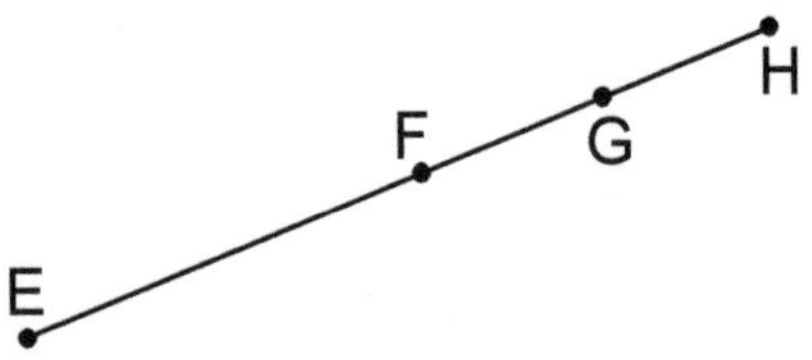

3-4. Refer to the figure at the right.

3. Which segments appear to be parallel to $\overline{QY}$?

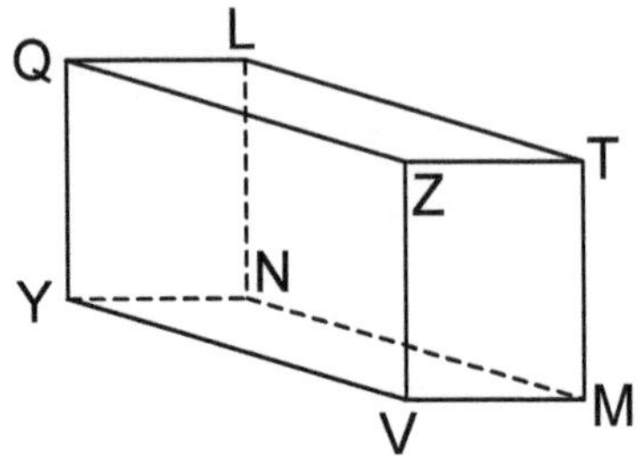

4. Which segments appear to be skew to $\overline{LT}$?

5. If 5 – 8x = 22x and 6x + 3y = 7, then 24x + 8y = ________.

6. If x + 2y = 7 and y – 5x = 20, then x = ________ and y = ________.

7. True or false: A quadrilateral is a parallelogram if and only its diagonals bisect each other.

8. True or false: Some trapezoids are parallelograms.

9. True or false: All numbers that are divisible by both 4 and 9 are also divisible by 6.

10. True or false: If a quadrilateral is not a rectangle, then it is not a square.

11. Draw a counterexample to show that the statement *No rhombus is also a rectangle* is false.

12. Give a counterexample to show that the statement *All numbers that are divisible by both 4 and 6 are also divisible by 24* is false.

13. In the figure at the right, y = _________.

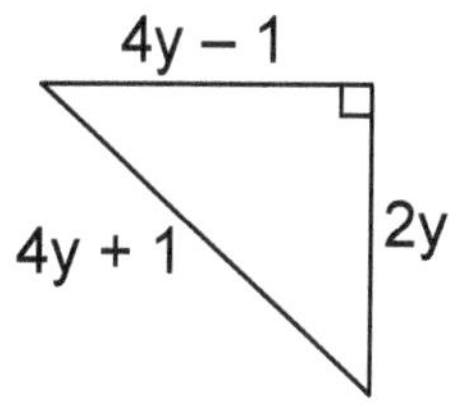

14-15. Refer to the number line below.

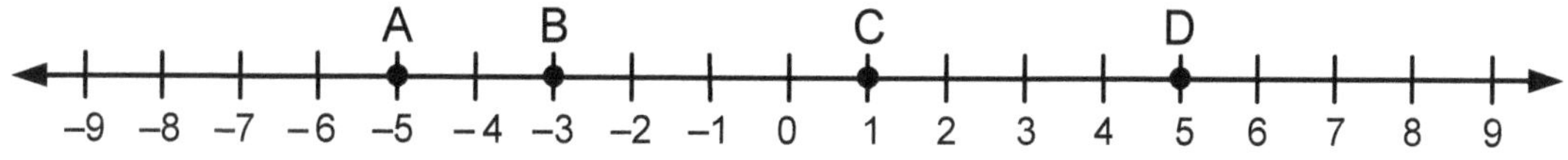

14. Is C the midpoint of $\overline{BD}$? __________

15. AC = __________

16. In the figure at the right, which segments, if any, must be parallel? State a postulate or theorem to support each answer.

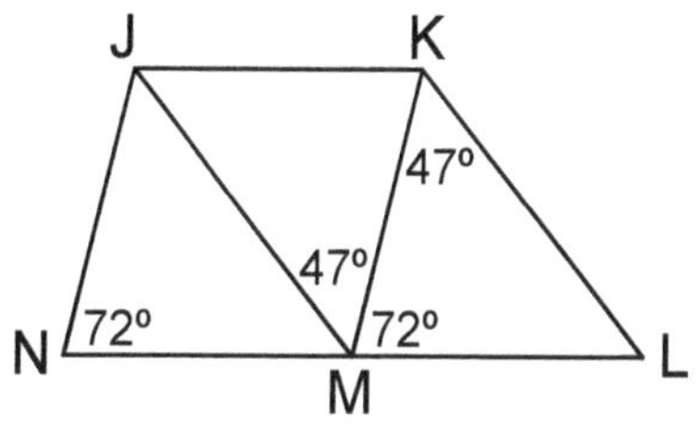

17. In the figure at the right, $\overline{OP} \parallel \overline{QR}$. Then x = __________

and y = __________.

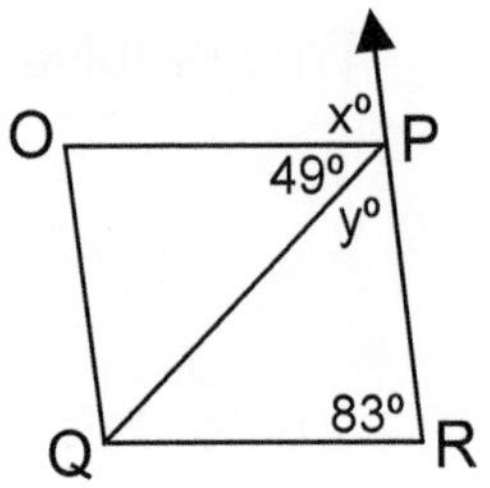

18. In the figure at the right, $\overline{DZ}$ is an altitude, m∠DZG = (4x + 6)°,

BZ = 5x – 3, and ZG = 4x + 9. Is $\overline{DZ}$ also a median? _______

Why or why not? ______________________________________

____

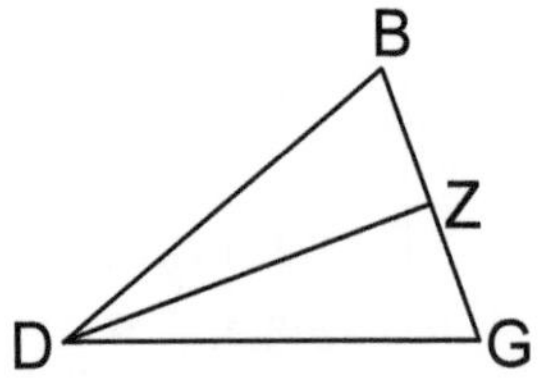

19-20. Quadrilateral LMNO at the right is a rectangle, ON = 16, LN = 20, and m∠OMN = 53°.

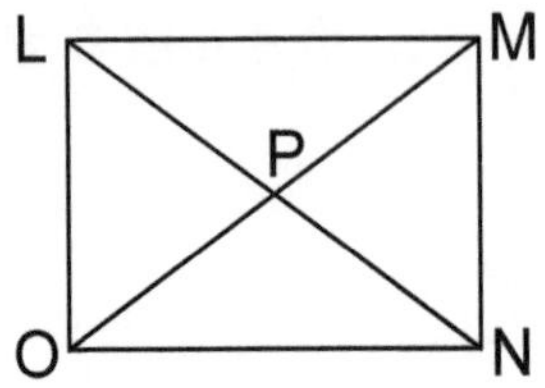

19. MP = __________, MN = __________, and

LM = __________

20. m∠MLO = __________, m∠MON = __________, and m∠ONP = __________

21-23. Quadrilateral RSTU at the right is a rhombus, RV = 3, and SV = 6.

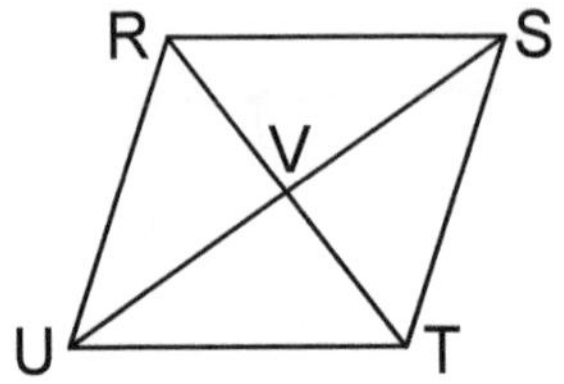

21. m∠ RVS = __________

22. RS = __________ and SU = __________

23. If m∠URT = (5x + 18)° and m∠RSU = 3x°, then x = __________ and

m∠URS = __________.

24-26. Quadrilateral WXYZ at the right is an isosceles trapezoid.

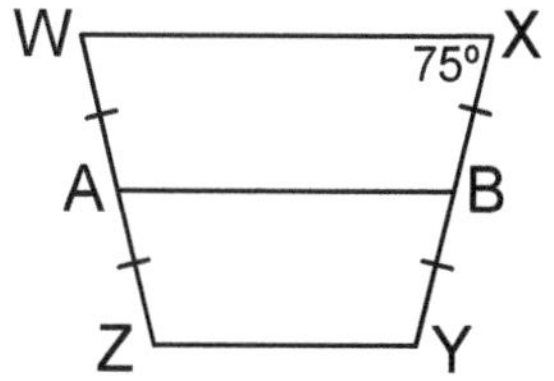

24. m∠W = ___________ and m∠Y = ___________

25. If WX = 7 and ZY = 15, then AB = ___________.

26. If WX = 8k + 1, ZY = 6k – 3, and AB = k + 35, then k = ___________ and WX = ___________.

27-29. Decide if each quadrilateral below is a *parallelogram*, *rectangle*, *rhombus*, *square*, *trapezoid*, *kite*, or *none of these*. Name all that apply.

27. $\overline{LC}$, $\overline{CJ}$, $\overline{SC}$, and $\overline{CU}$ are all congruent to each other

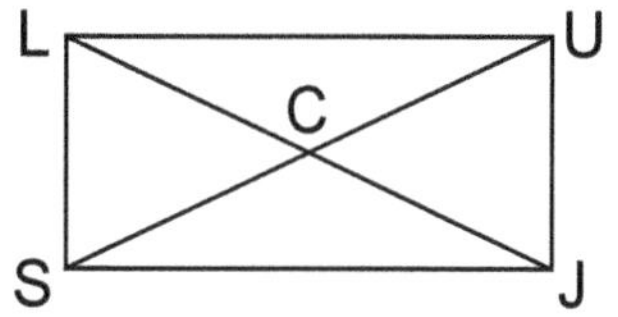

28.

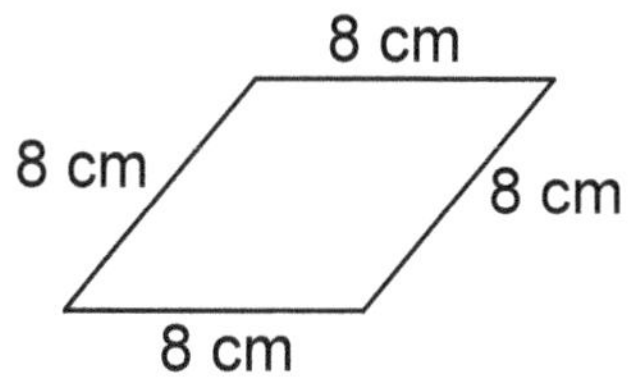

29.

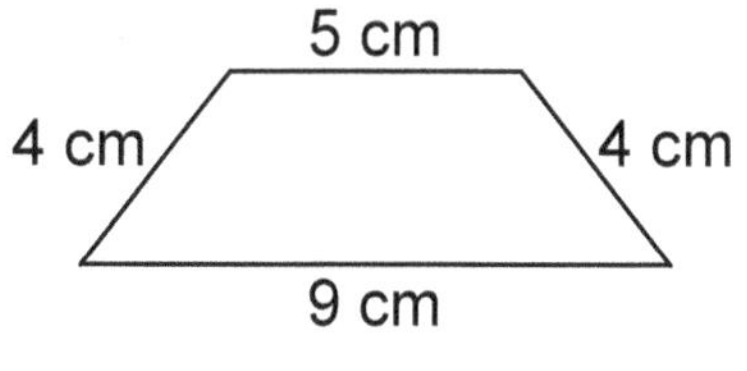

30. In the figure at the right, a = ___________, b = ___________, and c = ___________.

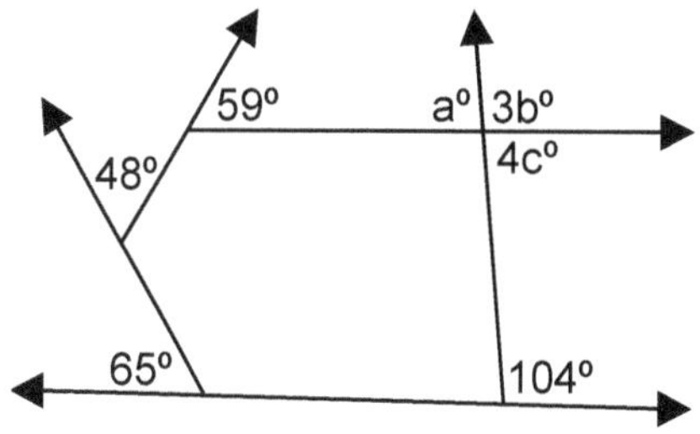

31. In the figure at the right, d = __________.

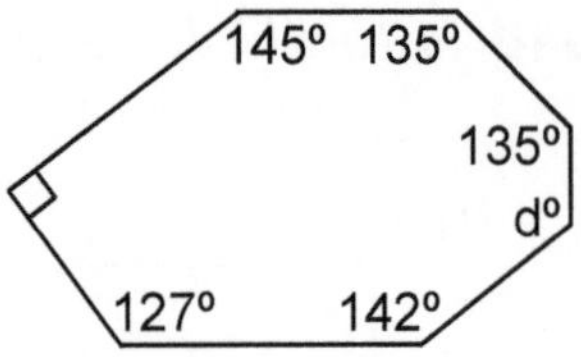

32. The measure of one interior angle of a regular nonagon equals __________, and the measure of one exterior angle of a regular nonagon equals __________.

33. In the figure at the right, $\Delta STU \cong \Delta KWA$. Then x = __________ and y = __________.

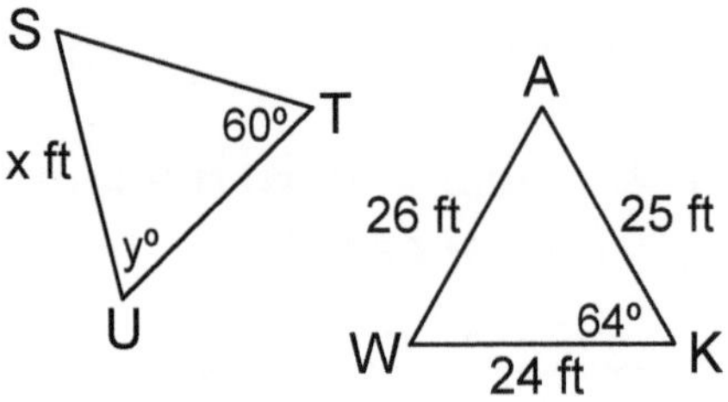

34. Given that $\Delta EHN \cong \Delta WNH$, $\overline{TN} \perp \overline{EH}$, and $\overline{TH} \perp \overline{NW}$ in the figure at the right, prove that $\Delta TEH \cong \Delta TWN$.

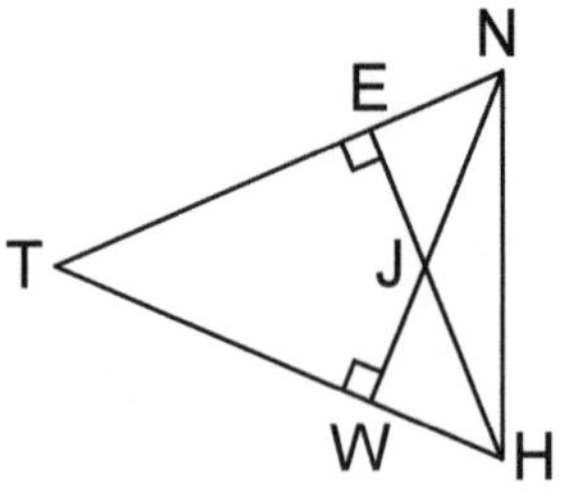

35. Given that $\overline{QR} \cong \overline{YR}$, $QR \neq QW$, and $\overline{RP} \perp \overline{QY}$ in the figure at the right, prove that quadrilateral QRYW is a kite.

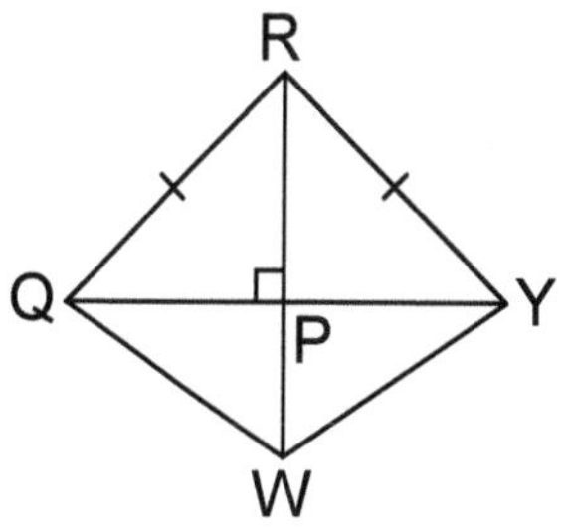

Chapter 7 – Similar Polygons

Part I – Ratios and Proportions

We will begin this section with two definitions and a property.

A <u>ratio</u> is a comparison of two or more numbers.

A <u>proportion</u> is an equation that states that two ratios are equal to each other.

Cross Products Property of Proportions

If $\frac{a}{b} = \frac{c}{d}$, then (a)(d) = (b)(c).*

We will review how we use these terms and the Cross Products Property of Proportions in purely algebraic problems in Examples 1 and 2, and then we will discuss how they relate to Geometry in Examples 3, 4, and 5.

Example 1: Over the course of the last 15 baseball games that he has played in, Gary has gotten 18 hits. (a) Find the ratio of games he has played in to hits. Leave your answer in simplest form. (b) Find the ratio of hits to games he has played in. Leave your answer in simplest form. (c) At this rate, how many hits will Gary get in 24 games?

(a) We can write the ratio of games Gary has played in to his hits as 15 to 18, 15 : 18, or $\frac{15}{18}$. To simplify this, we divide both numbers by the greatest common factor, which in this case is 3. This tells us that the final answer to this question can be written as 5 to 6, 5 : 6, or $\frac{5}{6}$. This means that, for every five games Gary has played in, he has gotten six hits (or, equivalently, for every six hits Gary has gotten, he has played in five games).

(b) Notice that this question is asking exactly the same thing as part (a); it's just that we need to reverse the order of the numbers. This means that we can write the ratio of hits to games Gary has played in as 18 to 15, 18 : 15, or $\frac{18}{15}$. To simplify this, we divide both numbers by the greatest common factor, which in this case is still 3. This tells us that the final answer to this question can be written as 6 to 5, 6 : 5, or $\frac{6}{5}$. We would **not** want to write it as $1\frac{1}{5}$ because this is not a comparison of two or more numbers.

*To see why this is true, start with the proportion $\frac{a}{b} = \frac{c}{d}$ and then multiply both sides by the least common denominator, bd.

(c) We can solve this problem using proportions. If we let x represent the number of hits Gary will get in 24 games, then we can write $\frac{15}{18} = \frac{24}{x}$ or $\frac{18}{x} = \frac{15}{24}$.

Both of these proportions are equally correct and will give us the correct answer, and there are many others we can write to solve this problem as well.

When you write a proportion, you should make sure that the top two numbers go together, the bottom two numbers go together, the left two numbers go together, and the right two numbers go together. The pictures below show how the numbers are related for the two proportions we stated above.

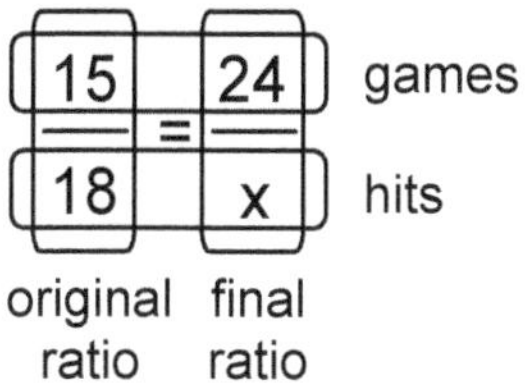

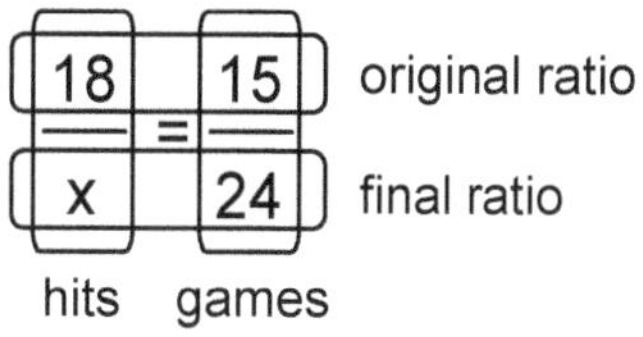

Generally, if you can draw a picture similar to these pictures, then your proportion is set up correctly. You will see this throughout this chapter.

Now, to finish solving this problem, we will note that the Cross Products Property of Proportions tells us that we can say that 15x = 432, and so $x = 28\frac{4}{5}$. However, it does not make sense to say that Gary will get $28\frac{4}{5}$ hits, and so we will say that Gary will get about 29 hits if he continues hitting at the same rate.

Example 2: Solve for x in the proportion $\frac{x+2}{3x-1} = \frac{3}{4}$.

We can work this problem by following the steps shown below.

$$\frac{x+2}{3x-1} = \frac{3}{4}$$

$4(x + 2) = 3(3x - 1)$	Use the Cross Products Property of Proportions.*
$4x + 8 = 9x - 3$	Use the Distributive Property.
$-5x = -11$	Subtract 8 and 9x from both sides.
$x = \frac{11}{5}$	Divide both sides by –5.

We can check this answer by substituting $\frac{11}{5}$ in for x in the original equation and then making sure that this gives us a true equation, as shown on the next page.

*As a first step, many people try to "reduce" the first fraction by canceling out the x's, but you **cannot** do this. In our Algebra I and Algebra II courses, we discuss how you can only cancel something on the top with something on the bottom if that something is *multiplied by everything else on both the top and the bottom*. In this case, neither x is multiplied by everything else on the top and bottom, and so neither x can cancel with anything else.

$$\frac{\frac{11}{5}+2}{3\bullet\frac{11}{5}-1} \stackrel{?}{=} \frac{3}{4}$$

$$\frac{\frac{21}{5}}{\frac{28}{5}} \stackrel{?}{=} \frac{3}{4}$$ Note that $\frac{11}{5}+2 = \frac{11}{5}+\frac{10}{5} = \frac{21}{5}$ and that $3\bullet\frac{11}{5}-1 = \frac{33}{5}-1 = \frac{33}{5}-\frac{5}{5} = \frac{28}{5}$.

$$\frac{3}{4} = \frac{3}{4}\ \checkmark$$ Note that $\frac{21}{5}\div\frac{28}{5} = \frac{21}{5}\bullet\frac{5}{28} = \frac{3}{4}$.

Since this did give us a true equation, we can conclude that our answer of $x = \frac{11}{5}$ must be correct.

Example 3: Look at $\triangle ABC$ at the right. What is the ratio AB : AC : BC? Leave your answer in simplest form.

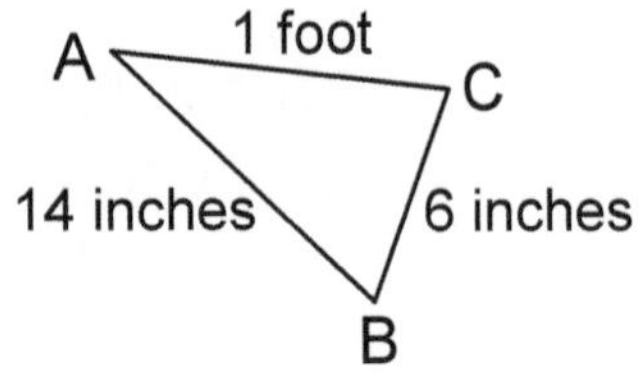

We will begin by stating that, whenever we want to write a ratio, the units must all be the same whenever possible. Hence, we do not want to write the length of $\overline{AC}$ as 1 foot; we want to write is as 12 inches instead. This means that we can write the ratio AB : AC : BC as 14 inches : 12 inches : 6 inches. To simplify this ratio, we can divide each piece by 2 inches. This tells us that the final answer to this question is 7 : 6 : 3. (We could also write this in words as "7 to 6 to 3," but we could not write it as a fraction because we have more than two numbers.)

Example 4: The ratio of the lengths of the sides of a triangle is 5 : 6 : 8, and the perimeter of the triangle is 190 centimeters. Find the lengths of the sides of the triangle.

We will begin by noting that the ratio 5 : 6 : 8 has been simplified by dividing each of the lengths of the sides by the least common denominator. Let's call this number that each of the sides were divided by x. Now, if "undivide" (or, in other words, multiply) each of the sides by x, we find that the lengths of the sides are 5x, 6x, and 8x.

Now, since the perimeter of the triangle is equal to the lengths of the sides added together, we can write 5x + 6x + 8x = 190 centimeters. This tells us that x = 10 centimeters. So, since we represented the lengths of the sides of the triangle by 5x, 6x, and 8x, the lengths of the sides of the triangle must be 50 centimeters, 60 centimeters, and 80 centimeters.

Example 5: On a blueprint of a certain house, 1 inch on the blueprint represents 5 feet in real life. (This is called the <u>scale</u> of the blueprint.) If a room is 6 inches wide and 4 inches long on the blueprint, what are the dimensions of the room in real life?

We will solve this problem using two proportions.

To find the width of the room in real life:

If we let x represent the width of the room in real life, then two of the proportions that we can write to solve this part of the problem are $\frac{1}{5} = \frac{6}{x}$ and $\frac{1}{6} = \frac{5}{x}$. Both of these proportions are equally correct, and they will both give the same answer. You can see how these numbers are related by looking at the pictures below.

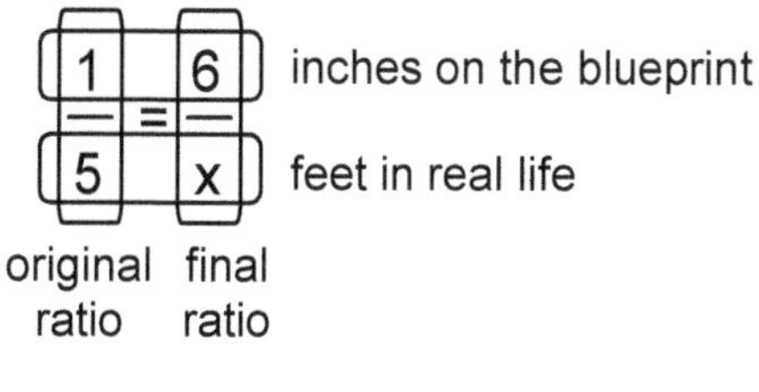

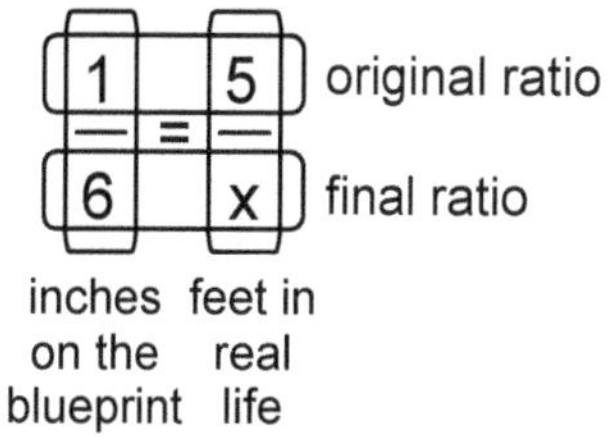

(We could change the inches to feet or the feet to inches, but, since we can draw the pictures above, we do not really need to.) Now, we can use the Cross Products Property of Proportions to say that x = 30, and so the room must be 30 feet wide in real life.

To find the length of the room in real life:

If we let y represent the width of the room in real life, then two of the proportions that we can write to solve this part of the problem are $\frac{1}{5} = \frac{4}{y}$ and $\frac{1}{4} = \frac{5}{y}$. You can see how these numbers are related by looking at the pictures below.

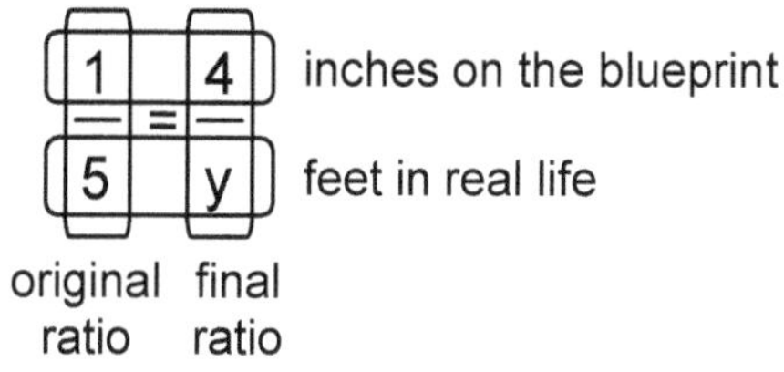

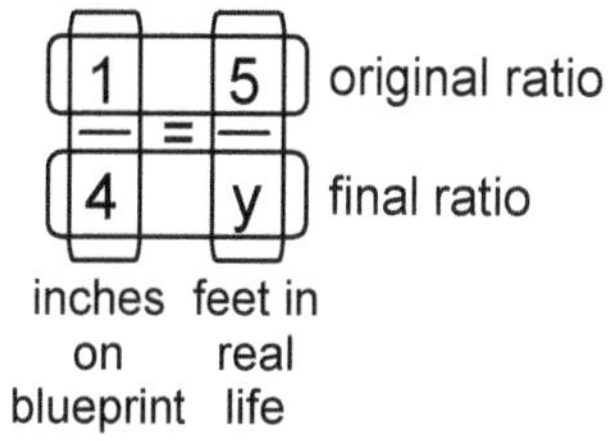

(Once again, we could change the inches to feet or the feet to inches, but, since we can draw the pictures above, we do not really need to.) Now, we can use the Cross Products Property of Proportions to say that y = 20, and so the room must be 20 feet wide in real life.

Problems:

1-14. Solve for the indicated variable in each proportion.

1. $\frac{4}{x} = \frac{6}{9}$ x = _______

3. $\frac{7}{2.8} = \frac{n}{6.2}$ n = _______

2. $\frac{4}{20} = \frac{y}{30}$ y = _______

4. $\frac{4.25}{p} = \frac{2.5}{0.9}$ p = _______

5. $\frac{4c-3}{5} = \frac{3c+1}{7}$ c = _______

11. $\frac{r+3}{r} = \frac{r}{4}$ r = _______

Hint: You might want to refer to the section in Appendix A on solving quadratic equations before you try to work this problem and the next three problems.

6. $\frac{4}{7} = \frac{5b+1}{9b-2}$ b = _______

7. $\frac{a+3}{10a+5} = \frac{2}{11}$ a = _______

12. $\frac{q+7}{4} = \frac{10}{7-q}$ q = _______

8. $\frac{4}{m} = \frac{11}{3m+2}$ m = _______

13. $\frac{1}{5w} = \frac{3w-2}{6-w}$ w = _______

9. $\frac{u-2}{u} = \frac{u}{u+1}$ u = _______

14. $\frac{h+3}{3h-5} = \frac{3h+5}{8h}$ h = _______

10. $\frac{2k}{8k-3} = \frac{k+5}{4k+6}$ k = _______

15-20. Round your answers for these problems to the nearest hundredth where necessary.

15. Isabella is working on drawing a map. She wants 2 centimeters on the map to represent 5 miles. If the distance between two towns is 27 miles in real life, how far apart should the towns be on the map? _______________

16. At least since the time of the ancient Greeks, mathematicians have been fascinated by a number called the golden ratio, which is equal to approximately 1 : 1.618. If you want to construct a rectangle so that the length and width have a ratio of 1 : 1.618, and if you want the shorter two sides to be 7 feet long, then the other two sides must be approximately _____________ feet long.

17. Eva has a picture that is 2.5 inches tall and 3.5 inches wide. If she wants to have it enlarged so that it is 10 inches wide, how tall will it be? _____________

18. Ethan has a picture that is 5 inches tall and 7 inches wide. If he wants to have it made smaller so that it is 4 inches tall, how wide will it be? _____________

19. When an architectural firm wants to build a large building or a series of buildings, it will sometimes construct scale models of the buildings. If an architectural firm has built a model of a shopping center so that 3 centimeters represents 10 feet, and if the model is 72 centimeters long, 9 centimeters wide, and 3.6 centimeters tall, then the real-life version of this shopping center would be ___________ feet long, ___________ feet wide, and ___________ feet tall.

20. A model car kit states that the scale of the assembled model to the real car is 1 : 14. If the model is 6 inches long, then the real-life version of this car would be ___________ **feet** long.

21-25. In the figure at the right, $\frac{AC}{CE} = \frac{BC}{CD}$ and $\frac{AC}{CE} = \frac{AB}{DE}$.

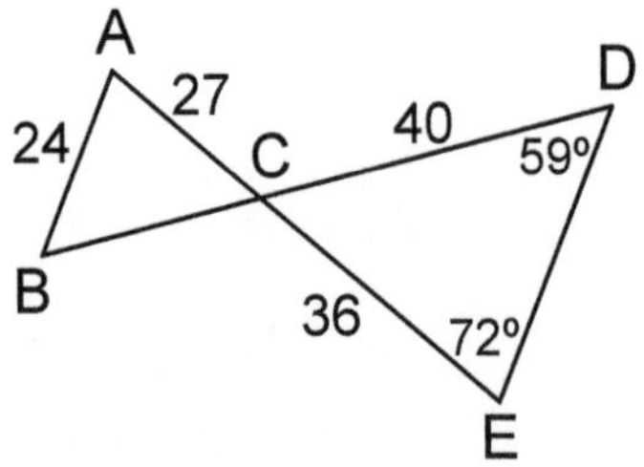

21. BC = ____________

22. DE = ____________

23. Find the ratio AB : BC : AC. Leave your answer in simplest form.

____

24. Find the ratio $m\angle D : m\angle E : m\angle DCE$. Leave your answer in simplest form.

____

25. Find the ratio of CE to AC. Leave your answer in simplest form.

____

26-27. In the figure at the right, $\frac{OP}{OQ} = \frac{PR}{QS}$ and $\frac{OS}{OQ} = \frac{RS}{PQ}$.

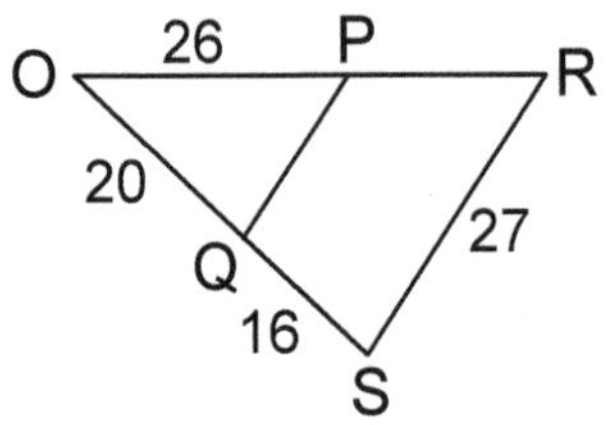

26. PR = ___________ and OR = ___________

27. PQ = ___________

28. The ratio of the lengths of the sides of a triangle is 5 : 6 : 2, and the perimeter of the triangle is 52 centimeters. Find the lengths of the sides of the triangle.

______________, ______________, and ______________

29. The ratio of the lengths of the sides of a triangle is 7 : 4 : 5, and the perimeter of the triangle is 96 feet. Find the lengths of the sides of the triangle. ______________, ______________, and ______________

30. The ratio of the measures of two angles that form a linear pair is 8 : 1. Find the measures of the angles. _________ and _________

31. In the figure at the right, the ratio a : b : c equals 7 : 2 : 1. Then a = ______ and c = ______.

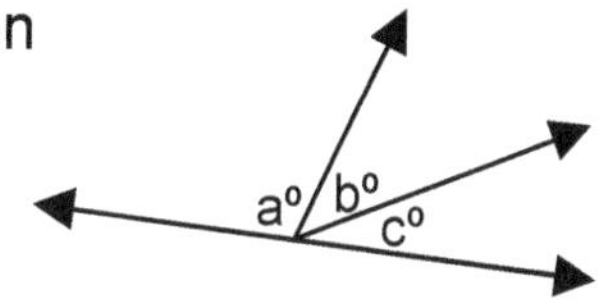

32. In the figure at the right, the ratio of EF : FG : GH is 2 : 5 : 3. If EH = 90 inches, then EF = ___________ and EG = ___________.

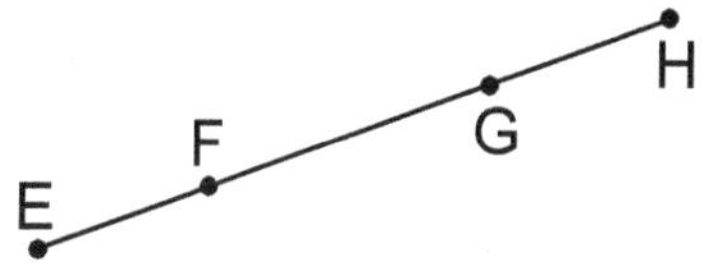

33. In the figure at the right, the ratio of JK : KL : LM is 6 : 4 : 3. If JL = 60 yards, then JK = ___________ and LM = ___________.

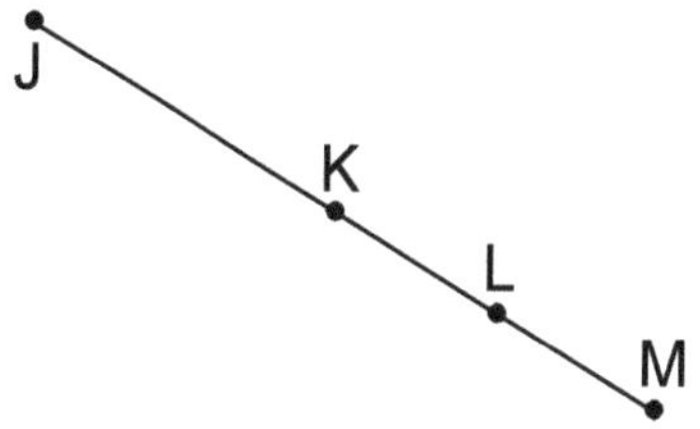

Part II – Congruent and Similar Polygons

We talked about congruent triangles in Chapter 4, but we never talked about congruent polygons with four or more sides each. We will do this in this section, and we will also discuss a concept called *similar polygons*.

We will begin this section with two definitions.

Two polygons are congruent if and only if their corresponding angles are congruent and their corresponding sides are congruent.

Two polygons are similar if and only if their corresponding angles are congruent and their corresponding sides are proportional. We use the symbol "~" to say "is similar to."

Essentially, these two definitions say that congruent polygons have the same shape *and* the same size, while similar polygons have the same shape but not necessarily the same size. We will talk more about what we mean when we say that the corresponding sides of two polygons are proportional in Examples 3, 4, and 5.

Example 1: In the figure at the right, are the two quadrilaterals congruent? If so, state a congruence statement.

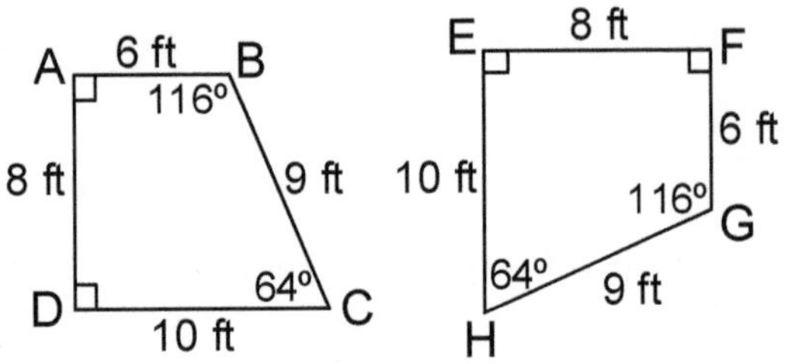

Notice that we have four sets of congruent segments ($\overline{AB} \cong \overline{FG}$, $\overline{BC} \cong \overline{GH}$, $\overline{CD} \cong \overline{HE}$, and $\overline{AD} \cong \overline{FE}$) and four sets of congruent corresponding angles ($\angle A \cong \angle F$, $\angle B \cong \angle G$, $\angle C \cong \angle H$, and $\angle D \cong \angle E$). We can therefore say that quadrilateral ABCD is congruent to quadrilateral FGHE. There are many other ways we could write this, too – for example, we could also say that quadrilateral CBAD is congruent to quadrilateral HGFE.

As we said about triangles in Chapter 4, the order in which we name the congruent polygons is important. We could **not**, for instance, say that "quadrilateral ABCD is congruent to quadrilateral EFGH," because this would tell anyone reading this statement that, among other things, $\overline{AB} \cong \overline{EF}$, $\overline{BC} \cong \overline{FG}$, $\angle B \cong \angle F$, and $\angle D \cong \angle H$.

Example 2: In the figure at the right, hexagon JKLMNO is congruent to hexagon RQPUTS. Find the values of w, x, and y.

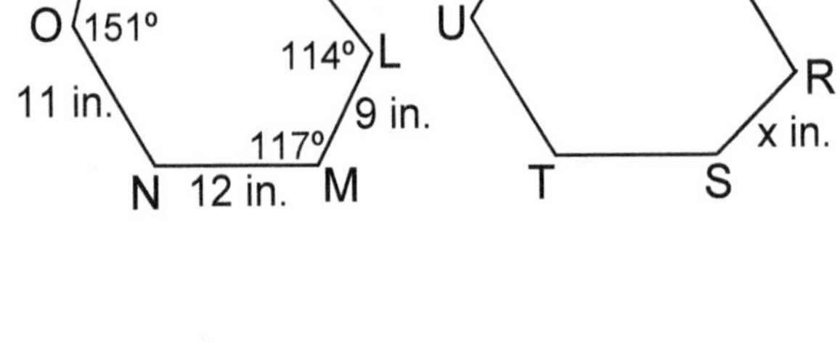

To find the value of w:

Since Q and P were named second

and third in the statement, "hexagon JKLMNO is congruent to hexagon RQPUTS," and since K and L were also named second and third, we can say that $\overline{KL}$ corresponds with $\overline{QP}$. Since we were told that the two hexagons are congruent, this means that $\overline{KL} \cong \overline{QP}$, and so w must equal 13.

To find the value of x:

Since R and S were named first and last in the statement, "hexagon JKLMNO is congruent to hexagon RQPUTS," and since J and O were also named first and last, we can say that $\overline{JO}$ corresponds with $\overline{RS}$. Since we were told that the two hexagons are congruent, this means that $\overline{JO} \cong \overline{RS}$, and so x must equal 8.

To find the value of y:

Since K was named second in the statement, "hexagon JKLMNO is congruent to hexagon RQPUTS," and since Q was also named second, we can say that $\angle K$ corresponds with $\angle Q$. Since we were told that the two hexagons are congruent, this means that $\angle K \cong \angle Q$, and so y must equal 129.

Example 3: Are the two triangles shown at the right similar to each other? If so, state a similarity statement.

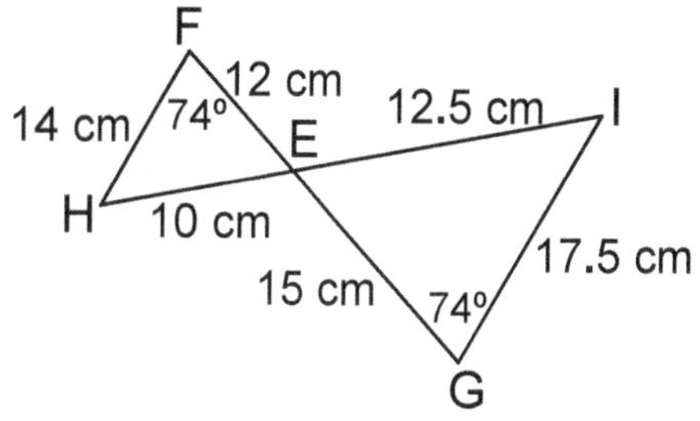

We will begin by noting that the definition of similar polygons tells us that, in order for us to decide that these two triangles are similar, we must decide that the corresponding angles are congruent *and* that the corresponding sides are proportional.

We will begin by noting that we do have three sets of congruent angles. We were given that $\angle F \cong \angle G$, $\angle FEH \cong \angle GEI$ because vertical angles are congruent to each other, and $\angle H \cong \angle I$ because we proved in Chapter 4 that, if two angles of one triangle are congruent to two angles of another triangle, then the third angles are also congruent. (You could also note that $\angle F$ and $\angle G$ are two congruent alternate interior angles, and so the Alternate Interior Angles Converse Theorem tells us that $\overline{FH} \parallel \overline{GI}$. Therefore, $\angle H$ must be congruent to $\angle I$ by the Alternate Interior Angles Theorem.) So, if the two triangles are similar (and we don't know whether or not they are similar yet), then we will be able to say that $\Delta FEH \sim \Delta GEI$. Like we said about congruent polygons, we must be careful about the order in which we name similar polygons. We would **not**, for instance, be able to say that $\Delta EHF \sim \Delta EGI$ because this would suggest to anyone reading this that $\angle F \cong \angle I$ and $\angle H \cong \angle G$.

Now, to decide if the corresponding sides are proportional, we must decide if the ratios $\frac{FE}{GE}$, $\frac{EH}{EI}$, and $\frac{FH}{GI}$ are all equal to each other. (Note the position of each of the letters in the similarity statement $\Delta FEH \sim \Delta GEI$. For instance, F and E are named first and second, and G and E are also named first and second. Hence, we talk about the ratio $\frac{FE}{GE}$.) With this in mind, we will make the following observations.

$$\frac{FE}{GE} = \frac{12}{15} = 0.8 \qquad \frac{EH}{EI} = \frac{10}{12.5} = 0.8 \qquad \frac{FH}{GI} = \frac{14}{17.5} = 0.8$$

Since these ratios are all equal to each other, we can conclude that the two triangles are similar to each other, and so we can write $\Delta FEH \sim \Delta GEI$. (We could also write $\Delta FHE \sim \Delta GIE$, $\Delta HFE \sim \Delta IGE$, or several other similarity statements. As we noted on the previous page, however, we could would **not**, for instance, be able to say that $\Delta EHF \sim \Delta EGI$ because, among other things, this would suggest to anyone reading this that $\angle F \cong \angle I$.)

Example 4: Are the two pentagons shown at the right similar to each other? If so, state a similarity statement.

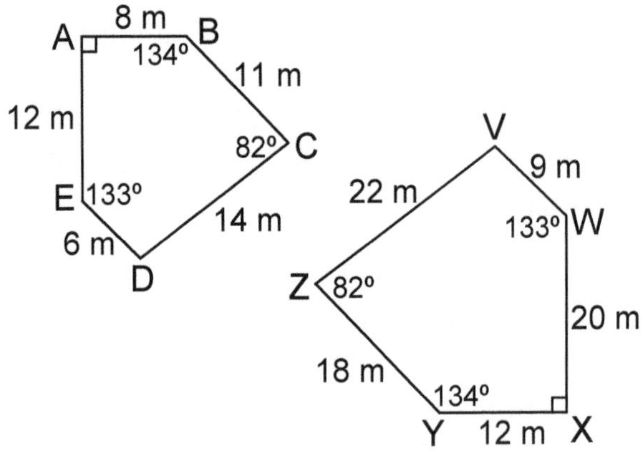

We do, in fact, have five sets of congruent corresponding angles. (Note that $\angle D \cong \angle V$ because the measures of the interior angles of a pentagon must add up to 540°, and so both $\angle D$ and $\angle V$ must have measures of 101°. Also note that $\angle A \cong \angle X$, $\angle B \cong \angle Y$, $\angle C \cong \angle Z$, and $\angle E \cong \angle W$.) So, if the two pentagons are similar (and we don't know whether or not they are yet), then we will be able to say that pentagon ABCDE is similar to pentagon XYZVW.

Now, to decide if the corresponding sides are proportional, we must decide if the ratios of the corresponding sides are all equal to each other. In other words, we must decide if the ratios $\frac{AB}{XY}$, $\frac{BC}{YZ}$, $\frac{CD}{ZV}$, $\frac{DE}{VW}$, and $\frac{AE}{XW}$ are all equal to each other. With this in mind, we will make the following observations.

$$\frac{AB}{XY} = \frac{8}{12} \approx 0.667 \qquad \frac{DE}{VW} = \frac{6}{9} \approx 0.667$$

$$\frac{BC}{YZ} = \frac{11}{18} \approx 0.611 \qquad \frac{AE}{XW} = \frac{12}{20} = 0.6$$

$$\frac{CD}{ZV} = \frac{14}{22} \approx 0.636$$

Since these ratios are not all equal to each other, we can conclude that the pentagons are **not** similar to each other.

Example 5: In the figure at the right, $\triangle LKM \sim \triangle LJN$. Find the values of w, x, and y.

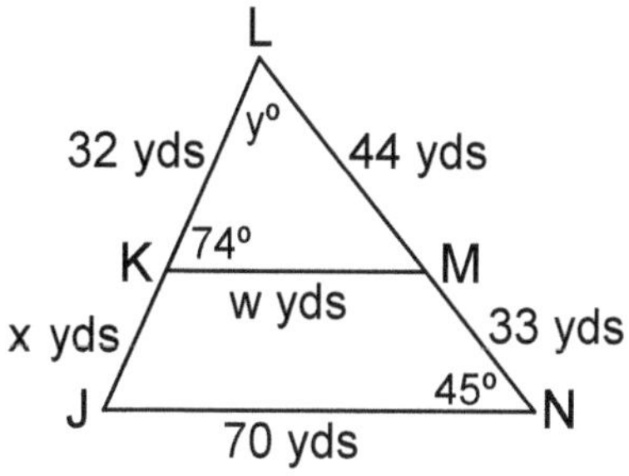

To find the values of w and x:

We will begin by noting that $\frac{LK}{LJ} = \frac{KM}{JN} = \frac{LM}{LN}$.

To find the value of w, we will use the proportion $\frac{KM}{JN} = \frac{LM}{LN}$. When we substitute the information given to us in the problem into this proportion, we see that $\frac{w}{70} = \frac{44}{77}$. When we use the Cross Product Property of Proportions and solve the resulting equation for w, we find that w = 40. To find the value of x, we will use the proportion $\frac{LK}{LJ} = \frac{LM}{LN}$. When we substitute the information given to us in the problem into this proportion, we see that $\frac{32}{x+32} = \frac{44}{77}$. When we use the Cross Products Property of Proportions and solve the resulting equation for x, we find that x = 24.

To find the value of y:

We will start by noting that $\angle N$ and $\angle LMK$ are corresponding angles of similar triangles, and so they must be congruent. Thus, we can say that $m\angle LMK = 45°$. Since the measures of all the interior angles of $\triangle LKM$ must add up to 180°, this means that y must equal 61.

Now, we need one more definition.

> The ratio of the lengths of two corresponding sides of two similar polygons is called the scale factor. Usually, scale factors are written as reduced fractions.

Example 6: Using the figure from Example 5, find the scale factor of $\triangle LKM$ to $\triangle LJN$, and then find the scale factor of $\triangle LJN$ to $\triangle LKM$.

To find the scale factor of $\triangle LKM$ to $\triangle LJN$:

Since the ratio of the length any of the sides of $\triangle LKM$ to the length of the corresponding side of $\triangle LJN$ is equal to $\frac{4}{7}$, the scale factor of $\triangle LKM$ to $\triangle LJN$ is $\frac{4}{7}$.

To find the scale factor of $\triangle LJN$ to $\triangle LKM$:

Since the ratio of any of the sides of $\triangle LJN$ to the corresponding side of $\triangle LKM$ is equal to $\frac{7}{4}$, the scale factor of $\triangle LJN$ to $\triangle LKM$ is $\frac{7}{4}$.

Finally, we will state that, if your proportions for similar figures are set up correctly, then you should be able to draw the same picture that we talked about for proportions in the last section. For example, look back at Example 5. When we were working this example, we said that $\frac{LK}{LJ} = \frac{KM}{JN} = \frac{LM}{LN}$. You can see that how the sides of these triangles are related by looking at the picture below.

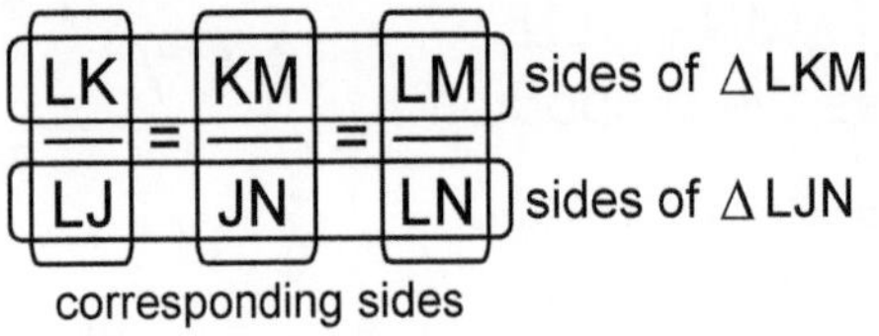

Problems:

1-6. (a) Decide if the two figures are congruent. (b) If your answer to part (a) was *yes*, complete the congruence statement.

1a. Are the two figures congruent to each other? __________

b. If your answer to (a) was *yes*, then hexagon DVSOZF is congruent to hexagon ______________.

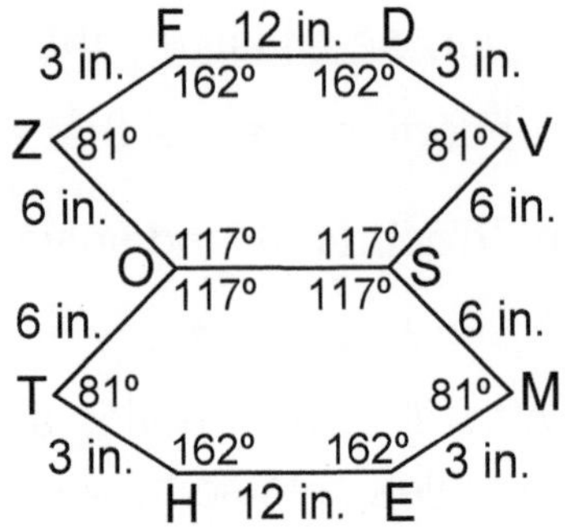

2a. Are the two figures congruent to each other? __________

b. If your answer to (a) was *yes*, then rectangle RAWL is congruent to rectangle ____________.

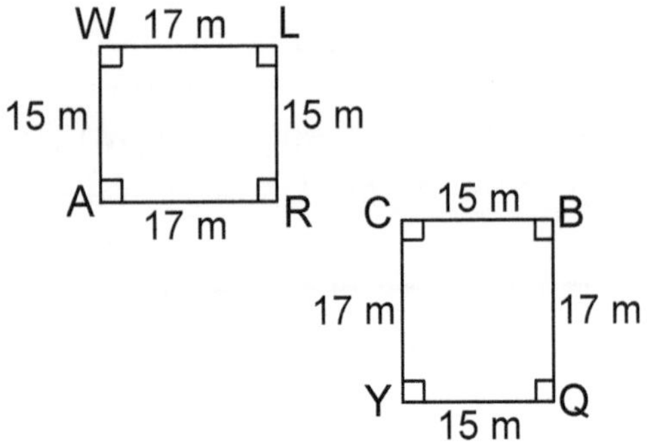

3a. Are the two figures congruent to each other? __________

b. If your answer to (a) was *yes*, then quadrilateral GJUX is congruent to quadrilateral ___________.

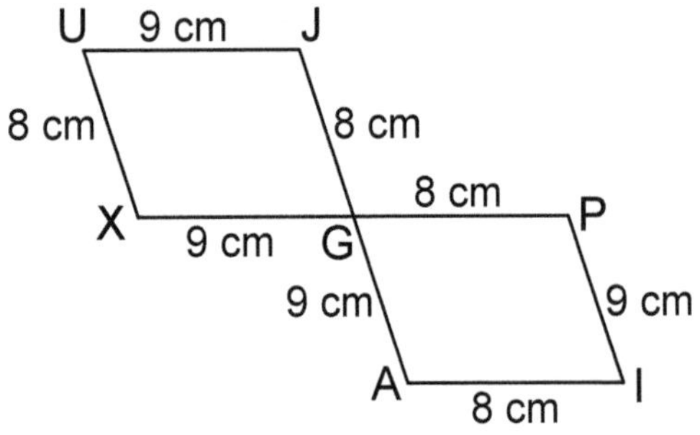

4a. Are the two figures congruent to each other? _________

b. If your answer to (a) was *yes*, then pentagon NJKDZ is congruent to pentagon ___________.

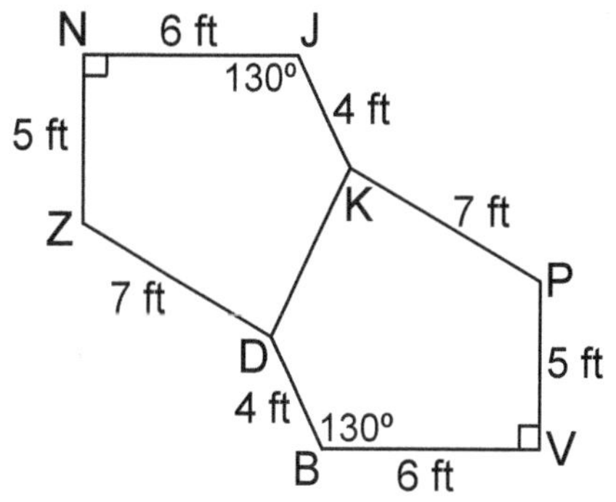

5a. Are the two figures congruent to each other? _________

b. If your answer to (a) was *yes*, then octagon ABCDLMNO is congruent to nonagon _______________.

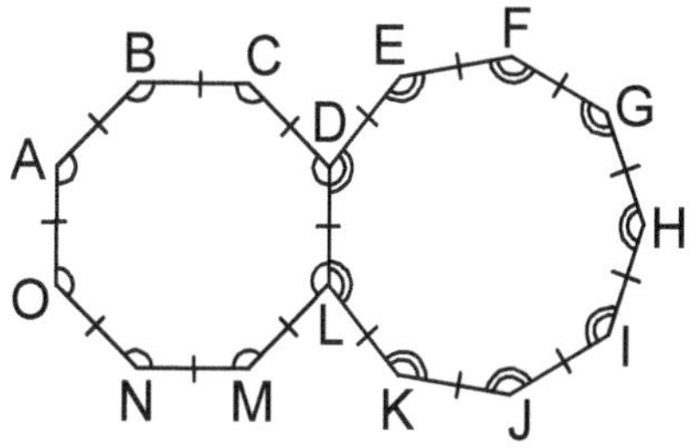

6a. Are the two figures congruent to each other? _________

b. If your answer to (a) was *yes*, then heptagon PQRSYZA is congruent to heptagon _____________.

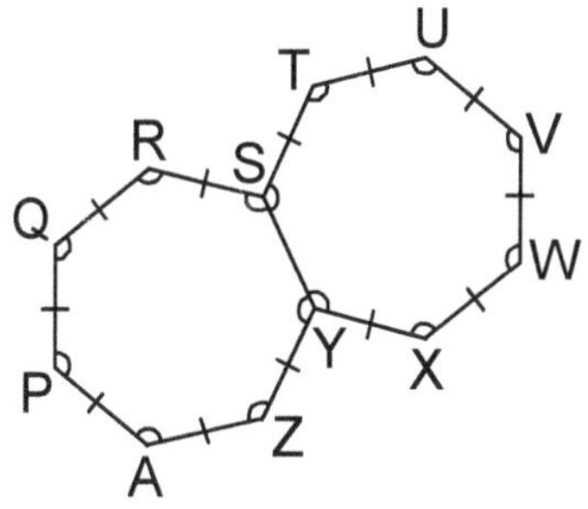

7. Are the two figures from #6 *similar* to each other? ___________ If your answer was *yes*, then the scale factor of heptagon PQRSYZA to heptagon STUVWXY is _____________.

8-13. (a) Decide if the two figures are similar. (b) If your answer to part (a) was *yes*, complete the similarity statement.

8a. Are the two figures similar to each other? _________

b. If your answer to (a) was *yes*, then pentagon TLDAH is similar to pentagon ___________.

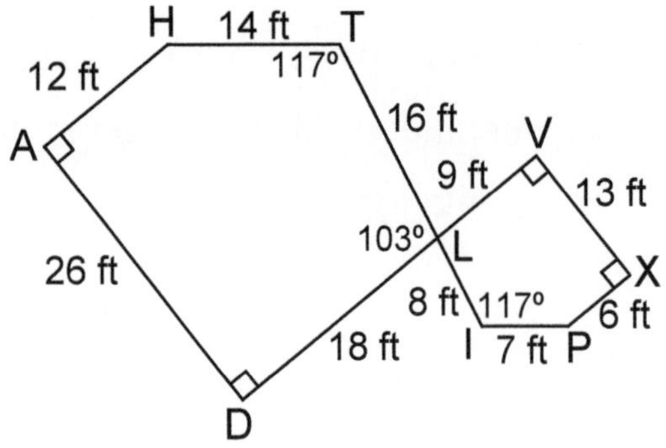

9a. Are the two figures similar to each other? _________

b. If your answer to (a) was *yes*, then parallelogram KCMG is similar to parallelogram ___________.

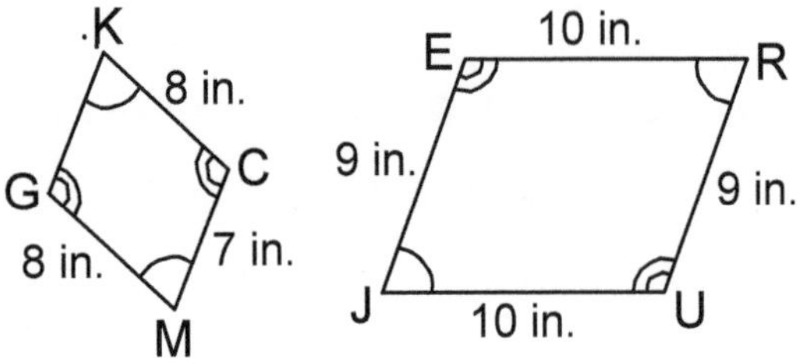

10a. Are the two figures similar to each other? _________

b. If your answer to (a) was *yes*, then parallelogram FWZB is similar to parallelogram ___________.

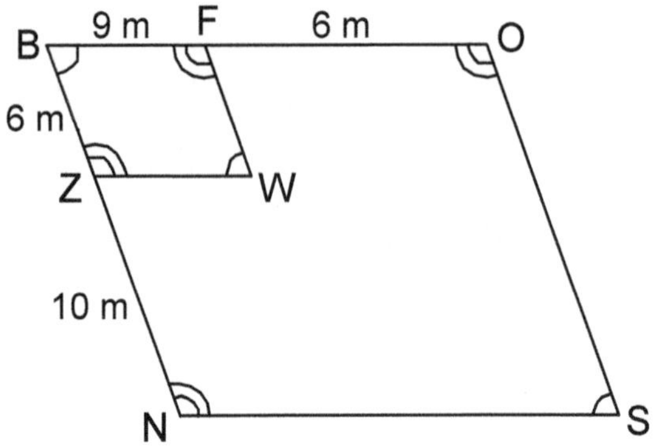

11a. Are the two triangles similar to each other? _________

b. If your answer to (a) was *yes*, then $\Delta CYV \sim \Delta$___________.

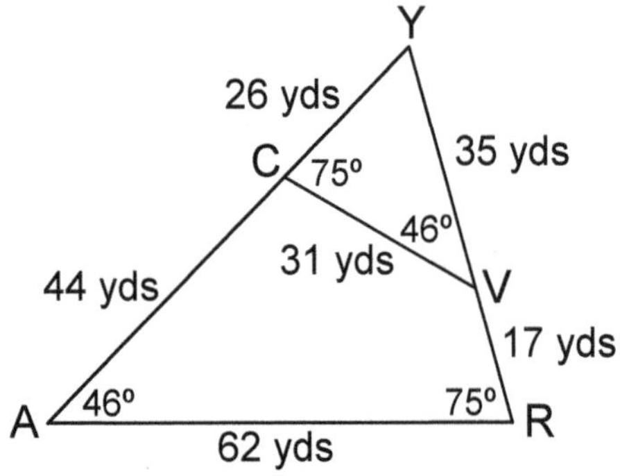

12a. Are the two figures similar to each other? __________

b. If your answer to (a) was *yes*, then hexagon XIKLUB is similar to hexagon ________________.

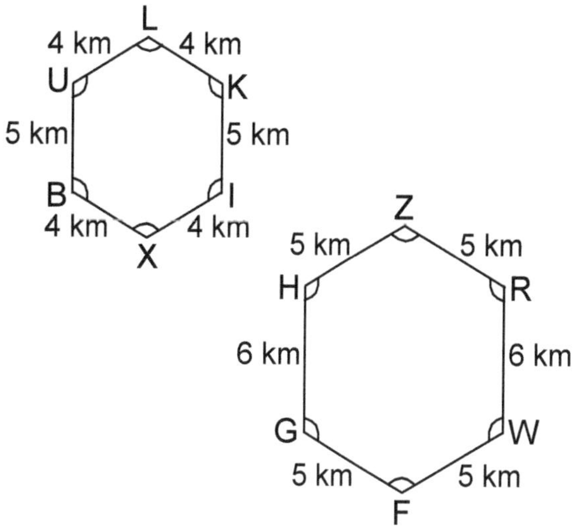

13a. Are the two figures similar to each other? __________

b. If your answer to (a) was *yes*, then octagon QSMRPNGJ is similar to octagon ________________.

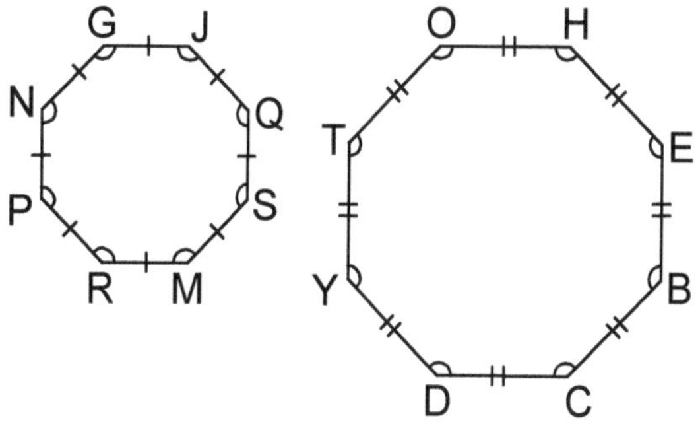

14-20. In the figure at the right, $\triangle CNT \sim \triangle GNQ$.

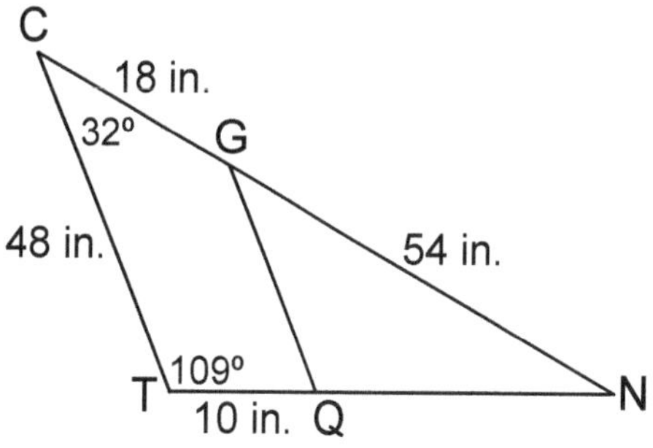

14. GQ = ___________

15. QN = ___________

16. $m\angle GQN$ = ___________

17. $m\angle N$ = ___________

18. What is the scale factor of $\triangle CNT$ to $\triangle GNQ$? ___________

19. the perimeter of ΔCNT = __________ and the perimeter of ΔGNQ = __________

20. Find the ratio of the perimeter of ΔCNT to the perimeter of ΔGNQ. __________

21-27. In the figure at the right, pentagon UBESL is similar to pentagon POHJZ.

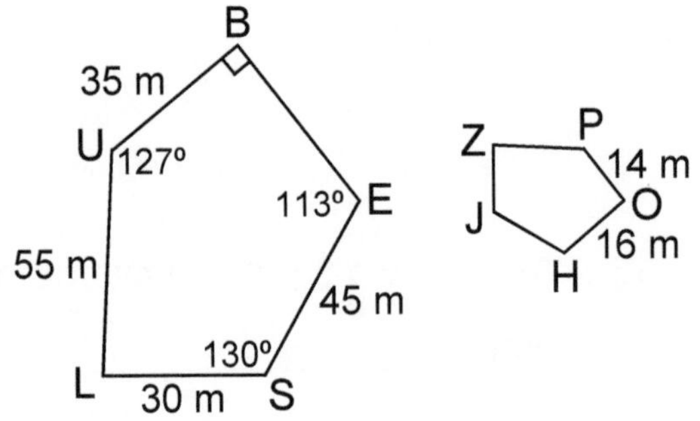

21. BE = __________

22. JZ = __________

23. m$\angle$H = __________

24. m$\angle$Z = __________

25. What is the scale factor of pentagon POHJZ to pentagon UBESL? __________

26. the perimeter of pentagon POHJZ = __________ and the perimeter of pentagon UBESL = __________

27. Find the ratio of the perimeter of pentagon POHJZ to the perimeter of pentagon UBESL. __________

28-33. Fill each blank with *might be, must be*, or *cannot be*.

28. If two quadrilaterals are similar, then they ________________ congruent.

29. If two quadrilaterals are congruent, then they ________________ similar.

30. Two regular hexagons ________________ congruent.

31. Two regular hexagons ________________ similar.

32. A regular pentagon and a regular heptagon ________________ congruent.

33. A regular pentagon and a regular heptagon ________________ similar.

Part III – Similar Triangles

Up to this point, if we wanted to prove that two triangles were similar, we had to use the definition of similar polygons and show that there were three sets of congruent corresponding angles *and* that all three sets of sides were proportional. However, as the postulate and the theorems below state, we can show that two triangles are similar with less information.

> **AAA Similarity Postulate**
> If the angles of one triangle are congruent to the angles of another triangle, then the triangles are similar.

> **AA Similarity Theorem**
> If two angles of one triangle are congruent to two angles of another triangle, then the triangles are similar.

> **SSS Similarity Theorem**
> If the lengths of the sides of one triangle are proportional to the lengths of the sides of another triangle, then the triangles are similar.

> **SAS Similarity Theorem**
> If the lengths of two sides of one triangle are proportional to the lengths of two sides of another triangle and the angles between the sides are congruent, then the triangles are similar.

You will prove the theorems in the exercises for this section.

Example 1: For each pair of triangles, (a) determine whether or not the triangles are similar, and (b) if your answer to part (a) was *yes*, then complete the similarity statement and state a similarity postulate or theorem to support your conclusion.

(i) $\Delta DOF \sim \Delta$________

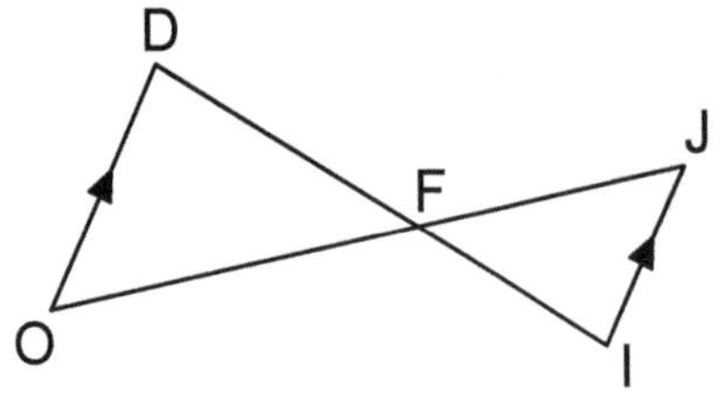

(ii) $\Delta ACS \sim \Delta$________

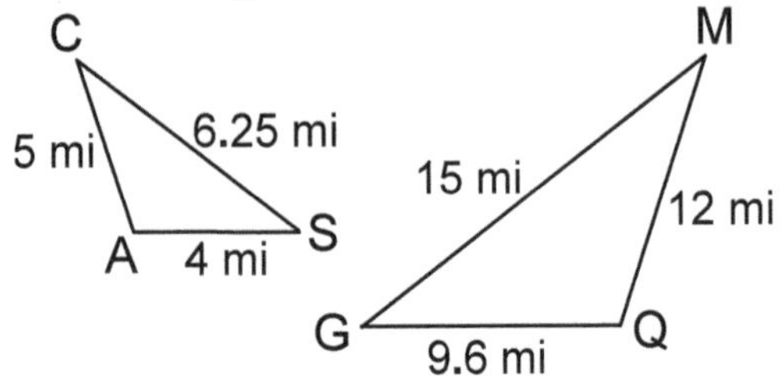

(iii) $\Delta BEY \sim \Delta$________

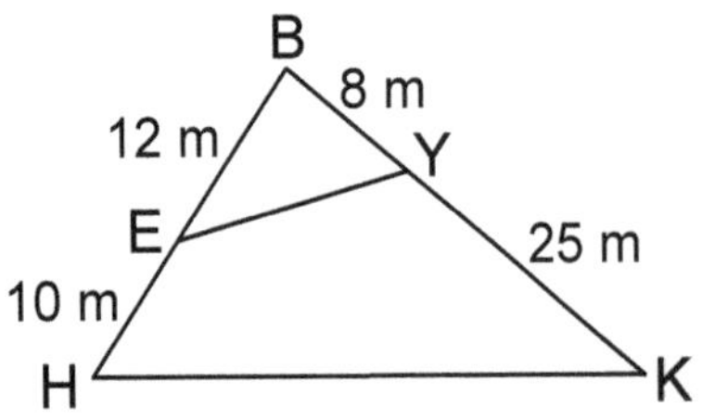

(iv) $\Delta OLN \sim \Delta$________

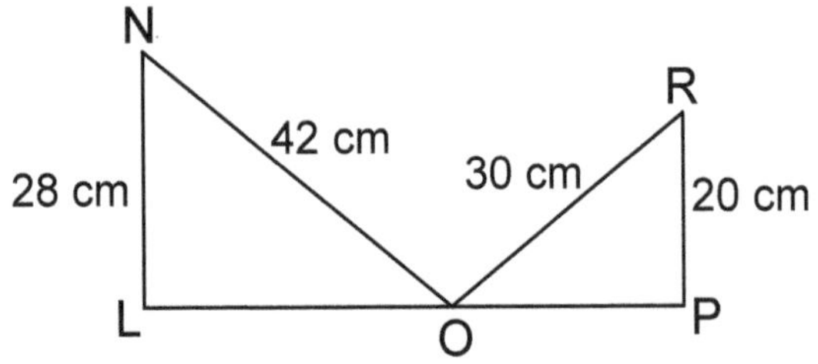

(v) $\Delta TWX \sim \Delta$________

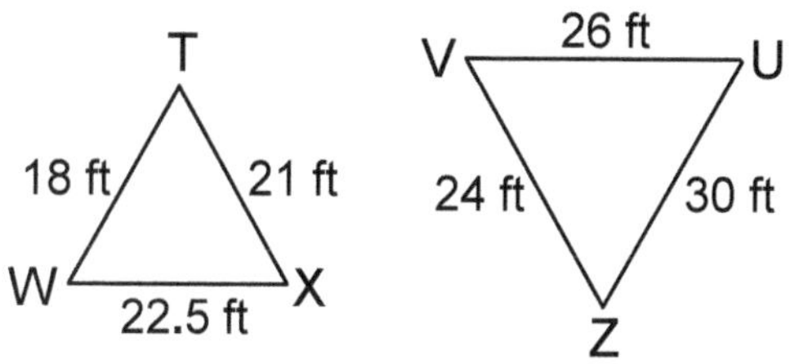

(i) Since that the arrowheads on $\overline{DO}$ and $\overline{IJ}$ tell us that $\overline{DO} \parallel \overline{IJ}$, we can use the Alternate Interior Angles Theorem to say that $\angle D \cong \angle I$ and $\angle O \cong \angle J$. Thus, the AA Similarity Theorem allows us to say that $\Delta DOF \sim \Delta IJF$. (Alternatively, we could have said that $\angle D \cong \angle I$ and $\angle O \cong \angle J$ by the Alternate Interior Angles Theorem and that $\angle OFD \cong \angle JFI$ by the Vertical Angles Theorem, and so $\Delta DOF \sim \Delta IJF$ by the AAA Similarity Postulate. Or, as another alternative, we could have named other combinations of two sets of congruent angles and used the AA Similarity Theorem.)

(ii) We will begin by noting that the ratios $\frac{MQ}{CA}$, $\frac{GQ}{SA}$, and $\frac{MG}{CS}$ are all equal to each other. (To see why, put $12 \div 5$, $9.6 \div 4$, and $15 \div 6.25$ into a calculator. Note that you get 2.4 each time.) Hence, we can use the SSS Similarity Postulate to say that $\Delta ACS \sim \Delta QMG$.

(iii) Notice that the ratios $\frac{BY}{BH}$ and $\frac{BE}{BK}$ are equal to each other. (Like we said in (ii), you can use a calculator to see that this is true.) Also notice that $\angle B$ is the angle between these sides in both cases, and $\angle B \cong \angle B$ by the Reflexive Property of Angle Congruence. Therefore, we can say that $\Delta BEY \sim \Delta BKH$ by the SAS Similarity Postulate.

(iv) The ratios $\frac{NL}{RP}$ and $\frac{NO}{RO}$ are equal to each other, but we do not know anything about the angles between these two sets of sides ($\angle N$ and $\angle R$) or the ratio of the lengths of the third sides. Therefore, we cannot say that these triangles must be similar, and so we cannot complete the similarity statement.

(v) From looking at the picture, it is difficult to tell which side of ΔUVZ might correspond with $\overline{TW}$, which side of ΔUVZ might correspond with $\overline{TX}$, and which side of ΔUVZ might correspond with $\overline{WX}$. The trick here is that, if the triangles are similar, then the longest side of ΔUVZ will correspond with the longest side of ΔTWX, the second longest side of ΔUVZ will correspond with the second longest side of ΔTWX, and the shortest side of ΔUVZ will correspond with the shortest side of ΔTWX. Therefore, if these two triangles are similar, then the ratios $\frac{WX}{UZ}$, $\frac{TX}{VU}$, and $\frac{TW}{ZV}$ will all equal each other. Since this is not the case, we can say that the triangles are not similar to each other, and so we cannot complete the similarity statement.

Example 2: At 2:00 p.m. one day, Brandon and his brother Thomas measured the lengths of their shadows. Brandon's shadow was 32 inches long, and Thomas's shadow was 28 inches long. If Thomas was 5 feet 3 inches tall, how tall was Brandon?

We will begin by noting that the sun hits the tops of both boys' heads at the same angle and that both boys form right angles with the ground. This allows us to use the AA Similarity Postulate to say that we have two similar triangles, as shown below.

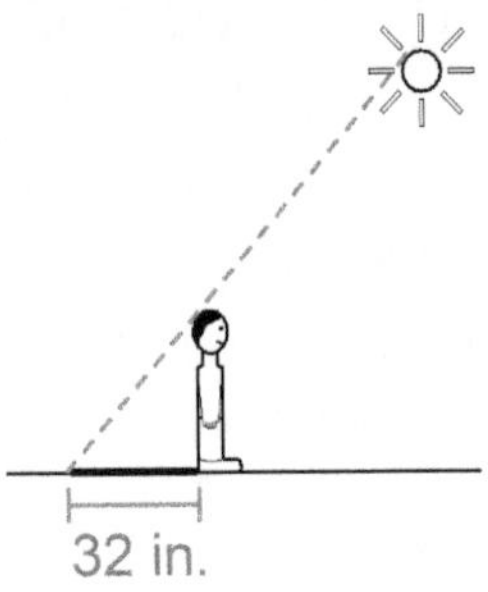

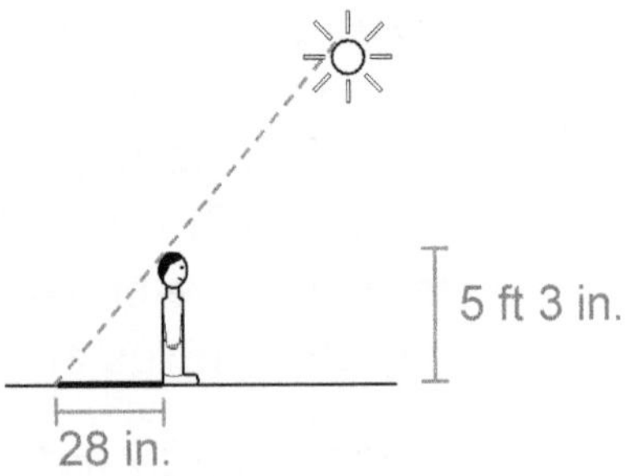

This tells us that $\frac{\text{Brandon's height}}{\text{Thomas's height}} = \frac{\text{length of Brandon's shadow}}{\text{length of Thomas's shadow}}$. If we let x represent Brandon's height and substitute the numbers given to us in the problem, we get the proportion $\frac{x}{63} = \frac{32}{28}$ (note that the fact that Thomas was 5 feet 3 inches tall tells us that he was 63 inches tall). This tells that x = 72, and so Thomas must have been 72 inches (or, equivalently, 6 feet) tall.

Now, we need five more theorems. You will prove them in the exercises for this section.

> Similarity of triangles is reflexive, symmetric, and transitive.

> If two triangles are similar, then the ratio of the corresponding angle bisectors is equal to the ratio of the corresponding sides.

> If two triangles are similar, then the ratio of the corresponding medians is equal to the ratio of the corresponding sides.

> If two triangles are similar, then the ratio of the corresponding altitudes is equal to the ratio of the corresponding sides.

> If two triangles are similar, then the ratio of the corresponding midsegments is equal to the ratio of the corresponding sides.

Example 3: In the figure at the right, $\triangle ABD \sim \triangle EFH$, $\overline{AC}$ is a median of $\triangle ABD$, and $\overline{EG}$ is a median of $\triangle EFH$. Find the length of $\overline{GE}$.

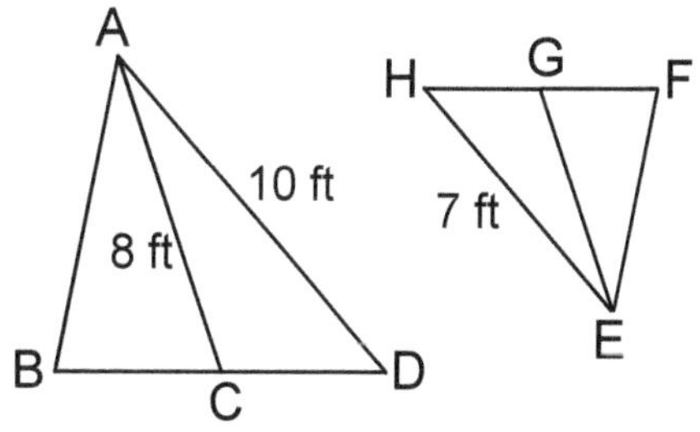

If we let x represent the length of $\overline{GE}$, then we can use the theorem *If two triangles are similar, then the ratio of the corresponding medians is equal to the ratio of the corresponding sides* to write the proportion $\frac{8}{x} = \frac{10}{7}$.

Using the Cross Products Property of Proportions, this tells us that 10x = 56, and so we can say that x = 5.6. Thus, $\overline{GE}$ must be 5.6 feet long.

Problems:

1-14. For each pair of triangles, (a) determine whether or not the triangles must be similar to each other, and (b) if your answer to part (a) was *yes*, then complete the similarity statement and state a similarity postulate or theorem to support your conclusion.

1a. Must the two triangles be similar to each other? _________

b. If your answer to (a) was *yes*, then $\triangle SPO \sim \triangle$___________.

Similarity postulate or theorem used:

____

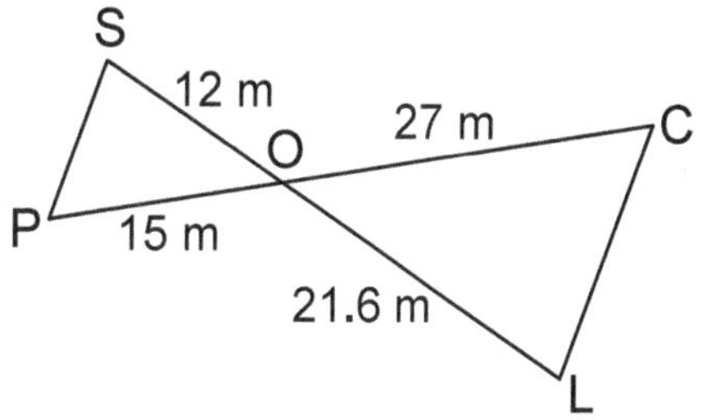

2a. Must the two triangles be similar to each other? _________

b. If your answer to (a) was *yes*, then $\triangle BHM \sim \triangle$___________.

Similarity postulate or theorem used:

____

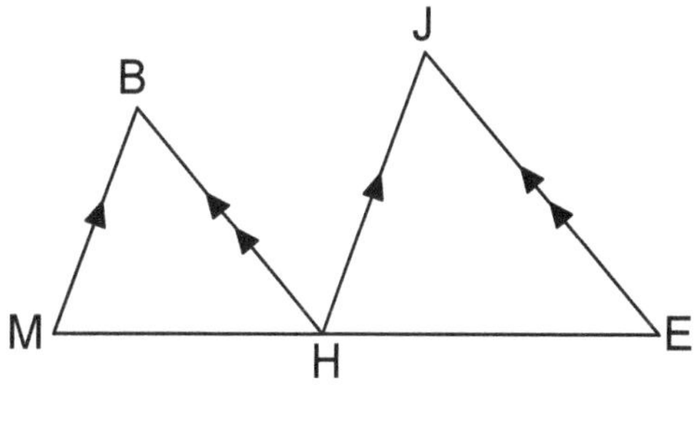

3a. Must the two triangles be similar to each other? _________

b. If your answer to (a) was *yes*, then $\Delta GXR \sim \Delta$___________.

Similarity postulate or theorem used:

____

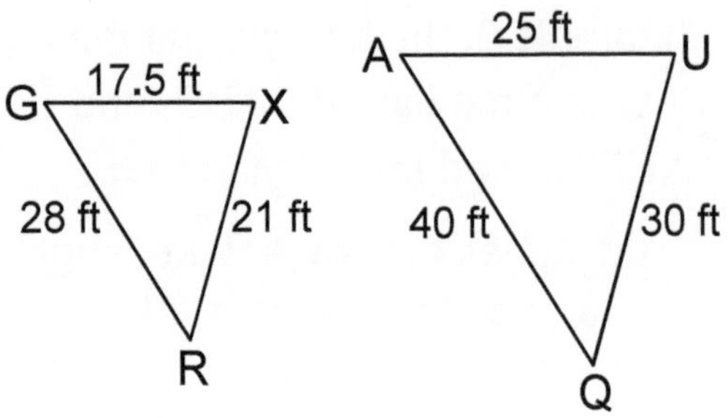

4a. Must the two triangles be similar to each other? _________

b. If your answer to (a) was *yes*, then $\Delta DFT \sim \Delta$___________.

Similarity postulate or theorem used:

____

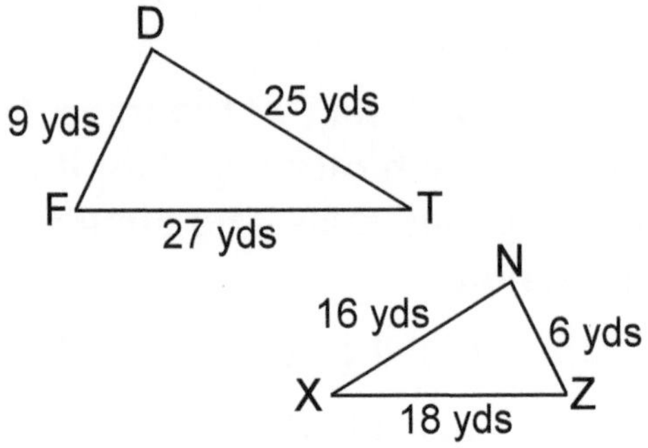

5a. Must the two triangles be similar to each other? _________

b. If your answer to (a) was *yes*, then $\Delta KWC \sim \Delta$___________.

Similarity postulate or theorem used:

____

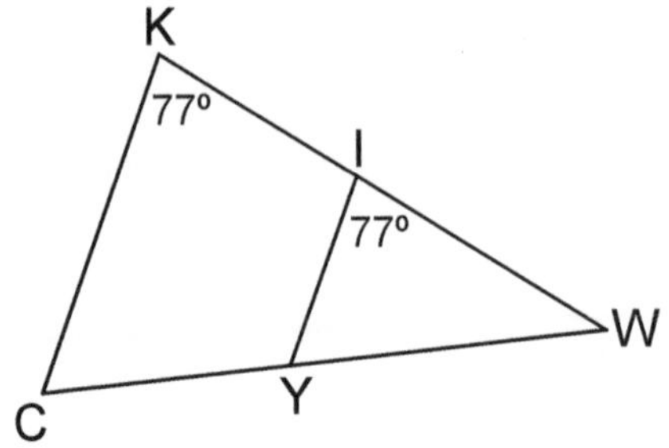

6a. Must the two triangles be similar to each other? _________

b. If your answer to (a) was *yes*, then $\Delta LGM \sim \Delta$___________.

Similarity postulate or theorem used:

____

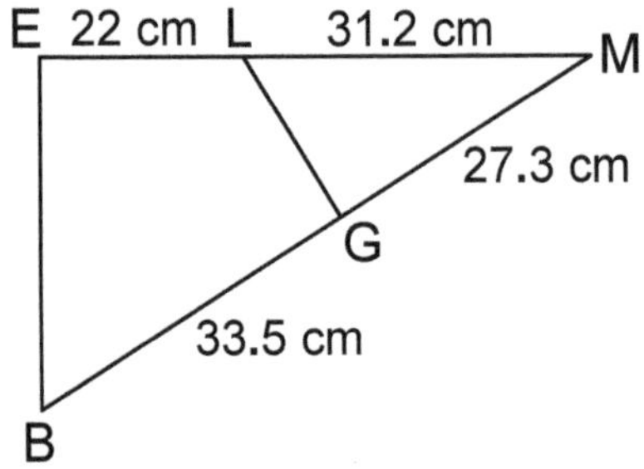

7a. Must the two triangles be similar to each other? _________

b. If your answer to (a) was *yes*, then $\Delta KHP \sim \Delta$___________.

Similarity postulate or theorem used:

____

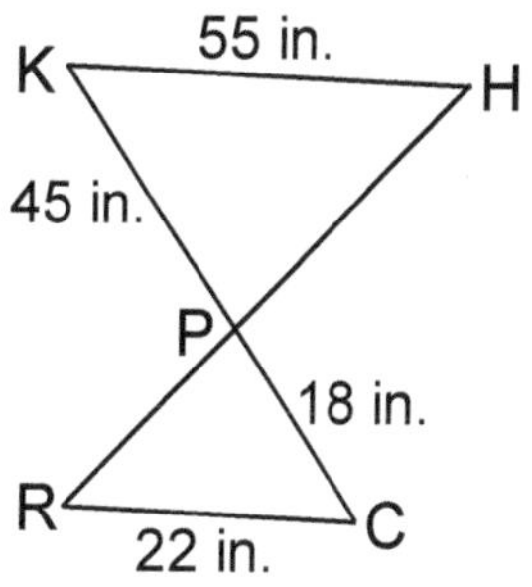

8a. Must the two triangles be similar to each other? _________

b. If your answer to (a) was *yes*, then $\Delta JNS \sim \Delta$___________.

Similarity postulate or theorem used:

____

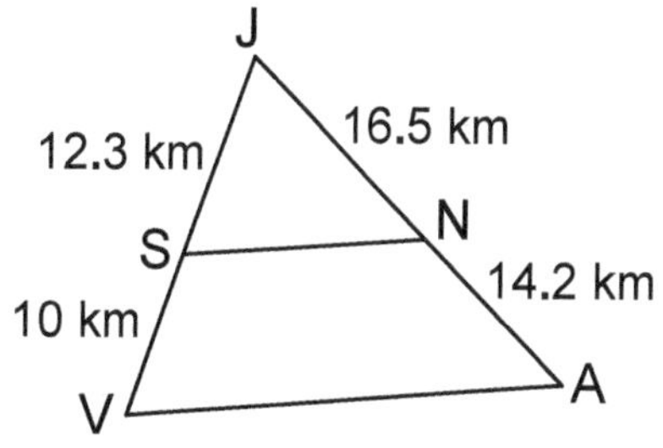

9a. Must the two triangles be similar to each other? _________

b. If your answer to (a) was *yes*, then $\Delta ZWD \sim \Delta$___________.

Similarity postulate or theorem used:

____

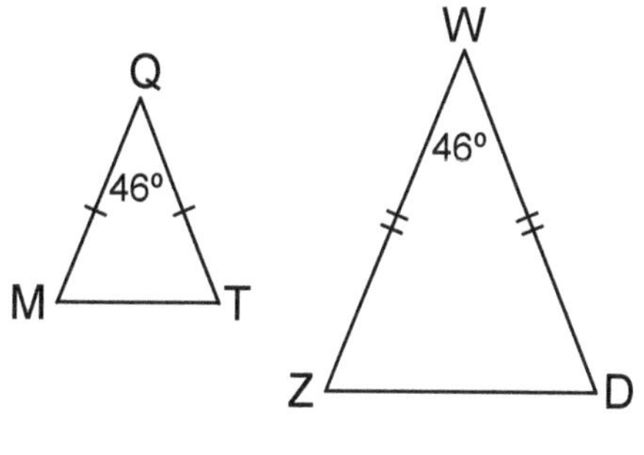

10a. Must the two triangles be similar to each other? _________

b. If your answer to (a) was *yes*, then $\Delta BEO \sim \Delta$___________.

Similarity postulate or theorem used:

____

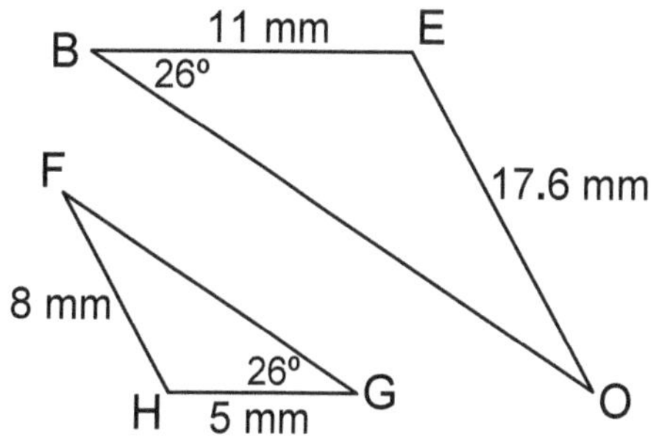

11a. Must the two triangles be similar to each other? __________

b. If your answer to (a) was *yes*, then $\Delta IJK \sim \Delta$____________.

Similarity postulate or theorem used:

____

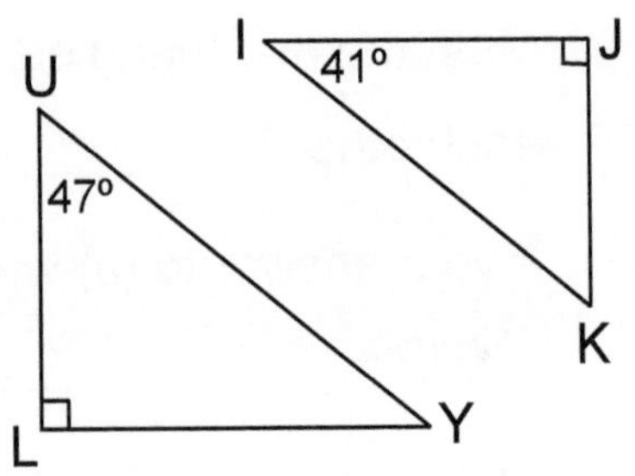

12a. Must the two triangles be similar to each other? __________

b. If your answer to (a) was *yes*, then $\Delta VWX \sim \Delta$____________.

Similarity postulate or theorem used:

____

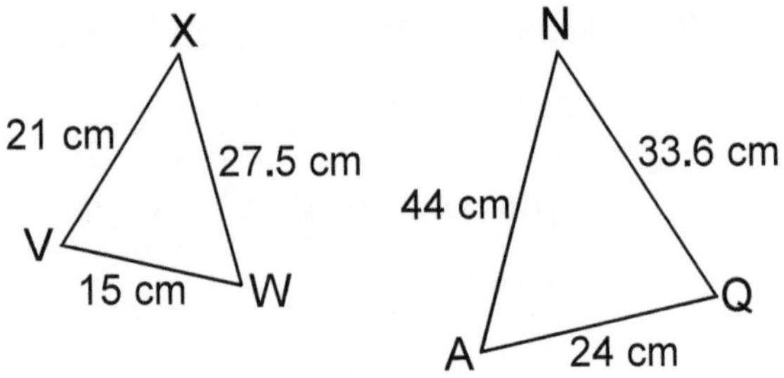

13a. Must the two triangles be similar to each other? __________

b. If your answer to (a) was *yes*, then $\Delta QTB \sim \Delta$____________.

Similarity postulate or theorem used:

____

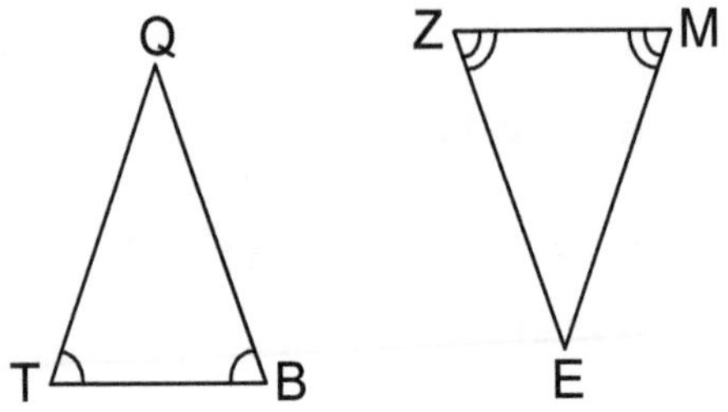

14a. Must the two triangles be similar to each other? __________

b. If your answer to (a) was *yes*, then $\Delta DSO \sim \Delta$____________.

Similarity postulate or theorem used:

____

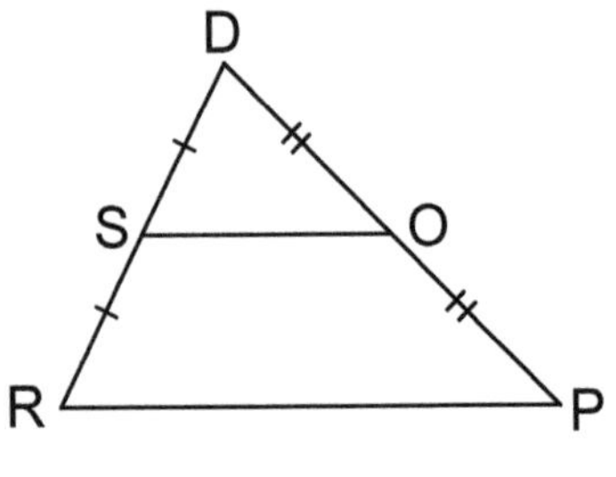

15-17. In the figure at the right, $\triangle ABC \sim \triangle FGE$, $\overline{AD}$ is a median of $\triangle ABC$, and $\overline{FH}$ is a median of $\triangle FGE$.

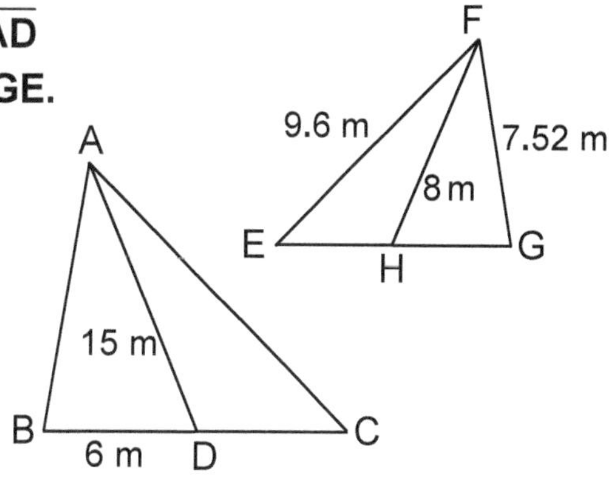

15. AC = __________

16. AB = __________

17. BC = __________, EG = __________, and EH = __________

18-21. In the figure at the right, $\triangle IJK \sim \triangle ONM$, $\overline{NP}$ is an angle bisector of $\triangle ONM$, and $\overline{JL}$ is an angle bisector of $\triangle IJK$.

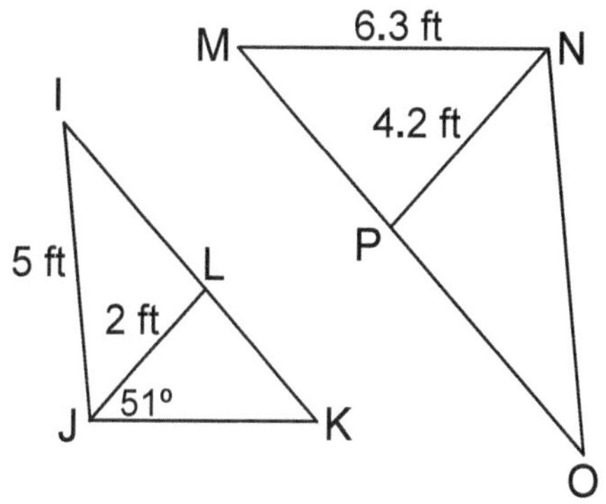

18. m∠ONP = _________ and

    m∠MNO = _________

19. NO = _________

20. JK = _________

21. Prove that $\triangle LJK \sim \triangle PNM$. (You may use the AA Similarity Theorem even though you have not proven it yet. You may not, however, use the any of the other theorems from this section.)

22-28. In the figure at the right, $\triangle QRS \sim \triangle UXW$, $\overline{RT}$ is an altitude of $\triangle QRS$, and $\overline{XV}$ is an altitude of $\triangle UXW$.

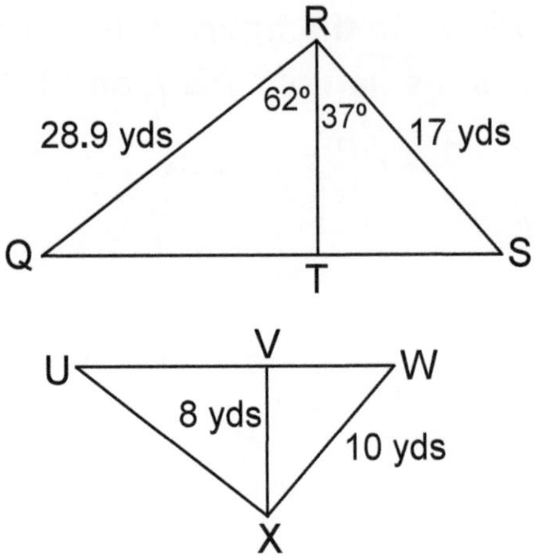

22. $m\angle QTR =$ _________

23. $m\angle U =$ _________ and $m\angle W =$ _________

24. $m\angle UXW =$ _________

25. $RT =$ _________

26. $UX =$ _________

27. $UW =$ _________

(Hint: You will need to use the Pythagorean Theorem twice.)

28. Prove that $\triangle QRT \sim \triangle UXV$. (You may use the AA Similarity Theorem even though you have not proven it yet. You may not, however, use the any of the other theorems from this section.)

29. The picture at the right shows a roof and some of its supports. Tell which two triangles must be similar, and state a similarity postulate or theorem that tells us that these two triangles must be similar. _______

____

What is the length of $\overline{BF}$? ____________

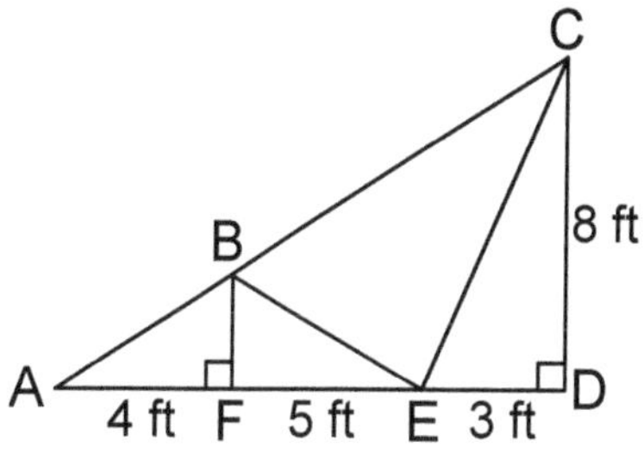

30. Zachary wants to know the distance across a river that is next to a site where he is camping. His campsite is at point G in the picture at the right, and he measures the distances shown in the picture. Name a postulate or theorem that tells us that we have two similar triangles. ________________

________________ What is the distance across the river? ____________

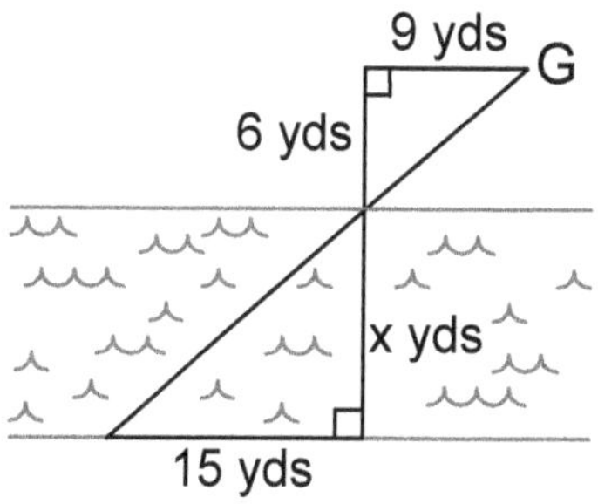

31. At a time of day when Eduardo's shadow is 0.9 meter long, the shadow of a tree is 11 meters long. If Eduardo knows that he is 1.7 meters tall, about how tall is the tree? (Round your answer to the nearest tenth of a meter.) ______________

32. At a time of day when Ava's shadow is 3 feet long, the shadow of a building is 20 feet long. If Ava knows that she is 5 feet 4 inches tall, about how tall is the building? (Round your answer to the nearest tenth of an inch.) ______________

33. At 5:00 p.m. one day, Sophia noticed that her shadow was 9 inches longer than her friend Hannah's shadow. Sophia knows that she is 5 feet 8 inches tall, and Hannah knows that she is 5 feet 2 inches tall. How long was Sophia's shadow?

____

34. Another method that a person can use to measure the height of objects is to hold a pole vertically in front of his or her face so that he or she can just barely see the top and bottom of the object. Emma wants to use this method to find out the height of a tree. If she stands 55 feet from the base of the tree, she must hold the pole 15 inches away from her face. Which similarity postulate or theorem tells us that we have similar triangles? _______ __________________ If the pole is 21 inches tall, how tall is the tree? _______________

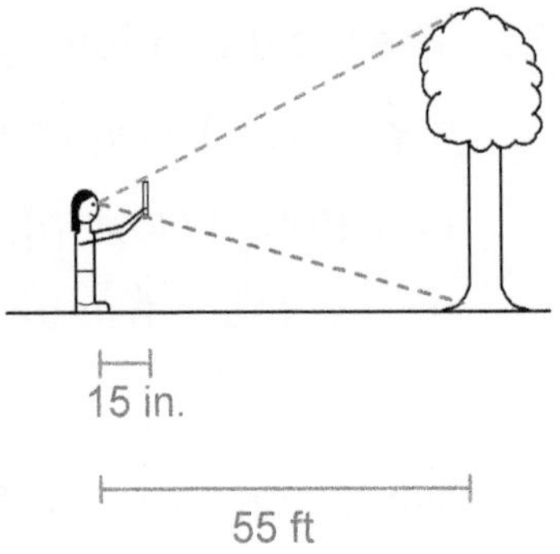

35. Andrew wants to use the method described in #34 to find the height of a building. If he stands 75 feet from the building, he must hold the pole 17 inches from his face. If he is using a pole that is 22 inches tall, about how tall is the building? (Round your answer to the nearest tenth of a foot.) _______________

36. Prove the AA Similarity Theorem.

Given: $\angle I \cong \angle L$ and $\angle J \cong \angle M$

Prove: $\triangle HIJ \sim \triangle KLM$

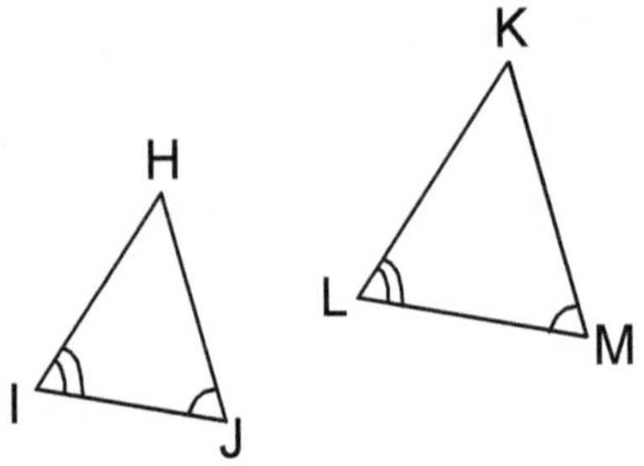

37. Prove the SAS Similarity Theorem using a paragraph proof.

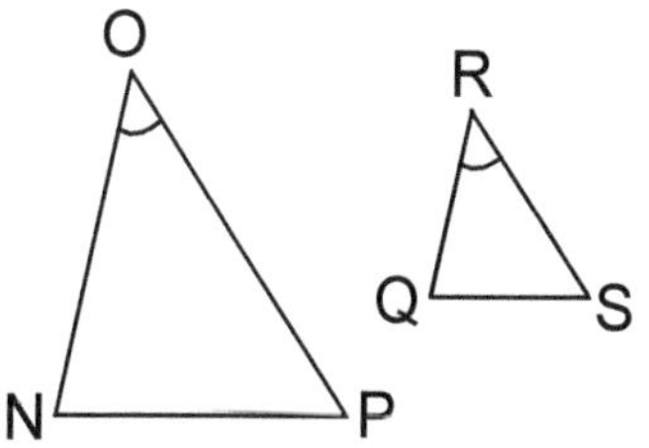

Given: $\frac{ON}{RQ} = \frac{OP}{RS}$ and $\angle O \cong \angle R$

Prove: $\Delta NOP \sim \Delta QRS$

We are given that $\frac{ON}{RQ} = \frac{OP}{RS}$ and that $\angle O \cong \angle R$. We will assume that the lengths of the sides of ΔNOP are longer than those of ΔQRS. If this is not the case, then the proof will essentially stay the same; only the next picture will change. We will begin by using the Ruler Postulate to label point T on $\overrightarrow{ON}$ so that OT = RQ. Then, by the ___________________________________, $\overline{OT} \cong \overline{RQ}$. Next, we will use the __________________ Postulate to draw $\overline{TU}$ so that $\overline{TU} \parallel \overline{NP}$ and U is on $\overrightarrow{OP}$.

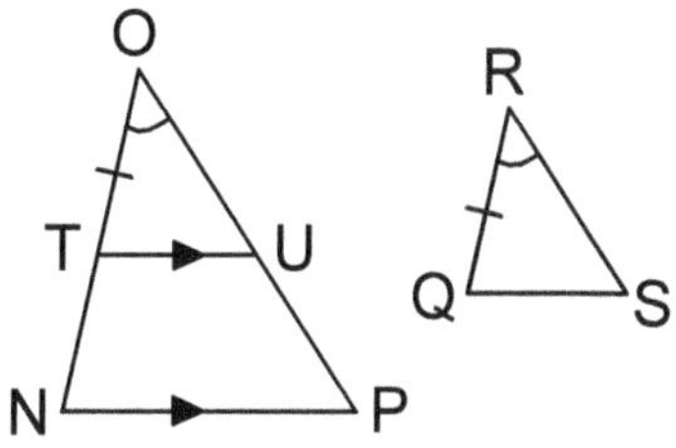

Then, by the ______________________________, $\angle N \cong \angle OTU$. By the Reflexive Property of Angle Congruence, $\angle O \cong \angle O$. Then, by the ____________________ Theorem, $\Delta TOU \sim \Delta NOP$. By the definition of similar triangles, $\frac{ON}{OT} = \frac{OP}{OU}$. By the ___________________________________, $\frac{ON}{RQ} = \frac{OP}{OU}$. By the _______________ __________________, $\frac{OP}{RS} = \frac{OP}{OU}$. By the Cross Products Property of Proportions and the Division Property of Equality, RS = OU. By the definition of congruent segments, ______________. Since we were given that $\angle O \cong \angle R$, we can now use the ______________________________________ to say that $\Delta TOU \cong \Delta QRS$. Then $\angle OTU \cong \angle Q$ by _______________. Since we already said that $\angle N \cong \angle OTU$, we can use the Transitive Property of Angle Congruence to say that $\angle N \cong \angle Q$. Therefore, $\Delta NOP \sim \Delta QRS$ by the __________________________ Theorem.

38. Prove the SSS Similarity Theorem using a paragraph proof.

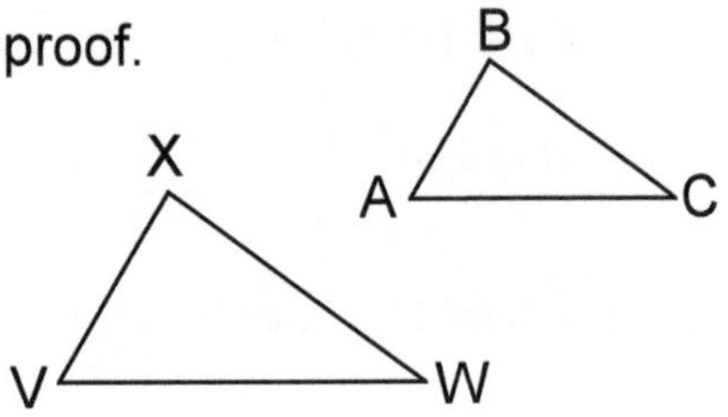

Given: $\frac{BA}{XV} = \frac{BC}{XW} = \frac{AC}{VW}$

Prove: $\Delta VXW \sim \Delta ABC$

We are given that $\frac{BA}{XV} = \frac{BC}{XW} = \frac{AC}{VW}$. Then, by the ____________________________ ____________, $\frac{(BA)(XW)}{XV} = BC$ and $\frac{(BA)(VW)}{XV} = AC$. Now, we will assume that the lengths of the sides of ΔVXW are longer than those of ΔABC. If this is not the case, then the proof will essentially stay the same; only the next picture will change. Next, we will use the Ruler Postulate to label point Y on $\overrightarrow{XV}$ so that XY = BA. Then, by the ______________________________________, $\overline{XY} \cong \overline{BA}$. Next, we will use the __________________ Postulate to draw $\overline{YZ}$ so that $\overline{YZ} \parallel \overline{VW}$ and is Z on $\overrightarrow{XW}$.

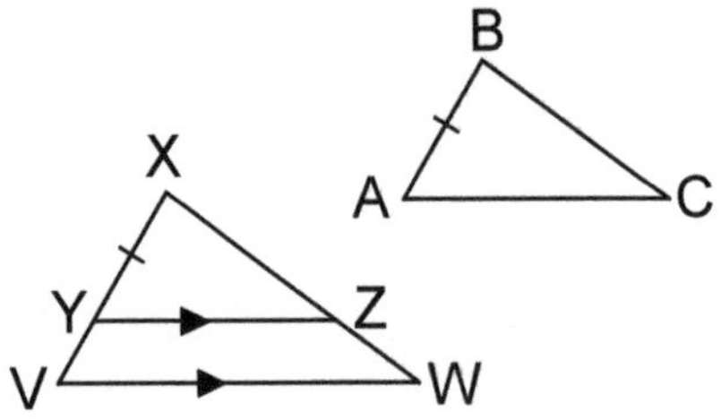

Then, by the ______________________________, $\angle XYZ \cong \angle V$. By the Reflexive Property of Angle Congruence, $\angle X \cong \angle X$. Then, by the ______________________ Theorem, $\Delta XYZ \sim \Delta XVW$. By the ____,

$\frac{XY}{XV} = \frac{XZ}{XW} = \frac{YZ}{VW}$. By the ____,

$\frac{BA}{XV} = \frac{XZ}{XW} = \frac{YZ}{VW}$. By the ____,

$\frac{(BA)(XW)}{XV} = XZ$ and $\frac{(BA)(VW)}{XV} = YZ$. By the ______________________________,

XZ = BC and YZ = AC. Then, by the ____,

$\overline{XZ} \cong \overline{BC}$ and $\overline{YZ} \cong \overline{AC}$. Since we already said that $\overline{XY} \cong \overline{BA}$, we can now use the ________________________________ to say that $\Delta XYZ \cong \Delta BAC$. Therefore, $\angle X \cong \angle B$ and $\angle XYZ \cong \angle A$ by _______________. Thus, $\angle V \cong \angle A$ by the ________ ___________________________. We can now use the _______________________ _______________ to say that $\Delta VXW \sim \Delta ABC$.

39. Prove that similarity of triangles is reflexive.

Given: ΔDEF

Prove: $\Delta DEF \sim \Delta DEF$

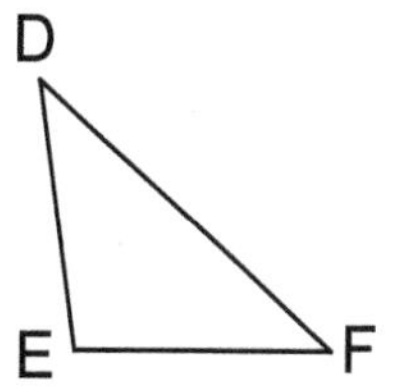

40. Prove that similarity of triangles is symmetric.

Given: $\Delta GHI \sim \Delta JKL$

Prove: $\Delta JKL \sim \Delta GHI$

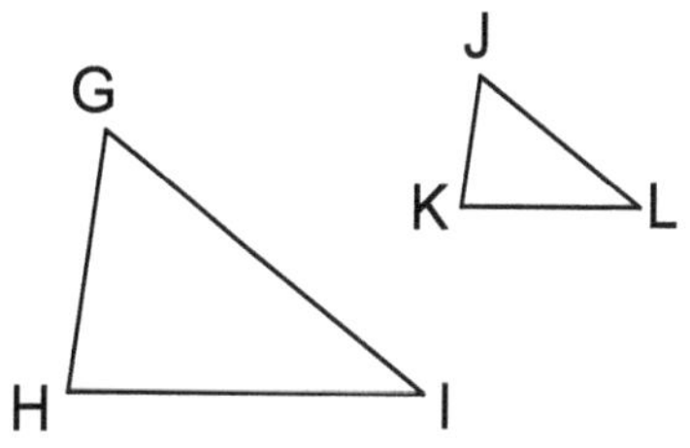

41. Prove that similarity of triangles is transitive.

Given: $\Delta MNO \sim \Delta PQR$ and $\Delta PQR \sim \Delta STU$

Prove: $\Delta MNO \sim \Delta STU$

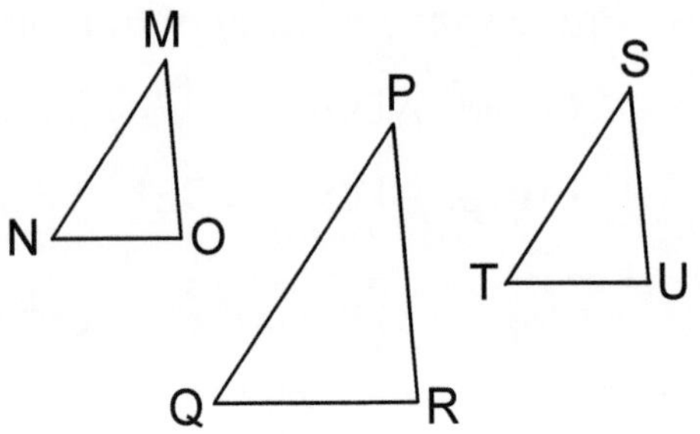

42. Prove the Midsegment of a Triangle Theorem, which says that, if a segment is a midsegment of a triangle, then it is parallel to a side of a triangle, and the length of this side of the triangle is equal to twice the length of the midsegment.

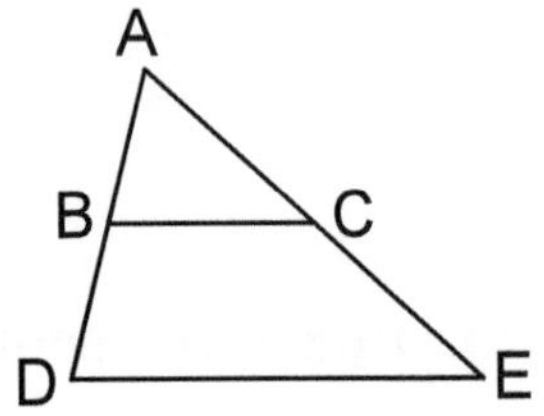

Given: ______________________________________

Prove: ______________________________________

43. Since we proved the Midsegment of a Triangle Theorem in the last problem, we can now use it to prove the Midsegment of a Trapezoid Theorem.

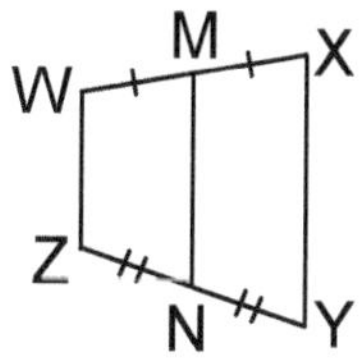

Given: Quadrilateral WXYZ is a trapezoid with bases $\overline{WZ}$ and $\overline{XY}$, and $\overline{MN}$ is a midsegment of trapezoid WXYZ

Prove: $\overline{MN}$ is parallel to both $\overline{WZ}$ and $\overline{XY}$ and $MN = \frac{WZ + XY}{2}$

We are given that quadrilateral WXYZ is a trapezoid with bases $\overline{WZ}$ and $\overline{XY}$. Then, by the ______________________________, $\overline{WZ} \parallel \overline{XY}$. We are also given that $\overline{MN}$ is a midsegment of trapezoid WXYZ. Then, by the definition of a midsegment of a trapezoid, M is the midpoint of $\overline{WX}$ and N is the midpoint of $\overline{ZY}$. By the ________________ Theorem, $\overline{ZN} \cong \overline{NY}$. Now, we can use the postulate ________ ____________________________________ to draw $\overrightarrow{XY}$ and $\overrightarrow{WN}$, and we will call the point where they intersect V.

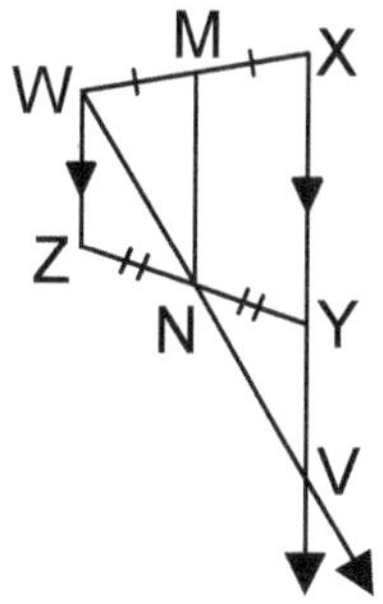

The ______________________________ Theorem tells us that $\angle ZWN \cong \angle NVY$ and $\angle WZN \cong \angle VYN$. Then $\Delta WZN \cong \Delta$__________ by the ____________________ Theorem. Therefore, $\overline{WN} \cong \overline{NV}$ and $\overline{WZ} \cong \overline{YV}$ by ______________.

Since $\overline{WN} \cong \overline{NV}$, the definition of ________________________ and the definition of congruent segments tell us that N is the midpoint of $\overline{WV}$, and so we can use the ____ to say that $\overline{MN}$ is a midsegment of ΔWXV. The Midsegment of a Triangle Theorem tells us that $\overline{MN} \parallel \overline{XY}$. Then, by the Transitive Property of Parallel Lines, $\overline{MN} \parallel \overline{WZ}$. The Midsegment of a Triangle Theorem also tells us that $MN = \frac{XV}{2}$. The ______________________________ tells us that XY + YV = XV, and so we can use the Substitution Property of Equality to say that ________________. We already said that $\overline{WZ} \cong \overline{YV}$, and so we can use the ____ to say that WZ = YZ. Then, by the ____, $MN = \frac{WZ + XY}{2}$.

44. Prove that, if two triangles are similar, then the ratio of the corresponding angle bisectors is equal to the ratio of the corresponding sides.

Given: ______________________________

____

Prove: ______________________________

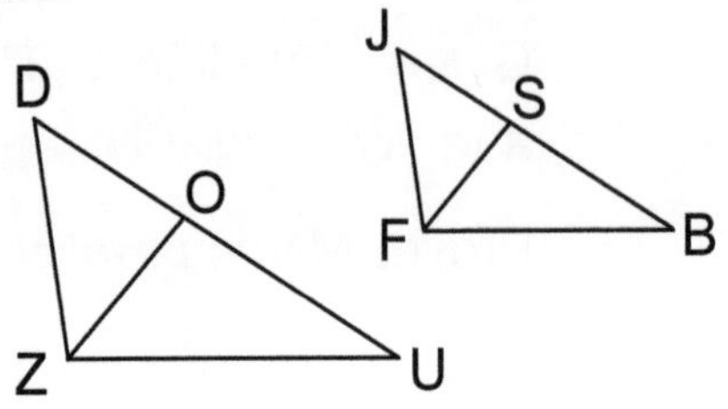

45. Prove that, if two triangles are similar, then the ratio of the corresponding medians is equal to the ratio of the corresponding sides.

Given: ______________________________

____

Prove: ______________________________

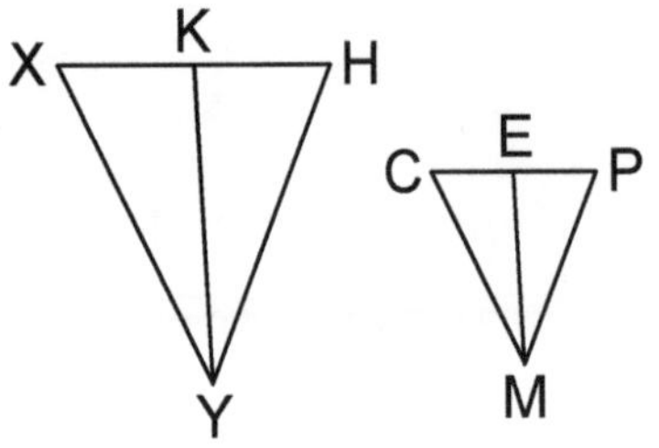

46. Prove that, if two triangles are similar, then the ratio of the corresponding altitudes is equal to the ratio of the corresponding sides.

Given: ______________________________

____

Prove: ______________________________

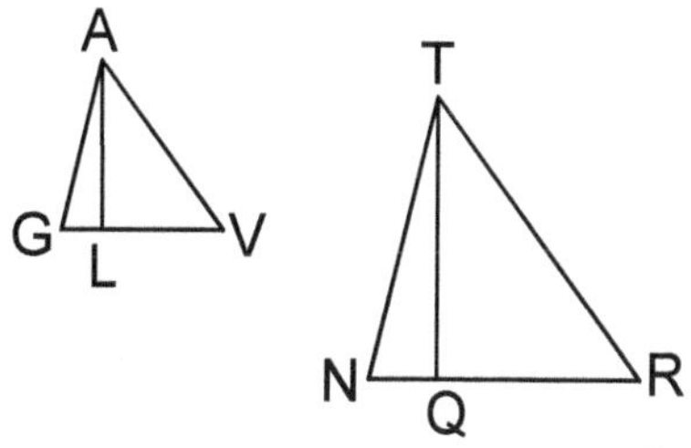

47. Prove that, if two triangles are similar, then the ratio of the corresponding midsegments is equal to the ratio of the corresponding sides.

Given: ______________________________

____

Prove: ______________________________

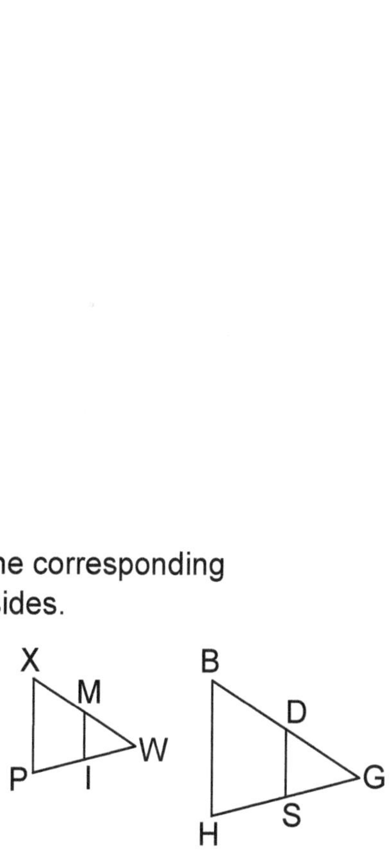

Part IV – Parallel Lines and Proportional Parts

We will begin this section with two theorems. We will prove the Side-Splitter of a Triangle Theorem in Example 1, and you will prove its converse in the exercises for this section.

> **Side-Splitter of a Triangle Theorem**
> If a segment is parallel to one side of a triangle and intersects the other two sides of the triangle in two distinct points, then it separates these sides into segments of proportional lengths.

> **Side-Splitter of a Triangle Converse Theorem**
> If a line intersects two sides of a triangle in two distinct points and separates these sides into segments so that the corresponding segments are proportional, then the line is parallel to the third side of the triangle.

To understand what these theorems tell us, look at the following picture.

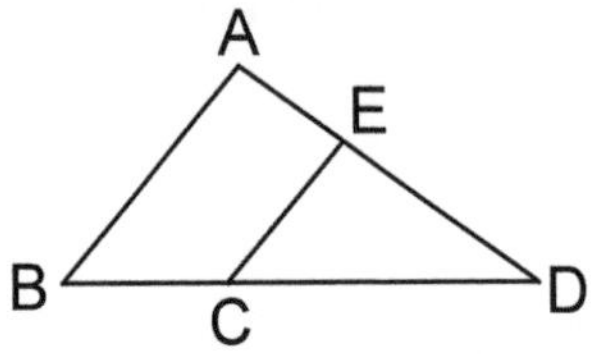

The Side Splitter of a Triangle Theorem tells us that, if we know that $\overline{AB} \parallel \overline{CE}$, then we can say that $\frac{AE}{ED} = \frac{BC}{CD}$. (There are actually many other proportions we could write. For instance, if we know that $\overline{AB} \parallel \overline{EC}$, then we can also say that $\frac{AE}{BC} = \frac{ED}{CD}$, $\frac{BC}{AE} = \frac{CD}{ED}$, and $\frac{BC}{CD} = \frac{AE}{ED}$. Notice that, for each of these proportions, we can draw a picture like we talked about in Part I of this chapter. Also note that the Cross Products Property of Proportions tells us that all of these proportions are equivalent because they all tell us that $AE \cdot CD = ED \cdot BC$.) The Side Splitter of a Triangle Converse Theorem tells us that, if we know that one of the proportions stated above is true, then $\overline{AB}$ must be parallel to $\overline{CE}$.

Example 1: Prove the Side Splitter of a Triangle Theorem.

The proof that we will give here is only one of several possible proofs.

We must, of course, begin by drawing a generic picture that describes the part of the theorem that follows the "if."

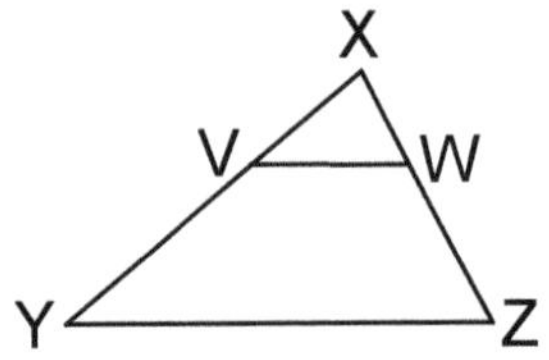

Using this picture, we can say that we are given that $\overline{VW} \parallel \overline{YZ}$, and we want to prove that $\frac{VY}{XV} = \frac{WZ}{XW}$.

Since we know that $\overline{VW} \parallel \overline{YZ}$, we can use the Corresponding Angles Postulate to say that $\angle Y \cong \angle XVW$. Since we also know that $\angle X \cong \angle X$ by the Reflexive Property of Angle Congruence, we can use the AA Similarity Theorem to say that $\Delta XVW \sim \Delta XYZ$. Then, by the definition of similar triangles, $\frac{XY}{XV} = \frac{XZ}{XW}$.

Now, we can use the Segment Addition Postulate to say that XY = XV + VY and that XZ = XW + WZ. Then, by the Substitution Property of Equality, $\frac{XV+VY}{XV} = \frac{XW+WZ}{XW}$. Now, note that $\frac{XV+VY}{XV} = \frac{XV}{XV} + \frac{VY}{XV} = 1 + \frac{VY}{XV}$ and $\frac{XW+WZ}{XW} = \frac{XW}{XW} + \frac{WZ}{XW} = 1 + \frac{WZ}{XW}$. Then, by the Substitution Property of Equality, $1 + \frac{VY}{XV} = 1 + \frac{WZ}{XW}$. Then $\frac{VY}{XV} = \frac{WZ}{XW}$ by the Subtraction Property of Equality.

Example 2: In the figure at the right, which segments, if any, must be parallel?

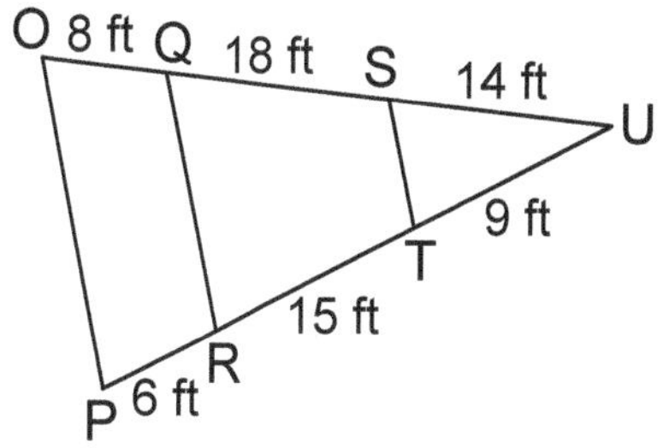

We will begin by noting that we can use the Side Splitter of a Triangle Theorem and its converse to say that $\overline{OP} \parallel \overline{QR}$ if and only if $\frac{OQ}{QU} = \frac{PR}{RU}$. This is true, and so we can say that $\overline{OP}$ must be parallel to $\overline{QR}$.

Next, we will note that we can use the Side Splitter of a Triangle Theorem and its converse to say that $\overline{ST} \parallel \overline{OP}$ if and only if $\frac{OS}{SU} = \frac{PT}{TU}$. Since $\frac{OS}{SU} \neq \frac{PT}{TU}$, we can say that $\overline{ST}$ is not parallel to $\overline{OP}$. Since we already said that $\overline{OP} \parallel \overline{QR}$, we can also say that $\overline{ST}$ is not parallel to $\overline{QR}$ either. (We could have also determined that $\overline{ST}$ is not parallel to either $\overline{QR}$ or $\overline{OP}$ by looking at ΔQRU and noting that $\overline{ST} \parallel \overline{QR}$ if and only if $\frac{QS}{SU} = \frac{RT}{TU}$. Since the ratios $\frac{QS}{SU}$ and $\frac{RT}{TU}$ are not equal to each other, $\overline{ST}$ cannot be parallel to $\overline{QR}$. Since $\overline{OP} \parallel \overline{QR}$, we can say that $\overline{ST}$ cannot be parallel to $\overline{OP}$ either.)

Now, we need two more theorems. We will prove the Parallel Lines and Proportionality Theorem in Example 4, and you will prove the other theorem in the exercises for this section.

Parallel Lines and Proportionality Theorem
If three or more parallel lines intersect two transversals, then they separate the transversals into segments of proportional lengths.

If three or more parallel lines cut off congruent segments on one transversal, then they cut off congruent segments on every transversal.

To understand what these theorems tell us, look at the following picture.

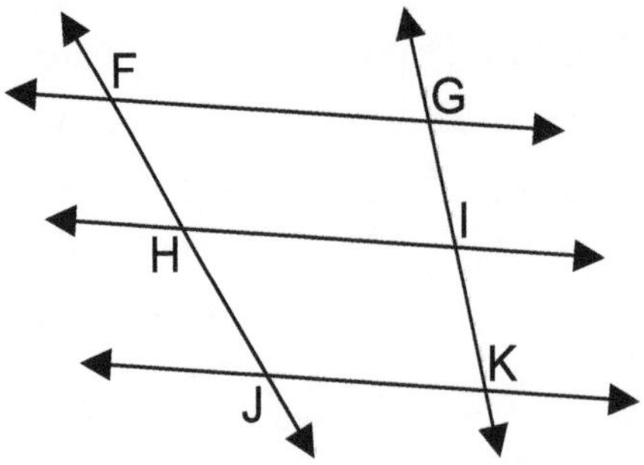

The Parallel Lines and Proportionality Theorem tells us that, if we know that $\overline{FG}$, $\overline{HI}$, and $\overline{JK}$ are all parallel to each other, then we can say that $\frac{FH}{HJ} = \frac{GI}{IK}$. Like we said with the Side Splitter of a Triangle Theorem, there are many other equivalent proportions we can write. For example, if we know that $\overline{FG}$, $\overline{HI}$, and $\overline{JK}$ are all parallel to each other, then we can also say that $\frac{FH}{GI} = \frac{HJ}{IK}$, $\frac{IK}{HJ} = \frac{GI}{FH}$, $\frac{IK}{GI} = \frac{HJ}{FH}$, $\frac{HJ}{FH} = \frac{IK}{GI}$, and $\frac{FJ}{HJ} = \frac{GK}{IK}$. The converse of this theorem, however, is not true. If we know that one the equations stated above is true, then we would **not** be able to conclude that any of the segments are parallel to each other.

The theorem *If three or more parallel lines cut off congruent segments on one transversal, then they cut off congruent segments on every transversal* tells us that, if $\overline{FG}$, $\overline{HI}$, and $\overline{JK}$ are all parallel to each other and $\overline{FH} \cong \overline{HJ}$, then $\overline{GI} \cong \overline{IK}$. It also tells us that, if $\overline{FG}$, $\overline{HI}$, and $\overline{JK}$ are all parallel to each other and $\overline{GI} \cong \overline{IK}$, then $\overline{FH} \cong \overline{HJ}$.

Example 3: In the figure at the right, lines ℓ, m, and n are all parallel to each other. Find the possible values of x.

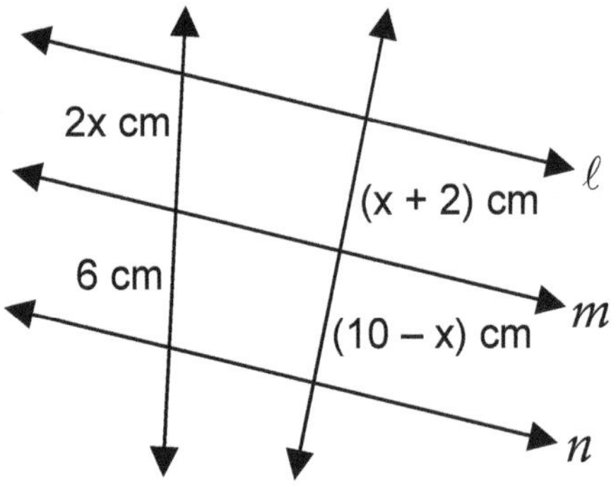

We can use the Parallel Lines and Proportionality Theorem to say that $\frac{2x}{6} = \frac{x+2}{10-x}$. We can solve this proportion as shown below and continued on the next page.

$$\frac{2x}{6} = \frac{x+2}{10-x}$$

$(2x)(10 - x) = (6)(x + 2)$ Use the Cross Products Property of Proportions.

$$\begin{aligned} 20x - 2x^2 &= 6x + 12 \\ 0 &= 2x^2 - 14x + 12 \\ 0 &= 2(x^2 - 7x + 6) \\ 0 &= 2(x - 1)(x - 6) \\ 2 = 0,\ x - 1 = 0,&\text{ or } x - 6 = 0 \\ x = 1 \quad &\text{or} \quad x = 6 \end{aligned}$$

We chose to finish solving this problem using factoring. We could have chosen to solve finish solving this problem using the quadratic formula instead; we would have gotten the same answers.

Finally, we will note that it is a good idea to go back and check and make sure that the answers work in the problem (especially when you get two answers, like we did here). If x = 1, then this gives us the picture on the left below; if x = 6, then this gives us the picture on the right below.

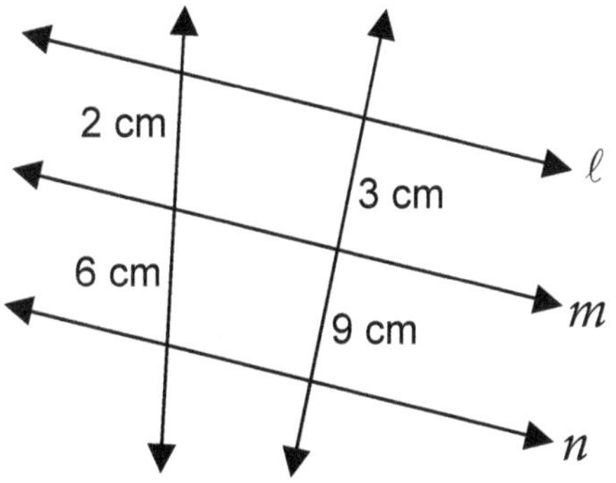

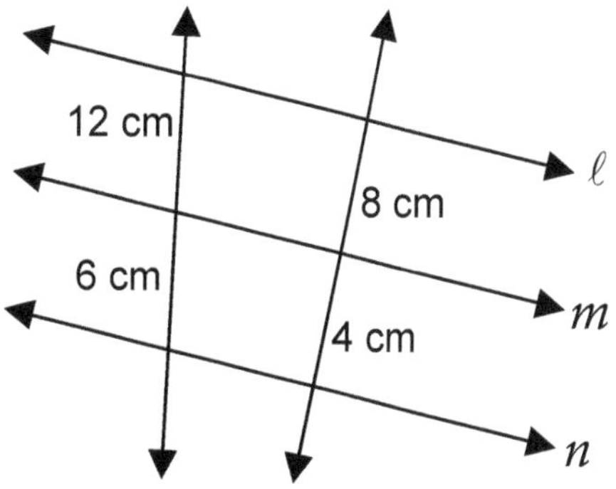

Neither of these answers gave us segments of negative length, and the segments are actually proportional for both pictures. Thus, our final answer is that x can equal 1 or 6.

Example 4: Prove Parallel Lines and Proportionality Theorem.

We will begin by drawing a generic picture that shows the part of the theorem that follows the "if."

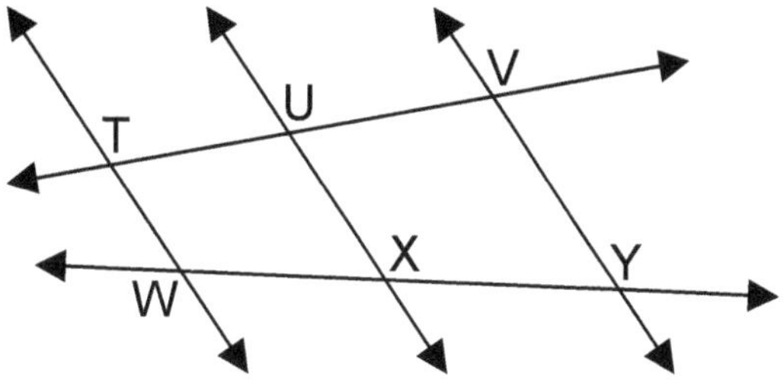

We can use this picture to say that we are given that $\overline{TW}$, $\overline{UX}$, and $\overline{VY}$ are all parallel to each other, and we want to prove that $\frac{TU}{WX} = \frac{UV}{XY}$.

We will consider two cases: either $\overleftrightarrow{TV} \parallel \overleftrightarrow{WY}$, or $\overleftrightarrow{TV}$ is not parallel to $\overleftrightarrow{WY}$.

Case 1: $\overleftrightarrow{TV} \parallel \overleftrightarrow{WY}$

If $\overleftrightarrow{TV} \parallel \overleftrightarrow{WY}$, then we can use the definition of a parallelogram to say that both quadrilateral TUXW and quadrilateral UVYX must be parallelograms. Then the Opposite Sides of a Parallelogram Theorem tells us that $\overline{TU} \cong \overline{WX}$ and

$\overline{UV} \cong \overline{XY}$. Then, by the definition of congruent segments, TU = WX and UV = XY. Then, by the Division Property of Equality, $\frac{TU}{WX} = 1$ and $\frac{UV}{XY} = 1$. Hence, we can now use the Substitution Property of Equality to say that $\frac{TU}{WX} = \frac{UV}{XY}$.

Case 2: $\overleftrightarrow{TV}$ is not parallel to $\overleftrightarrow{WY}$

If $\overleftrightarrow{TV}$ is not parallel to $\overleftrightarrow{WY}$, then we can use the theorem *If two distinct lines intersect, then they intersect in exactly one point* to say that $\overleftrightarrow{TV}$ and $\overleftrightarrow{WY}$ must intersect each other in exactly one point. We will call this point Z, and we will assume that Z is on the left side of $\overleftrightarrow{TW}$. (If $\overleftrightarrow{TV}$ intersects $\overleftrightarrow{WY}$ on the right side of $\overleftrightarrow{TW}$ instead, then the proof will be very similar but not identical.)

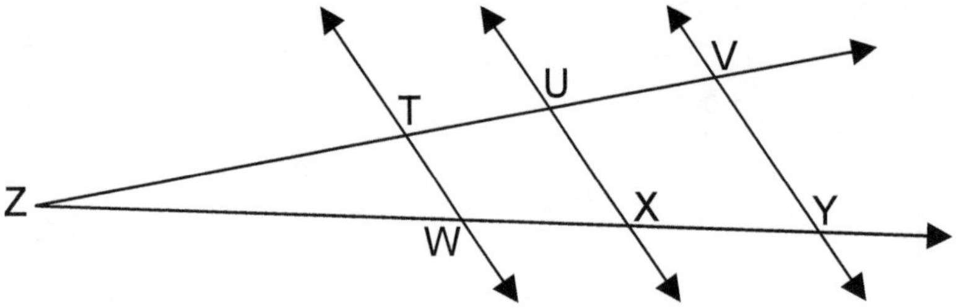

Now, we can use the Side Splitter of a Triangle Theorem to say that $\frac{TU}{WX} = \frac{ZT}{ZW}$ and $\frac{UV}{XY} = \frac{ZU}{ZX}$.

Next, we will note that the Corresponding Angles Postulate tells us that $\angle ZTW \cong \angle ZUX$ and $\angle ZWT \cong \angle ZXU$, and so we can use the AA Similarity Theorem to say that $\Delta ZTW \sim \Delta ZUX$. Then $\frac{ZT}{ZU} = \frac{ZW}{ZX}$ by the definition of similar triangles. By the Cross Products Property of Proportions and the Division Property of Equality, $\frac{ZT}{ZW} = \frac{ZU}{ZX}$.

Since we already said that $\frac{TU}{WX} = \frac{ZT}{ZW}$ and $\frac{UV}{XY} = \frac{ZU}{ZX}$, we can now use the Substitution Property of Equality to say that $\frac{TU}{WX} = \frac{UV}{XY}$.

Now, we need one more theorem.

An angle bisector of a triangle separates the opposite side into two segments whose lengths have the same ratio as the lengths of the other two sides.

We will talk about what this theorem says in Example 5, and then we will prove this theorem in Example 6.

Example 5: In the figure at the right, $\overline{NM}$ is an angle bisector of ΔONL. What is the value of y?

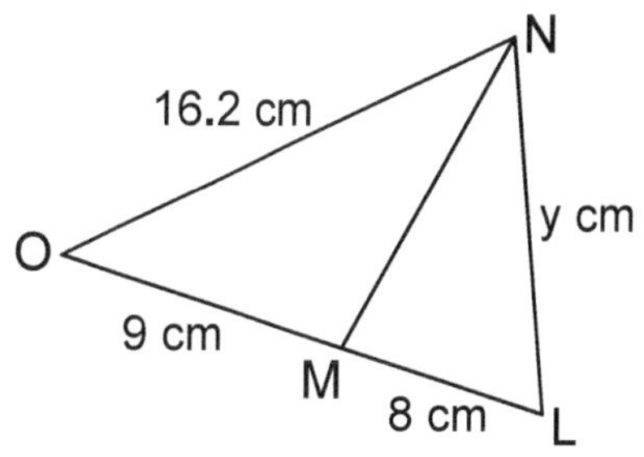

We can use the theorem in the box on the previous page to write the proportion $\frac{9}{8} = \frac{16.2}{y}$.

If we use the Cross Products Property of Proportions and then divide both sides of the resulting equation by 9, we find that y = 14.4.

Example 6: Prove that an angle bisector of a triangle separates the opposite side into two segments whose lengths have the same ratio as the lengths of the other two sides.

As usual, we will begin by drawing a generic picture that describes the part of this theorem that follows the "if."

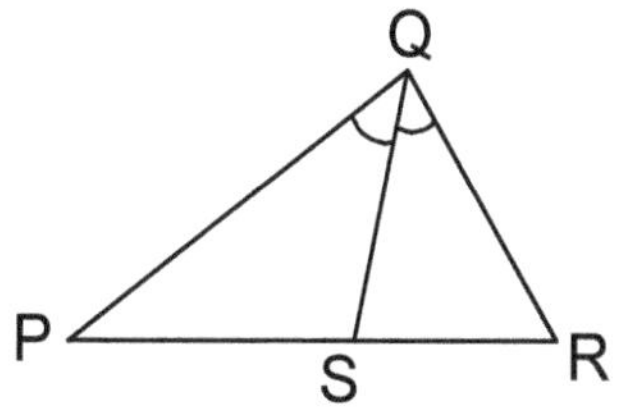

We can now say that we are given that $\overline{QS}$ bisects $\angle PQR$, and we want to prove that $\frac{PQ}{QR} = \frac{PS}{SR}$.

We will begin by using the Parallel Postulate and the theorem *If two lines intersect, then they intersect in exactly one point* to construct $\overline{RA}$ so that $\overline{RA} \parallel \overline{QS}$ and $\overrightarrow{PQ}$ intersects this segment at the point A.

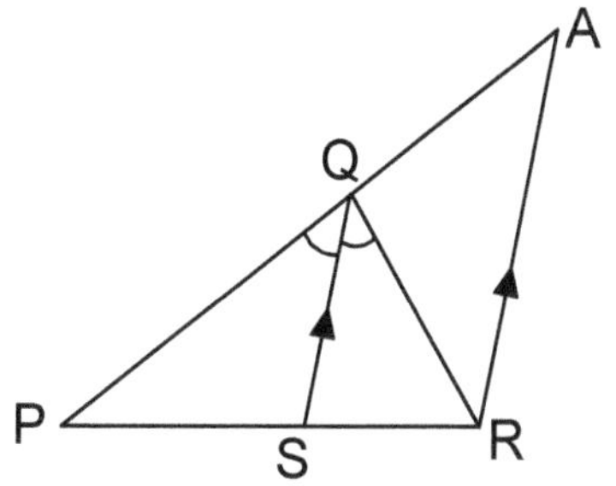

Now, we can use the Corresponding Angles Postulate to say that $\angle A \cong \angle PQS$ and the Alternate Interior Angles Theorem to say that $\angle SQR \cong \angle ARQ$. The definition of an angle bisector tells us that $\angle PQS \cong \angle SQR$, and so we can say that $\angle A \cong \angle ARQ$ by the Transitive Property of Angle Congruence. Therefore, $\overline{QR} \cong \overline{QA}$ by the Isosceles Triangle Converse Theorem, and so QR = QA by the definition of congruent segments.

Next, we will use the Side Splitter of a Triangle Theorem to say that $\frac{PQ}{QA} = \frac{PS}{SR}$.

Then, by the Substitution Property of Equality, $\frac{PQ}{QR} = \frac{PS}{SR}$.

Problems:

1-4. In the figures below, $\overline{AB} \parallel \overline{CD}$. Find the possible values of x.

1. x = ____________

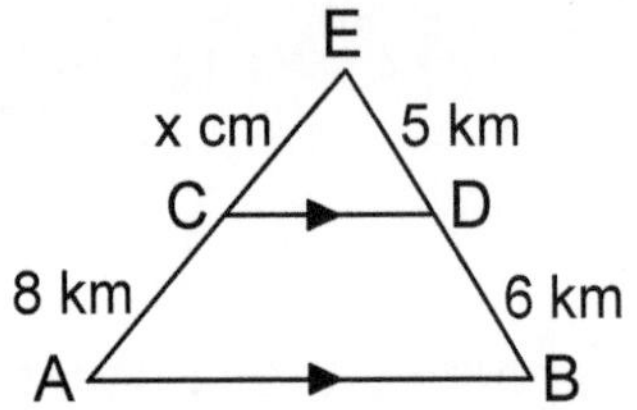

2. x = ____________

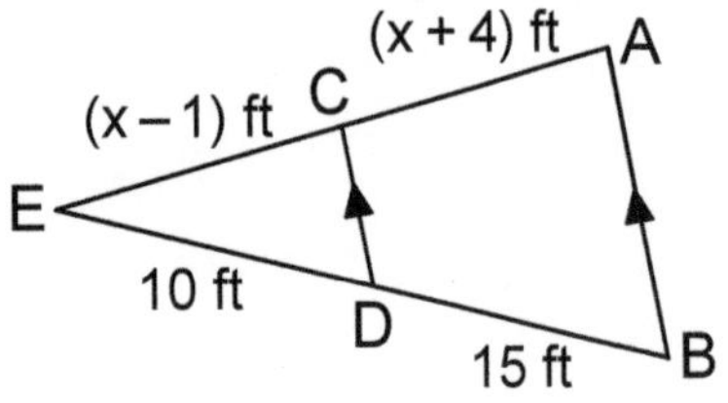

3. x = ____________

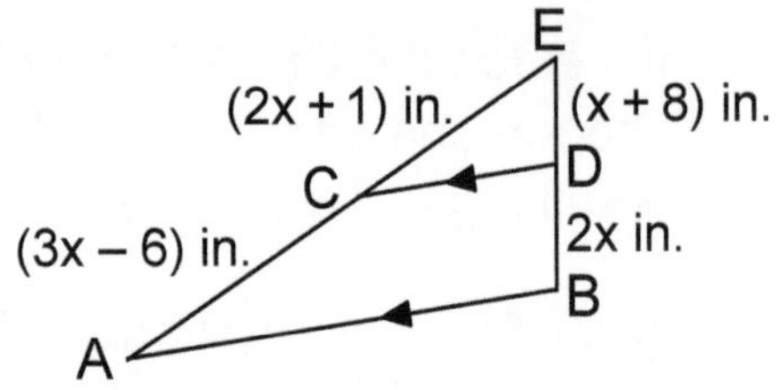

4. x = ____________

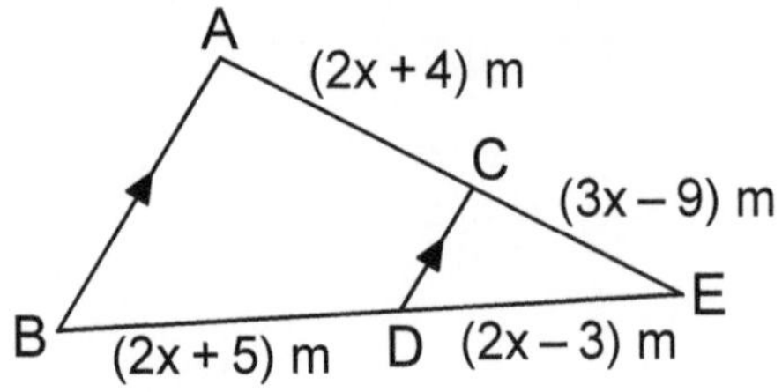

5-6. In the figures below, $\overline{FG} \parallel \overline{HI} \parallel \overline{JK}$. Find the values of x and y.

5. x = ____________

y = ____________

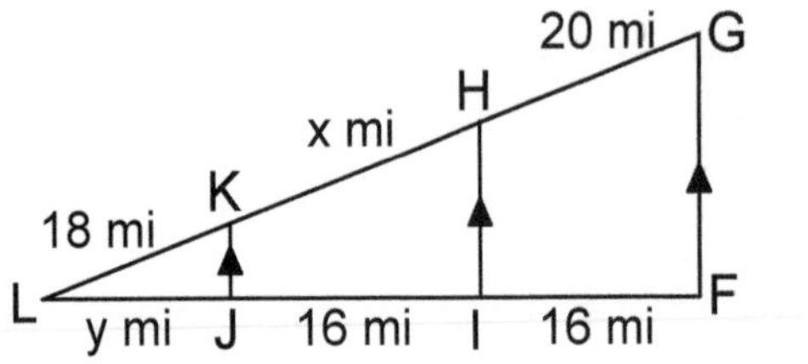

6. x = ____________

y = ____________

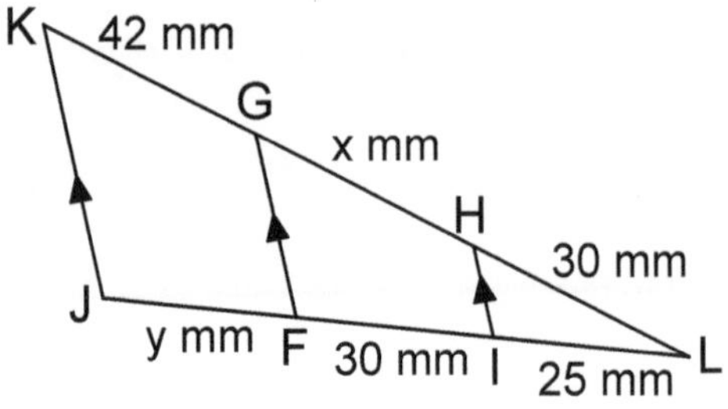

7-11. In the figures below, lines *m*, *n*, and *p* are all parallel to each other. Find the possible values of w.

7. w = ____________

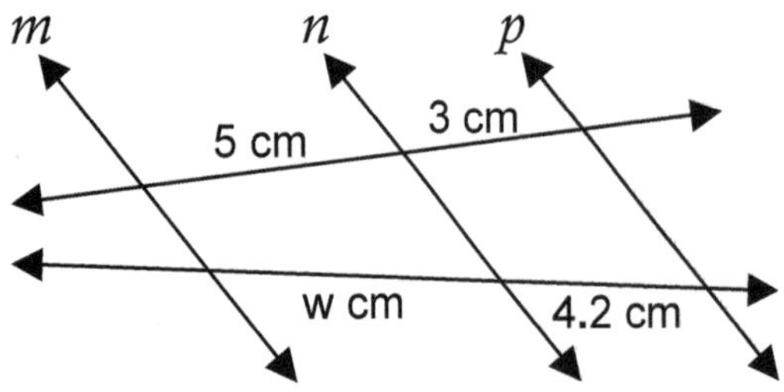

8. w = ____________

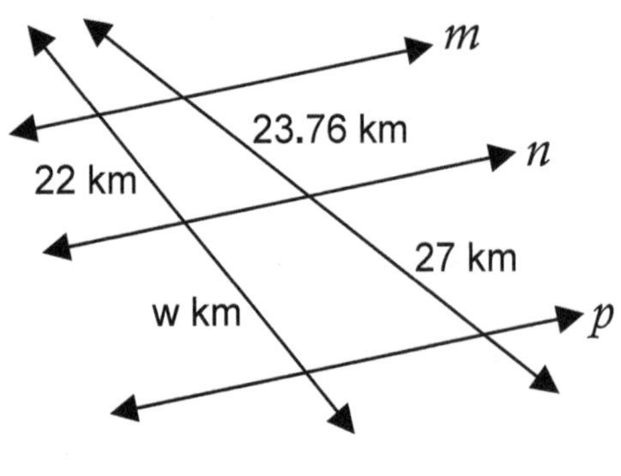

9. w = ____________

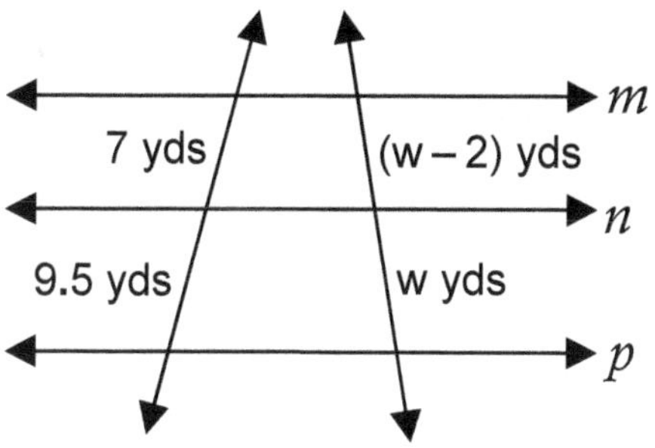

10. w = ____________

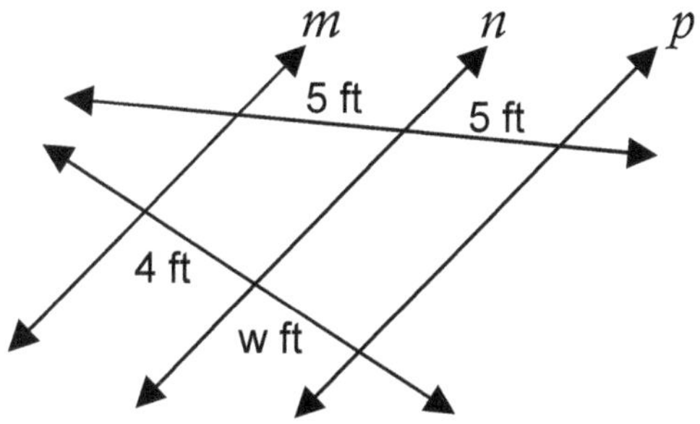

11. w = ____________

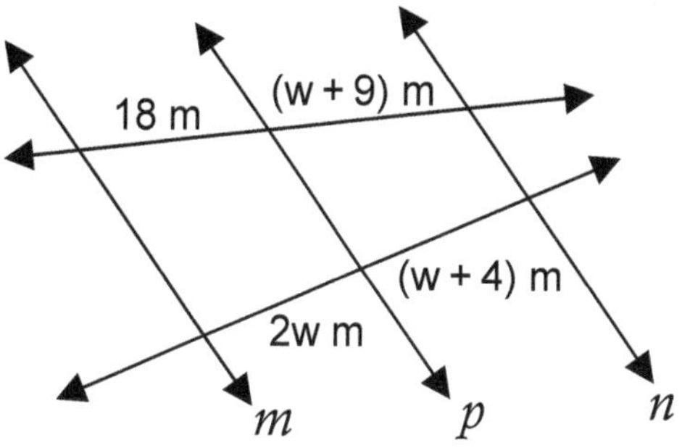

12. w = ____________

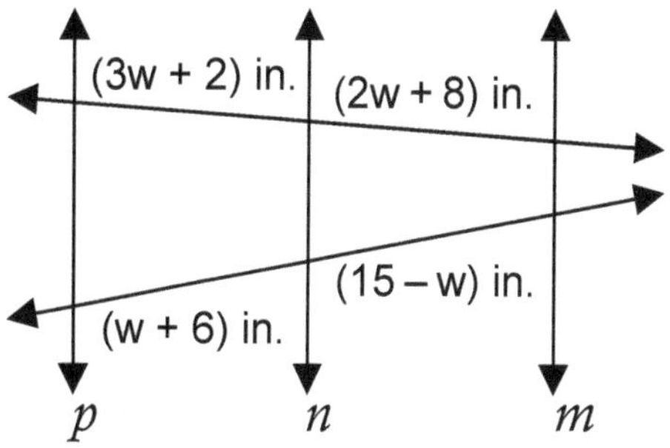

13-18. For each of the figures below, state which segments, if any, must be parallel to each other.

13. ____________________

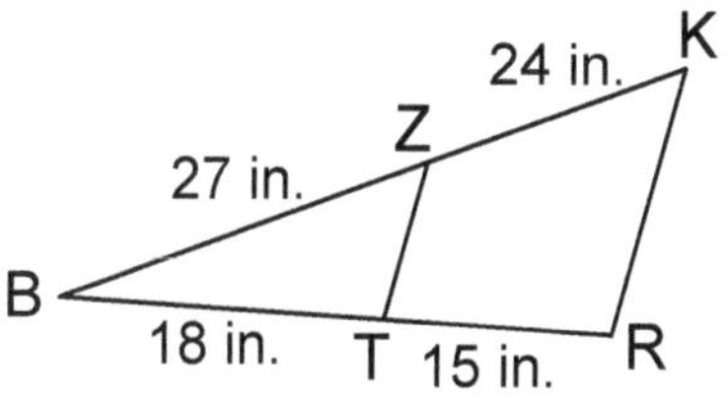

14. ____________________

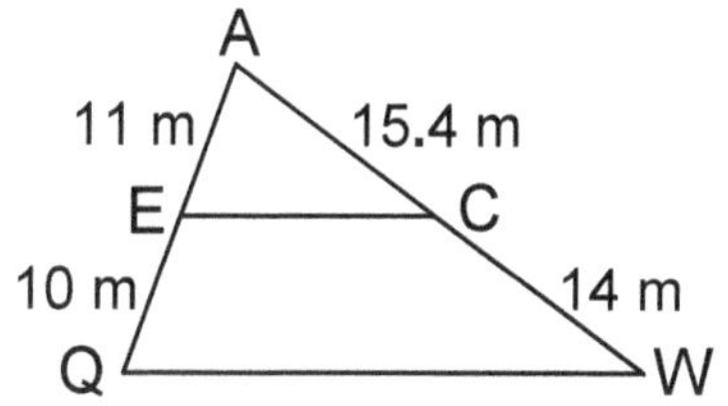

15. ____________________

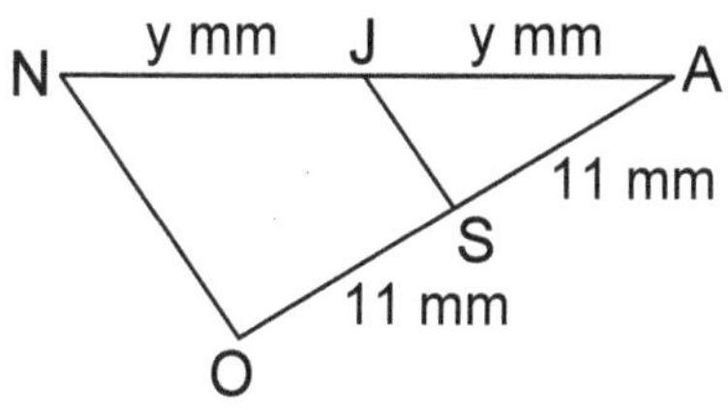

16. ____________________

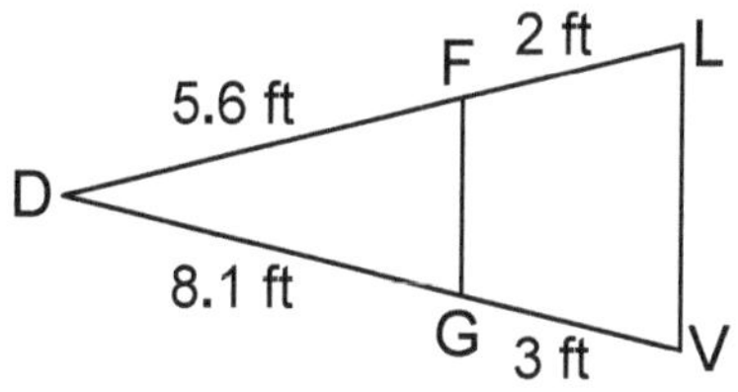

17. ____________________

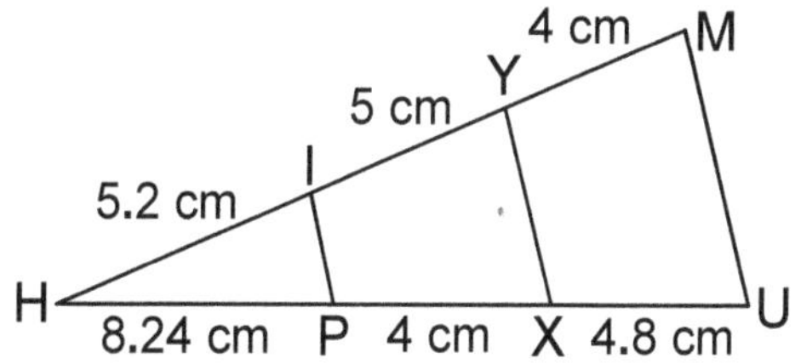

18. ____________________

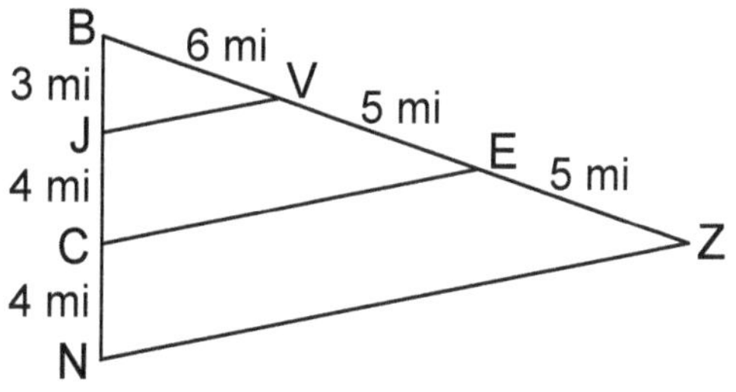

19-26. In each of the figures below, $\overline{QR}$ bisects $\angle SQT$. Find the possible values of k.

19. k = ___________

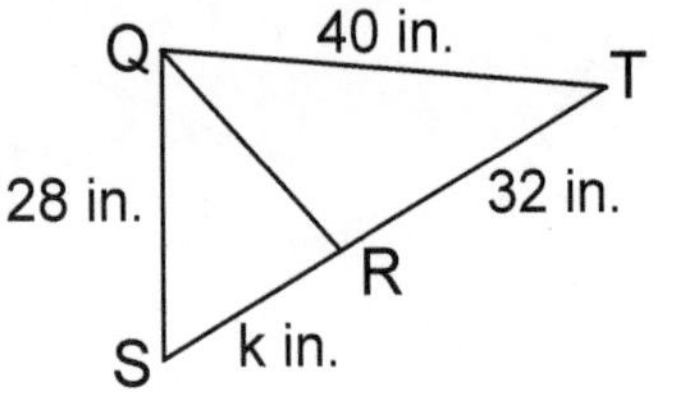

20. k = ___________

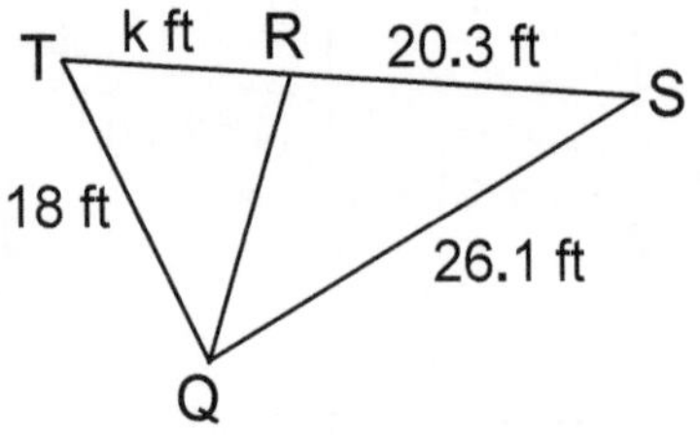

21. k = ___________

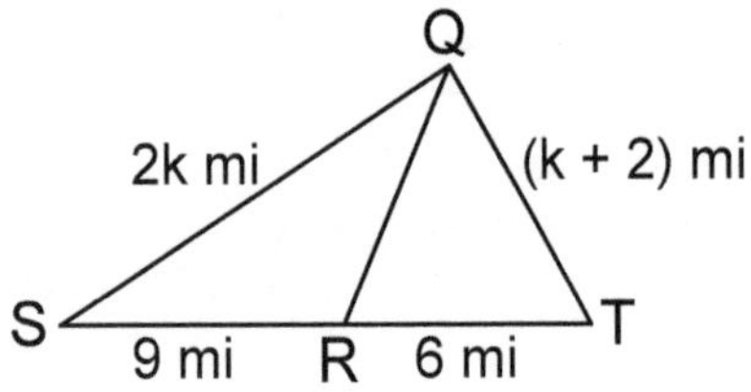

22. k = ___________

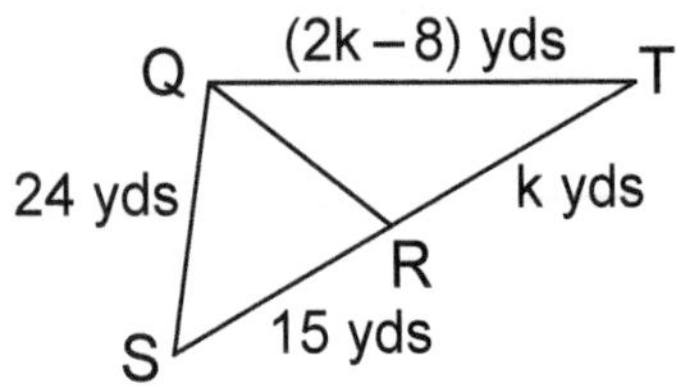

23. k = ___________

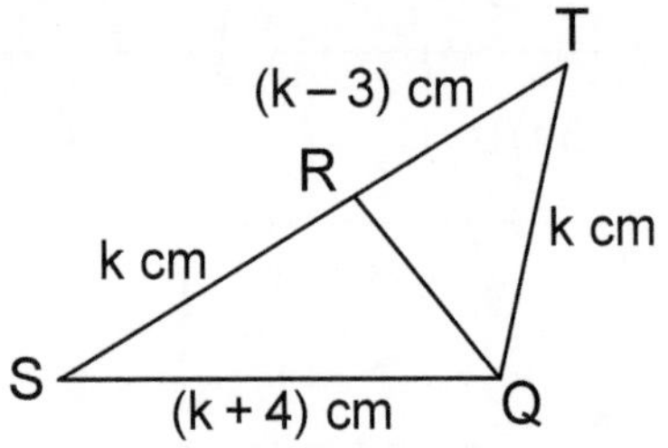

24. k = ___________

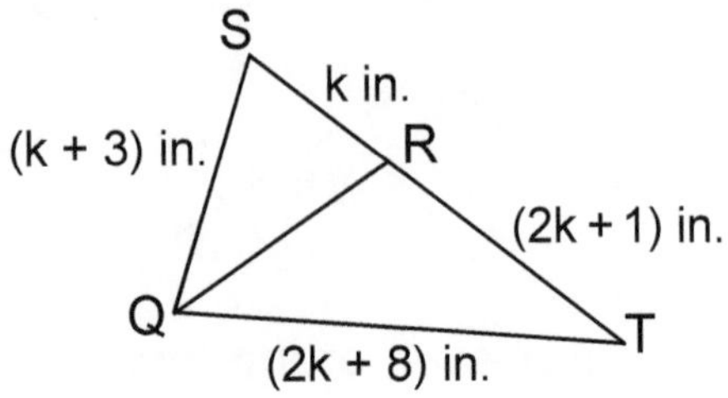

25. k = ___________

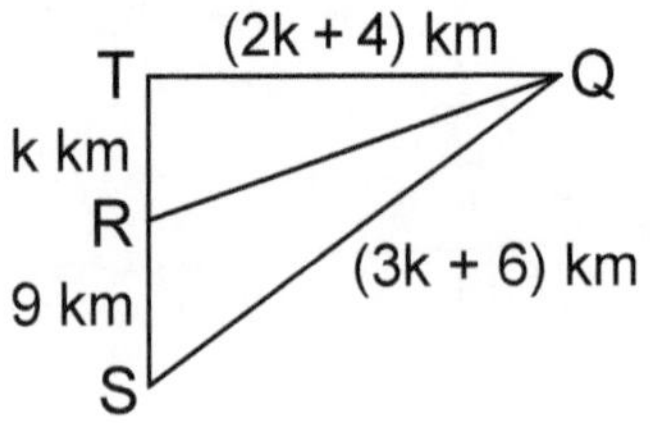

26. k = ___________

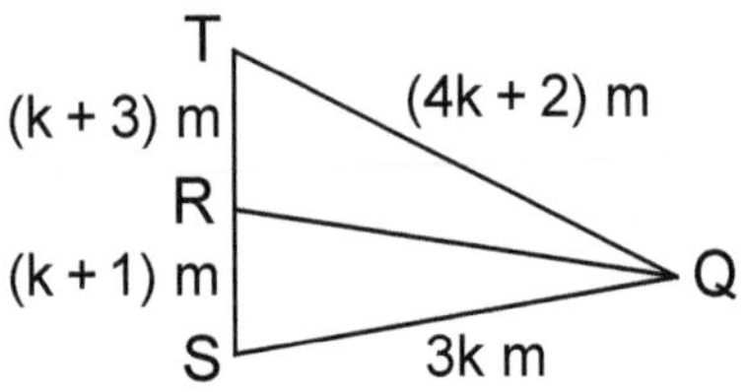

27. Prove the Side-Splitter of a Triangle Converse Theorem.

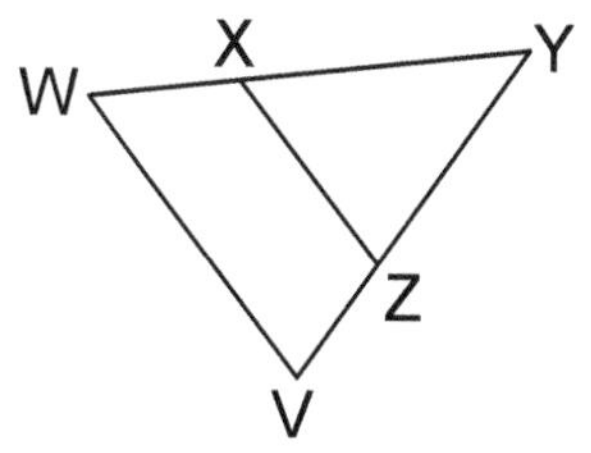

Given: $\frac{WX}{XY} = \frac{VZ}{ZY}$

Prove: ______________________________

28. Prove that, if three or more parallel lines cut off congruent segments on one transversal, then they cut off congruent segments on every transversal.

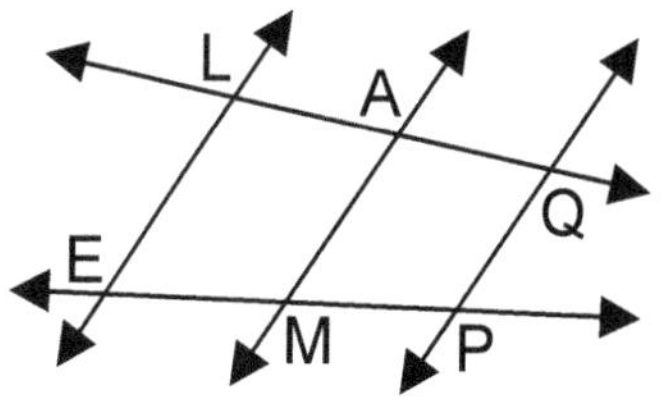

Given: $\overleftrightarrow{LE} \parallel \overleftrightarrow{AM} \parallel \overleftrightarrow{QP}$ and $\overline{EM} \cong \overline{MP}$

Prove: ______________________

Part V – Mixed Review

1-2. Solve for x in each of the following proportions.

1. $\frac{3-x}{x-1} = \frac{2x+5}{3x+3}$ x = ________

2. $\frac{x+1}{2x} = \frac{3x-5}{6x+8}$ x = ________

3-5. Use proportions to solve the following problems.

3. If a truck can travel 105 miles on 4.9 gallons of gasoline, how far can it travel on 14 gallons of gasoline? ____________

4. If a car travels 70 kilometers in 50 minutes, how far will the car travel in two hours (120 minutes) if it continues traveling at the same rate? ____________

5. If a doctor can see 10 patients in 2½ hours, how long will he need to see 28 patients? ____________

6. In the figure at the right, quadrilateral ABCD is similar to quadrilateral EFGH. Find the values of w, x, y, and z.

w = ________

x = ________

y = ________

z = ________

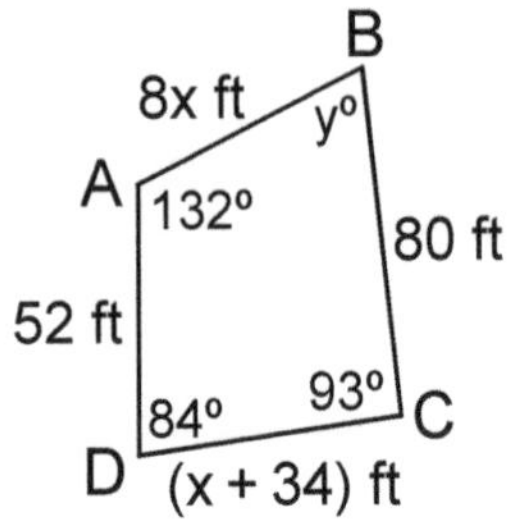

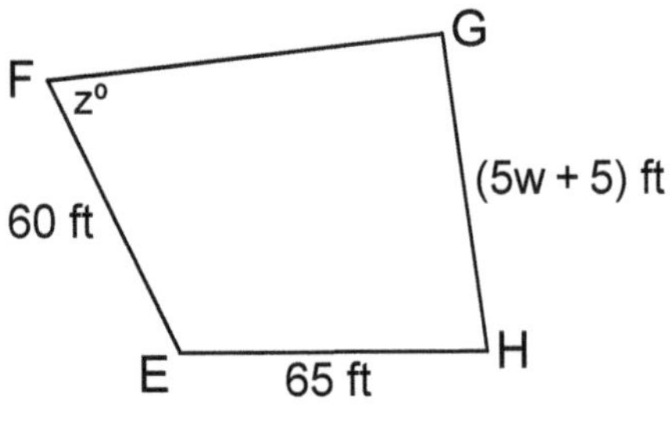

7. When Brian positions himself and his son in front of a mirror as shown at the right, he can just barely see the top of his son's head. If Brian knows that his eyes are 5 feet 10 inches from the ground, how tall is his son? _______________

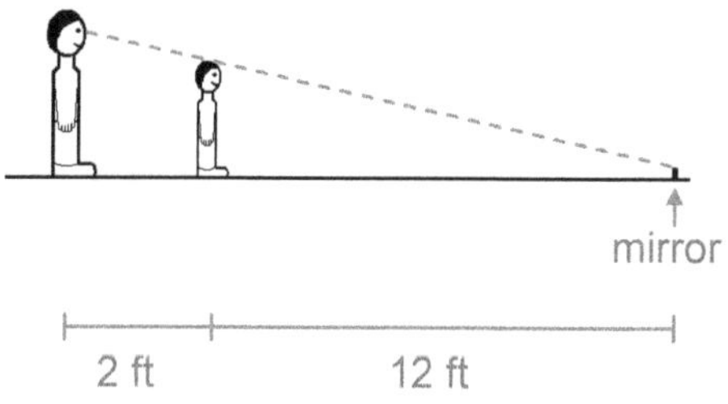

8-10. For each pair of figures below, (a) decide whether or not the two figures are similar, and (b) if you decide that the figures are similar, complete the similarity statement and then state a similarity definition, postulate, or theorem to support your conclusion.

8a. Are the two trapezoids similar? _________

b. If your answer to (a) was *yes*, then trapezoid GADU is similar to trapezoid _________.

Similarity definition, postulate, or theorem used:

____

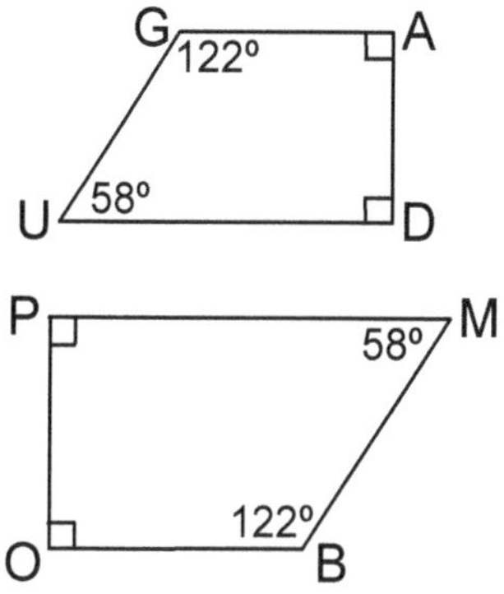

9a. Are the two triangles similar? _________

b. If your answer to (a) was *yes*, then

$\Delta CEU \sim \Delta$_________.

Similarity definition, postulate, or theorem used:

____

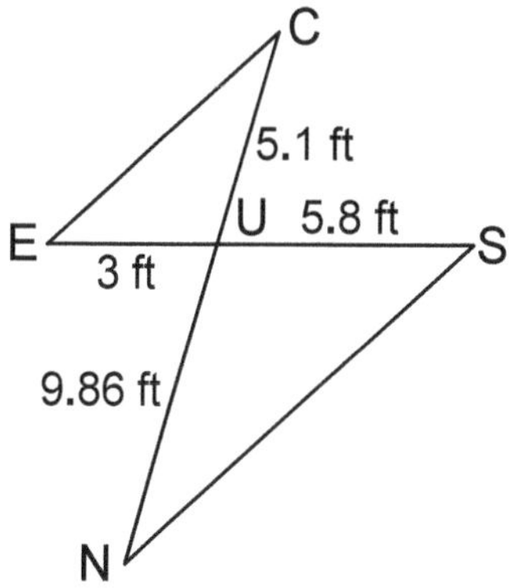

10a. Are the two triangles similar? _________

b. If your answer to (a) was *yes*, then

$\Delta VYL \sim \Delta$_________.

Similarity definition, postulate, or theorem used:

____

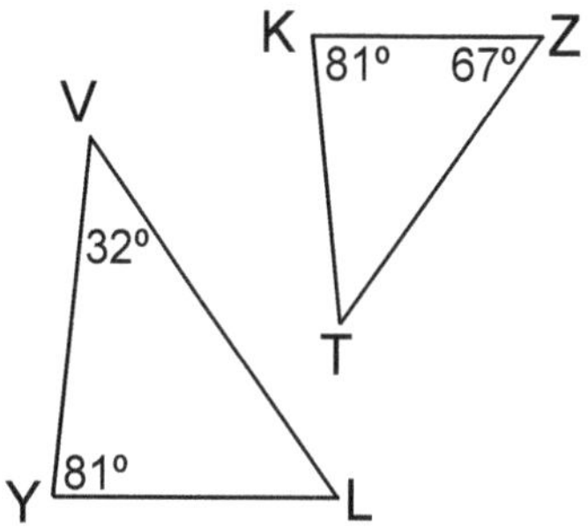

11. In the figure at the right, $\overline{PQ}$ bisects $\angle OPR$. Find the values of x and y, and then find $m\angle OPR$.

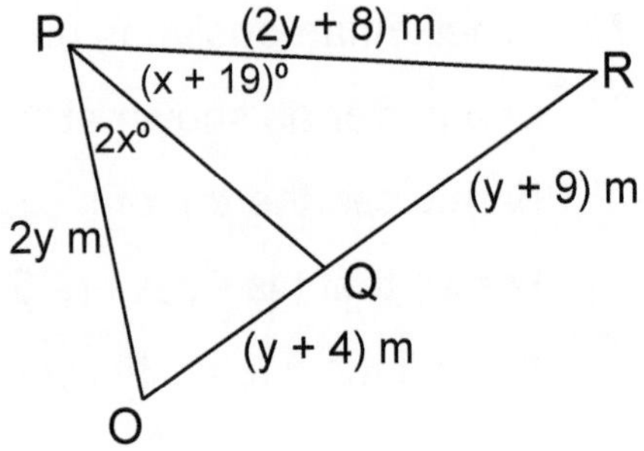

x = ____________

y = ____________

$m\angle OPR$ = ________

12. In the figure at the right, $\Delta WJZ \sim \Delta IYM$, $\overline{ZG}$ is a median of ΔWJZ, and $\overline{MK}$ is a median of ΔIYM. Find the values of x and y.

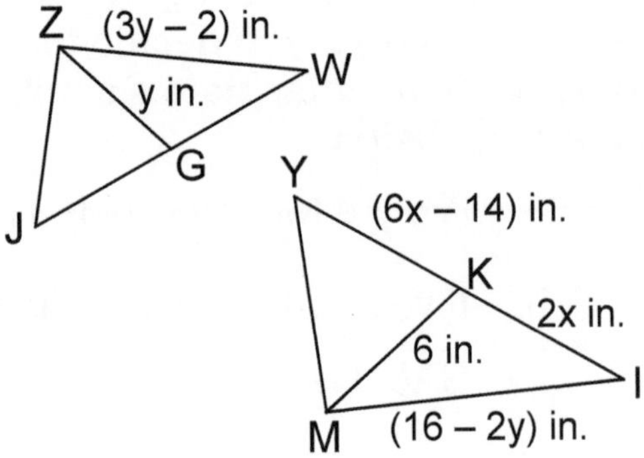

x = __________

y = __________

13. In the figure at the right, $\ell \perp m$ and x < 90. Which of the following MUST be true? Circle all that apply.

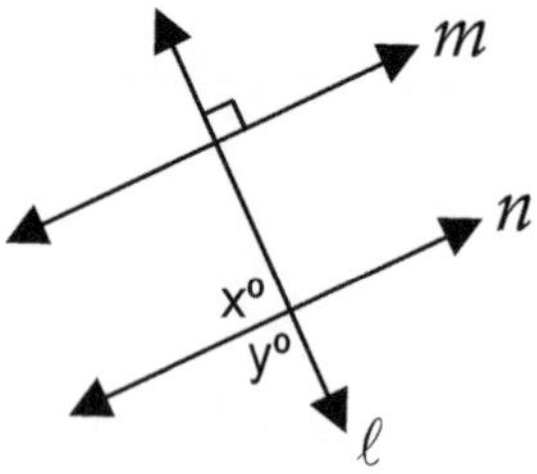

(A) y < 90 (B) y = 90 (C) y > 90

(D) $m \parallel n$ (E) m is not parallel to n

14. Are the triangles shown at the right congruent to each other? __________ If your answer was *yes*, which congruence definition, postulate, or theorem supports your conclusion? __________

____

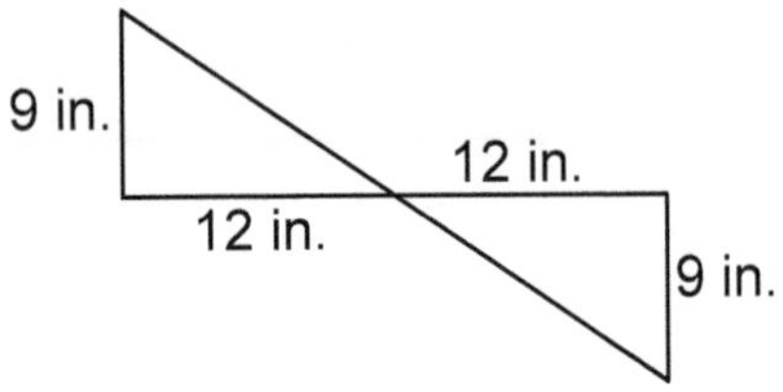

15. In the figure at the right, $\overline{OP} \cong \overline{NO}$. Then w = __________, x = __________, and y = __________.

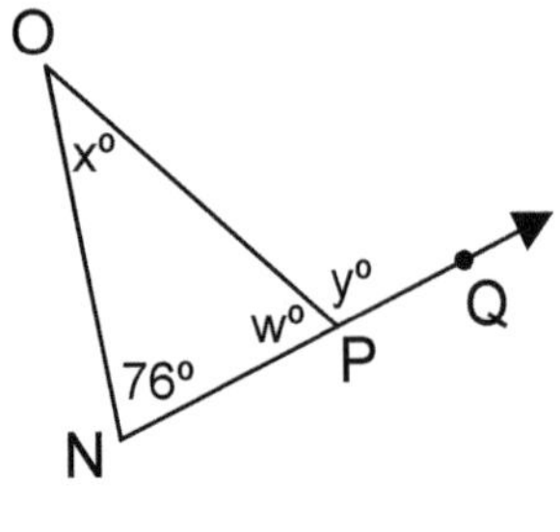

16. In the figure at the right, $\overrightarrow{CB} \perp \overrightarrow{CD}$. Then

$x =$ __________ and $m\angle BCE =$ __________.

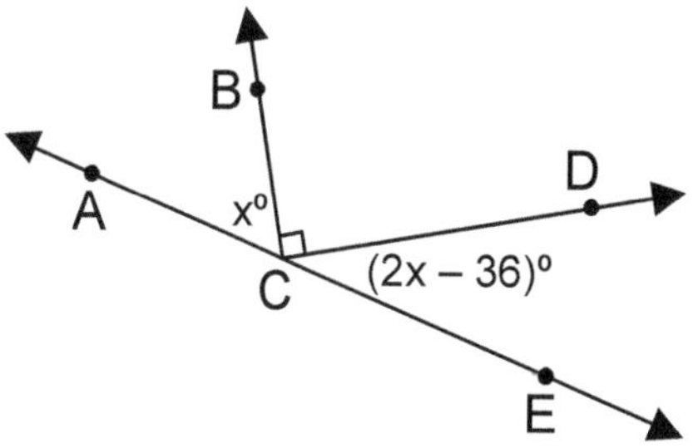

17. In the figure at the right, $\overrightarrow{GT}$ bisects $\angle MGK$. Find each of the following.

$x =$ __________

$y =$ __________

$m\angle LGW =$ ________

$m\angle TGW =$ ________

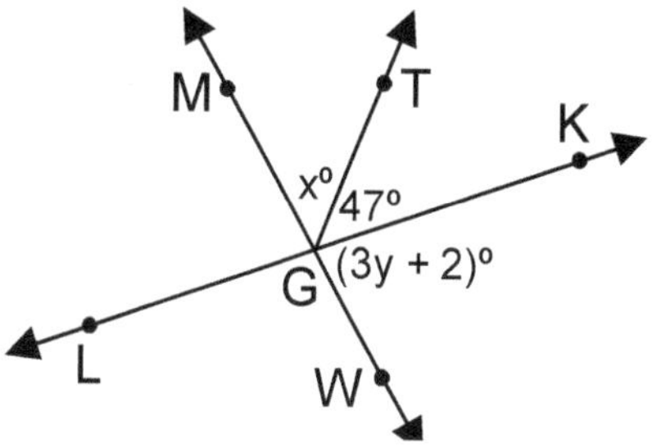

18. In the figure at the right, PE = 28, PZ = 16, ZH = 5, and $\overline{AZ} \cong \overline{HE}$. Find each of the following.

AZ = __________

PA = __________

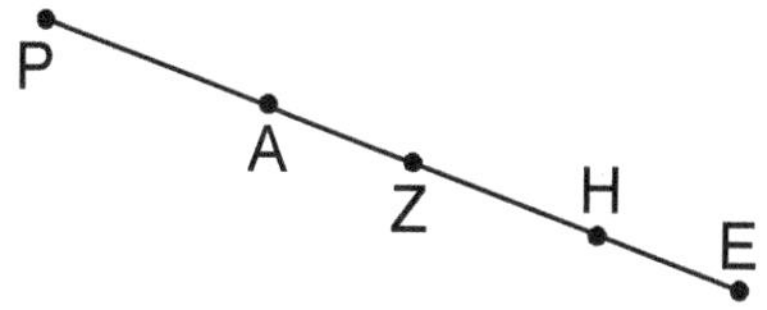

19. In the figure at the right, C is the midpoint of $\overline{BN}$, BC = 5x – 2, CN = 26 – 2x, and CU = 2x + 1. Find each of the following.

$x =$ __________

CU = __________

BC = __________

BN = __________

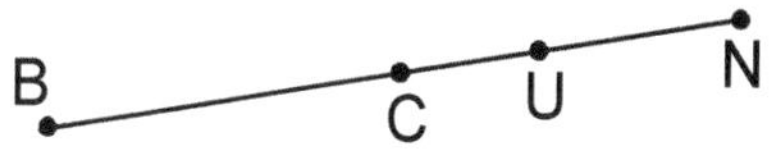

20. On line ℓ below, 3AB = 5BC. Then $\frac{AB}{BC} =$ ______, $\frac{AC}{BC} =$ ______, and $\frac{AC}{AB} =$ ______.

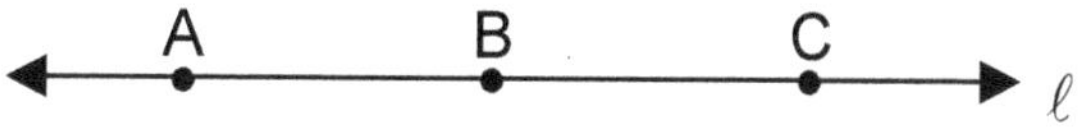

21. Given that quadrilateral JKLM at the right is a trapezoid, prove that $\frac{KZ}{MZ} = \frac{LZ}{JZ}$.

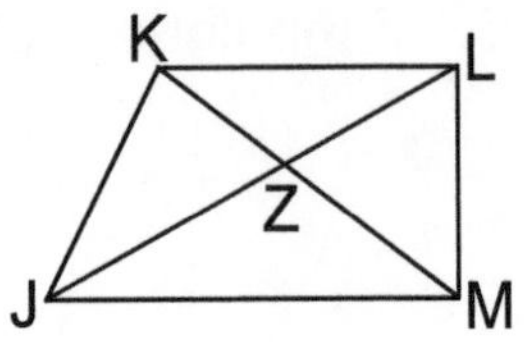

22. If quadrilateral AQYN is a parallelogram, which of the following MUST be true? Circle all that apply.

(A) $\overline{AQ} \cong \overline{YN}$ (B) $\overline{AY} \cong \overline{QN}$ (C) $\overline{AQ} \parallel \overline{YN}$

(D) $\overline{AY} \parallel \overline{QN}$ (E) $\angle NAQ \cong \angle AQY$ (F) $\angle NAQ \cong \angle QYN$

(G) $\angle NAQ$ and $\angle AQY$ are supplementary (H) $\angle ANQ \cong \angle AQN$

(I) $\angle NAQ$ and $\angle QYN$ are supplementary (J) $\angle YAQ \cong \angle NAQ$

23. If quadrilateral AQYN is a parallelogram, which of the following CANNOT be true? Circle all that apply.

(A) $\overline{AQ} \cong \overline{YN}$ (B) $\overline{AY} \cong \overline{QN}$ (C) $\overline{AQ} \parallel \overline{YN}$

(D) $\overline{AY} \parallel \overline{QN}$ (E) $\angle NAQ \cong \angle AQY$ (F) $\angle NAQ \cong \angle QYN$

(G) $\angle NAQ$ and $\angle AQY$ are supplementary (H) $\angle ANQ \cong \angle AQN$

(I) $\angle NAQ$ and $\angle QYN$ are supplementary (J) $\angle YAQ \cong \angle NAQ$

24. In the figure at the right, Q is the midpoint of $\overline{HR}$, HR = 18, and RY = 25. Then YQ = __________.

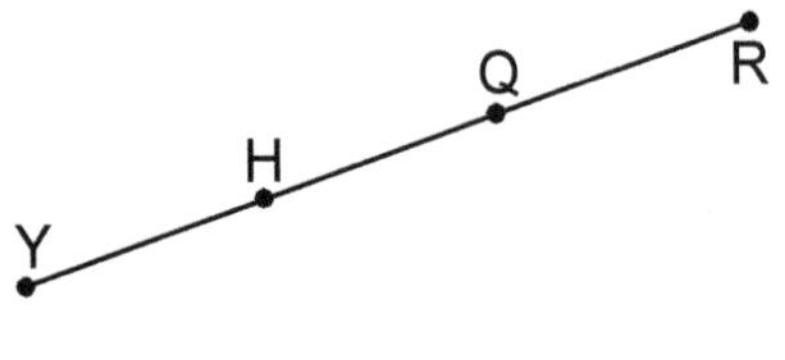

25. If $x = \frac{2}{3}$, then $\frac{1}{x} + \frac{1}{x-2}$ = ______________.

Hint: Recall that $1 \div \frac{2}{3} = 1 \bullet \frac{3}{2}$.

26. The measure of an interior angle of a regular pentagon is ______________, and the measure of an exterior angle of a regular pentagon is ______________.

27. In the figure at the right, x = ______________.

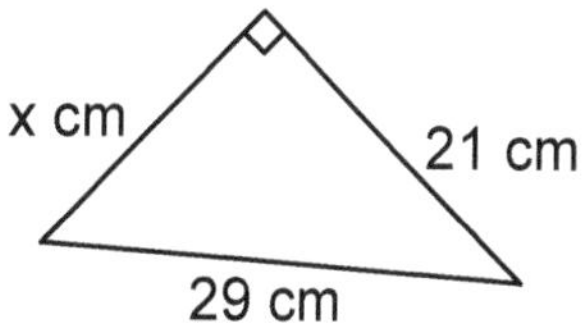

28. In the figure at the right, y = ______________.

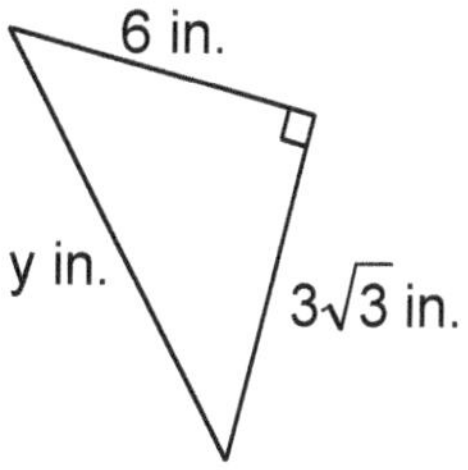

29. In the triangle shown at the right, JK > KL. Describe the possible values of x and y.

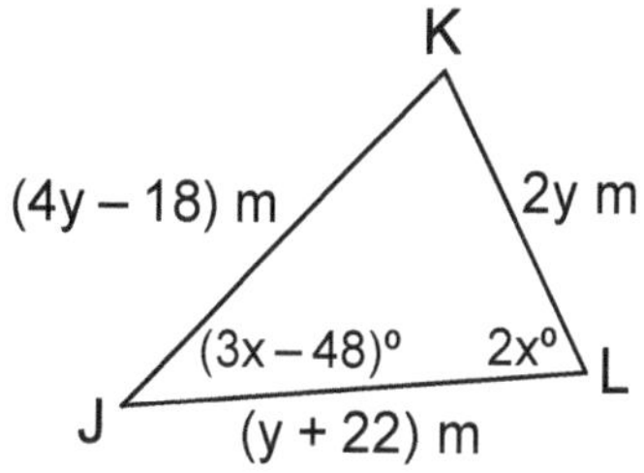

30. Decide if the statement *For all real numbers x,* $(x + 3)^2 = x^2 + 9$ is true or false. If you think that it is false, state a counterexample.

31. Decide if the statement *For all real numbers x,* $(x + 3)^2 \neq x^2 + 9$ is true or false. If you think that it is false, state a counterexample.

Chapter 8 – Right Triangles and Trigonometry

Part I – The Geometric Mean and Its Application to Right Triangles

We will begin this section with a theorem.

> If the altitude from the right angle of a right triangle is drawn, then the two smaller triangles formed are similar to each other and the original triangle.

Example 1: Prove that, if the altitude from the right angle of a right triangle is drawn, then the two smaller triangles formed are similar to each other and the original triangle.

As always, we will begin by drawing a generic picture that describes the part of the theorem that follows the "if."

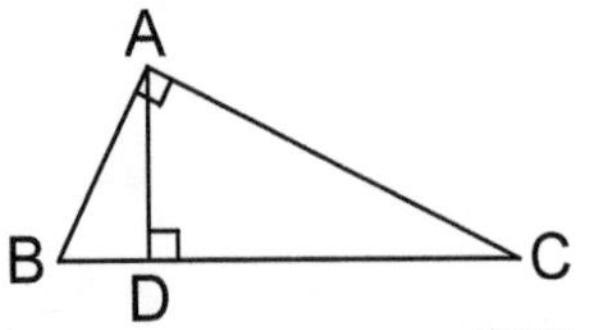

We can say that we are given that $\overline{AD}$ is an altitude of $\triangle ABC$ and that $\angle BAC$ is a right angle, and we want to prove that $\triangle ABC$, $\triangle DBA$, and $\triangle DAC$ are all similar to each other. We can prove this as shown below and continued on the next page.

Statements	Reasons	Explanations
1. $\overline{AD}$ is an altitude of $\triangle ABC$ and $\angle BAC$ is a right angle	1. Given	This was given to us.
2. $\overline{AD} \perp \overline{BC}$	2. Definition of an altitude	The definition of an altitude of a triangle says that it starts at a vertex of the triangle and is perpendicular to the opposite side of the triangle.
3. $\angle BDA$ and $\angle CDA$ are right angles	3. If two lines are perpendicular, then they intersect to form four right angles.	We said in Chapter 2 that, if we start with two perpendicular lines or segments, then they must form four right angles. So, since we said in Statement (2) that $\overline{AD} \perp \overline{BC}$, we can say that $\angle BDA$ and $\angle CDA$ must be right angles.
4. $\angle BAC \cong \angle BDA$ and $\angle BAC \cong \angle CDA$	4. If two angles are right angles, then they are congruent.	We proved in Chapter 2 that, if we have two right angles, then they must be congruent. Therefore, since we said in Statements (1) and (3) that $\angle BAC$, $\angle BDA$, and $\angle CDA$ are right angles, we can say that $\angle BAC \cong \angle BDA$ and $\angle BAC \cong \angle CDA$.

Statements continued	Reasons continued	Explanations continued
5. $\angle ABC \cong \angle ABD$ and $\angle ACB \cong \angle ACD$	5. Reflexive Property of Angle Congruence	The Reflexive Property of Angle Congruence tells us that an angle is congruent to itself.
6. $\Delta ABC \sim \Delta DBA$ and $\Delta ABC \sim \Delta DAC$	6. AA Similarity Theorem	We can use the AA Similarity Theorem to say that $\Delta ABC \sim \Delta DBA$ because we said in Statements (4) and (5) that we have two sets of congruent angles for these triangles ($\angle BAC \cong \angle BDA$ and $\angle ABC \cong \angle ABD$). We can also use the AA Similarity Theorem to say that $\Delta ABC \sim \Delta DAC$ because we said in Statements (4) and (5) that we have two sets of congruent angles for these triangles ($\angle BAC \cong \angle CDA$ and $\angle ACB \cong \angle ACD$).
7. $\Delta ABC \sim \Delta DBA \sim \Delta DAC$	7. Similarity of triangles is symmetric and transitive.	The fact that similarity is symmetric tells us that $\Delta DBA \sim \Delta ABC$. Since we know that $\Delta DBA \sim \Delta ABC$ and that $\Delta ABC \sim \Delta DAC$, we can use the fact that similarity is transitive to say that $\Delta DBA \sim \Delta DAC$.

Example 2: Find the values of x and y in the figure at the right.

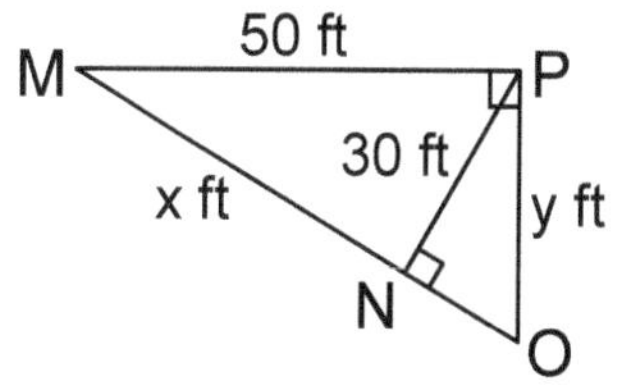

To find the value of x, we will note that we can look at ΔPMN and use the Pythagorean Theorem to say that $(MN)^2 + (PN)^2 = (PM)^2$. Therefore, we can find the value of x as shown below.

$$(MN)^2 + (PN)^2 = (PM)^2$$
$$x^2 + 900 = 2500$$
$$x^2 = 1600$$
$$x = \pm 40$$

Since x represents the length of a side of a triangle, and since lengths are always positive, x must equal 40.

To find the value of y, we will write a similarity statement with the vertices in the correct order and then use this to write a proportion. So, we will begin by stating that $\Delta POM \sim \Delta NOP \sim \Delta NPM$. (To see why we can name the vertices in this order, note that we named each of the right angles first, $\angle O \cong \angle O$, and $\angle M \cong \angle M$.) This tells us that $\frac{MP}{PO} = \frac{MN}{NP}$, and so we can say that $\frac{50}{y} = \frac{40}{30}$. By the Cross Product Property of Proportions, $1500 = 40y$, and so y must equal 37.5.

Now, we need a definition.

> If x, m, and n are positive real numbers, then x is called the <u>geometric mean of m and n</u> if and only if $\frac{m}{x} = \frac{x}{n}$.

Example 3: Find the geometric mean of 6 and 2.

The geometric mean of 6 and 2 is the positive value of x that satisfies the equation $\frac{6}{x} = \frac{x}{2}$. We can follow the steps below to finish solving this problem.

$$\frac{6}{x} = \frac{x}{2}$$

$12 = x^2$ — Use the Cross Products Property of Proportions.

$\pm 2\sqrt{3} = x$ — Take the square root of both sides, and remember that, whenever you take the square root of both sides of an equation, you need to put a symbol in front of one of the sides. Also, note that $\sqrt{12} = \sqrt{4} \cdot \sqrt{3} = 2 \cdot \sqrt{3} = 2\sqrt{3}$.

$2\sqrt{3} = x$ — The definition of the geometric mean of two numbers tells us that we only want the positive value of x.

Now, we need two more theorems. You do not have to understand these theorems in order to work the problems in this section, but they will make your life easier if you do. You will prove them in the exercises for this section.

> If the altitude from the right angle of a right triangle is drawn, then the length of the altitude is the geometric mean of the lengths of the two segments of the hypotenuse.

> If the altitude from the right angle of a right triangle is drawn, then the length of a leg of the largest right triangle is the geometric mean of the length of the entire hypotenuse and the length of the piece of the hypotenuse that is adjacent to that leg.

Example 4: Find the values of w, x, and y in the figure at the right.

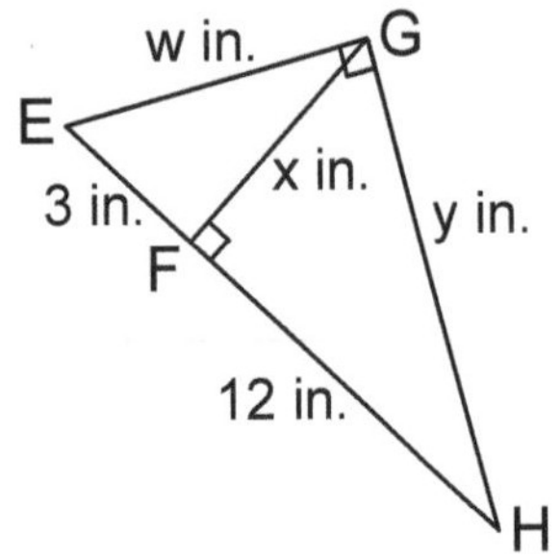

We will begin by noting that the first theorem above tells us that the length of $\overline{GF}$ is the geometric mean of the lengths of $\overline{EF}$ and $\overline{FH}$. This means that we can say that $\frac{3}{x} = \frac{x}{12}$. Then, by the Cross Products Property of Proportions, $x^2 = 36$. When we take the square root of both sides of this equation and realize that we only want the positive value of x, we find that x must equal 6.

To find the value of y, we will note that the second theorem above tells us that the length of $\overline{GH}$ is the geometric mean of the lengths of $\overline{EH}$ and $\overline{FH}$. This tells us that $\frac{15}{y} = \frac{y}{12}$. We can use the Cross Product Property of Proportions to say that this tells us that $y^2 = 180$. When we take the square root of both sides of this equation and realize that we only want the positive value of y, this tells us that $y = 6\sqrt{5}$.

To find the value of w, we will note that the second theorem on the previous page tells us that the length of $\overline{EG}$ is the geometric mean of the lengths of $\overline{EH}$ and $\overline{EF}$. Therefore, we can say that $\frac{15}{w} = \frac{w}{3}$. This gives us $w^2 = 45$, which means that w must equal $3\sqrt{5}$.

Example 5: Find the values of w, x, and y in the figure at the right.

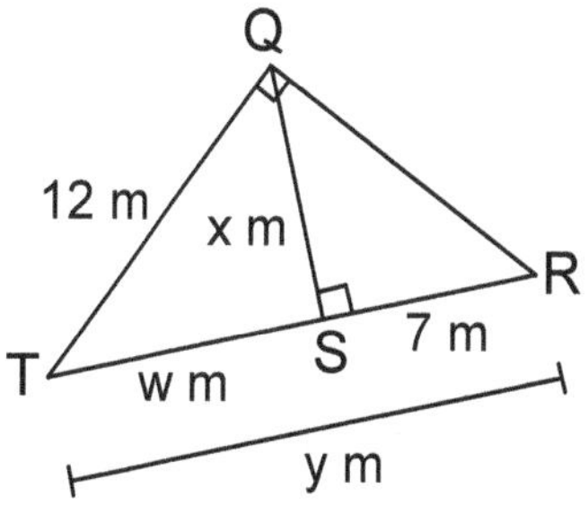

We will begin by noting that second theorem on the previous page tells us that the length of $\overline{QT}$ is the geometric mean of the lengths of $\overline{RT}$ and $\overline{ST}$. Hence, we can say that $\frac{w+7}{12} = \frac{12}{w}$.* We can finish solving this part of the problem as shown below.

$$\frac{w+7}{12} = \frac{12}{w}$$
$$w(w + 7) = 144$$
$$w^2 + 7w = 144$$
$$w^2 + 7w - 144 = 0$$
$$(w + 16)(w - 9) = 0$$
$$w + 16 = 0 \text{ or } w - 9 = 0$$
$$w = -16 \text{ or } w = 9$$

Since w represents the length of a side of a triangle, and since lengths are always positive, w must equal 9.

Since TR = ST + SR, this means that y must equal 16.

Now, to find the value of x, we will note that the first theorem on the previous page tells us that the length of $\overline{QS}$ is the geometric mean of the lengths of $\overline{TS}$ and $\overline{RS}$. This gives us $\frac{9}{x} = \frac{x}{7}$, which means that $x = 3\sqrt{7}$ (note that the Cross Products Property of Proportions tells us that $x^2 = 63$, and $\sqrt{63} = \sqrt{9} \cdot \sqrt{7} = 3\sqrt{7}$).

*We could have said that $\frac{y}{12} = \frac{12}{y-7}$ instead. This would have given us y = 16, and so w would have to equal 9. Note that these answers are exactly the same as what we came up with using the other method.

Problems:

1-6. Find the geometric mean of each of the following sets of numbers.

1. 4 and 16
2. 7 and 6
3. 5 and 9
4. 12 and 3
5. 5 and 30
6. 5 and 15

7-12. For each of the figures below, complete the similarity statement, and then use this to complete the proportion.

7. $\Delta GKA \sim \Delta$________ $\sim \Delta$________,

   and so $\frac{GA}{GE} = \frac{GK}{\_\_\_}$.

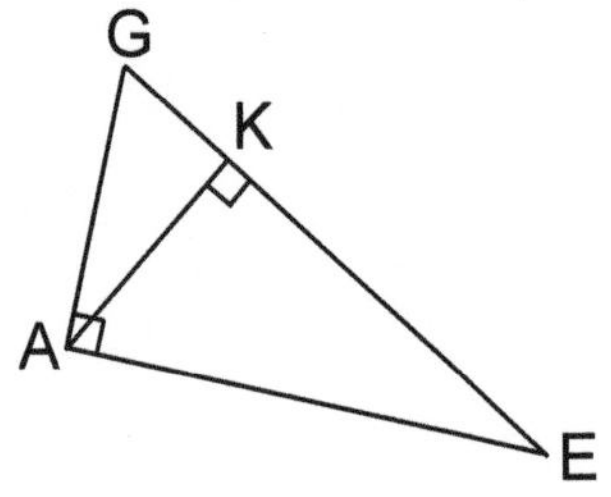

8. $\Delta DJV \sim \Delta$________ $\sim \Delta$________,

   and so $\frac{DV}{DQ} = \frac{\_\_\_}{QV}$.

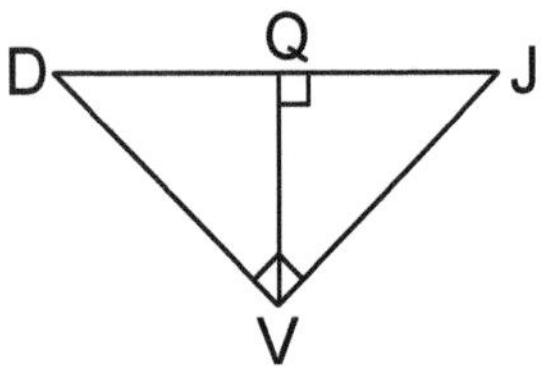

9. $\Delta MBZ \sim \Delta$________ $\sim \Delta$________,

   and so $\frac{BZ}{\_\_\_} = \frac{BM}{IZ}$.

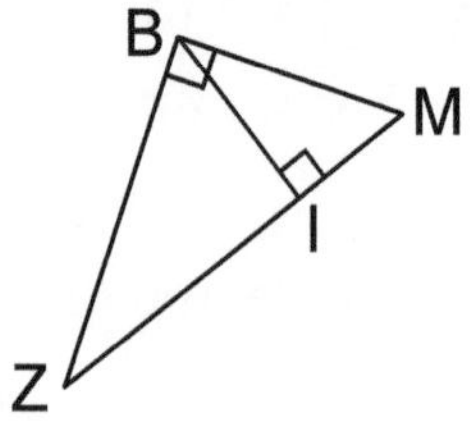

10. $\Delta RHU \sim \Delta$________ $\sim \Delta$________,

   and so $\frac{RU}{CU} = \frac{RH}{\_\_\_}$.

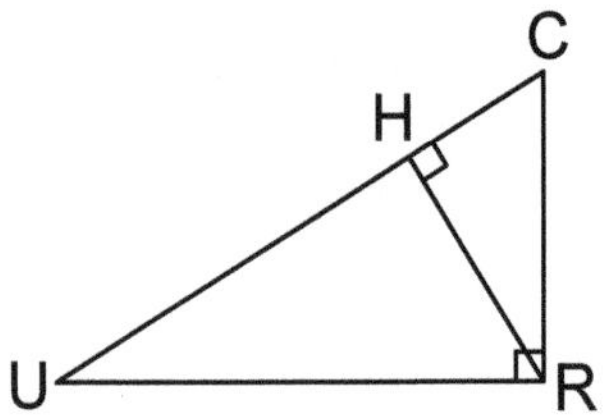

11. ΔLYW ~ Δ________ ~ Δ________,

and so $\frac{YL}{LO} = \frac{\_\_\_}{OW}$.

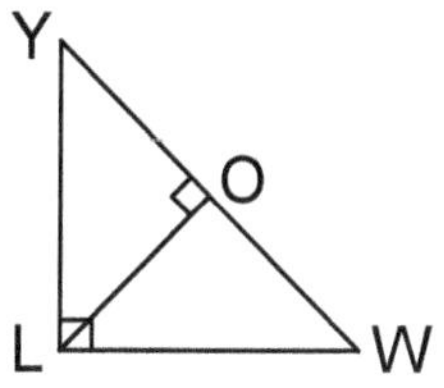

12. ΔNPS ~ Δ________ ~ Δ________,

and so $\frac{NP}{\_\_\_} = \frac{PS}{PN}$.

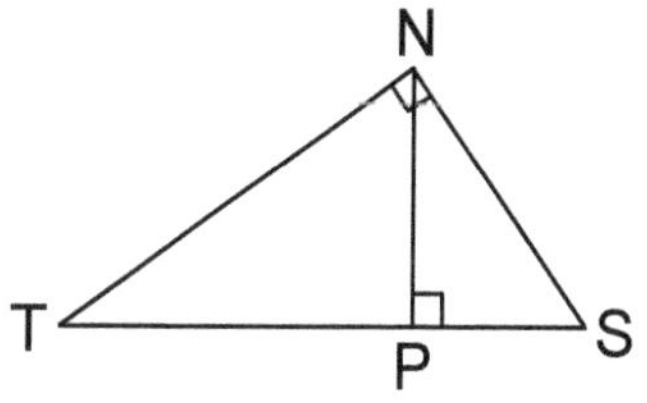

13-28. Find the values of each of the variables in the figures below.

13. x = ____________

y = ____________

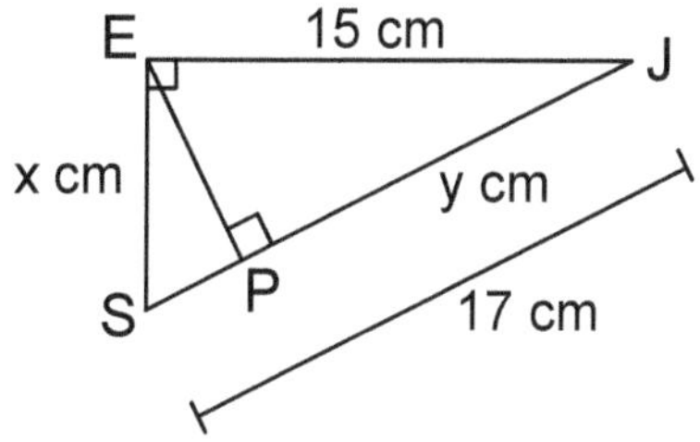

16. x = ____________

y = ____________

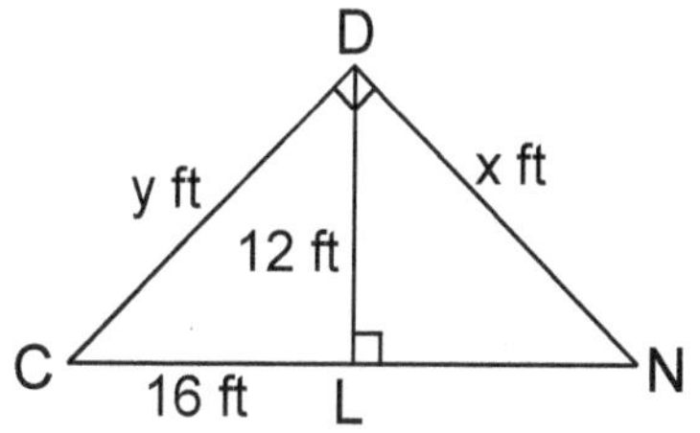

14. x = ____________

y = ____________

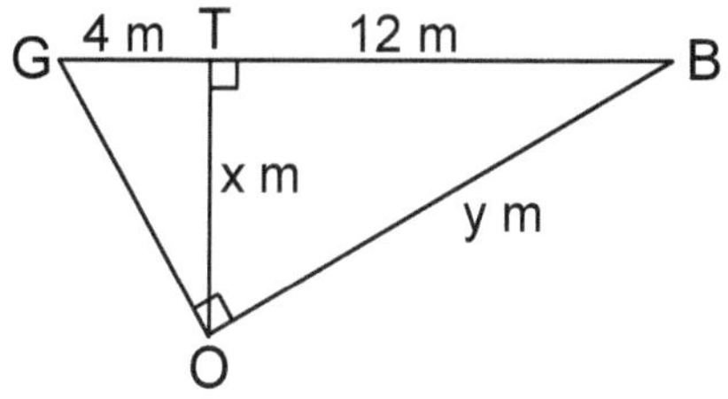

17. x = ____________

y = ____________

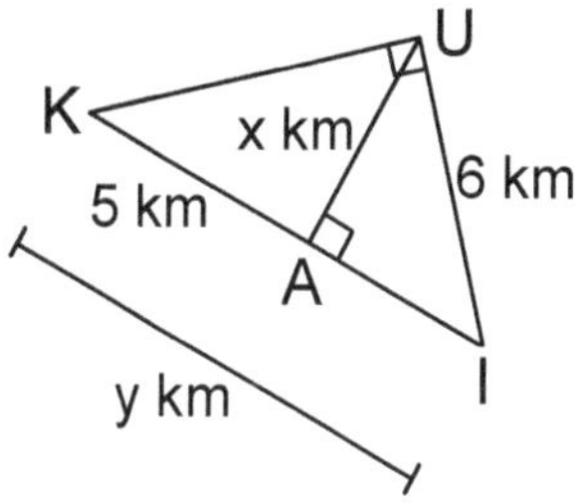

15. x = ____________

y = ____________

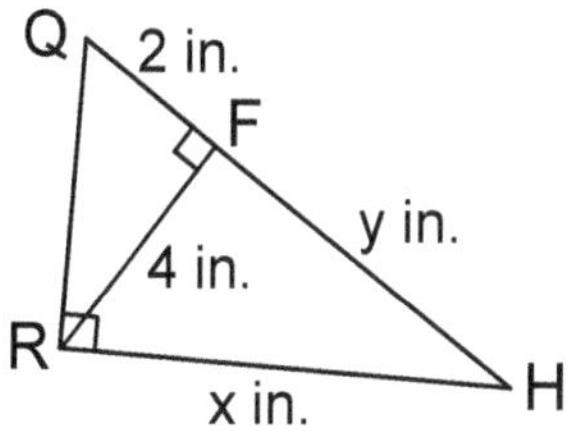

18. x = ____________

y = ____________

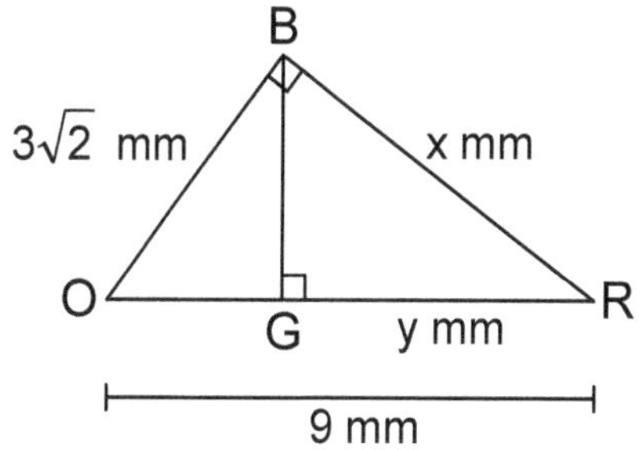

19. x = ____________

y = ____________

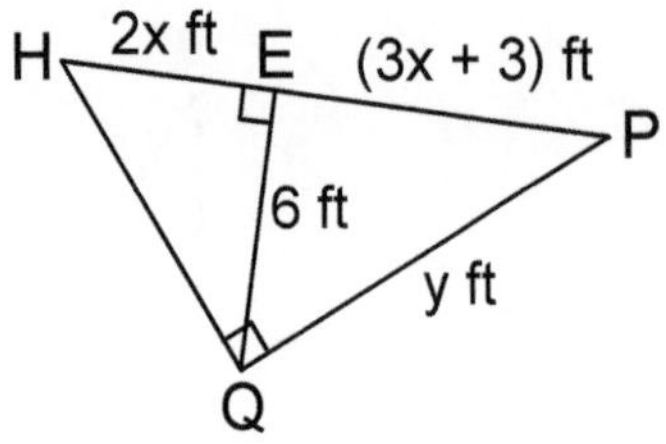

20. x = ____________

y = ____________

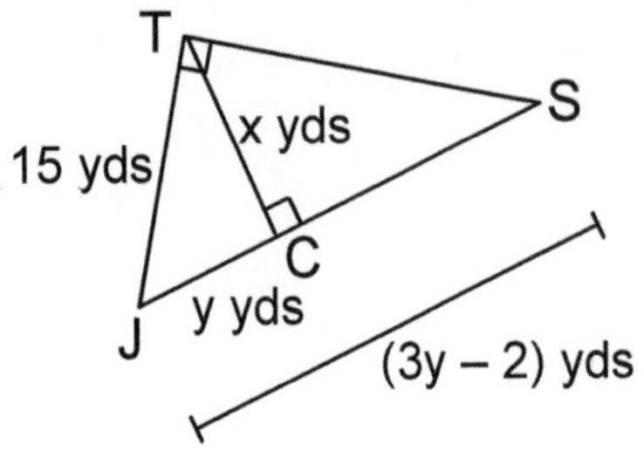

21. x = ____________

y = ____________

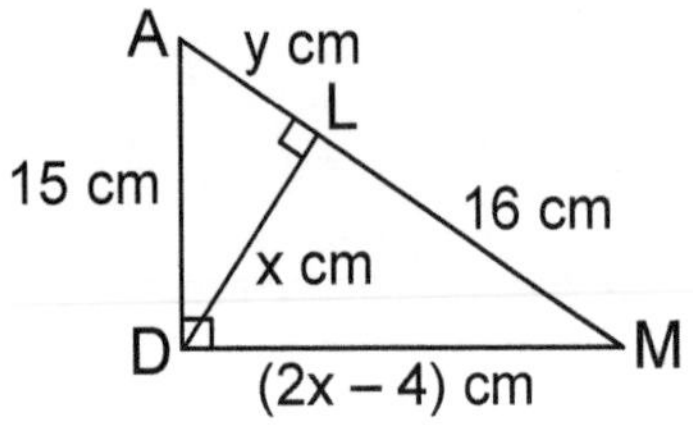

22. x = ____________

y = ____________

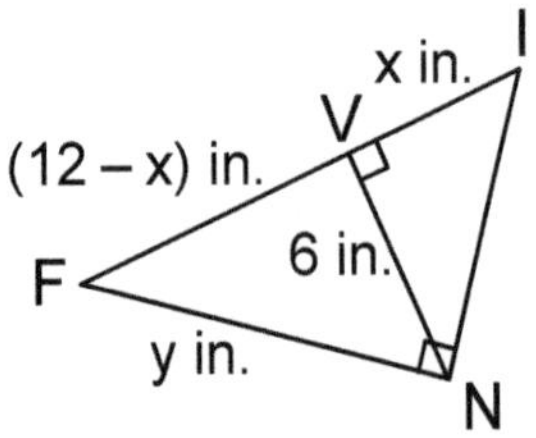

23. x = ____________

y = ____________

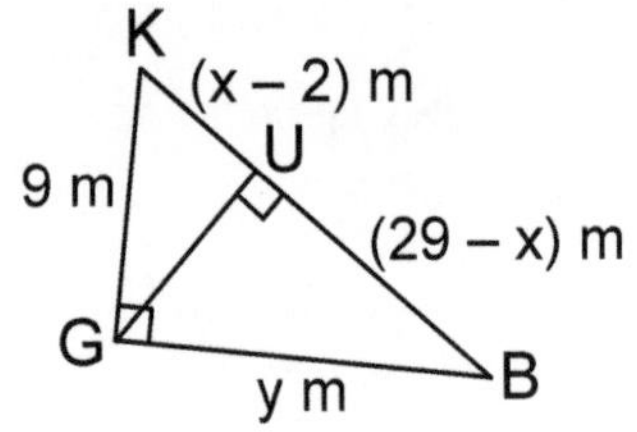

24. x = ____________

y = ____________

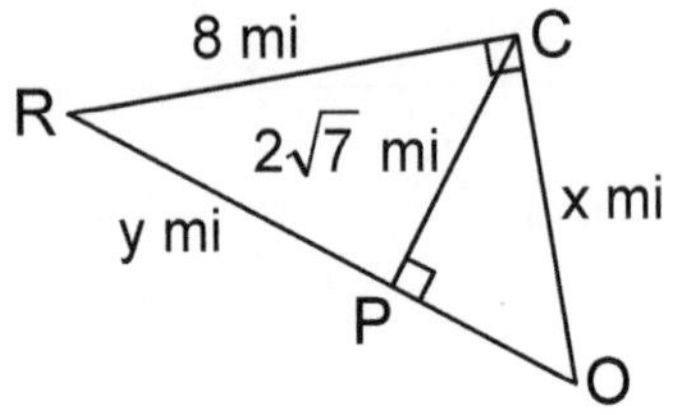

25. x = ____________

y = ____________

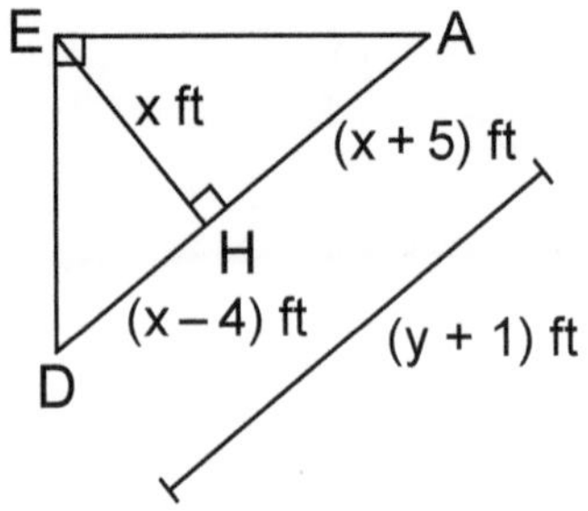

26. x = ____________

y = ____________

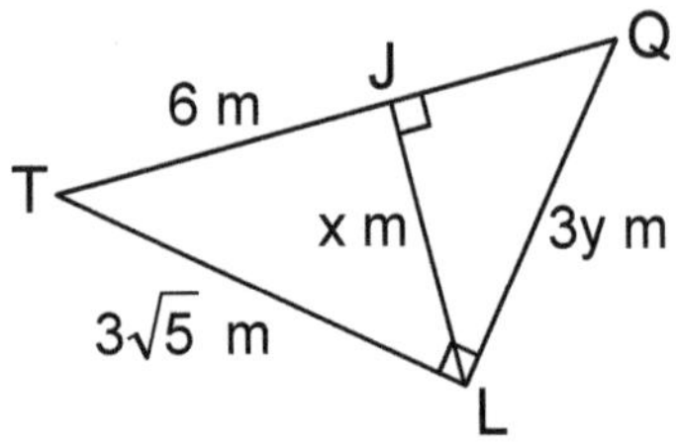

27. x = ____________

y = ____________

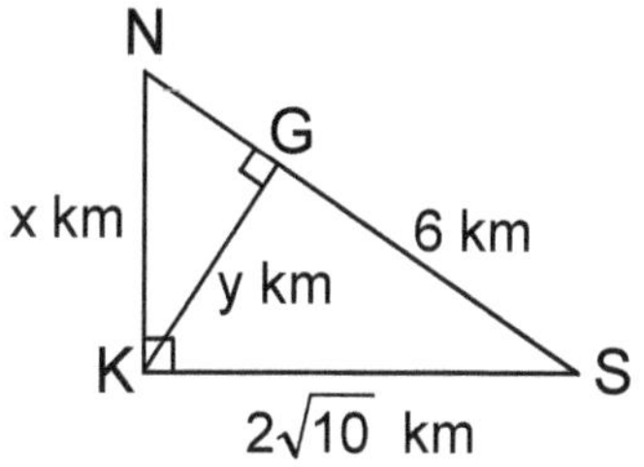

29. x = ____________

y = ____________

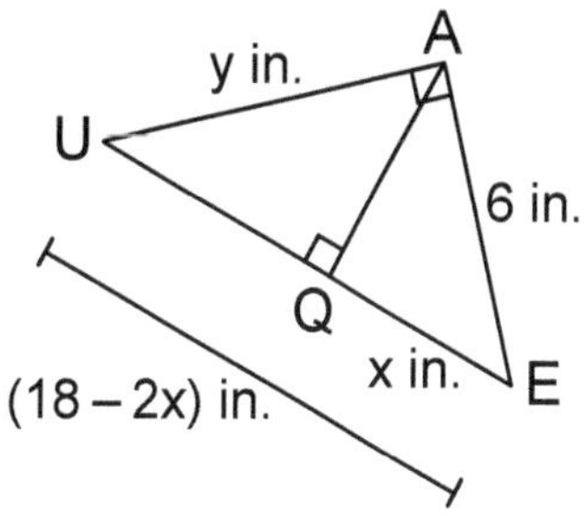

28. x = ____________

y = ____________

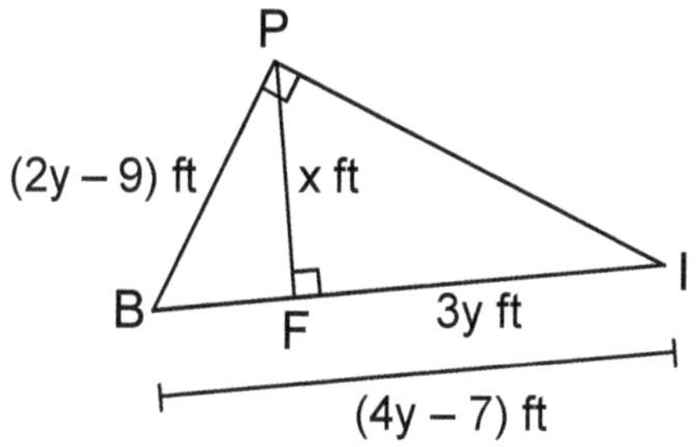

30. Prove that, if the altitude from the right angle of a right triangle is drawn, then the length of the altitude is the geometric mean of the lengths of the two segments of the hypotenuse.

Given: ________________________________

____

Prove: ________________________________

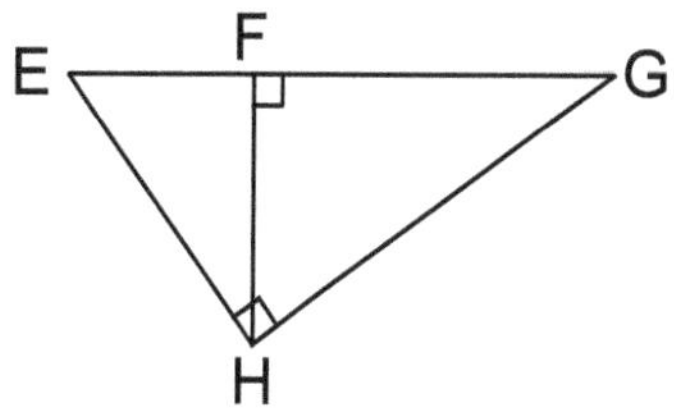

31. Prove that, if the altitude from the right angle of a right triangle is drawn, then the length of a leg of the largest right triangle is the geometric mean of the length of the entire hypotenuse and the length of the piece of the hypotenuse that is adjacent to that leg.

Given: ______________________________

____

Prove: ______________________________

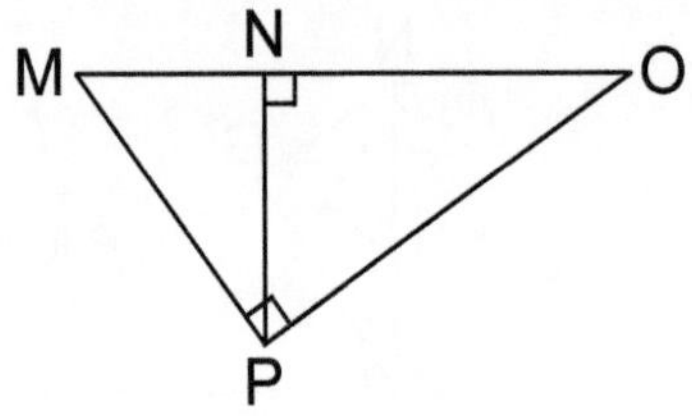

Part II – Special Right Triangles

In this section, we will discuss right triangles with angles that measure 45°, 45°, and 90° (called 45°-45°-90° triangles) and right triangles with angles that measure 30°, 60°, and 90° (called 30°-60°-90° triangles).

We will begin with two theorems. We will prove the 30°-60°-90° Triangle Theorem in Example 1, and you will prove the 45°-45°-90° Triangle Theorem in the exercises for this section.

45°-45°-90° Triangle Theorem

In a triangle with angles that measure 45°, 45°, and 90°, the length of the hypotenuse is equal to $\sqrt{2}$ times the length of either leg.

30°-60°-90° Triangle Theorem

In a triangle with angles that measure 30°, 60°, and 90°, the length of the longer leg is equal to $\sqrt{3}$ times the length of the shorter leg, and the length of the hypotenuse is equal to twice the length of the shorter leg.

These two theorems can be summarized by the pictures below.

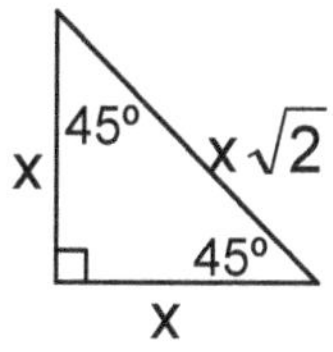

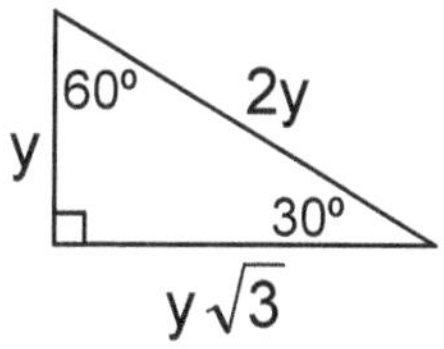

Example 1: Prove the 30°-60°-90° Triangle Theorem using a paragraph proof.

We will begin by drawing an equilateral triangle and calling the length of each side of the triangle 2y. We said in Chapter 5 that a triangle is equilateral if and only if each angle measures 60°, and so we can say that each angle of this triangle measures 60°.

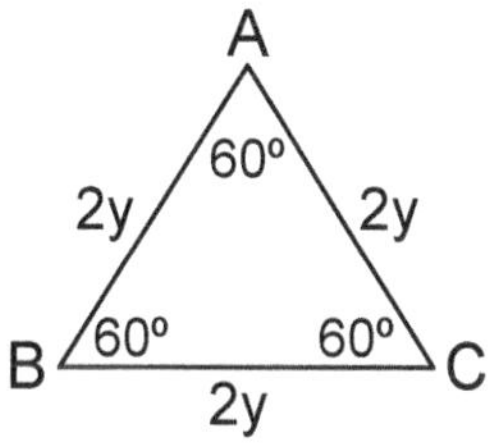

Next, we will use the theorem *Through a point P not on a line, there is exactly one line perpendicular to the given line* to draw the altitude of $\triangle ABC$ that starts at A. We will use the theorem *If two lines intersect, then they intersect at exactly one point* to call the point where this altitude intersects $\overline{BC}$ the point D. Then, by the definition of an altitude of a triangle, $\overline{BC} \perp \overline{AD}$. By the theorem *If two lines*

are perpendicular, then they intersect to form four right angles and the definition of a right angle, we can say that m$\angle$BDA = 90° and m$\angle$CDA = 90°.

You proved in Chapter 5 that the altitude from the vertex angle of a triangle is also a perpendicular bisector, a median, and an angle bisector of the triangle. The definition of a perpendicular bisector tells us that the midpoint of a segment tells us that D is the midpoint of $\overline{BC}$. Then, by the definition of a midpoint, BD = DC, and so we can say that BD = y and DC = y. Since $\overline{BC}$ is also an angle bisector of $\triangle$ABC, we can say that m$\angle$DAB = 30° and m$\angle$DAC = 30°. This gives us the picture shown below.

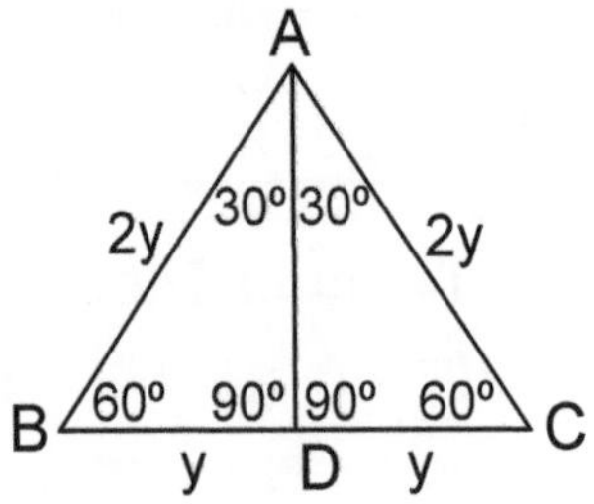

Now, let's look at just $\triangle$ABD.

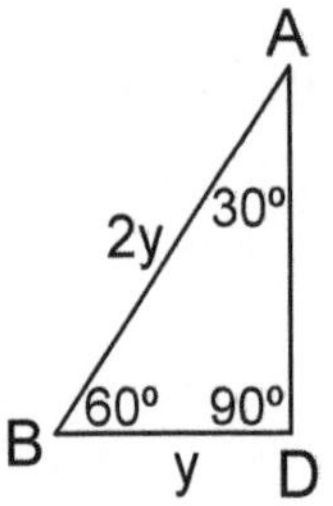

We can use the Pythagorean Theorem to say the following.

$$(AD)^2 + (BD)^2 = (AB)^2$$
$$(AD)^2 + y^2 = (2y)^2$$
$$(AD)^2 + y^2 = 4y^2$$
$$(AD)^2 = 3y^2$$
$$AD = \pm y\sqrt{3}$$

Since the length of $\overline{AD}$ must be a positive number, we can say that AD = $y\sqrt{3}$.

Example 2: Find the values of c and m in the figure at the right.

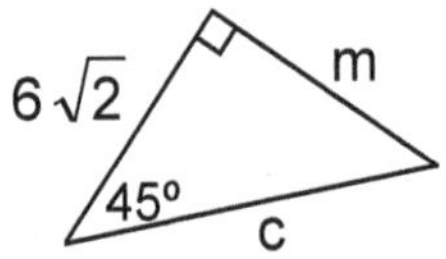

We will begin by noting that, since the measures of the angles in a triangle must add up to 180°, we can say that the measure of the third angle in this triangle is 45°. This means that this triangle is a 45^0-45^0-90^0 triangle, and m must equal $6\sqrt{2}$. Since the length of the hypotenuse is equal to $\sqrt{2}$ multiplied by the length of a leg, we can say that $c = 6\sqrt{2} \cdot \sqrt{2}$, or c = 12.

Example 3: Find the values of n and p in the figure at the right.

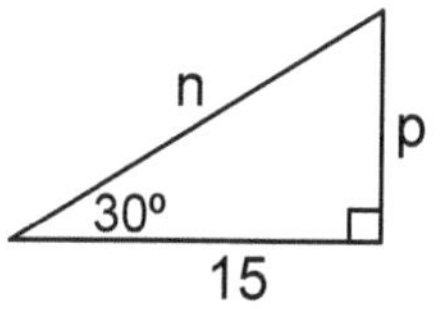

We will begin by noting that, since the measures of the angles in a triangle must add up to 180°, the measure of the third angle must be 60°. This tells us that this triangle is a 30°-60°-90° triangle, the side labeled p is the shorter leg (recall that the shortest side in a triangle is opposite the smallest angle), the side labeled 15 is the longer leg, and the side labeled n is the hypotenuse. So, using the notation that we used in the 30°-60°-90° triangle on page 366, we can say the following.

$15 = y\sqrt{3}$

$\frac{15}{\sqrt{3}} = y$ Solve for y by dividing both sides of the equation by $\sqrt{3}$.

$5\sqrt{3} = y$ Since we cannot leave a radical sign in the denominator, we must multiply both the numerator and denominator of the fraction $\frac{15}{\sqrt{3}}$ by $\sqrt{3}$ and then simplify the result.

Since the notation that we used on page 366 tells us that y represents the length of the shorter leg, we can now say that, in this triangle, p must equal $5\sqrt{3}$. Since the length of the hypotenuse is twice the length of the shorter leg (or, using the notation that we used on page 366, 2y), we can say that $n = 2 \cdot 5\sqrt{3}$, or $10\sqrt{3}$.

Example 4: In the figure at the right, $\triangle EFG$ is an equilateral triangle and $EH = 7\sqrt{3}$ feet. Find the area of $\triangle EFG$.

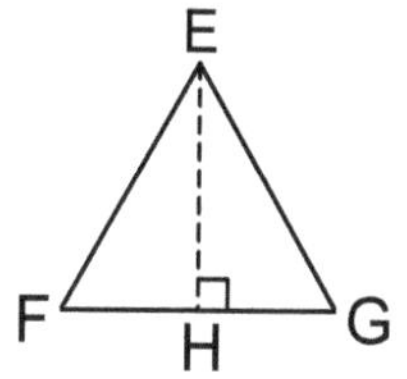

Since a triangle is equilateral if and only if each angle measures 60°, we can say that $m\angle F = 60°$ and $m\angle G = 60°$. This tells us that both $\triangle EFH$ and $\triangle EGH$ are 30°-60°-90° triangles, as shown in the figures below.

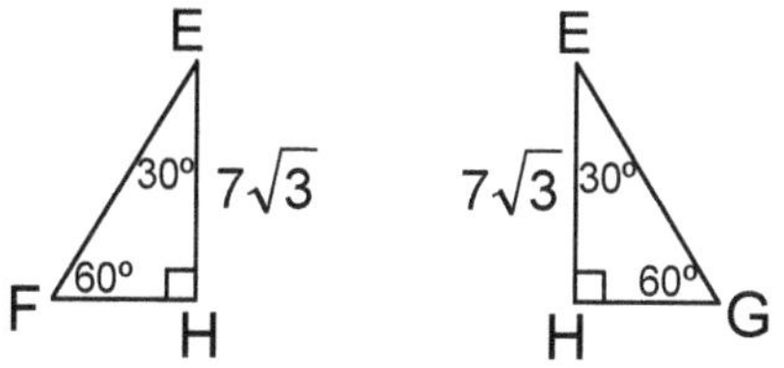

Using the notation that we used in the 30°-60°-90° triangle on page 366, we can say that $y\sqrt{3} = 7\sqrt{3}$, and so we can say that y = 7. This tells us that HG = 7 feet, FH = 7 feet, EF = 14 feet, and EG = 14 feet. Since FH = 7 feet and HG = 7 feet, we can say that FG = 14 feet. (Or you could use the fact that $\triangle EFG$ is an equilateral triangle to say that FG = 14 feet.) Now, recall that the formula we use to find the area of a triangle is $A = \frac{1}{2}$(base)(height), where the base and height form 90° angles. This tells us that we can find the area of $\triangle EFG$ as shown on the next page.

Area of $\Delta EFG = \frac{1}{2}(FG)(EH)$

Area of $\Delta EFG = \frac{1}{2}(14 \text{ ft})(7\sqrt{3} \text{ ft})$

Area of $\Delta EFG = 49\sqrt{3} \text{ ft}^2$

Note that $\frac{1}{2} \bullet 14 \bullet 7\sqrt{3} = 49\sqrt{3}$ and that $\text{ft} \bullet \text{ft} = \text{ft}^2$.

Example 5: Find the length of a diagonal of the square at the right. (Recall that a diagonal of a square or rectangle starts at one corner of the square or rectangle and goes to the opposite corner of the square or rectangle. For instance, the diagonals in the figure at the right are $\overline{IK}$ and $\overline{JL}$.)

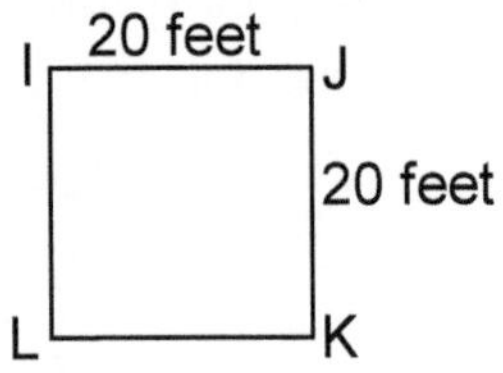

We will begin by drawing the diagonal $\overline{IK}$.

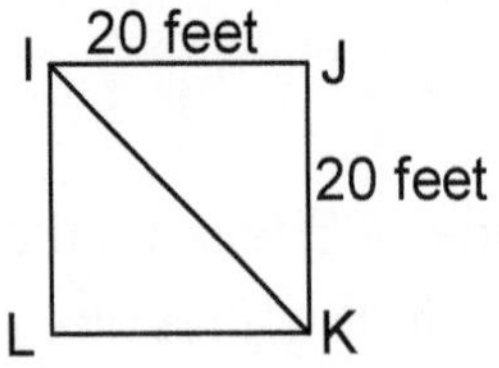

The definition of a square tells us that $\angle J$ is a right angle. Since the Isosceles Triangle Theorem tells us that $\angle JIK \cong \angle JKI$, and since the measures of the angles in a triangle must add up to 180°, we can say that $m\angle JIK = 45°$ and $m\angle JKI = 45°$. This tells us that ΔIJK is a 45°-45°-90° triangle, and so the length of $\overline{IK}$ must equal $20\sqrt{2}$ feet.

1-18. Find the values of each of the variables in the figures below. Leave your answers in simplified radical form where necessary.

1. b = ________

   c = ________

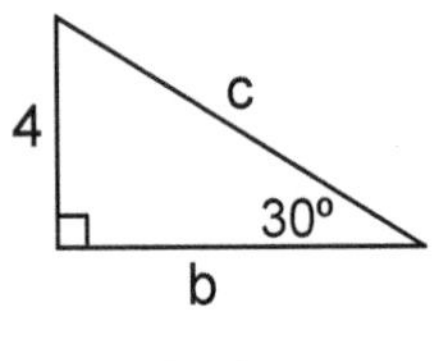

3. k = ________

   w = ________

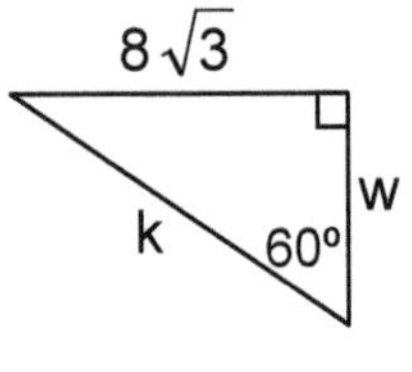

2. a = ________

   c = ________

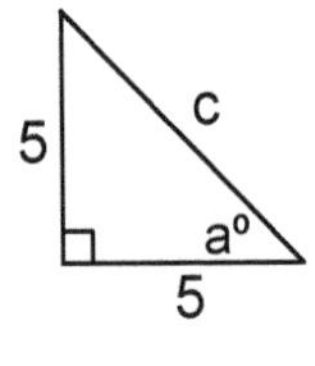

4. a = ________

   b = ________

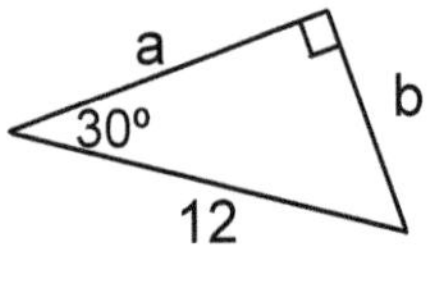

5. q = __________

v = __________

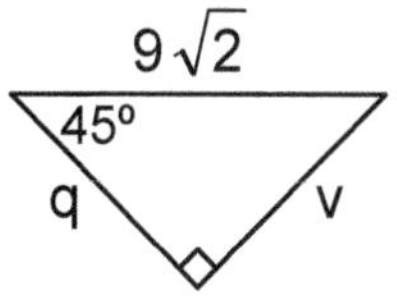

6. p = __________

m = __________

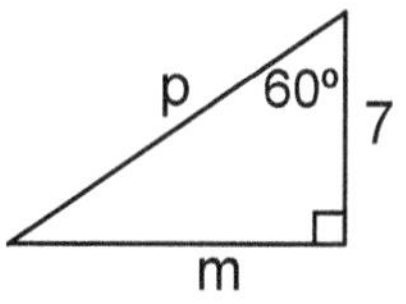

7. c = __________

d = __________

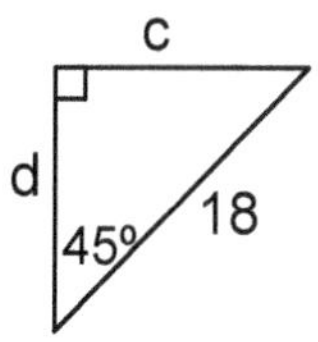

8. a = __________

u = __________

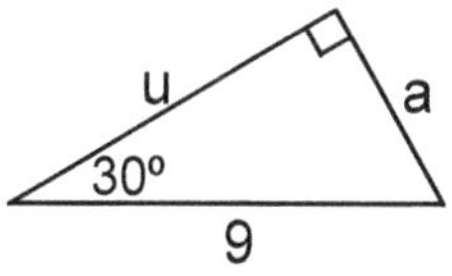

9. p = __________

r = __________

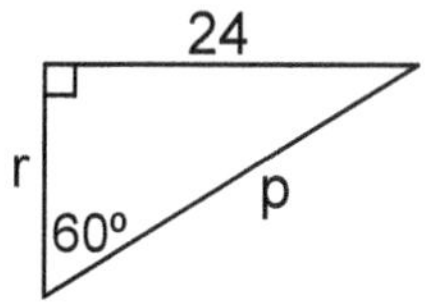

10. g = __________

y = __________

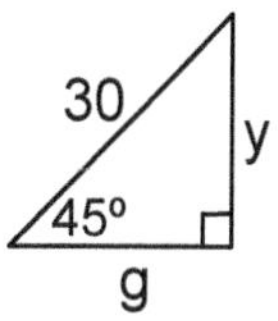

11. b = __________

k = __________

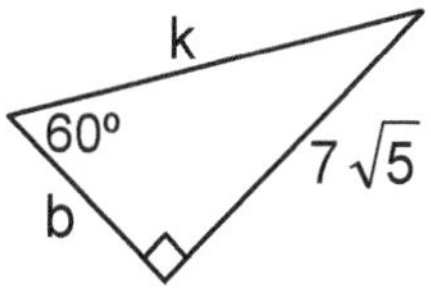

12. c = __________

n = __________

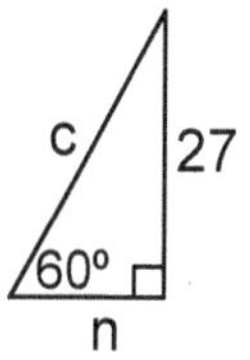

13. x = __________

y = __________

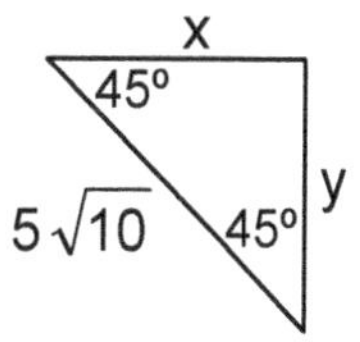

14. k = __________

z = __________

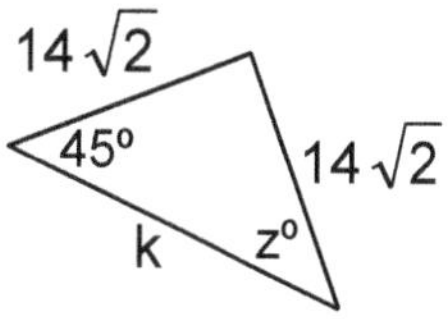

15. a = ________

b = ________

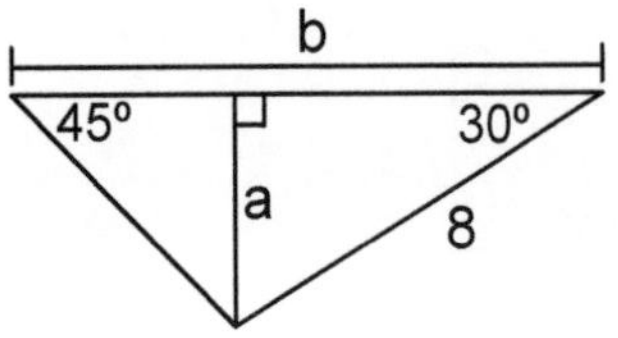

17. b = ________

w = ________

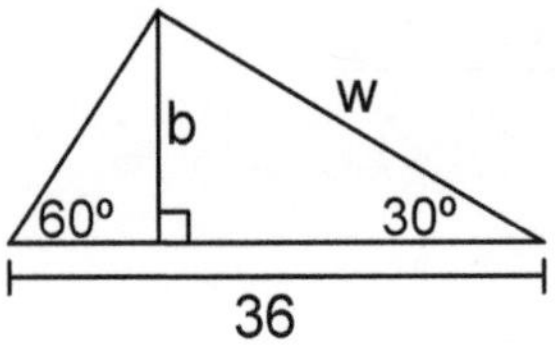

16. n = ________

q = ________

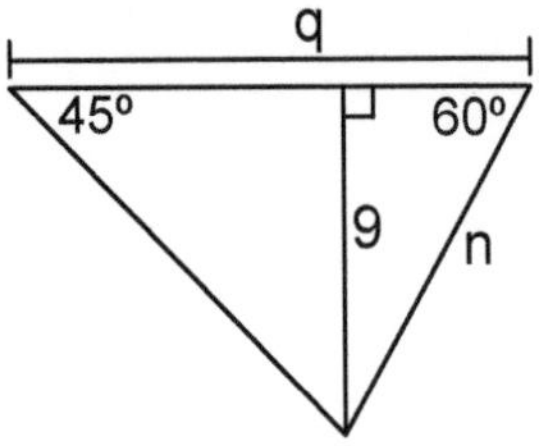

18. u = ________

v = ________

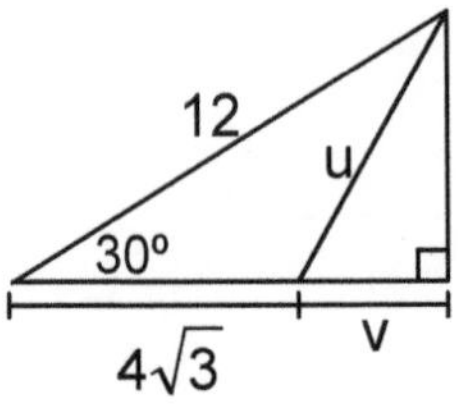

19. Find the length of a diagonal of a square that has sides with lengths of 5 inches each. ____________

20. If the length of a diagonal of a square is 12 feet, what is the length of one side of the square? ____________

21. If the length of a diagonal of a square is $9\sqrt{2}$ meters, what is the perimeter of the square? ____________ (Recall that the perimeter of a figure is the distance around the outside of the figure.)

22. If the perimeter of a square is $20\sqrt{2}$ meters, what is the length of a diagonal of the square? _______________

23. In the figure at the right, BD = 6 feet and $\triangle ABC$ is an equilateral triangle. Find the area of $\triangle ABC$. _______________

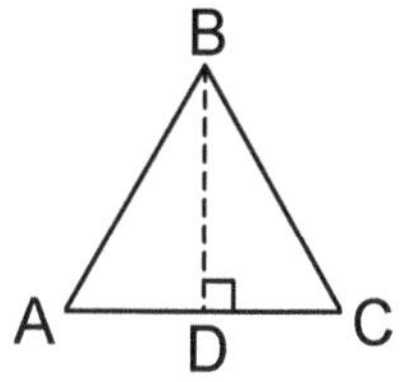

24. In the figure at the right, PO = 24 miles and $\triangle NPQ$ is an equilateral triangle. Find the perimeter of $\triangle NPQ$. _______________

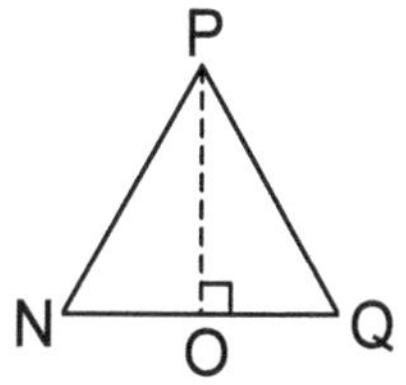

25. If each side of an equilateral triangle has a length of $18\sqrt{3}$ inches, what is the area of the triangle? _______________

26. If each side of an equilateral triangle has a length of s units, show that the area of the triangle can be found using the formula $A = \frac{\sqrt{3}}{4}s^2$. (You do not need to do a formal proof.)

27. If the perimeter of an equilateral triangle is 6 centimeters, what is its area?

____

28. If the area of an equilateral triangle is $16\sqrt{3}$ square inches, what is the perimeter of the triangle? Hint: Use the formula you proved in #26. ____________

29. If the area of an equilateral triangle is $2\sqrt{3}$ square feet, what is the perimeter of the triangle? ____________

30. If a side of a square has a length of n units, then a diagonal of the square is ____________ units long.

31. If a diagonal of a square has a length of d units, what is the *area* of the square? (Recall that, to find the area of a square, you multiply the length and the width.)

____

32. The figure at the right is a cube, and each side of the cube is p units long. Then DB = ________, DE = ________, and DF = ________. Hint: Recall that the edges of a cube all have the same length.

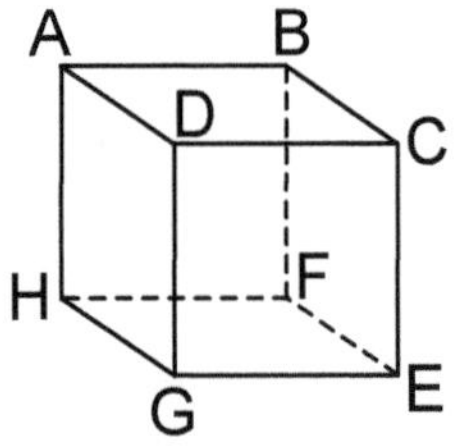

33. What is the perimeter of the figure at the right?

____

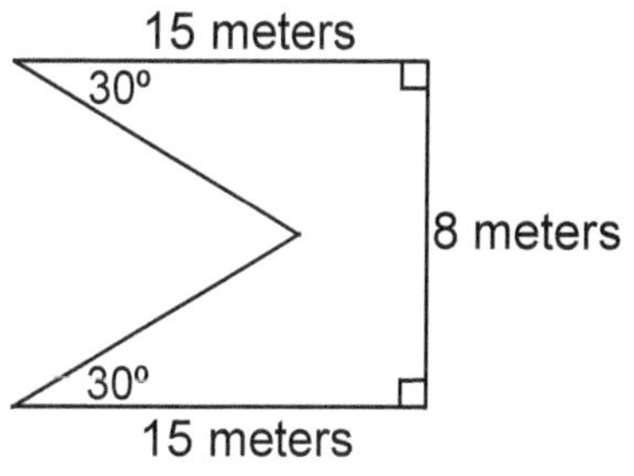

34. Prove the 45°-45°-90° Triangle Theorem.

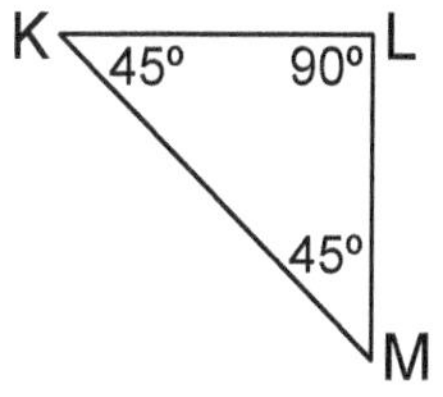

Given: $\triangle KLM$ is a 45°-45°-90° triangle with $m\angle K = 45°$, $m\angle M = 45°$, and $m\angle L = 90°$

Prove: $KM = (KL)(\sqrt{2}) = (LM)(\sqrt{2})$

We are given that $\triangle KLM$ is a 45°-45°-90° triangle with $m\angle K = 45°$, $m\angle M = 45°$, and $m\angle L = 90°$. By the definition of congruent angles, $\angle K \cong \angle M$. By the ____, $\overline{LM} \cong \overline{KL}$. Then LM = KL by the ____.

Since $\triangle KLM$ is a right triangle, we can use the Pythagorean Theorem to say that $(KL)^2 + (LM)^2 = (KM)^2$. Then, by the ____________________________________ ___________, $(KL)^2 + (KL)^2 = (KM)^2$. By the Distributive Property, $2(KL)^2 = (KM)^2$. We can now use the Multiplication Property of Equality to take the square root of both sides. When do this and use the Substitution Property of Equality to simplify the result, we get _______________. Since KM must be positive, we can say that $KM = (KL)(\sqrt{2})$. Then, by the Substitution Property of Equality and the Transitive Property of Equality, $KM = (KL)(\sqrt{2}) = (LM)(\sqrt{2})$.

Part III – Trigonometric Ratios in Right Triangles

In this section, we will discuss how we can use a concept called trigonometric ratios to find the lengths of sides and the measures of angles in right triangles.

We will begin with three definitions.

> In a right triangle,
>
> - the sine of an acute angle is equal to $\dfrac{\text{the length of the leg opposite the angle}}{\text{the length of the hypotenuse}}$,
> - the cosine of an acute angle is equal to $\dfrac{\text{the length of the leg adjacent to the angle}}{\text{the length of the hypotenuse}}$,
>
> and
>
> - the tangent of an acute angle is equal to $\dfrac{\text{the length of the leg opposite the angle}}{\text{the length of the leg adjacent to the angle}}$.

You can remember these definitions by remembering the acronym "soh-cah-toa," as shown below.

s	**o**	**h**	**c**	**a**	**h**	**t**	**o**	**a**
i	p	y	o	d	y	a	p	d
n	p	p	s	j	p	n	p	j
e	o	o	i	a	o	g	o	a
	s	t	n	c	t	e	s	c
	i	e	e	e	e	n	i	e
	t	n		n	n	t	t	n
	e	u		t	u		e	t
		s			s			
	leg	e		leg	e		leg	leg

We usually abbreviate sine as *sin*, cosine as *cos*, and tangent as *tan*. Now, let's look at some examples that illustrate how we use these definitions.

Example 1: In the figure at the right, find the values of each of the following: (a) sin J, (b) cos J, (c) tan J, (d) sin L, (e) cos L, and (f) tan L.

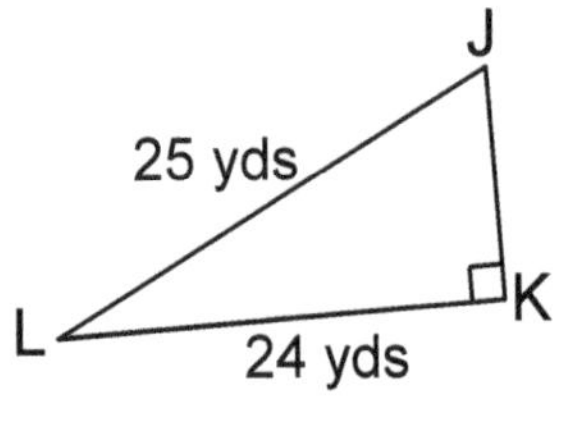

(a) Since $\overline{KL}$ is the leg opposite $\angle J$ in the triangle at the right, and since $\overline{JL}$ is the hypotenuse in this triangle, we can say that $\sin J = \dfrac{24}{25}$. (Notice that $\dfrac{24 \text{ yds}}{25 \text{ yds}} = \dfrac{24}{25}$ because the yards on the top of the fraction can cancel with the yards on the bottom of the fraction.)

(b) Since $\overline{JK}$ is the leg that is adjacent to (or next to) $\angle J$ in this triangle, and since $\overline{JL}$ is the hypotenuse, we can say that $\cos J = \frac{JK}{JL}$. Thus, in order to answer this question, we must find the length of $\overline{JK}$. We can do this by using the Pythagorean Theorem, as shown below.

$$(JK)^2 + (KL)^2 = (JL)^2$$
$$(JK)^2 + (24\text{ yds})^2 = (25\text{ yds})^2$$
$$(JK)^2 + 576\text{ yds}^2 = 625\text{ yds}^2$$
$$(JK)^2 = 49\text{ yds}^2$$ Subtract 576 yds^2 from both sides.
$$JK = 7\text{ yds}$$ Take the square root of both sides, and keep in mind that we want the positive value of JK.

We can now say that $\cos J = \frac{7\text{ yards}}{25\text{ yards}}$, or $\frac{7}{25}$.

(c) Since $\overline{KL}$ is the leg that is opposite $\angle J$ in this triangle, and since $\overline{JK}$ is the leg next to $\angle J$, we can say that $\tan J = \frac{KL}{JK}$. Hence, $\tan J = \frac{24\text{ yards}}{7\text{ yards}}$, or $\frac{24}{7}$.

(d) Notice that $\overline{JK}$ is the leg that is opposite $\angle L$ in this triangle and that $\overline{JL}$ is still the hypotenuse. Therefore, we can say that $\sin L = \frac{JK}{JL}$, or $\frac{7}{25}$.

(e) The leg that is adjacent to $\angle L$ in this triangle is $\overline{KL}$, and the hypotenuse is $\overline{JL}$. Thus, $\cos L = \frac{KL}{JL}$, or $\frac{24}{25}$.

(f) Since $\overline{JK}$ is the leg that is opposite $\angle L$ in this triangle, and since $\overline{KL}$ is the leg that is adjacent to $\angle L$, we can say that $\tan L = \frac{JK}{KL}$, or $\frac{7}{24}$.

Example 2: In the figure at the right, find the values of each of the following: (a) sin P, (b) cos P, (c) tan P, (d) sin Q, (e) cos Q, and (f) tan Q.

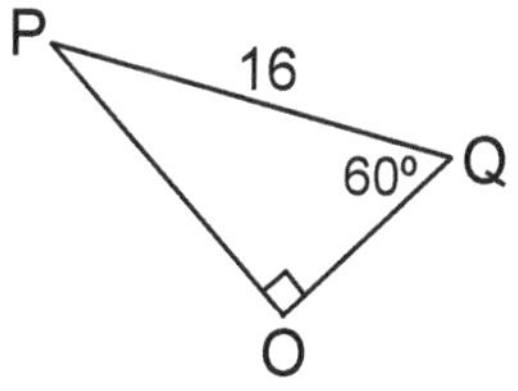

We will begin by noting that we can use the 30°-60°-90° Triangle Theorem that we discussed in the last section to say that OQ = 8 and OP = $8\sqrt{3}$. Thus, we can redraw ΔOPQ as shown below.

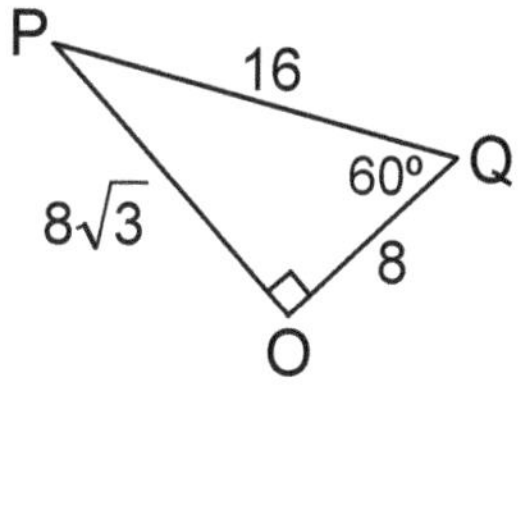

(a) Note that $\overline{OQ}$ is the leg that is opposite $\angle P$ in this triangle, and $\overline{PQ}$ is the hypotenuse. Thus, $\sin P = \frac{8}{16}$, or $\frac{1}{2}$.

(b) $\overline{OP}$ is the leg that is adjacent to $\angle P$ in this triangle, and $\overline{PQ}$ is the hypotenuse. Hence, $\cos P = \frac{8\sqrt{3}}{16}$, or $\frac{\sqrt{3}}{2}$.

(c) Since $\overline{OQ}$ is the leg that is opposite $\angle P$ and $\overline{OP}$ is the leg that is adjacent to $\angle P$, we can say that $\tan P = \frac{8}{8\sqrt{3}}$. This reduces to $\frac{1}{\sqrt{3}}$, but, as discussed in the section on simplifying square roots in Appendix B, we cannot leave our answer like this because we never want to leave a square root in the denominator of a fraction. Thus, we must multiply both the top and bottom of this fraction by $\sqrt{3}$, giving us $\frac{\sqrt{3}}{3}$. Thus, our final answer is that $\tan P = \frac{\sqrt{3}}{3}$.

(d) $\overline{OP}$ is the leg that is opposite $\angle Q$ in this triangle, and $\overline{PQ}$ is the hypotenuse. Therefore, $\sin Q = \frac{8\sqrt{3}}{16}$, or $\frac{\sqrt{3}}{2}$.

(e) $\overline{OQ}$ is the leg that is adjacent to $\angle Q$ in this triangle, and $\overline{PQ}$ is the hypotenuse. Thus, $\cos Q = \frac{8}{16}$, or $\frac{1}{2}$.

(f) Note that $\overline{OP}$ is the leg that is opposite $\angle Q$ in this triangle, and $\overline{OQ}$ is the leg that is adjacent to $\angle Q$. Hence we can say that $\tan Q = \frac{8\sqrt{3}}{8}$, or $\sqrt{3}$.

Before we talk about the next example, we need to talk about your calculator. To work the remainder of the problems in this section, you will need a scientific or graphing calculator. These calculators will have buttons that say sin, cos, and tan.

First, you need to determine what type of calculator you have. To do this, start by clearing your screen. Then type "0," and then hit the button that says "cos." If your calculator now displays a "1," then we will say that you have a type A calculator. If your calculator did not do anything, then we will say that you have a type B calculator.

Now, we need to make sure that your calculator is in the correct mode. To do this using a type A calculator, type 90 first, and then hit the "sin" key. If the calculator now displays "1," then your calculator is in the correct mode. If it displays 0.8939966..., then your calculator is in radian mode. Consult your calculator's manual and change your calculator to degree mode. If the calculator now displays 0.987688..., then your calculator is in gradient mode. Consult your calculator's manual and change your calculator to degree mode. If you have a type B calculator, hit the "sin" key first, then type 90, and then hit the "=" or "Enter" button. If the calculator says 1, then your calculator is in the correct mode. If it says either 0.8939966... or 0.987688..., then your calculator is in the wrong mode. Consult the calculator's manual and change it to degree mode.

Example 3: Find the values of w, x and y in the triangle at the right. Round the final answers to two decimal places where necessary.

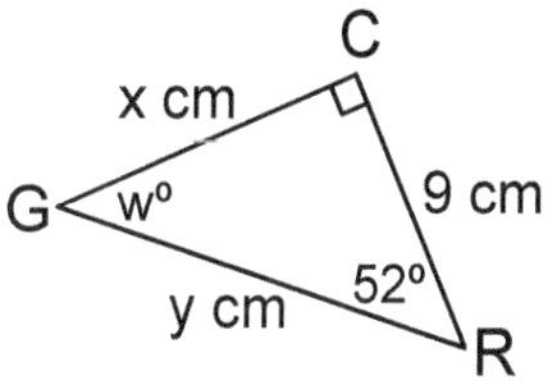

To find the value of w:

Since $m\angle G + m\angle C + m\angle R = 180°$, we can conclude that w must equal 38.

To find the value of x:

We will begin by noting that $\overline{GC}$ is the leg that is opposite $\angle R$ in this triangle, and $\overline{CR}$ is the leg that is adjacent to $\angle R$. Thus, we can say that $\tan R = \frac{x}{9}$.

(We could also have said $\tan G = \frac{9}{x}$. In the end, we would have come up with the same final answer.) We can finish solving this part of the problem as shown below.

$\tan R = \frac{x}{9}$

$\tan 52° = \frac{x}{9}$ — Notice that $m\angle R = 52°$.

$1.2799 \approx \frac{x}{9}$ — The AAA Similarity Postulate tells us that all triangles with measures of 52°, 38°, and 90° are similar to each other. Therefore, in a triangle that has angles with measures of 52°, 38°, and 90°, the ratio of the length of the leg opposite the 52° angle to the length of the leg next to the 52° angle will always be the same. So, we can find the tangent of 52° using a calculator. To do this using a type A calculator, type the 52 first, and then hit the "tan" button. To do this using a type B calculator, hit the "tan" key first, then type 52, and the hit the "=" or "Enter" button. Also, whenever you are using the trigonometric functions, you should round the answers to four decimal places. We will round the final answer to two decimal places (since that is what the question tells us to do), but we will keep at least four decimal places until the final answer.

$11.52 \approx x$ — Multiply both sides of the equation by 9.

To find the value of y:

Note that $\overline{CR}$ is the leg that is adjacent to $\angle R$ in this triangle, and $\overline{GR}$ is the hypotenuse. Thus, we can say that $\cos R = \frac{9}{y}$. We can finish solving this part of the problem as shown on the next page.

$\cos R = \frac{9}{y}$

$\cos 52^\circ = \frac{9}{y}$ Notice that $m\angle R = 52^\circ$.

$0.6157 \approx \frac{9}{y}$ The AAA Similarity Postulate tells us that all triangles with measures of 52°, 38°, and 90° are similar to each other. Therefore, in a triangle that has angles with measures of 52°, 38°, and 90°, the ratio of the length of the leg adjacent to the 52° angle to the length of the hypotenuse will always be the same. So, we can find the cosine of 52° using a calculator. To do this using a type A calculator, type the 52 first, and then hit the "cos" button. To do this using a type B calculator, hit the "cos" key first, then type 52, and then hit the "=" or "Enter" button. Also, whenever you are using the trigonometric functions, you should round the answers to four decimal places. We will round the final answer to two decimal places (since that is what the question says to do), but we will keep at least four decimal places until the final answer.

$0.6157y \approx 9$ To get the y out of the denominator of the fraction, multiply both sides by y.

$y \approx 14.62$ Divide both sides by 0.6157

By the way, we could have found y using one of several other methods instead. We could have used the Pythagorean Theorem, the fact that that $\sin G = \frac{9}{y}$, the fact that $\cos G \approx \frac{11.52}{y}$, or the fact that $\sin R \approx \frac{11.52}{y}$. However, if we had used any of these methods, then we would have been assuming that the answers we found earlier were correct. If we had made a mistake in finding the values for w and/or x, then this could have given us the wrong value for y. Therefore, it is better to use the fact that $\cos R = \frac{9}{y}$ than to use any of these other methods.

Example 4: Find the values of w, x and y in the triangle at the right. Round the final answers to two decimal places where necessary.

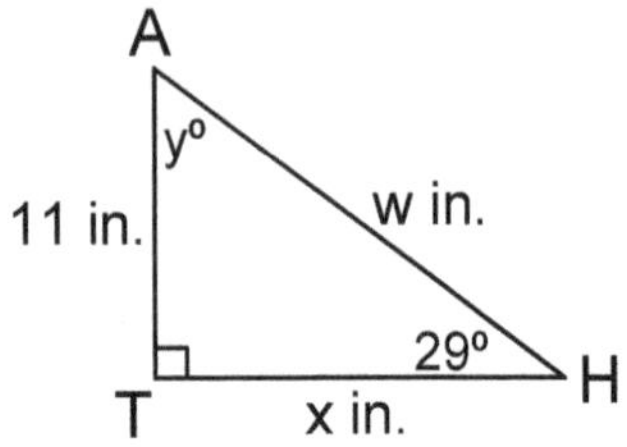

To find the value of w:

Note that $\overline{AT}$ is the leg that is opposite $\angle H$ in this triangle, and $\overline{AH}$ is the hypotenuse. This tells us that we can say that $\sin H = \frac{11}{w}$. We can finish solving this part of the problem as shown on the next page.

$\sin H = \frac{11}{w}$

$\sin 29^\circ = \frac{11}{w}$ — Notice that $m\angle H = 29^\circ$.

$0.4848 \approx \frac{11}{w}$ — Using a calculator, $\sin 29^\circ \approx 0.4848$.

$0.4848w \approx 11$ — To get the w out of the denominator of the fraction, multiply both sides by w.

$w \approx 22.69$ — Divide both sides by 0.4848.

To find the value of x:

$\overline{AT}$ is the leg that is opposite $\angle H$ in this triangle, and $\overline{TH}$ is the leg that is next to $\angle H$ in this triangle. This tells us that we can say that $\tan H = \frac{11}{x}$. We can finish solving this part of the problem as shown below.

$\tan H = \frac{11}{x}$

$\tan 29^\circ = \frac{11}{x}$ — Notice that $m\angle H = 29^\circ$.

$0.5543 \approx \frac{11}{x}$ — Using a calculator, $\tan 29^\circ \approx 0.5543$.

$0.5543x \approx 11$ — To get the x out of the denominator of the fraction, multiply both sides by x.

$x \approx 19.84$ — Divide both sides by 0.5543.

There are several other ways that we could have found the value of x (for instance, we could have used the fact that $\cos H \approx \frac{x}{22.69}$ or the Pythagorean Theorem), but they all require us to find the values of one or more of the other variables first. Since it is possible to make an error finding these other values, it is best to use the fact that $\tan H = \frac{11}{x}$ instead of one of the other methods.

To find the value of y:

Since $m\angle A + m\angle H + m\angle T = 180^\circ$, we can conclude that y must equal 61.

Problems:

1-8. For each triangle below, find the sine, cosine, and tangent of both acute angles. Simplify all answers with square roots, and do not round your answers to these problems.

1. sin A = ________

   cos A = ________

   tan A = ________

   sin B = ________

   cos B = ________

   tan B = ________

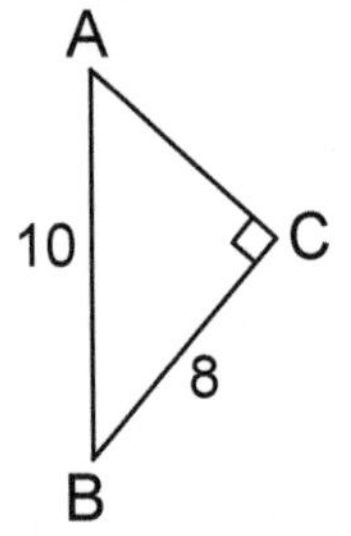

4. sin K = ________

   cos K = ________

   tan K = ________

   sin J = ________

   cos J = ________

   tan J = ________

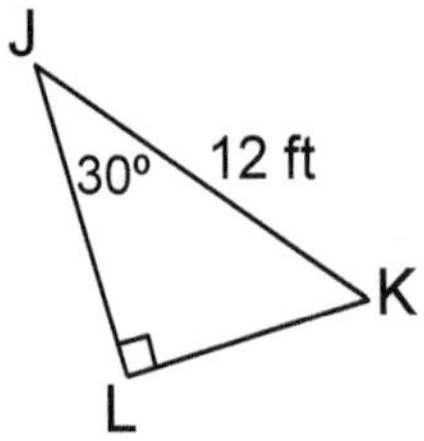

2. sin D = ________

   cos D = ________

   tan D = ________

   sin E = ________

   cos E = ________

   tan E = ________

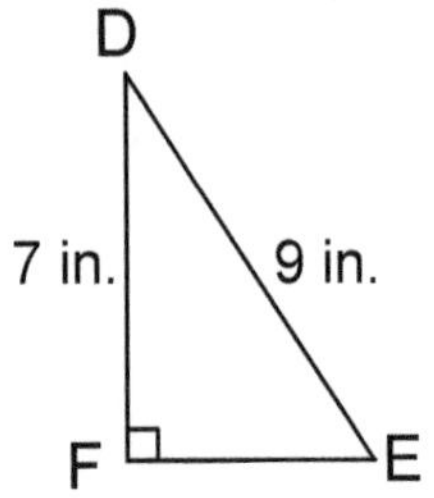

5. sin N = ________

   cos N = ________

   tan N = ________

   sin O = ________

   cos O = ________

   tan O = ________

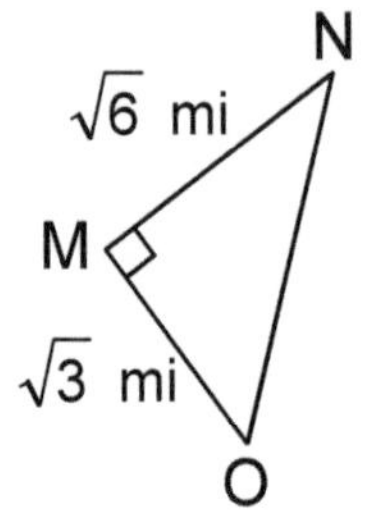

3. sin G = ________

   cos G = ________

   tan G = ________

   sin H = ________

   cos H = ________

   tan H = ________

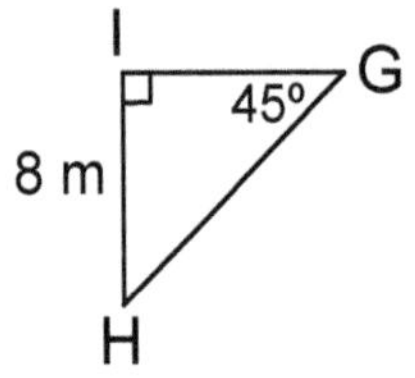

6. sin P = ________

   cos P = ________

   tan P = ________

   sin R = ________

   cos R = ________

   tan R = ________

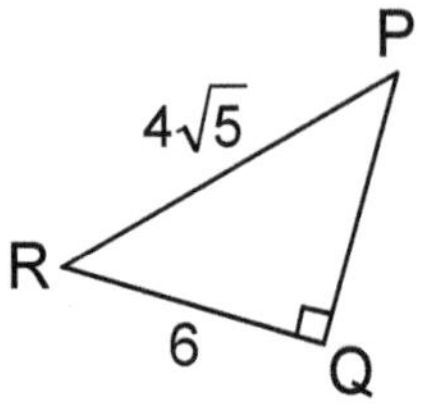

7. sin U = ________

cos U = ________

tan U = ________

sin T = ________

cos T = ________

tan T = ________

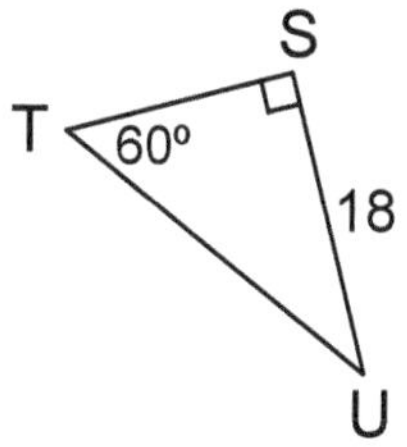

8. sin V = ________

cos V = ________

tan V = ________

sin Z = ________

cos Z = ________

tan Z = ________

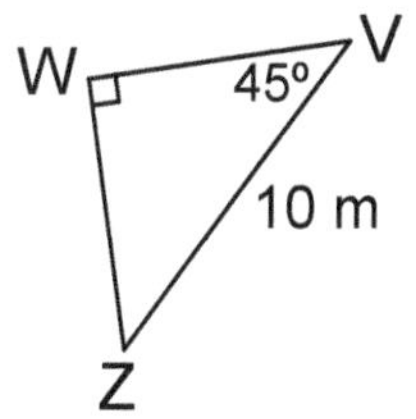

9-22. For each figure below, find the values of w, x, and y. Round your final answers to two decimal places where necessary.

9. w = ____________

x = ____________

y = ____________

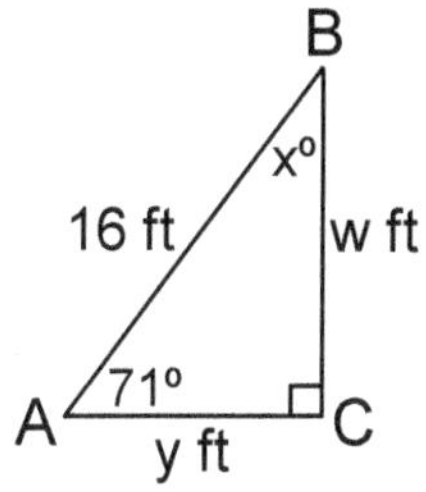

12. w = ____________

x = ____________

y = ____________

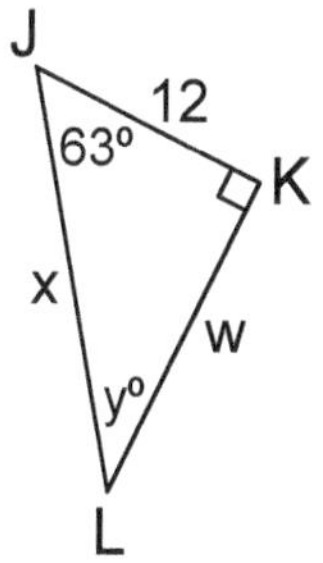

10. w = ____________

x = ____________

y = ____________

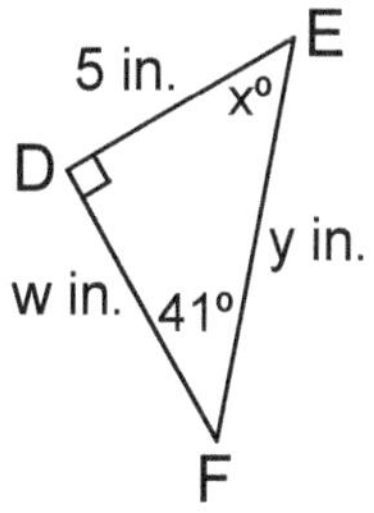

13. w = ____________

x = ____________

y = ____________

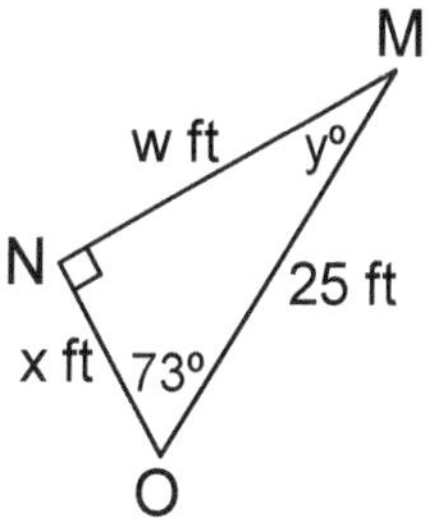

11. w = ____________

x = ____________

y = ____________

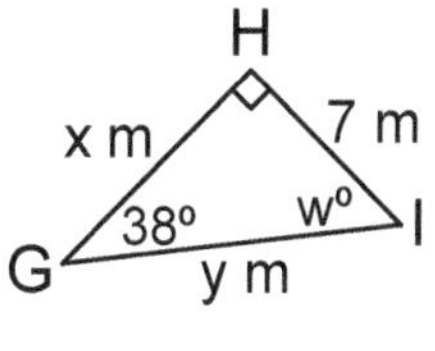

14. w = ____________

x = ____________

y = ____________

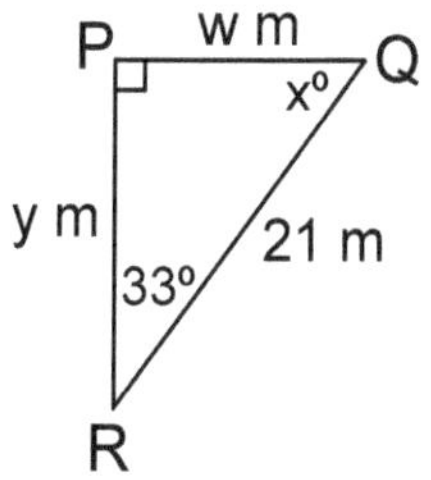

15. w = ____________

x = ____________

y = ____________

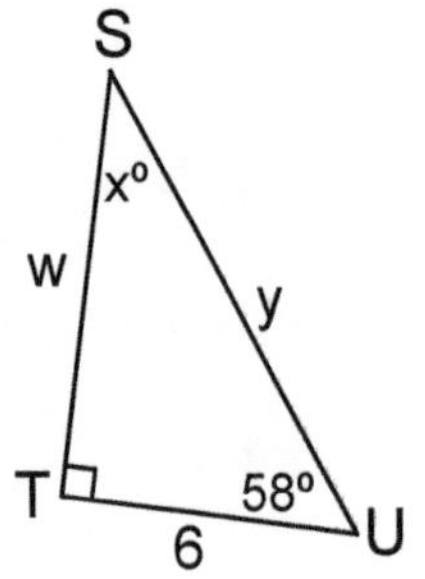

16. w = ____________

x = ____________

y = ____________

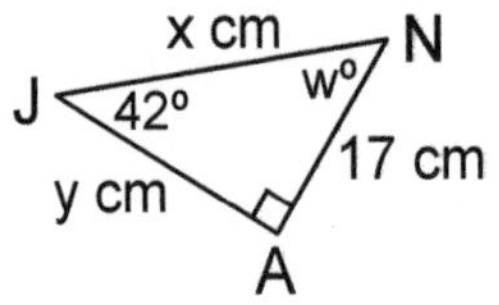

17. w = ____________

x = ____________

y = ____________

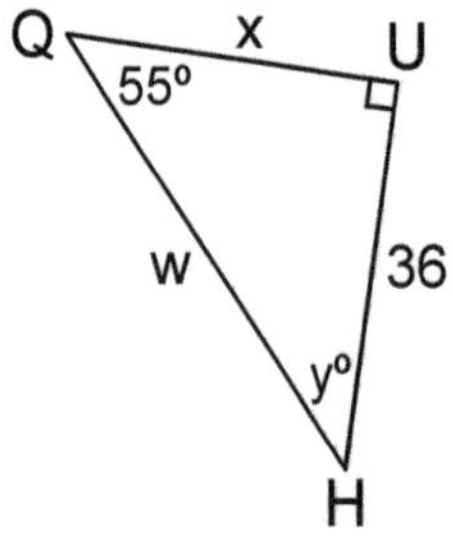

18. w = ____________

x = ____________

y = ____________

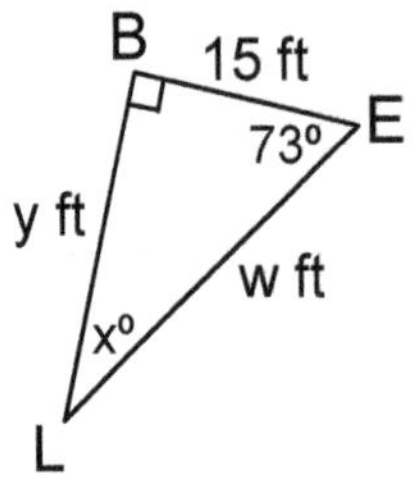

19. w = ____________

x = ____________

y = ____________

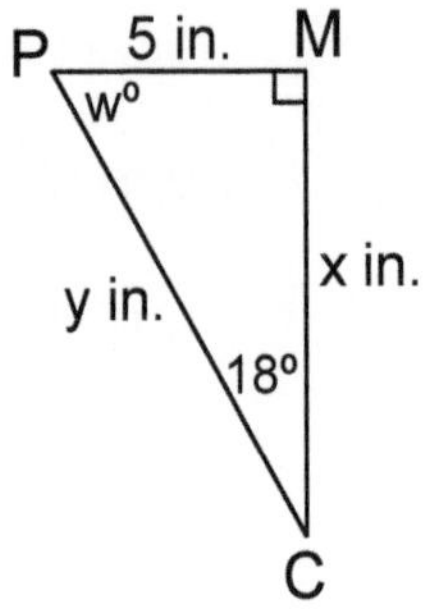

20. w = ____________

x = ____________

y = ____________

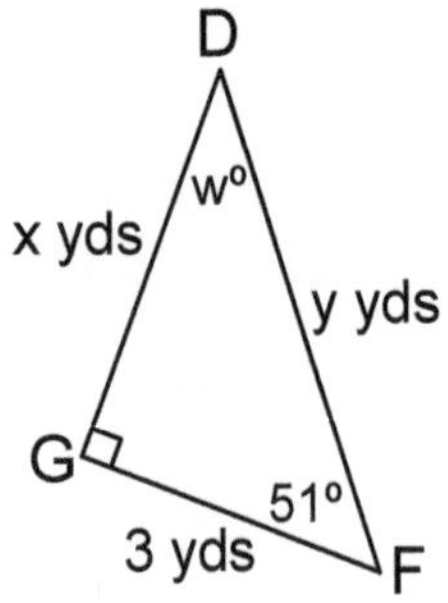

21. w = ____________

x = ____________

y = ____________

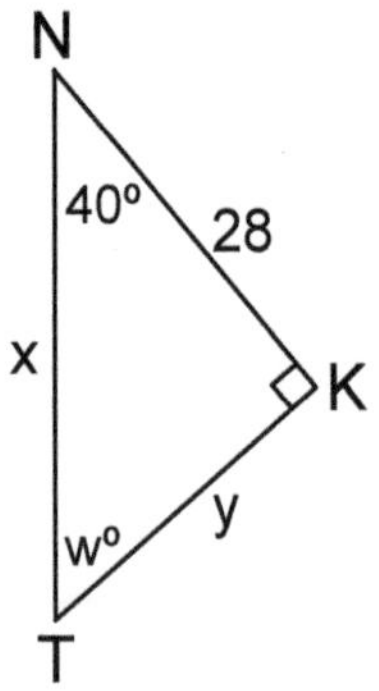

22. w = ____________

x = ____________

y = ____________

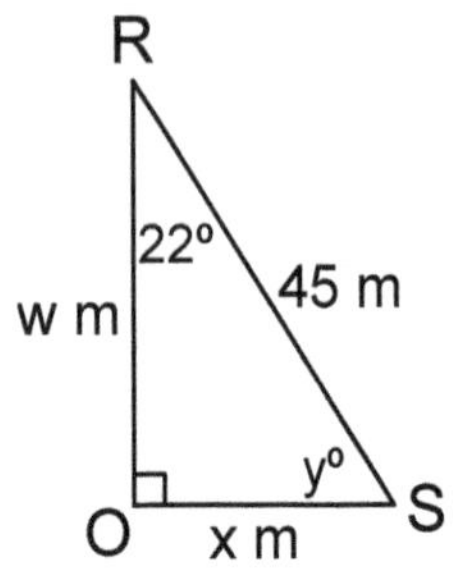

Part IV – More on Trigonometric Ratios in Right Triangles

In this section, we will expand on what we discussed in the last section.

Example 1: Find the values of w, x and y in the triangle at the right. Round the final answers to two decimal places where necessary.

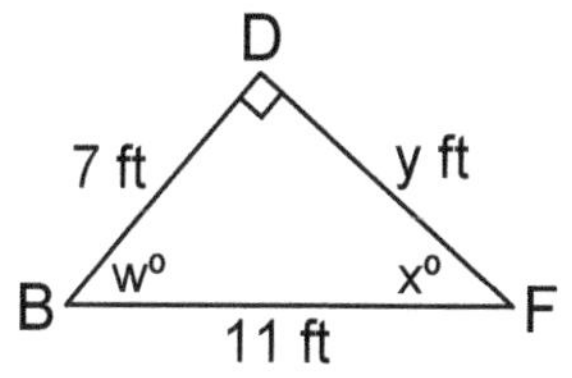

To find the value of w:

Note that $\overline{BD}$ is the leg that is next to $\angle B$ in this triangle, and $\overline{BF}$ is the hypotenuse. Hence, we can say that $\cos B = \frac{7}{11}$. We can finish solving this part of the problem as shown below.

$\cos B = \frac{7}{11}$

$\cos w^\circ \approx 0.6364$ — Notice that $\frac{7}{11} \approx 0.6364$ and that $m\angle B = w^\circ$. Also, like we said in the last section, we will round to four decimal places until we get to our final answer, and then we will round the final answer to two decimal places.

$w \approx 50.48$ — To find the value of w, we must find the **inverse** cosine of 0.6364. (Note the difference between this problem and the one in Example 3 in the last section. In Example 3 in the last section, we knew the measure of the angle, and we wanted to tell the calculator to find the cosine. In this example, we know the cosine of the angle, and we want to know the measure of the angle.) To do this using a type A calculator, type 0.6364, then hit the "2nd" or "inv" key, and then the "cos" key. To do this using a type B calculator, hit the "2nd" or "inv" key, then the "cos" key, and then type 0.6364.

To find the value of x:

Note that $\overline{BD}$ is the leg that is opposite $\angle F$ in this triangle, and $\overline{BF}$ is the hypotenuse. Therefore, we can say that $\sin F = \frac{7}{11}$. We can finish solving this part of the problem as shown below.

$\sin F = \frac{7}{11}$

$\sin x^\circ \approx 0.6364$ — Notice that $\frac{7}{11} \approx 0.6364$ and that $m\angle F = x^\circ$.

$x \approx 39.52$ — To find the value of x, we must find the **inverse** sine of 0.6364. (Note the difference between this problem and the one in Example 4 in the last section. In Example 4 in the last section, we knew the measure of the angle, and we wanted to tell the calculator to find the sine of the angle. In this example, we know the sine of the angle, and we want to know the measure of the angle.) To do this using a type A calculator, type 0.6364, then hit the "2nd" or "inv" key, and then the "sin" key. To do this using a type B calculator, hit the "2nd" or "inv" key, then the "sin" key, and then type 0.6364.

To find the value of y:

We can use the Pythagorean Theorem to say that $(BD)^2 + (DF)^2 = (BF)^2$. This tells us that $y = 6\sqrt{2}$. Since the question tells us to round the final answer to two decimal places, we will say our final answer is that $y \approx 8.49$.

There are several other ways we could find the values of w, x, and y in this problem, but they all require you to find the value of another variable first and then assume that the value you found is correct. Therefore, the methods we discussed here are the preferred methods of finding the values of w, x, and y in this problem.

Example 2: Find the values of w, x and y in the triangle at the right. Round the final answers to two decimal places where necessary.

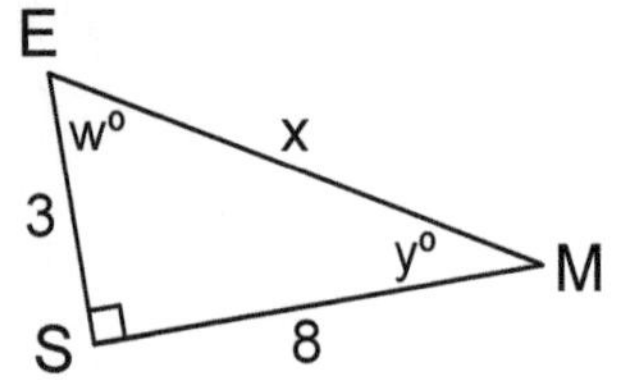

To find the value of w:

Since $\overline{SM}$ is the leg that is opposite $\angle E$ and $\overline{ES}$ is the leg that is adjacent to $\angle E$ in this triangle, we can say that $\tan E = \frac{8}{3}$. We can finish solving this part of the problem by following the steps shown below.

$\tan E = \frac{8}{3}$

$\tan w^\circ \approx 2.6667$ — Note that $\frac{8}{3} \approx 2.6667$ and that $m\angle E = w^\circ$.

$w \approx 69.44$ — To find the value of w in this problem, we must find the **inverse** tangent of 2.6667.

To find the value of x:

We can use the Pythagorean Theorem to say that $(ES)^2 + (SM)^2 = (EM)^2$. This tells us that $x = \sqrt{73}$, or approximately 8.54.

To find the value of y:

$\overline{ES}$ is the leg that is opposite $\angle M$ in this triangle, and $\overline{SM}$ is the leg that is adjacent to $\angle M$. Thus, we can say that $\tan M = \frac{3}{8}$. We can finish solving this part of the problem as shown below.

$\tan M = \frac{3}{8}$

$\tan y^\circ = 0.375$ — Note that $\frac{3}{8} = 0.375$ and that $m\angle M = y^\circ$.

$y \approx 20.56$ — To find the value of y in this problem, we must find the **inverse** tangent of 0.375.

In the next two examples, we will show how we can use trigonometric ratios to solve word problems. Before we can do this, however, we need to discuss two definitions.

Suppose that you are on the ground looking up at a friend who is looking at you from the third floor of a building, as shown in the figure at the right. The angle labeled $\angle DCB$ is the <u>angle of elevation</u> for you looking up at the person on the third floor, and the angle labeled $\angle ABC$ is the <u>angle of depression</u> for the person on the third floor looking down at you.

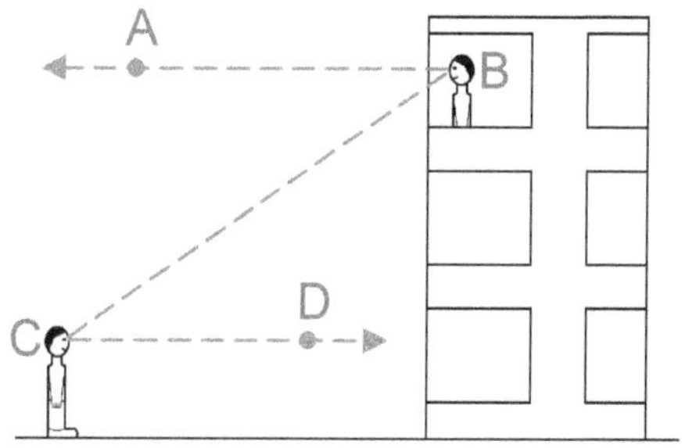

Example 3: A person in a lighthouse looks out and sees a sailboat at an angle of depression of 25°. If the person in the lighthouse knows that he is 34 meters above sea level, how far away is the sailboat from the base of the lighthouse? Round the final answer to two decimal places if necessary.

We will begin by drawing a picture to describe the information we are given, and we will label the distance we want to find as "x meters."

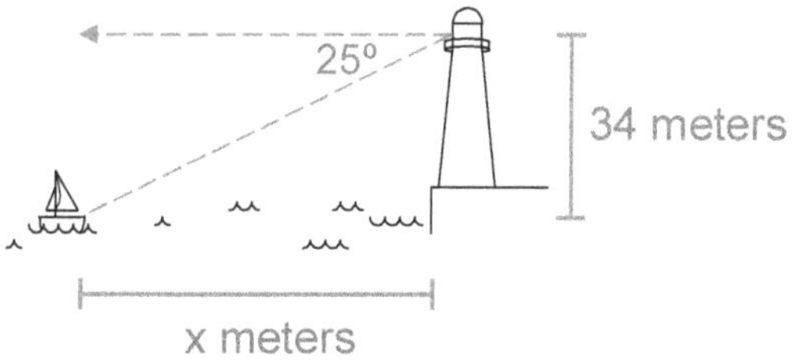

Now, we will redraw part of this picture as shown below. (We will also label some of the points so that we can talk about them.)

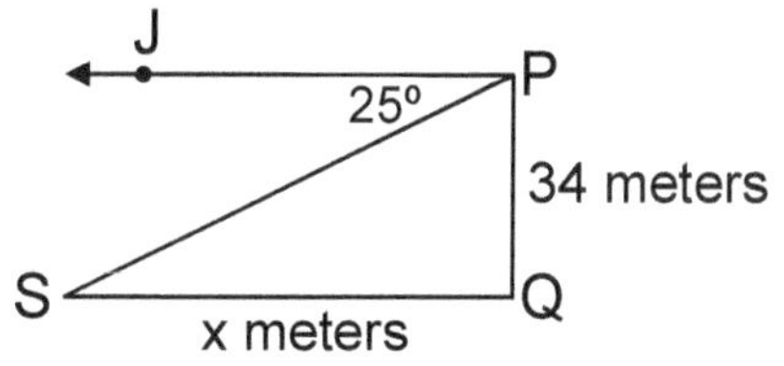

Next, we will note that $\angle JPS$ and $\angle S$ are two alternate interior angles formed by two parallel lines and a transversal, and so they must be congruent to each other. Also note that the angle we labeled $\angle Q$ must be a right angle. This tells us that we can say that $\tan 25° = \frac{34}{x}$ (because $m\angle S = 25°$, $\overline{PQ}$ is the leg in ΔPQS that is opposite $\angle S$, and $\overline{SQ}$ is the leg in ΔPQS that is adjacent to $\angle S$). We can finish solving this problem as shown below.

$$\tan 25° = \frac{34}{x}$$

$$0.4663 \approx \frac{34}{x}$$ Notice that $\tan 25° \approx 0.4663$.

$$0.4663x \approx 34$$ To get the x out of the denominator of the fraction, multiply both sides by x.

$$x \approx 72.91$$ Divide both sides by 0.4336.

Thus, the sailboat must be approximately 72.91 meters from the base of the lighthouse.

Example 4: A person in an airport control tower sees an airplane flying toward him at an angle of elevation of 22°. If the plane is flying at height of 480 feet above the ground, and if the person in the control tower knows that he is 128 feet from the ground, how far away from the control tower is the airplane? Round the final answer to two decimal places if necessary.

We will begin by drawing the following picture.

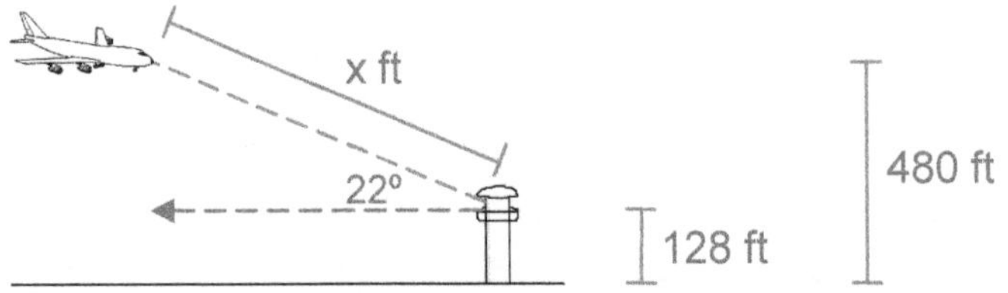

This tells us that we can draw the following triangle. (Note that 480 – 128 = 352, and so we can say that the plane is flying 352 feet above the person in the control tower.)

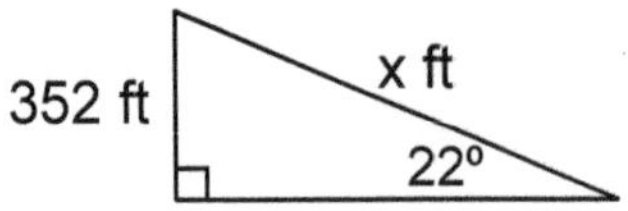

This tells us that we can write $\sin 22^\circ = \frac{352}{x}$, and so we can solve this problem by following the steps shown below.

$\sin 22^\circ = \frac{352}{x}$

$0.3746 \approx \frac{352}{x}$ — Note that $\sin 22^\circ \approx 0.3746$.

$0.3746x \approx 352$ — To get the x out of the denominator of the fraction, multiply both sides by x.

$x \approx 939.67$ — Divide both sides by 0.3746.

Therefore, the airplane must be approximately 939.67 feet away from the tower.

Finally, we will note that the answers you get to the problems in this section may be slightly different from the answers we get because you might round differently from us.

Problems:

1-22. For each figure below, find the values of w, x, and y. Round your final answers to two decimal places where necessary.

1. w = ___________
x = ___________
y = ___________

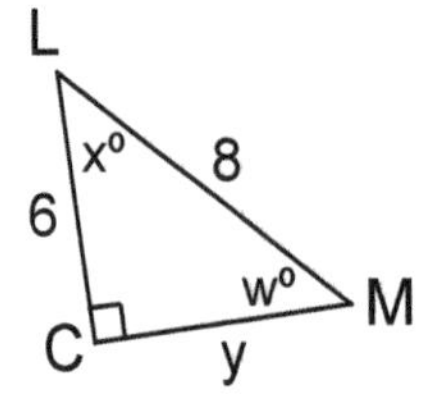

2. w = ___________
x = ___________
y = ___________

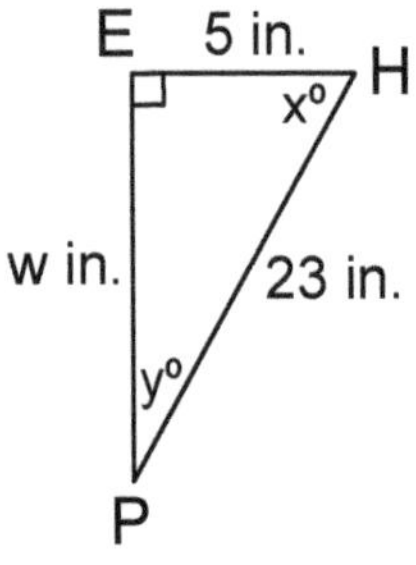

3. w = ____________
x = ____________
y = ____________

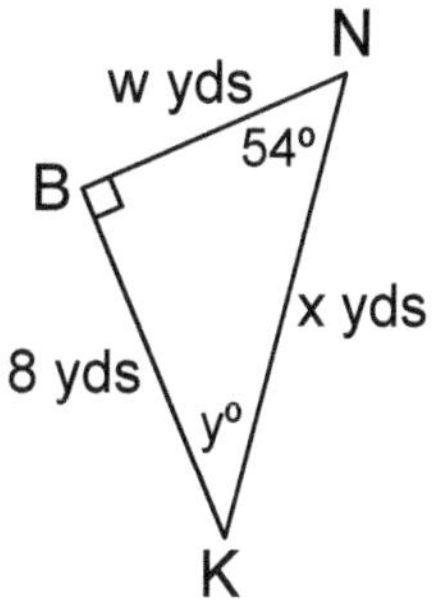

4. w = ____________
x = ____________
y = ____________

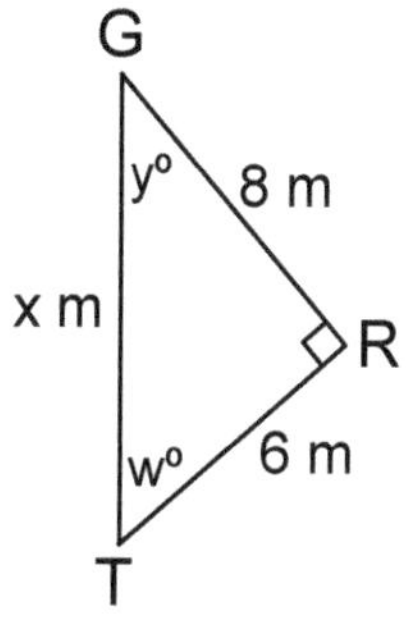

5. w = ____________
x = ____________
y = ____________

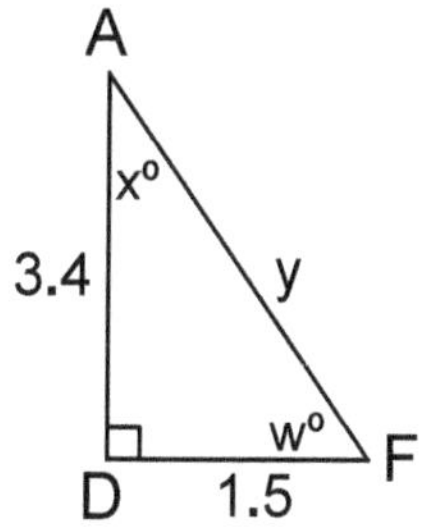

6. w = ____________
x = ____________
y = ____________

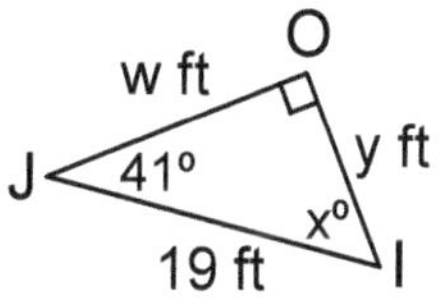

7. w = ____________
x = ____________
y = ____________

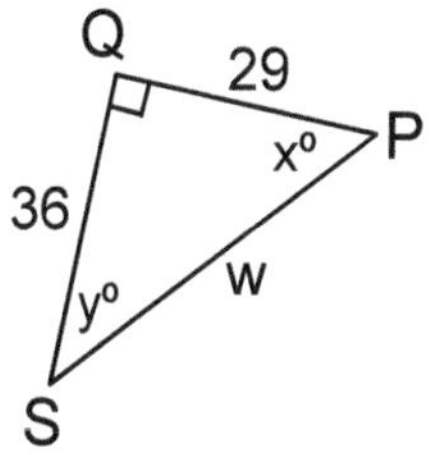

8. w = ____________
x = ____________
y = ____________

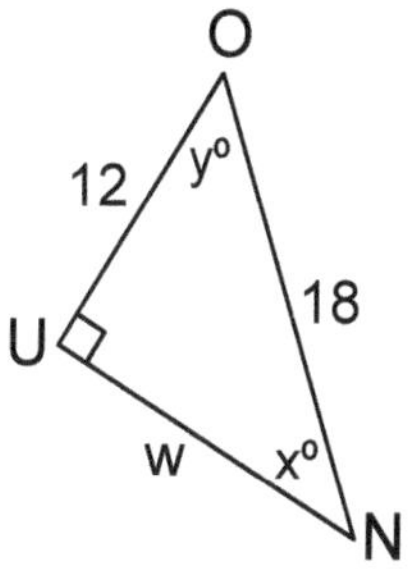

9. w = ____________
x = ____________
y = ____________

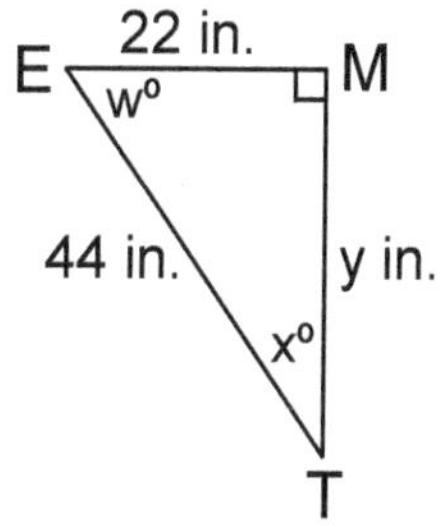

10. w = ____________
x = ____________
y = ____________

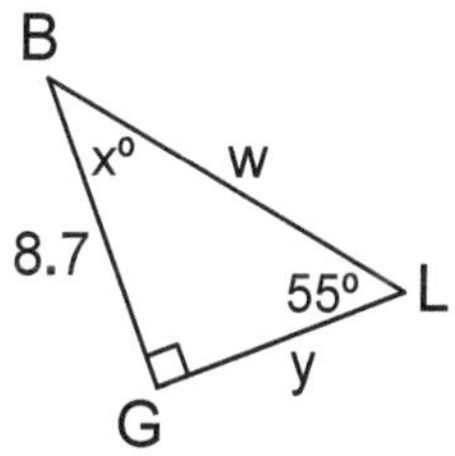

11. w = ____________
x = ____________
y = ____________

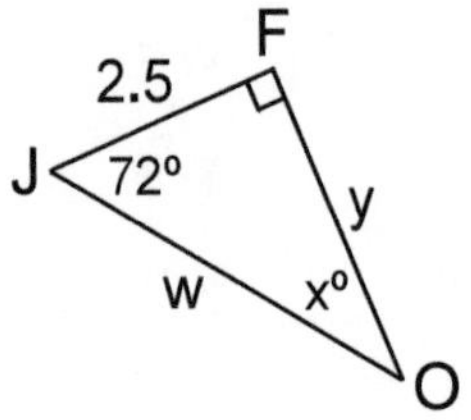

12. w = ____________
x = ____________
y = ____________

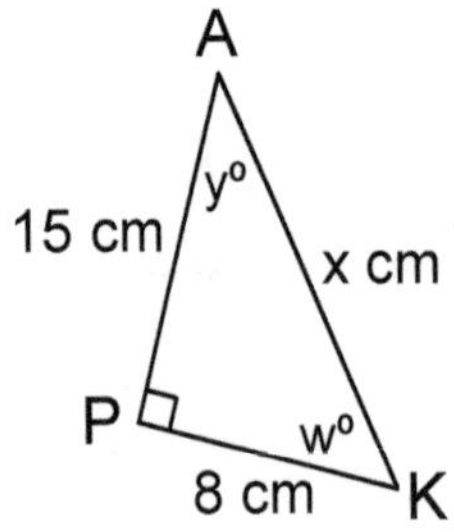

13. w = ____________
x = ____________
y = ____________

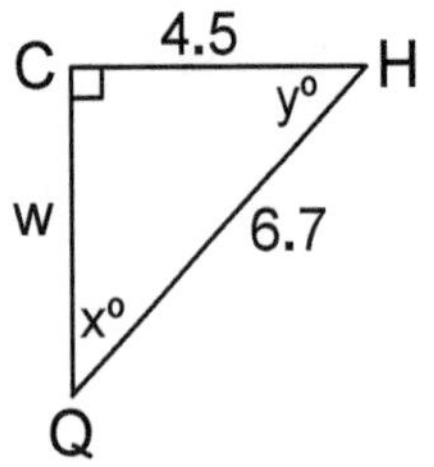

14. w = ____________
x = ____________
y = ____________

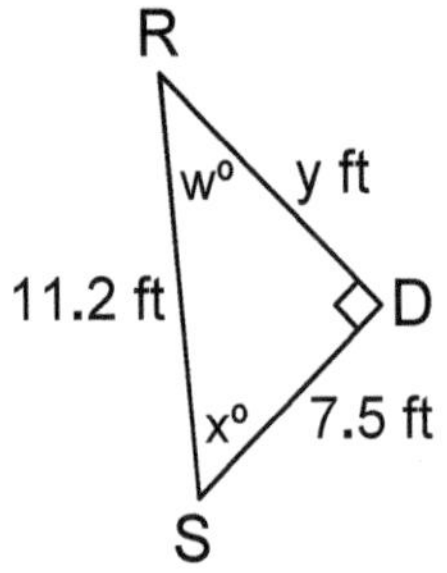

15. w = ____________
x = ____________
y = ____________

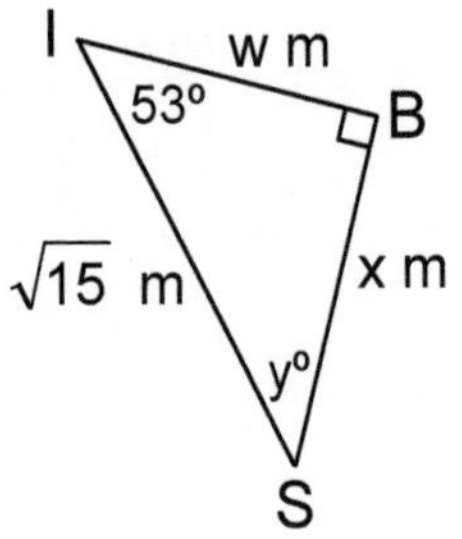

16. w = ____________
x = ____________
y = ____________

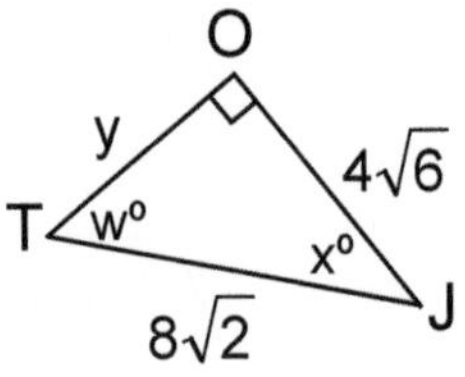

17. w = ____________
x = ____________
y = ____________

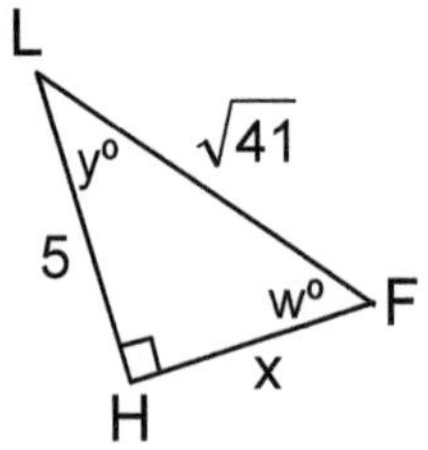

18. w = ____________
x = ____________
y = ____________

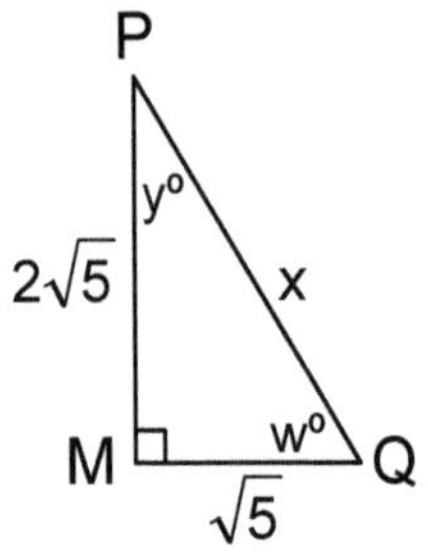

19. w = ____________

x = ____________

y = ____________

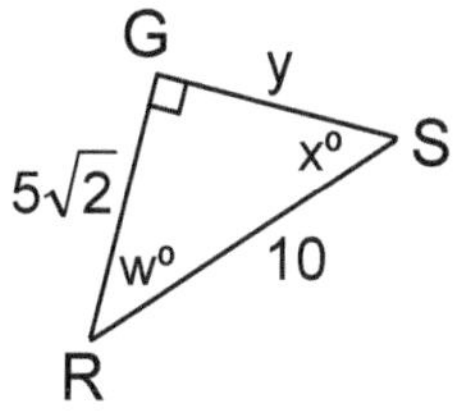

21. w = ____________

x = ____________

y = ____________

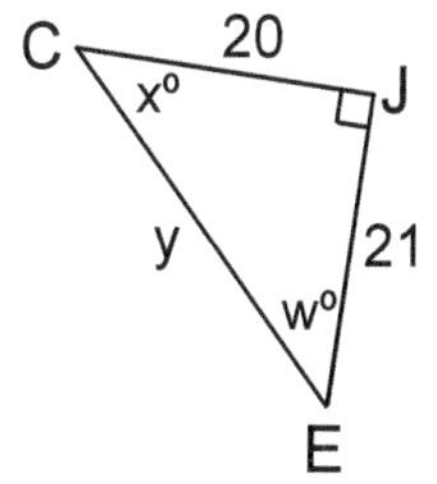

20. w = ____________

x = ____________

y = ____________

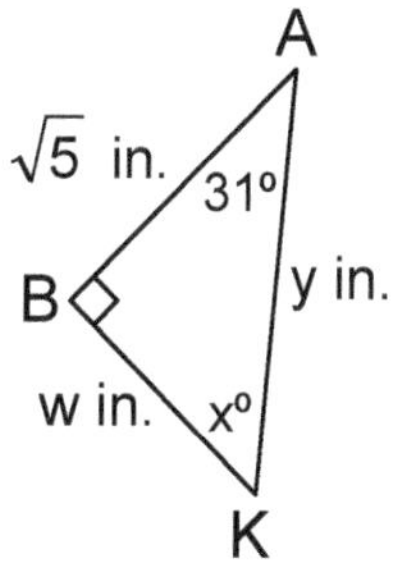

22. w = ____________

x = ____________

y = ____________

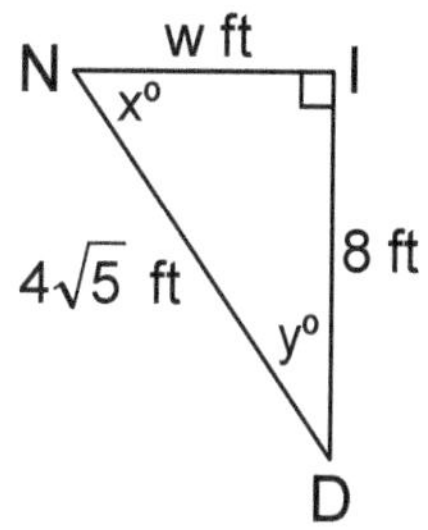

23-36. For these questions, round your answers to two decimal places where necessary, and assume that all of these problems take place on level ground.

23. Pamela is standing 18 meters from the base of a tree. When she looks at the top of the tree, the angle of elevation is 39°. If Pamela is 1.5 meters tall, how tall is the tree? ____________

24. A wheelchair ramp rises 1 foot while covering 12 feet horizontally. How long is the ramp? ____________ What is the angle of elevation? ____________

25. An airplane is flying at a height of 4 miles above the ground when it is about to begin its descent towards a runway. If the airplane's ground distance from the runway is 117 miles, what is the angle of depression for the pilot looking at the runway? ____________

26. Little Johnny has just built and launched a small homemade rocket. When the rocket is 9 feet in the air, he notices a spider on the tip of the rocket.

 a. The spider notices a grasshopper on the ground 8 feet from the spot on the ground where the rocket was launched. What is the angle of depression for the spider looking at the grasshopper when the rocket is 9 feet in the air? ____________

 b. The spider then looks up and sees a bird in a tree. If the bird is 25 feet above the ground, and if the angle of elevation for the spider looking at the bird is 23°, how far away from the spider is the bird? ____________

 c. Johnny is 4 feet tall, and he is standing 12 feet away from where the rocket was launched. When the rocket is 9 feet in the air, would we talk about an angle of depression or an angle of elevation for Johnny looking at the spider? ______________ What is the angle of depression or angle of elevation? ____________

27. Little Katie is 3 feet tall and is learning to ski. She has just skied down a section of a ski slope that is 100 feet long and has a vertical drop of 11 feet.

 a. Katie's mother is standing where Katie started. What is the angle of elevation for Katie when she looks up at her mother's feet? ____________

 b. How far did Katie travel horizontally? ____________

28. One of the weather conditions the Federal Aviation Administration looks at to determine whether or not airplanes can take off is the *cloud ceiling*, or the height above the earth's surface of the lowest layer of clouds. To find the cloud ceiling, one can beam a light vertically into space and then measure the angle of elevation to look at the spot of light on the clouds from some point on the ground far away from the point where the light was turned on. If the angle of elevation to look at a spot of light on the clouds is 54° when you are standing 380 yards away from the point where the light was turned on, what is the cloud ceiling? ____________

29. A person in a lighthouse is 115 feet above sea level. When a ship is 400 feet away from the base of the lighthouse, what is the angle of depression for the person in the top of lighthouse looking out at the ship? ____________

30. A ladder is 25 feet long, and the base of the ladder is placed 8 feet away from the base of a building.

    a. What angle does the ladder make with the ground? ____________

    b. How far up the side of the building does the ladder reach? ____________

31. Zachary is flying a kite, and he has let out 94 feet of string. If the string makes an angle of 73° with the ground, how far above the ground is the kite if Zachary is holding the end of the string 2 feet above the ground? ____________

32. As a train travels up a mountain, it rises 125 feet vertically for every 2000 feet of track. What is the angle of elevation of the track? ____________

33. Casey is standing 95 meters away from the base of a factory with a smokestack on its roof, and he knows that he is 2 meters tall. When he looks at the roof of the factory, the angle of elevation is 48°. When he looks at the top of the smokestack, the angle of elevation is 63°. How tall is the smokestack alone? ____________ Hint: You will need to draw *two* triangles.

34. Television antennas and other tall thin structures are often supported by *guy wires*, or wires that have one end attached to the top of the structure and the other end anchored to the ground. One end of a guy wire is attached to a certain radio antenna 52 feet from the base of the antenna, and the guy wire makes an angle of 61° with the ground.

    a. How long is the wire? ____________

    b. How tall is the antenna? ____________

35. Becky is looking at the top of a flagpole. She knows that the flagpole is 32 feet tall and that she is standing 20 feet from the base of the flagpole. If Becky is 5 feet tall, what is the angle of elevation for her looking at the top of the flagpole?

    ____

36. Leonard is standing 30 feet from the base of a tree, and he finds that, when he lays down on the ground, the angle of elevation to look at the top of the tree is 58°. If the tree is cut down, could it hit the house that is 45 feet from the base of the tree? ____________ Why or why not? ____________________________

Part V – Mixed Review

1-4. Do not round your answers; leave them in simplified radical form.

1. In the figure at the right, a = _________, b = _________, and c = _________.

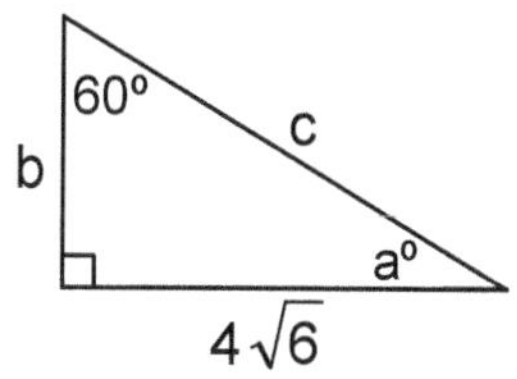

2. In the figure at the right, k = _________, u = _________, and v = _________.

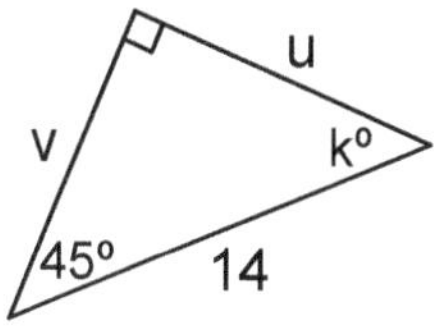

3. In the figure at the right, w = ___________, x = ___________, and y = ___________.

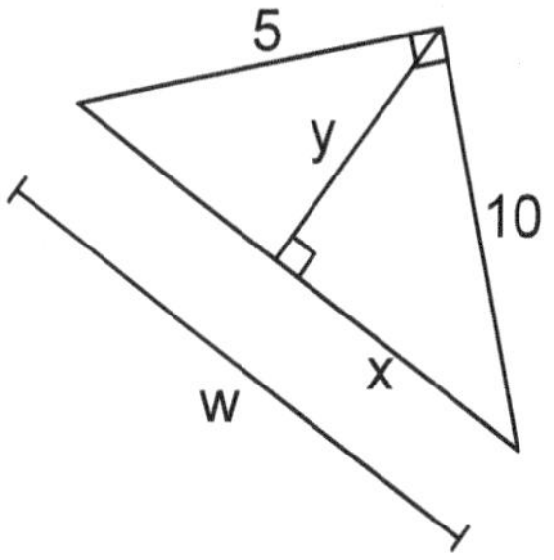

4. In the figure at the right, w = ___________, x = ___________, and y = ___________.

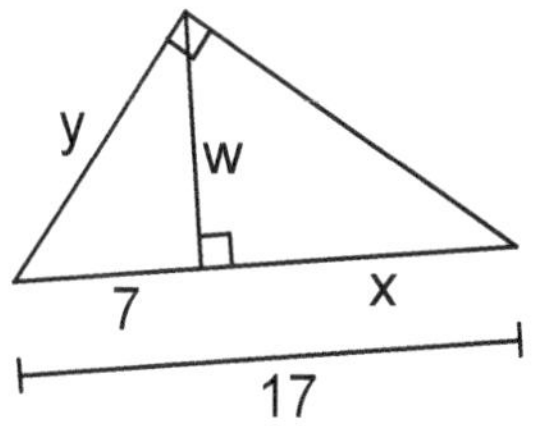

5-11. Round your answers to two decimal places where necessary, and assume that all of these problems take place on level ground.

5. In the figure at the right, m$\angle$B = _____________, BC = _____________, and AC = _____________.

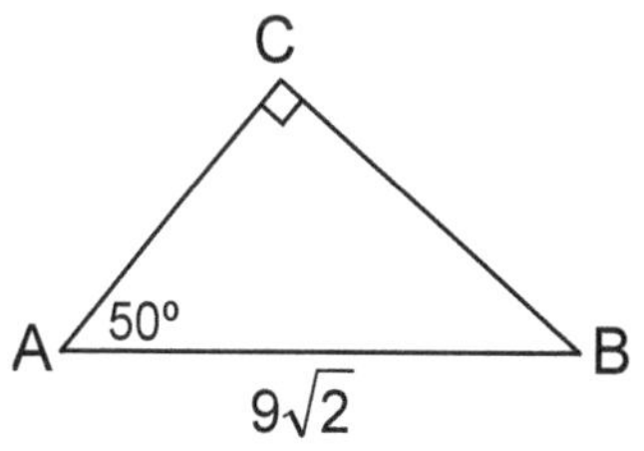

6. In the figure at the right, m$\angle$A = ____________,

m$\angle$B = ____________, and AB = ____________.

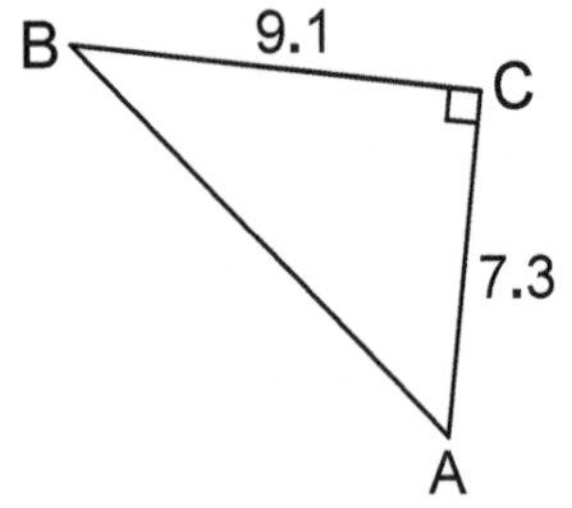

7. Tijuan was flying a kite until it got caught in the top of a tree. When he stands 35 feet away from the tree, the angle of elevation to look at the kite is 63°. If Tijuan is 4 feet tall, how high above the ground is the kite? ____________

8. A hawk is sitting on top of a building that is 16 meters high when the hawk sees a mouse on the ground at an angle of depression of 22°. How far away from the hawk is the mouse? ____________

9. Refer back to #8, and use the formula distance = (rate)(time) to find out how long it will take the hawk to reach the mouse if the hawk flies at an average speed of 45 meters per second. ____________

10. The diagram at the right shows four <u>roof trusses</u>, or boards that are used to hold up the roof of a building. If DE = EF = FG = 20 ft and AD = AG = 39 ft, then AF = ____________,

m$\angle$G = __________, and CF = ____________.

Hint: Begin by drawing the altitude of $\triangle$ADG that starts at A.

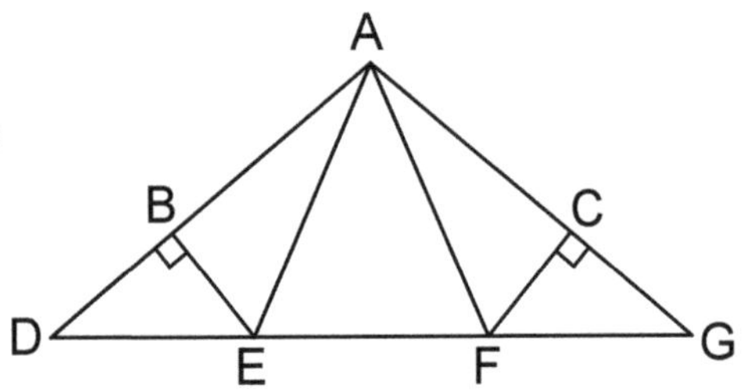

11. When Clarissa stands 25 yards from the base of a building, she notices that the angle of elevation for her to look at the roof of the building is 37°. Adriana is standing farther away from the same building, and, she notices that the angle of elevation for her to look at the roof of the building is 28°. If both girls are the same height, how far away from the base of the building is Adriana standing?

____

12. Prove the Pythagorean Theorem using the theorems discussed in Part I of this chapter.

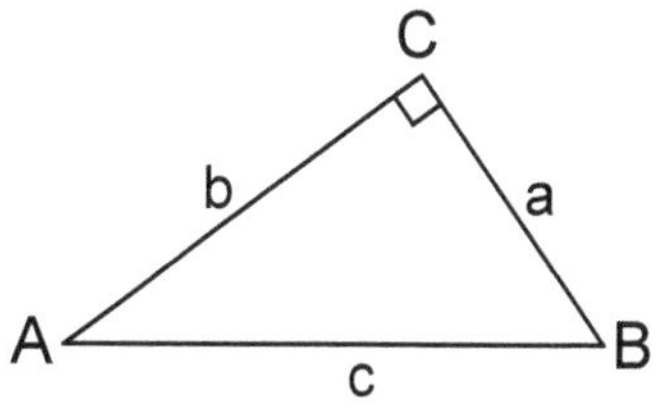

Given: $\triangle ABC$ is a right triangle with $\angle C$ as its right angle

Prove: ____________________

Begin by drawing the altitude from C to $\overline{AB}$, and label the point where the altitude intersects $\overline{AB}$ as the point D, as shown below.

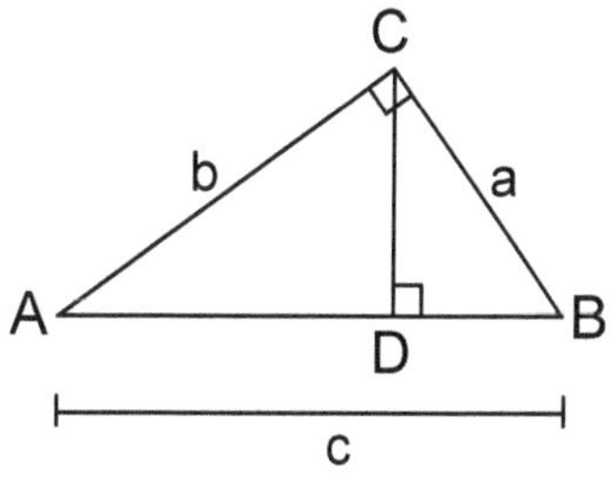

Since the length of each leg of the largest right triangle is the geometric mean of the length of the entire hypotenuse and the length of the piece of the hypotenuse that is adjacent to that leg, we can say that $\frac{c}{a} = \frac{a}{DB}$ and $\frac{c}{b} = \frac{b}{AD}$. By the Cross Products Property of Proportions____________ and ____________. Next, we will use the Addition Property of Equality to add these two equations together. When we do this, we get $a^2 + b^2 = c(DB) + c(AD)$. By the Distributive Property, ________________.
The ____________________________ tells us that c = DB + AD. So, by the ____________________________, we can say that $a^2 + b^2 = c(c)$, or $a^2 + b^2 = c^2$.

13. What is the measure of one interior angle of a regular decagon? __________

What is the measure of one exterior angle of a regular decagon? __________

14. Use a protractor to draw all the altitudes in each triangle below.

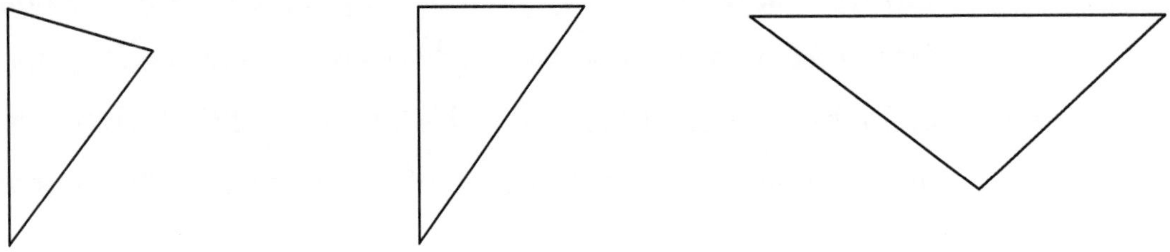

15. Given that $\overline{SG} \cong \overline{SW}$ and that $\overline{SE} \perp \overline{GW}$ in the figure at the right, prove that $\overline{GE} \cong \overline{WE}$.

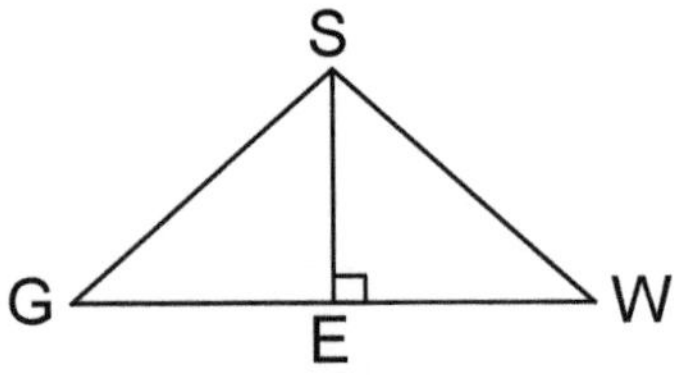

16-18. In the figure at the right, $\triangle EGJ$ is an equilateral triangle and $\overline{HF} \cong \overline{IF}$.

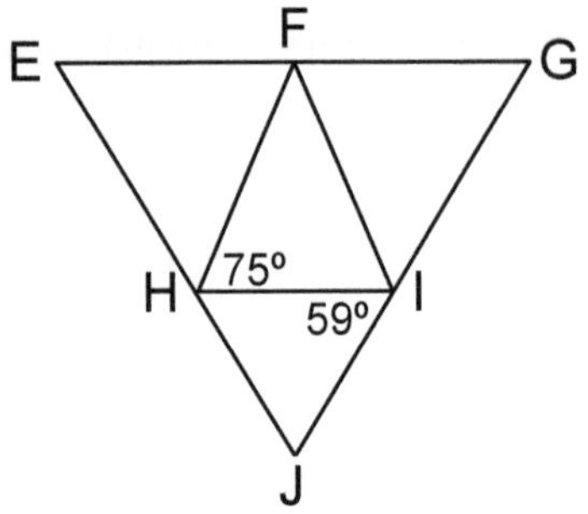

16. $m\angle IFG$ = __________

17. $m\angle IFH$ = __________

18. Is $\overline{HI} \parallel \overline{EG}$? __________ If your answer is *yes*, name a definition, theorem, or postulate to support your answer. ______________________________

19. In the figure at the right, $m \parallel n$. Find the values of x and y.

    x = ___________

    y = ___________

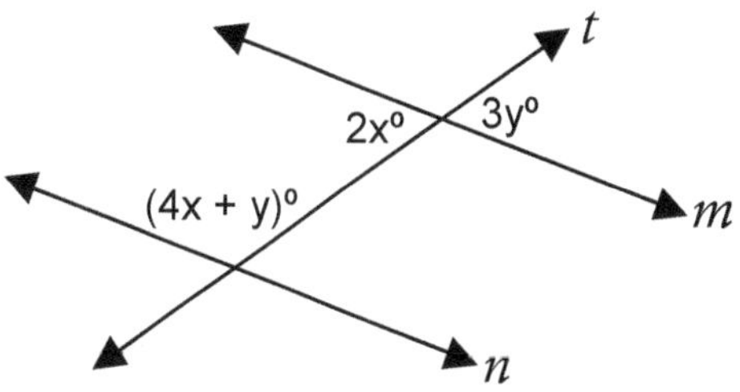

20-22. Fill in each blank with <, >, or =, and then state the definitions, postulates, and/or theorems used.

20. AD _______ DC

    Definitions, postulates, and/or theorems used:

    ____

    ____

    ____

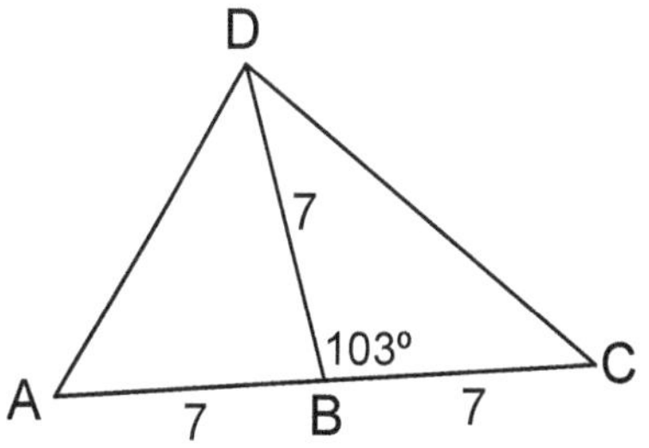

21. DC _______ DB

    Definitions, postulates, and/or theorems used:

    ____

    ____

    ____

22. $m\angle C$ _______ $m\angle BDC$

    Definitions, postulates, and/or theorems used:

    ____

    ____

    ____

23. Classify the triangle at the right according to the lengths of its sides and the measures of its angles. Name all of the terms that apply. ___________________________________

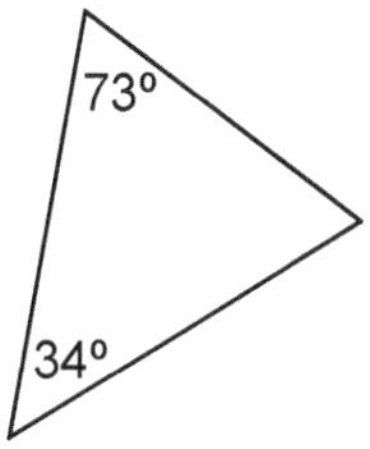

24. Classify the triangle at the right according to the lengths of its sides and the measures of its angles. Name all of the terms that apply. ______________________________

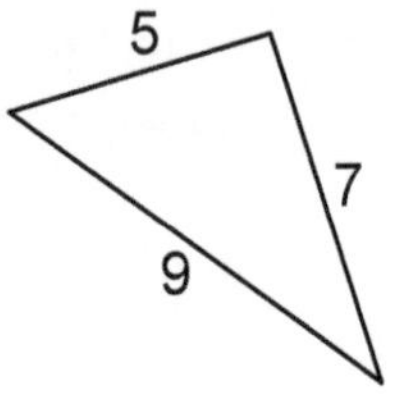

25a. In the figure at the right, must the two triangles be similar to each other? _________

b. If your answer to (a) was *yes*, then $\Delta DCQ \sim \Delta$___________.

Postulate(s) or Theorem(s) used: ______________________

____

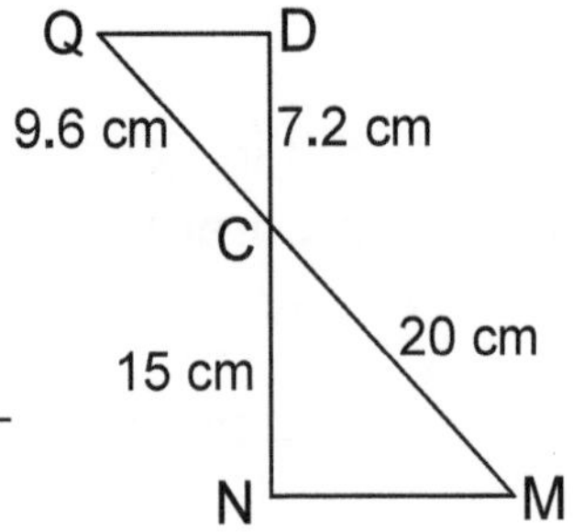

26a. In the figure at the right, must the two triangles be similar to each other? _________

b. If your answer to (a) was *yes*, then $\Delta OAP \sim \Delta$___________.

Postulate(s) or Theorem(s) used: ______________________

____

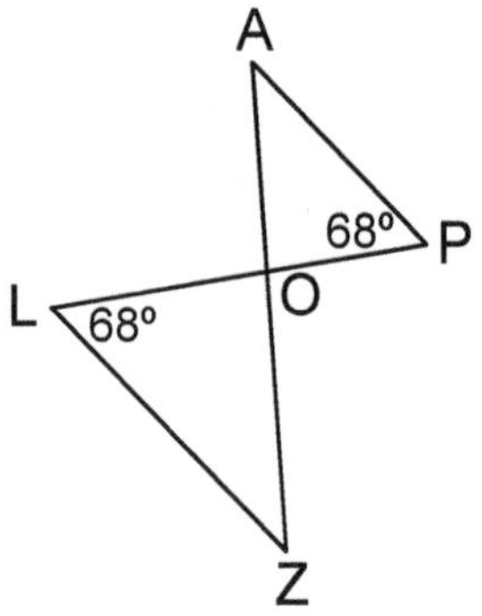

27-28. In the figure at the right, $\overline{BJ}$, $\overline{UM}$, and $\overline{RH}$ are all medians of ΔUBH.

27. If BM = 6x + 5 and MH = 33 – x, then x = _________ and BH = _________.

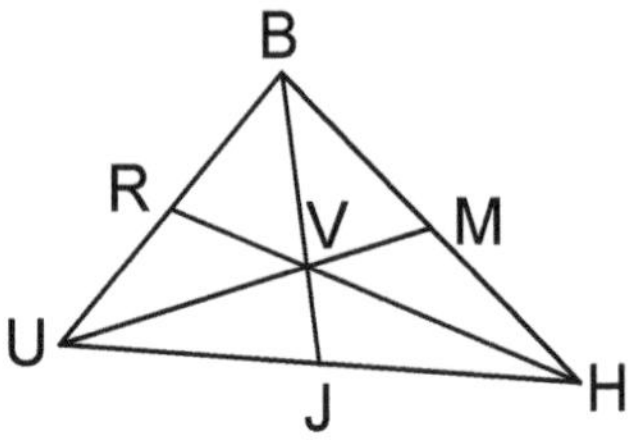

28. If HV = 30, then RV = _________ and HR = _________.

29-30. During a solar eclipse, the sun is completely blocked from view on parts of the earth as the moon passes between the earth and the sun. In reality, the sun is much bigger than the moon, but, because the sun is so much farther away from the earth, the sun and the moon appear to be about the same size, and, in a solar eclipse, the moon appears to just barely cover up the sun (and even then, only small parts of the earth observe a *total* solar eclipse, where the moon completely covers up the view of the sun). The figure below shows a solar eclipse.

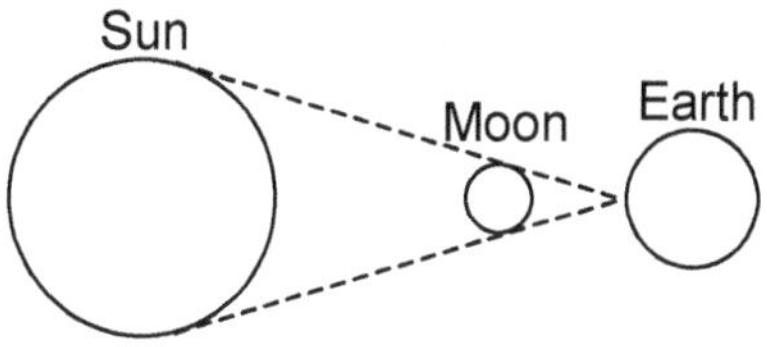

Note: This figure is not drawn to scale.

29. The caption below the picture says that the picture is not drawn to scale. What does this mean? (Hint: Look back at Example 5 from Part I of Chapter 7.)

____

____

____

30. The average distance from the center of the moon to the surface of the earth is 378,089 km, the average distance from the center of the sun to the surface of the earth is about 149.6 million km, and the diameter of the moon is about 3475 km. (Recall that the length of a diameter of a circular object is the distance from its center to its surface.) Name a similarity postulate or theorem tells us that we have similar triangles. (Actually, we do not have two similar triangles with these numbers because the points where the rays of the sun drawn in the picture above do not quite touch the sun and moon at the endpoints of diameters, but it's very close.) ____________________ Use the numbers given above to find the approximate length of the diameter of the sun. ____________________ (By the way, the *actual* diameter of the sun is about 1.391 million km.)

Chapter 9 – Circles

Part I – Terms and Definitions Associated With Circles

In this section, we will discuss the definition of a circle as well as the definitions of some of the terms we associate with circles.

A circle is a set of points that are equidistant from a fixed point. The fixed point is called the center of the circle.

We usually name circles by writing the symbol "⊙" and then naming the center of the circle. So, for example, we could refer to the circle on the left below by writing "⊙C" (read "circle C"), and we could refer to the circle on the right below by writing "⊙G" (read "circle G").

Now, we need some more definitions.

A segment is a radius (plural: radii) of a circle if and only if it has one endpoint at the center of the circle and one endpoint on the circle. (We can also call the length of such a segment a radius, but, to avoid some confusion, we will not do this. When we talk about a radius of a circle in this chapter, you may assume that we are talking about the segment, and not its length, unless we specifically say otherwise.) Note that the definition of a circle tells us that, in any given circle, all radii of the circle are congruent to each other.

A segment is a diameter of a circle if and only if it passes through the center of the circle and has both endpoints on the circle. Its length is equal to twice the length of the radius.

A segment is a chord of a circle if and only if it has both endpoints on the circle.

A line, segment, or ray is called a secant of a circle if and only if it contains two points that are on the circle but are not both endpoints.

A line is said to be tangent to a circle if and only if it touches the circle at exactly one point. A segment or ray is said to be tangent to a circle if and only if it is part of a line that is tangent to the circle. The point where a tangent line, segment, or ray touches the circle is called the point of tangency.

Example 1: Use the terms from the previous page to describe $\overline{WX}$, $\overline{ZX}$, $\overline{YX}$, $\overline{MO}$, $\overrightarrow{MO}$, and point X as they relate to $\odot W$ and $\odot L$.

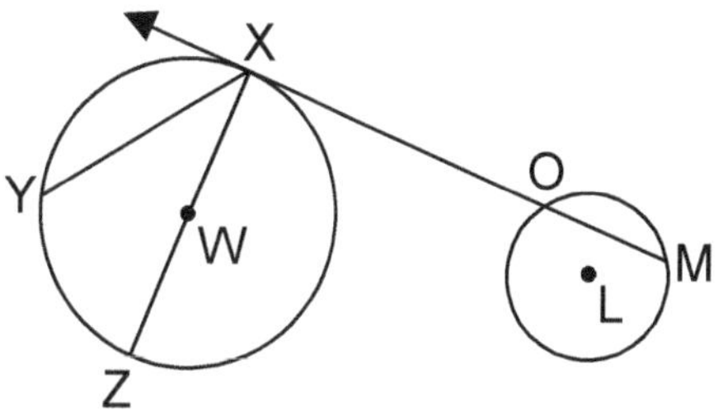

We will begin by noting that we can say that the points W and L are the centers of these two circles because the question told us that we can refer to them as $\odot W$ and $\odot L$.

$\overline{WX}$ is a radius of $\odot W$. One of its endpoints is on the circle, and the other endpoint is at the center of the circle.

$\overline{ZX}$ is a diameter of $\odot W$ because it passes through the point W (the center of the circle) and it has both of its endpoints on the circle. We can also say that it is a chord of $\odot W$ because both of its endpoints are on the circle.

$\overline{YX}$ is a chord of $\odot W$ because both of its endpoints are on the circle. We cannot call it a diameter because it does not pass through the center of the circle. We cannot call it a secant because both of its endpoints are on the circle.

$\overline{MO}$ is a chord of $\odot L$ because both of its endpoints are on $\odot L$.

$\overrightarrow{MO}$ is a secant of $\odot L$ because both points M and O lie on the circle but O is not an endpoint. It is also tangent to $\odot W$ because it touches $\odot W$ at one, and only one, point.*

Point X is a point of tangency because it is the point where $\overrightarrow{MO}$ (which we just said is tangent to $\odot W$) intersects $\odot W$.*

Example 2: Name all of the radii, diameters, chords, secants, and tangents of $\odot P$ drawn in the figure at the right.

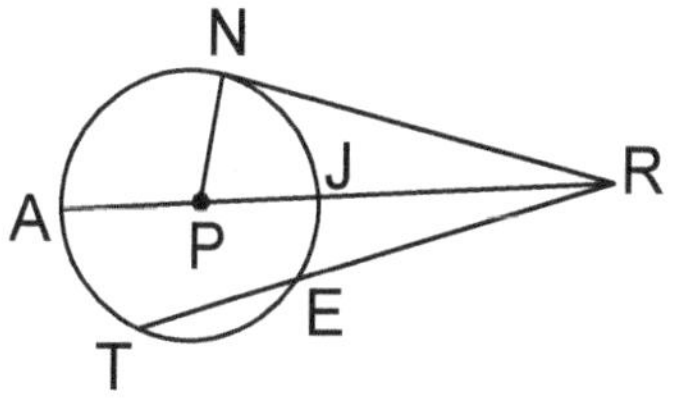

The radii of $\odot P$ drawn in the figure at the right are $\overline{AP}$, $\overline{JP}$, and $\overline{NP}$.

The only diameter of $\odot P$ drawn in the figure at the right is $\overline{AJ}$.

The chords of $\odot P$ drawn in the figure at the right are $\overline{AJ}$ and $\overline{TE}$.

The secants of $\odot P$ drawn in the figure at the right are $\overline{AR}$ and $\overline{RT}$.

The only tangent of $\odot P$ drawn in the figure at the right is $\overline{NR}$.*

We can also talk about two circles being tangent to each other, as the following definition shows.

Two or more circles are called <u>tangent</u> to each other if and only if they intersect at exactly one point. The point where they intersect is called the <u>point of tangency</u>.

*Technically, we are usually not allowed to assume that a line, segment, ray, or circle is tangent to a circle just because it appears to be tangent. However, you may assume that all lines, segments, rays, and other circles that appear to be tangent are actually tangent for the problems and examples in this section.

For example, in the pictures below, ⊙S is tangent to ⊙F at the point L, and ⊙C is tangent to ⊙I at the point T.

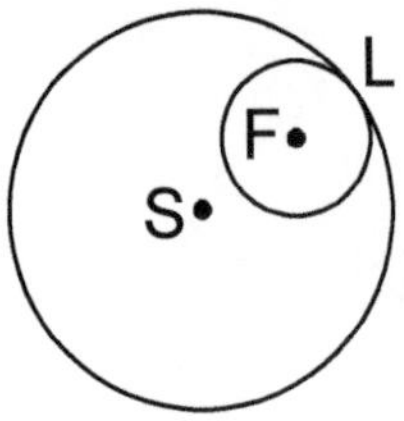

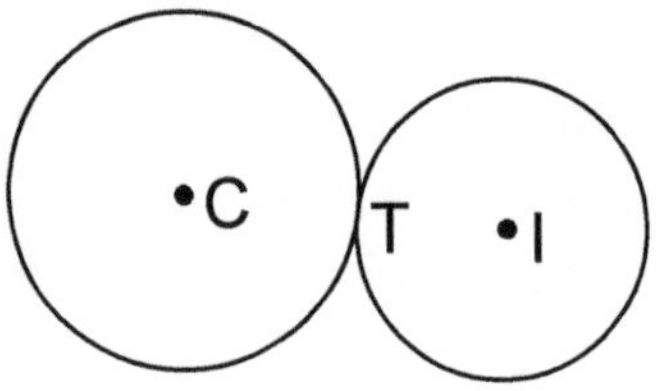

Now, we need two more definitions.

Two or more circles are called <u>concentric</u> if and only if they have the same center but radii of different lengths.

Two or more circles are <u>congruent</u> if and only if their radii have the same length.

For instance, the figure below shows three concentric circles, and Example 3 talks about congruent circles.

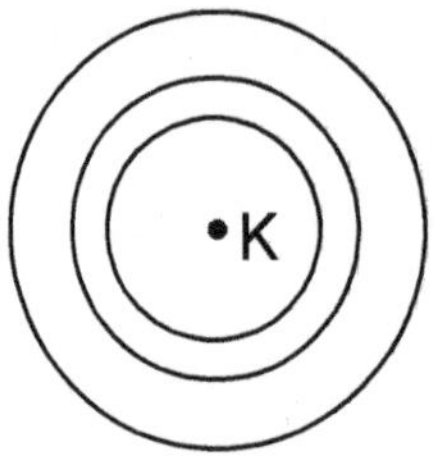

Example 3: In the figure at the right, D, A, and H are the centers of their respective circles. If QB = 30, AU = 15, and HV = 14, which circles are congruent to each other?

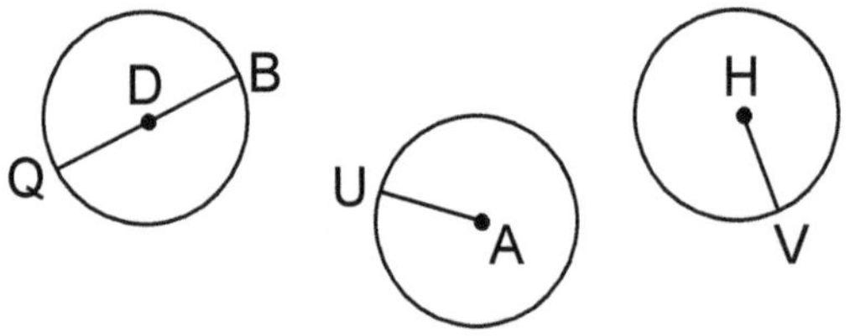

We will begin by noting that, since the length of a diameter of a circle is equal to twice the length of a radius of a circle, we can say that DB = 30 ÷ 2, or 15. Therefore, DB = AU, and so we can say that ⊙A is congruent to ⊙D. We cannot say that ⊙H is congruent to either ⊙D or ⊙A because all the radii of ⊙H have a length of 14 instead of 15.

Problems:

1-22. Refer to the figure at the right to answer these questions.

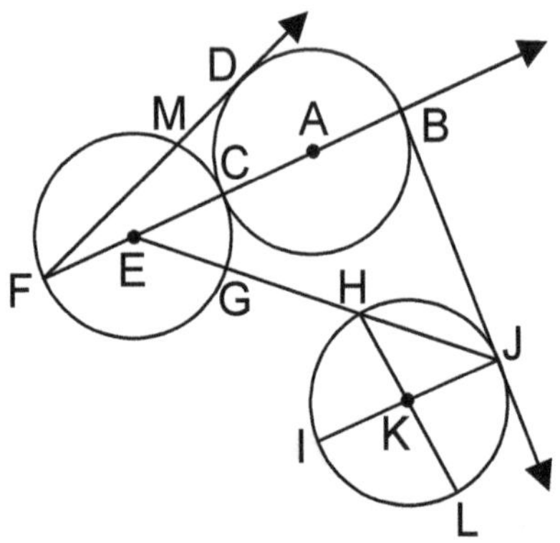

1. Name all the radii of ⊙E drawn.

   ____

2. Name all the diameters of ⊙E drawn.

   ____

3. Name all the chords of ⊙ E drawn. _______________

4. Name all the rays drawn that are secants of ⊙ E. _______________

5. Name all the rays tangent to ⊙ E drawn. _______________

6. Name all the radii of ⊙ K drawn. _______________

7. Name all the diameters of ⊙ K drawn. _______________

8. Name all the chords of ⊙ K drawn. _______________

9. Name all the secants of ⊙ K drawn. _______________

10. Name all the rays tangent to ⊙ K drawn. _______________

11. Are any of the circles concentric to each other? _____________ If so, what is their center? _____________

12. If AB = 12, what is the length of all the diameters of ⊙ A? _______________

13. If HL = 22, what is the length of all the radii of ⊙ K? _______________

14. If AB = 12, HL = 22, and CF = 24, which two circles are congruent to each other? _______________

15. Which point is the center of ⊙ A? _______________

16. Are any of the circles tangent to each other? _____________ If so, what is the point of tangency? _____________

17. True or false: $\overline{HL}$ is a both a chord and a diameter of ⊙ K. _____________

18. True or false: $\overline{CB}$ is a both a chord and a secant of ⊙ A. _____________

19. True or false: $\overline{AC}$ is a diameter of ⊙ A. _____________

20. True or false: $\overrightarrow{AB}$ is tangent to ⊙A. ____________

21. True or false: $\overrightarrow{BJ}$ is tangent to both ⊙A and ⊙K. ____________

22. Which point is the center of ⊙K? ____________

23-30. Refer to the figure at the right to answer these questions.

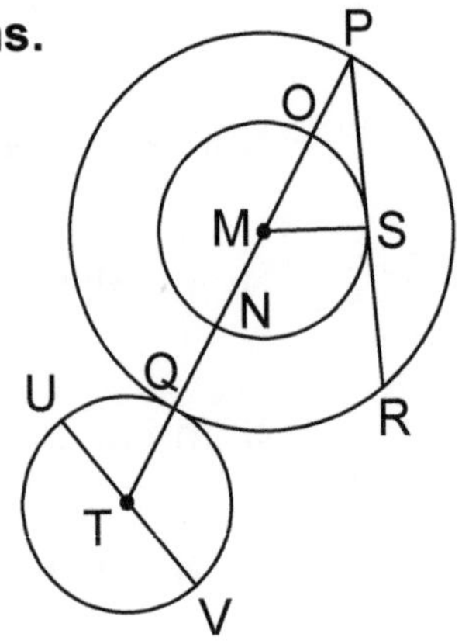

23. Name all the radii of ⊙T drawn. ______________

24. Name all the diameters of ⊙T drawn. __________

25. If MN = 5, then OM = ________ and NO = ________.

26. If UT = 7, then QT = ________ and UV = ________.

27. If OM = 14 and MQ = 23, then MN = ________, NQ = ________, and PQ = ________.

28. If SM = 16 and PM = 33, then NO = ________, MN = ________, and OP = ________.

29. Are any of the circles tangent to each other? __________ If so, what is the point of tangency? ____________

30. Are any of the circles concentric to each other? __________ If so, what is their center? ____________

Part II – Central Angles and Measures of Arcs

We will begin this section with six definitions.

A central angle is an angle whose vertex is at the center of a circle.

An arc is a part of a circle.

The measure of an arc is defined to be the measure of the corresponding central angle.

An arc is called a minor arc if and only if its measure is less than 180°. To name minor arcs, we usually name their endpoints with the symbol "$\frown$" over the top of them.

An arc is called a semicircle if and only if its measure is equal to 180°. We name semicircles using three letters and the symbol "$\frown$" over the top of them. The first and last letters are always the endpoints, and the middle letter is another point on the arc.

An arc is called a major arc if and only if its measure is more than 180°. We name major arcs using three letters and the symbol "$\frown$" over the top of them. The first and last letters are always the endpoints, and the middle letter is another point on the arc.

To discuss what these definitions mean, we will talk about the picture below.

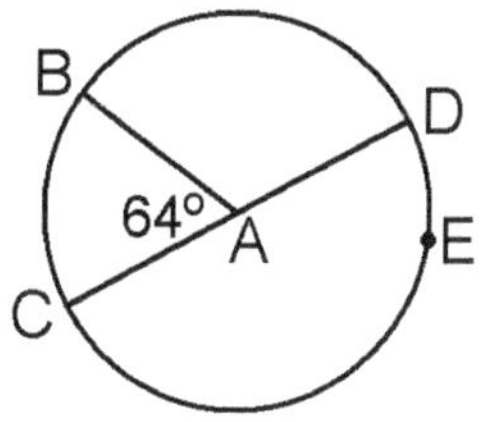

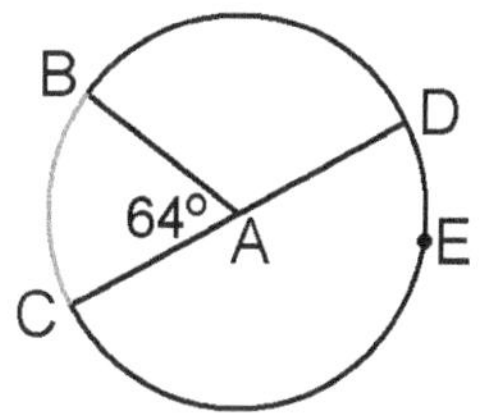

We can say that $\angle BAC$ is a central angle because its vertex is at the point A, which is the center of the circle. We can also say that $m\overset{\frown}{BC}$ (this is read, "the measure of arc BC," and $\overset{\frown}{BC}$ is the arc outlined in gray in the picture at the right) equals 64° because the measure of the corresponding central angle ($\angle BAC$) is 64°. Since 64° < 180°, we can also say that $\overset{\frown}{BC}$ is a minor arc.

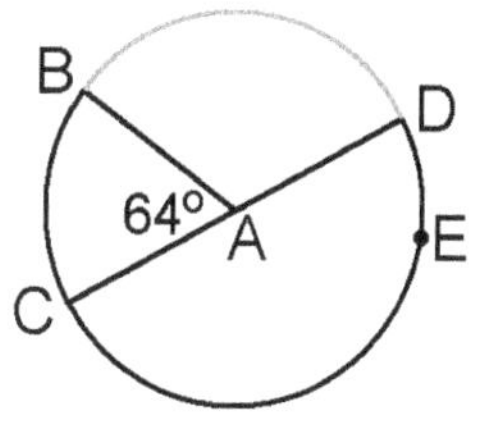

We can also say that $m\overset{\frown}{BD} = 116°$. To see why, note that $\angle BAD$ and $\angle BAC$ form a linear pair, and so $m\angle BAD$ must equal 116°. Since $\angle BAD$ is the central angle that corresponds with $\overset{\frown}{BD}$, we can conclude that $m\overset{\frown}{BD} = 116°$. Since this is less than 180°, we can also conclude that $\overset{\frown}{BD}$ is also a minor arc.

Next, we will note that m$\overset{\frown}{CBD}$ = 180° because $\overset{\frown}{CBD}$ corresponds with the straight angle ∠CAD and m∠CAD = 180°. Since m$\overset{\frown}{CBD}$ = 180°, we can also say that $\overset{\frown}{CBD}$ is a semicircle.

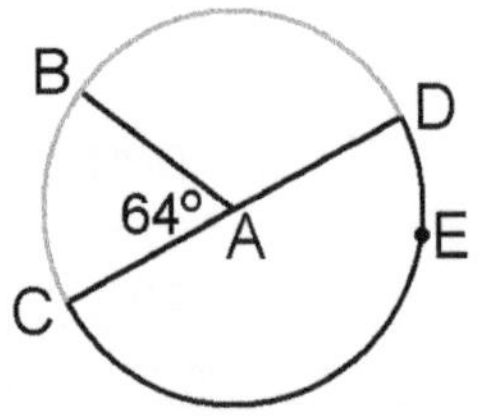

Before we can talk about the next part of this example, we need a postulate and a theorem.

Arc Addition Postulate
If $\overset{\frown}{AB}$ and $\overset{\frown}{BC}$ are adjacent arcs in a circle, then m$\overset{\frown}{AB}$ + m$\overset{\frown}{BC}$ = m$\overset{\frown}{ABC}$.

The arc measure of an entire circle is 360°.

The theorem *The arc measure of an entire circle is 360°* can be easily proven by noting that two semicircles with measures of 180° each make up a full circle.

Now, we can say that m$\overset{\frown}{CDB}$ = 296°. To see why, note that $\overset{\frown}{CDB}$ is composed of two arcs: $\overset{\frown}{CED}$ (which has a measure of 180°) and $\overset{\frown}{BD}$ (which, as we said on the previous page, has a measure of 116°). Since 180° + 116° = 296°, we can use the Arc Addition Postulate to say that m$\overset{\frown}{CDB}$ = 296°. (We could have also found that m$\overset{\frown}{CDB}$ = 296° in the following way. Since the arc measure of an entire circle is 360°, we can say that m$\overset{\frown}{CDB}$ = 360° – 64°, or 296°.) Since this measure is greater than 180°, we can also say that $\overset{\frown}{CDB}$ is a major arc.

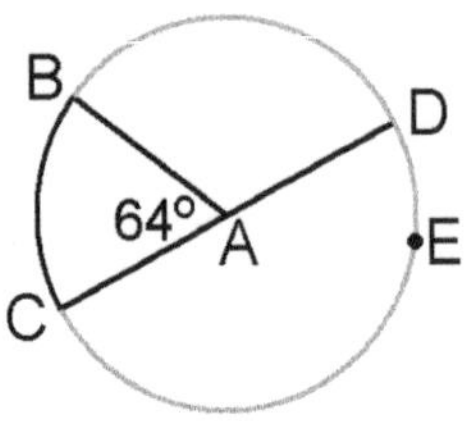

Example 1: In ⊙Y at the right, m$\overset{\frown}{XW}$ = 62°. Find m∠ZYW, m$\overset{\frown}{ZUV}$, m$\overset{\frown}{XUW}$, and m$\overset{\frown}{UW}$. Also classify each arc as a *minor arc*, a *major arc*, or a *semicircle*.

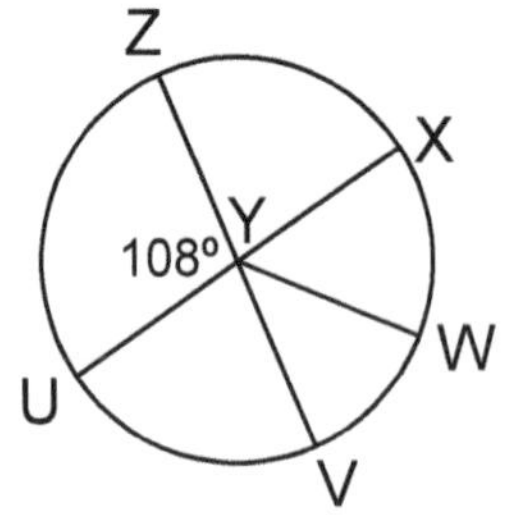

We will begin by noting the following. (By the way, there are many other ways you could arrive at each of the following conclusions).

- Since we were told that m∠ZYU = 108°, we can use the fact that ∠ZYX and ∠ZYU form a linear pair to say that m∠ZYX = 72°.
- Since we were told that m∠ZYU = 108°, we can use the fact that ∠UYV and ∠ZYU form a linear pair to say that m∠UYV = 72°.
- Since we were told that m∠ZYU = 108°, we can use the fact that ∠XYV and ∠ZYU are vertical angles to say that m∠XYV = 108°.
- Since we were told that m$\overset{\frown}{XW}$ = 62°, we can use the definition of the measure of an arc to say that m∠XYW = 62°.
- Since we just said that m∠XYV = 108° and m∠XYW = 62°, we can use the Angle Addition Postulate to say that m∠WYV = 46°.

Now, we can answer the questions as shown on the next page.

We can say that $m\angle ZYW = m\angle ZYX + m\angle XYW$, or 134°.

We can say that $m\overset{\frown}{ZUV} = m\overset{\frown}{ZU} + m\overset{\frown}{UV} = m\angle ZYU + m\angle UYV$, or 180°. Since this measure is equal to 180°, we can say that $\overset{\frown}{ZUV}$ is a *semicircle*.

We can say that $m\overset{\frown}{XUW} = m\overset{\frown}{XZ} + m\overset{\frown}{ZUV} + m\overset{\frown}{VW} = m\angle ZYX + 180° + m\angle WYV$, or 298°. (We could also find this by saying that $m\overset{\frown}{XUW} = 360° - m\overset{\frown}{XW}$.) Since this measure is more than 180°, we can say that $\overset{\frown}{XUW}$ is a *major arc*.

We can say that $m\overset{\frown}{UW} = m\overset{\frown}{UV} + m\overset{\frown}{VW} = m\angle UYV + m\angle WYV$, or 118°. Since this measure is less than 180°, we can say that $\overset{\frown}{UW}$ is a *minor arc*.

Example 2: In ⊙G at the right, $m\overset{\frown}{DEH} = 233°$ and $m\overset{\frown}{EF} = 71°$. Find $m\angle DGF$ and $m\overset{\frown}{EDF}$.

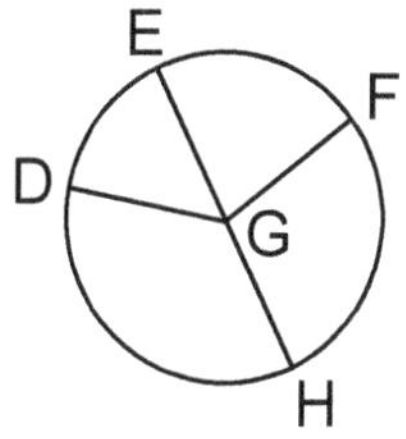

We will begin by noting the following. (Like we said about the conclusions we made in Example 1, there are many ways of arriving at each of the following conclusions.)

- Since $\overset{\frown}{EFH}$ is formed by the straight angle $\angle EGH$, we can say that $\overset{\frown}{EFH}$ is a semicircle and that $m\overset{\frown}{EFH} = 180°$. Since we were told that $m\overset{\frown}{DEH} = 233°$, we can use the Arc Addition Postulate to say that $m\overset{\frown}{DE} = 233° - 180°$, or 53°. This means that we can say that $m\angle DGE = 53°$ by the definition of the measure of an arc.
- We already said that $m\overset{\frown}{EFH} = 180°$, and we were told that $m\overset{\frown}{EF} = 71°$. Thus, we can use the Arc Addition Postulate to say that $m\overset{\frown}{FH} = 180° - 71°$, or 109°.

Now, we can answer the questions as follows.

Since we were given that $m\overset{\frown}{EF} = 71°$, we can use the definition of the measure of an arc to say that $m\angle EGF = 71°$. Since the Angle Addition Postulate tells us that $m\angle DGF = m\angle DGE + m\angle EGF$, this means that $m\angle DGF$ must equal 124°.

We can find $m\overset{\frown}{EDF}$ either by noting that $m\overset{\frown}{EDF} = 360° - m\overset{\frown}{EF}$ or by noting that $m\overset{\frown}{EDF} = m\overset{\frown}{ED} + m\overset{\frown}{DH} + m\overset{\frown}{FH}$. Either way, we find that $m\overset{\frown}{EDF} = 289°$.

Now, we need another definition and three theorems. You will prove the theorems in the exercises for this section.

In a circle or in congruent circles, two arcs are called <u>congruent</u> if and only if their measures are equal.

In a circle or in congruent circles, two chords are congruent if and only if their corresponding arcs are congruent.

If a radius of a circle is perpendicular to a chord of the circle, then it bisects the chord and its arc.

In a circle or in congruent circles, two chords are congruent if and only if they are equidistant from the center.

To understand what this definition and these theorems tell us, look at the following picture, and assume that $\odot P \cong \odot T$. (Recall that two circles are congruent if and only if their radii are congruent, and so you can assume that $\overline{KP} \cong \overline{NP} \cong \overline{TW}$).

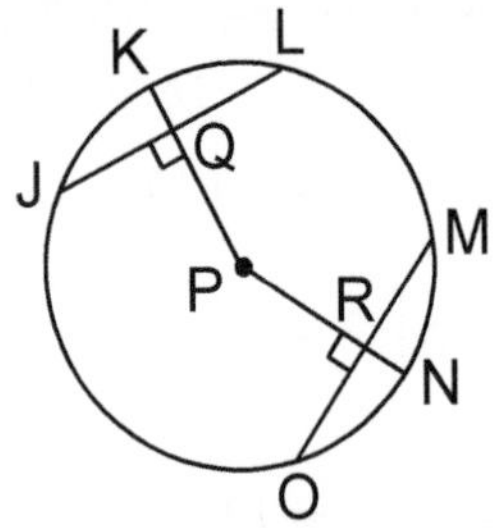

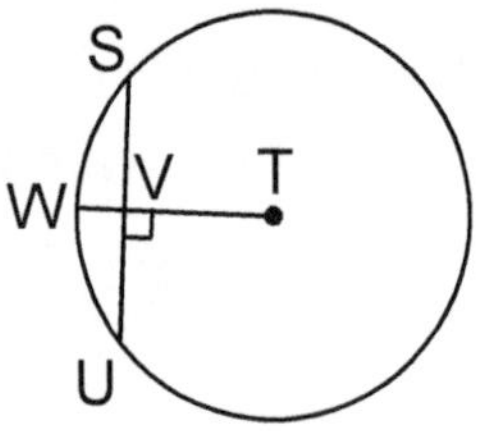

The definition of congruent arcs tells us that $\overset{\frown}{JL} \cong \overset{\frown}{MO}$ if and only if $m\overset{\frown}{JL} = m\overset{\frown}{MO}$. Since we said that you can assume that $\odot P \cong \odot T$, it also tells us that $\overset{\frown}{JL} \cong \overset{\frown}{SU}$ if and only if $m\overset{\frown}{JL} = m\overset{\frown}{SU}$.

The theorem *In a circle or in congruent circles, two chords are congruent if and only if their corresponding arcs are congruent* tells us that $\overset{\frown}{JL} \cong \overset{\frown}{MO}$ if and only if $\overline{JL} \cong \overline{MO}$. Since we said that you can assume that $\odot P \cong \odot T$, it also tells us that $\overset{\frown}{JL} \cong \overset{\frown}{SU}$ if and only if $\overline{JL} \cong \overline{SU}$.

The theorem *If a radius of a circle is perpendicular to a chord of the circle, then it bisects the chord and its arc* tells us that, since the picture tells us that $\overline{PK} \perp \overline{JL}$, we can conclude that $\overline{JQ} \cong \overline{QL}$ and that $\overset{\frown}{JK} \cong \overset{\frown}{KL}$. It also tells us that, since the picture tells us that $\overline{PN} \perp \overline{MO}$ and $\overline{TW} \perp \overline{SU}$, we can conclude that $\overline{MR} \cong \overline{RO}$, $\overset{\frown}{MN} \cong \overset{\frown}{NO}$, $\overline{SV} \cong \overline{VU}$, and $\overset{\frown}{SW} \cong \overset{\frown}{WU}$.

The theorem *In a circle or in congruent circles, two chords are congruent if and only if they are equidistant from the center* tells us that $\overline{JL} \cong \overline{MO}$ if and only if $\overline{PQ} \cong \overline{PR}$. Since we said that you can assume that $\odot P \cong \odot T$, it also tells us that $\overline{JL} \cong \overline{SU}$ if and only if $\overline{PQ} \cong \overline{TV}$. (To understand this better, you may want to refer back to Part III of Chapter 5 to refresh your memory on how we defined the distance from a point to a line or line segment.)

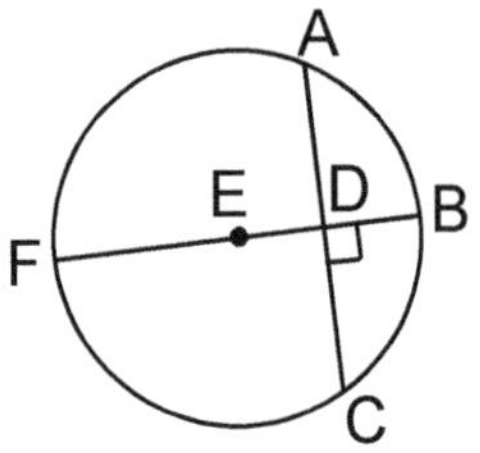

Example 3: In $\odot E$ at the right, FB = 52 and DE = 10. What is the length of $\overline{AC}$?

We will begin by noting that, since the picture tells us that $\overline{AC} \perp \overline{BF}$, we can use the theorem *If a radius of a circle is perpendicular to a chord of the circle, then it bisects the chord and its arc* to say that $\overline{AD} \cong \overline{DC}$.

Next, we will note that, since the length of a radius of a circle is equal to half the length of a diameter of the circle, we can say that all radii of $\odot E$ have a length of

$52 \div 2$, or 26. Therefore, we can say that EC = 26 in the circle shown below.

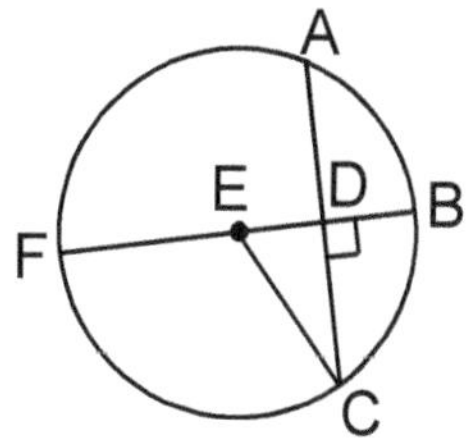

Now, we can use the Pythagorean Theorem to say that $(DE)^2 + (DC)^2 = (EC)^2$. This tells us that DC = 24, as shown below.

$$\begin{aligned} (DE)^2 + (DC)^2 &= (EC)^2 \\ 10^2 + (DC)^2 &= 26^2 \\ 100 + (DC)^2 &= 676 \\ (DC)^2 &= 576 \\ DC &= 24 \end{aligned}$$

Since we said on the previous page that $\overline{AD} \cong \overline{DC}$, we can now say that AC = 48.

Problems:

1-10. In ⊙A at the right, $m\angle BAC = 41°$ and $m\overset{\frown}{DF} = 128°$.

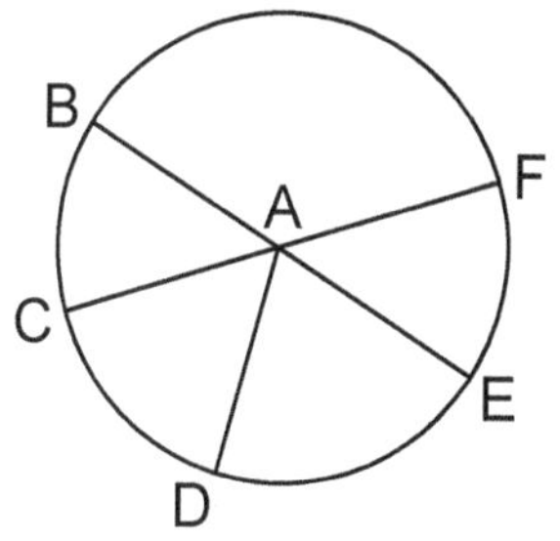

1. $m\angle EAF$ = _______
2. $m\angle BAF$ = _______
3. $m\angle CAD$ = _______
4. $m\angle EAD$ = _______
5. $m\overset{\frown}{EF}$ = _______

   Is this arc a *minor arc*, a *major arc*, or a *semicircle*? ___________

6. $m\overset{\frown}{CDF}$ = _______

   Is this arc a *minor arc*, a *major arc*, or a *semicircle*? ___________

7. $m\overset{\frown}{CFD}$ = _______

   Is this arc a *minor arc*, a *major arc*, or a *semicircle*? ___________

8. $m\overset{\frown}{CD}$ = _______

   Is this arc a *minor arc*, a *major arc*, or a *semicircle*? ___________

9. $m\overset{\frown}{EFB}$ = _______

   Is this arc a *minor arc*, a *major arc*, or a *semicircle*? ___________

10. $m\overset{\frown}{BFD}$ = _______

   Is this arc a *minor arc*, a *major arc*, or a *semicircle*? ___________

11-16. In ⊙Q at the right, m∠KQL = 28° and $\overline{KM} \cong \overline{MO}$.

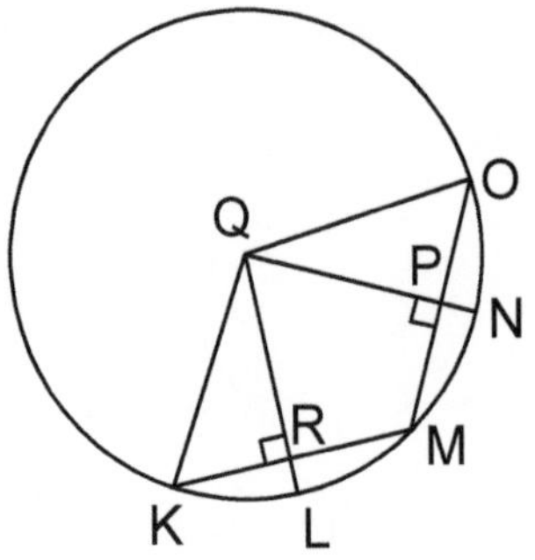

11. m$\overset{\frown}{KL}$ = _______

Is this arc a *minor arc*, a *major arc*, or a *semicircle*?

____

12. m$\overset{\frown}{KM}$ = _______

Is this arc a *minor arc*, a *major arc*, or a *semicircle*? _____________

13. m$\overset{\frown}{OM}$ = _______

Is this arc a *minor arc*, a *major arc*, or a *semicircle*? _____________

14. m$\overset{\frown}{MN}$ = _______

Is this arc a *minor arc*, a *major arc*, or a *semicircle*? _____________

15. m$\overset{\frown}{LOK}$ = _______

Is this arc a *minor arc*, a *major arc*, or a *semicircle*? _____________

16. m$\overset{\frown}{MKO}$ = _______

Is this arc a *minor arc*, a *major arc*, or a *semicircle*? _____________

17. In ⊙W at the right, SW = 17 and TW = 8. Then TV = _______, UT = _______, and UV = _______.

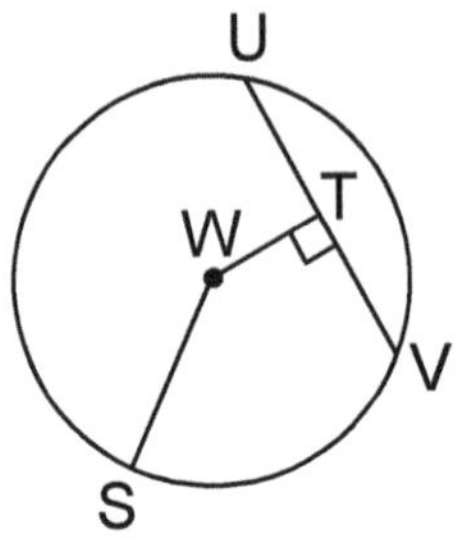

18. In ⊙E at the right, m∠GEY = 30° and NG = 22. Then YN = _______, EY = _______, and AG = _______.

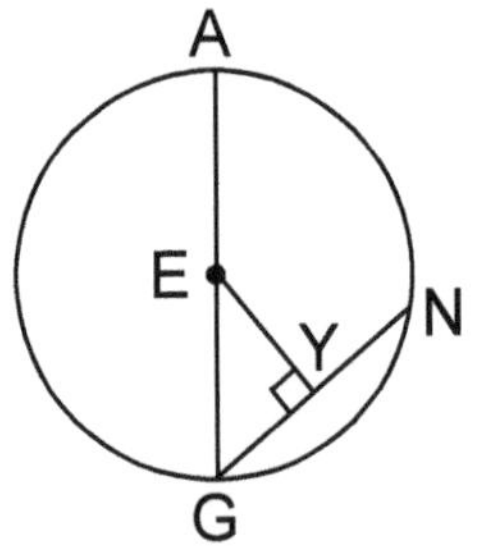

19. In $\odot H$ at the right, $m\angle LHQ = 70°$ and $\overline{MO} \cong \overline{LQ}$. Then $m\angle HLQ =$ _______, $m\angle OMH =$ _______, and $m\widehat{MO} =$ _______.

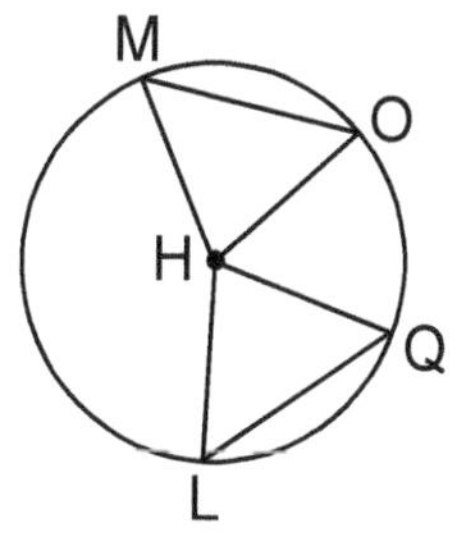

20. In $\odot B$ at the right, RJ = 50 and BG = 15. Then ZG = _______, GC = _______, and ZC = _______.

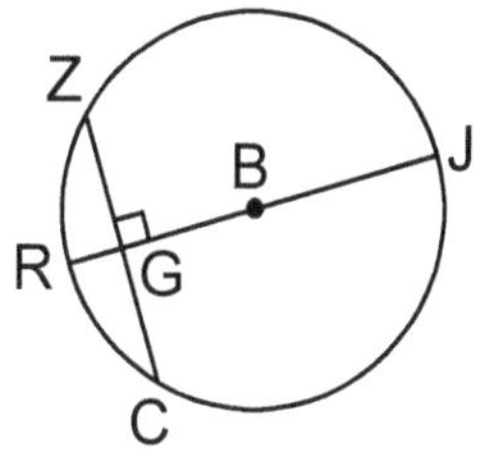

21-24. For each figure below, (a) decide if you can conclude that $\widehat{AB} \cong \widehat{CD}$, and (b) if your answer to part (a) was *yes*, state the definitions, postulates, and/or theorems you used.

21a. In $\odot T$ and $\odot U$ at the right, $\overline{TA} \cong \overline{UC}$. Can you conclude that $\widehat{AB} \cong \widehat{CD}$? __________

b. If your answer to (a) was *yes*, what definitions, theorems, and/or postulates did you use? ____________________

____

____

____

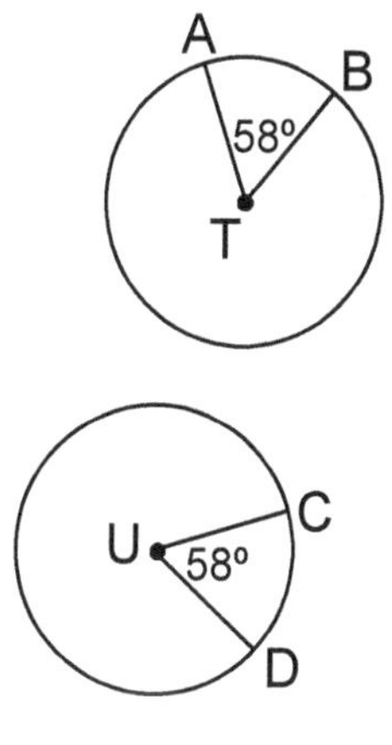

22a. In $\odot S$ at the right, $\overline{DY} \cong \overline{AB}$. Can you conclude that $\widehat{AB} \cong \widehat{CD}$? __________

b. If your answer to (a) was *yes*, what definitions, theorems, and/or postulates did you use? ____________________

____

____

____

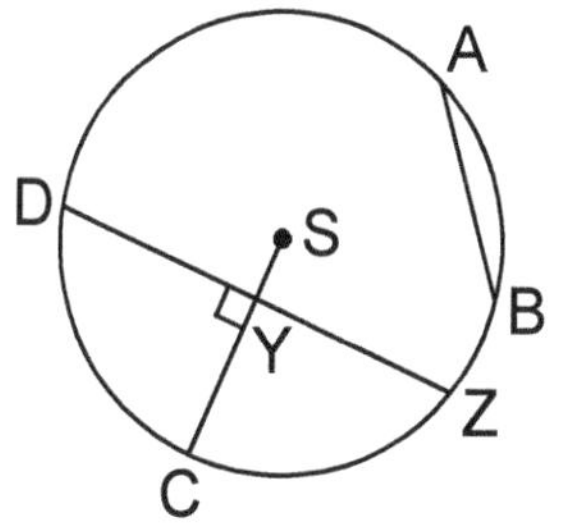

23a. In ⊙K and ⊙N at the right, $\overline{AB} \cong \overline{CD}$, KA = 9, and ND = 10. Can you conclude that $\overset{\frown}{AB} \cong \overset{\frown}{CD}$? ___________

b. If your answer to (a) was *yes*, what definitions, theorems, and/or postulates did you use? ____________________

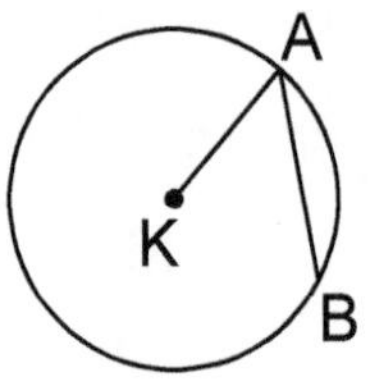

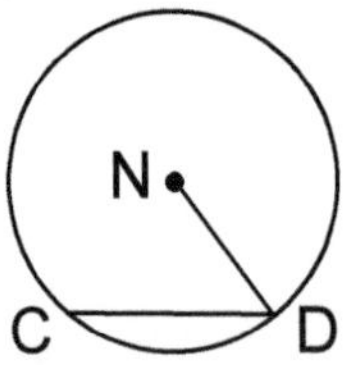

24a. In ⊙V at the right, $\overline{WV} \cong \overline{VX}$. Can you conclude that $\overset{\frown}{AB} \cong \overset{\frown}{CD}$? ___________

b. If your answer to (a) was *yes*, what definitions, theorems, and/or postulates did you use? ____________________

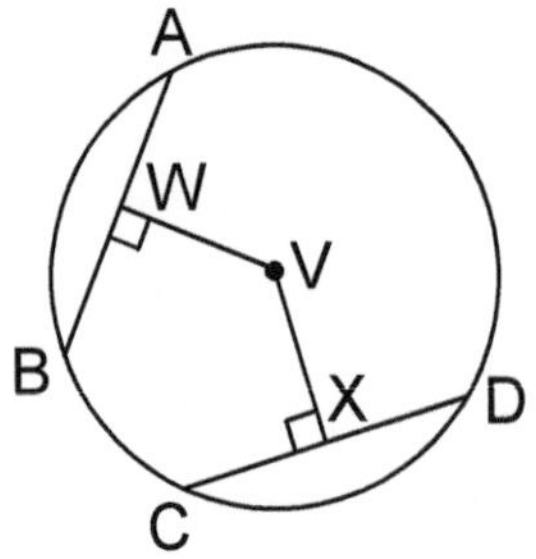

25-27. For each figure below, (a) decide if you can conclude that $\overline{PQ} \cong \overline{QR}$, and (b) if your answer to part (a) was *yes*, state the definitions, postulates, and/or theorems you used.

25a. In ⊙L at the right, $\overline{LP}$, $\overline{LQ}$, and $\overline{LR}$ are all congruent to each other. Can you conclude that $\overline{PQ} \cong \overline{QR}$?

____

b. If your answer to (a) was *yes*, what definitions, theorems, and/or postulates did you use? ____________________

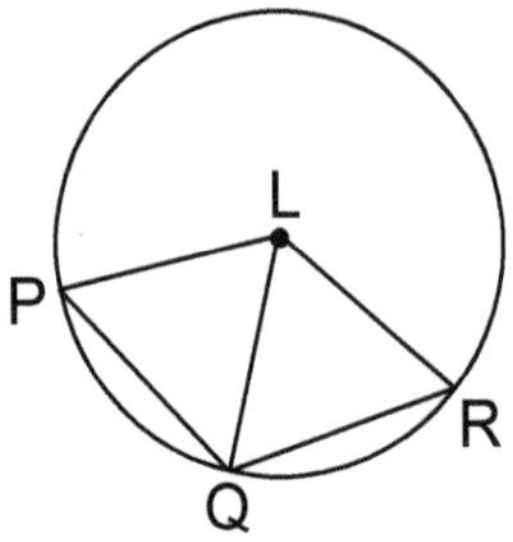

26a. In $\odot M$ at the right, can you conclude that $\overline{PQ} \cong \overline{QR}$?

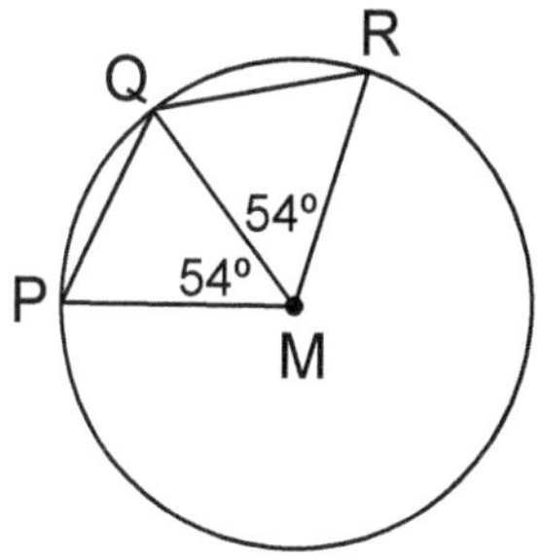

____

b. If your answer to (a) was *yes*, what definitions, theorems, and/or postulates did you use? ____________________

____

____

____

27a. In $\odot E$ at the right, can you conclude that $\overline{PQ} \cong \overline{QR}$?

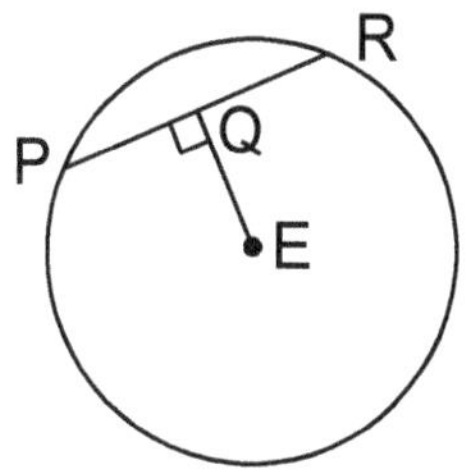

____

b. If your answer to (a) was *yes*, what definitions, theorems, and/or postulates did you use? ____________________

____

____

____

28. Prove that, in a circle, if two chords are congruent, then their corresponding arcs are congruent. (The proof of the statement *In congruent circles, if two chords are congruent, then their corresponding arcs are congruent* is very similar.)

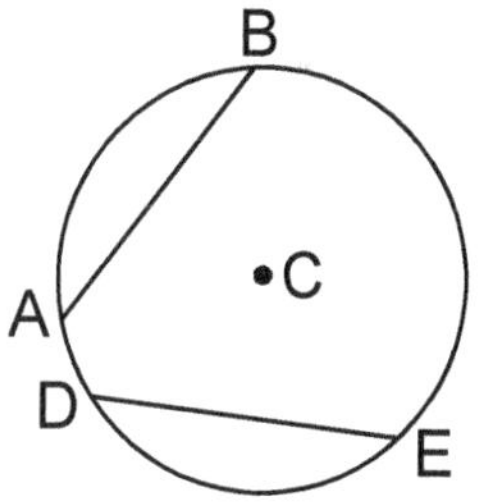

Given: In $\odot C$, $\overline{AB} \cong \overline{DE}$

Prove: $\overset{\frown}{AB} \cong \overset{\frown}{DE}$

Hint: Start by using the postulate *Through any two points there is exactly one line* to draw $\overline{AC}$, $\overline{BC}$, $\overline{DC}$, and $\overline{EC}$.

29. Prove that, in a circle, if two arcs are congruent, then their corresponding chords are congruent.

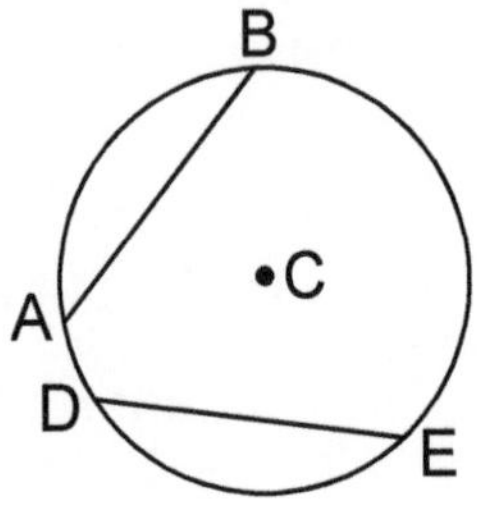

Given: In $\odot C$, $\overset{\frown}{AB} \cong \overset{\frown}{DE}$

Prove: $\overline{AB} \cong \overline{DE}$

30. Prove that, if a radius of a circle is perpendicular to a chord of the circle, then it bisects the chord and its arc.

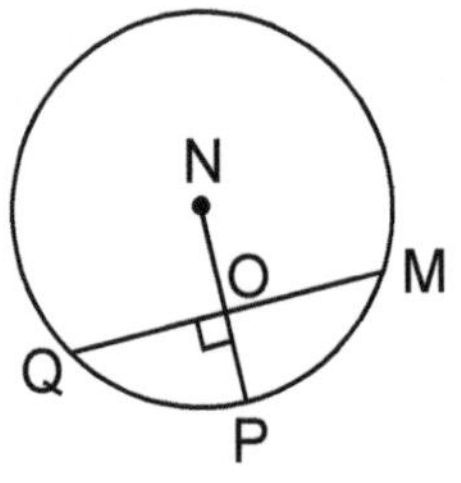

Given: In $\odot N$, $\overline{NP} \perp \overline{QM}$

Prove: $\overline{NP}$ bisects $\overline{QM}$ and $\overset{\frown}{QM}$

31. Prove that, in a circle, if two chords are congruent, then they are equidistant from the center.

Given: In ⊙U, $\overline{RS} \cong \overline{WX}$, $\overline{RS} \perp \overline{TU}$, and $\overline{WX} \perp \overline{UV}$

Prove: $\overline{UT} \cong \overline{UV}$

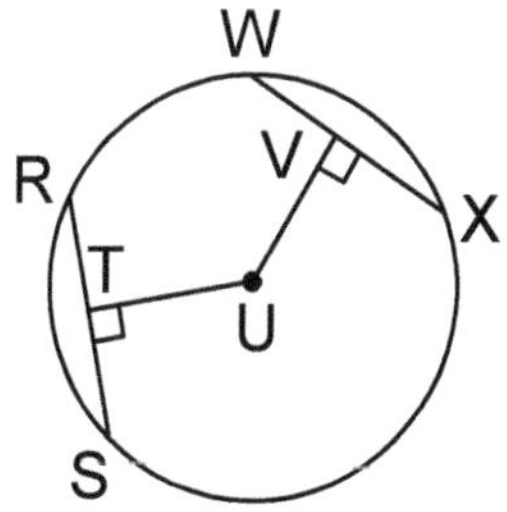

32. Prove that, in a circle, if two chords are equidistant from the center, then they are congruent.

Given: In ⊙U, $\overline{UT} \cong \overline{UV}$, $\overline{RS} \perp \overline{TU}$, and $\overline{WX} \perp \overline{UV}$

Prove: $\overline{RS} \cong \overline{XW}$

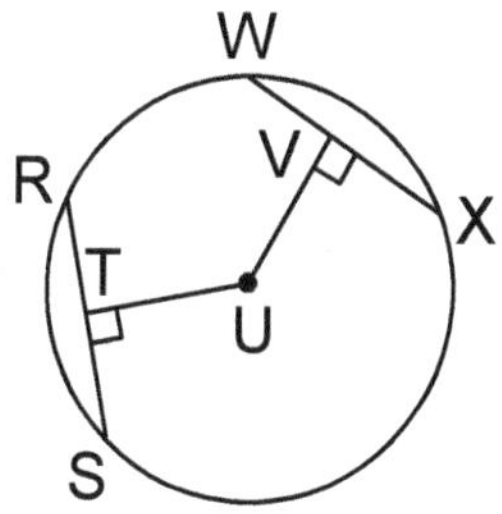

Part III – Inscribed Angles

We will begin this section with two definitions.

> In a circle, an angle is called an <u>inscribed angle</u> if and only if its vertex is on the circle and both of its sides pass through the interior of the circle.

> A polygon is <u>inscribed</u> in a circle if and only if all of its angles are inscribed angles of the circle.

For example, in the figures below, we can say that $\angle ABC$ is inscribed in $\odot D$ because its vertex is on the circle and both of its sides are secants that pass through the interior of the circle. We can also say that quadrilateral ENSR is inscribed in $\odot Q$ because all of its angles are inscribed angles of $\odot Q$.

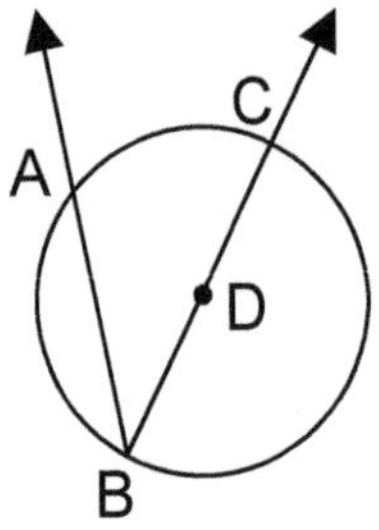

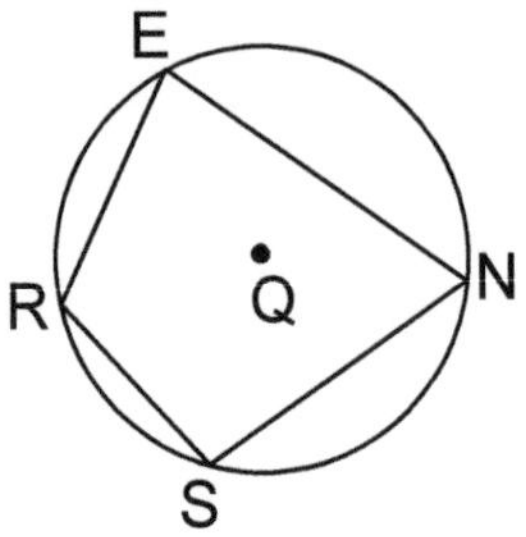

Now, we need a theorem. You will prove this theorem in the exercises for this section.

> **Measure of an Inscribed Angle Theorem**
>
> In a circle, the measure of an inscribed angle is equal to half the measure of the intercepted arc.

Now, look back at the pictures above. This theorem tells us that $m\angle ABC = \frac{1}{2}m\overset{\frown}{AC}$, $m\angle R = \frac{1}{2}m\overset{\frown}{SNE}$, $m\angle S = \frac{1}{2}m\overset{\frown}{REN}$, $m\angle N = \frac{1}{2}m\overset{\frown}{ES}$, and $m\angle E = \frac{1}{2}m\overset{\frown}{RN}$.

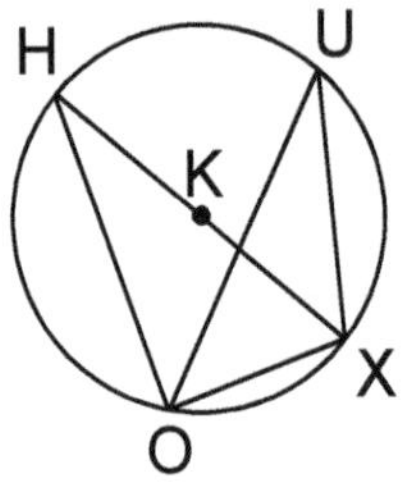

Example 1: In $\odot K$ at the right, $m\overset{\frown}{UX} = 87°$ and $m\angle OUX = 27°$. Find (a) $m\angle OHX$, (b) $m\angle XOH$, (c) $m\overset{\frown}{OH}$, (d) $m\overset{\frown}{OX}$, (e) $m\overset{\frown}{OU}$, (f) $m\angle HOU$, and (g) $m\overset{\frown}{OHU}$.

(a) We will begin by noting that the Measure of an Inscribed Angle Theorem tells us $m\angle OUX = \frac{1}{2}m\overset{\frown}{OX}$. Since we know that $m\angle OUX = 27°$, we can say that $27° = \frac{1}{2}m\overset{\frown}{OX}$. When we divide both sides of this equation by $\frac{1}{2}$ (or, equivalently, multiply both sides by 2), we find that $m\overset{\frown}{OX} = 54°$. Now, since $m\angle OHX = \frac{1}{2}m\overset{\frown}{OX}$, this tells us that $m\angle OHX = 27°$.

(b) The Measure of an Inscribed Angle Theorem tells us that $m\angle XOH = \frac{1}{2} m\overset{\frown}{HUX}$.

Since the question said that K is the center of the circle, we can say that $\overline{HX}$ must be a diameter of the circle. Therefore, $\overset{\frown}{HUX}$ is a semicircle with a measure of 180°, and so $\angle XOH$ must have a measure of 90°.

(c) Note that $\overset{\frown}{HOX}$ is a semicircle with a measure of 180°. This tells us that $m\overset{\frown}{OH} + m\overset{\frown}{OX} = 180°$. Since we said in part (a) that $m\overset{\frown}{OX} = 54°$, we can conclude that $m\overset{\frown}{OH} = 126°$.

(d) As we said in part (a), $m\overset{\frown}{OX} = 54°$.

(e) Note that $m\overset{\frown}{OU} = m\overset{\frown}{OX} + m\overset{\frown}{UX}$. Since we were given that $m\overset{\frown}{UX} = 87°$, and since we said in part (a) that $m\overset{\frown}{OX} = 54°$, this means that $m\overset{\frown}{OU} = 87° + 54°$, or 141°.

(f) One way of finding $m\angle HOU$ is to start by noting that $m\overset{\frown}{UH} + m\overset{\frown}{UX} = 180°$. Since we were given that $m\overset{\frown}{UX} = 87°$, we can say that $m\overset{\frown}{UH} = 93°$. Now, since $m\angle HOU = \frac{1}{2} m\overset{\frown}{UH}$, we can say that $m\angle HOU = \frac{1}{2} \cdot 93°$, or 46.5°.

(g) The easiest way to solve this part of this problem is to note that $m\overset{\frown}{OHU} = 360° - m\overset{\frown}{OU}$, and so we can say that $m\overset{\frown}{OHU} = 219°$. (We could also have found this answer by using the fact that $m\overset{\frown}{OHU} = m\overset{\frown}{OH} + m\overset{\frown}{UH}$. Since we said in part (f) that $m\overset{\frown}{UH} = 93°$, and since we said in part (c) that $m\overset{\frown}{OH} = 126°$, we can conclude that $m\overset{\frown}{OHU} = 126° + 93°$, or 219°.)

The thought process behind parts (a) and (b) of this example give rise to the following theorems. You will prove them in the exercises for this section.

> In a circle or in congruent circles, if two inscribed angles intercept the same arc or congruent arcs, then the inscribed angles are congruent to each other.

> If an angle is inscribed in a semicircle, then it is a right angle.

To understand what these theorems tell us, look back at parts (a) and (b) of Example 1. The theorem *In a circle or in congruent circles, if two inscribed angles intercept the same arc or congruent arcs, then the inscribed angles are congruent to each other* tells us that, since $\angle OHX$ and $\angle OUX$ intercept the same arc, we know that $\angle OHX$ must be congruent to $\angle OUX$. (Note that this agrees with what we found earlier.) The theorem *If an angle is inscribed in a semicircle, then it is a right angle* tells us that, since $\angle XOH$ is inscribed in a semicircle, we can conclude that $\angle XOH$ is a right angle. (Note that this also agrees with what we found earlier.)

Example 2: In $\odot J$ at the right, $m\overset{\frown}{TP} = (10w + 24)^\circ$, $m\angle TMP = 7w^\circ$, $m\overset{\frown}{PM} = (50 - x)^\circ$, $m\angle PGM = (2x + 75)^\circ$, $m\angle MTG = (2y + 3)^\circ$, and $m\angle GPM = (4y - 17)^\circ$. Find $m\overset{\frown}{GT}$.

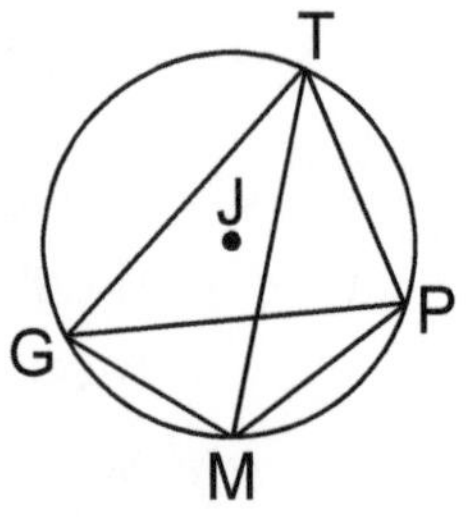

We will solve this problem by finding $m\overset{\frown}{TP}$, $m\overset{\frown}{PM}$, and $m\overset{\frown}{GM}$, and then we will use the fact that the arc measure of an entire circle is 360°.

To find $m\overset{\frown}{TP}$, we must first find the value of w. To do this, we will note that $\frac{1}{2}m\overset{\frown}{TP} = m\angle TMP$. This tells us that w = 6, as shown below.

$$\frac{1}{2}m\overset{\frown}{TP} = m\angle TMP$$
$$\frac{1}{2}(10w + 24) = 7w$$
$$5w + 12 = 7w$$
$$12 = 2w$$
$$6 = w$$

Now, since we were told that $m\overset{\frown}{TP} = (10w + 24)^\circ$, we can say that $m\overset{\frown}{TP} = 84^\circ$.

To find $m\overset{\frown}{PM}$, we must first find the value of x. To do this, we will note that $\frac{1}{2}m\overset{\frown}{PM} = m\angle PGM$. This tells us that x = –20, as shown below.

$$\frac{1}{2}m\overset{\frown}{PM} = m\angle PGM$$
$$\frac{1}{2}(50 - x) = 2x + 75$$
$$25 - \frac{1}{2}x = 2x + 75$$

$-\frac{5}{2}x = 50$ Subtract 25 and 2x from both sides.

$x = -20$ Divide both sides by $-\frac{5}{2}$. (Note that $50 \div -\frac{5}{2} = 50 \cdot -\frac{2}{5}$, or –20.)

Now, since we were told that $m\overset{\frown}{PM} = (50 - x)^\circ$, we can say that $m\overset{\frown}{PM} = 70^\circ$.

To find $m\overset{\frown}{GM}$, we must first find the value of y. To do this, we will note that $\angle MTG$ and $\angle GPM$ correspond to the same arc. Thus, we can use the theorem *In a circle or in congruent circles, if two inscribed angles intercept the same arc or congruent arcs, then the inscribed angles are congruent to each other* to say that y = 10, as shown below.

$$m\angle MTG = m\angle GPM$$
$$2y + 3 = 4y - 17$$

$20 = 2y$ Subtract 2y from both sides and add 17 to both sides.

$10 = y$ Divide both sides by 2.

Now, since we were told that $m\angle MTG = (2y + 3)°$, we can say $m\angle MTG = 23°$. The Measure of an Inscribed Angle Theorem tells us that $m\angle MTG = \frac{1}{2} m\overset{\frown}{GM}$, and so $m\overset{\frown}{GM}$ must equal $2 \cdot 23°$, or $46°$.

Finally, since $m\overset{\frown}{TP} + m\overset{\frown}{PM} + m\overset{\frown}{GM} + m\overset{\frown}{GT} = 360°$, $m\overset{\frown}{GT}$ must equal $160°$.

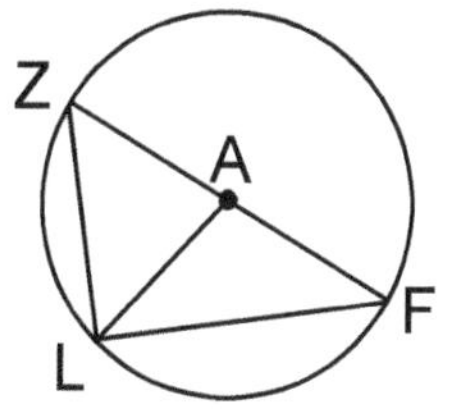

Example 3: In ⊙A at the right, $m\overset{\frown}{LZ} = 81°$. Find (a) $m\angle LAF$, (b) $m\angle Z$, (c) $m\angle ZLF$, and (d) $m\angle ZLA$.

For each part of this question, we will only discuss one of the methods we can use to find the measure of the angle, but there are many other ways you could find each of these angle measures.

(a) We will begin by noting that, since $\angle ZAL$ is a central angle that corresponds to $\overset{\frown}{LZ}$, we can say that $m\angle ZAL = 81°$. Next, since $\angle ZAL$ and $\angle LAF$ form a linear pair, we can conclude that $m\angle LAF = 99°$.

(b) Note that $m\overset{\frown}{LZ} + m\overset{\frown}{LF} = 180°$, and so we can say that $m\overset{\frown}{LF} = 99°$. The Measure of an Inscribed Angle Theorem tells us that $m\angle Z = \frac{1}{2} m\overset{\frown}{LF}$, and so $\angle Z$ must have a measure of $49.5°$.

(c) Since $\angle ZLF$ is inscribed in a semicircle, we can use the theorem *If an angle is inscribed in a semicircle, then it is a right angle* to say that $m\angle ZLF = 90°$.

(d) Since all radii of a circle are congruent, we can say that $\overline{ZA} \cong \overline{LA}$. This tells us that we can use the Isosceles Triangle Theorem to say that $\angle Z \cong \angle ZLA$. Since we said in part (b) that $m\angle Z = 49.5°$, $m\angle ZLA$ must also equal $49.5°$.

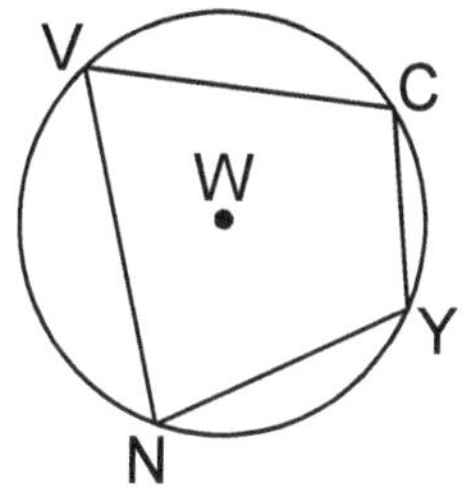

Example 4: In ⊙W at the right, $m\angle V = 75°$, $m\overset{\frown}{VYN} = 247°$, and $m\overset{\frown}{CY} = 46°$. Find (a) $m\angle Y$, (b) $m\angle N$, and (c) $m\angle C$.

(a) Since we were told that $m\angle V = 75°$, we can use the Measure of an Inscribed Angle Theorem to say that $m\overset{\frown}{CN} = 2 \cdot 75°$, or $150°$. Since the arc measure of an entire circle is $360°$, we can say that $m\overset{\frown}{CVN} = 360° - 150°$, or $210°$. The Measure of an Inscribed Angle Theorem tells us that $m\angle Y = \frac{1}{2} m\overset{\frown}{CVN}$, and so we can say that $m\angle Y = \frac{1}{2} \cdot 210°$, or $105°$.

(b) We were given that $m\overset{\frown}{VYN} = 247°$, and we said in part (a) that $m\overset{\frown}{CN} = 150°$. Thus, we can use the Arc Addition Postulate to say that $m\overset{\frown}{VC} = 247° - 150°$, or $97°$. The Arc Addition Postulate also tells us that $m\overset{\frown}{VY} = m\overset{\frown}{VC} + m\overset{\frown}{CY}$, and so, since we were given that $m\overset{\frown}{CY} = 46°$, we can now say that $m\overset{\frown}{VY}$

must equal 97° + 46°, or 143°. The Measure of an Inscribed Angle Theorem tells us that $m\angle N = \frac{1}{2}m\overset{\frown}{VY}$, and so $m\angle N$ must equal $\frac{1}{2} \cdot 143°$, or 71.5°.

(c) Since we said in part (b) that $m\overset{\frown}{VY} = 143°$, we can use the fact that the arc measure of an entire circle is equal to 360° to say that $m\overset{\frown}{VNY} = 360° - 143°$, or 217°. The Measure of an Inscribed Angle Theorem tells us that $m\angle C = \frac{1}{2}m\overset{\frown}{VNY}$, and so $m\angle C$ must equal $\frac{1}{2} \cdot 217°$, or 108.5°.

The thought process behind parts (a) and (c) of this example gives rise to the following theorem, which you will prove in the exercises for this section.

If a quadrilateral is inscribed in a circle, then its opposite angles are supplementary.

To understand what this theorem tells us, look back at the picture from Example 4. This theorem tells us that, since quadrilateral VCYN is inscribed in ⊙W, we can say that ∠V and ∠Y are supplementary to each other and that ∠C and ∠N are supplementary to each other. (Notice that this agrees with the answers we found for this example.)

Problems:

1-7. In ⊙E at the right, m∠ABD = 58°.

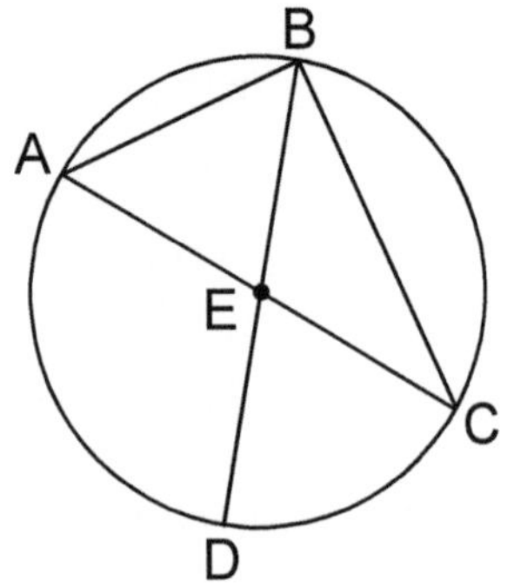

1. $m\overset{\frown}{AD}$ = _________ and $m\overset{\frown}{DC}$ = _________

2. m∠DBC = _________ and m∠ACB = _________

3. m∠AED = _________ and m∠CED = _________

4. $m\overset{\frown}{AB}$ = _________ and $m\overset{\frown}{BC}$ = _________

5. m∠ABC = _________ and m∠CAB = _________

6. m∠AEB = _________ and m∠BEC = _________

7. $m\overset{\frown}{ADC}$ = _________ and $m\overset{\frown}{ACD}$ = _________

8-13. In ⊙U at the right, $m\angle QTR = 34^\circ$, $m\angle RTS = 28^\circ$, and $m\overparen{QST} = 219^\circ$.

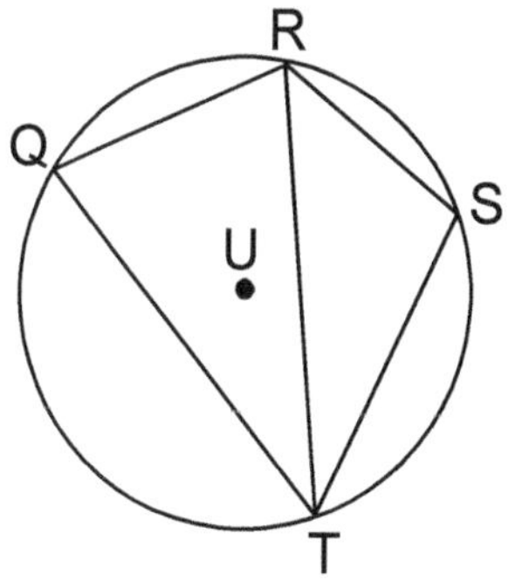

8. $m\overparen{QR}$ = _________ and $m\overparen{RS}$ = _________

9. $m\overparen{ST}$ = _________ and $m\overparen{QT}$ = _________

10. $m\angle QRT$ = _________ and $m\angle TRS$ = _________

11. $m\angle QRS$ = _________ and $m\angle QTS$ = _________

12. $m\angle S$ = _________ and $m\angle Q$ = _________

13. $m\overparen{TQS}$ = _________ and $m\overparen{QTS}$ = _________

14-19. In ⊙P at the right, $m\angle LMO = (4w + 17)^\circ$, $m\angle LNO = 6w^\circ$, $m\angle MLO = (8x + 2)^\circ$, $m\angle ONM = (11x + 7)^\circ$, $m\angle LMN = (4y - 33)^\circ$, and $m\overparen{LON} = (5y + 36)^\circ$.

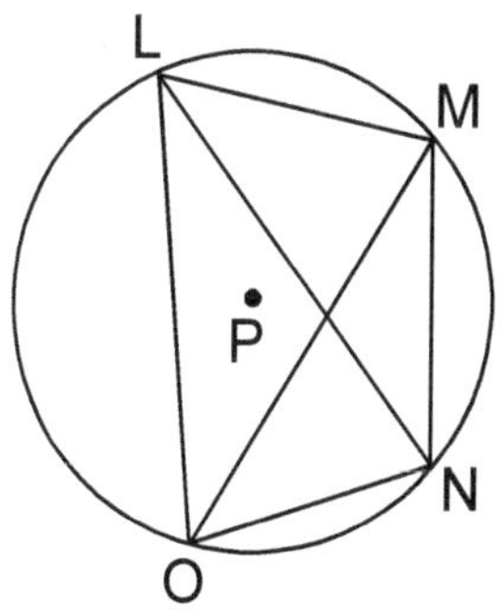

14. w = _________

15. x = _________

16. y = _________

17. $m\angle MLO$ = _________ and $m\angle ONM$ = _________

18. $m\angle LMO$ = _________ and $m\angle LNO$ = _________

19. $m\overparen{MLO}$ = _________, $m\overparen{LO}$ = _________, and $m\overparen{ML}$ = _________

20. Prove the Measure of an Inscribed Angle Theorem.

(We will assume here that the inscribed angle is an acute angle, and will therefore intercept a minor arc. If it isn't, then the proof is very similar; only the notation that we use to represent the arcs will change.)

Given: $\angle ABC$ is inscribed in $\odot D$

Prove: $m\angle ABC = \frac{1}{2} m\overset{\frown}{AC}$

We are given that $\angle ABC$ is inscribed in $\odot D$. There are three possible ways that this can happen: one of the sides of $\angle ABC$ is a diameter of $\odot D$, the center D is in the interior of $\angle ABC$, or the center D is in the exterior of $\angle ABC$.

Case 1: One of the sides of $\angle ABC$ is a diameter of $\odot D$. (We will assume that it is $\overline{AB}$; if it is $\overline{BC}$ instead, then the proof is very similar.)

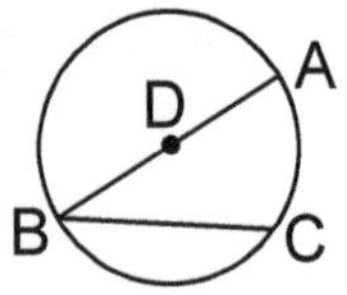

We will use the postulate ______________________________

to draw $\overline{DC}$, as shown in the figure below.

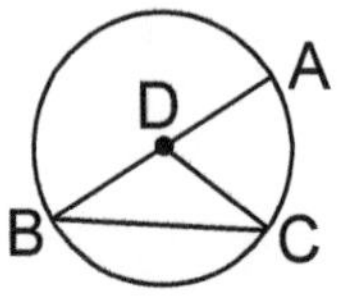

The ______________ Theorem tells us that $m\angle ADC = m\angle B + m\angle C$.

By the definition of a circle, $\overline{BD} \cong \overline{CD}$. Therefore, we can use the ________ ________________ to say that $\angle B \cong \angle C$. The definition congruent angles tells us that ____________. By the ________________ ____________, we can now say that ________________.

Next, we will use the Distributive Property to say that $m\angle ADC = 2(m\angle B)$. By the ____________________, we can now say that $\frac{1}{2} m\angle ADC = m\angle B$.

The definition of the measure of an arc tells us that $m\angle ADC = m\overset{\frown}{AC}$, and so we can use the ____________________ to say that $\frac{1}{2} m\overset{\frown}{AC} = m\angle B$.

Case 2: The center D is in the interior of $\angle ABC$.

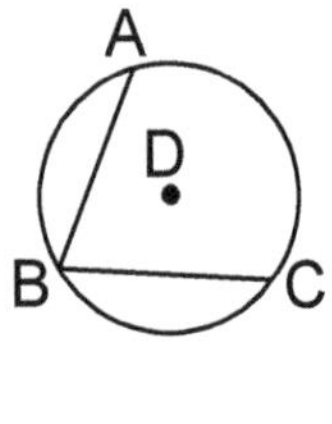

We will use the postulate ____________________ __________ to draw $\overrightarrow{BD}$, as shown in the figure on the next page. Also, we will call the point where $\overrightarrow{BD}$ intersects $\odot D$ point E.

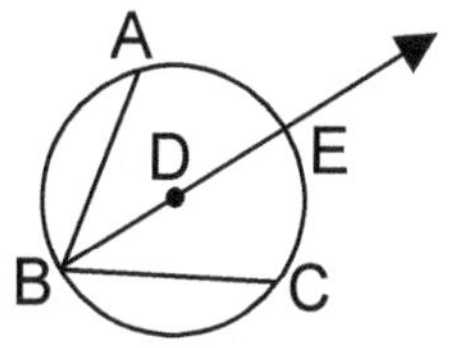

We can use the ______________________________ to say that $m\angle ABC = m\angle ABE + m\angle EBC$. Using what we proved in Case 1, we can say that $m\angle ABE = \frac{1}{2}m\overset{\frown}{AE}$ and $m\angle EBC = \frac{1}{2}m\overset{\frown}{EC}$. By the ______________________________, we can say that $m\angle ABC = \frac{1}{2}m\overset{\frown}{AE} + \frac{1}{2}m\overset{\frown}{EC}$.

Next, we will use the Distributive Property to say that $m\angle ABC = \frac{1}{2}(m\overset{\frown}{AE} + m\overset{\frown}{EC})$.

The ______________________________ tells us that $m\overset{\frown}{AC} = m\overset{\frown}{AE} + m\overset{\frown}{EC}$.

By the ______________________________, we can now conclude that ____________________.

Case 3: The center D is in the exterior of $\angle ABC$.

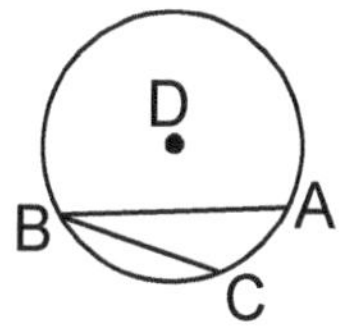

We will use the postulate ______________________________ to draw $\overrightarrow{BD}$, as shown in the figure below. Also, we will call the point where $\overrightarrow{BD}$ intersects $\odot D$ point E.

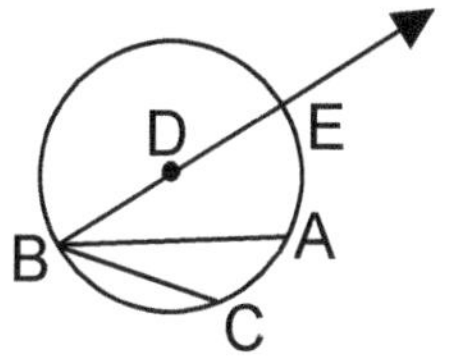

We can use the ______________________________ to say that $m\angle EBA + m\angle ABC = m\angle EBC$. Then, by the ______________________________, $m\angle ABC = m\angle EBC - m\angle EBA$. Using what we proved in Case 1, we can say that $m\angle EBC = \frac{1}{2}m\overset{\frown}{EC}$ and $m\angle EBA = \frac{1}{2}m\overset{\frown}{EA}$.

By the ______________________________, we can now say that $m\angle ABC = \frac{1}{2}m\overset{\frown}{EC} - \frac{1}{2}m\overset{\frown}{EA}$. Then $m\angle ABC = \frac{1}{2}(m\overset{\frown}{EC} - m\overset{\frown}{EA})$ by the ______________________________. The ______________________________ tells us that $m\overset{\frown}{EA} + m\overset{\frown}{AC} = m\overset{\frown}{EC}$. By the ______________________________, we can say that $m\overset{\frown}{AC} = m\overset{\frown}{EC} - m\overset{\frown}{EA}$. Using the ______________________________, we can now conclude that ____________________.

21. Prove that, in a circle, if two inscribed angles intercept the same arc, then the inscribed angles are congruent to each other. (The proof of the statement *In congruent circles, if two inscribed angles intercept the same arc, then the inscribed angles are congruent to each other* is very similar.)

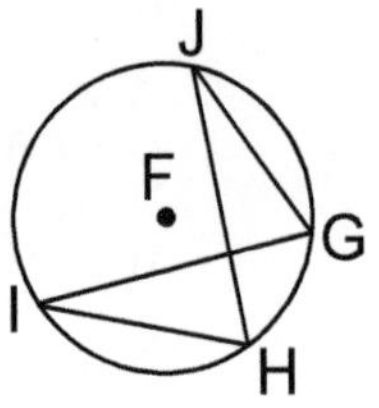

Given: In $\odot F$, $\angle HJG$ and $\angle GIH$ intercept the same arc

Prove: $\angle HJG \cong \angle GIH$

22. Prove that, in a circle, if two inscribed angles intercept congruent arcs, then the inscribed angles are congruent to each other. (The proof of the statement *In congruent circles, if two inscribed angles intercept congruent arcs, then the inscribed angles are congruent to each other* is very similar.)

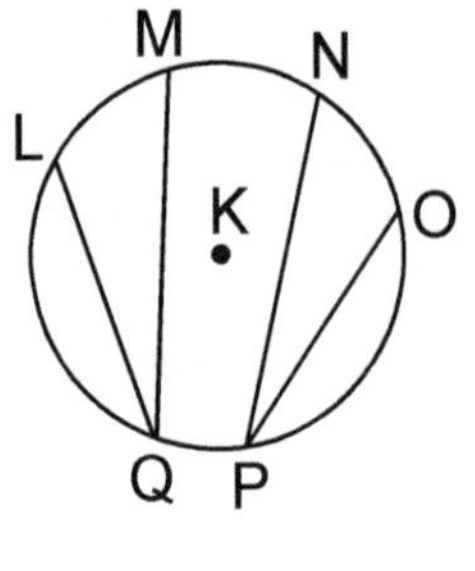

Given: In $\odot F$, $\overset{\frown}{ML} \cong \overset{\frown}{NO}$

Prove: ______________________________

23. Prove that, if an angle is inscribed in a semicircle, then it is a right angle.

Given: $\angle RST$ is inscribed in the semicircle $\overset{\frown}{RVT}$

Prove: $\angle RST$ is a right angle

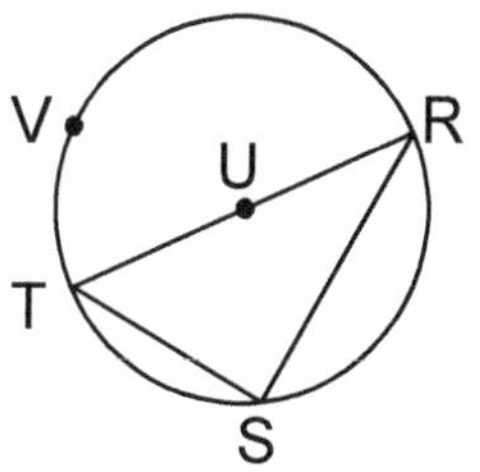

24. Prove that, if a quadrilateral is inscribed in a circle, then its opposite angles are supplementary.

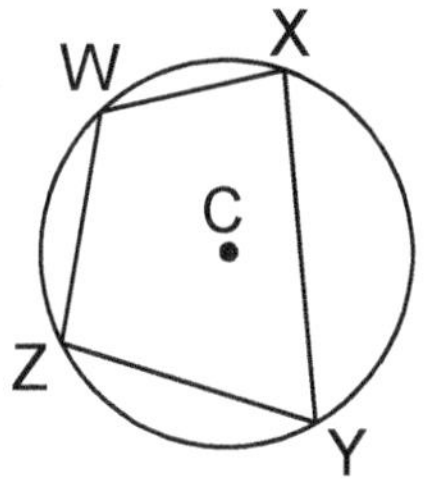

Given: ____

Prove: $\angle W$ is supplementary to $\angle Y$

(The proof that $\angle X$ is supplementary to $\angle Z$ is very similar.)

We are given that ____________________________________. The ______________________ Postulate and the theorem *The arc measure of an entire circle is 360°* tell us that $m\overset{\frown}{XYZ} + m\overset{\frown}{XZ} = 360°$. The Measure of an Inscribed Angle Theorem tells us that $m\angle W =$ ___________ and that $m\angle Y =$ ___________. When we use the Addition Property of Equality to add these two equation together, we find that $m\angle W + m\angle Y = \frac{1}{2}m\overset{\frown}{XYZ} + \frac{1}{2}m\overset{\frown}{XZ}$. The ____________________ Property tells us that $m\angle W + m\angle Y = \frac{1}{2}(m\overset{\frown}{XYZ} + m\overset{\frown}{XZ})$, and so now we can use the Substitution Property of Equality to say that $m\angle W + m\angle Y = \frac{1}{2}(360°)$, or $m\angle W + m\angle Y = 180°$. Then, by the ______________________________________, $\angle W$ and $\angle Y$ must be supplementary.

25-30. Fill in each of the following blanks with *must be*, *might be*, or *cannot be*.

25. In ⊙Z at the right, $\overline{QY} \parallel \overline{NS}$. Then $\overset{\frown}{QN}$ ____________ ______ congruent to $\overset{\frown}{SY}$, and $\overset{\frown}{QS}$ __________________ congruent to $\overset{\frown}{NY}$.

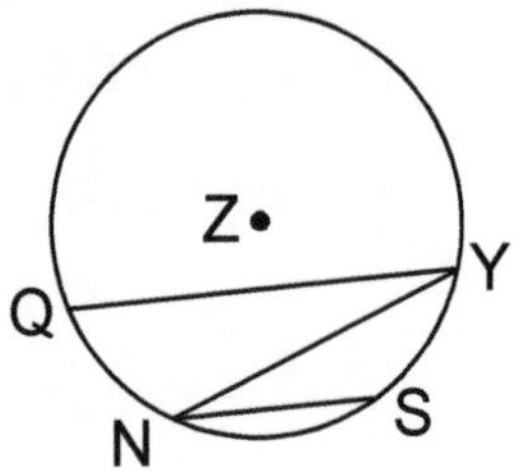

26. In a circle, if a central angle and an inscribed angle intercept the same arc, then the angles ________________ congruent to each other.

27. If a hexagon is inscribed in a circle, then it ________________ a regular hexagon.

28. If a trapezoid is inscribed in a circle, then it ________________ an isosceles trapezoid.

29. If a parallelogram is inscribed in a circle, then it ________________ a rectangle.

30. In the ⊙G and ⊙J at the right, FG = 12, MJ = 11, and $\angle FIH \cong \angle KML$. Then $\overset{\frown}{FH}$ ________________ congruent to $\overset{\frown}{KL}$.

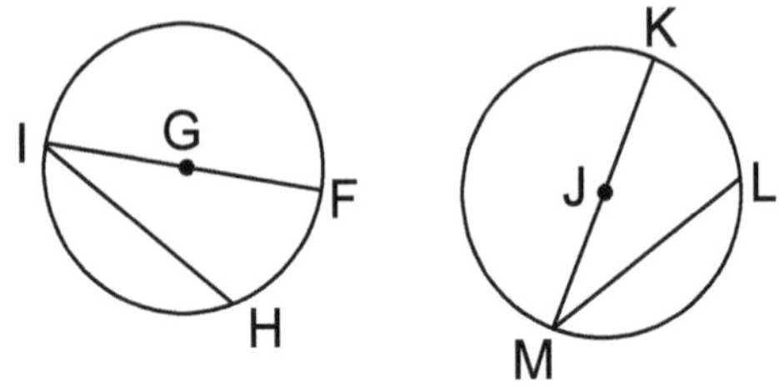

Part IV – More on Measures of Arcs

We will begin this section with two theorems. We will prove these theorems in Examples 1 and 2.

If a line is tangent to a circle, then it is perpendicular to the radius drawn to the point of tangency.

If a line is perpendicular to a radius of a circle at the endpoint on the circle, then the line is tangent to the circle.

To explain what these theorems tell us, we will use the picture below.

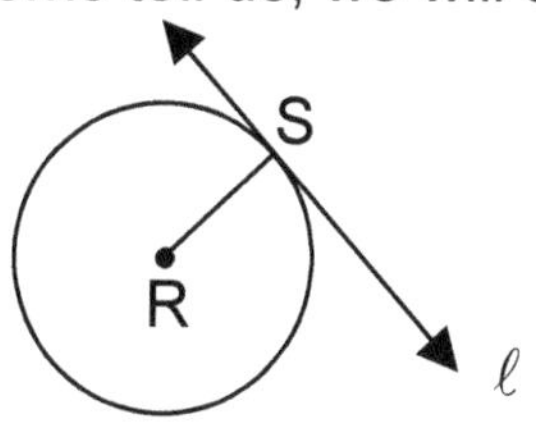

The theorem *If a line is tangent to a circle, then it is perpendicular to the radius drawn to the point of tangency* tells us that, if we know that ℓ is tangent to $\odot$R at the point S, then we can conclude that $\overline{RS} \perp \ell$.

The theorem *If a line is perpendicular to a radius of a circle at the endpoint on the circle, then the line is tangent to the circle* tells us that, if we know that the radius $\overline{RS}$ is perpendicular to ℓ at the point S, then we can conclude that ℓ is tangent to $\odot$R at the point S.

Example 1: Prove that, if a line is tangent to a circle, then it is perpendicular to the radius drawn to the point of tangency.

As usual, we will start by drawing a generic picture to describe the part of this theorem that follows the "if".

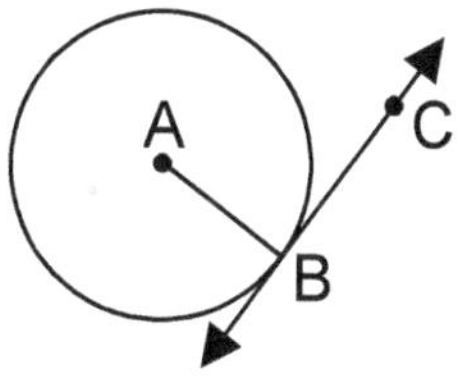

Now, we can say that we are given that $\overleftrightarrow{BC}$ is tangent to $\odot$A at the point B, and we want to prove that $\overline{AB} \perp \overleftrightarrow{BC}$.

We will prove this theorem indirectly, and so we will assume that $\overline{AB}$ is not perpendicular to $\overleftrightarrow{BC}$. Next, we will use the theorem *Through a point P not on a line, there is exactly one line perpendicular to the given line* to draw a line through A that is perpendicular to $\overleftrightarrow{BC}$, and we will call the point where this line intersects $\overleftrightarrow{BC}$ point D. You proved in Chapter 5 that, given a line and a point not on the line, the shortest segment from the point to the line is the perpendicular segment, and so $\overline{AD}$ must be the shortest segment between the point A and $\overleftrightarrow{BC}$.

However, by the definition of a line tangent to a circle, the point D must lie outside the circle, and therefore $\overline{AD}$ must be longer than the radius $\overline{AB}$. Thus, we have a contradiction, and so our assumption must be false. $\overline{AB}$ must be perpendicular to $\overleftrightarrow{BC}$.

Example 2: Use an indirect proof to prove that, if a line is perpendicular to a radius of a circle at the endpoint on the circle, then the line is tangent to the circle.

We will begin by drawing a generic picture to describe the part of the theorem that follows the "if."

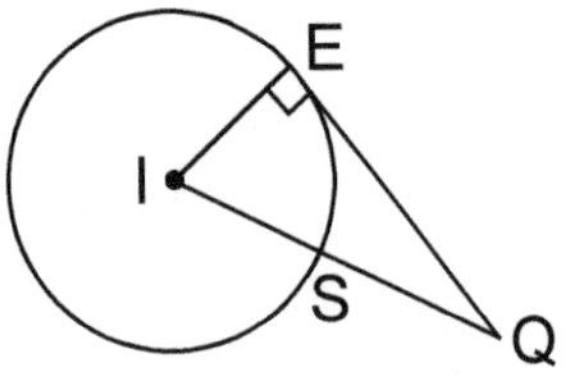

Now, we can say that we are given that $\overline{QE} \perp \overline{IE}$, and we want to prove that $\overline{QE}$ is tangent to ⊙I at E. Since we are using an indirect proof here, we will assume that $\overline{QE}$ is *not* tangent to ⊙I at E. Then $\overrightarrow{QE}$ intersects ⊙I at more than one point, as shown in one of the two pictures below. We will call the additional point where $\overrightarrow{QE}$ and ⊙I intersect point O.

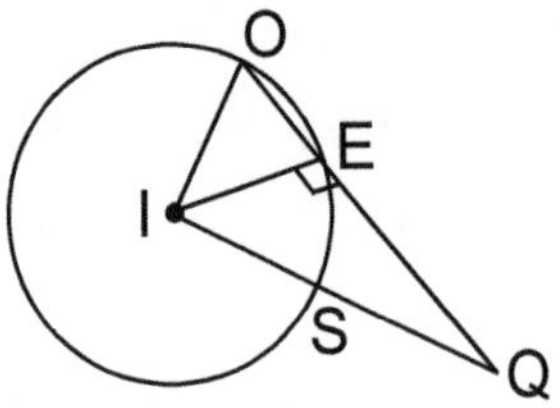

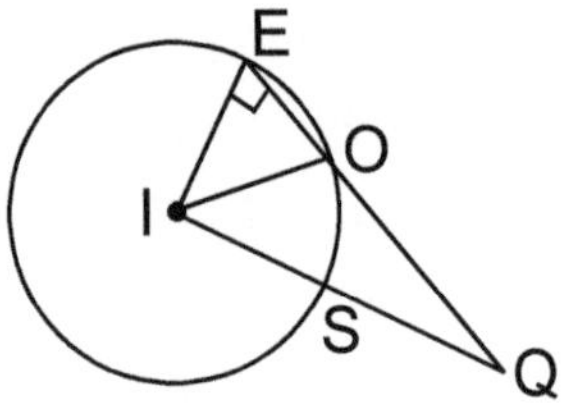

Case 1: QE < QO (as shown in the picture on the left above)

The theorem *If two lines are perpendicular, then they intersect to form four right angles* tells us that ∠QEI and ∠OEI are both right angles. Then, by the definition of right angles, m∠OEI = 90°. Since all radii of a circle are congruent to each other, we can say that $\overline{IO} \cong \overline{IE}$. Then, by the Isosceles Triangle Theorem and the definition of congruent angles, m∠IOE = 90°.

Case 2: QE > QO (as shown in the picture on the right above)

The definition of perpendicular lines tells us that ∠OEI is a right angle. The definition of right angles tells us that this means that m∠OEI = 90°. Since all radii of a circle are congruent to each other, we can say that $\overline{IO} \cong \overline{IE}$. Then, by the Isosceles Triangle Theorem and the definition of congruent angles, m∠IOE = 90°.

Then, by the definition of a right angle, ∠IOE must be a right angle. However, both of these cases are impossible because we proved in Chapter 5 that a triangle can have no more than one right angle. Thus, our assumption must be false, and so $\overline{QE}$ is must be tangent to ⊙I at E.

Example 3: In the figure at the right, $\overline{LM}$ is tangent to $\odot J$ at point M, JK = 7, and KL = 18. Find the length of $\overline{LM}$.

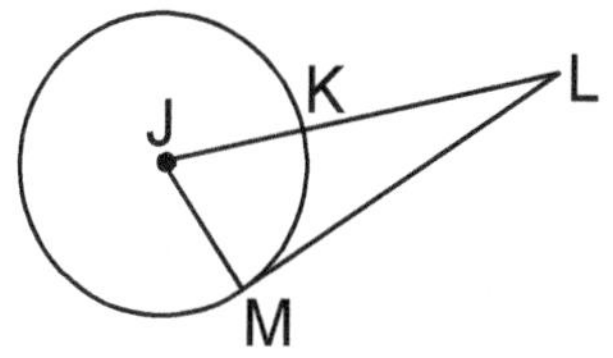

We will begin by noting that, since the question says that $\overline{LM}$ is tangent to $\odot J$ at point M, we can use the theorem *If a line is tangent to a circle, then it is perpendicular to the radius drawn to the point of tangency* to say that $\overline{LM} \perp \overline{JM}$. Therefore, we can use the Pythagorean Theorem as shown below.

$$(JM)^2 + (LM)^2 = (JL)^2$$

$$7^2 + (LM)^2 = 25^2$$

Note that $\overline{JM}$ and $\overline{JK}$ are both radii of $\odot J$, and so, since the definition of a circle tells us that all radii of a circle are congruent to each other, we can say that JM = 7. Also note that the Segment Addition Postulate tells us that JL = JK + KL, and so we can say that JL = 25.

$$49 + (LM)^2 = 625$$

$$(LM)^2 = 576$$

$$LM = 24$$

Take the square root of both sides, and note that LM must be positive.

Now, we need another theorem. You will prove this theorem in the exercises for this section.

> If an angle is formed by a chord that intersects a line tangent to a circle at the point of tangency, then the measure of each angle formed is equal to half the measure of the corresponding arc.

This theorem tells us that, in $\odot R$ below, $m\angle EVQ = \frac{1}{2} m\overset{\frown}{VTQ}$ and $m\angle GVQ = \frac{1}{2} m\overset{\frown}{VQ}$.

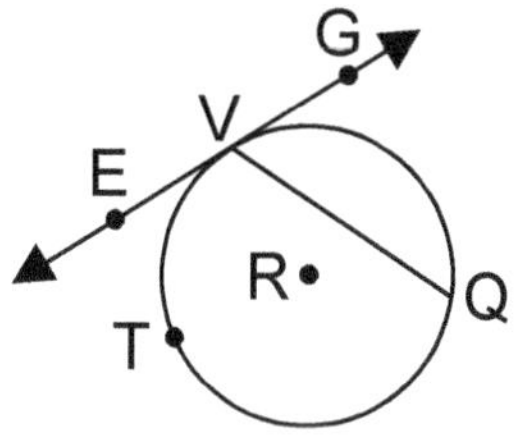

Example 4: In $\odot R$ above, $m\overset{\frown}{VTQ} = (38 + 2x)°$ and $m\overset{\frown}{VQ} = (x - 14)°$. Find $m\angle EVQ$ and $m\angle GVQ$.

We will begin by noting that $m\overset{\frown}{VTQ} + m\overset{\frown}{VQ} = 360°$, and so we can say that $38 + 2x + x - 14 = 360$. This tells us that $x = 112$.

Now, we will note that this tells us that $m\overset{\frown}{VTQ} = 262°$ and $m\overset{\frown}{VQ} = 98°$. Since we said earlier that $m\angle EVQ = \frac{1}{2} m\overset{\frown}{VTQ}$ and $m\angle GVQ = \frac{1}{2} m\overset{\frown}{VQ}$, this means that $m\angle EVQ = 131°$ and $m\angle GVQ = 49°$.

Now, we need another theorem. You will prove this theorem in the exercises for this section.

> If two secants, two tangents, or a tangent and a secant intersect *outside* a circle, then the measure of the angle formed is equal to half the difference of the measures of the intercepted arcs.

This tells us that we can talk about the measures of the angles below as shown underneath each of the pictures.

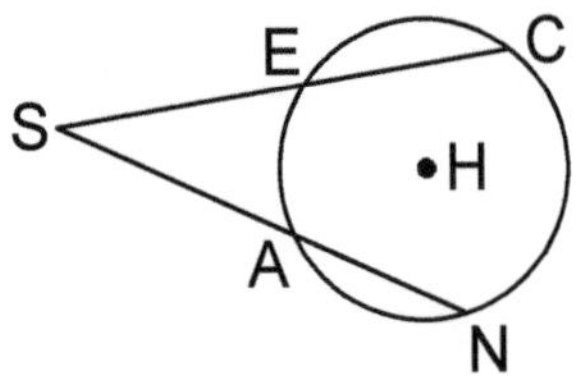

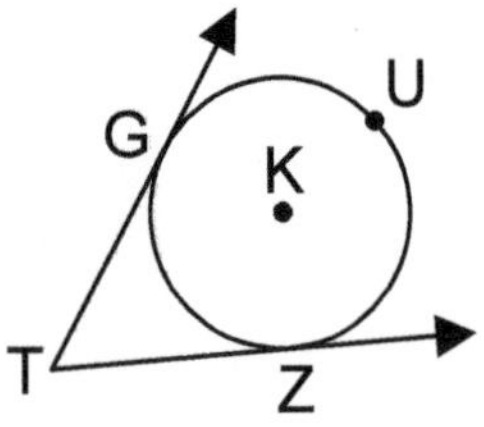

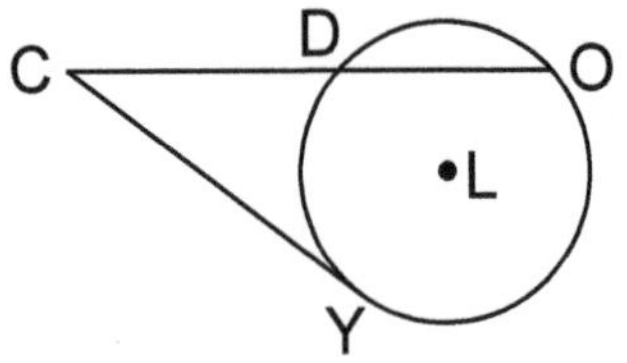

$m\angle CSN = \frac{1}{2}(m\overset{\frown}{CN} - m\overset{\frown}{EA})$ $m\angle GTZ = \frac{1}{2}(m\overset{\frown}{GUZ} - m\overset{\frown}{GZ})$ $m\angle OCY = \frac{1}{2}(m\overset{\frown}{OY} - m\overset{\frown}{DY})$

Example 5: In the figure at the right, $\overrightarrow{QT}$ is tangent to $\odot P$ at T, $m\overset{\frown}{ST} = 103°$, and $m\overset{\frown}{RT} = 152°$. Find the measure of $\angle Q$.

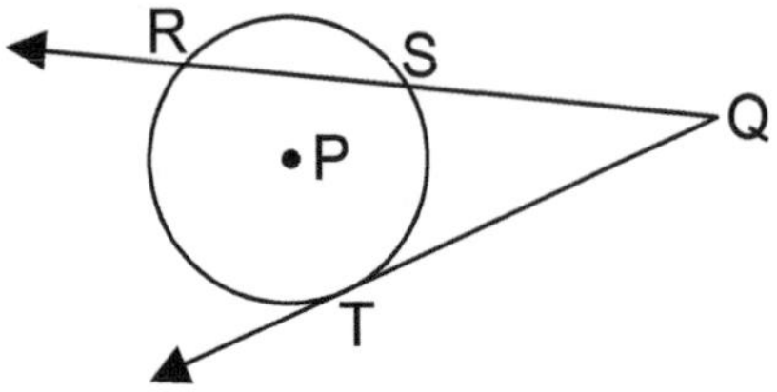

We will begin by noting that the theorem above tells us that $m\angle Q = \frac{1}{2}(m\overset{\frown}{RT} - m\overset{\frown}{ST})$, and so we can finish answering this question as shown below.

$$m\angle Q = \frac{1}{2}(m\overset{\frown}{RT} - m\overset{\frown}{ST})$$

$$m\angle Q = \frac{1}{2}(152° - 103°)$$

$$m\angle Q = \frac{1}{2} \cdot 49°$$

$$m\angle Q = 24.5°$$

Example 6: In the figure at the right, $\overline{BH}$ is tangent to $\odot M$ at H, $\overline{BV}$ is tangent to $\odot M$ at V, $m\overset{\frown}{HJV} = (30 + 2x)°$, and $m\angle B = 50°$. Find $m\overset{\frown}{HV}$.

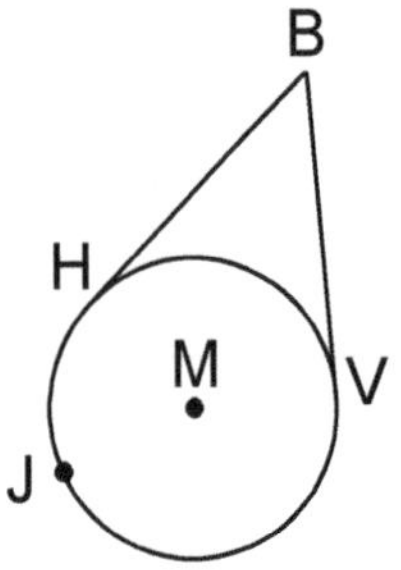

We will begin by noting that $m\angle B = \frac{1}{2}(m\overset{\frown}{HJV} - m\overset{\frown}{HV})$. This tells us that we can work this problem as shown below and continued on the next page.

$$m\angle B = \frac{1}{2}(m\overset{\frown}{HJV} - m\overset{\frown}{HV})$$

$$50 = \frac{1}{2}[30 + 2x - (330 - 2x)]$$

Note that $m\overset{\frown}{HJV} + m\overset{\frown}{HV} = 360°$, and so we can say that $m\overset{\frown}{HV} = 360° - (30 + 2x)°$, or $(330 - 2x)°$.

$$50 = \frac{1}{2}[30 + 2x - 330 + 2x]$$

Distribute the −1 in front of the (330 − 2x).

$$50 = \frac{1}{2}[4x - 300]$$

$$50 = 2x - 150$$

Distribute the $\frac{1}{2}$.

$$100 = x$$

Add 150 to both sides and then divide both sides by 2.

Now, we can find $m\overset{\frown}{HV}$ by noting that we said in the explanations on the previous page that $m\overset{\frown}{HV} = (330 - 2x)^\circ$. This tells us that $m\overset{\frown}{HV} = (330 - 2 \cdot 100)^\circ$, or 130°.

Finally, we need one more theorem. You will prove this theorem in the exercises for this section.

> If two secants or two chords intersect *inside* a circle, then the measure of each angle formed is equal to half the sum of the measures of the arc corresponding to that angle and the arc corresponding to the vertical angle.

Example 7: In ⊙Z at the right, $m\overset{\frown}{VW} = 81^\circ$ and $m\overset{\frown}{XY} = 43^\circ$. Find $m\angle VUW$, $m\angle XUY$, and $m\angle VUY$.

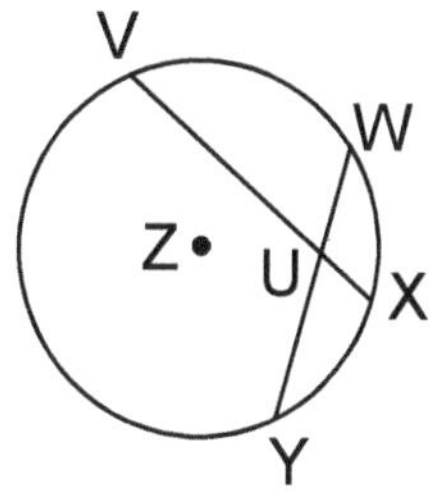

Since $\overset{\frown}{VW}$ is the arc that corresponds with $\angle VUW$, and since $\overset{\frown}{XY}$ is the arc that corresponds with its vertical angle ($\angle XUY$), we can use the theorem above to say that $m\angle VUW = \frac{1}{2}(m\overset{\frown}{VW} + m\overset{\frown}{XY})$.

Thus, we can solve this problem as shown below.

$$m\angle VUW = \frac{1}{2}(m\overset{\frown}{VW} + m\overset{\frown}{XY})$$

$$m\angle VUW = \frac{1}{2}(81^\circ + 43^\circ)$$

$$m\angle VUW = \frac{1}{2} \cdot 124^\circ$$

$$m\angle VUW = 62^\circ$$

$$m\angle XUY = 62^\circ$$

Since $\angle VUW$ and $\angle XUY$ are vertical angles, we can say that $m\angle XUY$ also equals 62°.

$$m\angle VUY = 118^\circ$$

Since $\angle VUW$ and $\angle VUY$ form a linear pair, we can say that $m\angle VUY = 180^\circ - 62^\circ$, or 118°.

Example 8: In $\odot D$ at the right, $m\overset{\frown}{BA} = (3n - 12)°$, $m\overset{\frown}{EC} = 2n°$, and $m\angle AFB = (2n + 16)°$. Find $m\overset{\frown}{EAC}$.

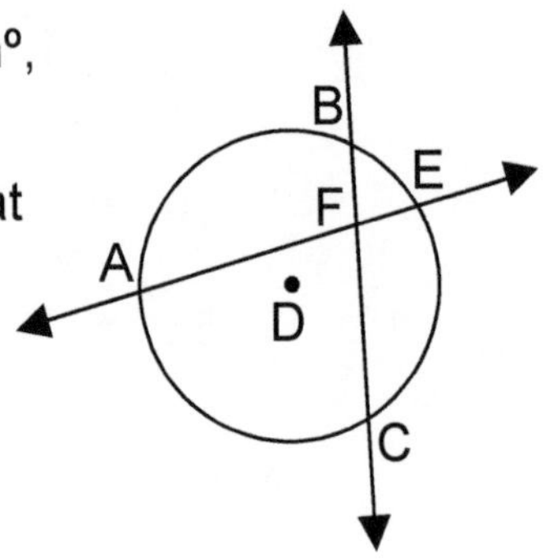

We can use the theorem on the previous page to say that $m\angle AFB = \frac{1}{2}(m\overset{\frown}{BA} + m\overset{\frown}{EC})$, and so we can solve this problem as shown below.

$$m\angle AFB = \frac{1}{2}(m\overset{\frown}{BA} + m\overset{\frown}{EC})$$

$$2n + 16 = \frac{1}{2}(3n - 12 + 2n)$$

$$2n + 16 = \frac{1}{2}(5n - 12)$$

$$2n + 16 = \frac{5}{2}n - 6$$

$$22 = \frac{1}{2}n$$ Subtract 2n from both sides and add 6 to both sides.

$$44 = n$$ Divide both sides by $\frac{1}{2}$. (Note that $22 \div \frac{1}{2} = 22 \cdot \frac{2}{1}$, or 44.)

$$m\overset{\frown}{EC} = 88°$$ Since we were given that $m\overset{\frown}{EC} = 2n°$, we can say that $m\overset{\frown}{EC} = 2 \cdot 44°$, or 88°.

$$m\overset{\frown}{EAC} = 272°$$ Since $m\overset{\frown}{EAC} + m\overset{\frown}{EC} = 360°$, we can say that $m\overset{\frown}{EAC} = 360° - 88°$, or 272°.

Problems:

1-6. In the figure at the right, $\overline{PR}$ is tangent to $\odot O$ at R, $m\overset{\frown}{RT} = 93°$, $m\angle PRU = 109°$, and $m\overset{\frown}{RS} = 36°$.

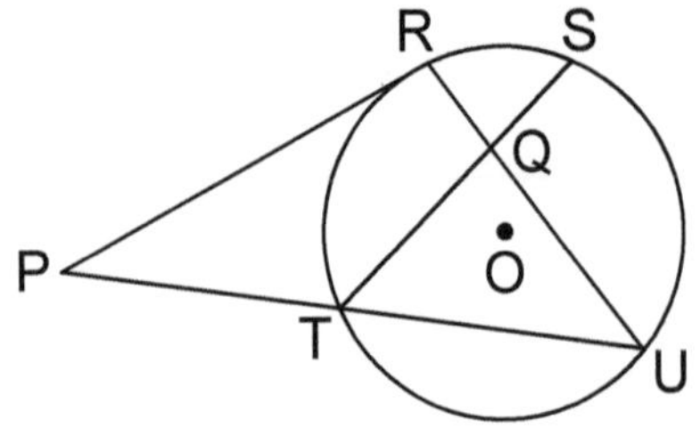

1. $m\overset{\frown}{RTU}$ = ____________

2. $m\overset{\frown}{TU}$ = ____________

3. $m\angle P$ = ____________

4. $m\angle RQS$ = ____________

5. $m\angle U$ = ____________

6. $m\angle STU$ = ____________

7-19. In the figure at the right, $\overrightarrow{MG}$ is tangent to ⊙K at G, m$\overset{\frown}{GHJ}$ = 186°, m∠GMJ = 46°, m$\overset{\frown}{GHN}$ = 331°, and m∠GMH = 12°.

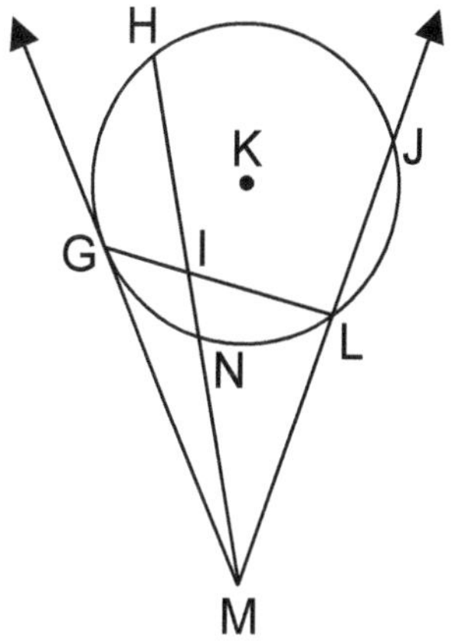

7. m$\overset{\frown}{GL}$ = ____________

8. m$\overset{\frown}{JL}$ = ____________

9. m$\overset{\frown}{GN}$ = ____________

10. m$\overset{\frown}{GH}$ = ____________

11. m$\overset{\frown}{LN}$ = ____________

12. m$\overset{\frown}{HJ}$ = ____________

13. m∠MGL = ____________

14. m∠LIM = ____________

15. m∠HMJ = ____________

16. m∠HIG = ____________

17. m∠GLJ = ____________

18. m∠GLM = ____________

19. m∠LIH = ____________

20-27. In the figure at the right, $\overrightarrow{CB}$ is tangent to ⊙P at B, $\overrightarrow{CW}$ is tangent to ⊙P at W, m$\overset{\frown}{WB}$ = 105°, and m$\overset{\frown}{VO}$ = 28°.

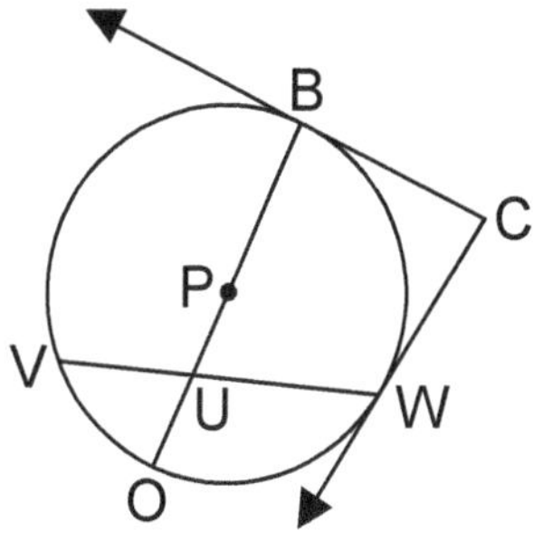

20. m$\overset{\frown}{BVO}$ = ____________

21. m$\overset{\frown}{VB}$ = ____________

22. m$\overset{\frown}{OW}$ = ____________

23. m∠C = ____________

24. m∠OBC = ____________

25. m∠WUB = ____________

26. m∠VWC = ____________

27. m∠VUB = ____________

28-29. In ⊙K at the right, m∠N = 4x°, m∠PQO = (11y + 3)°, m$\overset{\frown}{MR}$ = (16y – 22)°, m$\overset{\frown}{SO}$ = (2x + 40)°, m$\overset{\frown}{PMO}$ = (19y – 26)°, and m$\overset{\frown}{LR}$ = (5y + 8)°.

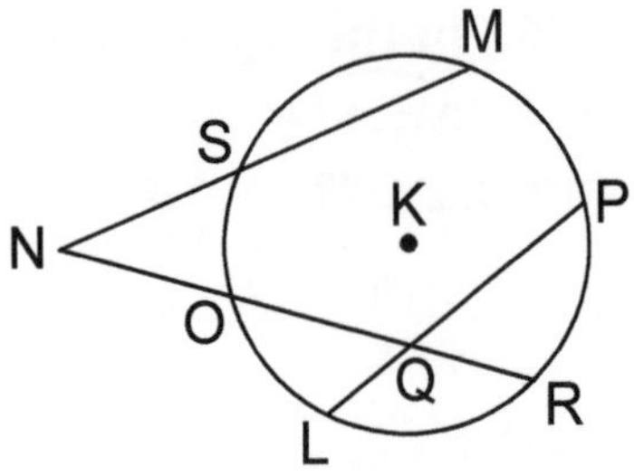

28. m∠N = ____________

29. m∠PQO = ____________

30-36. In the figure at the right, $\overline{EG}$ is tangent to ⊙J at F, AJ = 5, m∠JEF = 30°, m∠G = (10w + 8)°, and m$\overset{\frown}{HF}$ = (6w + 8)°.

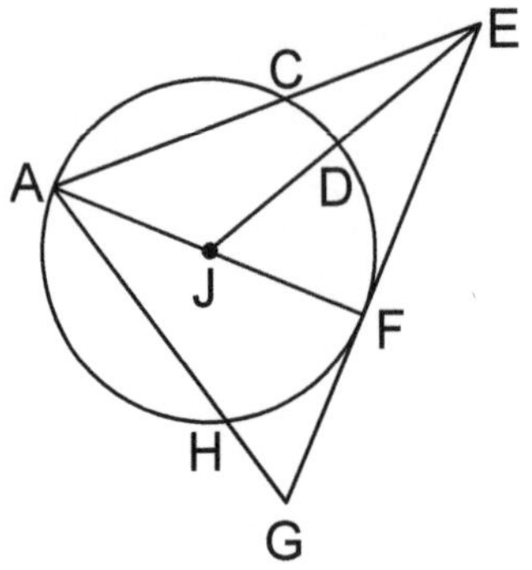

30. m∠EJF = ____________

31. m∠AFG = ____________

32. EF = ____________

33. JE = ____________

34. AE = ____________

35. m∠G = ____________

36. m$\overset{\frown}{DF}$ = ____________

37. In the figure at the right, $\overleftrightarrow{QV}$ is tangent to ⊙U at V, m∠QVT = (7x + 10y)°, and m$\overset{\frown}{VIT}$ = (8x + 5y)°. Then x = ____________ and y = ____________.

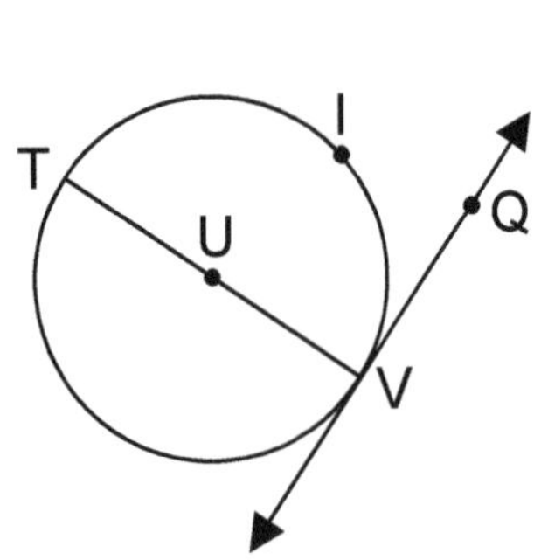

38. In the figure at the right, $\overline{ZP}$ is a radius of ⊙Z, BP = 15, BR = 9, and RZ = 8. Is $\overline{BP}$ tangent to ⊙Z at P?

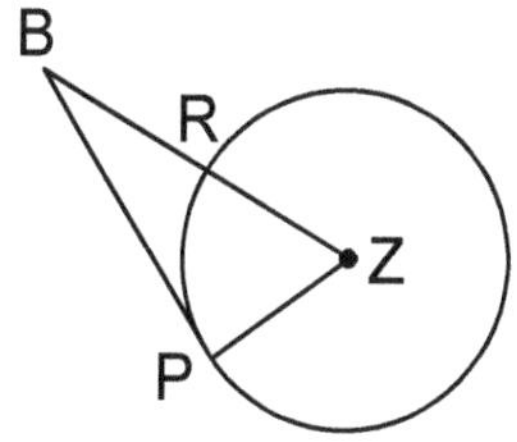

39. In the figure at the right, $\overline{AL}$ is a radius of ⊙A, AL = 10, CL = 40, and CW = 31. Is $\overline{CL}$ tangent to ⊙A at L?

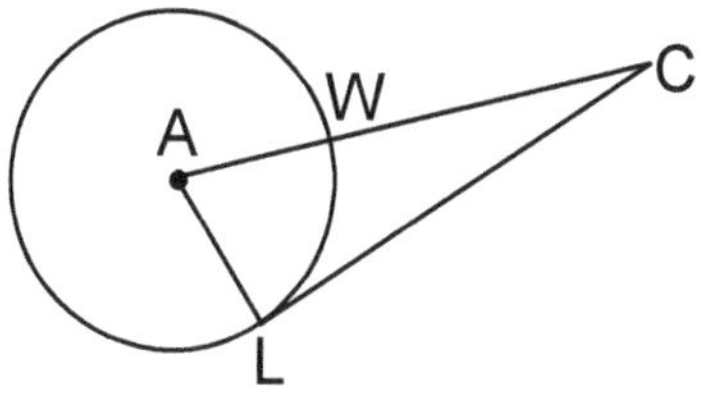

40. Prove that, if an angle is formed by a chord that intersects a line tangent to a circle at the point of tangency, then the measure of each angle formed is equal to half the measure of the corresponding arc.

Case 1: The chord passes through the center of the circle.

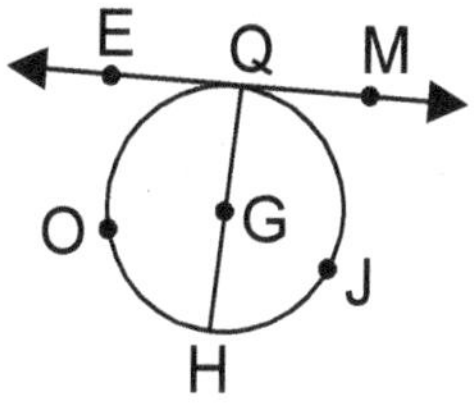

We are given that ________________________________,

and we want to prove that __________________________.

By the definition of a semicircle, we can say that $\overset{\frown}{QOH}$ and $\overset{\frown}{QJH}$ are semicircles with measures of 180°. We can use the theorem ________

____ to say that $\overline{QH} \perp \overleftrightarrow{EM}$.

Then, by the theorem ____

________, ∠EQH and ∠MQH must be right angles. By the definition of right angles, m∠EQH = 90° and m∠MQH = 90°. Then we can use the Substitution Property of Equality to say that $m\angle EQH = \frac{1}{2} m\overset{\frown}{QOH}$ and $m\angle MQH = \frac{1}{2} m\overset{\frown}{QJH}$.

Case 2: The chord does not pass through the center of the circle.

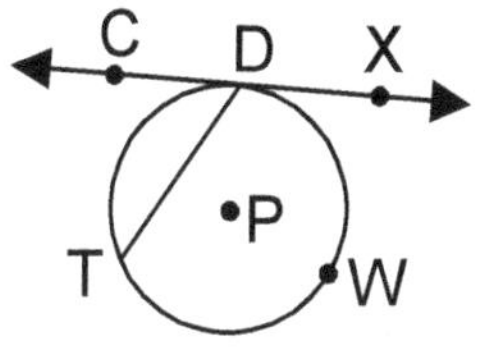

We are given that ________________________________

______, and we want to prove that $m\angle XDT = \frac{1}{2} m\overset{\frown}{DWT}$ and $m\angle CDT = \frac{1}{2} m\overset{\frown}{DT}$. We can use the postulate ____________________________

________________________________ to draw $\overrightarrow{DP}$, and we will call the second point where $\overrightarrow{DP}$ intersects ⊙P the point R, as shown in the figure on the next page.

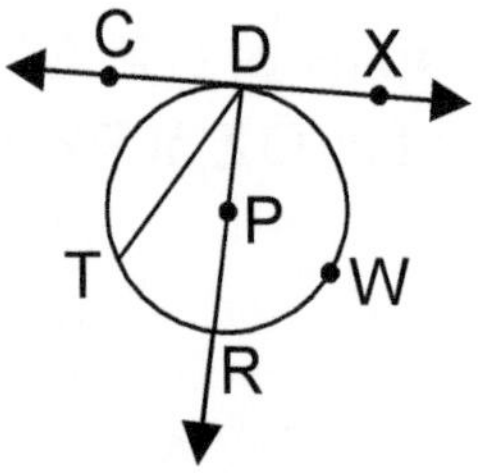

Now, we can use what we proved in Case 1 to say that $m\angle RDC = \frac{1}{2} m\overset{\frown}{RTD}$ and $m\angle XDR = \frac{1}{2} m\overset{\frown}{DWR}$. We can also use the ________________________ ____________ Theorem to say that $m\angle RDT = \frac{1}{2} m\overset{\frown}{TR}$.

Now, we can use the ________________________________ and the Subtraction Property of Equality to say that $m\angle XDT = m\angle XDR + m\angle RDT$ and $m\angle CDT = m\angle RDC - m\angle RDT$. Then, by the ________________________ ____________________, $m\angle XDT =$ ________________________ and $m\angle CDT =$ ________________________. By the Distributive Property, $m\angle XDT = \frac{1}{2}(m\overset{\frown}{DWR} + m\overset{\frown}{TR})$ and $m\angle CDT = \frac{1}{2}(m\overset{\frown}{RTD} - m\overset{\frown}{TR})$. The ________ ____________________ Postulate and the ________________ Property of Equality tell us that $m\overset{\frown}{DWT} = m\overset{\frown}{DWR} + m\overset{\frown}{TR}$ and $m\overset{\frown}{DT} = m\overset{\frown}{RTD} - m\overset{\frown}{TR}$, and so now we can use the ____________________________________ to say that ____________________ and ____________________.

41. Prove that, if two secants intersect outside a circle, then the measure of the angle formed is equal to half the difference of the measures of the intercepted arcs.

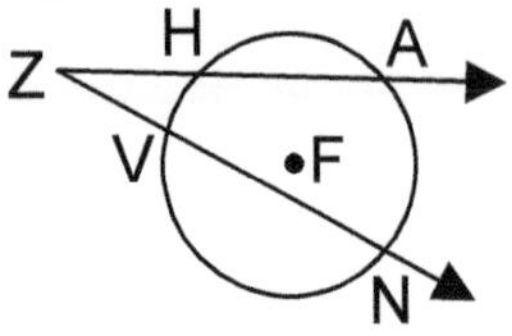

Given: ________________________________

Prove: ________________________________

We are given that ________________________________.

We can use the postulate ____ to draw $\overline{VA}$, as shown at the right. We can use the ____________ ________________ Theorem, the ____________ Property of Equality, and the Symmetric Property of Equality to say that $m\angle Z = m\angle AVN - m\angle ZAV$. The Measure of an Inscribed Angle Theorem tells us that $m\angle AVN =$ __________ and $m\angle ZAV =$ __________. Then, by the Substitution Property of Equality, $m\angle Z =$ ____________________. By the Distributive Property, $m\angle Z =$ ________________.

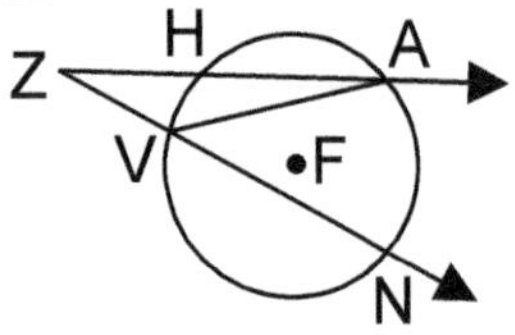

42. Prove that, if two tangents intersect outside a circle, then the measure of the angle formed is equal to half the difference of the measures of the intercepted arcs.

Given: $\overrightarrow{SU}$ is tangent to ⊙K at U, and $\overrightarrow{SY}$ is tangent to ⊙K at Y

Prove: $m\angle S = \frac{1}{2}(m\overset{\frown}{UPY} - m\overset{\frown}{UY})$

Hint: After you state the information given to you, draw $\overline{UY}$.

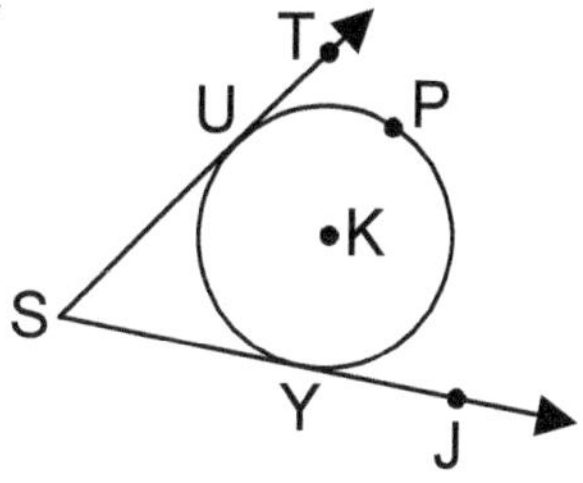

43. Prove that, if a tangent and a secant intersect outside a circle, then the measure of the angle formed is equal to half the difference of the measures of the intercepted arcs.

Given: $\overrightarrow{QX}$ is tangent to ⊙L at X; $\overrightarrow{QI}$ is a secant of ⊙L

Prove: $m\angle Q = \frac{1}{2}(m\overset{\frown}{IBX} - m\overset{\frown}{XR})$

Hint: After you state the information given to you, draw $\overline{XI}$.

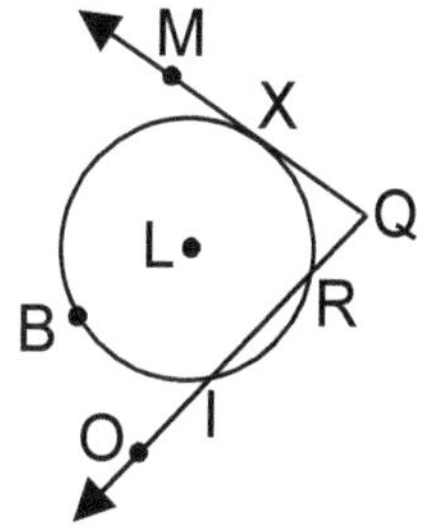

44. Prove that, if two chords intersect inside a circle, then the measure of each angle formed is equal to half the sum of the measures of the corresponding arc and the arc corresponding to the vertical angle. (The proof of the statement *If two* secants *intersect inside a circle, then the measure of each angle formed is equal to half the sum of the measures of the corresponding arc and the arc corresponding to the vertical angle* is, of course, nearly identical.)

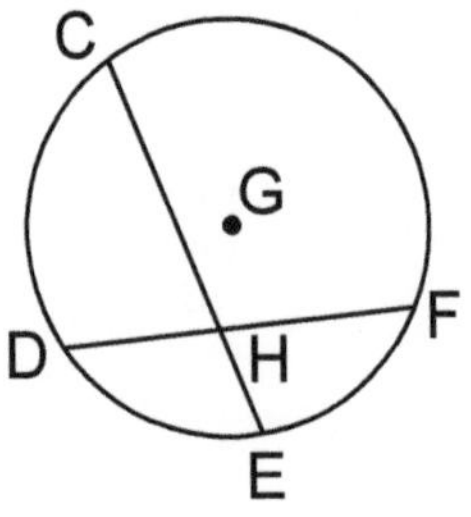

Given: $\overline{CE}$ and $\overline{DF}$ are chords of $\odot G$

Prove: $m\angle CHD = \frac{1}{2}(m\overset{\frown}{EF} + m\overset{\frown}{CD})$,

$m\angle FHE = \frac{1}{2}(m\overset{\frown}{EF} + m\overset{\frown}{CD})$,

$m\angle EHD = \frac{1}{2}(m\overset{\frown}{DE} + m\overset{\frown}{CF})$, and

$m\angle CHF = \frac{1}{2}(m\overset{\frown}{DE} + m\overset{\frown}{CF})$

Hint: After you state the information given to you, draw $\overline{DE}$ and $\overline{FE}$.

Part V – Lengths of Chords, Secant Segments, and Tangent Segments

In this section, we will talk about different theorems that talk about the lengths of segments associated with circles.

We will begin this section with two theorems. You will prove them in the exercises for this section.

> **Two Tangent Segments Theorem**
>
> Suppose that $\overline{AB}$ and $\overline{AC}$ are tangent to $\odot D$ at points B and C. Then $\overline{AB} \cong \overline{AC}$.

> **Chord Segments Theorem**
>
> Suppose that $\overline{AB}$ and $\overline{CD}$ are chords of $\odot E$ that intersect at the point F. Then (AF)(FB) = (CF)(FD).

Example 1: In the figure at the right, $\overline{QP}$ is tangent to $\odot U$ at P, $\overline{QR}$ is tangent to $\odot U$ at R, QP = 28, SV = 5, SP = 4, and ST = 20. Find the lengths of $\overline{QR}$ and $\overline{SR}$.

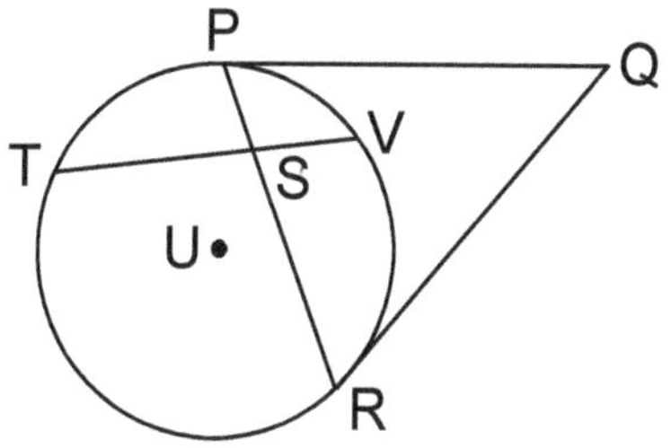

We will begin by noting that the Two Tangent Segments Theorem tells us that $\overline{QP} \cong \overline{QR}$, and so QR must equal 28.

Next, we will note that the Chord Segments Theorem tells us that (PS)(SR) = (TS)(SV). Therefore, we can say that (4)(SR) = (20)(5), and so $\overline{SR}$ must have a length of 25.

Example 2: In the figure at the right, $\overline{IG}$ is tangent to $\odot K$ at G, $\overline{IJ}$ is tangent to $\odot K$ at J, IG = 5x – 4, IJ = 6x – 2y, GM = 3x – 9, MJ = 8, HM = 6, and ML = 2y + 20. Find the values of x and y.

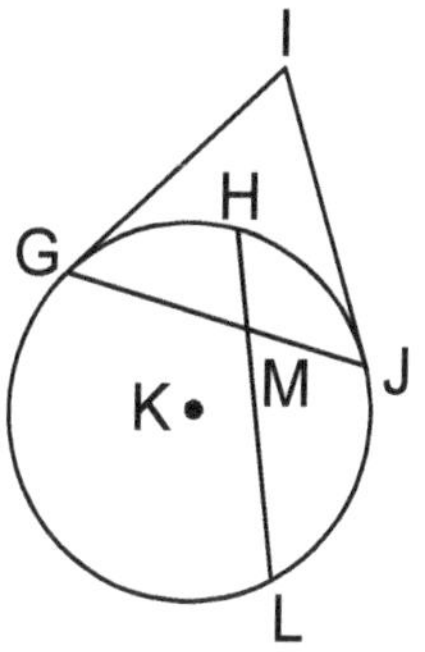

The Two Tangent Segments Theorem tells us that IG = IJ, and so we can say that 5x – 4 = 6x – 2y. The Chord Segments Theorem tells us that (MJ)(GM) = (HM)(ML), and so we can say that 8(3x – 9) = 6(2y + 20). Now, we can solve this system of equations using either the substitution or elimination method. (If you have forgotten how to use one or both of these methods, they are discussed in Appendix A in the section titled "Solving Systems of Equations.") There are many different ways of working this problem from here, and one of them is shown below.

$5x - 4 = 6x - 2y$	$8(3x - 9) = 6(2y + 20)$
$-4 = x - 2y$	$24x - 72 = 12y + 120$
$2y - 4 = x$	$24x = 12y + 192$

$$24(2y - 4) = 12y + 192$$

Since we said that x = 2y – 4, we can substitute (2y – 4) for x in the equation 24x = 12y + 192.

$$48y - 96 = 12y + 192$$
$$36y = 288$$
$$y = 8$$
$$2(8) - 4 = x$$

Since we now know that y = 8, we can substitute 8 for y in one of the equations we found earlier. (We could have chosen to substitute it in any of the other equations from the two columns on the previous page instead. In the end, we would have come up with the same answer.)

$$12 = x$$

Thus, the final answer to this question is that x = 12 and y = 8.

Now, we need two more theorems. You will prove them in the exercises for this section.

Two Secant Segments Theorem

If two secant segments intersect outside a circle, then the product of the length of a secant segment's external part and the length of the entire segment is equal to the product of the length of the other secant segment's external part and the length of the entire segment.

One Tangent Segment and One Secant Segment Theorem

If a secant segment and a tangent segment intersect outside a circle, then the product of the length of a secant segment's external part and the length of the entire segment is equal to the square of the length of the tangent segment.

Example 3: In the figure at the right, $\overline{OC}$ and $\overline{OF}$ are secant segments of ⊙N, OA = 10, AC = 26, and OE = 15. Find the length of $\overline{EF}$.

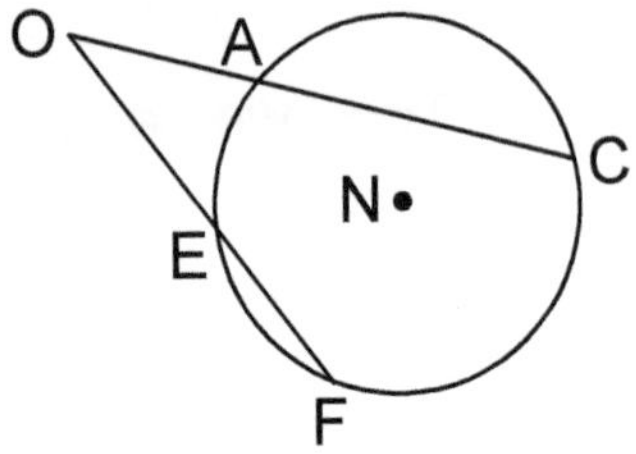

The Two Secant Segments Theorem above tells us that (OA)(OC) = (OE)(OF). Thus, we can solve this problem as shown below.

$$(OA)(OC) = (OE)(OF)$$
$$(10)(36) = (15)(OF)$$
$$360 = (15)(OF)$$
$$24 = OF$$
$$EF = OF - OE$$
$$EF = 24 - 15$$
$$EF = 9$$

Note that OC = OA + AC.

Example 4: In the figure at the right, $\overline{QS}$ is tangent to ⊙L at S, QS = 2x – 2, MQ = 3x – 8, and MD = 9 – x. Find the length of $\overline{QS}$.

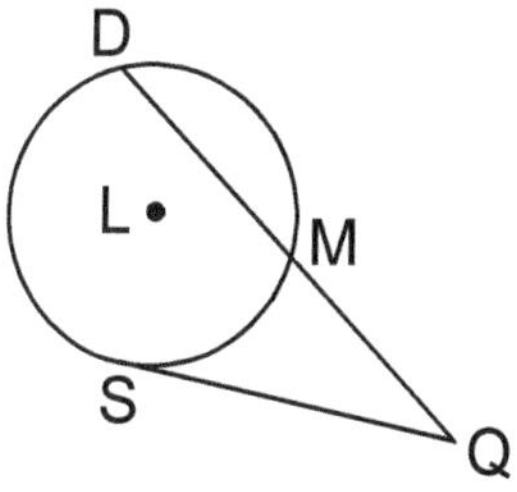

The One Tangent Segment and One Secant Segment Theorem tells us that (MQ)(DQ) = $(SQ)^2$, and so we can work this problem as shown below. (You may need to review the section in Appendix A on solving quadratic equations in order to understand this solution completely.)

$(MQ)\quad(DQ) = (SQ)^2$

$(3x - 8)(2x + 1) = (2x - 2)^2$ — Note that DQ = MD + MQ, or 2x + 1.

$6x^2 - 13x - 8 = 4x^2 - 8x + 4$ — Note that $(2x - 2)^2 = (2x - 2)(2x - 2)$, or $4x^2 - 8x + 4$.

$2x^2 - 5x - 12 = 0$

$(2x + 3)(x - 4) = 0$

$2x + 3 = 0$ or $x - 4 = 0$

$x = -\frac{3}{2}$ or $x = 4$

$QS = 2(4) - 2$

Note that, if $x = -\frac{3}{2}$, then SQ would have to equal –5. Since the length of a segment cannot be negative, x must equal 4.

$QS = 6$

Example 5: In the figure at the right, TE = 13, KG = 2y – 4, EK = y – 5, and GR = y. Find all the possible values of y.

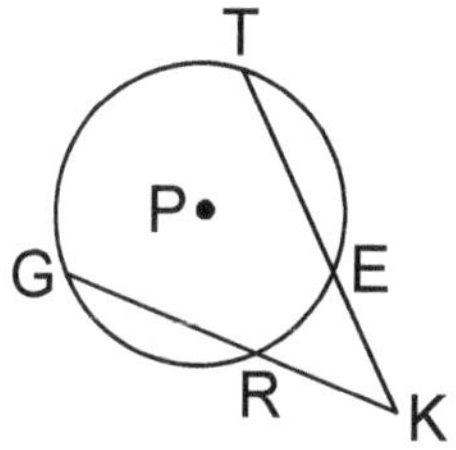

We will begin by noting that the Two Secant Segments Theorem tells us that (KE)(KT) = (KR)(KG). This means that we can work this problem as shown below.

$(KE)\quad(KT) = (KG)\quad(KR)$

$(y - 5)(y + 8) = (2y - 4)(y - 4)$ — Note that KT = TE + EK and that KR = KG – GR.

$y^2 + 3y - 40 = 2y^2 - 12y + 16$

$0 = y^2 - 15y + 56$

$0 = (y - 7)(y - 8)$ — Solve using the factoring method discussed in Appendix A. (We could have also gotten the correct answer by using the quadratic formula.)

$y - 7 = 0$ or $y - 8 = 0$

$y = 7$ or $y = 8$

Neither of these answers give us zero or negative values for any of the lengths of our segments, and so our final answer is that y can equal either 7 or 8.

Problems:

1-7. In the figure at the right, $\overline{EM}$ is tangent to ⊙C at E, and $\overline{AM}$ is tangent to ⊙C at A.

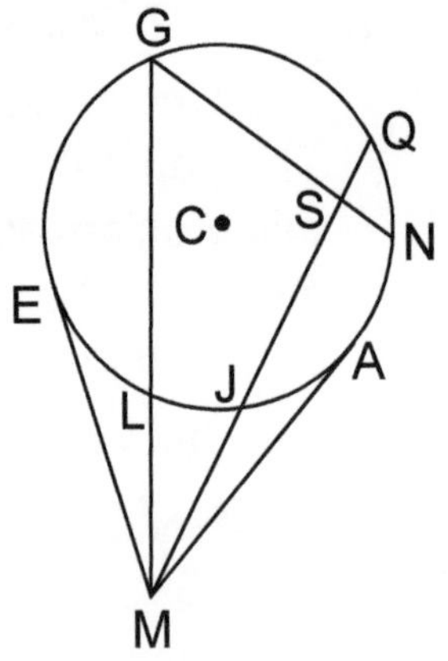

1. If GM = 44, LM = 15, and QM = 33, then
   JM = ___________ and QJ = ___________.

2. If GL = 28, LM = 12, and QM = 30, then
   QJ = ___________ and JM = ___________.

3. If EM = 18 and GM = 27, then LM = ___________ and LG = ___________.

4. If GS = 16, QS = 4, and SN = 6, then SJ = ___________ and QJ = ___________.

5. If GN = 20, SN = 2, and SJ = 9, then QJ = ___________ and QS = ___________.

6. If GL = 5 and AM = 6, then MG = ___________ and LM = ___________.

7. If EM = $x^2 + 11$ and AM = $2x^2 - 14$, what are the possible value(s) of x?

   ____

8-16. In the figure at the right, $\overline{AB}$ is tangent to ⊙D at B, and $\overline{AI}$ is tangent to ⊙D at I.

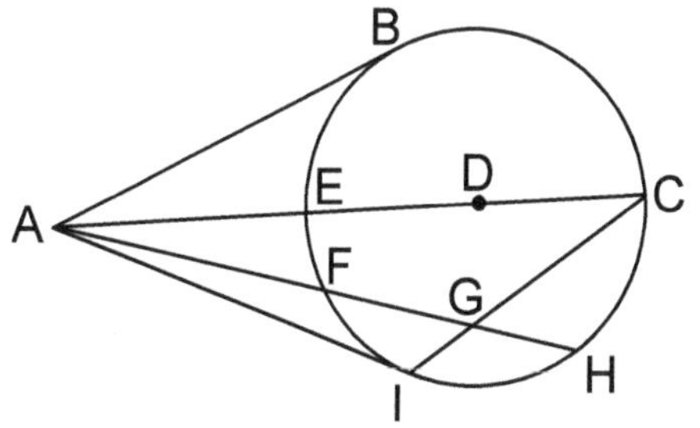

8. If AI = 12 meters, then AB = _______ meters.

9. If FG = 9 yards, GH = 8 yards, and GI = 6 yards, then GC = _______ yards.

10. If AE = 4 feet and AI = 6 feet, then AC = _______ feet and EC = _______ feet.

11. If AC = 29 centimeters, AE = 16 centimeters, and AH = 40 centimeters, then FH = _______ centimeters and AF = _______ centimeters.

12. If AE = 15 inches, EC = 19 inches, and HF = 13 inches, then AH = _______ inches and AF = _______ inches.

13. If AB = x – 2, AE = x – 8, and AC = x + 7, then x = _______ and AC = _______.

14. If AE = 2w – 9, AF = w + 2, AC = 2w + 4, and AH = w + 9, then w = _______ and AF = _______.

15. If AB = 2q + 5 and AI = 10q – 7, then q = _______ and AB = _______.

16. If FG = p + 7, GH = 2p, GC = 2p + 5, and IG = p + 3, then p = _______.

17-23. In the figure at the right, $\overline{JO}$ is tangent to ⊙R at O, and $\overline{JK}$ is tangent to ⊙R at K.

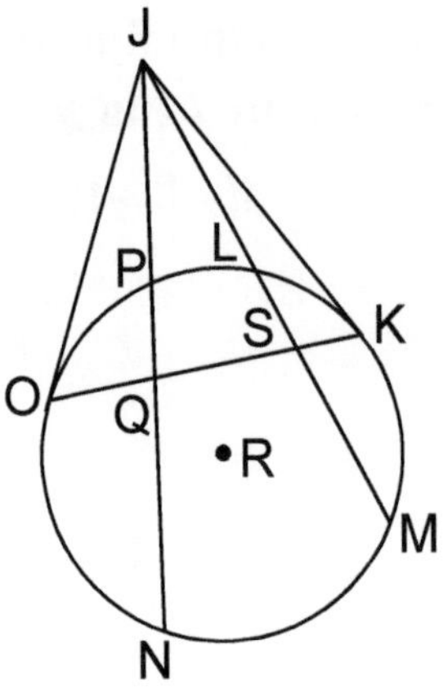

17. If PN = 41, OQ = 10, and QK = 40, what are the possible length(s) of $\overline{PQ}$? ____________

18. If JO = 12 and PN = 10, then JP = _______ and JN = _______.

19. If LM = 10, JN = 25, and PN = 17, then JL = _______ and JM = _______.

20. If JO = 2v – 8, JM = 8, and LM = v, then v = _______ and JL = _______.

21. If PQ = 7u – 4, OQ = 5u + 2, PN = 7u + 20, and QK = 20, then u = _______ and OK = _______.

22. If JO = x^2 and JK = 4x + 5, what are the possible value(s) of x? ____________

23. If JP = y – 2, PN = 2y – 9, JL = y + 3, and LM = 10, what are the possible value(s) of y? ____________

24-28. In the figure at the right, $\overline{CG}$ is tangent to ⊙B at G, and $\overline{CE}$ is tangent to ⊙B at E.

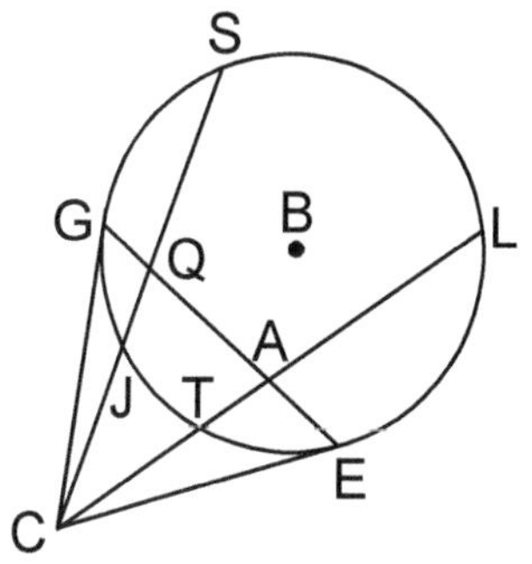

24. If SJ = 7 – w, SC = 9, and GC = w + 4, what are the possible value(s) of w? ____________

25. If GQ = 6, QA = y, AE = 14, SQ = 3x + 6, JQ = 8, AT = 5x – 6, and LA = 16, then x = ________ and y = ________.

26. If GC = 8, LC = x + 3y, TC = 4, and CE = –x – y, then x = ________ and y = ________.

27. If SC = x + 6y, JC = 5, LC = x + 5y, TC = 4, and GC = 10, then x = ________ and y = ________.

28. If GQ = 6, GE = 26, SQ = x, QJ = 8, EC = x + 3y, and GC = 3x – 7y, then x = ________ and y = ________.

29. Prove the Two Tangent Segments Theorem.

Given: ____

Prove: ____

Hint: After you state the information given to you, draw $\overline{BD}$, $\overline{CD}$, and $\overline{DA}$.

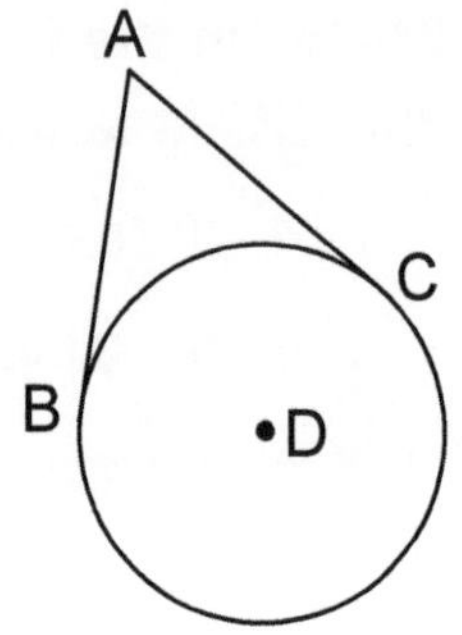

30. Prove the Chord Segments Theorem.

Given: ____

Prove: ____

Hint: After you state the information given to you, draw $\overline{AD}$ and $\overline{BC}$. Then prove that $\Delta ADF \sim \Delta CBF$ by the AA Similarity Theorem.

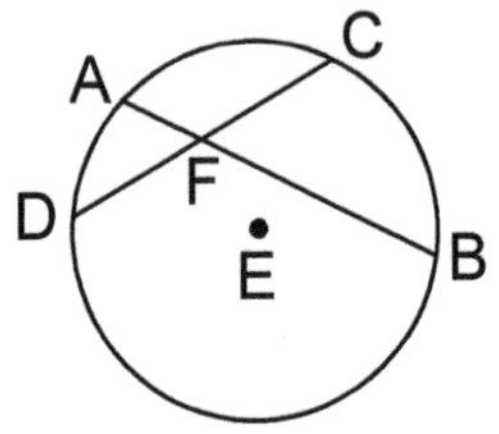

31. Prove the Two Secant Segments Theorem.

Given: ______________________________________

Prove: ______________________________________

Hint: After you state the information given to you, draw $\overline{AB}$ and $\overline{DC}$. Then prove that $\Delta ABF \sim \Delta CDF$ by the AA Similarity Theorem.

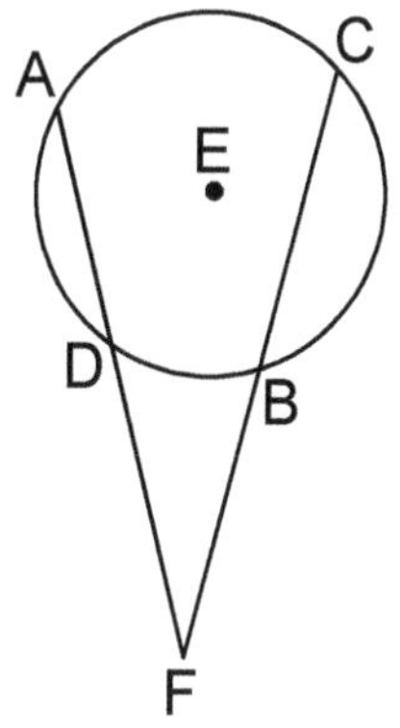

32. Prove the One Tangent Segment and One Secant Segment Theorem.

Given: ______________________________________

Prove: ______________________________________

Hint: After you state the information given to you, draw $\overline{BD}$ and $\overline{CD}$. Then prove that $\Delta ABD \sim \Delta ADC$ by the AA Similarity Theorem.

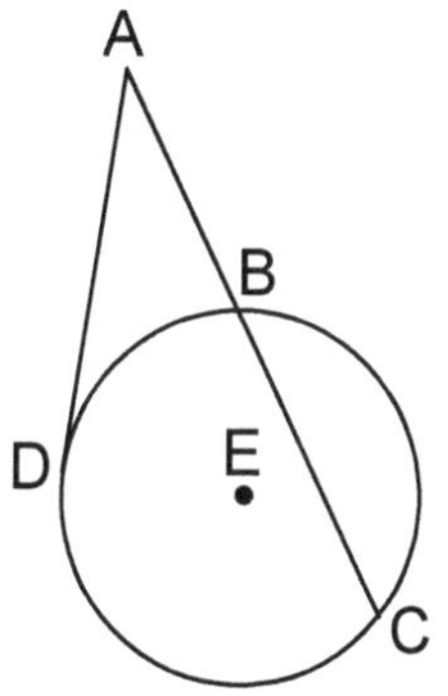

Part VI – Mixed Review

1. In $\triangle ABC$, $\overline{AB} \cong \overline{BC}$. If $m\angle B = 73^\circ$, then $m\angle A =$ ________ and $m\angle C =$ ________.

2. In $\triangle DEF$, the measure of $\angle D$ is three times the measure of $\angle E$, and the measure of $\angle F$ is 18° fewer than twice the measure of $\angle E$. Then $m\angle D =$ __________, $m\angle E =$ __________, and $m\angle F =$ __________.

3-4. In the figure at the right, $\ell \perp m$ and $m\angle 3 > 90^\circ$.

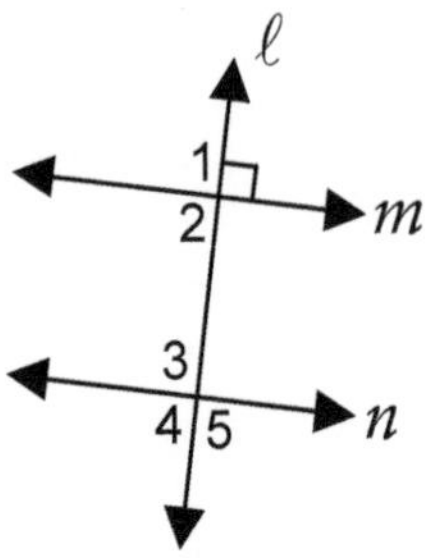

3. Which of the following *must* be true? Circle all that apply.

   (A) $m \parallel n$ (B) $\ell \perp n$

   (C) $m\angle 1 > 90^\circ$ (D) $m\angle 1 = 90^\circ$

   (E) $m\angle 1 = m\angle 2$ (F) $m\angle 1 < m\angle 4$

   (G) $m\angle 1 + m\angle 4 < 180^\circ$ (H) $m\angle 5 > 90^\circ$

4. Which of the following *cannot* be true? Circle all that apply.

   (A) $m \parallel n$ (B) $\ell \perp n$

   (C) $m\angle 1 > 90^\circ$ (D) $m\angle 1 = 90^\circ$

   (E) $m\angle 1 = m\angle 2$ (F) $m\angle 1 < m\angle 4$

   (G) $m\angle 1 + m\angle 4 < 180^\circ$ (H) $m\angle 5 > 90^\circ$

5. In the figure at the right, $\overline{RQ} \parallel \overline{UZ}$, RQ = n + 3, UZ = 2n – 3, RZ = n + 8, and ZV = 3n + 8. What are the possible value(s) of n? ______________

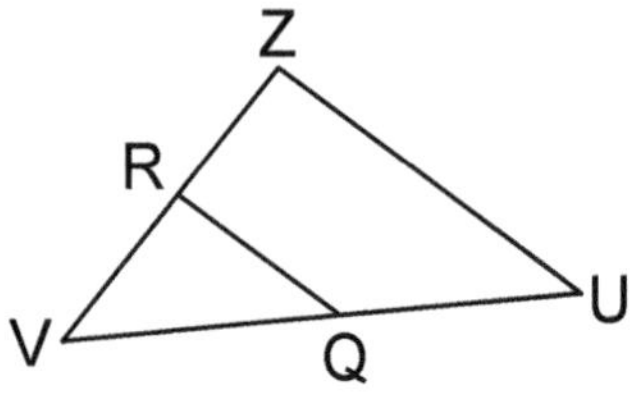

6. Draw a counterexample to show that the following statement is false.
If $\overset{\frown}{AB}$ and $\overset{\frown}{BC}$ are arcs of $\odot D$, then $m\overset{\frown}{AB} + m\overset{\frown}{BC} = m\overset{\frown}{ABC}$.

7-11. In the figure at the right, C and G are the centers of their respective circles, AD = 16 feet, and EG = 8 feet.

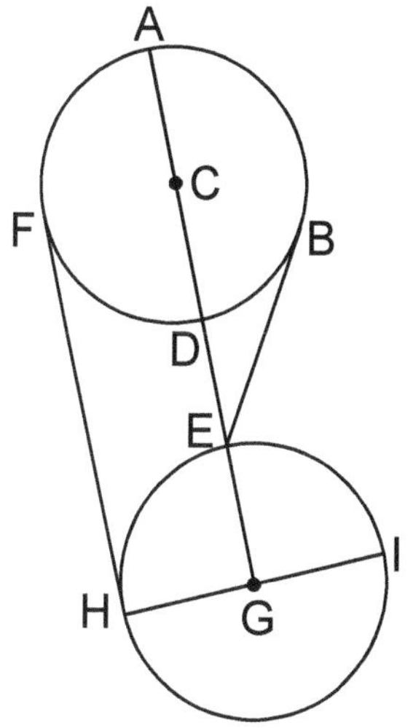

7. Which of the following terms apply to $\overline{GH}$? Circle all that apply.

   radius   secant   chord

   diameter   tangent

8. Which of the following terms apply to $\overline{AD}$? Circle all that apply.

   radius   secant   chord

   diameter   tangent

9. Name all the segments that appear to be tangent to ⊙G. ______________

10. AC = ___________ feet and HI = ___________ feet

11. Is ⊙C congruent to ⊙G? ___________ Why or why not? ________________

____

12. In the figure at the right, $\overline{TU}$ is tangent to ⊙Z at U, $\overline{TV}$ is tangent to ⊙Z at V, and $m\angle T = 62°$. Then $m\overset{\frown}{UV}$ = ___________ and $m\overset{\frown}{UWV}$ = ___________.

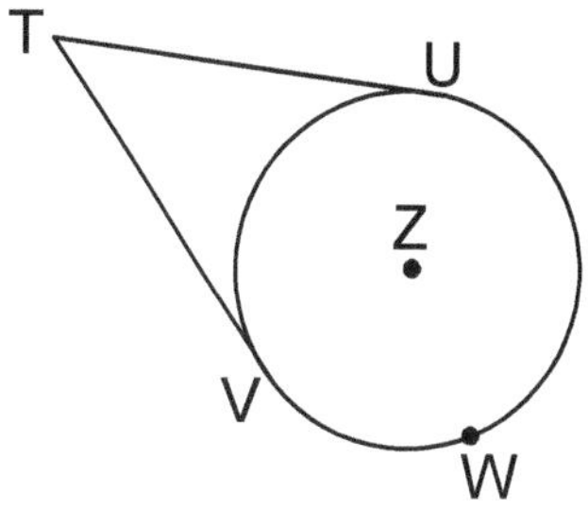

13. In the figure at the right, $m\overset{\frown}{RL} = (3x - 19)°$, $m\overset{\frown}{CM} = (x + 33)°$, and $m\angle LHM = 141°$. Then x = ___________, $m\overset{\frown}{CM}$ = ___________, and $m\overset{\frown}{CRM}$ = ___________.

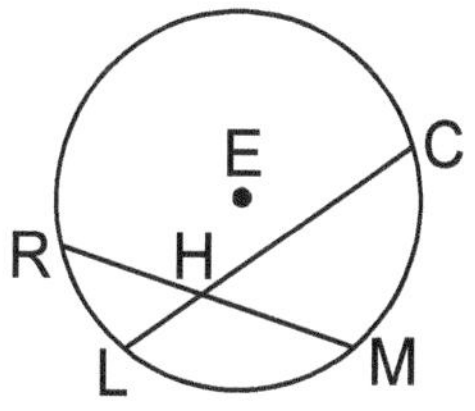

14-23. In the figure at the right, $\overline{JK}$ is tangent to $\odot O$ at K, $\overrightarrow{JN}$ is tangent to $\odot O$ at N, m$\overset{\frown}{KM}$ = 72°, and m$\overset{\frown}{QP}$ = 46°.

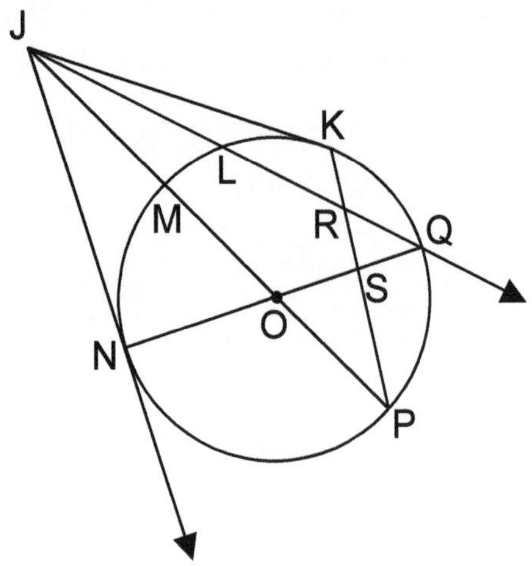

14. m $\overset{\frown}{NLQ}$ = ___________

    Is this a *minor arc*, a *major arc*, or a *semicircle*? ____________________

15. m $\overset{\frown}{KP}$ = ___________

    Is this a *minor arc*, a *major arc*, or a *semicircle*? ____________________

16. m $\overset{\frown}{KNP}$ = ___________

    Is this a *minor arc*, a *major arc*, or a *semicircle*? ____________________

17. m $\overset{\frown}{KQ}$ = ___________

    Is this a *minor arc*, a *major arc*, or a *semicircle*? ____________________

18. Is $\overset{\frown}{QP}$ congruent to $\overset{\frown}{MN}$? ___________ Why or why not? ____________________

    ____

19. m∠PJK = ___________

20. m∠QOP = ___________

21. m∠KPM = ___________

22. m$\angle$JNQ = ___________

23. m$\angle$QSP = ___________

24-25. In the figure at the right, $\overline{QI}$ is tangent to $\odot$O at I, $\overline{OK}$ is a radius of $\odot$O, QK = 24, OK = 10, and SQ = 16.

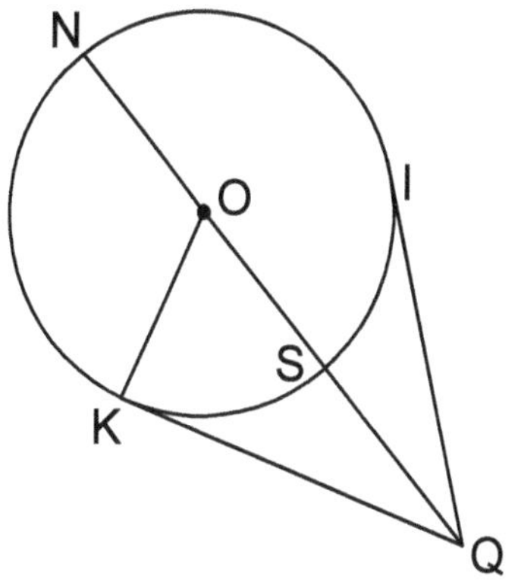

24. Is $\overline{QK}$ tangent to $\odot$O? ____________ How do you know? ______________________________

____

25. QI = __________

26-29. In the figure at the right, $\overline{ZG}$ is tangent to $\odot$B at Z, BP = 10, ZA = 8, PF = 12, BA = 4, ZG = 24, VG = x + 15, and TG = x + 7.

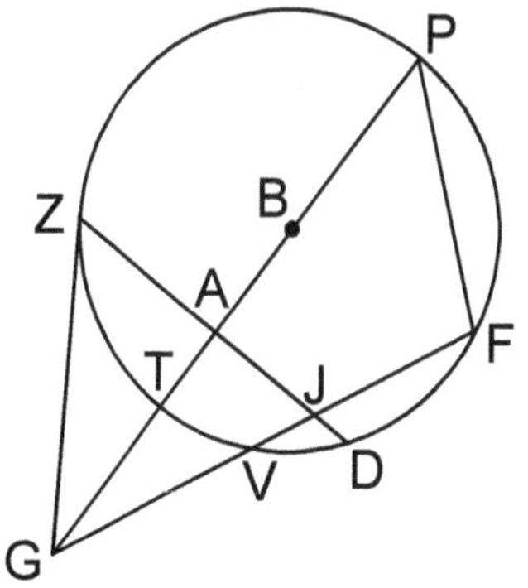

26. Is $\overline{ZD} \perp \overline{PA}$? ____________ How do you know?

____

____

27. Is $\overset{\frown}{ZD} \cong \overset{\frown}{PF}$? ____________ How do you know?

____

____

28. AT = __________

29. x = __________ and TG = __________

30-31. In the figure at the right, EB = 2x + 18, BN = 12 – x, CB = x + 15, CH = 21, UH = y, UN = 2y + 9, and MN = y + 8.

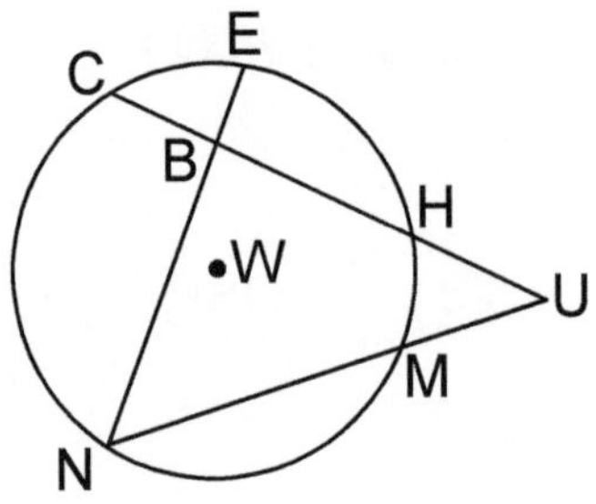

30. CB = __________ and HB = __________

31. What are the possible value(s) of y?

____

32-33. In the figure at the right, $\overline{FD} \perp \overline{HJ}$, $\overline{JD} \perp \overline{HD}$, FD = $2\sqrt{3}$, and HD = $\sqrt{30}$.

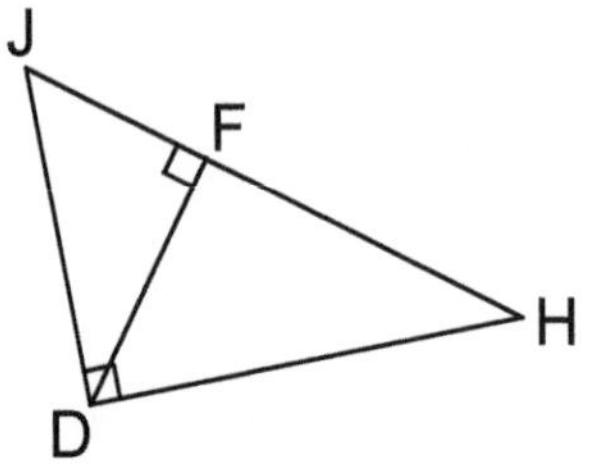

32. HF = __________, JF = __________,

JH = __________, and DJ = __________

33. m∠J ≈ __________ and m∠H ≈ __________

34-35. In the figure at the right, quadrilateral RTUV is a rectangle, m∠UTV = 32°, and TU = 7 inches.

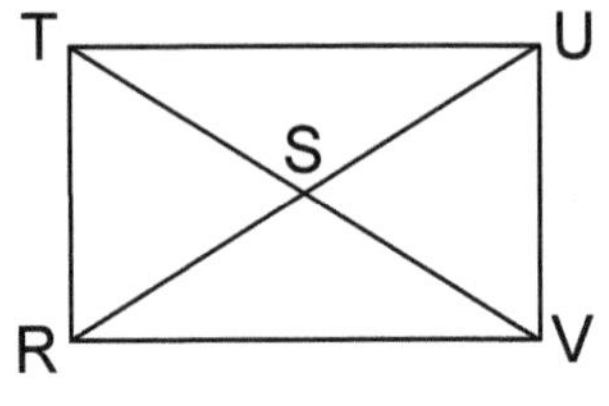

34. TV ≈ __________ and TS ≈ __________

35. m∠URV = __________, m∠TUR = __________, and m∠TSU = __________

36-37. Quadrilateral LQRA at the right is a parallelogram.

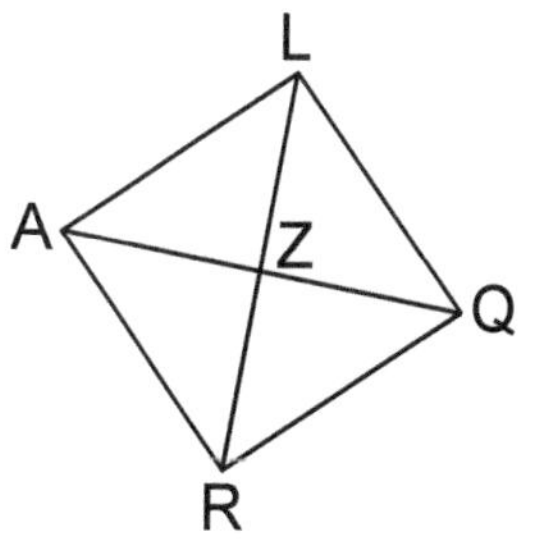

36. Which of the following *must* be true? Circle all that apply.

(A) $\overline{LA} \perp \overline{AR}$ (B) $\overline{AQ} \perp \overline{LR}$

(C) $\angle LAQ \cong \angle RQA$ (D) $\angle LAR \cong \angle LQR$

(E) $\angle LZA \cong \angle QZR$ (F) $m\angle LAQ + m\angle RQA = 180°$

37. Which of the following *could* be true? Circle all that apply.

(A) $\overline{LA} \perp \overline{AR}$ (B) $\overline{AQ} \perp \overline{LR}$

(C) $\angle LAQ \cong \angle RQA$ (D) $\angle LAR \cong \angle LQR$

(E) $\angle LZA \cong \angle QZR$ (F) $m\angle LAQ + m\angle RQA = 180°$

38. If $a \blacklozenge b = \dfrac{a+2b}{a-2b}$, then $3 \blacklozenge 5 =$ ______________.

Chapter 10 – Geometry in the Coordinate Plane

Part I – The Distance Formula

In this section, we will discuss how to find the distance between two points in the coordinate plane.

Example 1: Find the distance between the points (1, 4) and (1, –2).

We will start by plotting these points.

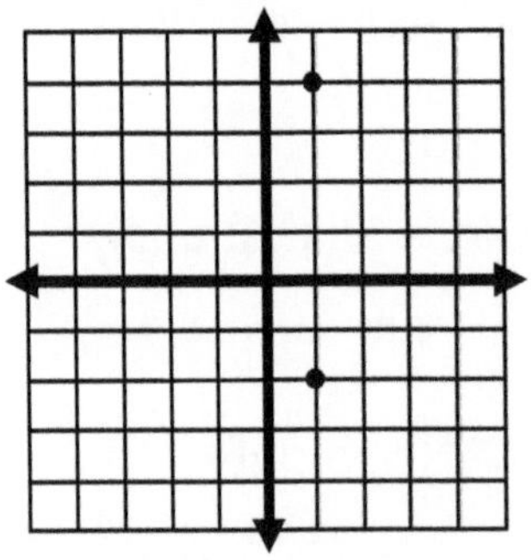

If you count the spaces between these points, you should find that the distance between them is 6 spaces.

Example 2: Find the distance between the points (–3, 4) and (1, 4).

Again, we will start by plotting these points.

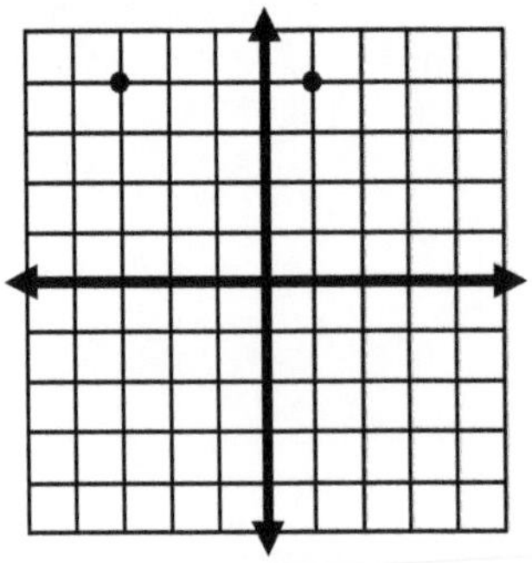

If you count the spaces between these points, you should find that the distance between them is 4 spaces.

Example 3: Find the distance between the points (–3, 4) and (1, –2).

Once again, we will start by plotting these points.

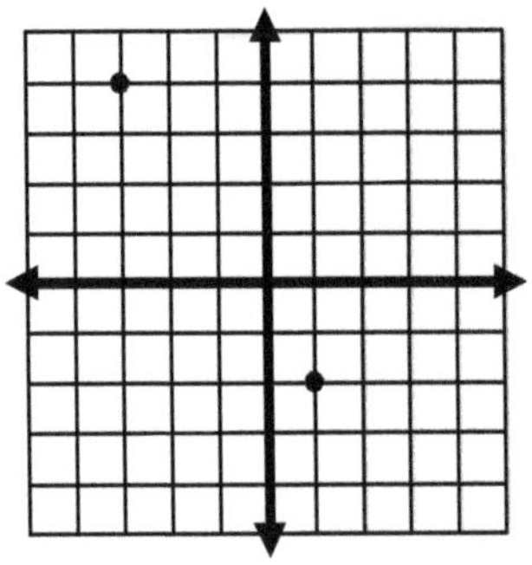

This time, we cannot count the spaces between the points like we did in Examples 1 and 2. However, we can use the Pythagorean Theorem to find the distance between these points. Notice that the figure below shows a right triangle, and the length of the hypotenuse is equal to the distance between the points (–3, 4) and (1, –2).

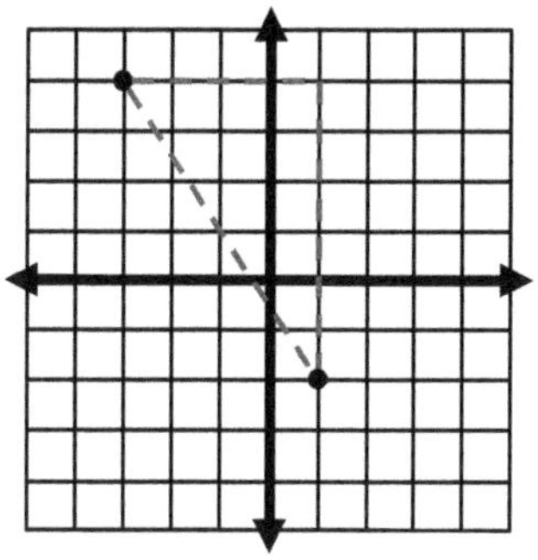

Now, if we let c represent the length of the hypotenuse of this triangle, we can say that $4^2 + 6^2 = c^2$. This tells us that $c^2 = 52$, and so c must equal $2\sqrt{13}$. (You may want to refresh your memory on square roots by reviewing the section in the Appendix on this topic.) Therefore, the distance between the points (–3, 4) and (1, –2) must equal $2\sqrt{13}$.

These three examples and the thought process behind them give rise to the distance formula.

The Distance Formula

The distance between the points (x_1, y_1) and (x_2, y_2) is given by

$$d = \sqrt{(x_2 - x_1)^2 + (y_2 - y_1)^2}$$

In the next example, we will re-work Example 3, except we will use the Distance Formula.

Example 4: Find the distance between the points (–3, 4) and (1, –2) using the distance formula.

We will let the point (–3, 4) be our (x_1, y_1), and we will let the point (1, –2) be our (x_2, y_2). This tells us that the distance between these points is given by $d = \sqrt{(1-(-3))^2 + (-2-4)^2}$. This simplifies to $\sqrt{52}$, which simplifies further to $2\sqrt{13}$. (Notice that this agrees with the answer we found earlier in Example 3.)

Example 5: Find the distance between the points (1, –3) and (7, –11) using the distance formula.

We will let the point (1, –3) be our (x_1, y_1), and we will let the point (7, –11) be our (x_2, y_2). This tells us that the distance between these points is given by $d = \sqrt{(7-1)^2 + (-11-(-3))^2}$. This simplifies to $\sqrt{100}$. Since $\sqrt{100} = 10$, we can say that the distance between the points (1, –3) and (7, –11) is equal to 10 units.

Example 6: A triangle has its vertices at the points (2, –3), (4, 5), and (–4, 3). Is this a scalene, isosceles, or equilateral triangle?

To answer this question, we must find the lengths of each of the sides of the triangle. Or, in other words, we must find the distance between each set of points.

The distance between the points (2, –3) and (4, 5) is equal to $\sqrt{(4-2)^2+(5-(-3))^2}$. This simplifies to $\sqrt{68}$, which simplifies further to $2\sqrt{17}$.

The distance between the points (4, 5) and (–4, 3) is equal to $\sqrt{(-4-4)^2+(3-5)^2}$. This simplifies to $\sqrt{68}$, which simplifies further to $2\sqrt{17}$.

The distance between the points (2, –3) and (–4, 3) is equal to $\sqrt{(-4-2)^2+(3-(-3))^2}$. This simplifies to $\sqrt{72}$, which simplifies further to $6\sqrt{2}$.

Since two of the sides have lengths of $2\sqrt{17}$, we can say that this triangle is an isosceles triangle.

Problems:

1. Find the distance between the points (0, 5) and (0, –2). _________

2. Find the distance between the points (–5, –8) and (4, –8). _________

3. Find the distance between the points (3, 2) and (–8, 2). _________

4. Find the distance between the points (–6, 0) and (–2, –1). _________

5. Find the distance between the points (7, –1) and (3, –5). _________

6. Find the distance between the points (9, –2) and (3, 1). _________

7. Find the distance between the points (0, –2) and (3, –4). _________

8. Find the distance between the points (–4, 7) and (–3, 9). _________

9. Find the distance between the points (5, –6) and (11, –14). _________

10. Find the distance between the points (–2, 4) and (–12, –6). _________

11. Find the distance between the points (2, 9) and (5, 6). _________

12. Find the distance between the points (0, –7) and (5, –10). _________

13. Find the distance between the points (–7, 9) and (–3, 12). _________

14. Find the distance between the points (4, –2) and (10, –8). _________

15. Find the distance between the points (5, –4) and (6, –11). _________

16. Find the distance between the points (10, 0) and (1, –3). _________

17. Find the distance between the points (0, –1) and ($\sqrt{3}$, 3). _________

18. Find the distance between the points (2, $-3\sqrt{6}$) and (–3, $-\sqrt{6}$). _________

19. Find the distance between the points ($8\sqrt{5}$, –3) and ($6\sqrt{5}$, –7). _________

20. Find the distance between the points (0, $2\sqrt{3}$) and (4, $5\sqrt{3}$). _________

21-28. The coordinates of the vertices of eight different triangles are given below. Determine if each triangle is a *scalene triangle*, *isosceles triangle*, or *equilateral triangle*.

21. (3, 2), (7, 2), (5, –1)

22. (2, 0), (4, –3), (–1, 0)

23. (0, –1), (–2, 7), (–6, 2)

24. (5, −3), (5, 6), (−4, −3)

25. (−5, 0), (7, 0), $(1, 6\sqrt{3})$

26. $(3\sqrt{2}, -4)$, (0, 5), $(8\sqrt{2}, 3)$

27. (0, −1), $(6\sqrt{2}, -2)$, $(5\sqrt{2}, 4)$

28. (0, −8), $(6\sqrt{3}, -5)$, $(\sqrt{3}, 2)$

Part II – The Midpoint Formula

In this section, we will discuss how to find the midpoint of a segment in the coordinate plane.

Example 1: Find the midpoint of the segment that has its endpoints at (–5, 4) and (1, 4).

We will start by plotting these points and the corresponding segment.

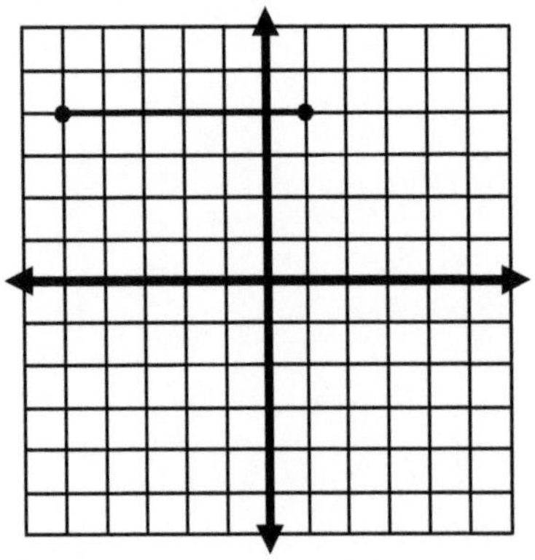

You should be able to look at this picture and see that the point that is halfway in the middle between the endpoints of this segment is at (–2, 4).

Example 2: Find the midpoint of the segment that has its endpoints at (2, 3) and (2, –2).

We will start by plotting these points and the corresponding segment again.

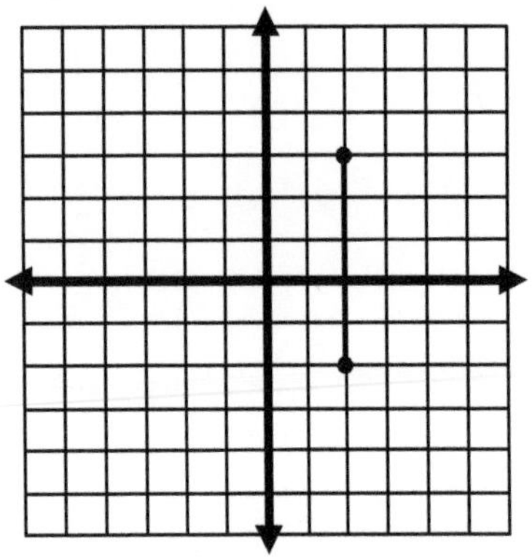

This problem is a little harder than the one in Example 1, but, if you think about it hard enough, you should be able to see that the point that is halfway in the middle between the endpoints of this segment is at $\left(2, \frac{1}{2}\right)$.

Example 3: Find the midpoint of the segment that has its endpoints at (3, –1) and (–5, 5).

Once again, we will start by graphing these points. This is done on the next page.

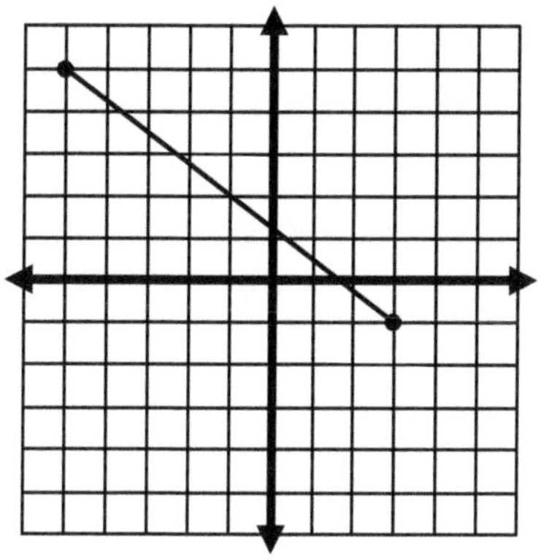

This problem is a little harder than either of the previous two, but, if you think about it, you should realize that the point that is halfway between the endpoints of this segment is (–1, 2).

If you think about what we did in these examples a little harder, you might realize that, in order to find the midpoint of a segment when you are given the endpoints, you need to average the x-coordinates of the endpoints, and you also need to average the y-coordinates of the endpoints. This gives rise to the Midpoint Formula.

The Midpoint Formula

If the endpoints of a segment are at (x_1, y_1) and (x_2, y_2), then the midpoint of the segment is at $\left(\frac{x_2+x_1}{2}, \frac{y_2+y_1}{2}\right)$.

In the next example, we will re-work Example 3, except we will use the Midpoint Formula this time.

Example 4: Find the midpoint of the segment that has its endpoints at (3, –1) and (–5, 5) using the Midpoint Formula.

We will let the point (3, –1) be our (x_1, y_1), and we will let the point (–5, 5) be our (x_2, y_2). This tells us that the midpoint of this segment is given by $\left(\frac{-5+3}{2}, \frac{5+(-1)}{2}\right)$, which simplifies to (–1, 2). (Note that this agrees with the answer we found in Example 3.)

Example 5: Find the midpoint of the segment that has its endpoints at $(2\sqrt{3}, 7)$ and $(8\sqrt{3}, 15)$ using the Midpoint Formula.

We will let the point $(2\sqrt{3}, 7)$ be our (x_1, y_1), and we will let the point $(8\sqrt{3}, 15)$ be our (x_2, y_2). This tells us that the midpoint of this segment is given by $\left(\frac{8\sqrt{3}+2\sqrt{3}}{2}, \frac{15+7}{2}\right)$. This simplifies to $\left(\frac{10\sqrt{3}}{2}, \frac{22}{2}\right)$, which simplifies further to $(5\sqrt{3}, 11)$.

Example 6: If one endpoint of a segment is at (–1, 5), and if the midpoint of the segment is at (3, –2), what are the coordinates of the other endpoint?

Notice that this example is different from the last five examples because, in the previous examples, we were given the coordinates of the endpoints and asked to find the midpoint; in this example, we are given the midpoint and one of the endpoints and asked to find the other endpoint.

Next, we will note that the formula for the x-coordinate of the midpoint is $x_M = \frac{x_2 + x_1}{2}$, and the formula for the y-coordinate of the midpoint is $y_M = \frac{y_2 + y_1}{2}$.

This tells us that we can work this problem as shown below.

$$x_M = \frac{x_2 + x_1}{2} \qquad y_M = \frac{y_2 + y_1}{2}$$

$$3 = \frac{x_2 + (-1)}{2} \qquad -2 = \frac{y_2 + 5}{2}$$

$$6 = x_2 - 1 \qquad -4 = y_2 + 5$$ (by multiplying both sides of each equation by 2)

$$7 = x_2 \qquad -9 = y_2$$

This tells us that the other endpoint is at (7, –9).

Problems:

1. Find the midpoint of the segment with endpoints at (3, –1) and (9, –1). (____, ____)

2. Find the midpoint of the segment with endpoints at (5, 8) and (5, –10). (____, ____)

3. Find the midpoint of the segment with endpoints at (2, –3) and (4, –5). (____, ____)

4. Find the midpoint of the segment with endpoints at (–1, 0) and (3, –7). (____, ____)

5. Find the midpoint of the segment with endpoints at (4, –5) and (–3, 1). (____, ____)

6. Find the midpoint of the segment with endpoints at (5, 12) and (–3, 8). (____, ____)

7. Find the midpoint of the segment with endpoints at (–4, –3) and (5, 0). (____, ____)

8. Find the midpoint of the segment with endpoints at (–10, 1) and (–5, 3). (____, ____)

9. Find the midpoint of the segment with endpoints at (–18, –7) and (–3, 6).
(____, ____)

10. Find the midpoint of the segment with endpoints at (–11, 15) and (–5, –9).
(____, ____)

11. Find the midpoint of the segment with endpoints at (–17, 0) and (–15, 3).
(____, ____)

12. Find the midpoint of the segment with endpoints at (–1, –8) and (–9, –19).
(____, ____)

13. Find the midpoint of the segment with endpoints at (–15, 5) and (23, –5).
(____, ____)

14. Find the midpoint of the segment with endpoints at (–10, 22) and (10, –9).
(____, ____)

15. Find the midpoint of the segment with endpoints at (6, –5) and (12, 3). (____, ____)

16. Find the midpoint of the segment with endpoints at (–4, –1) and (–14, –10).

(____, ____)

17. Find the midpoint of the segment with endpoints at (–2, $3\sqrt{7}$) and (8, 0).

(______, ______)

18. Find the midpoint of the segment with endpoints at ($-5\sqrt{6}$, –4) and ($7\sqrt{6}$, 3).

(______, ______)

19. Find the midpoint of the segment with endpoints at ($9\sqrt{5}$, –10) and ($-3\sqrt{5}$, 2).

(______, ______)

20. Find the midpoint of the segment with endpoints at ($3\sqrt{10}$, 9) and ($4\sqrt{10}$, 12).

(______, ______)

21. Find the midpoint of the segment with endpoints at ($\sqrt{2}$, $9\sqrt{2}$) and ($-3\sqrt{2}$, $6\sqrt{2}$).

(______, ______)

22. Find the midpoint of the segment with endpoints at (0, $7\sqrt{5}$) and ($\sqrt{6}$, $4\sqrt{5}$).

(______, ______)

23. If one endpoint of a segment is at (4, –2), and if the midpoint of the segment is at (3, –7), what are the coordinates of the other endpoint? (______, ______)

24. If one endpoint of a segment is at (–5, 8), and if the midpoint of the segment is at (–1, 0), what are the coordinates of the other endpoint? (_____, _____)

25. If one endpoint of a segment is at (–9, –3), and if the midpoint of the segment is at (–4, 5), what are the coordinates of the other endpoint? (_____, _____)

26. If one endpoint of a segment is at (0, –1), and if the midpoint of the segment is at (–2, –7), what are the coordinates of the other endpoint? (_____, _____)

27. If one endpoint of a segment is at (–3, 4), and if the midpoint of the segment is at (–7, –5), what are the coordinates of the other endpoint? (_____, _____)

28. If one endpoint of a segment is at ($9\sqrt{2}$, –3), and if the midpoint of the segment is at ($4\sqrt{2}$, 1), what are the coordinates of the other endpoint? (_____, _____)

29. If one endpoint of a segment is at (–5, $\sqrt{3}$), and if the midpoint of the segment is at (–2, $-\sqrt{3}$), what are the coordinates of the other endpoint? (_____, _____)

30. If one endpoint of a segment is at (0, $-\sqrt{10}$), and if the midpoint of the segment is at ($2\sqrt{7}$, $2\sqrt{10}$), what are the coordinates of the other endpoint? (_____, _____)

Part III – Verifying Conjectures Related to Triangles and Quadrilaterals

In this section, we will discuss how we can use the coordinate plane to discover and prove properties about triangles and quadrilaterals.

Example 1: Quadrilateral WXYZ has its vertices at the following points: W (6, –1), X (2, 5), Y (–4, 1), and Z (0, –5). Tell which of the following terms apply to quadrilateral WXYZ: parallelogram, rhombus, rectangle, square, trapezoid, isosceles trapezoid, and/or kite. Name all that apply.

We will begin by plotting the points on the coordinate plane and drawing quadrilateral WXYZ.

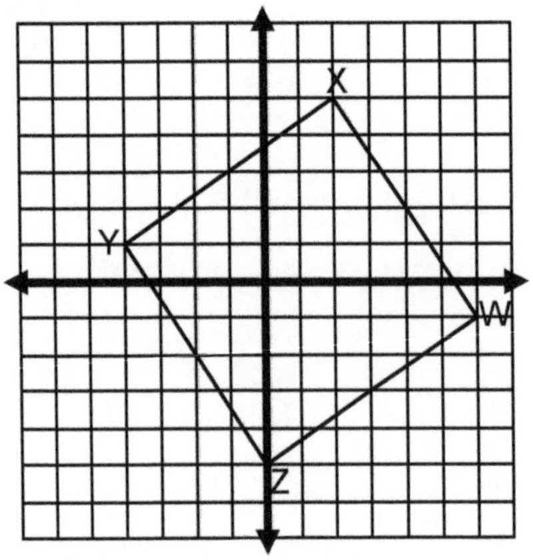

We will show that the terms *rectangle*, *rhombus*, *square*, and *parallelogram* all apply to quadrilateral WXYZ.

The easiest way to show that quadrilateral WXYZ is a rectangle is to show that all four of its angles are right angles. To do this, we must show that the consecutive sides of quadrilateral WXYZ have slopes that are opposite reciprocals. (Recall that the formula for the slope of a line that passes through (x_1, y_1) and (x_2, y_2) is $m = \frac{y_2 - y_1}{x_2 - x_1}$ and that perpendicular lines have slopes that are opposite reciprocals.)

slope of $\overline{XY} = \frac{1-5}{-4-2} = \frac{2}{3}$ slope of $\overline{ZW} = \frac{-1-(-5)}{6-0} = \frac{2}{3}$

slope of $\overline{YZ} = \frac{-5-1}{0-(-4)} = -\frac{3}{2}$ slope of $\overline{WX} = \frac{5-(-1)}{2-6} = -\frac{3}{2}$

Since each set of consecutive sides have slopes that are opposite reciprocals, we can say that all the angles of quadrilateral WXYZ must be right angles, and so quadrilateral WXYZ must be a rectangle.

The easiest way to show that quadrilateral WXYZ is a rhombus is to show that all of its sides are congruent to each other. We will use the distance formula to do this, as shown below.

$XY = \sqrt{(-4-2)^2+(1-5)^2} = 2\sqrt{13}$ $ZW = \sqrt{(6-0)^2+(-1-(-5))^2} = 2\sqrt{13}$

$YZ = \sqrt{(0-(-4))^2+(-5-1)^2} = 2\sqrt{13}$ $WX = \sqrt{(2-6)^2+(5-(-1))^2} = 2\sqrt{13}$

Since this shows that $\overline{WX}$, $\overline{XY}$, $\overline{YZ}$, and $\overline{WZ}$ all have the same length, we can now say that quadrilateral WXYZ must be a rhombus.

Since we have shown that quadrilateral WXYZ is both a rectangle and a rhombus, we can say that it is also a square. Finally, since all squares are also parallelograms, we can say that quadrilateral WXYZ is also a parallelogram.

As we stated earlier, the methods we used here are the easiest ways to prove that the terms *parallelogram*, *rectangle*, *rhombus*, and *square* apply to quadrilateral WXYZ. There are, however, many other ways that we could have proven this.

To prove that quadrilateral WXYZ is a parallelogram, we could have done any of the following.

- We could have shown that $\overline{WX} \parallel \overline{YZ}$ and $\overline{XY} \parallel \overline{WZ}$ by showing that $\overline{WX}$ and $\overline{YZ}$ have equal slopes and that the slopes of $\overline{XY}$ and $\overline{WZ}$ are also equal. Then we could have used the definition of a parallelogram to say that quadrilateral WXYZ must be a parallelogram.
- We could have used the distance formula to show that $\overline{WX} \cong \overline{YZ}$ and $\overline{XY} \cong \overline{WZ}$. Then we could have used the Opposite Sides of a Parallelogram Converse Theorem to say that quadrilateral WXYZ must be a parallelogram.
- We could have shown that $\overline{XZ}$ and $\overline{WY}$ have the same midpoint. Then we could have used the Diagonals of a Parallelogram Converse Theorem to say that quadrilateral WXYZ must be a parallelogram.
- We could have shown that $\overline{WX} \cong \overline{YZ}$ (using the distance formula) and that $\overline{WX} \parallel \overline{YZ}$ (by showing that their slopes are equal). Then we could have used the theorem that states, "If one pair of opposite sides of a quadrilateral is both parallel and congruent, then the quadrilateral is a parallelogram" to say that quadrilateral WXYZ must be a parallelogram.
- We could have shown that $\overline{XY} \cong \overline{WZ}$ (using the distance formula) and that $\overline{XY} \parallel \overline{WZ}$ (by showing that their slopes are equal). Then we could have used the theorem that states, "If one pair of opposite sides of a quadrilateral is both parallel and congruent, then the quadrilateral is a parallelogram" to say that quadrilateral WXYZ must be a parallelogram.

To prove that quadrilateral WXYZ is a rectangle, we could have done either of the following.

- We could have shown that quadrilateral WXYZ is a parallelogram (using one of the methods above) and that $\overline{XZ} \cong \overline{WY}$ (using the distance formula). Then we could have used the theorem that states, "If the diagonals of a parallelogram are congruent, then it is a rectangle" to say that quadrilateral WXYZ must be a rectangle.

- Or, as we did in the example, we could have shown that consecutive sides of quadrilateral WXYZ are perpendicular.

To prove that quadrilateral WXYZ is a rhombus, we could have done either of the following.

- We could have shown that quadrilateral WXYZ is a parallelogram (using one of the methods discussed on the previous page) and that $\overline{XZ} \perp \overline{WY}$ (by showing that their slopes are opposite reciprocals). Then we could have used the theorem that states, "If the diagonals of a parallelogram are perpendicular, then it is a rhombus" to say that quadrilateral WXYZ must be a rhombus.
- Or, as we did in the example, we could have shown that $\overline{WX}$, $\overline{XY}$, $\overline{YZ}$, and $\overline{WZ}$ are all congruent to each other.

Example 2: Set up a generic isosceles trapezoid in the coordinate plane, and label the coordinates of its vertices using as few variables as possible.

There are four main ways that we can do this. There are many variations on each of these, but these pictures should give you an idea of how we set up generic figures in the coordinate plane and label the coordinates of the vertices. All of the answers shown in this example are equally correct.

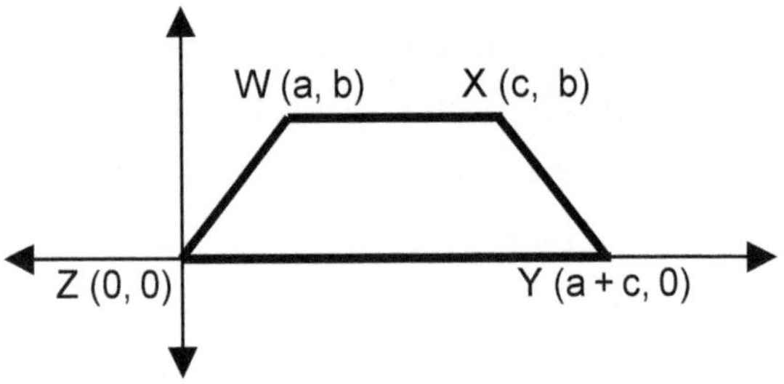

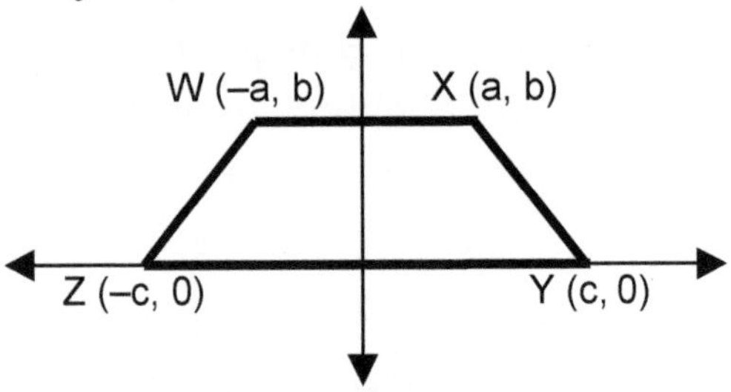

If the question wants us to talk about midpoints, we can multiply each of our coordinates by 2 so that we can avoid some of the fractions, as shown below.

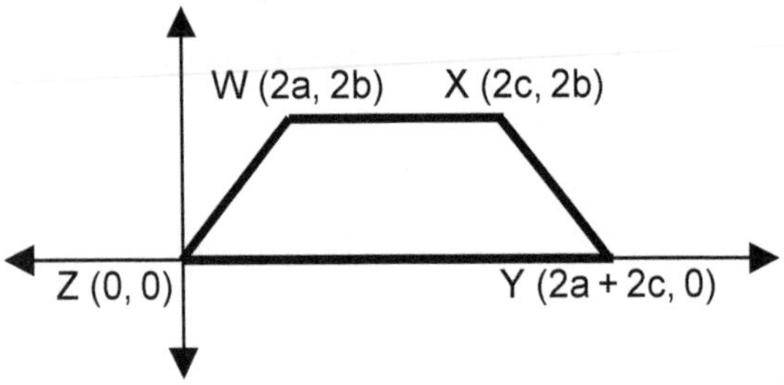

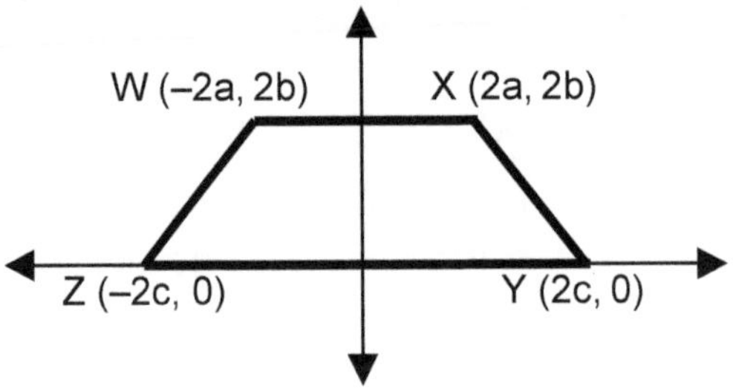

Example 3: Use a coordinate proof to show that, if the diagonals of a parallelogram are congruent, then the parallelogram must be a rectangle.

We will begin by drawing a generic parallelogram and labeling the coordinates of its vertices as shown on the next page.

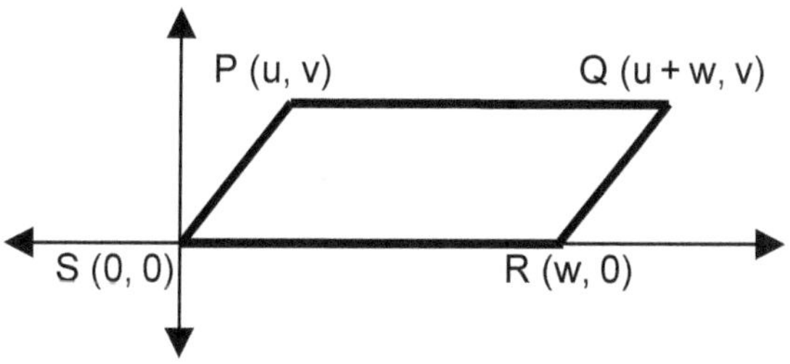

To see why we can say that point Q has the coordinates (u + w, v), look at the picture below. We can write the x-coordinate of point Q as u + w because, in order to get to point Q, we must go to the right u units (note that the length of the dotted gray segment below is u units) and then to the right w more units (note that the length of $\overline{RS}$ is w units, and so the length of $\overline{PQ}$ is also w units). Also, the point Q is at the same height above the x-axis as point P, and so the y-coordinate of point Q is v.

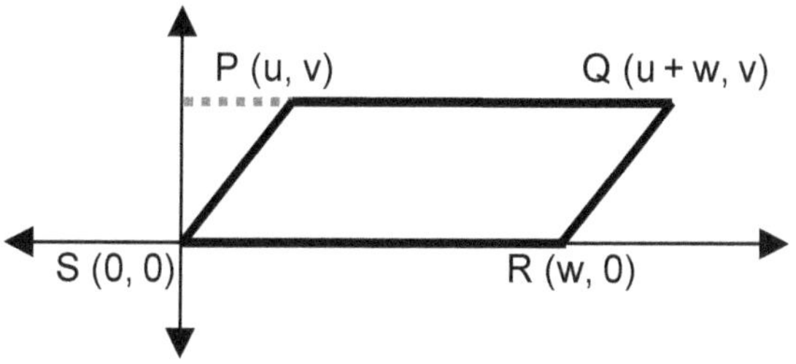

Now, we can say that we are given that quadrilateral PQRS is a parallelogram and that $\overline{PR} \cong \overline{QS}$. We can use the definition of congruent segments to say that this means that PR = QS. Next, we will use the distance formula to talk about the lengths of the diagonals.

$$PR = \sqrt{(w-u)^2 + (0-v)^2} = \sqrt{(w-u)^2 + v^2}$$

$$SQ = \sqrt{(u+w-0)^2 + (v-0)^2} = \sqrt{(u+w)^2 + v^2}$$

Now, we can use the Substitution Property of Equality to say the following.

$$\sqrt{(w-u)^2 + v^2} = \sqrt{(u+w)^2 + v^2}$$

$$(w-u)^2 + v^2 = (u+w)^2 + v^2 \quad \text{(by squaring both sides)}$$

$$(w-u)^2 = (u+w)^2 \quad \text{(using the Subtraction Property of Equality)}$$

$$w - u = \pm(u + w) \quad \text{(by taking the square root of both sides)}$$

$$w - u = u + w \quad \text{or} \quad w - u = -u - w$$

$$u = 0 \quad \text{or} \quad w = 0$$

If w = 0, then quadrilateral PQRS is not really a quadrilateral. Therefore, u = 0. Since this can only happen if $\overline{PS}$ lies on the y-axis, we can now say that quadrilateral PQRS must be a rectangle.

Example 4: Prove the Midsegment of a Trapezoid Theorem using a coordinate proof.

We will begin by drawing a generic trapezoid in the coordinate plane as shown below. Recall that the Midsegment of a Trapezoid Theorem talks about *all* trapezoids (and not just isosceles trapezoids), and so we must use more variables to label the coordinates of our vertices. Also, since the Midsegment of a Trapezoid Theorem talks about midpoints, we will multiply all of our coordinates by 2 so that we can avoid some fractions when we use the midpoint formula.

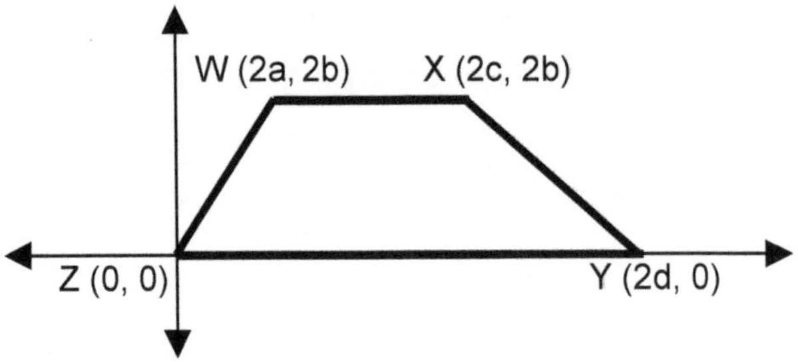

Next, we must find the coordinates of the midpoints of $\overline{WZ}$ and $\overline{XY}$. Using the midpoint formula, the midpoint of $\overline{WZ}$ is at $\left(\frac{2a+0}{2}, \frac{2b+0}{2}\right)$, or (a, b). We will call this point M. Using the midpoint formula again, the midpoint of $\overline{XY}$ is at $\left(\frac{2c+2d}{2}, \frac{2b+0}{0}\right)$, or (c + d, b). We will call this point N. This gives us the following picture.

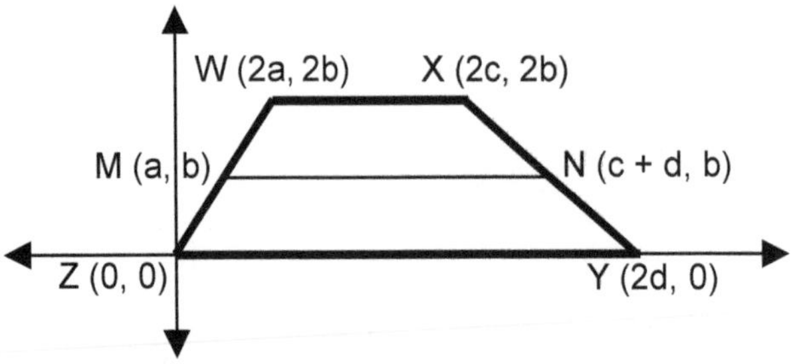

We can now say that we want to prove that $\overline{MN}$ is parallel to both $\overline{WX}$ and $\overline{ZY}$ and that MN = $\frac{WX+ZY}{2}$.

To prove that $\overline{MN}$ is parallel to both $\overline{WX}$ and $\overline{ZY}$, we will show that the slopes of $\overline{MN}$, $\overline{WX}$, and $\overline{YZ}$ are all equal to each other.

$$\text{slope of } \overline{MN} = \frac{b-b}{c+d-a} = 0$$

$$\text{slope of } \overline{WX} = \frac{2b-2b}{2c-2a} = 0$$

$$\text{slope of } \overline{ZY} = \frac{0-0}{2d-0} = 0$$

All of these slopes are equal, and so $\overline{MN}$ must be parallel to both $\overline{WX}$ and $\overline{ZY}$.

To prove that MN = $\frac{WX + ZY}{2}$, we will use the distance formula to say the following.

$$MN = \sqrt{(c + d - a)^2 + (b - b)^2} = \sqrt{(c + d - a)^2} = c + d - a$$

$$WX = \sqrt{(2c - 2a)^2 + (2b - 2b)^2} = \sqrt{(2c - 2a)^2} = 2c - 2a$$

$$ZY = \sqrt{(2d - 0)^2 + (0 - 0)^2} = \sqrt{(2d)^2} = 2d$$

Now, we will note that we can use the Substitution Property of Equality to say that $\frac{WX + ZY}{2} = \frac{2c - 2a + 2d}{2}$, or $c - a + d$. Since MN also equals $c - a + d$, we can use the Substitution Property of Equality again to say that MN = $\frac{WX + ZY}{2}$.

Problems:

1-5. For each of the following sets of points, state if quadrilateral WXYZ is a *parallelogram*, *rhombus*, *rectangle*, *square*, *trapezoid*, *isosceles trapezoid*, and/or *kite*. Name all that apply.

1. W (–2, 6), X (4, 4), Y (2, 1), and Z (–4, 3)

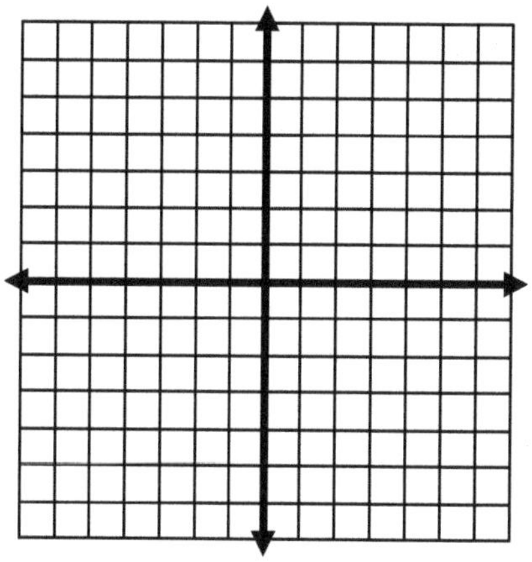

2. W (–4, 1), X (–1, –6), Y (5, 0), and Z (1, 6)

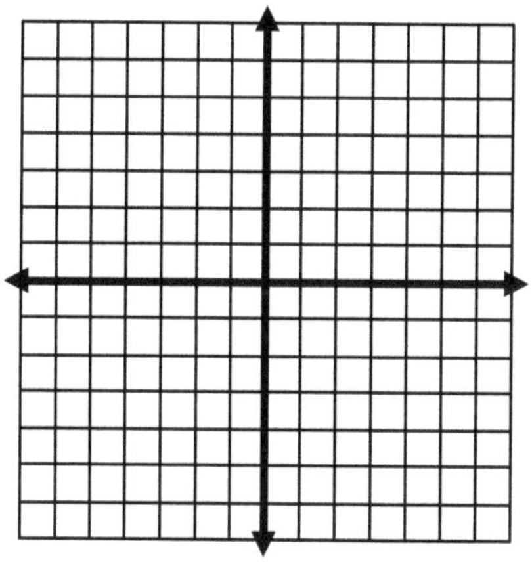

3. W (5, –1), X (2, –5), Y (2, 0), and Z (5, 4)

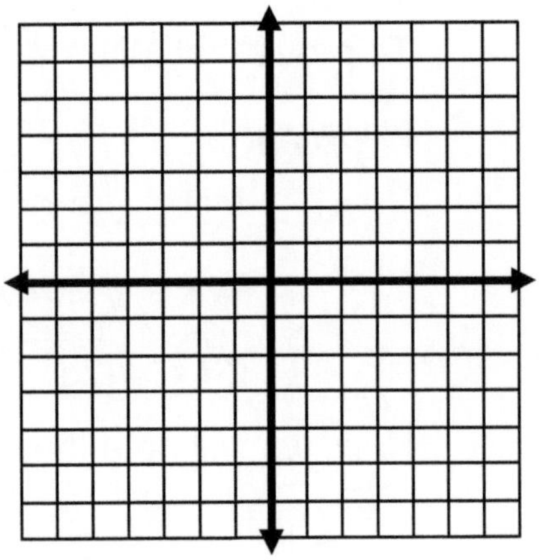

4. W (3, –3), X (5, 3), Y (–4, 6), and Z (–6, 0)

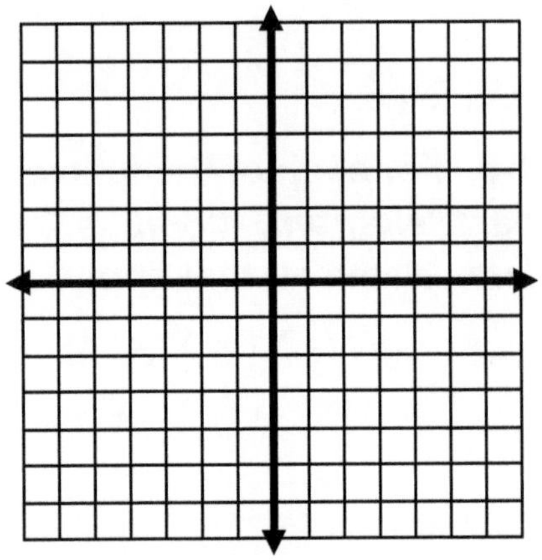

5. W (–6, 3), X(–1, –2), Y(6, 1), Z(2, 5)

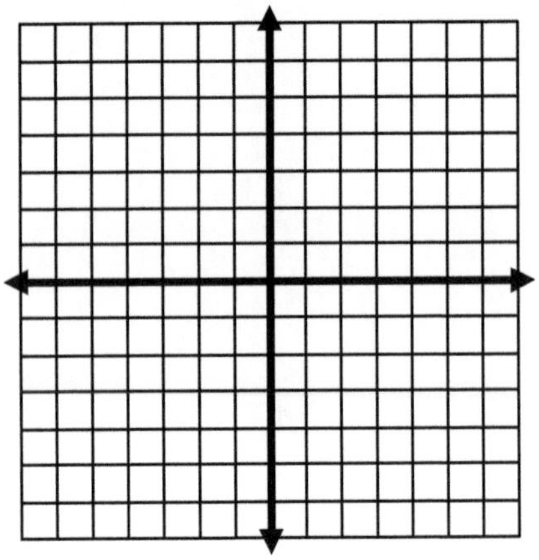

6. If two corners of a square are at (3, 1) and (–2, 1), then the other corners could be at

(______, ______) and (______, ______) OR at (______, ______) and (______, ______).

7-10. Fill in the missing coordinates of the vertices of each of the following figures without introducing any new variables.

7. Quadrilateral JKLM is a rectangle.

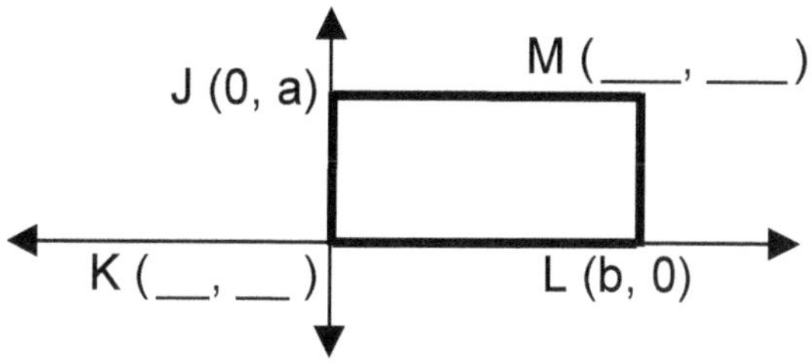

8. Quadrilateral NOPQ is a rectangle.

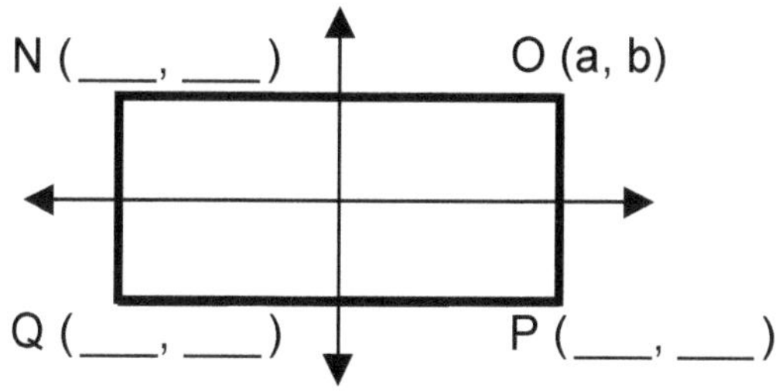

9. Quadrilateral RSTU is a parallelogram.

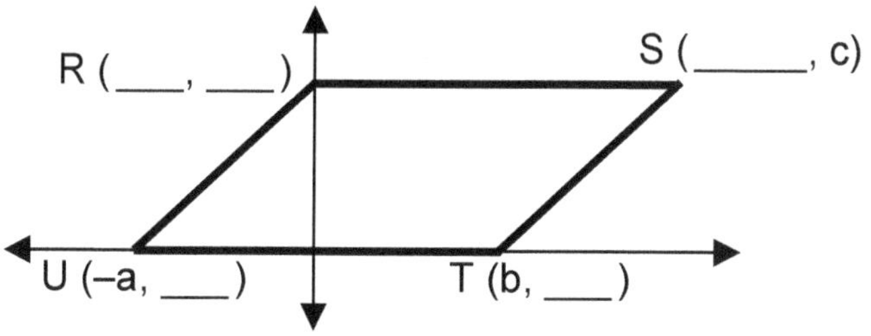

10. Quadrilateral VWXY is a parallelogram.

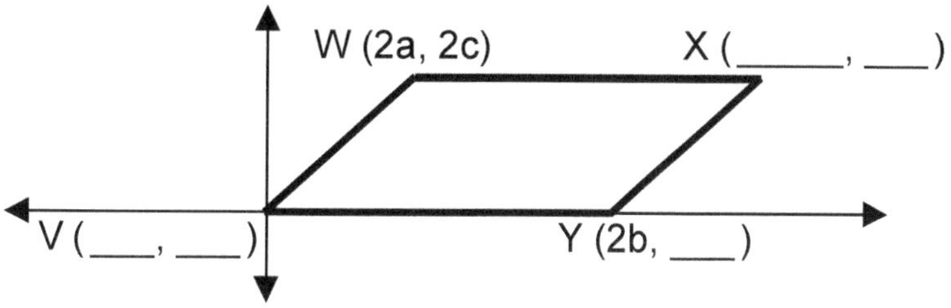

11-14. Fill in the coordinates of the vertices of each of the following figures using as few variables as possible.

11. Quadrilateral EFGH is a kite.

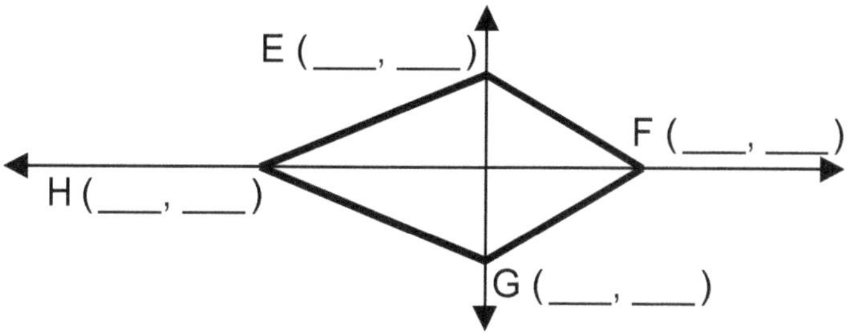

12. Triangle KLZ is an isosceles triangle.

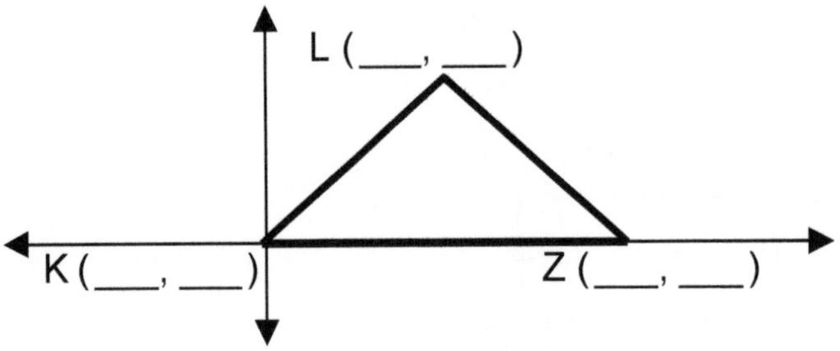

13. Triangle PQR is an isosceles triangle.

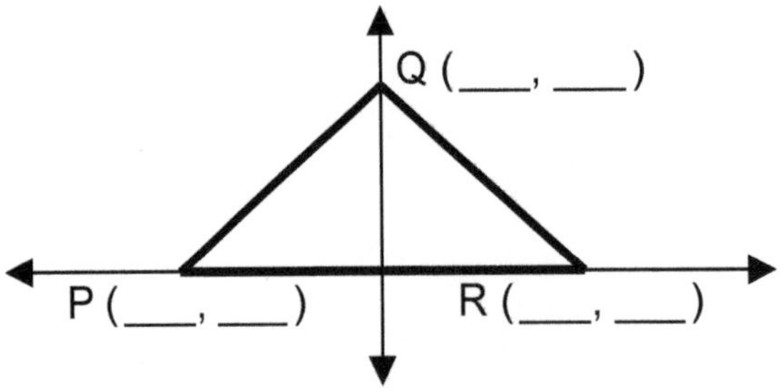

14. Triangle GTM is an equilateral triangle.

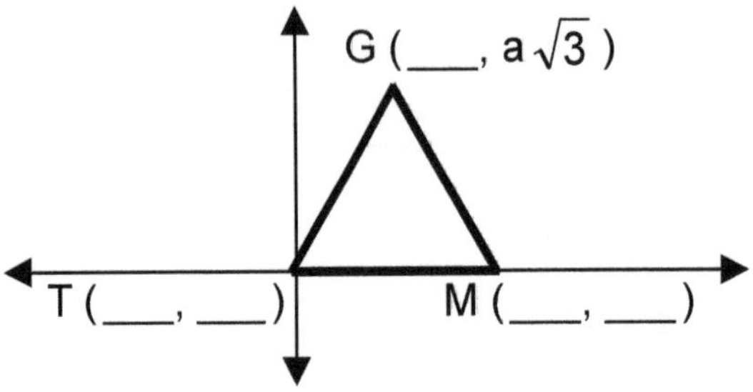

15. Set up a generic square in the coordinate plane and label the coordinates of its vertices.

16. Set up a generic isosceles right triangle in the coordinate plane and label the coordinates of its vertices.

17-29. Prove each of the following statements using a coordinate proof.

17. If a trapezoid is isosceles, then its diagonals are congruent.

18. If a quadrilateral is a rectangle, then its diagonals are congruent.

19. If a quadrilateral is a parallelogram, then its diagonals bisect each other.

20. If a quadrilateral is a rhombus, then its diagonals are perpendicular.
Hint: Set your rhombus up in the coordinate plane as shown below. Then, after you find the slope of both $\overline{JK}$ and $\overline{JK}$, use the following theorem: Two nonvertical lines are perpendicular if and only if the product of their slopes is −1.

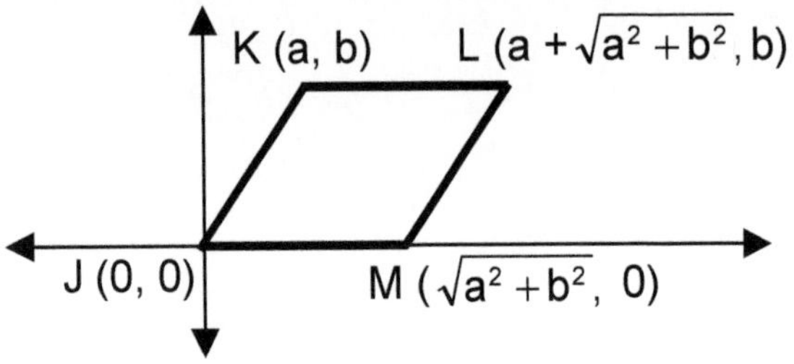

21. The medians to the legs of an isosceles triangle are congruent.

22. If a segment is a midsegment of a triangle, then it is parallel to a side of a triangle, and the length of this side of the triangle is equal to twice the length of the midsegment.

23. The segments joining the midpoints of consecutive sides of any quadrilateral form a parallelogram.

24. The segments joining the midpoints of consecutive sides of a rectangle form a rhombus.

25. The segments joining the midpoints of consecutive sides of a square form another square.

26. In a right triangle, the median to the hypotenuse is equidistant from each of the vertices of the triangle.

Given: $\triangle WXY$ is a right triangle with $\overline{WY}$ as its hypotenuse; M is the midpoint of $\overline{WY}$

Prove: WM = XM = YM

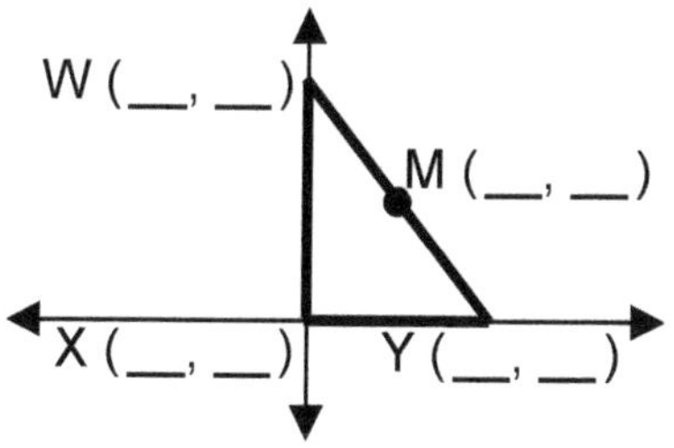

27. If the midpoint of a segment is equidistant from each of the vertices of a triangle, then the triangle is a right triangle.

Given: WM = XM = YM

Prove: $\triangle WXY$ is a right triangle

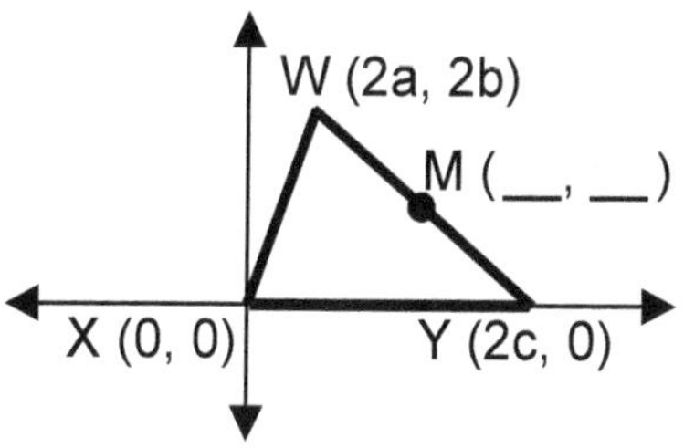

28. If a point P is equidistant from the endpoints of a segment, then the point lies on the perpendicular bisector of the segment.

29. If a point P is on the perpendicular bisector of a segment, then it is equidistant from the endpoints of the segment.

Part IV – Mixed Review

1-2. In the figure at the right, quadrilateral KLMN is a rhombus.

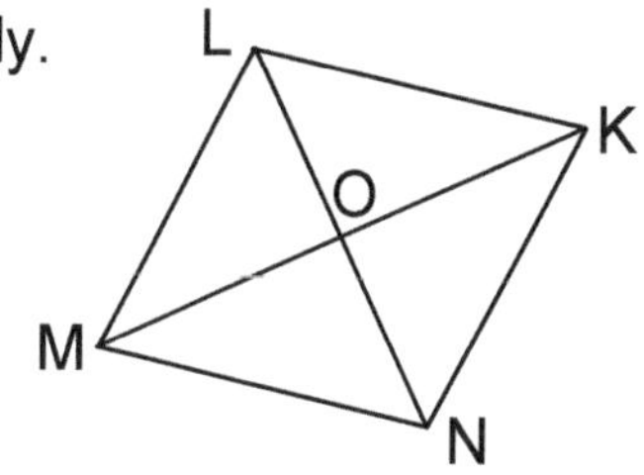

1. Which of the following *must* be true? Circle all that apply.

   (A) $\angle KLN \cong \angle KMN$ (B) $\overline{KL} \cong \overline{LM}$

   (C) $\angle KLN \cong \angle LNK$ (D) $\overline{KM} \perp \overline{LO}$

   (E) $m\angle LKN + m\angle LNM = 180°$ (F) $\overline{KO} \cong \overline{OM}$

2. Which of the following *cannot* be true? Circle all that apply.

   (A) $\angle KLN \cong \angle KMN$ (B) $\overline{KL} \cong \overline{LM}$

   (C) $\angle KLN \cong \angle LNK$ (D) $\overline{KM} \perp \overline{LO}$

   (E) $m\angle LKN + m\angle LNM = 180°$ (F) $\overline{KO} \cong \overline{OM}$

3. If $\boxed{a} = a^2 + 2a$, then $\boxed{3}$ = __________.

4. If $x \triangle y = 3x - 2y$, then $4 \triangle 6$ = __________.

5. If x is an odd integer, which of the following must also represent odd integers? Circle all that apply.

   (A) x^2 (B) $2x$ (C) $x - 1$ (D) $x - 2$ (E) $2x - 3$ (F) $(x - 1)^2$

6. If x is an odd integer, which of the following must represent even integers? Circle all that apply.

   (A) x^2 (B) $2x$ (C) $x - 1$ (D) $x - 2$ (E) $2x - 3$ (F) $(x - 1)^2$

7. In the figure at the right, x = __________.

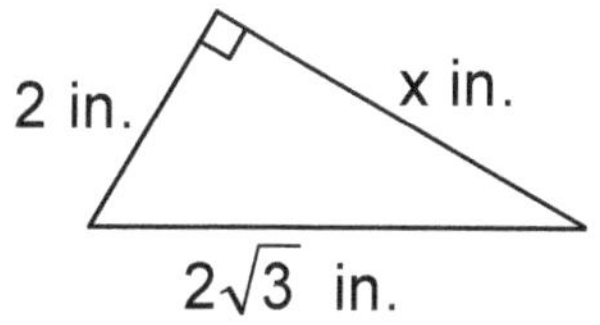

8. If a printer can print 100 pages in 6 minutes, how many pages can it print in an hour? ____________

9. While working at his job in a grocery store, Stan discovered that fifteen pears of equal mass had the same mass as two five-pound bags of apples. What was the mass of six pears? ____________

10. Find the values of x and y in the figure below.

x = __________

y = __________

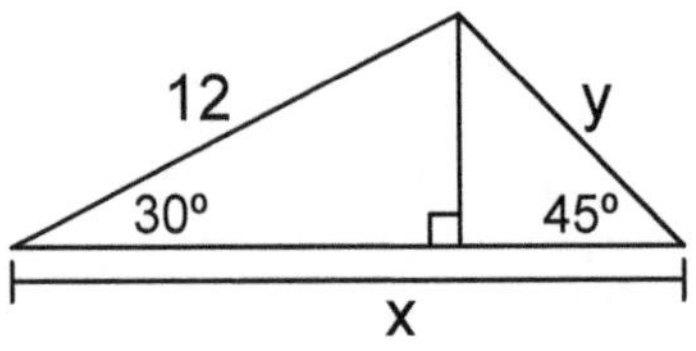

11. Given that P is the midpoint of both $\overline{BA}$ and $\overline{NK}$ in the figure at the right, prove that $\overline{BN} \parallel \overline{KA}$.

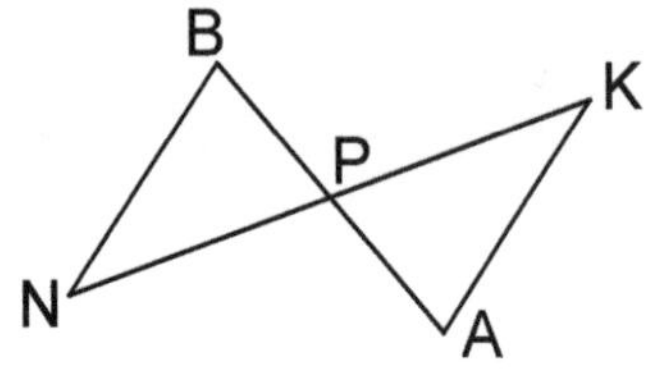

12. A triangle has sides with lengths of 7 cm, 8 cm, and 11 cm. Must this triangle be an *acute triangle*, an *obtuse triangle*, or a *right triangle*? ________________

13. The vertices of a triangle are at (–1, 4), (3, 7), and (0, –2). Must this triangle be an *acute triangle*, an *obtuse triangle*, or a *right triangle*? ________________

14. Can you form a triangle with vertices at (–5, 7), (–2, 5), and (4, 1)? ______________________

Why or why not? ______________________

____

____

____

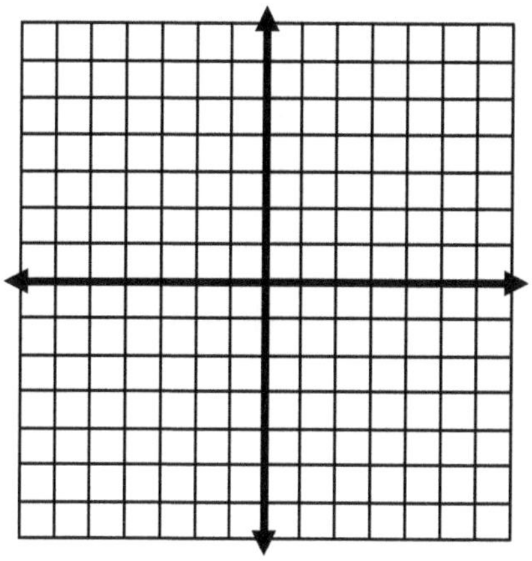

15. A quadrilateral has vertices at W(–5, 3), X(–1, 5), Y(4, 0), and Z(–3, –1). Is quadrilateral WXYZ a *parallelogram*, *rhombus*, *rectangle*, *square*, *trapezoid*, *isosceles trapezoid*, and/or *kite*? Name all that apply.

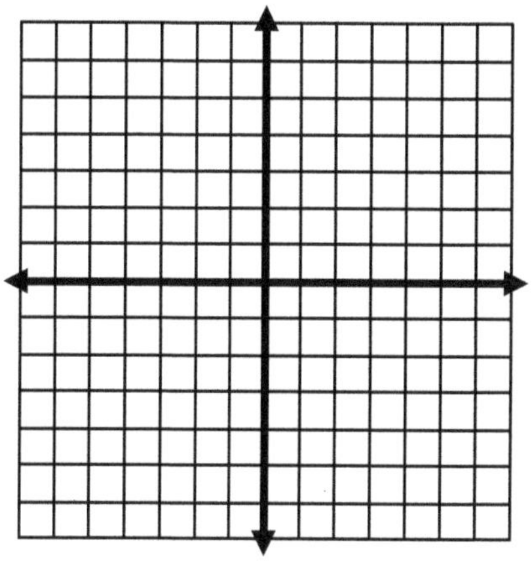

16. Prove the following statement using a coordinate proof: If the diagonals of a parallelogram are perpendicular, then it is a rhombus.

17. If one endpoint of a segment is at (–5, –2), and if the midpoint of the segment is at (7, –9), what are the coordinates of the other endpoint? (_____, _____)

18-20. In the figure at the right, quadrilateral ABCD is a rhombus, $m\angle AEB = (3w + 6x)°$, $m\angle DAC = (2w + 5)°$, and $m\angle BCA = (5x – 16)°$.

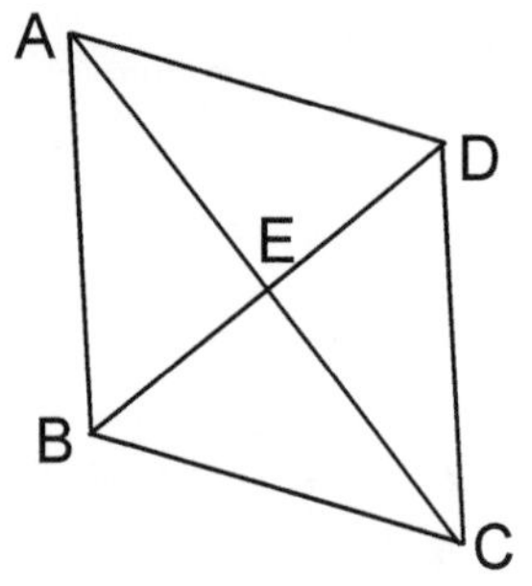

18. w = __________

19. x = __________

20. $m\angle DAB$ = __________

21-23. Use a protractor to measure each of the following angles in the figure at the right.

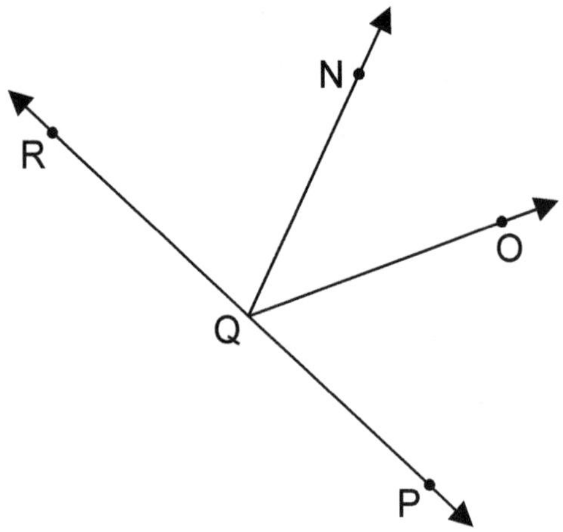

21. $m\angle RQO$ = __________

22. $m\angle NQO$ = __________

23. $m\angle PQN$ = __________

24. Use right triangle trigonometry and the Pythagorean Theorem to find the values of w, x, and y in the figure at the right. Round your final answers to the nearest tenth.

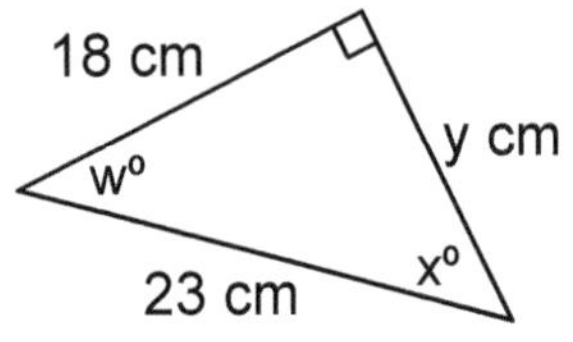

w = ____________

x = ____________

y = ____________

25. Use right triangle trigonometry and the Sum of the Measures of the Angles in a Triangle Theorem to find the values of k, m, and m∠L in the figure at the right. You may round your final answers to the nearest tenth.

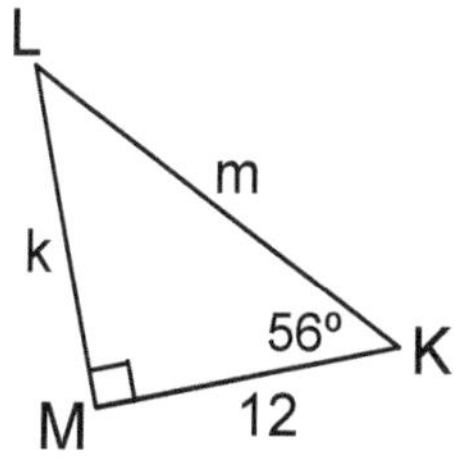

k = ____________

m = ____________

m∠L = _________

26. In ⊙Z at the right, m∠HUJ = 21°. Then m$\overset{\frown}{HJ}$ = ________, m$\overset{\frown}{JHU}$ = ________, m∠HZJ = ________, and m∠JZU = ________.

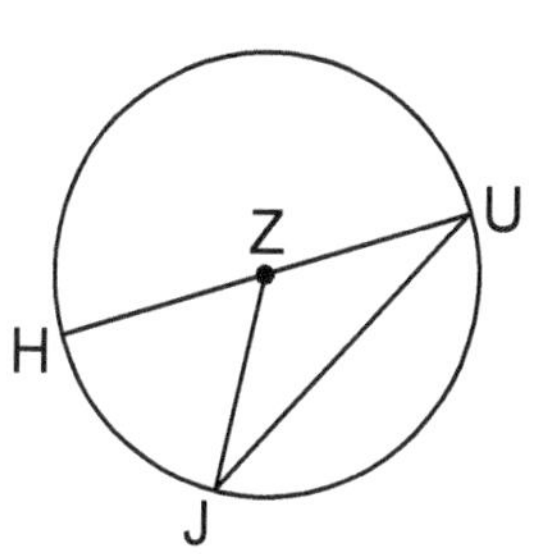

27. In ⊙O at the right, AQ = 8, EQ = 3, NS = 5, IS = 9, and NQ = 6. Then IA = __________ and QW = __________.

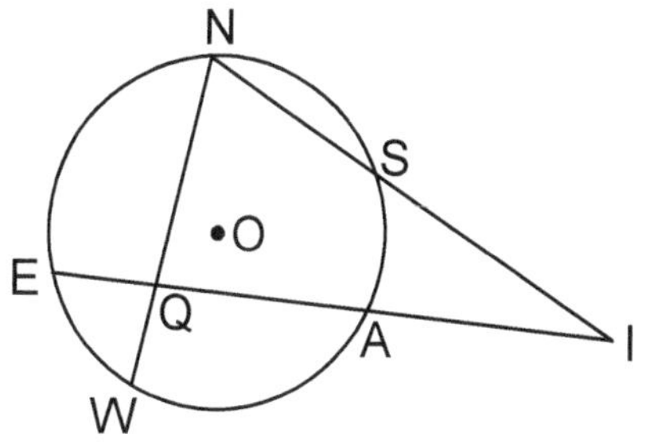

28. In the figure at the right, ΔLMB ~ ΔNMC. Then x = ________ and y = ________.

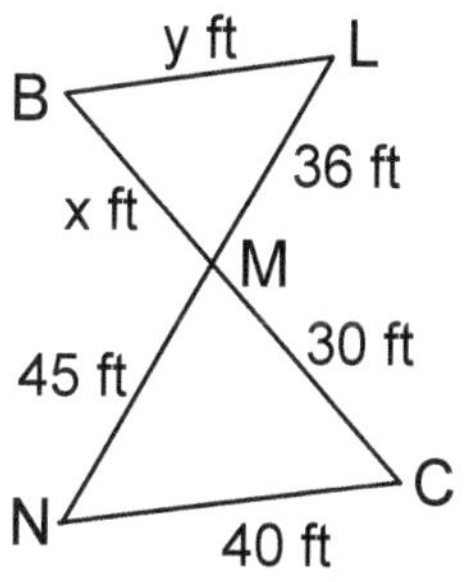

29. The measure of one interior angle of a regular pentagon is ________, and the measure of one exterior angle of a regular pentagon is ________.

Chapter 11 – Rotations, Reflections, Translations, and Dilations

Part I – Introduction to Rotations, Reflections, Translations, and Dilations

In this chapter, we will examine different ways of transforming shapes. We will begin this chapter with some definitions.

> A preimage of a figure is the original figure, and the image is a transformed version of the shape or picture.

> A transformation is an isometry if and only if an image and its preimage are congruent to each other.

> A rotation is a transformation that turns a figure about a fixed point. The fixed point is called the center of rotation.

> A transformation is a reflection in line ℓ if and only if which each point of the image is the same distance from ℓ as its corresponding preimage but is on the opposite side of ℓ.

> A transformation is a translation if and only every point of the preimage is moved a fixed distance in a fixed direction.

> A transformation of a figure is a dilation if and only all the distances from a fixed point are multiplied by a constant. The fixed point is called the center of dilation, and the constant is called the scale factor.

We will give more formal versions of some of these definitions in the later sections of this chapter, but these definitions and the examples in this section should help you gain a basic understanding of each of these words.

Example 1: For each set of figures below, the preimage is the black figure, and the gray figure is the image. Identify each transformation as a *rotation*, *reflection*, *translation*, or *dilation*. Also state whether or not each transformation is an isometry.

(a)

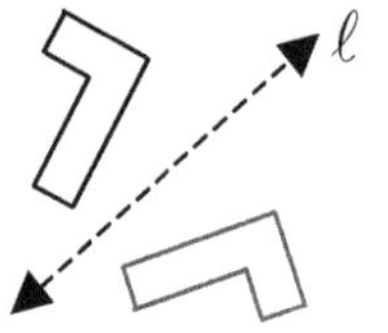

(b)

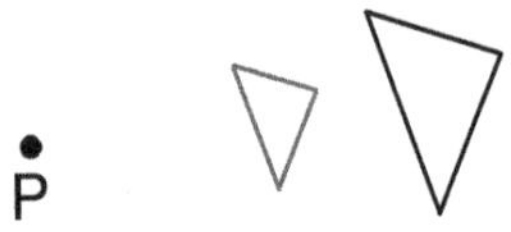

(c)

(d)

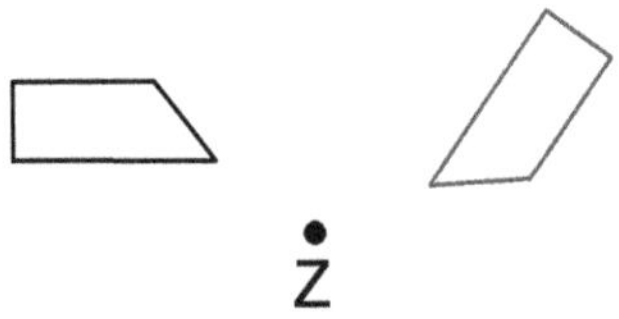

(a) This is a reflection in line ℓ. If you pick any point in the black figure (the preimage), you should notice that there is a corresponding point on the opposite side of ℓ that is exactly the same distance from ℓ as the original point. (To look at this another way, you can put a mirror on line ℓ and look at the preimage in the mirror. You should see an exact copy of the image.)

This is an example of an isometry because the preimage and the image are congruent to each other.

(b) This is an example of a dilation. If you pick a point in the black figure (the preimage) and measure its distance from P, you should notice that the distance from P to its corresponding point in the gray figure (the image) is equal to the original distance multiplied by $\frac{3}{5}$.

For this example, the image is smaller than the preimage, and so the image and the preimage are not congruent to each other. Therefore, this transformation is *not* an isometry.

(c) This is an example of a translation. Notice that each point of the preimage was picked up and moved to the right and down the same amount.

The preimage and the image are congruent to each other, and so we can say that this transformation is an isometry.

(d) This is an example of a 125° clockwise rotation about the point Z. To help you see why this is true, look at the pictures below. We have drawn dotted segments between the various points of the preimage and Z, and we have also drawn dotted segments from the corresponding points of the image to Z. Notice that the angle between each of these dotted segments is 125°, and each dotted segment is congruent to its partner.

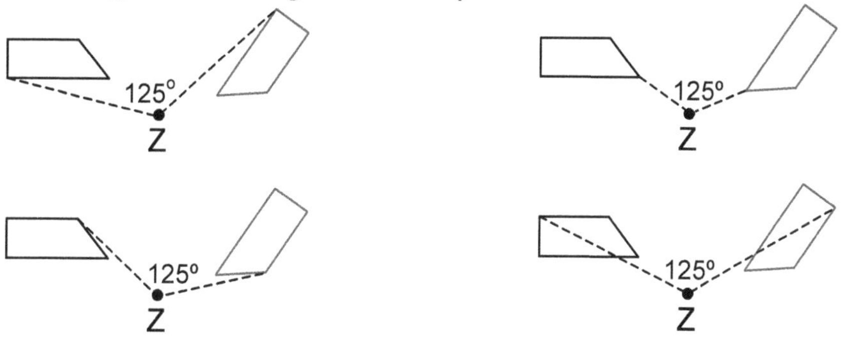

To see this another way, you can trace the preimage on a separate sheet of paper. Then you should be able to rotate the paper around until the picture you see is exactly the same as gray figure (the image).

Since the image and the preimage are congruent to each other, we can conclude that this transformation is an example of an isometry.

You may have noticed that we talked about measuring segments and angles with a ruler and a protractor in these problems. Normally, of course, you cannot use a ruler or a protractor to work the problems in this book because the pictures can be deceiving. Also, you are normally not allowed to assume that two figures are congruent (or that they're not congruent) just because that's what the picture makes it looks like. However, you may use a ruler and protractor to work the problems in this chapter, and you may assume that the pictures drawn in this chapter are not deceiving.

Example 2: For each set of figures below, the preimage is the black figure, and the gray figure is the image. Identify each transformation as a *rotation*, *reflection*, *translation*, or *dilation*. Also state whether or not each transformation is an isometry.

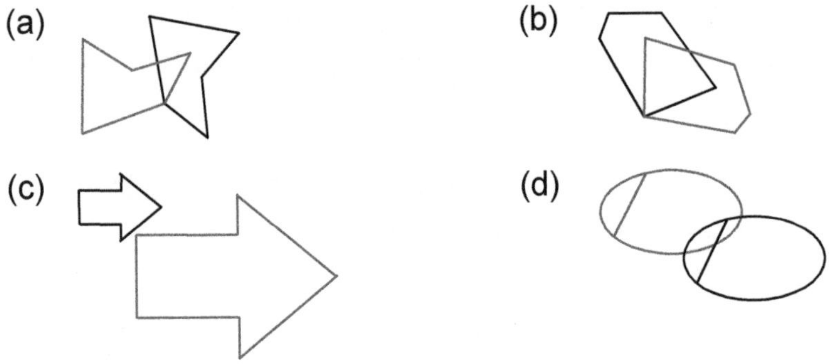

(a) This is a 100° counterclockwise rotation about the point labeled Q in the figure below.

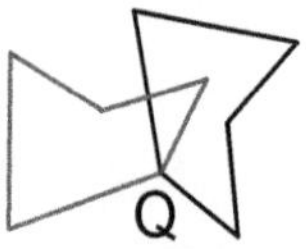

To see why this is true, you can draw a segment from Q to any of the points in the preimage and then draw another segment from Q to the corresponding point in the image. The two segments will be congruent to each other, and the angle between them will be 100°. (To see that this transformation is a rotation, you can also trace the preimage on another piece of paper and then rotate the paper around until the picture is exactly the same as that of the image.)

This transformation is an example of an isometry because the image and the preimage are congruent to each other.

(b) This transformation is an example of a reflection. To see why, look at the picture below.

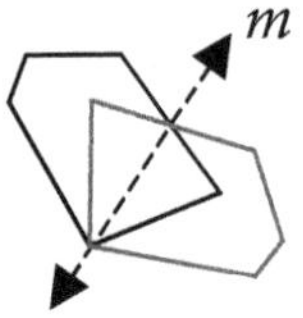

In this picture, each point of the image is the same distance from m as the corresponding point of the preimage, but it is on the opposite side of m. (You can also see this by placing a mirror on line m and then looking at the picture you see in the mirror. You should be able to see part of the image in the mirror. Then flip the mirror around and look at the other side. You should be able to see the rest of the image in the mirror.)

This transformation is an example of an isometry because the image and the preimage are congruent to each other.

(c) This is an example of a dilation. To see why this is true, look at the picture below and measure the distance from A to a point in the image and also the distance from A to the corresponding point in the preimage. For each set of points, you should find that the distance from A to each of the points in the image is equal to $\frac{5}{2}$ of the distance from A to the corresponding point in the preimage.

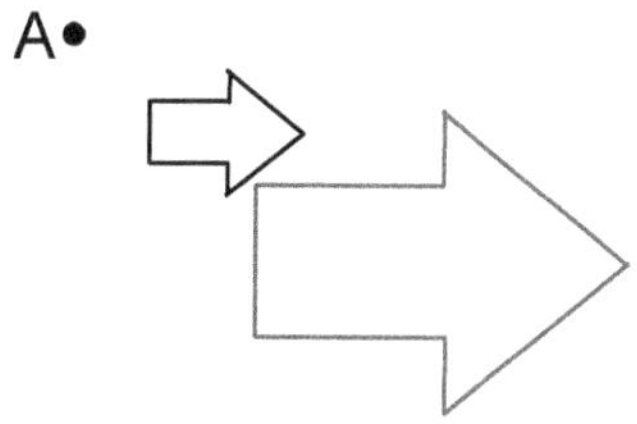

This transformation is not an example of an isometry because the image and the preimage are not congruent to each other.

(d) This is an example of a translation. You should notice that each point of the black figure (the image) was picked up and moved up and to the left, and they were all picked up and moved in exactly the same direction and exactly the same distance.

This transformation is an example of an isometry because the image and the preimage are congruent to each other.

Problems:

1-20. For each set of figures below, the preimage is the black figure, and the gray figure is the image. Classify each transformation as a *rotation*, *reflection*, *translation*, or *dilation*. Also state whether or not each transformation is an isometry.

1.

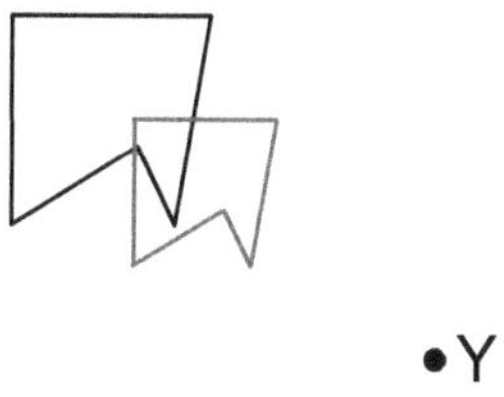

Is this transformation a *rotation*, *reflection*, *translation*, or *dilation*?

____

Is this an isometry? ___________

2.

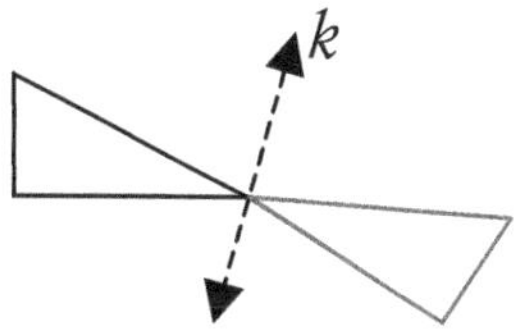

Is this transformation a *rotation*, *reflection*, *translation*, or *dilation*?

____

Is this an isometry? ___________

3. 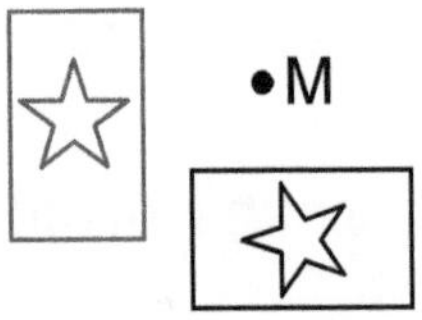

Is this transformation a *rotation*, *reflection*, *translation*, or *dilation*?

____

Is this an isometry? ___________

4. 

Is this transformation a *rotation*, *reflection*, *translation*, or *dilation*?

____

Is this an isometry? ___________

5. 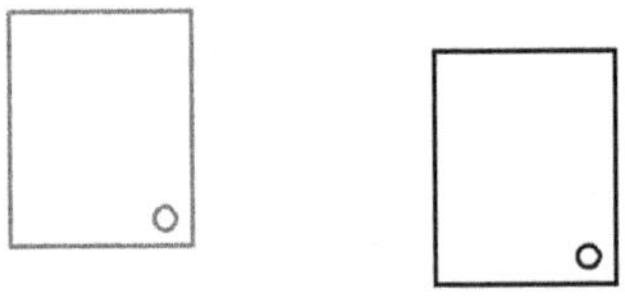

Is this transformation a *rotation*, *reflection*, *translation*, or *dilation*?

____

Is this an isometry? ___________

6. 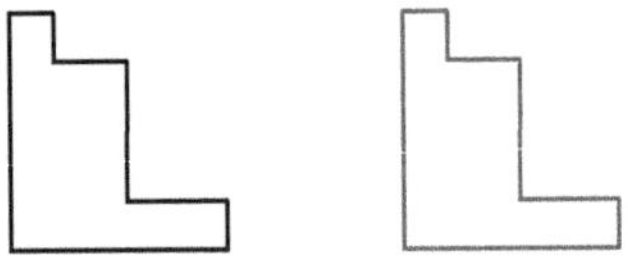

Is this transformation a *rotation*, *reflection*, *translation*, or *dilation*?

____

Is this an isometry? ___________

7. 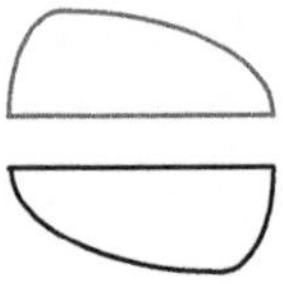

Is this transformation a *rotation*, *reflection*, *translation*, or *dilation*?

____

Is this an isometry? ___________

8. 

Is this transformation a *rotation*, *reflection*, *translation*, or *dilation*?

____

Is this an isometry? ___________

9. 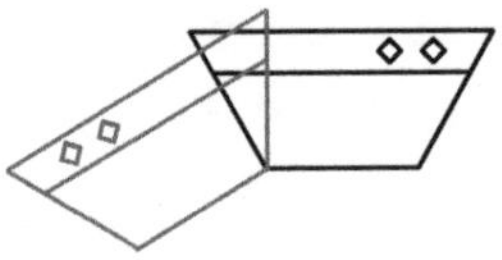

Is this transformation a *rotation*, *reflection*, *translation*, or *dilation*?

____

Is this an isometry? ___________

10. 

Is this transformation a *rotation*, *reflection*, *translation*, or *dilation*?

____

Is this an isometry? ___________

11. 

Is this transformation a *rotation*, *reflection*, *translation*, or *dilation*?

____

Is this an isometry? ____________

12. 

Is this transformation a *rotation*, *reflection*, *translation*, or *dilation*?

____

Is this an isometry? ____________

13. 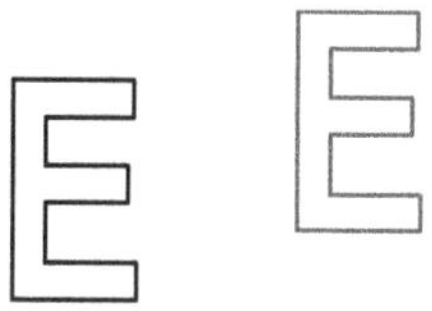

Is this transformation a *rotation*, *reflection*, *translation*, or *dilation*?

____

Is this an isometry? ____________

14. 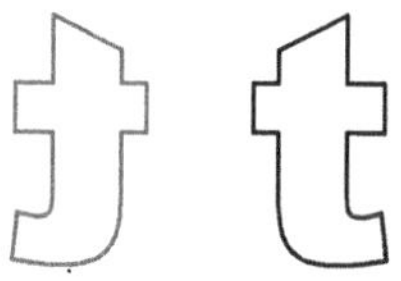

Is this transformation a *rotation*, *reflection*, *translation*, or *dilation*?

____

Is this an isometry? ____________

15. 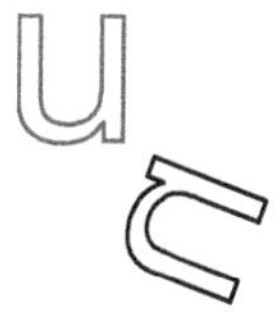

Is this transformation a *rotation*, *reflection*, *translation*, or *dilation*?

____

Is this an isometry? ____________

16. 

Is this transformation a *rotation*, *reflection*, *translation*, or *dilation*?

____

Is this an isometry? ____________

17. 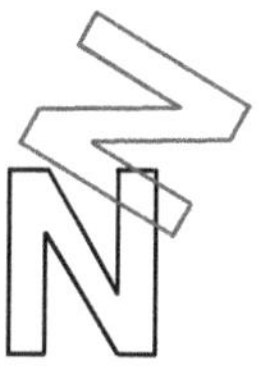

Is this transformation a *rotation*, *reflection*, *translation*, or *dilation*?

____

Is this an isometry? ____________

18. 

Is this transformation a *rotation*, *reflection*, *translation*, or *dilation*?

____

Is this an isometry? ____________

19. 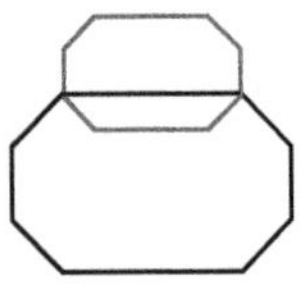

Is this transformation a *rotation*, *reflection*, *translation*, or *dilation*?

____

Is this an isometry? ____________

20. 

Is this transformation a *rotation*, *reflection*, *translation*, or *dilation*?

____

Is this an isometry? ____________

21-24. For each set of figures below, the preimage is the black figure, and the gray figure is the image. Each preimage can be transformed into its corresponding image by using two or more different types of transformations. For example, the preimage in the figure below could be transformed into the image using *either* a translation *or* a reflection.

In the problems that follow, name all the types of transformations that could transform the preimage into the image.

21. 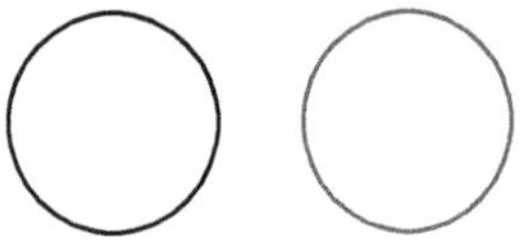

Types of transformations: ______

____

22. 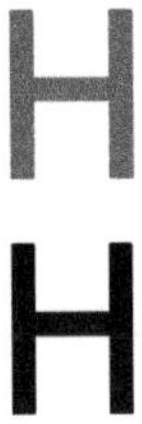

Types of transformations: ______

____

23. 

Types of transformations: ______

____

24. 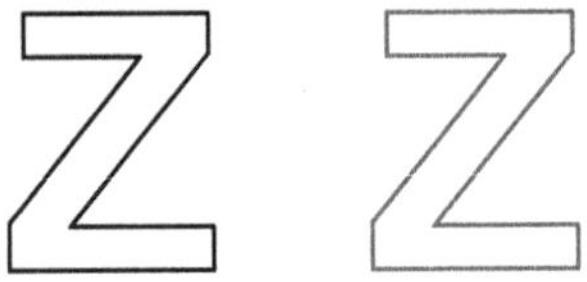

Types of transformations: ______

____

25-30. The next six problems use some new notation. The figure below shows a reflection in line ℓ. Notice that the point A corresponds to the point A′ (read, "A prime"). Or, in mathematical terms, we say that A <u>maps to</u> A′. We can also write this symbolically as $A \rightarrow A'$. Similarly, we can say that $B \rightarrow B'$, $\overline{AB} \rightarrow \overline{A'B'}$, and $\triangle ABC \rightarrow \triangle A'B'C'$. However, when we make statements such as $\triangle ABC \rightarrow \triangle A'B'C'$, we must be careful about the order in which we name points (like we discussed when we talked about congruent and similar triangles). We would *not*, for instance, be able to say that $\triangle ABC \rightarrow \triangle C'B'A'$ because this would suggest that A maps to C′ and that C maps to A′.

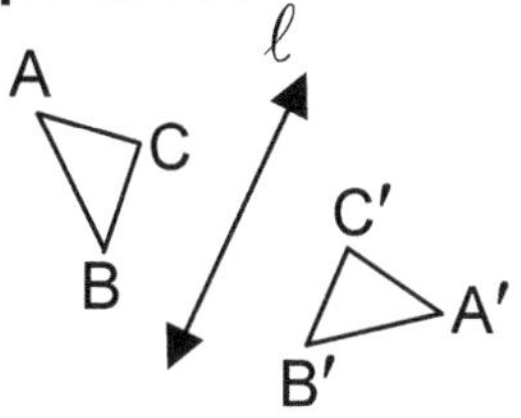

25.

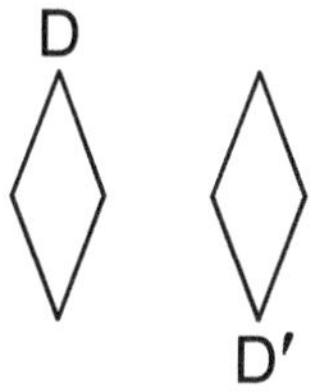

In the figure above, $D \rightarrow D'$.

What type of transformation is this? ____________________

26.

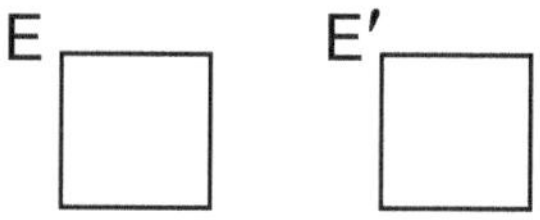

In the figure above, $E \rightarrow E'$.

What type of transformation is this? ____________________

27.

In the figure above, $L \rightarrow T$. Then

$\triangle LMN \rightarrow \triangle$____________.

What type of transformation is this? ____________________

28.

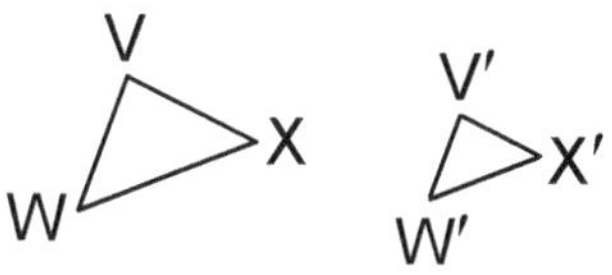

In the figure above, $V \rightarrow V'$. Then

$\triangle VWX \rightarrow \triangle$____________.

What type of transformation is this? ____________________

29.

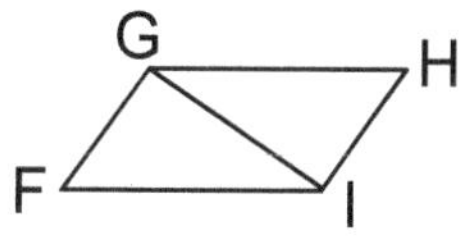

In the figure above, $\triangle GIF \rightarrow \triangle IGH$.

What type of transformation is this? ____________________

30.

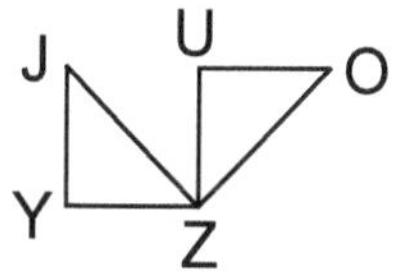

The figure above shows a 90° clockwise rotation of $\triangle JYZ$ about Z. Then $J \rightarrow$____, $\overline{YZ} \rightarrow$____, and $\triangle JYZ \rightarrow$________.

Part II – Rotations

In this section, we will discuss rotations in more detail.

Example 1: Draw a 130° clockwise rotation of the figure below about the point X.

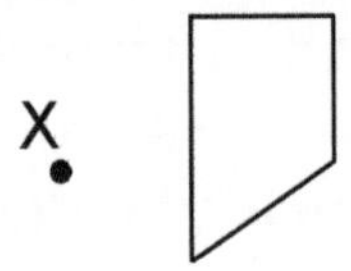

To draw this rotation, we will follow the steps shown below.

Step 1: Draw line segments from the vertices of the preimage to the center of rotation. (We will make these segments dotted, but you may choose to use a different colored pencil when you work the practice problems.) We will also label the vertices because it will make life a little less confusing when we get to Step 3.

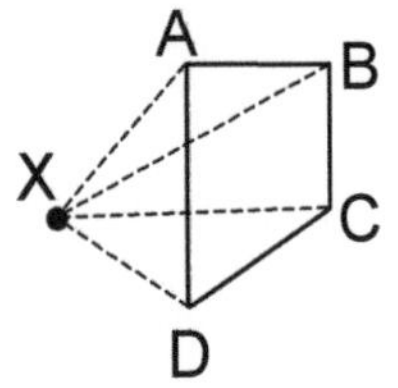

Step 2: Since the question asked us to draw a 130° rotation, we will now use a ruler and a protractor to draw segments congruent to the segments we drew in Step 1, each forming 130° angles with the corresponding segment. Since the question asked us to draw a 130° *clockwise* rotation, we will make sure that we move *clockwise* (like the hands of a clock move) 130° to draw the new segments. Also, we will label the endpoints of these segments using the notation that we introduced in Exercises 25-30 of the last section.

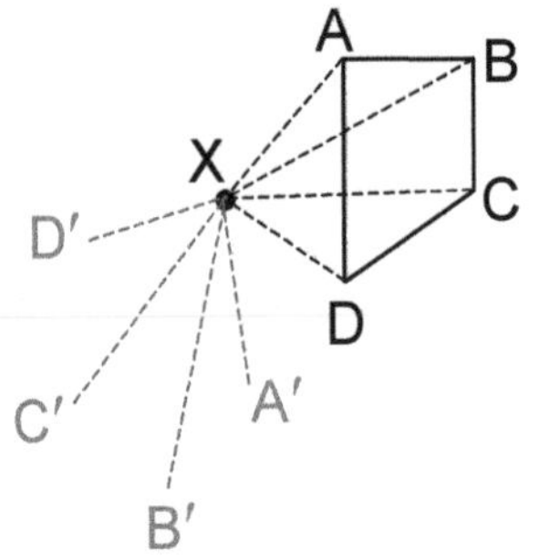

Step 3: Draw the segments that make up the image.

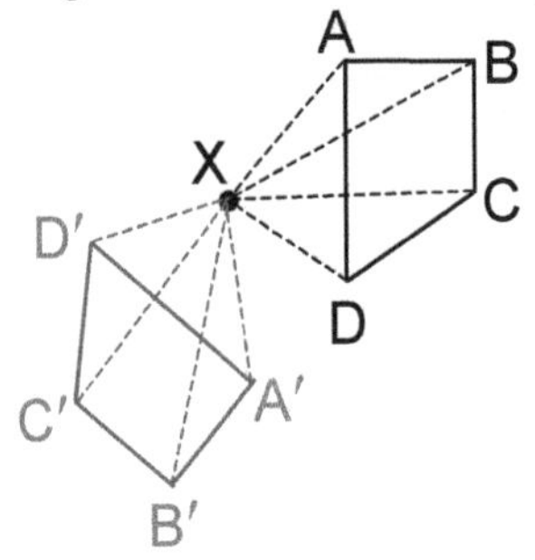

Notice that, in this last step, we connected only the images of the vertices that were connected in the preimage. We did not, for instance, draw $\overline{A'C'}$ because $\overline{AC}$ did not exist in the preimage.

Step 4: To make this picture less confusing to look at, we will erase the dotted segments.

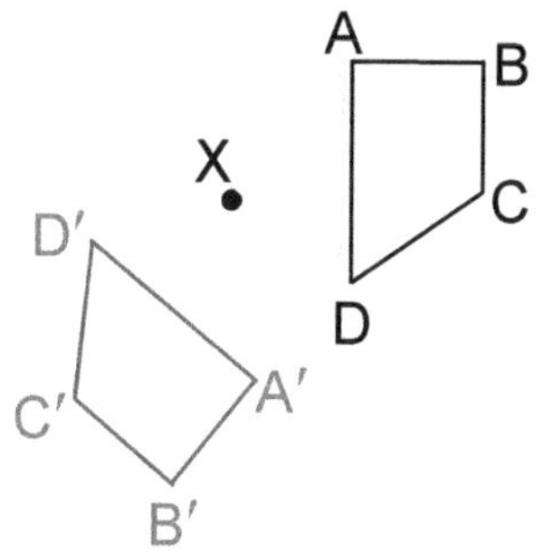

Example 2: Draw a 70° counterclockwise rotation of the figure below about the point J.

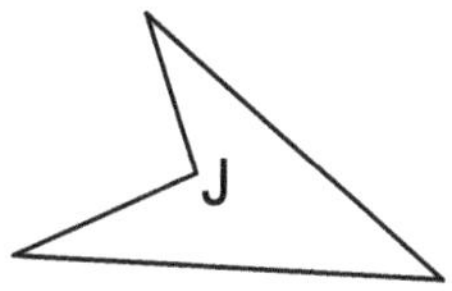

Step 1: Draw line segments from the vertices of the preimage to the center of rotation. (We will make these segments dotted, but you may choose to use a different colored pencil when you work the practice problems.) We will also label the vertices because it will make life a little less confusing when we get to Step 3.

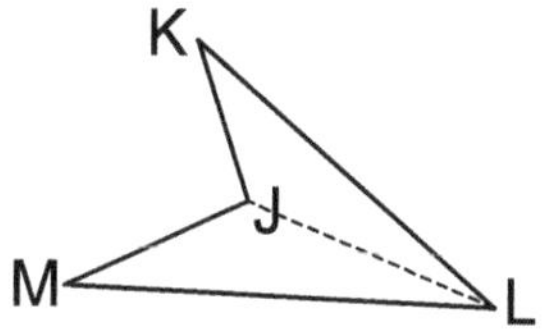

Step 2: Since the question asked us to draw a 70° rotation, we will now use a ruler and a protractor to draw segments congruent to the segments we drew in Step 1, each forming 70° angles with the corresponding segment. Since the question asked us to draw a 70° *counterclockwise* rotation, we will make sure that we move *counterclockwise* (in the direction opposite the way the hands of a clock move) 70° to draw the new segments. Also, we will label the endpoints of these segments using the notation that we introduced in Exercises 25-30 of the last section.

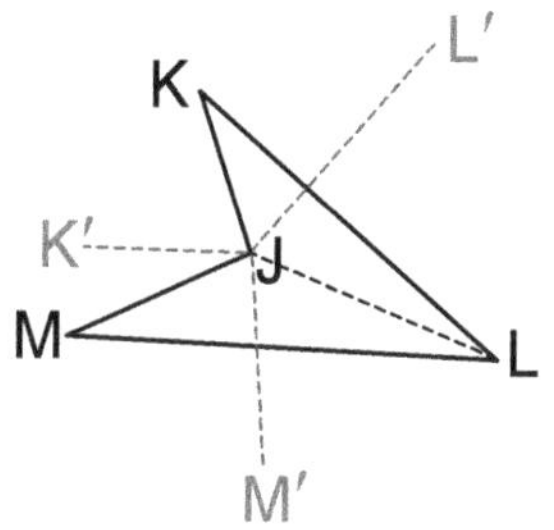

Notice that the image of J will be itself, so we did not label J′.

Step 3: Draw the segments that make up the image.

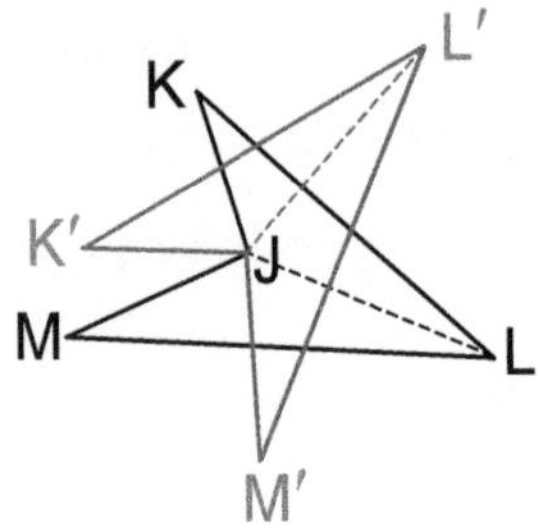

Step 4: To make this picture less confusing to look at, we can erase the dotted segments.

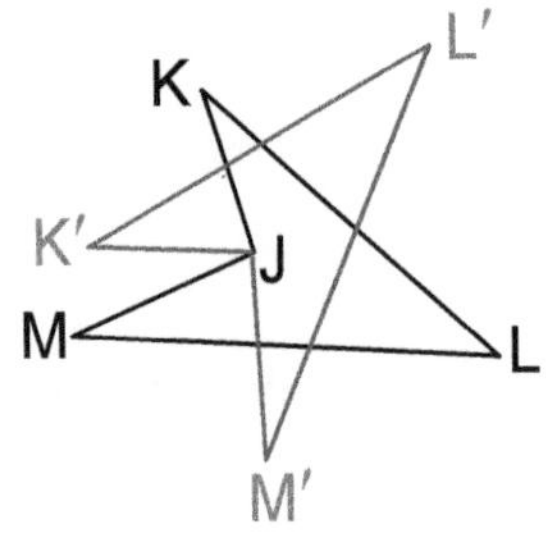

Example 3: In the figure at the right, all of the triangles are equilateral. Name the image of (a) a 120° clockwise rotation of point Q about point V, (b) a 180° clockwise rotation of $\overline{RS}$ about point R, (c) a 60° counterclockwise rotation of $\overline{ST}$ about point U, (d) a 60° counterclockwise rotation of ΔVTR about point T.

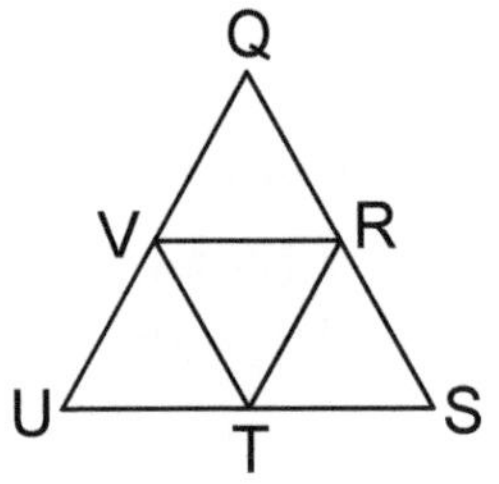

We will begin by noting that, since the all of the triangles are equilateral, all of their angles must have measures of 60°.

(a) Step 1: Draw a line segment from Q to V.

This has already been done for us; it is $\overline{QV}$.

Step 2: Since the question asked us to talk about a 120° rotation, draw a segment congruent to $\overline{QV}$ that forms an angle of 120° with $\overline{QV}$. Also, since the question asked us to draw a 120° *clockwise* rotation, we will make sure that we move *clockwise* (like the hands of a clock move) 120° to draw the new segment.

This has already been done for us; it is $\overline{VT}$.

Step 3: Draw the image.

This has already been done for us; it is the point T.

(b) Step 1: Draw line segments from the endpoints of $\overline{RS}$ to R.

This has already been done for us; the only segment we would need to draw is $\overline{RS}$.

Step 2: Since the question asked us to talk about a 180° rotation, draw a segment congruent to $\overline{RS}$ that forms an angle of 180° with $\overline{RS}$. Also, since the question asked us to draw a 180° *clockwise* rotation, we will make sure that we move *clockwise* (like the hands of a clock move) 180° to draw the new segment.

This has already been done for us; it is $\overline{RQ}$.

Step 3: Draw the image.

Note that the image of the point R is itself, and the image of the point S is the point Q. Thus, the image of a 180° counterclockwise rotation of $\overline{RS}$ about point R is $\overline{RQ}$.

By the way, you might notice that, if the question had asked us to name the image of a 180° *counterclockwise* rotation of $\overline{RS}$ about point R, our answer would still be $\overline{RQ}$ because a 180° clockwise rotation always produces exactly the same image as a 180° counterclockwise rotation.

(c) Step 1: Draw line segments from the endpoints of $\overline{ST}$ to U.

This has already been done for us; they are $\overline{US}$ and $\overline{UT}$.

Step 2: Since the question asked us to talk about a 60° rotation, draw segments congruent to $\overline{US}$ and $\overline{UT}$ that form angles of 60° with these segments. Also, since the question asked us to draw a 60° *counterclockwise* rotation, we will make sure that we move *counterclockwise* (in the direction opposite the way the hands of a clock move) 60° to draw the new segments.

This has already been done for us; the new segments are $\overline{UQ}$ and $\overline{UV}$.

Step 3: Draw the image.

Note that the image of the point S is the point Q, and the image of the point T is the point V. Thus, the image of a 60° counterclockwise rotation of $\overline{ST}$ about point U is $\overline{QV}$.

(d) Step 1: Draw line segments from the vertices of ΔVTR to T.

This has already been done for us; the only segments we would need to draw are $\overline{TR}$ and $\overline{TV}$.

Step 2: Since the question asked us to talk about a 60° rotation, draw segments congruent to $\overline{TR}$ and $\overline{TV}$ that form angles of 60° with these segments. Also, since the question asked us to draw a 60° *counterclockwise* rotation, we will make sure that we move *counterclockwise* (in the direction opposite the way the hands of a clock move) 60° to draw the new segments.

This has already been done for us; they are $\overline{TV}$ and $\overline{TU}$.

Step 3: Draw the image.

Note that the image of the point V is the point U, the image of the point T is itself, and the image of the point R is the point V. Thus, the image of a 60° counterclockwise rotation of ΔVTR about point T is ΔUTV.

Example 4: Triangle NZX has vertices at N(–1, –2), Z(4, –4), and X(5, 2). Draw ΔNZX and (a) a 90° counterclockwise rotation 90° about the origin and (b) a 180° clockwise rotation about the point (2, –1).

We will begin by drawing ΔNZX. This is done in the coordinate plane at the right.

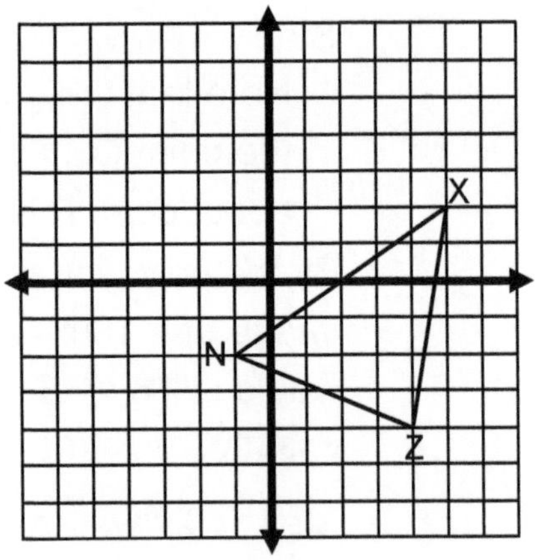

(a) Step 1: Draw line segments from the vertices of the preimage to the center of rotation.

Recall that the <u>origin</u> is the point (0, 0).

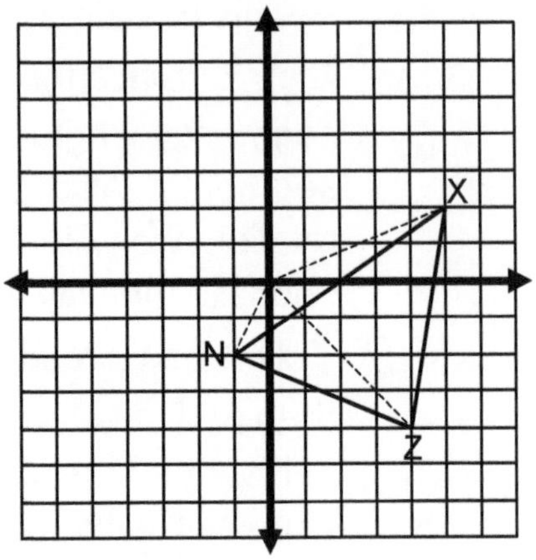

Step 2: Since the question asked us to draw a 90° rotation, we will now draw segments congruent to the segments we drew in Step 1, each forming 90° angles with the corresponding segment. Since the question asked us to draw a 90° *counterclockwise* rotation, we will make sure that we move *counterclockwise* (in the direction opposite the way the hands of a clock move) 90° to draw the new segments. Also, we will label the endpoints of these segments using the notation that we introduced in Exercises 25-30 of the last section.

To make sure that each of our segments form 90° angles with the corresponding segment, we will use a principle that we discussed in the last chapter: Two lines are perpendicular if and only if their slopes are opposite reciprocals. So, since we rise –2 and run –1 to go from the origin to the point N, we will rise +1 and run –2 to go to N′. (Note that this will also give us segments that are congruent to the original segments.)

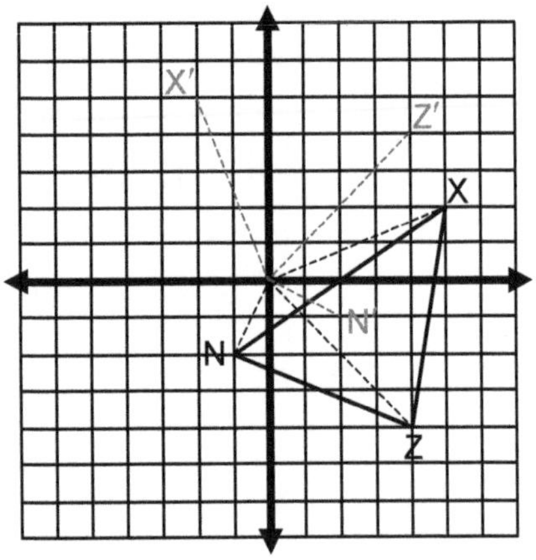

Step 3: Draw the segments that make up the image.

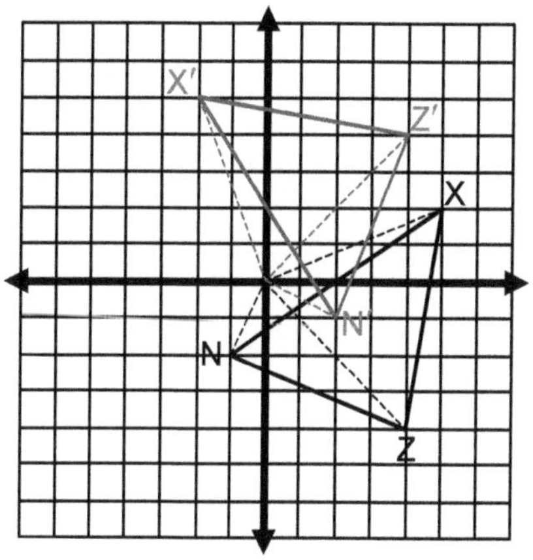

Step 4: To make this picture less confusing to look at, we will erase the dotted segments.

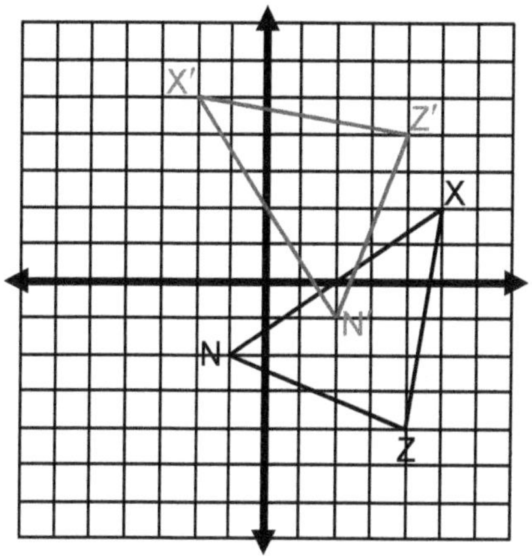

(b) Step 1: Draw line segments from the vertices of the preimage to the center of rotation.

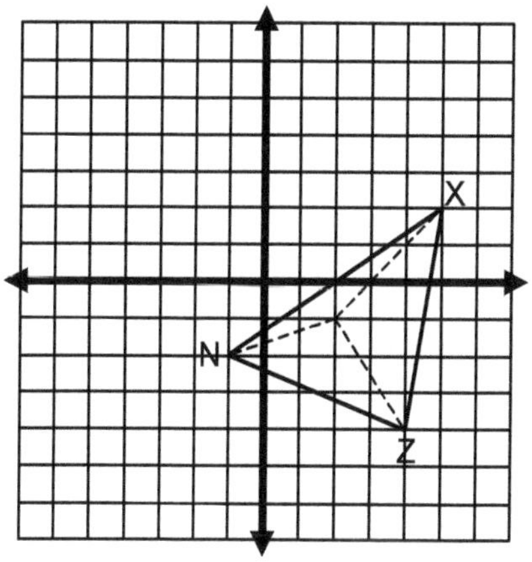

Step 2: Since the question asked us to draw a 180° rotation, we will now draw segments congruent to the segments we drew in Step 1, each forming 180° angles with the corresponding segment. We will move *clockwise* 180° to draw the new segments, but our picture would actually look identical if we moved 180° counterclockwise instead. Also, we will label the endpoints of these segments using the notation that we introduced in Exercises 25-30 of the last section.

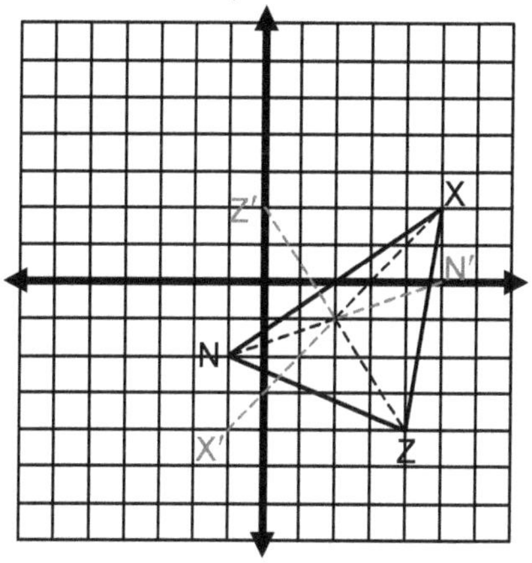

Step 3: Draw the segments that make up the image.

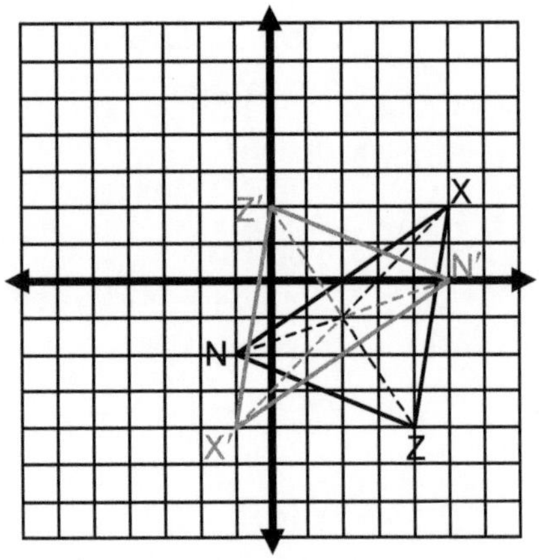

Step 4: To make this picture less confusing to look at, we will erase the dotted segments.

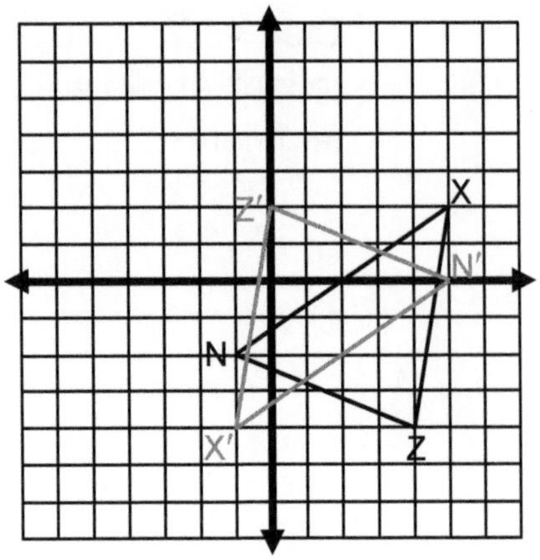

Now, we need another definition.

A figure has <u>rotational symmetry</u> if and only if it can be rotated about a center point a certain number of degrees and the resulting image is exactly the same as the preimage.

To understand this definition, look at the equilateral triangle and the square below. We can rotate the triangle either 120° clockwise or 120° counterclockwise and end up with an image that looks exactly like the preimage that we started with. Similarly, we can rotate the square 90° clockwise, 180° clockwise, 90° counterclockwise, or 180° counterclockwise and end up with an image that looks exactly like the preimage that we started with. Thus, we can say that both of these figures have rotational symmetry.

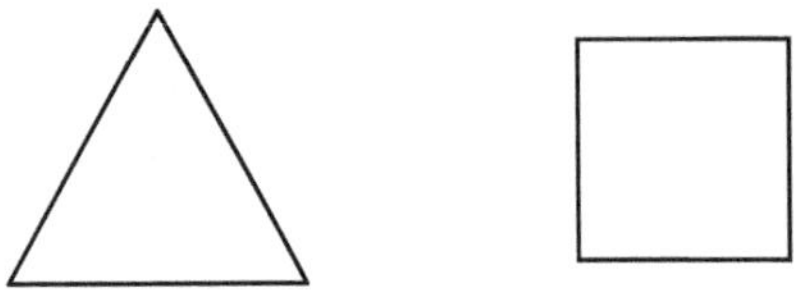

Example 5: For each of the figures on the next page, decide whether or not the figure has rotational symmetry. If you decide that it does have rotational symmetry, name the angles that the figure can be rotated about the center point so that the resulting image looks exactly like the preimage.

(a) 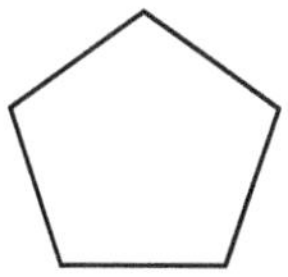 (b)  (c) 

(a) This figure does have rotational symmetry. You can rotate the figure 72° clockwise, 144° clockwise, 72° counterclockwise, or 144° counterclockwise and end up with a figure that looks exactly like the preimage.
To see why we picked these angle measures, look at the picture below.

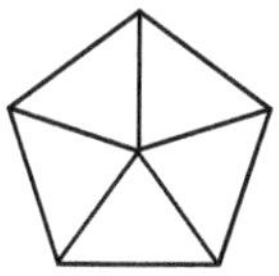

Since we said in the last section that you may assume that angles and segments that look congruent are actually congruent in this chapter, we can assume that this is a regular pentagon. Therefore, each of the smaller central angles drawn in the picture above must have measures of 72°.

(b) This figure does not have rotational symmetry. You cannot rotate this figure through any angle, either clockwise or counterclockwise, less than 360° and end up with an image that matches the preimage exactly.

(c) This figure does have rotational symmetry. You can rotate the figure either 180° clockwise or 180° counterclockwise and end up with a figure that looks exactly like the preimage.

Problems:

1. Draw a 90° clockwise rotation of the figure below about the point P.

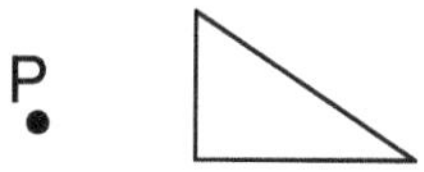

2. Draw a 120° clockwise rotation of the figure below about the point Q.

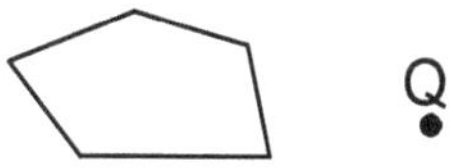

3. Draw a 80° clockwise rotation of the figure below about the point R.

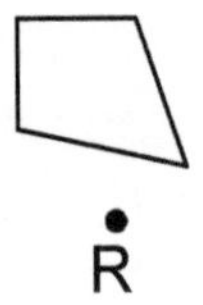

4. Draw a 114° counterclockwise rotation of the figure below about the point S.

5. Draw a 53° counterclockwise rotation of the figure below about the point T.

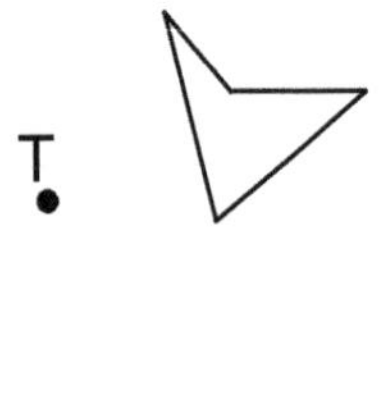

6. Draw a 90° counterclockwise rotation of the figure below about the point U.

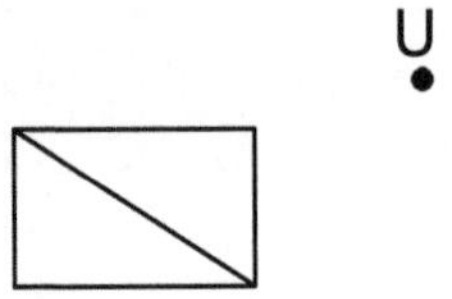

7. Draw a 180° counterclockwise rotation of the figure below about the point V.

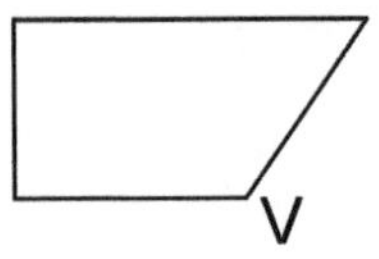

8. Draw a 180° clockwise rotation of the figure below about the point W.

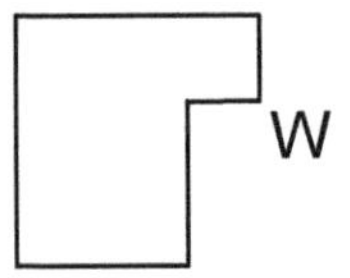

9. Draw a 45° clockwise rotation of the figure below about the point X.

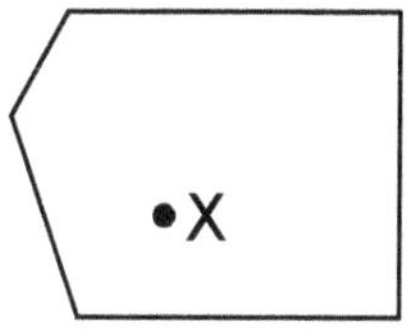

10. Draw a 180° clockwise rotation of the figure below about the point Y.

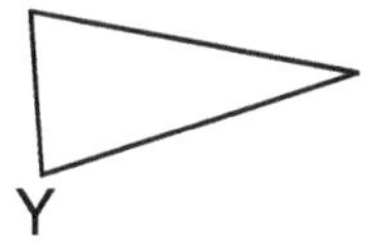

11. Draw a 38° clockwise rotation of the figure below about the point Z.

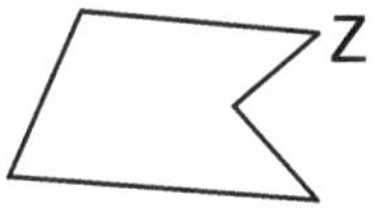

12. Draw a 108° clockwise rotation of the figure below about the point A.

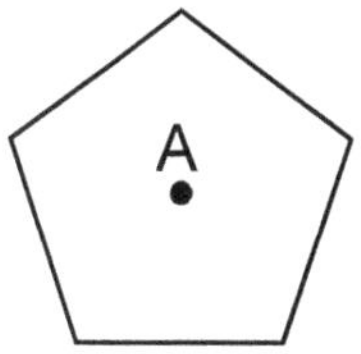

13. Draw a 57° counterclockwise rotation of the figure below about the point B.

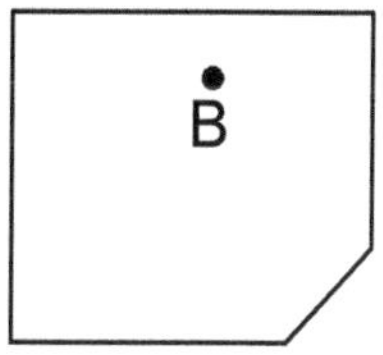

14. Draw a 141° counterclockwise rotation of the figure below about the point C.

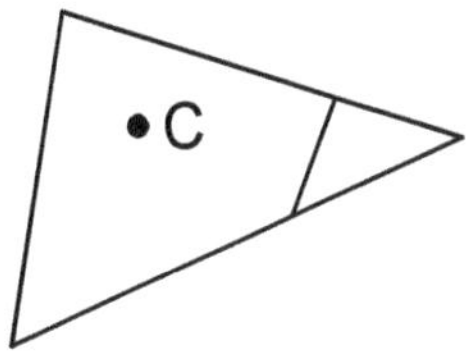

15. Draw a 180° counterclockwise rotation of the figure below about the point D.

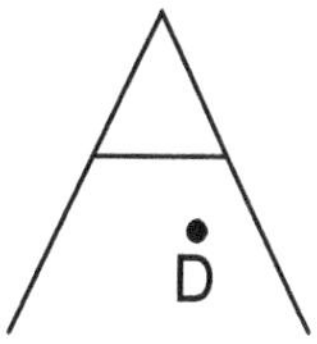

16. Draw a 55° counterclockwise rotation of the figure below about the point E.

17-27. Use the figure at the right to name the images of each of the following rotations. You may assume that all angles and segments that appear to be congruent to each other are actually congruent to each other.

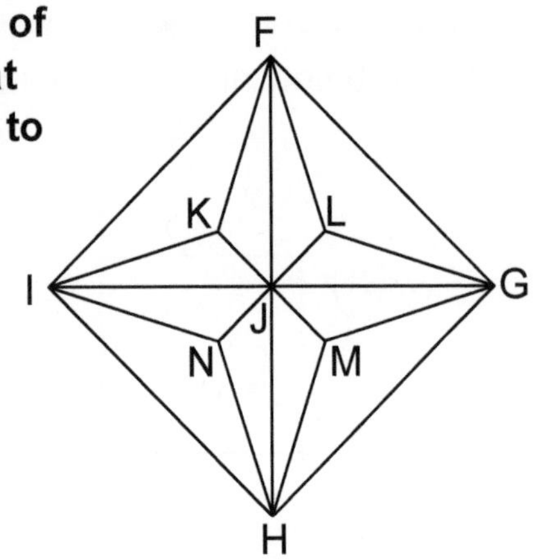

17. Name the image of a 90° clockwise rotation of point L about point J. __________

18. Name the image of a 180° clockwise rotation of point H about point J. __________

19. Name the image of a 90° counterclockwise rotation of point G about point H.

____

20. Name the image of a 90° clockwise rotation of $\overline{GJ}$ about point J. __________

21. Name the image of a 90° clockwise rotation of $\overline{GH}$ about point G. __________

22. Name the image of a 180° counterclockwise rotation of $\overline{HI}$ about point J.

____

23. Name the image of a 180° clockwise rotation of $\overline{MH}$ about point J. __________

24. Name the image of a 90° counterclockwise rotation of ΔIJK about point J.

____

25. Name the image of a 90° counterclockwise rotation of ΔGMH about point J.

____

26. Name the image of a 180° clockwise rotation of ΔINH about point J. __________

27. Name the image of a 180° counterclockwise rotation of ΔJLG about point J.

____

28-31. Triangle PQR has vertices at P(–3, 1), Q(1, –2), and R(3, 5). Draw ΔPQR and each of the rotations described.

28. a 90º clockwise rotation about the origin

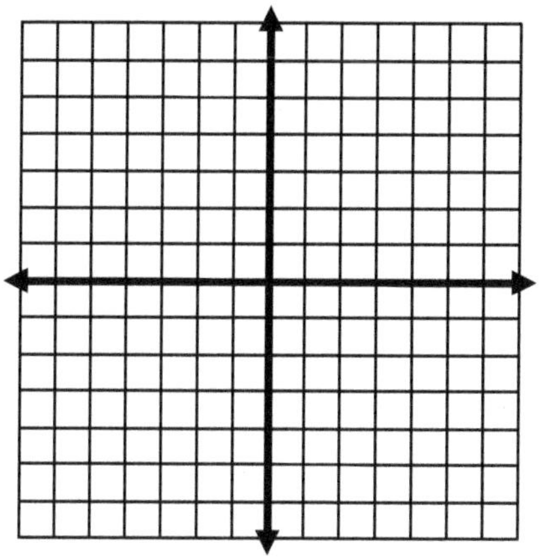

30. a 180º counterclockwise rotation about the point (1, 0)

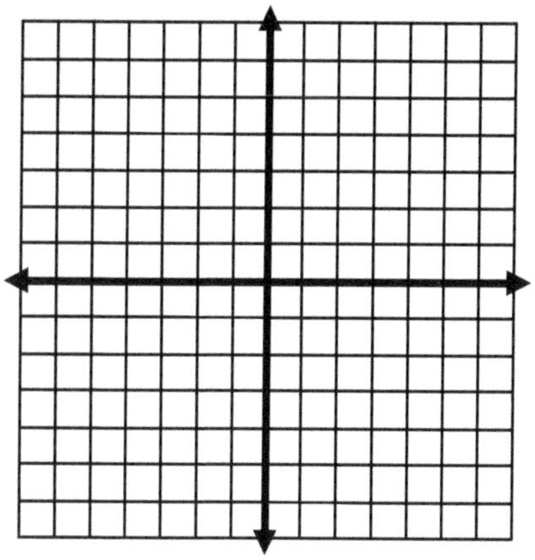

29. a 180º counterclockwise rotation about the origin

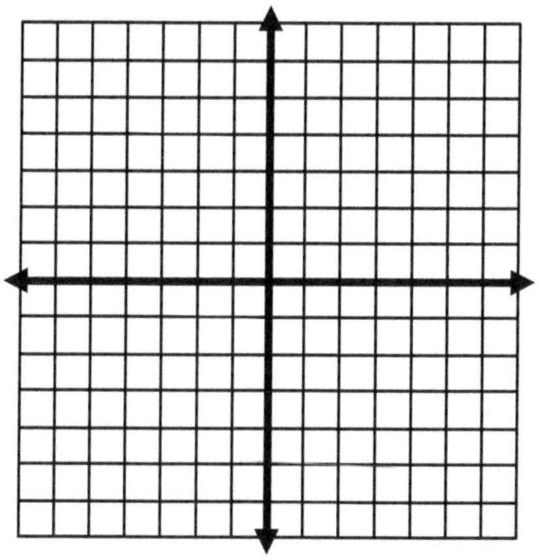

31. a 90º clockwise rotation about the point (–3, 1)

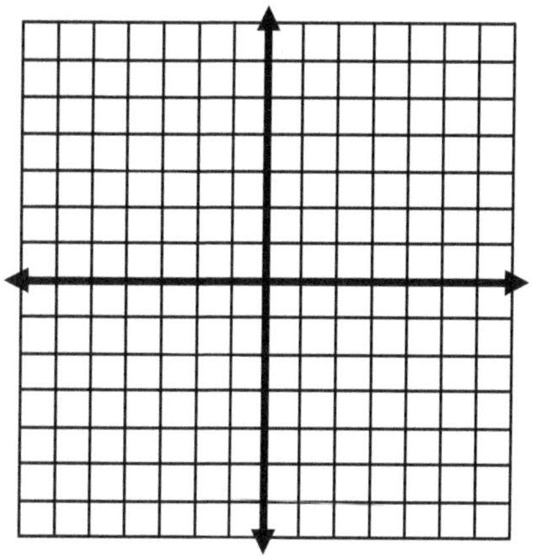

32-33. Quadrilateral STUV has vertices at S(–3, 3), T(3, 4), U(3, 2), and V(–2, –1). Draw quadrilateral STUV and each of the rotations described.

32. a 90º counterclockwise rotation about the point (3, 2)

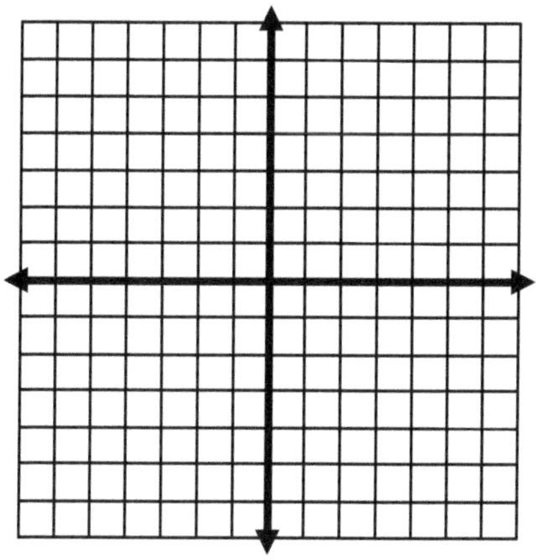

33. a 90º counterclockwise rotation about the point (–1, 1)

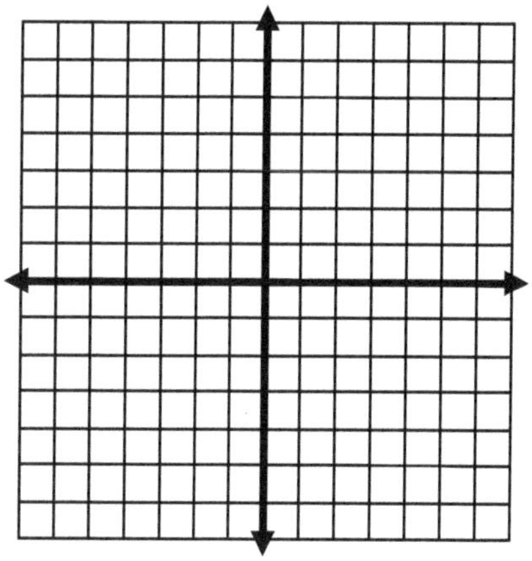

34-45. For each of the figures below, decide whether or not the figure has rotational symmetry. If you decide that it does have rotational symmetry, name the angles that the figure can be rotated about the center point so that the resulting image looks exactly like the preimage.

34.

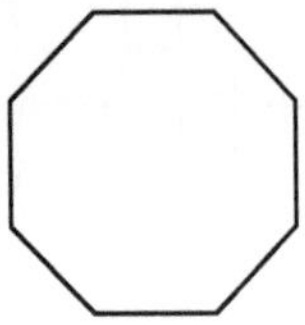

Does this figure have rotational symmetry? __________

If your answer was *yes*, name the angles that the figure can be rotated about the center point so that the resulting image looks exactly like the preimage.

____

____

35.

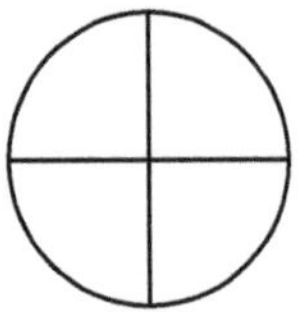

Does this figure have rotational symmetry? __________

If your answer was *yes*, name the angles that the figure can be rotated about the center point so that the resulting image looks exactly like the preimage.

____

____

36.

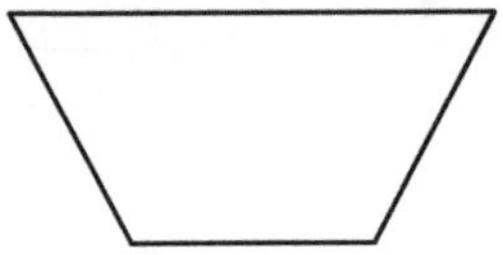

Does this figure have rotational symmetry? __________

If your answer was *yes*, name the angles that the figure can be rotated about the center point so that the resulting image looks exactly like the preimage.

____

____

37.

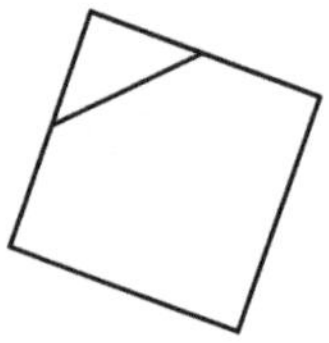

Does this figure have rotational symmetry? __________

If your answer was *yes*, name the angles that the figure can be rotated about the center point so that the resulting image looks exactly like the preimage.

____

____

38.

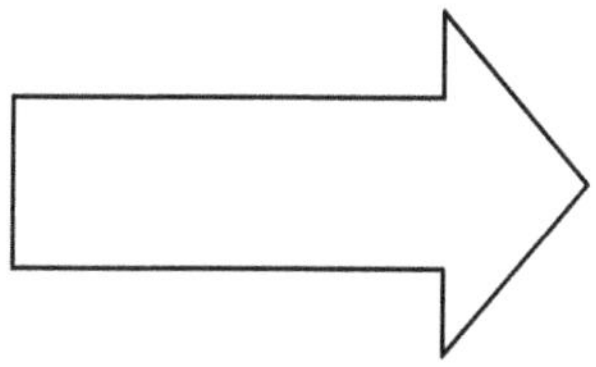

Does this figure have rotational symmetry? __________

If your answer was *yes*, name the angles that the figure can be rotated about the center point so that the resulting image looks exactly like the preimage.

____

____

39.

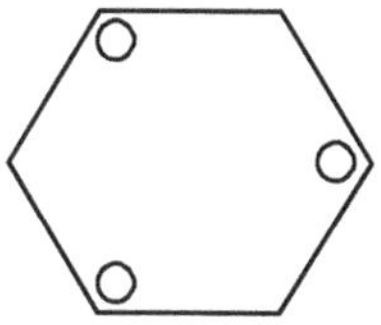

Does this figure have rotational symmetry? __________

If your answer was *yes*, name the angles that the figure can be rotated about the center point so that the resulting image looks exactly like the preimage.

____

____

40.

Does this figure have rotational symmetry? __________

If your answer was *yes*, name the angles that the figure can be rotated about the center point so that the resulting image looks exactly like the preimage.

____

____

41.

6

Does this figure have rotational symmetry? __________

If your answer was *yes*, name the angles that the figure can be rotated about the center point so that the resulting image looks exactly like the preimage.

____

____

42. 

Does this figure have rotational symmetry? __________

If your answer was *yes*, name the angles that the figure can be rotated about the center point so that the resulting image looks exactly like the preimage.

____

____

43. 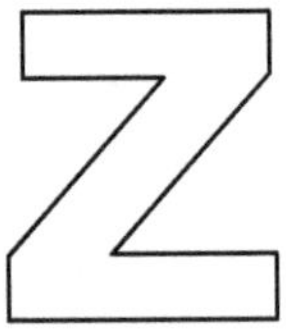

Does this figure have rotational symmetry? __________

If your answer was *yes*, name the angles that the figure can be rotated about the center point so that the resulting image looks exactly like the preimage.

____

____

44. 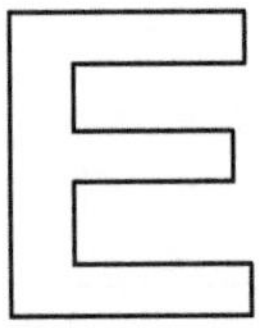

Does this figure have rotational symmetry? __________

If your answer was *yes*, name the angles that the figure can be rotated about the center point so that the resulting image looks exactly like the preimage.

____

____

45. 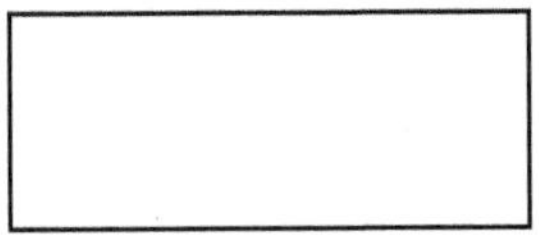

Does this figure have rotational symmetry? __________

If your answer was *yes*, name the angles that the figure can be rotated about the center point so that the resulting image looks exactly like the preimage.

____

____

Part III – Reflections

In this section, we will discuss reflections in more detail.

We will begin by stating a more formal definition of a reflection in a line.

> A point M is a <u>reflection in line ℓ</u> of the point N if and only if ℓ is the perpendicular bisector of $\overline{MN}$. If M is a point on line ℓ, then its image after a reflection in ℓ is M.

Example 1: In the figure below, the black figure is the preimage, and the gray figure is the image after a reflection in a line. Draw the line of reflection.

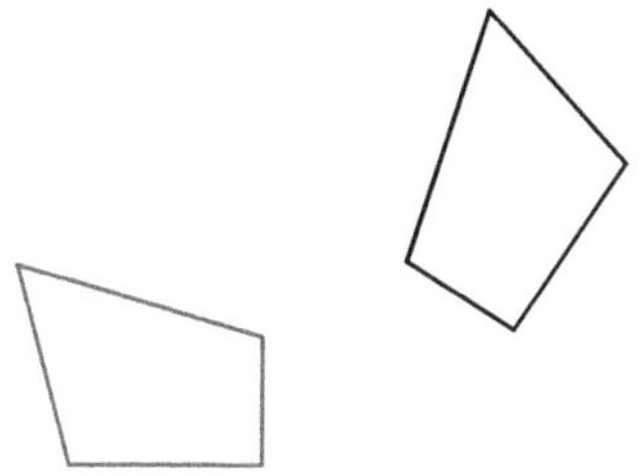

We will begin by drawing segments that connect the corresponding vertices in the figure above.

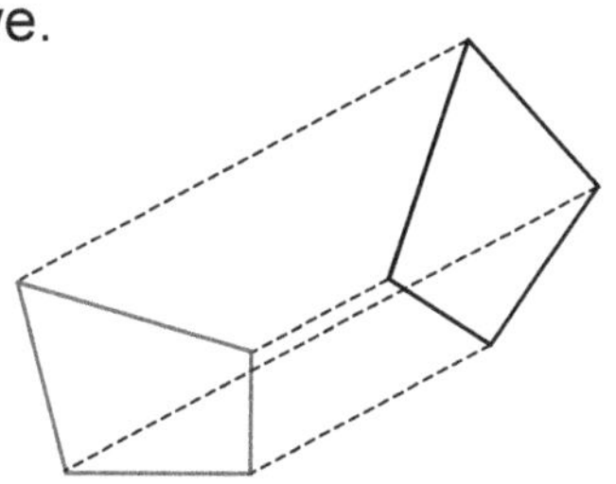

Now, the line of reflection is the line that contains the midpoints of all of these segments. You can use a ruler to find these midpoints, or you can use paper folding techniques. To use paper folding techniques, copy the figure above onto another sheet of paper and then fold the paper so that the two pictures are exactly on top of each other. The line of reflection is the fold in your paper. (If you have trouble understanding this, copy the next figure on another sheet of paper and then fold it on the dotted line. Notice how the image and the preimage are exactly on top of each other.) Using either technique, you should find that the line of reflection is the dotted line shown in the picture below.

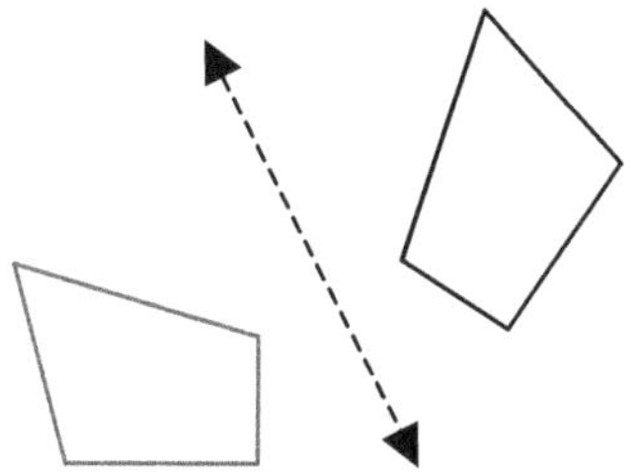

Example 2: Draw the image of a reflection in line ℓ of the figure shown on the below.

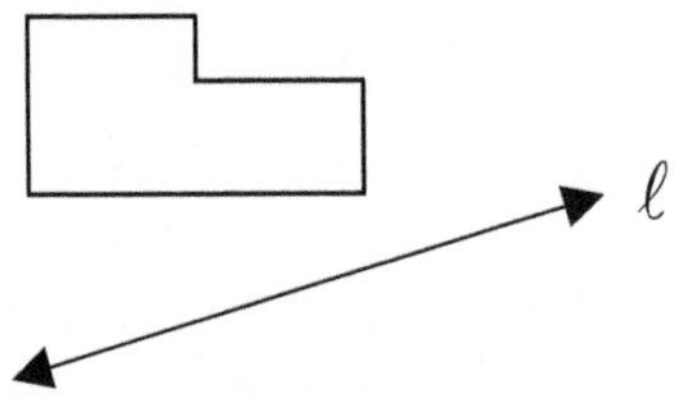

Step 1: Label the vertices of the preimage because this will make life a little less confusing when you get to Step 3, and draw segments from the vertices of the image to ℓ that are perpendicular to ℓ.

You can use a protractor to draw the perpendicular segments if you want, but the easiest way is to use the corner of a notecard. (Note that the corners of a notecard are right angles.) To use a notecard, line one edge of the notecard up with line ℓ, and also line one of the edges perpendicular to it up with one of the vertices of the preimage. Then draw the segment that follows this edge of the notecard from the vertex to ℓ.

This gives us the dotted segments shown in the figure below. (Like we said in the last section, you may want to use colored pencils to draw the different sets of segments when you work the exercises in this section.)

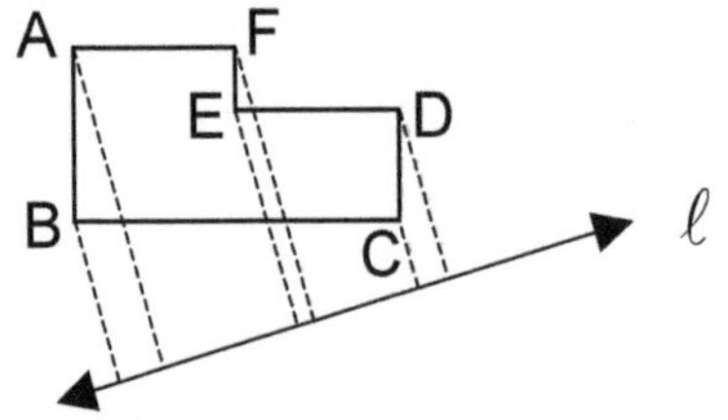

Step 2: Extend the segments that you drew in Step 1 so that they are twice as long as the original segments.

You can do this using a ruler, or you can mark the length on a notecard. Whichever way you choose to do this, make sure that the segments are straight, the segments are twice as long as they were in Step 1, and the extra length is all on the opposite side of line ℓ.

We will also label the endpoints of these new segments using the notation we discussed in Exercises 25-30 of Part I of this chapter.

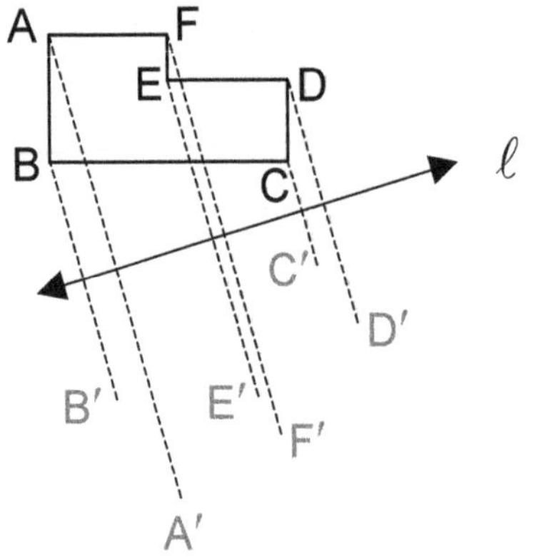

Step 3: Draw the image.

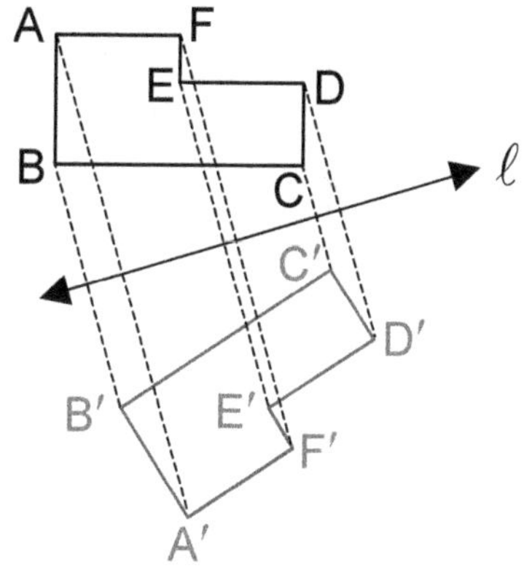

Step 4: To make this picture less confusing to look at, we will erase the dotted segments.

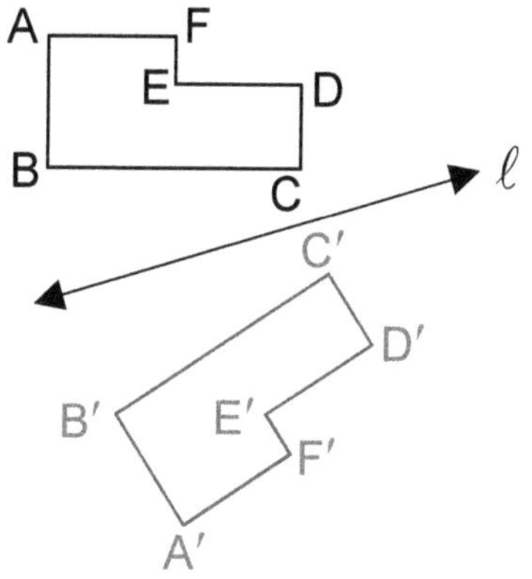

Example 3: Draw the image of a reflection in line m of the parallelogram shown below.

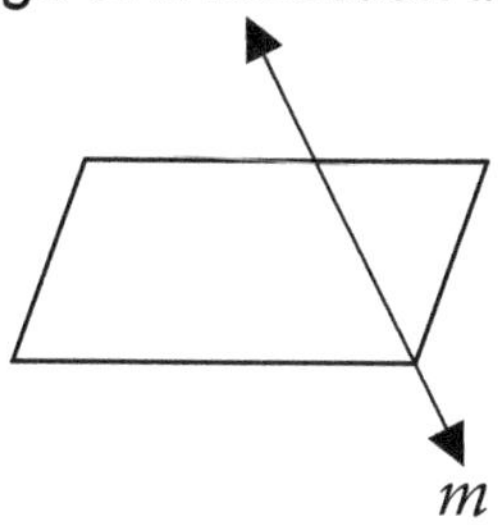

Step 1: Label the vertices of the preimage because this will make life a little less confusing when we get to Step 3, and draw segments from the vertices of the image to m that are perpendicular to m.

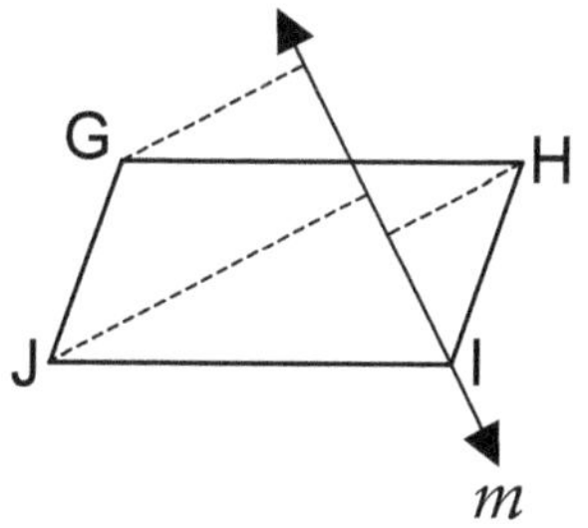

Step 2: Extend the segments that you drew in Step 1 so that they are twice as long as the original segments, and label the endpoints of these new segments using the notation we discussed in Exercises 25-30 of Part I of this chapter.

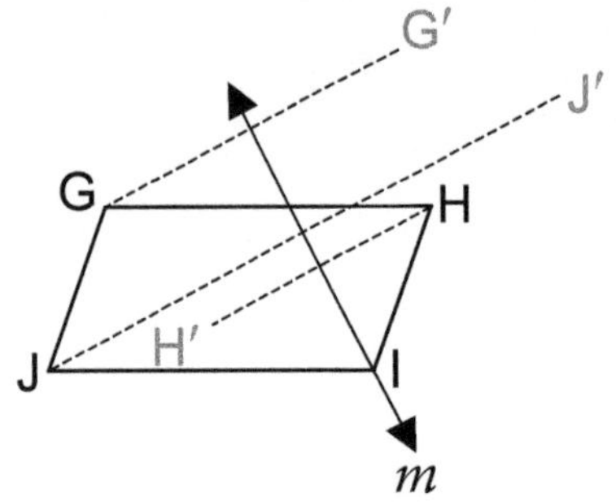

Notice that we did not label I′ because the image of I will be itself.

Step 3: Draw the image.

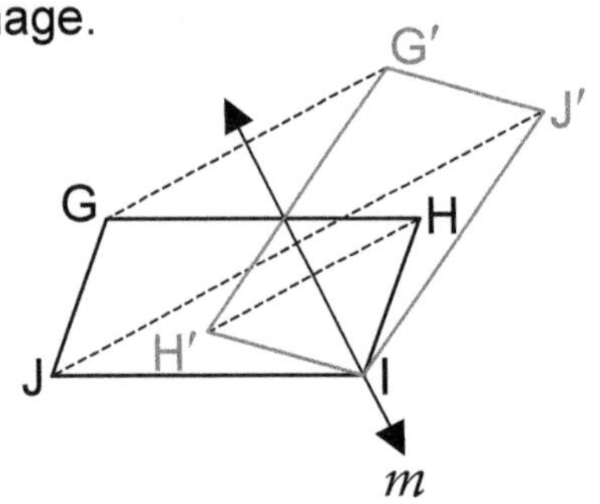

Step 4: To make this picture less confusing to look at, we will erase the dotted segments.

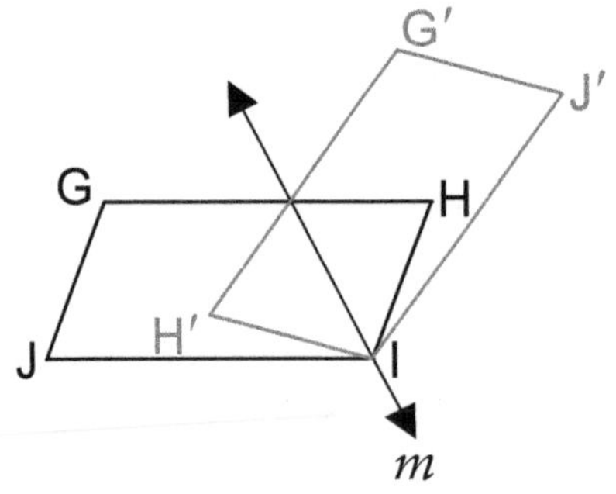

Example 4: The figure at the right shows a triangle graphed in the coordinate plane. Draw the image of (a) a reflection of the triangle in the x-axis, (b) a reflection of the triangle in the line y = 1, and (c) a reflection of the triangle in the line x = –2.

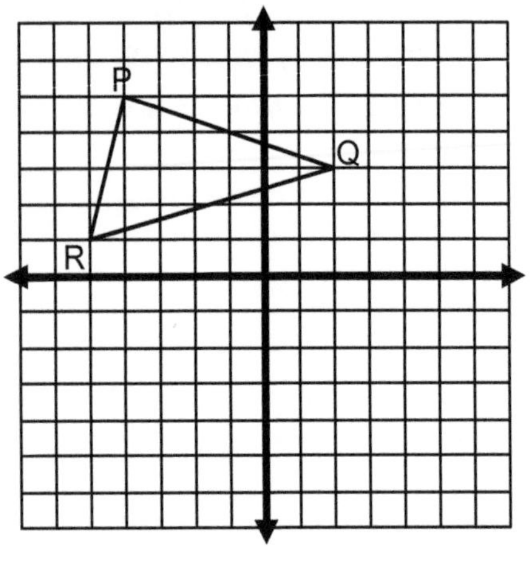

(a) Note that the reflection of the point P in the x-axis is the point (–4, –5), the reflection of the point Q in the x-axis is the point (2, –3), and the reflection of the point R in the x-axis is the point (–5, –1).

Thus, we can draw the image of a reflection of ΔPQR in the x-axis as shown below.

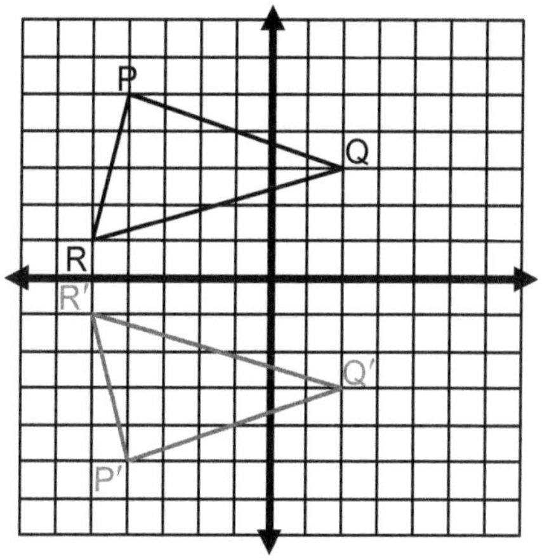

(b) We will begin by noting that the line y = 1 is the dotted line shown in the graph below. (To see why this is true, note that the y-coordinate is 1 at every point along this line.)

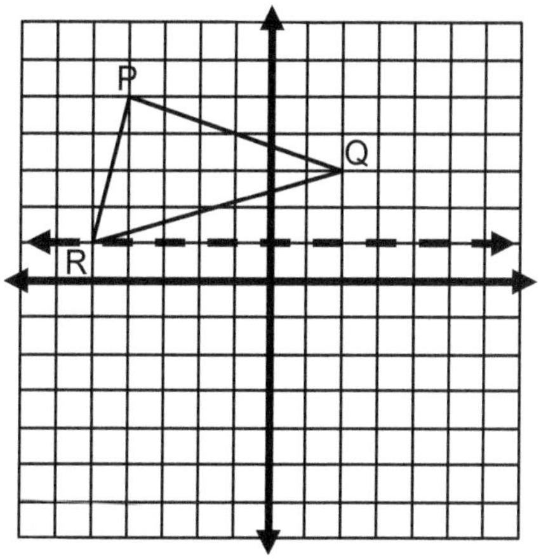

Now, note that the reflection of the point P in this line is the point (–4, –3), the reflection of the point Q in this line is the point (2, –1), and the reflection of the point R in this line is itself. Thus, we can draw the image of a reflection of ΔPQR in the line y = 1 as shown below.

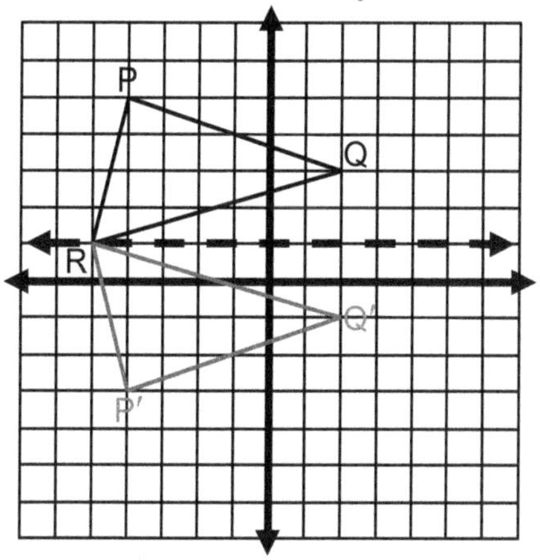

(c) We will begin by noting that the line x = –2 is the dotted line shown in the graph below. (To see why this is true, note that the x-coordinate is –2 at every point along this line.)

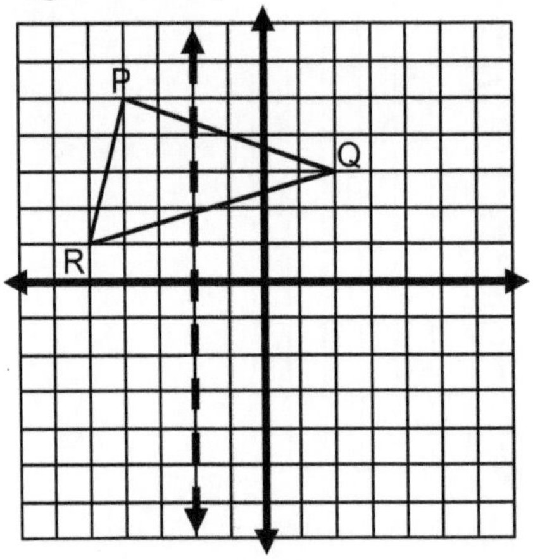

Now, note that the reflection of the point P in this line is the point (0, 5), the reflection of the point Q in this line is the point (–6, 3), and the reflection of the point R in this line is the point (1, 1). Thus, we can draw the image of a reflection of ΔPQR in the line x = –2 as shown below.

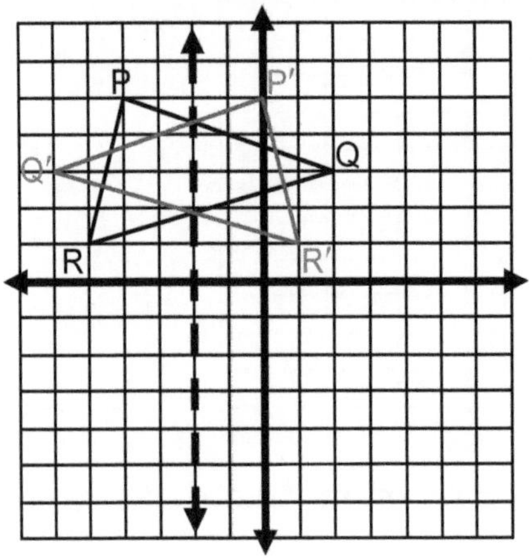

Example 5: The figure at the right shows two squares that share a common side and have their diagonals drawn. Name the image of (a) a reflection of the point S in $\overline{VW}$, (b) a reflection of the point T in $\overline{TV}$, (c) a reflection of $\overline{SU}$ in $\overline{TV}$, and (d) a reflection of ΔVXY in $\overline{VW}$.

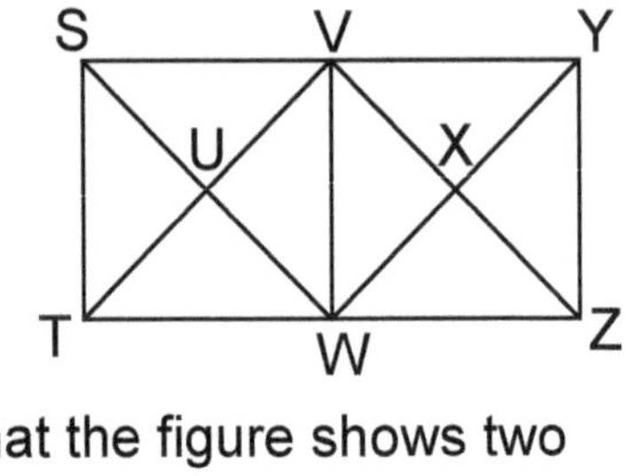

We will begin by noting that, since the question says that the figure shows two *squares* with their diagonals drawn, we can use the theorems we discussed in Chapter 6 to say that each of the angles in this figure has a measure of 45°, 90°, 135°, or 180°.

(a) If you follow the steps discussed in Examples 2 and 3 of this section, you should find that the image of the point S after a reflection in $\overline{VW}$ is the point Y.

(b) Since the point T is on $\overline{TV}$, we can use the definition at the beginning of this section to say that the image of T after a reflection in $\overline{TV}$ is the point T.

(c) If you follow the steps discussed in Examples 2 and 3 of this section, you should find that the image of the point S after a reflection in $\overline{TV}$ is the point W, and the image of the point U after a reflection in $\overline{TV}$ is the point U. Therefore, the image of $\overline{SU}$ after a reflection in $\overline{TV}$ is $\overline{WU}$.

(d) Note that the image of the point V after a reflection in $\overline{VW}$ is itself, the image of the point X after a reflection in $\overline{VW}$ is the point U, and the image of the point Y after a reflection in $\overline{VW}$ is the point S. Therefore, the image of ΔVXY after a reflection in $\overline{VW}$ is ΔVUS.

Now, we need another definition.

A figure has line symmetry if and only if there exists a line such that a reflection in the line gives an image that matches the preimage exactly. If there is such a line, then it is called a line of symmetry.

To understand these definitions, look at the figure below.

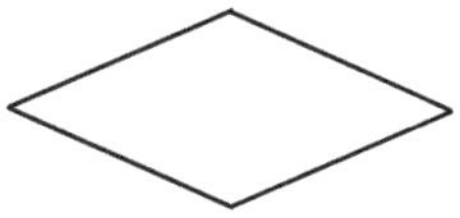

If you draw a reflection of this figure in either of the dotted lines shown below, then you should end up with an image that matches the preimage perfectly. Therefore, we can say that this figure does have line symmetry, and its lines of symmetry are the dotted lines shown below.

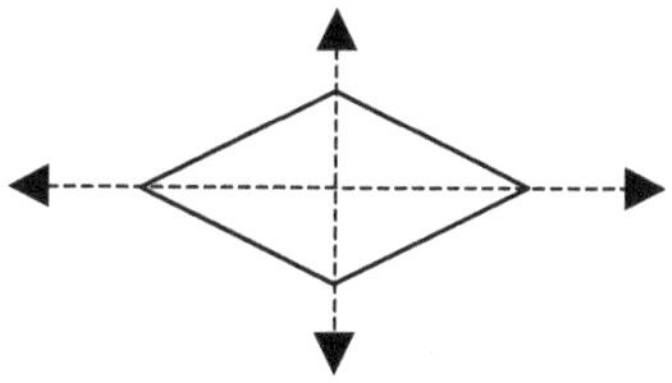

You should also notice that, if you try to draw a reflection of this figure in any other line, you will not end up with an image that matches the preimage perfectly. Therefore, the two lines of symmetry shown above are the *only* lines of symmetry that this figure has.

Example 6: Decide whether or not each of the figures below has line symmetry. For each figure that does have line symmetry, draw all the lines of symmetry.

(a)

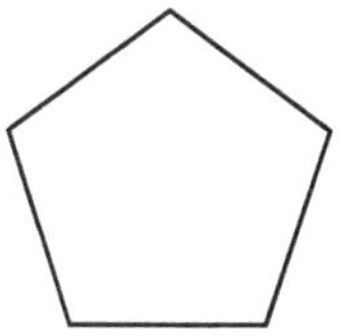

(b)

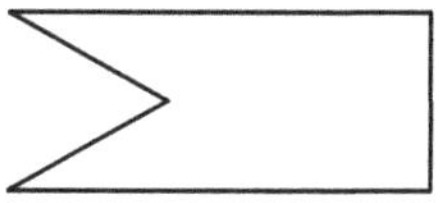

(c)

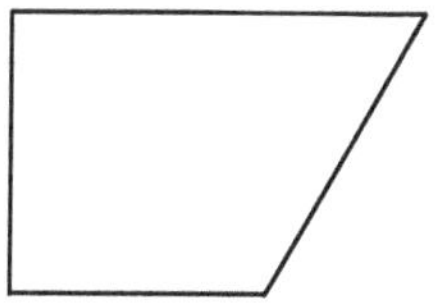

(a) This figure does exhibit line symmetry, and there are five lines of symmetry. If you draw a reflection of this figure in any of the dotted lines shown below, you will get an image that is exactly the same as the preimage.

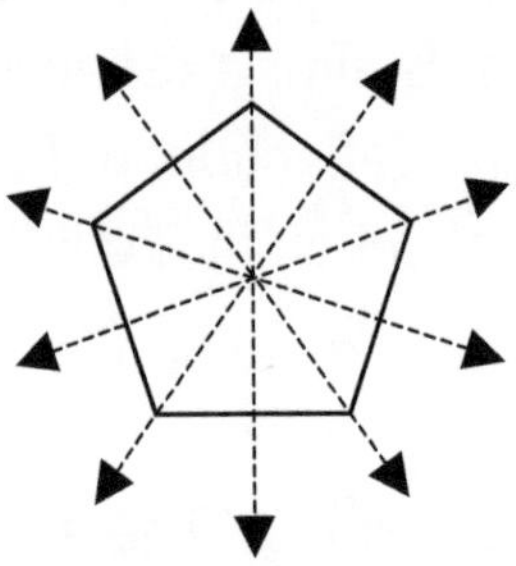

(b) This figure does have line symmetry, but there is only one line of symmetry. If you draw a reflection of this figure in the dotted line shown below, you will get an image that is exactly the same as the preimage. (However, if you draw a reflection in any other line, you will not get a figure that is exactly the same as the preimage. Therefore, this is the ONLY line of symmetry.)

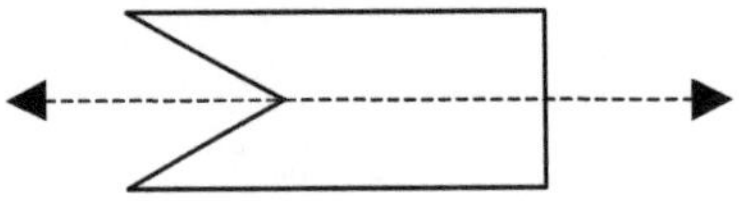

(c) This figure does not have line symmetry. You cannot draw a line such that a reflection in the line yields an image that matches the preimage exactly.

Problems:

1-4. In each of the figures below, the black figure is the preimage, and the gray figure is the image after a reflection in a line. Draw the lines of reflection.

1.

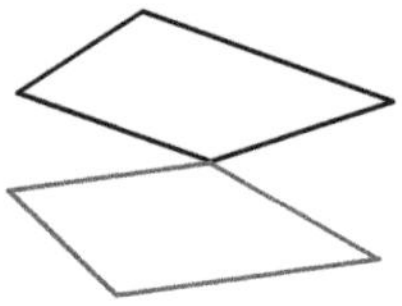

2.

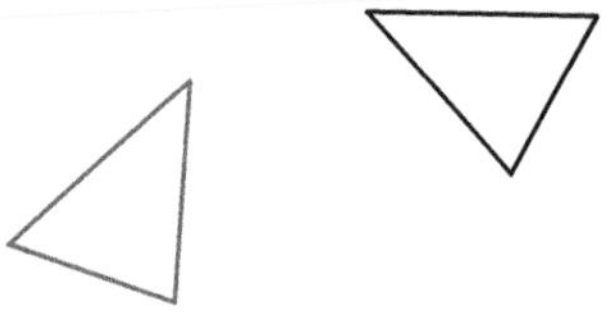

3.

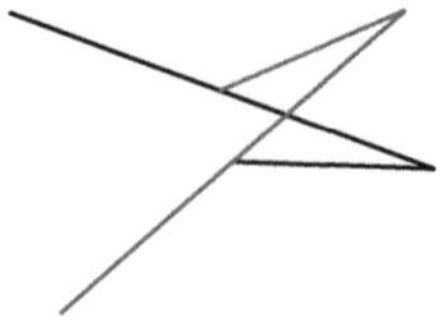

4.

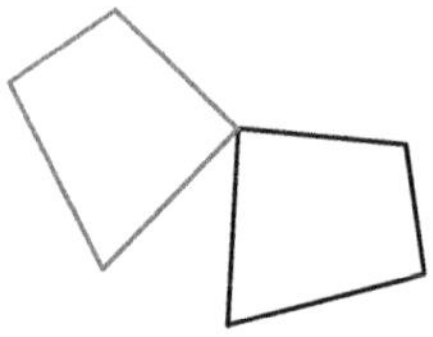

5-16. For each of the figures below, draw the image of a reflection of the figure in line ℓ.

5.

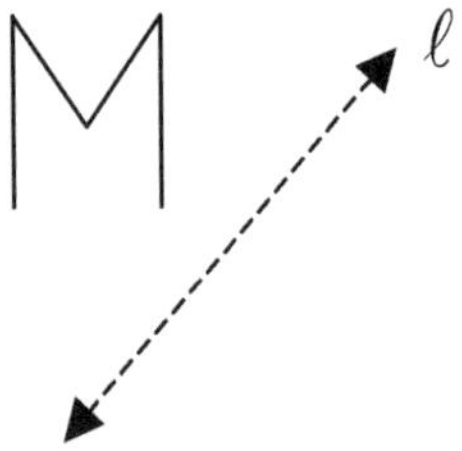

6.

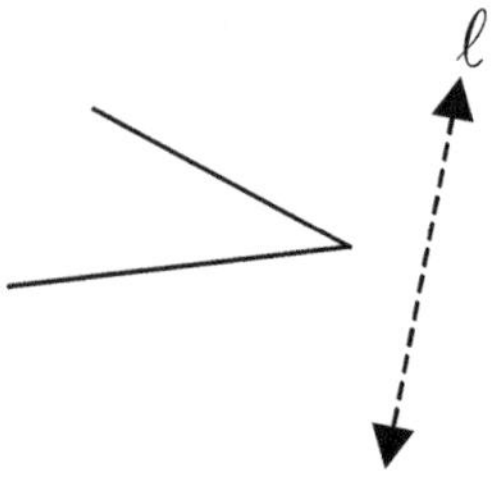

7.

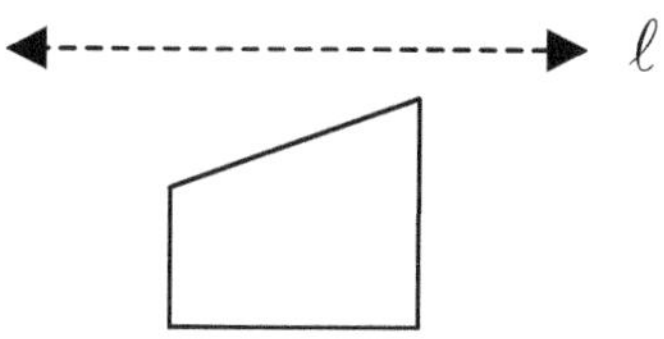

8.

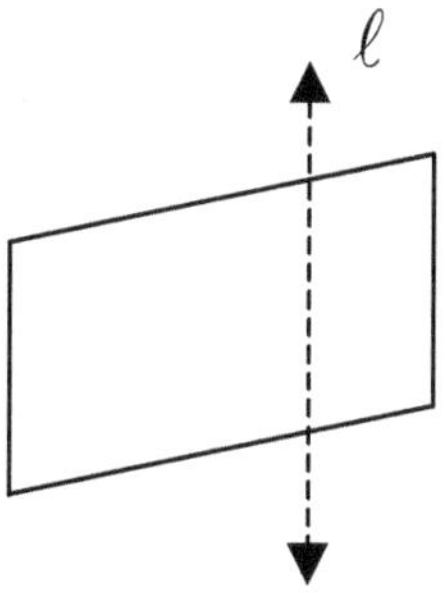

9.

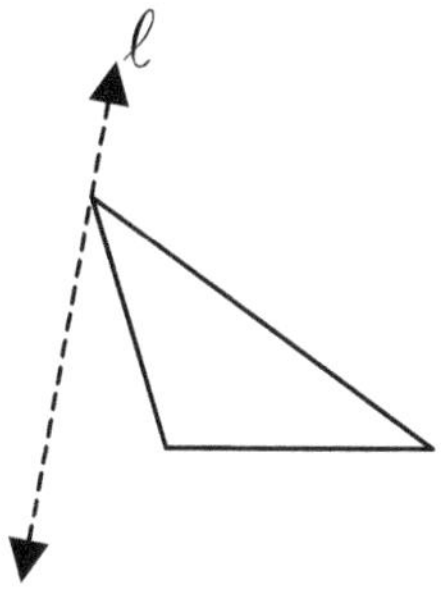

10.

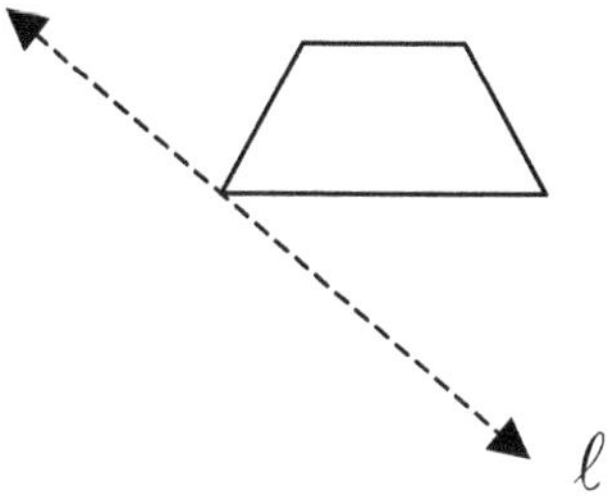

11.

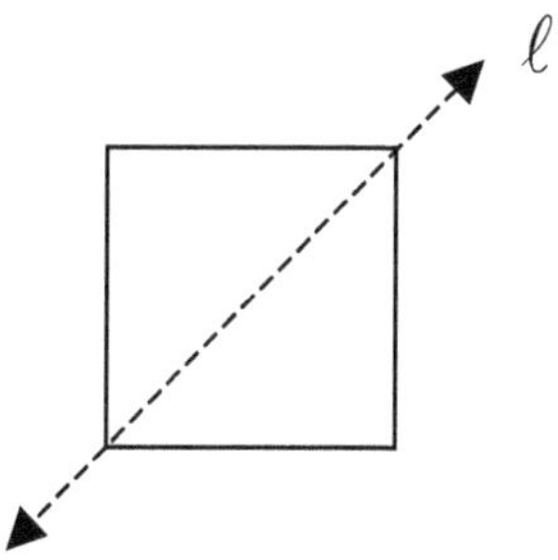

12.

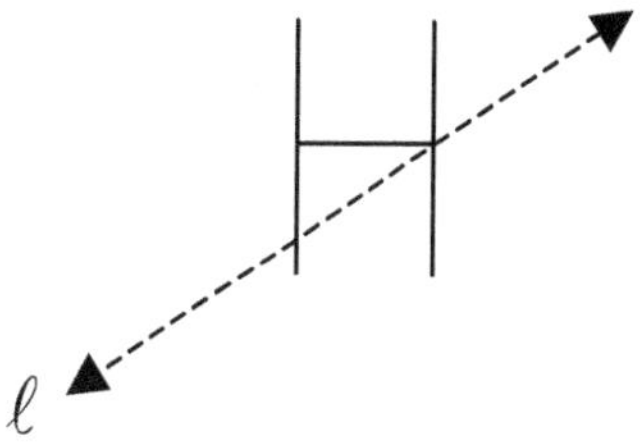

13.

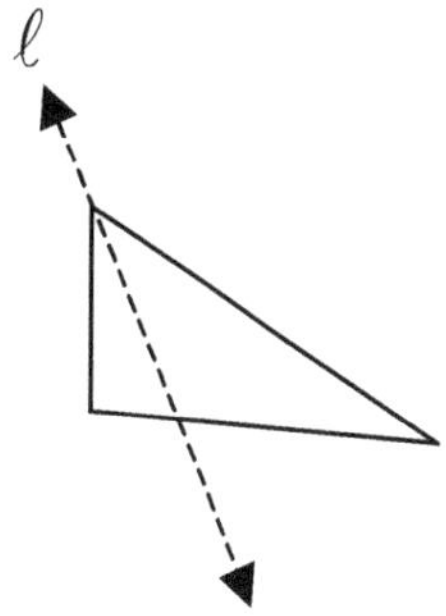

14.

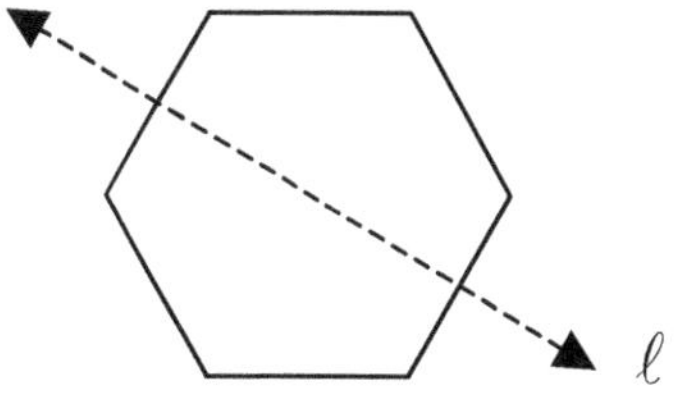

15.

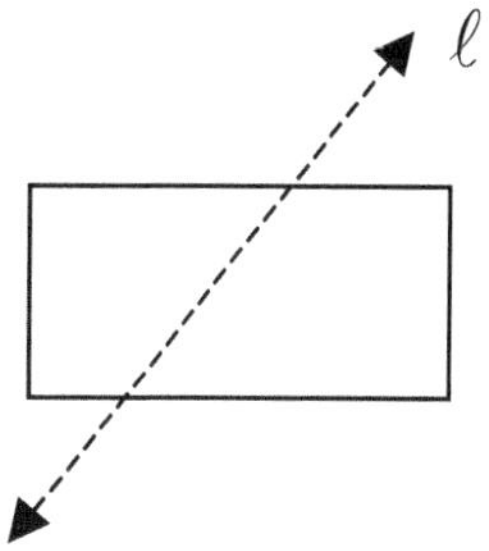

16.

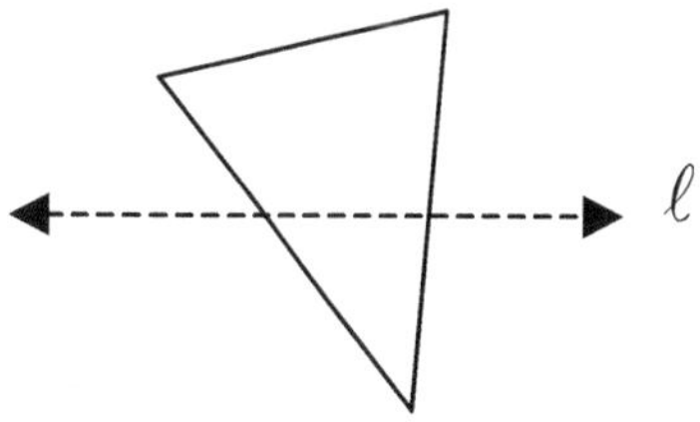

17. Draw the image of $\overline{AB}$ after a reflection in the x-axis.

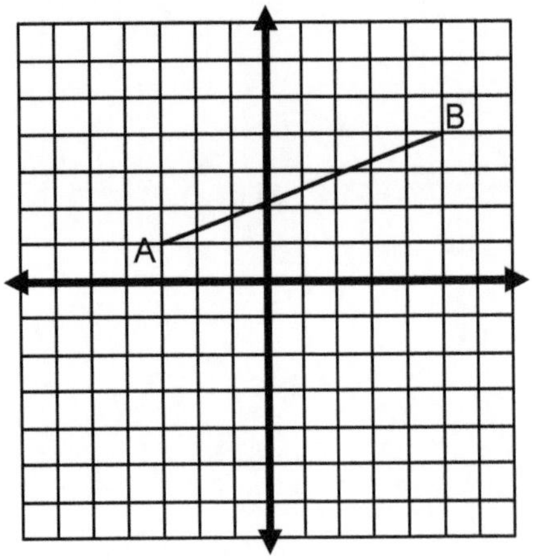

18. Draw the image of ΔCDE after a reflection in the x-axis.

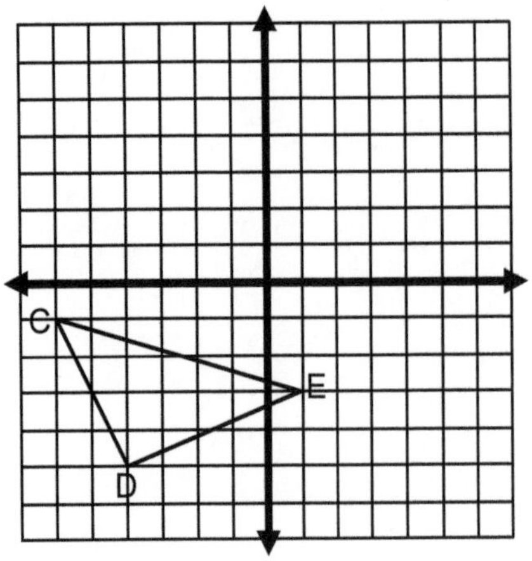

19. Draw the image of parallelogram FGHI after a reflection in the y-axis.

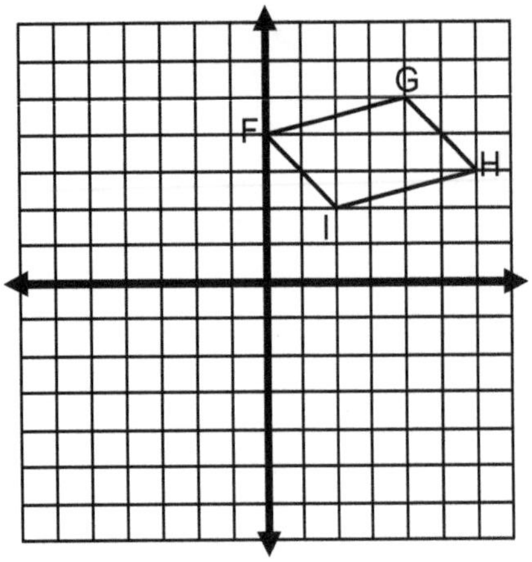

20. Draw the image of $\overline{JK}$ after a reflection in the line $y = 2$.

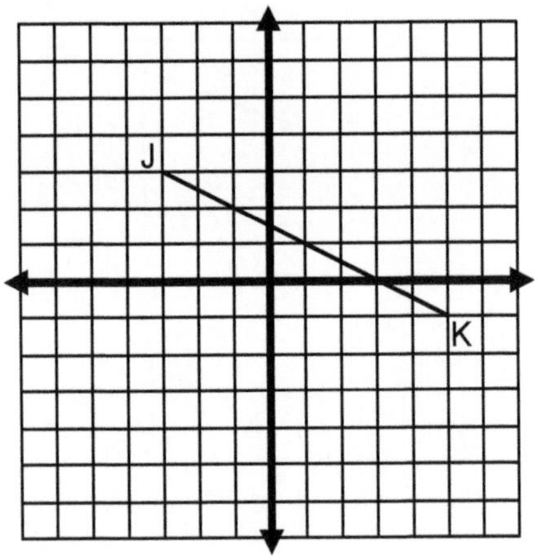

21. Draw the image of ΔLMN after a reflection in the line $x = -1$.

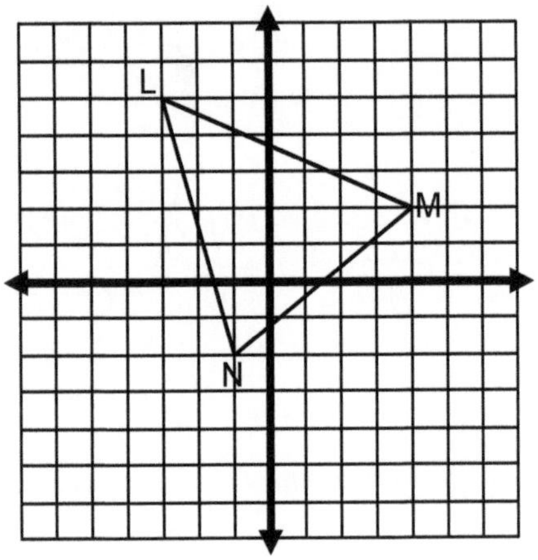

22. Draw the image of pentagon OPQRS after a reflection in the y-axis.

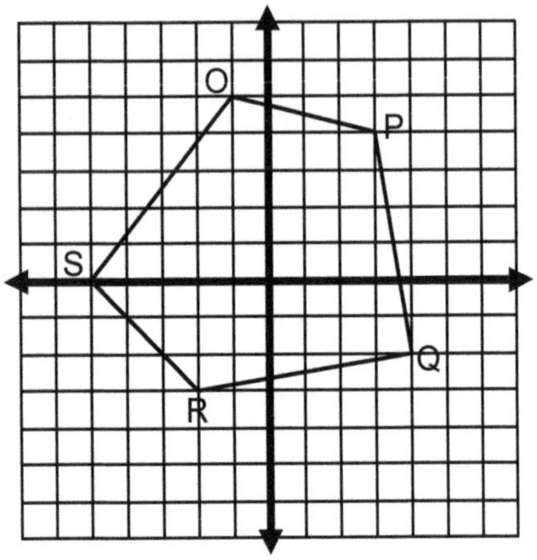

23. Draw the image of $\triangle TUV$ after a reflection in the line y = 3.

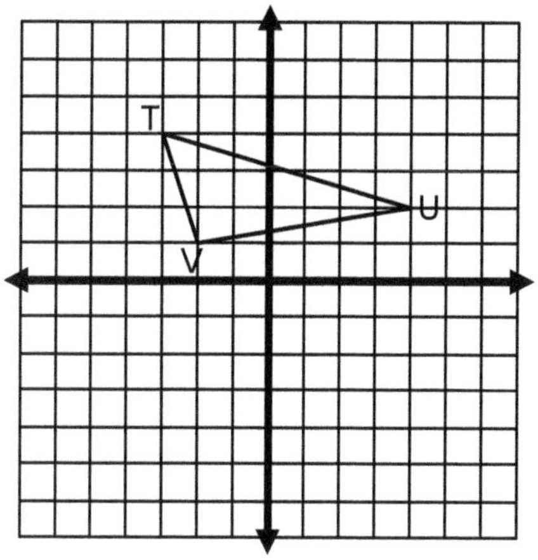

24. Draw the image of $\triangle WXY$ after a reflection in the line x = 2.

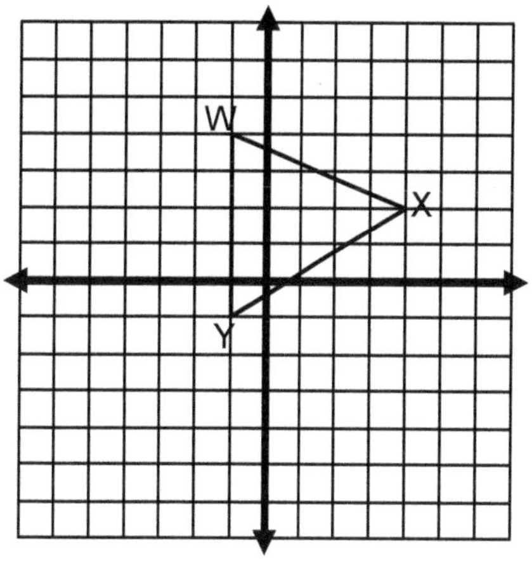

25-30. In the figure at the right, all of the triangles are isosceles right triangles.

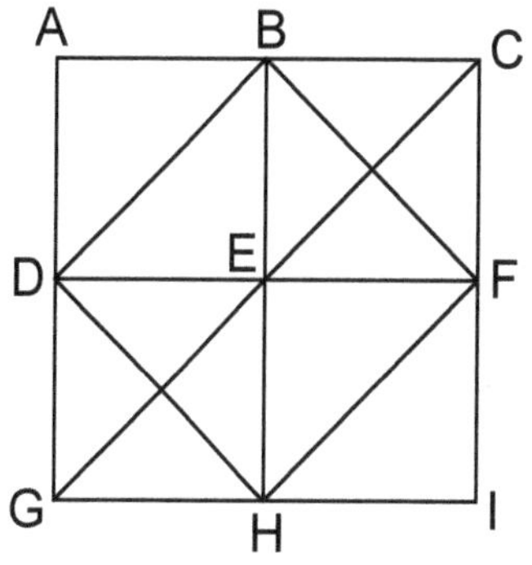

25. What is the image of $\overline{AB}$ after a reflection in $\overline{DF}$? ________________

26. What is the image of $\overline{BF}$ after a reflection in $\overline{DF}$? ________________

27. What is the image of $\triangle ABD$ after a reflection in $\overline{BH}$? ________________

28. What is the image of $\triangle BED$ after a reflection in $\overline{BH}$? ________________

29. What is the image of square BCFE after a reflection in $\overline{BH}$? ________________

30. What is the image of $\triangle IFH$ after a reflection in $\overline{CG}$? ________________

31-38. Decide whether or not each of the figures below has line symmetry. If you decide that the figure does have line symmetry, draw all the lines of symmetry.

31. Does this figure have line symmetry? ______________

32. Does this figure have line symmetry? ______________

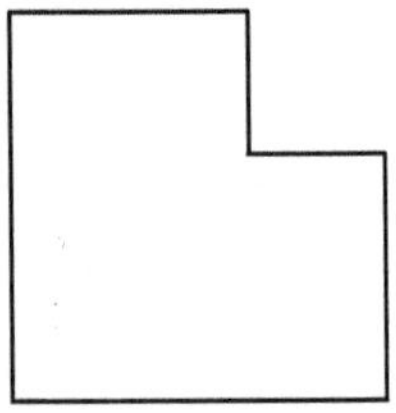

33. Does this figure have line symmetry? ______________

34. Does this figure have line symmetry? ______________

35. Does this figure have line symmetry? ______________

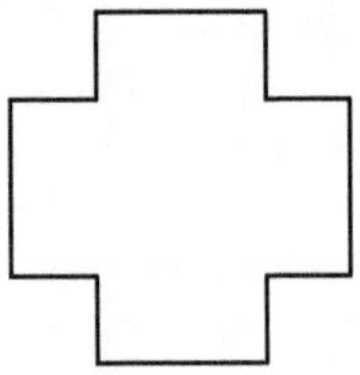

36. Does this figure have line symmetry? ______________

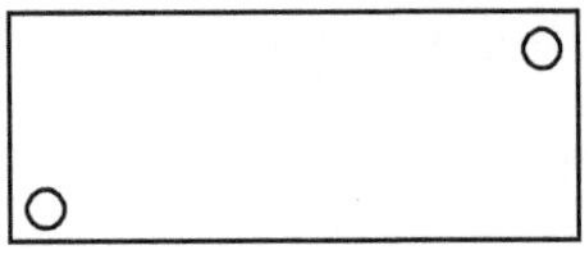

37. Does this figure have line symmetry? ______________

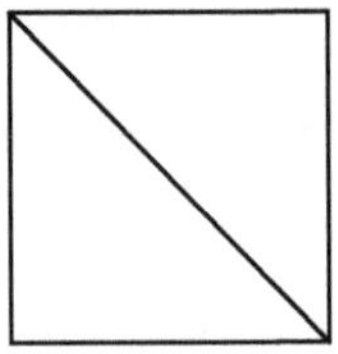

38. Does this figure have line symmetry? ______________

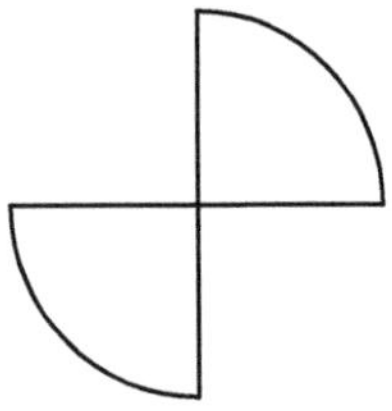

Part IV – Translations

We will begin by reviewing the definition of a translation that we discussed in Part I of this chapter.

A transformation is a translation if and only every point of the preimage is moved a fixed distance in a fixed direction.

Example 1: Triangle ABC has vertices at A(–5, 3), B(–1, 5), and C(–3, –4). Graph ΔABC, and then graph the image of ΔABC after a translation 6 units to the right and 1 unit down. Also name the coordinates of A′, B′, and C′.

We can graph ΔABC as shown at the right.

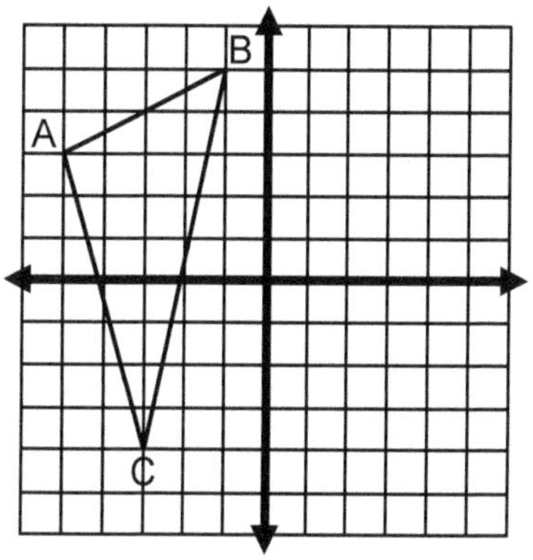

Now, the question tells us to translate ΔABC 6 units to the right and 1 unit down. This gives us ΔA′B′C′ shown at the right.

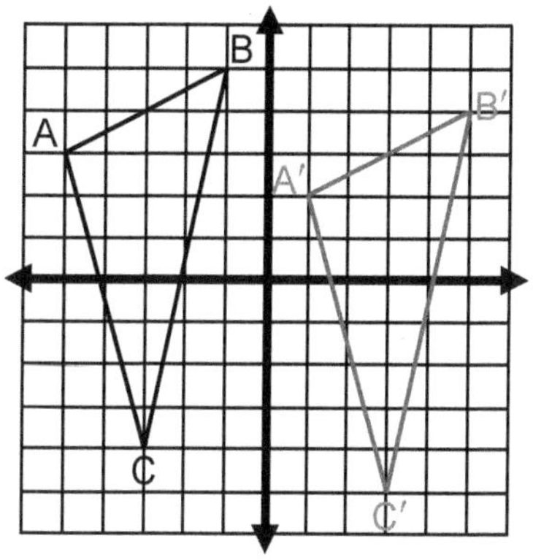

Now, we can say that the coordinates of A′ are (1, 2), the coordinates of B′ are (5, 4), and the coordinates of C′ are (3, –5).

Example 2: If parallelogram DEFG at the right is to be translated so that D′ is at (–3, 5), what will the coordinates of E′, F′, and G′ be?

We will begin by noting that, in order to translate parallelogram DEFG so that D′ is at (–3, 5), we must shift the parallelogram 2 units to the left and 3 units up. Therefore, the coordinates of E′ will be (2, 4), the coordinates of F′ will be (1, 1), and the coordinates of G′ will be (–4, 2).

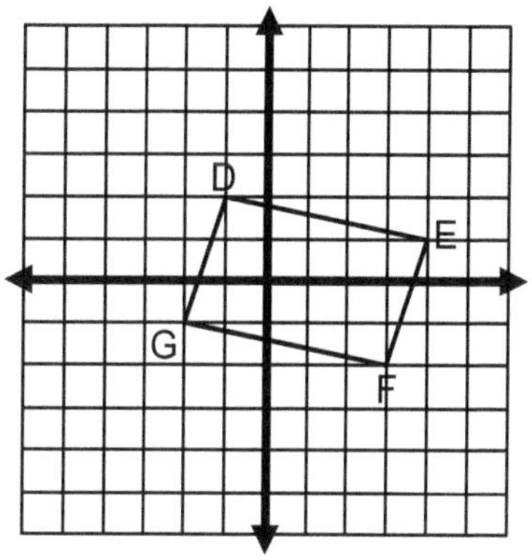

In the next example, we will discuss a concept called coordinate notation. If you look back at Example 1, you should notice that we added 6 to each of the x-coordinates, and we subtracted 1 from each of the y-coordinates. Therefore, we can describe this translation by writing "$(x, y) \rightarrow (x + 6, y - 1)$." In Example 2, we subtracted 2 from each of the x-coordinates, and we added 3 to each of the y-coordinates. Therefore, we can describe this translation by writing "$(x, y) \rightarrow (x - 2, y + 3)$."

Example 3: The vertices of ΔPQR are at P(1, 0), Q(3, 4), and R(–2, 3). Draw ΔPQR, and then draw the image after the translation $(x, y) \rightarrow (x, y - 4)$.

We will begin by drawing ΔPQR.

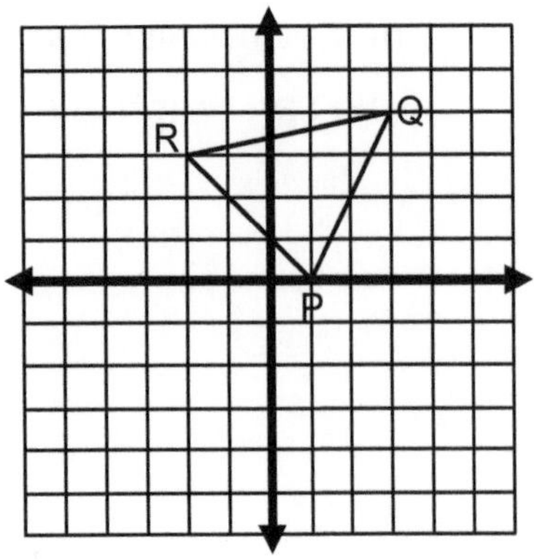

Now, the translation $(x, y) \rightarrow (x, y - 5)$ tells us to leave the x-coordinates the same and subtract 5 from each y-coordinate (or, equivalently, translate the triangle down 5 units). This gives us $\Delta P'Q'R'$ shown at the right.

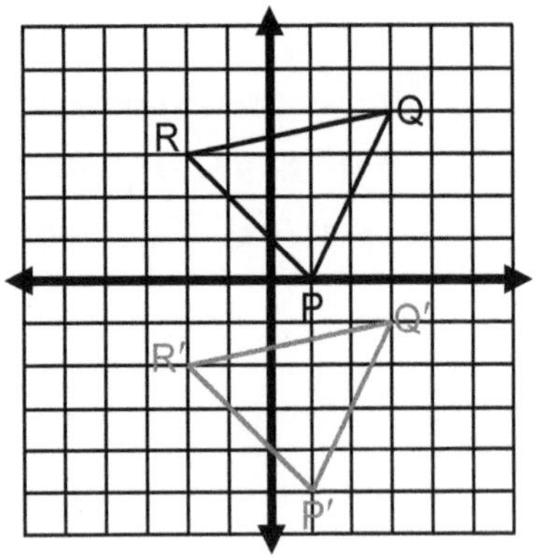

Now, we need another definition.

A vector is a type of directed segment. A vector has both a magnitude (or length) and a direction.

In Example 4, we will discuss how we name vectors and describe them using a notation called component form. In Examples 5 and 6, we will discuss how we can use vectors to talk about translations.

Example 4: Name the vector shown at the right and write its component form.

We can call this vector "vector MN," or, in symbols, "$\overrightarrow{MN}$." We could ***not***, however, call this "vector NM" or "$\overrightarrow{NM}$" because we must always name the starting point first.

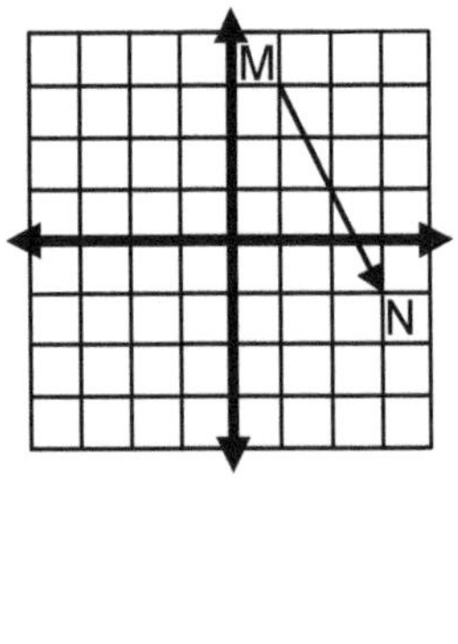

To write this vector in its component form, we will note that, in order to start at the point M and go to the point N, we must move 2 units to the right and 4 units down. This tells us that we write the component form of this vector as $\langle 2, -4 \rangle$. (Note that this is very similar to the way we name points in the coordinate plane.)

Finally, we will state that all of the vectors shown in the figure at the right are identical. They have different starting points, but they all have the same magnitude and direction.

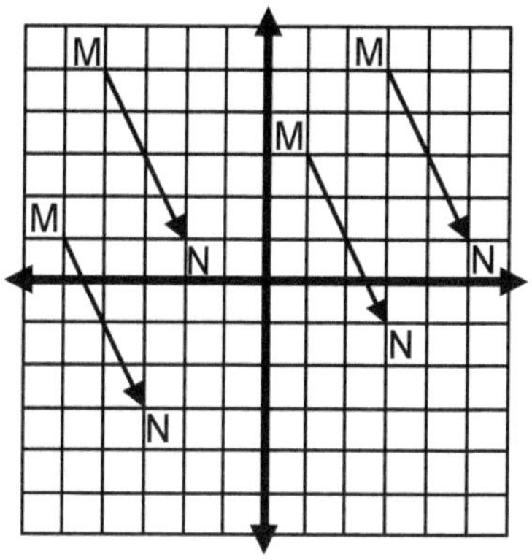

Example 5: Quadrilateral WXYZ has vertices at W(3, –1), X(2, –4), Y(0, –2), and Z(1, 2). Translate quadrilateral WXYZ by the vector $\langle -5, 3 \rangle$, and state the coordinates of the translated figure.

We will begin by drawing quadrilateral WXYZ.

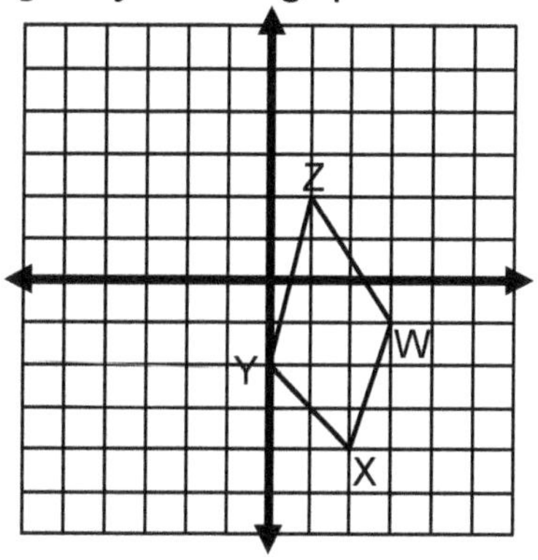

Next, we will note that the directions want us to translate quadrilateral WXYZ by the vector $\langle -5, 3 \rangle$. This means that we need to move each of the vertices 5 units to the left and 3 units up.

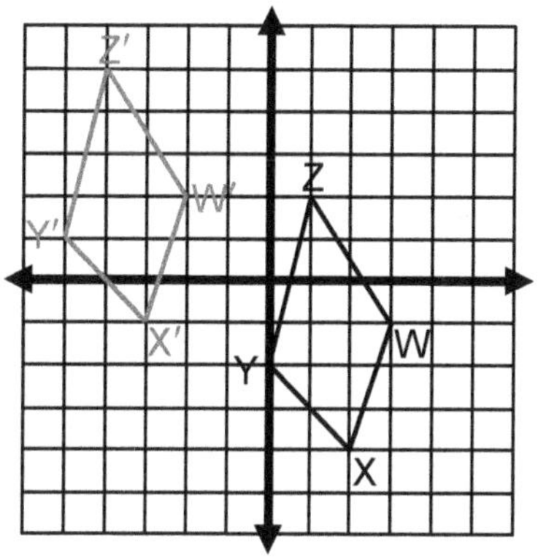

This tells us that the coordinates of the vertices of the translated figure are W′(–2, 2), X′(–3, –1), Y′(–5, 1), and Z′(–4, 5).

Problems:

1a. $\overline{AB}$ has endpoints at A(5, –1) and B(2, 3). Draw $\overline{AB}$ and a translation 4 units to the left and 3 units up.

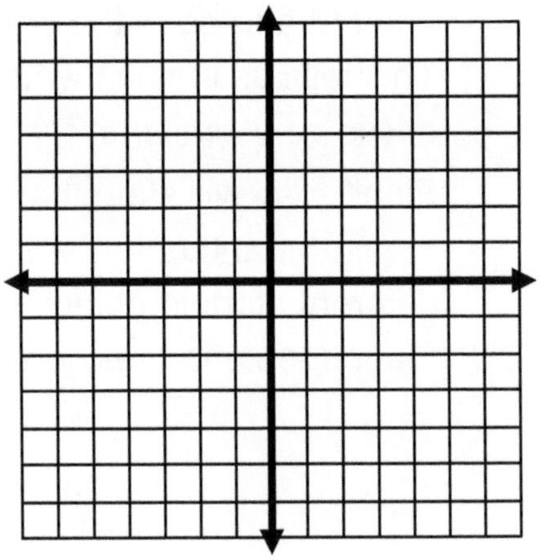

b. Give the coordinates of the endpoints of the translated segment.

A′: (____, ____), B′: (____, ____)

c. Describe this translation using coordinate notation.

(x, y) → (________, ________)

2a. ΔCDE has vertices at C(0, –2), D(–1, 5), and E(3, 1). Draw ΔCDE and a translation 3 units to the right.

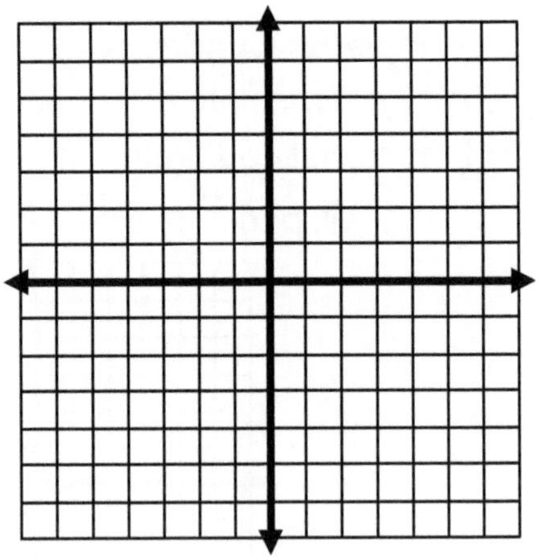

b. Give the coordinates of the vertices of the translated triangle.

C′: (____, ____), D′: (____, ____),

E′: (____, ____)

c. Describe this translation using coordinate notation.

(x, y) → (________, ________)

3a. Triangle FGH has vertices at F(–5, 6), G(–2, –3), and H(0, 1). Draw ΔFGH and a translation 6 units to the right and 1 unit down.

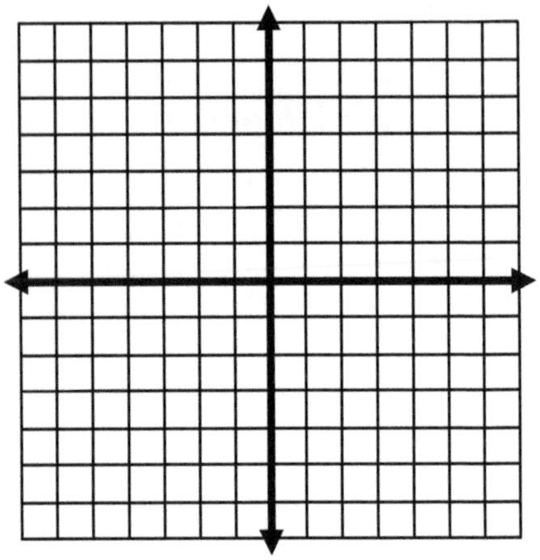

b. Give the coordinates of the vertices of the translated triangle.

F′: (____, ____), G′: (____, ____),

H′: (____, ____)

c. Describe this translation using coordinate notation.

____

4a. Quadrilateral JKLM has vertices at J(–1, –3), K(2, 0), L(3, –2), and M(1, –4). Draw JKLM and a translation 2 units to the left and 4 units up.

b. Give the coordinates of the vertices of the translated quadrilateral.

J′: (____, ____), K′: (____, ____),

L′: (____, ____), M′: (____, ____)

c. Describe this translation using coordinate notation.

____

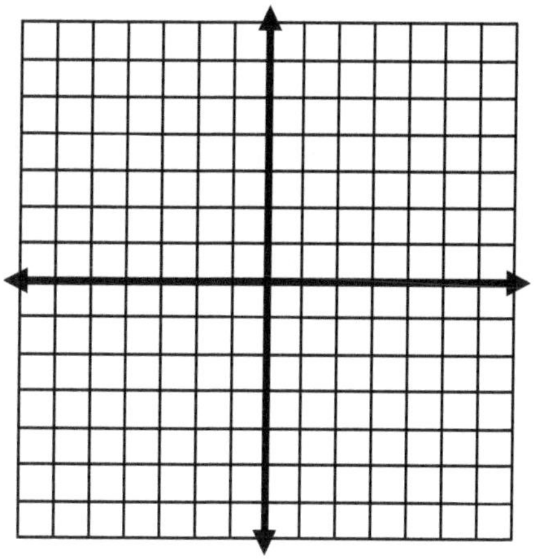

5a. Triangle NOP has vertices at N(3, 0), O(5, –1), and P(4, 4), and it is to be translated so that N′ is located at (–5, 2). Draw ΔNOP and this translation.

b. Give the coordinates of the remaining vertices of the translated triangle.

O′: (____, ____), P′: (____, ____)

c. Describe this translation using coordinate notation.

____

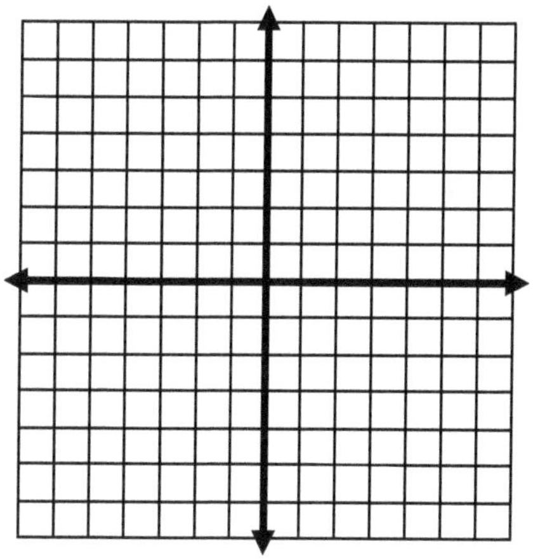

6a. Trapezoid QRST has vertices at Q(–5, 4), R(–2, 5), S(0, 3), and T(–6, 1), and it is to be translated so that R′ is located at (3, –2). Draw trapezoid QRST and this translation.

b. Give the coordinates of the remaining vertices of the translated trapezoid.

Q′: (____, ____), S′: (____, ____),

T′: (____, ____)

c. Describe this translation using coordinate notation.

____

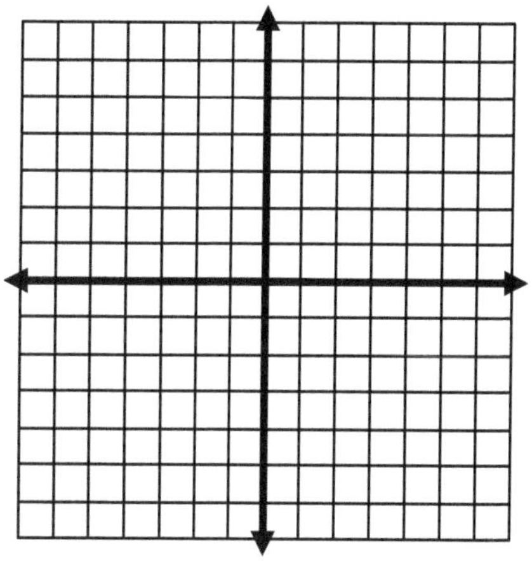

7a. Rectangle UVWZ has vertices at U(3, 3), V(2, 1), W(–2, 3), and Z(–1, 5), and it is to be translated so that W′ is located at (–5, –4). Draw rectangle UVWZ and this translation.

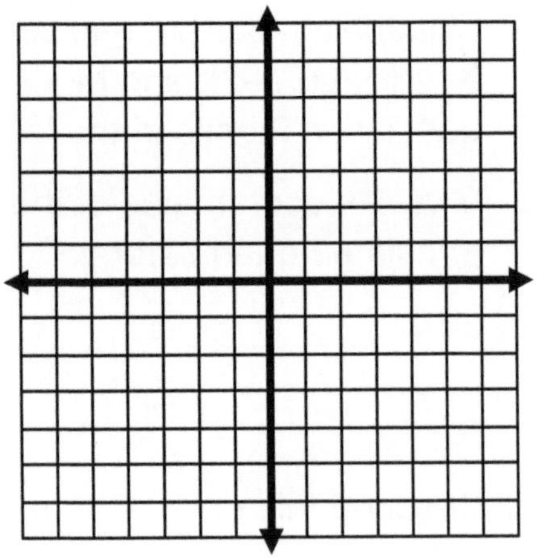

b. Give the coordinates of the remaining vertices of the translated rectangle.

U′: (_____, _____), V′: (_____, _____),

Z′: (_____, _____)

c. Describe this translation using coordinate notation.

____

8a. $\overline{LM}$ has endpoints at L(4, –1) and M(–2, 2), and it is to be translated so that L′ is located at (4, –6). Draw $\overline{LM}$ and this translation.

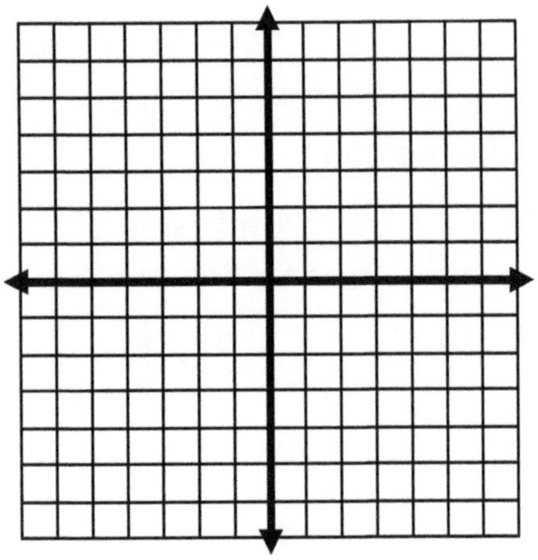

b. Give the coordinates of M′.

M′: (_____, _____)

c. Describe this translation using coordinate notation.

____

9. Name the vector drawn at the right. ______________

Write the component form of this vector. __________

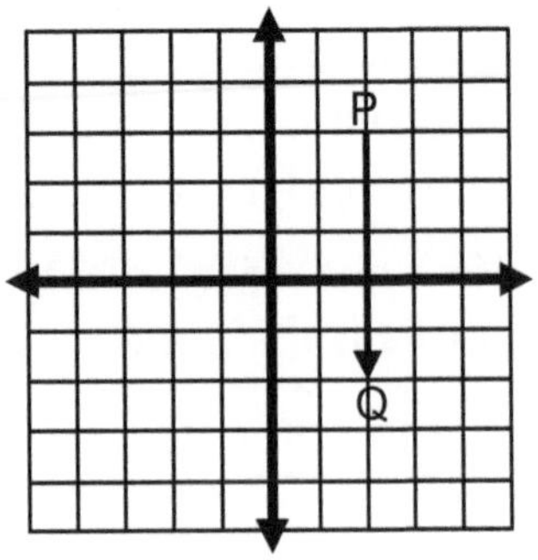

10. Name the vector drawn at the right. ______________

Write the component form of this vector. __________

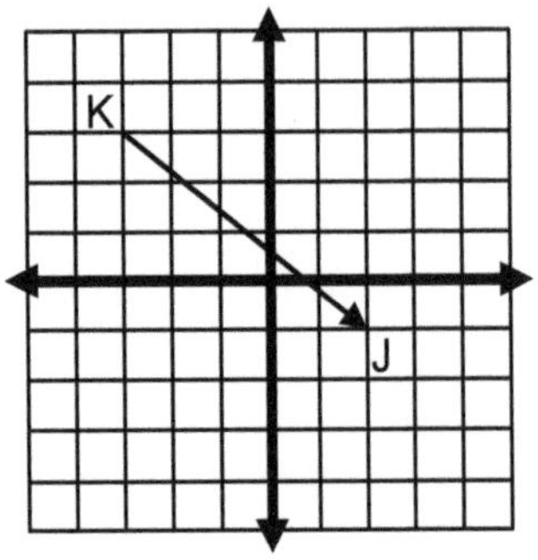

11. In the coordinate plane drawn at the right, draw three vectors that have the component form $\langle -2, 5 \rangle$.

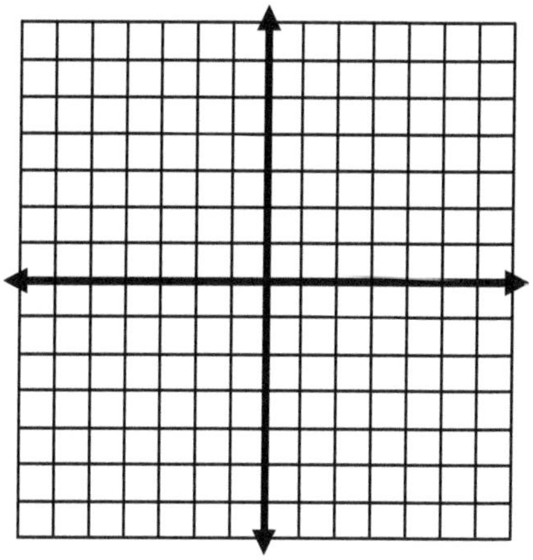

12. In the coordinate plane drawn at the right, draw three vectors that have the component form $\langle -1, -3 \rangle$.

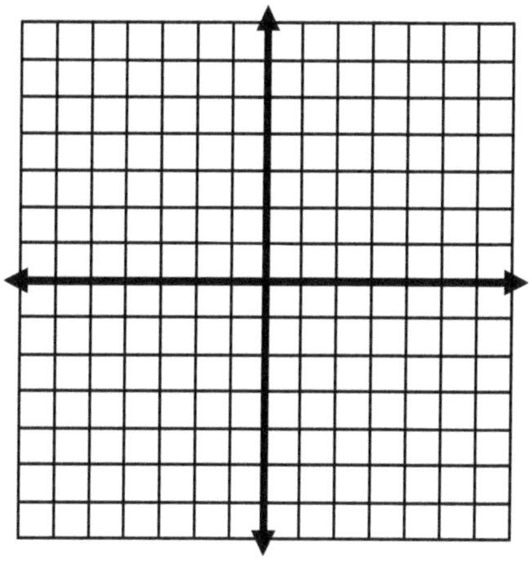

13a. $\overline{RB}$ has endpoints at R(−4, −1) and B(−6, 5). Draw $\overline{RB}$, and then draw the image after the translation $(x, y) \rightarrow (x + 4, y - 1)$.

b. Give the coordinates of the endpoints of the translated segment.

R′: (____, ____), B′: (____, ____)

c. We could also describe this translation by saying that $\overline{RB}$ was translated by the vector

⟨_____, _____⟩.

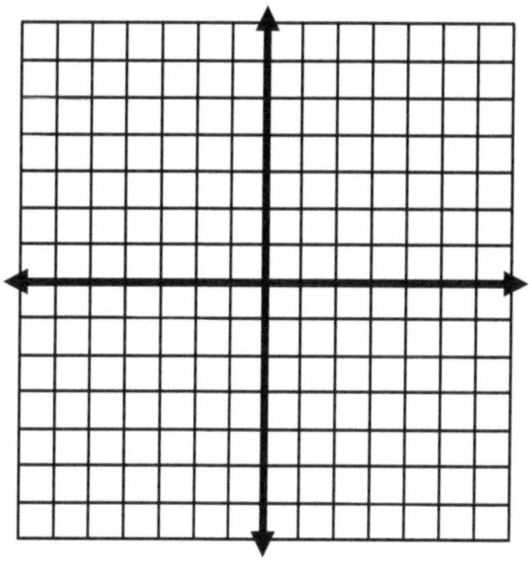

14a. Triangle GSC has vertices at G(−6, 2), S(−4, 3), and C(−3, 6). Draw ΔGSC, and then draw the image after the translation (x, y) → (x + 5, y − 1).

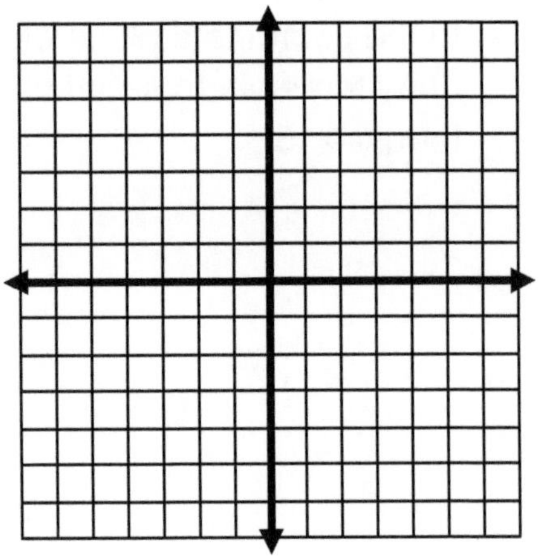

b. Give the coordinates of the vertices of the translated triangle.

G′: (_____, _____), S′: (_____, _____),

C′: (_____, _____)

c. We could also describe this translation by saying that ΔGSC was translated by the vector

⟨______, ______⟩.

15a. Parallelogram TJLR has vertices at T(−2, 1), J(3, 5), L(3, 0), and R(−2, −4). Draw parallelogram TJLR, and then draw the image after the translation (x, y) → (x − 4, y).

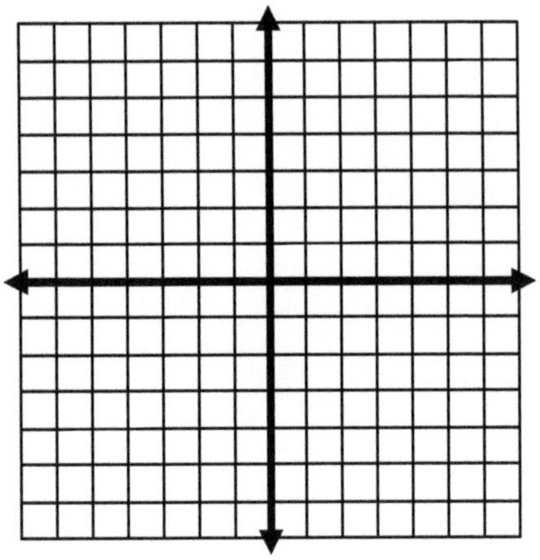

b. Give the coordinates of the vertices of the translated parallelogram.

T′: (_____, _____), J′: (_____, _____),

L′: (_____, _____), R′: (_____, _____)

c. We could also describe this translation by saying that parallelogram TJLR was translated by the vector ⟨______, ______⟩.

16a. Quadrilateral QNPA has vertices at Q(2, 1), N(−3, 0), P(−4, −4), and A(0, −3). Draw quadrilateral QNPA, and then draw the image after the translation (x, y) → (x − 2, y + 5).

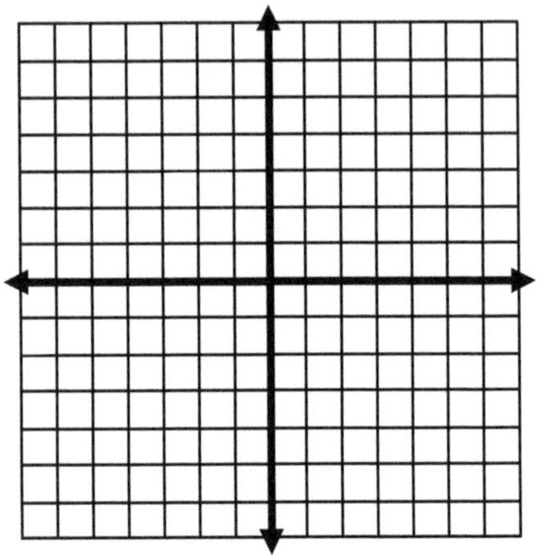

b. Give the coordinates of the vertices of the translated quadrilateral.

Q′: (_____, _____), N′: (_____, _____),

P′: (_____, _____), A′: (_____, _____)

c. We could also describe this translation by saying that quadrilateral QNPA was translated by the vector ⟨______, ______⟩.

17a. Triangle EKL has vertices at E(–2, –3), K(–1, 4), and L(– 4, 2). Draw ΔEKL, and then draw the image after a translation by the vector ⟨5, –3⟩.

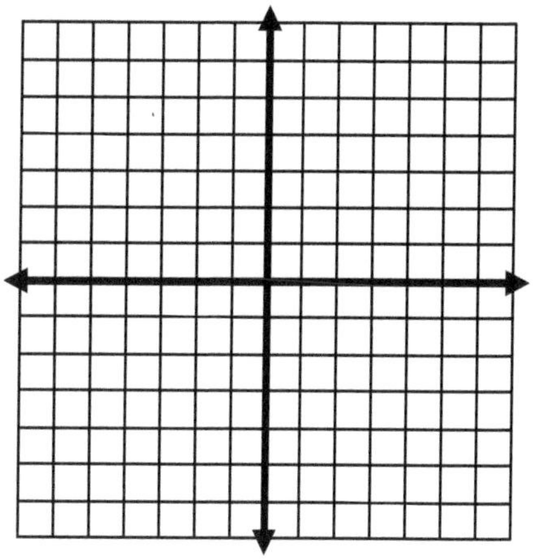

b. Give the coordinates of the vertices of the translated triangle.

E′: (_____, _____), K′: (_____, _____),

L′: (_____, _____)

c. Describe this translation using coordinate notation.

____

18a. $\overline{VN}$ has endpoints at V(3, 6) and N(4, –1). Draw $\overline{VN}$, and then draw the image after a translation by the vector ⟨–7, 0⟩.

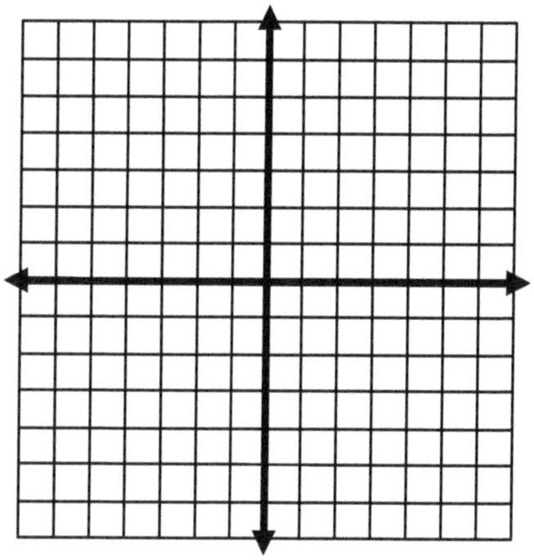

b. Give the coordinates of the endpoints of the translated segment.

V′: (_____, _____), N′: (_____, _____)

c. Describe this translation using coordinate notation.

____

19a. Quadrilateral MDXZ has vertices at M(–4, 2), D(2, 2), X(3, –2), and Z(–4, –1), and it is to be translated so that Z′ is located at (–2, 2). Draw quadrilateral MDXZ and this translation.

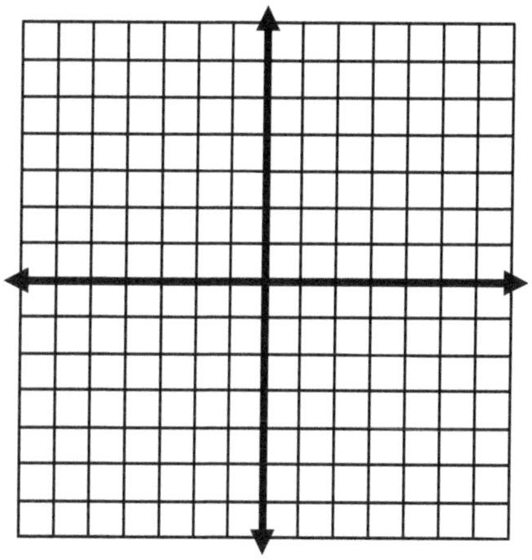

b. Give the coordinates of the remaining vertices of the translated quadrilateral.

M′: (_____, _____), D′: (_____, _____),

X′: (_____, _____)

c. We could describe this translation by saying that quadrilateral MDXZ was translated by the vector

⟨______, ______⟩.

20a. Triangle HWI has vertices at H(0, –2), W(4, –5), and I(1, –5), and it is to be translated so that H′ is located at (–2, 5). Draw ΔHWI and this translation.

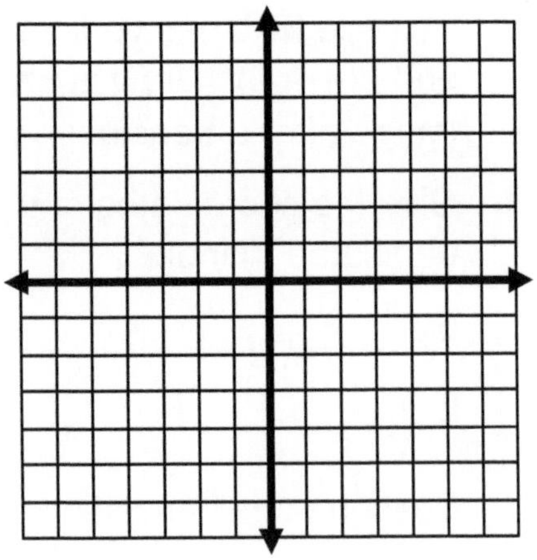

b. Give the coordinates of the remaining vertices of the translated triangle.

W′: (____, ____), I′: (____, ____)

c. We could describe this translation by saying that ΔHWI was translated by the vector

⟨_____, _____⟩.

21a. Triangle AYU has vertices at A(3, –5), Y(–2, –1), and U(–1, –6). Draw ΔAYU, and then draw the image after a translation by the vector ⟨0, 7⟩.

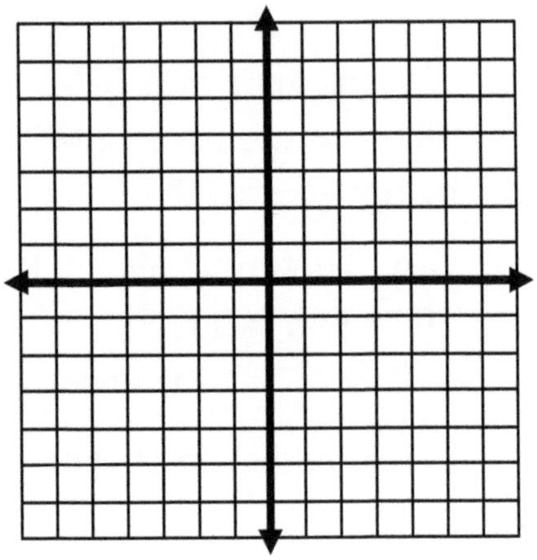

b. Give the coordinates of the endpoints of the translated segment.

A′: (____, ____), Y′: (____, ____),

U′: (____, ____)

c. Describe this translation using coordinate notation.

____

22a. $\overline{GT}$ has endpoints at G(5, 0) and T(–2, 1). Draw $\overline{GT}$, and then draw the image after a translation by the vector ⟨–4, –3⟩.

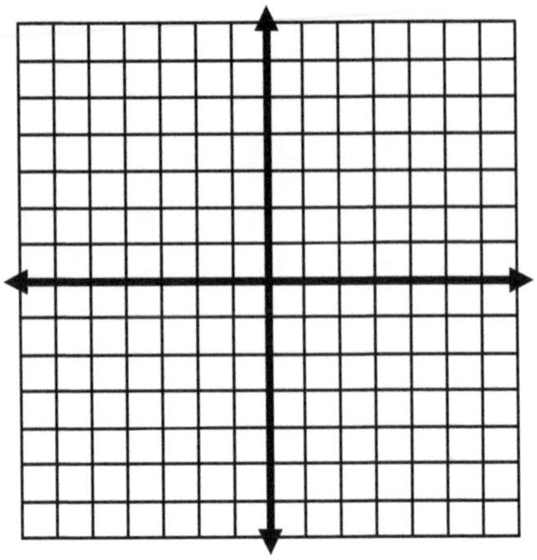

b. Give the coordinates of the endpoints of the translated segment.

G′: (____, ____), T′: (____, ____)

c. Describe this translation using coordinate notation.

____

Part V – Dilations

In this section, we will discuss dilations in further detail. We will begin by repeating the definition of a dilation that we discussed in Part I, and we will also discuss two additional definitions.

A transformation of a figure is a <u>dilation</u> if and only all the distances from a fixed point are multiplied by a constant. The fixed point is called the <u>center of dilation</u>, and the constant is called the <u>scale factor</u>.

A dilation is called a <u>reduction</u> if and only if the scale factor is greater than 0 and less than 1.

A dilation is called an <u>enlargement</u> if and only if the scale factor is greater than 1.

Example 1: Use a ruler to draw a dilation of the figure below with center N and a scale factor of 3.

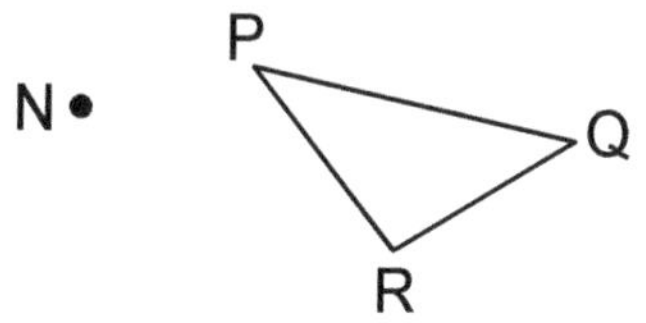

Step 1: Draw segments connecting N and the vertices of the preimage, and measure the lengths of each of these segments.

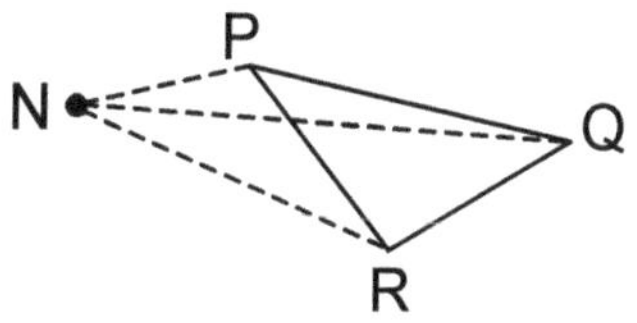

Step 2: Extend the segments drawn in Step 1. Since the scale factor is supposed to be 3, we must use a ruler to make sure that the length of each segment is equal to 3 times the length of the original segment. Also, we will label the endpoints of the segments using the notation that we discussed in Exercises 25-30 of Part I.

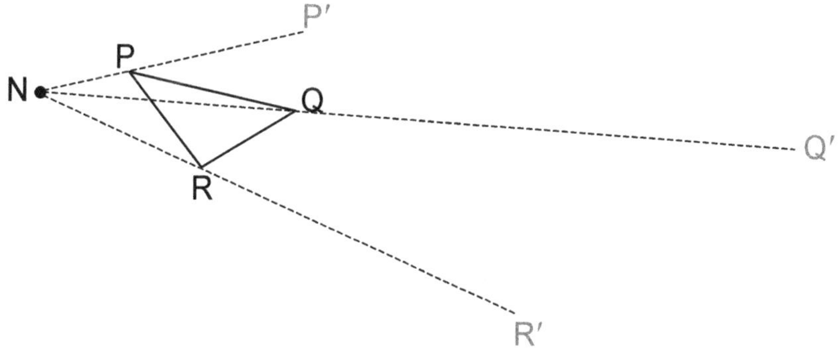

Step 3: Draw the image.

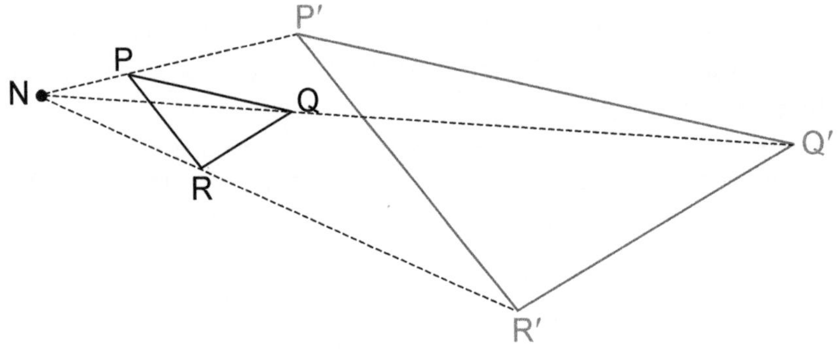

Step 4: Erase the dotted segments.

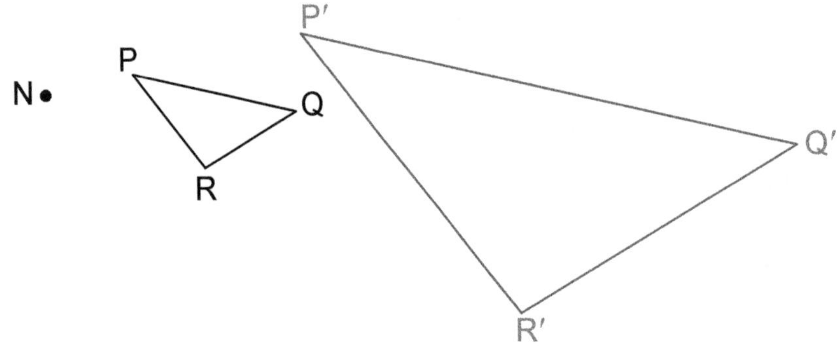

By the way, you might notice that this is an enlargement. The image is larger than the preimage, and the scale factor is larger than 1.

Example 2: Triangle ABC has vertices at A(4, –1), B(–4, –3), and C(–6, 6). Draw the dilation of ΔABC that has a scale factor of $\frac{1}{2}$ and center at (0, 0).

We will begin by drawing ΔABC.

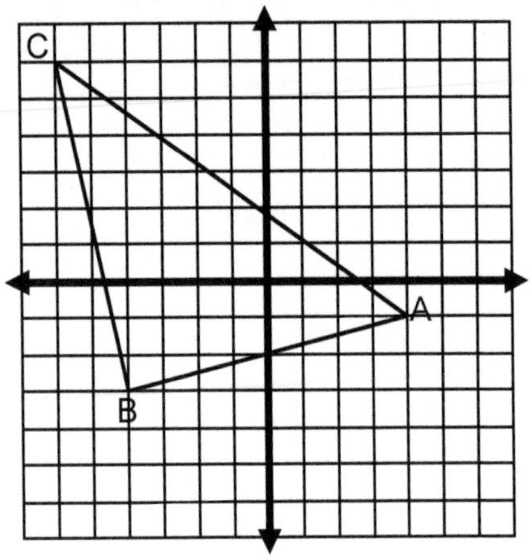

To draw a dilation with its center at the origin, all we have to do is multiply each of the coordinates by the scale factor and plot the new points. This tells us that the vertices of the new triangle will be A′(2, –½), B′(–2, –1½), and C′(–3, 3). This gives us the picture shown on the next page.

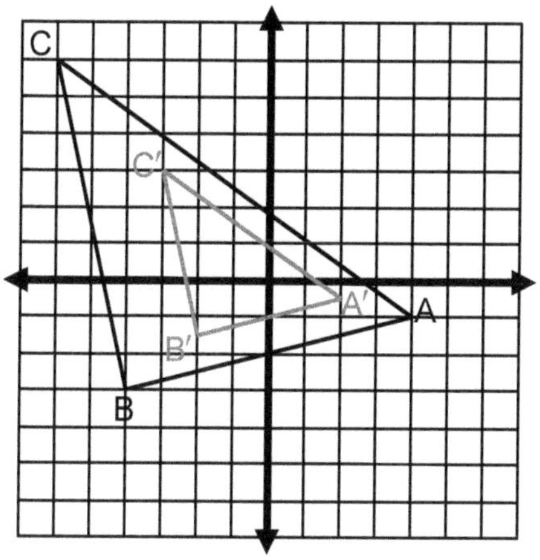

By the way, you might notice that this is an example of a reduction. The image is smaller than the preimage, and the scale factor is between 0 and 1.

Example 3: The figure at the right shows a dilation of quadrilateral EFGH with the center of dilation at (1, –3). What is the scale factor for this dilation? Is this an example of a *reduction* or an *enlargement*?

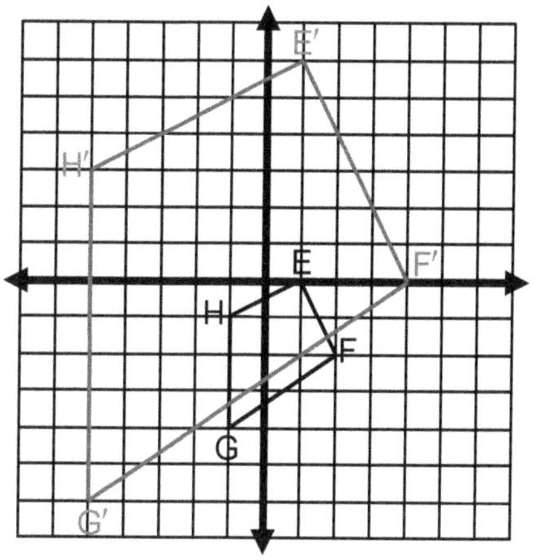

One way that we can find the scale factor for this dilation is to find the distance from the center of the dilation to a point of the image and the distance from the center of the dilation to the corresponding point of the preimage, and then find the ratio of these distances. (We used G′ and G, but you could use any other pair of points and end up with the same answer in the end.)

The distance between the center of dilation and the point G′ is given by $\sqrt{(-5-1)^2+(-6-(-3))^2}$, which simplifies to $3\sqrt{5}$.

The distance between the center of dilation and the point G is given by $\sqrt{(-1-1)^2+(-4-(-3))^2}$, which simplifies to $\sqrt{5}$.

Since the ratio of these distances reduces to 3 : 1, the scale factor for this dilation must be equal to 3.

Finally, this is an example of an *enlargement*. The scale factor is greater than 1, and the image is larger than the preimage.

As the following theorem shows, we could have found the scale factor for this dilation by finding the ratio of the lengths of corresponding sides of the image and preimage. This theorem tells us that the image and the preimage of a dilation are similar to each other and that the ratio of the corresponding sides is equal to the scale factor.

If a dilation with a scale factor of k maps A to A′ and B to B′, then $k = \frac{A'B'}{AB}$.

You will prove this theorem in the exercises for this section.

Example 4: The figure at the right shows a dilation of ΔJKL with a center of M. The distance between M and J is 24, KL = 20, JK = 25, and K′L′ = 12. Find (a) the distance between M and J′, (b) the length of $\overline{J'L'}$, (c) the measure of ∠J, (d) the measure of ∠J′, and (e) the scale factor. Where necessary, round the final answers to the nearest tenth.

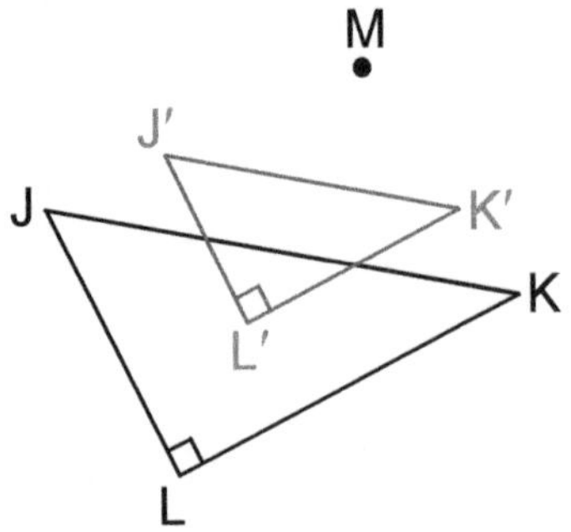

(a) We can work this part of the problem as shown below.

$$\frac{MJ'}{MJ} = \frac{K'L'}{KL}$$ Use the theorem above.

$$\frac{MJ'}{24} = \frac{12}{20}$$ Substitute the numbers we were given into the proportion we found in the last step.

$$20(MJ') = 288$$ Use the Cross Products Property of Proportions.

$$MJ' = 14.4$$ Divide both sides by 20.

(b) To find the length of $\overline{J'L'}$, we can either (i) find the length of $\overline{JL}$ and then use the theorem above, or (ii) find the length of $\overline{J'K'}$ using the theorem above and then use the Pythagorean Theorem. We will use the first method, but we would have gotten the same answer in the end if we had chosen the second method instead.

$$(JL)^2 + (KL)^2 = (JK)^2$$ Note that ΔJKL is a right triangle, and so we can use the Pythagorean Theorem to find the length of $\overline{JL}$.

$$(JL)^2 + 20^2 = 25^2$$

$$(JL)^2 + 400 = 625$$

$$(JL)^2 = 225$$

$$JL = 15$$

$$\frac{J'L'}{JL} = \frac{K'L'}{KL}$$ The theorem above tells us that the image and the preimage are similar to each other.

$$\frac{J'L'}{15} = \frac{12}{20}$$

$$20(J'L') = 180$$ Use the Cross Products Property of Proportions.

$$J'L' = 9$$ Divide both sides by 20.

(c) To find the measure of ∠J, we will use the right triangle trigonometry concepts that we discussed in Chapter 8.

$\sin J = \frac{KL}{JK}$

$\sin J = \frac{20}{25}$

$\sin J = 0.8$

$m\angle J \approx 53.1°$

Recall that the cosine of an angle is equal to the length of the leg adjacent to the angle divided by the length of the hypotenuse.

Take the inverse sine of 0.8.

(d) To find the measure of $\angle J'$, we will note that the theorem on the previous page tells us that $\Delta JKL \sim \Delta J'K'L'$. Therefore, we can say that $\angle J$ must be congruent to $\angle J'$, and so $m\angle J'$ must equal approximately 53.1°.

(e) We can find the scale factor by finding any of the following ratios: $\frac{MJ'}{MJ}$, $\frac{MK'}{MK}$, $\frac{ML'}{ML}$, $\frac{J'K'}{JK}$, $\frac{J'L'}{JL}$, and $\frac{K'L'}{KL}$. All of these ratios are equal to $\frac{3}{5}$, and so the scale factor for this dilation must equal $\frac{3}{5}$.

Problems:

1-9. Use a ruler to draw the following dilations.

1. Draw a dilation of ΔABC with center Z and a scale factor of 2.

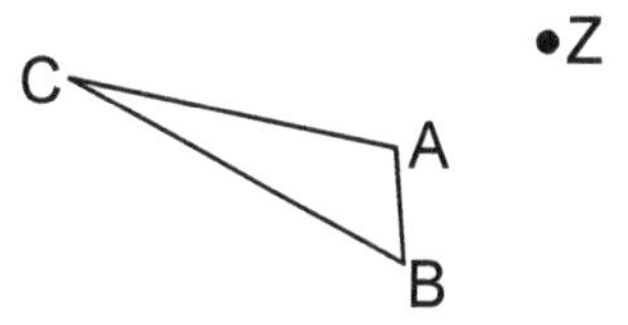

2. Draw a dilation of ΔDEF with center Q and a scale factor of 3.

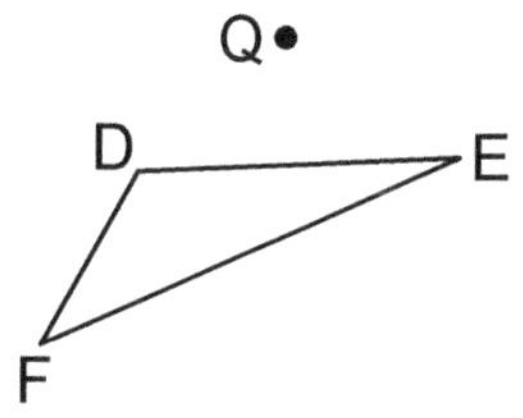

3. Draw a dilation of ΔGHI with center K and a scale factor of $\frac{1}{2}$.

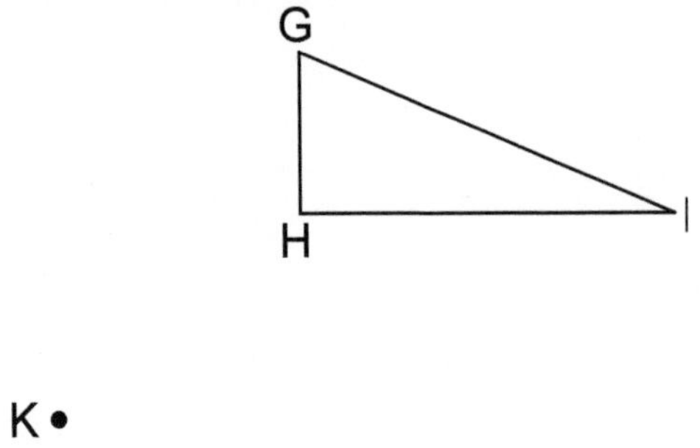

4. Draw a dilation of ΔMNO with center T and a scale factor of $2\frac{1}{2}$.

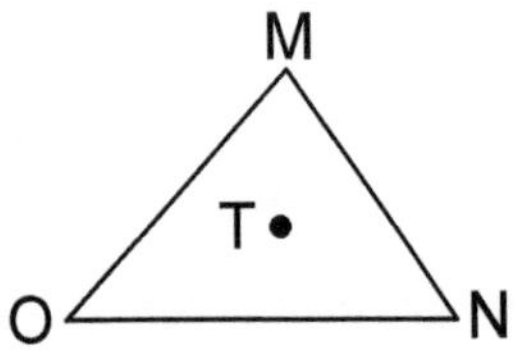

5. Draw a dilation of parallelogram PQRS with center L and a scale factor of 3.

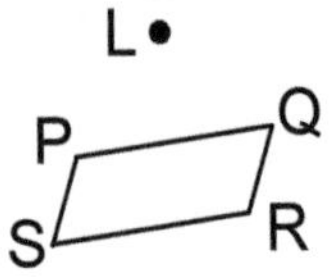

6. Draw a dilation of quadrilateral UVWX with center Y and a scale factor of 2.

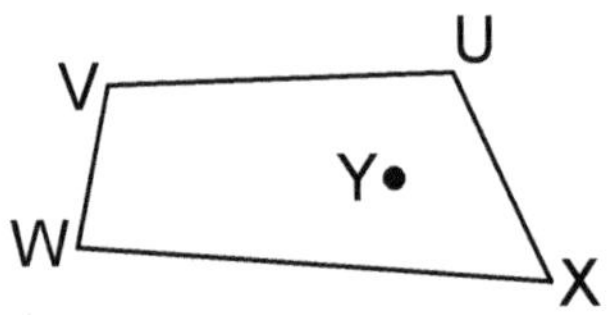

7. Draw a dilation of pentagon JPTZQ with center J and a scale factor of $1\frac{1}{2}$.

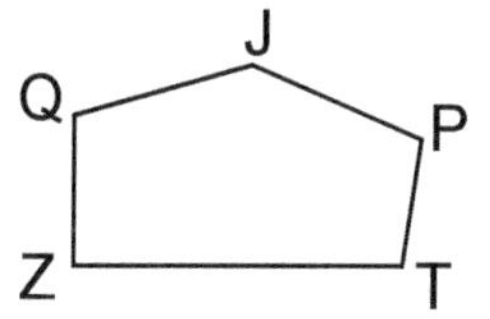

8. Draw a dilation of rectangle CRTL with center L and a scale factor of $\frac{3}{4}$.

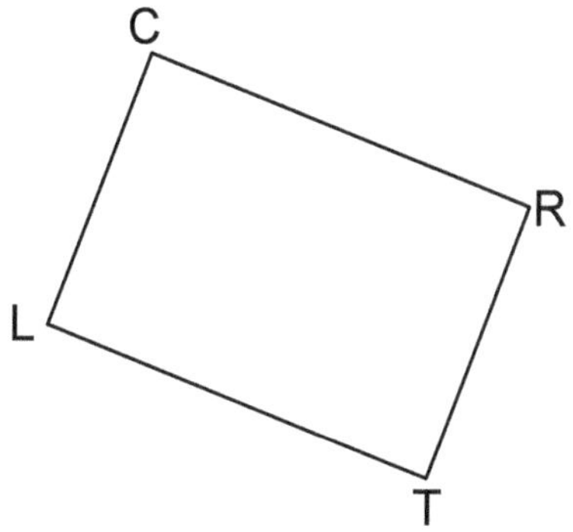

9. Draw a dilation of quadrilateral BNSM with center A and a scale factor of $\frac{1}{4}$.

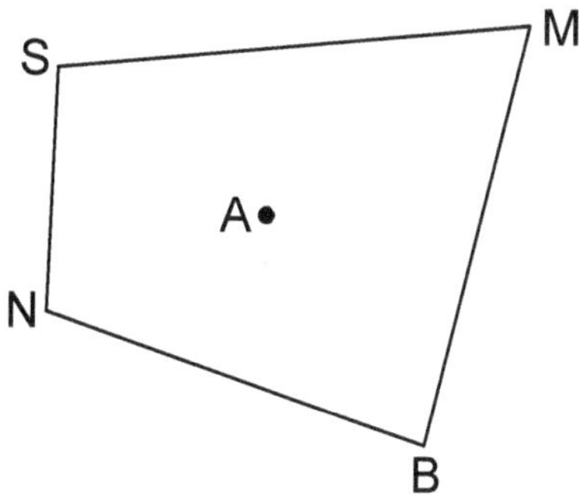

10a. Triangle ABC has vertices at A(–1, 2), B(–3, 1), and C(1, –2). Draw ΔABC, and then draw a dilation of ΔABC with the origin as the center and a scale factor of 2.

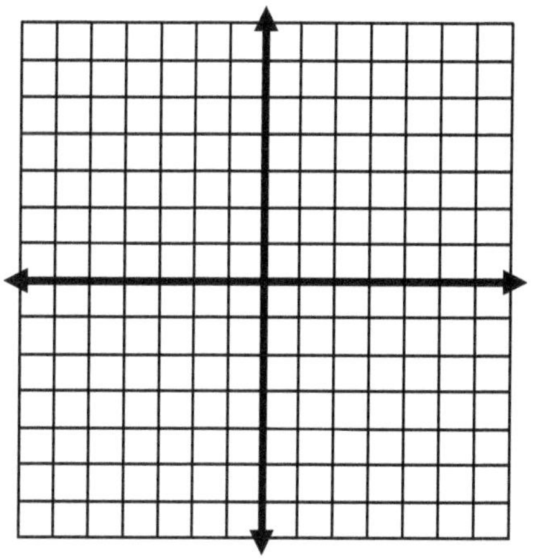

b. Give the coordinates of the vertices of the image.

A′: (_____, _____), B′: (_____, _____),

C′: (_____, _____)

11a. Triangle DEF has vertices at D(–1, –2), E(–1, 1), and F(1, 0). Draw ΔDEF, and then draw a dilation of ΔDEF with the origin as the center and a scale factor of 3.

b. Give the coordinates of the vertices of the image.

D′: (____, ____), E′: (____, ____),

F′: (____, ____)

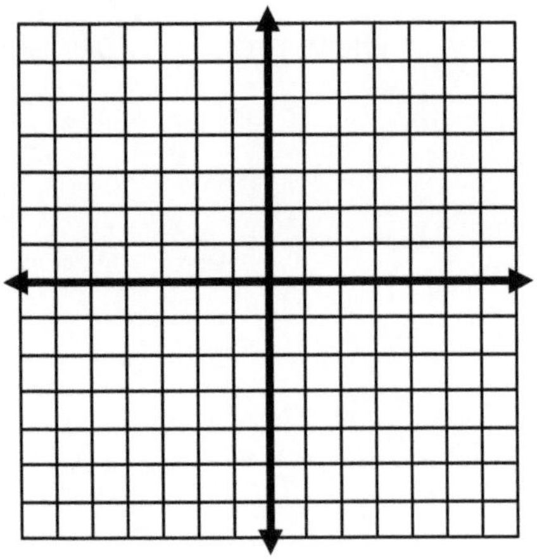

12a. Quadrilateral GHIJ has vertices at G(0, 4), H(4, 0), I(–2, –4), and J(–6, 2). Draw quadrilateral GHIJ, and then draw a dilation of quadrilateral GHIJ with the origin as the center and a scale factor of $\frac{1}{4}$.

b. Give the coordinates of the vertices of the image.

G′: (____, ____), H′: (____, ____),

I′: (____, ____), J′: (____, ____)

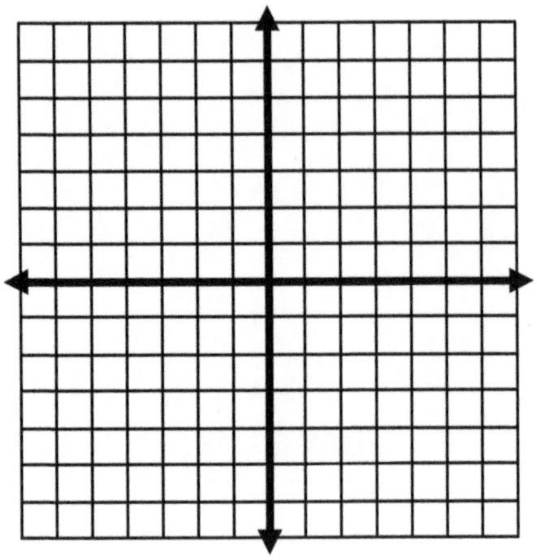

13a. Quadrilateral KLMN has vertices at K(–6, –3), L(–6, 6), M(0, 3), and N(–3, –3). Draw quadrilateral KLMN, and then draw a dilation of quadrilateral KLMN with the origin as the center and a scale factor of $\frac{2}{3}$.

b. Give the coordinates of the vertices of the image.

K′: (____, ____), L′: (____, ____),

M′: (____, ____), N′: (____, ____)

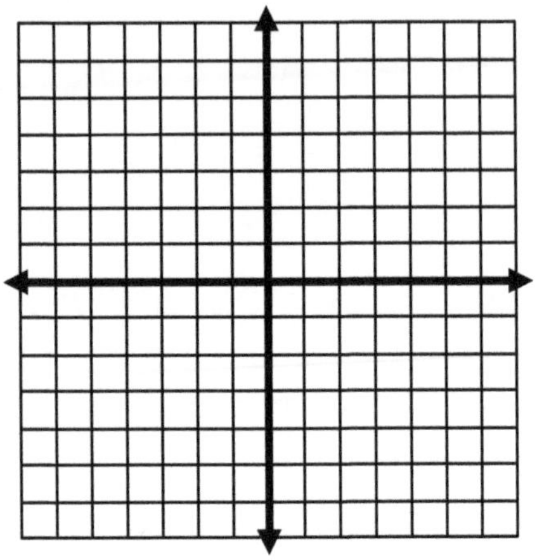

14a. Parallelogram OPQR has vertices at O(–1, 2), P(0, 4), Q(4, 0), and R(3, –2). Draw parallelogram OPQR, and then draw a dilation of parallelogram OPQR with the origin as the center and a scale factor of $1\frac{1}{2}$.

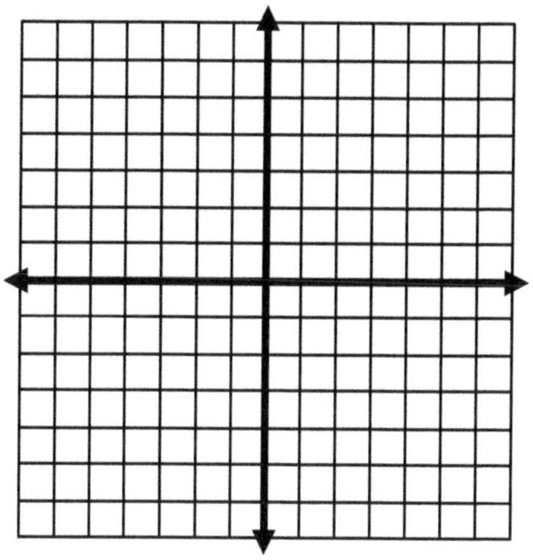

b. Give the coordinates of the vertices of the image.

O′: (_____, _____), P′: (_____, _____),

Q′: (_____, _____), R′: (_____, _____)

15a. Triangle STU has vertices at S(0, 0), T(4, 4), and U(–4, 6). Draw ΔSTU, and then draw a dilation of ΔSTU with the origin as the center and a scale factor of $\frac{3}{4}$.

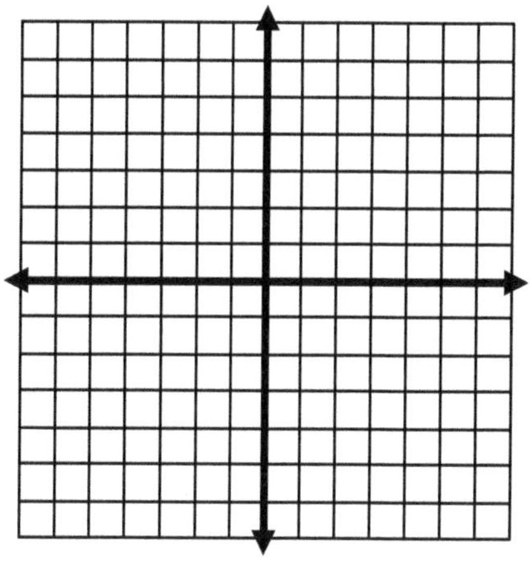

b. Give the coordinates of the vertices of the image.

S′: (_____, _____), T′: (_____, _____),

U′: (_____, _____)

16a. The figure at the right shows ΔVWX and a dilation of ΔVWX with the origin as the center of dilation. What is the scale factor?

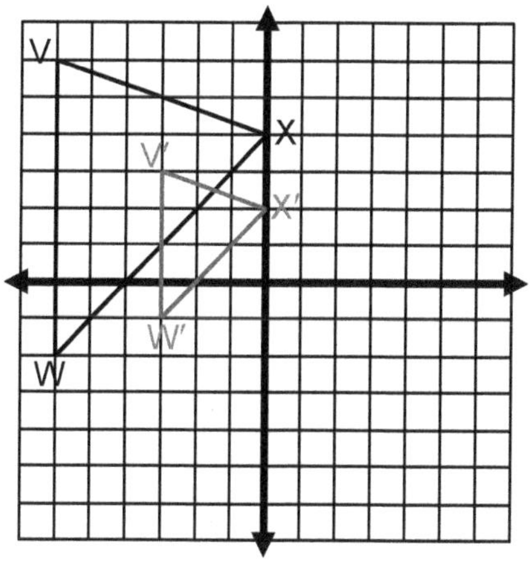

____

b. Is this an example of an *enlargement* or a *reduction*? ____________________

17a. The figure at the right shows ΔYLC and a dilation of ΔYLC with the origin as the center of dilation. What is the scale factor? ___________________

b. Is this an example of an *enlargement* or a *reduction*? ___________________

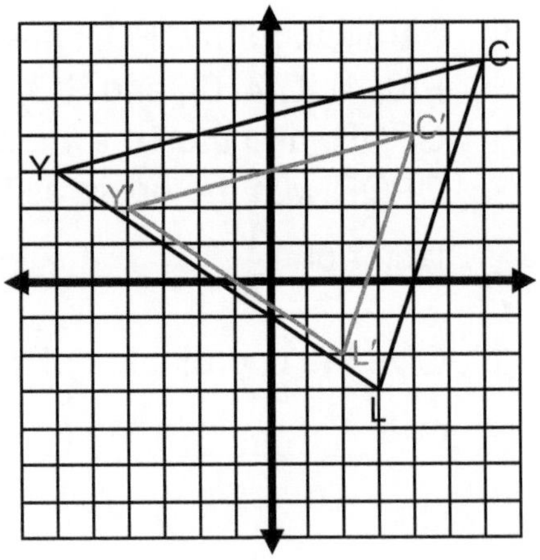

18a. The figure at the right shows quadrilateral QNAE and a dilation of quadrilateral QNAE with (1, 1) as the center of dilation. What is the scale factor?

____

b. Is this an example of an *enlargement* or a *reduction*? ___________________

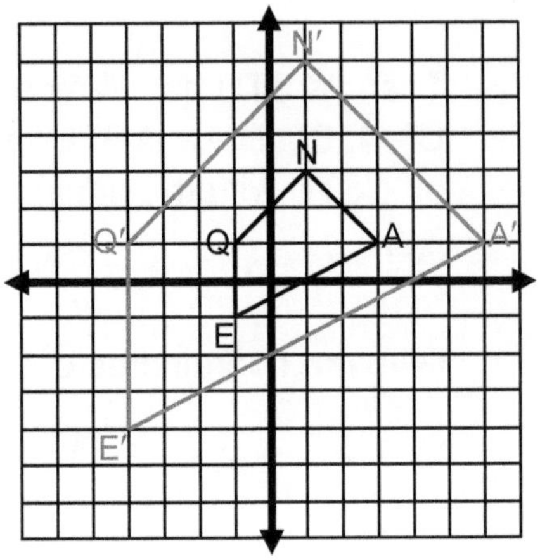

19a. The figure at the right shows parallelogram ZHMJ and a dilation of parallelogram ZHMJ with (–6, –3) as the center of dilation. What is the scale factor? ___________________

b. Is this an example of an *enlargement* or a *reduction*? ___________________

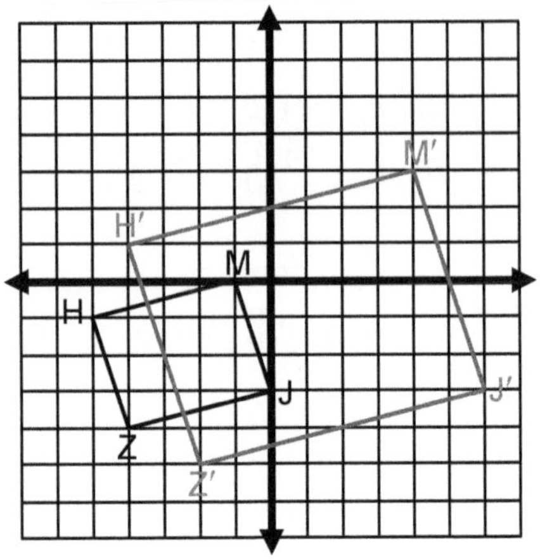

20a. The figure at the right shows ΔCBW and a dilation of ΔCBW with (−4, 5) as the center of dilation. (Note that the image of C is itself.) What is the scale factor? ________________

b. Is this an example of an *enlargement* or a *reduction*? ________________

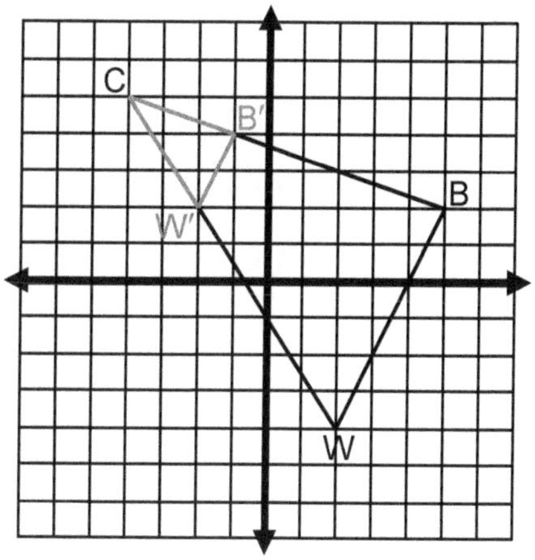

21-32. Do not use a ruler or a protractor to answer these questions, and round your final answers to the nearest tenth where necessary.

21. The figure at the right shows a dilation of ΔJAU with center R. If RJ = 45, RJ′ = 27, RU′ = 24, A′U′ = 12, UJ = 25, and AJ = 10, then A′J′ = ________, RU = ________, and the scale factor is ________.

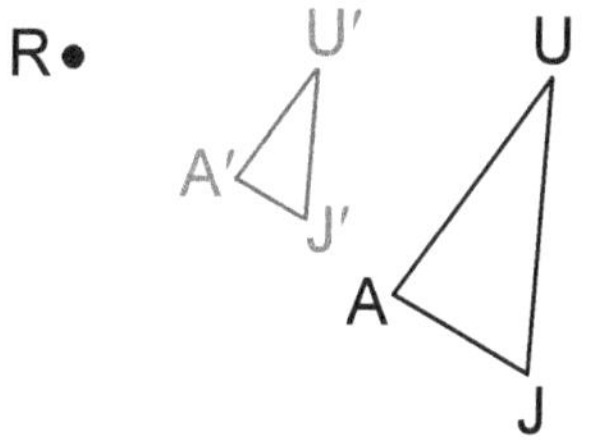

22. The figure at the right shows a dilation of ΔVSC with center E. If EV = 16, EC′ = 45, EV′ = 36, SC = 14, S′V′ = 27, and VC = 24, then the scale factor is ________, EC = ________, SV = ________, and V′C′ = ________.

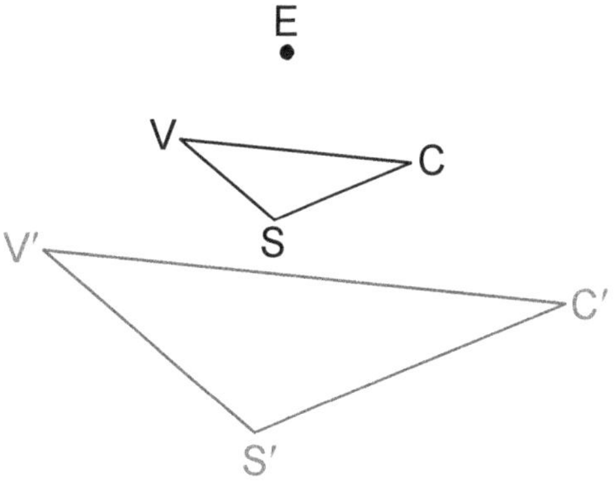

23. The figure at the right shows a dilation of parallelogram IOXP with center G. If XO = 22, XP = 10, GP′ = 45, and X′P′ = 15, then X′O′ = ________, GP = ________, I′P′ = ________, and the scale factor is ________.

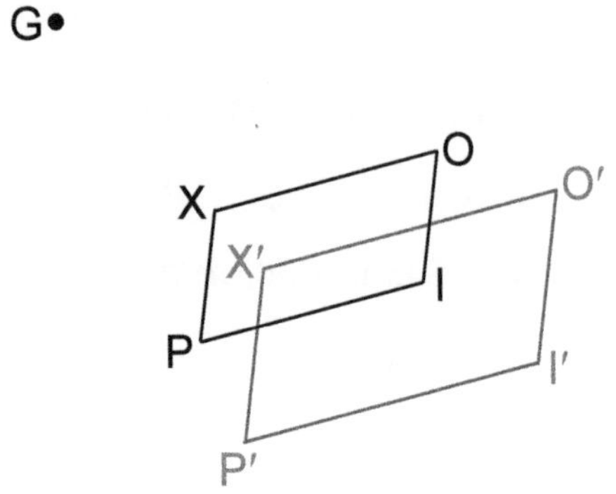

24. The figure at the right shows a dilation of ΔZDB with center Y and scale factor $\frac{4}{5}$. If B′D′ = 32, Z′D′ = 28, BZ = 40, B′Y = 20, and ZY = 55, then ZD = ________, Z′Y = ________, and BY = ________.

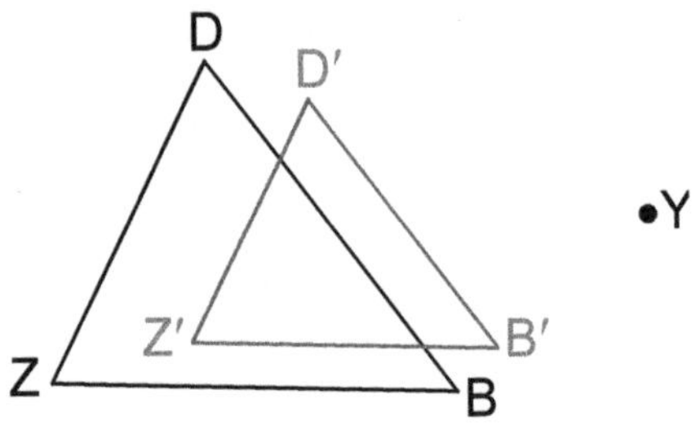

25. The figure at the right shows a dilation of isosceles trapezoid EFGH with center A. If AF = 28, FE = 20, AG′ = 18, E′H′ = 23, and F′E′ = 10, then AF′ = ________, the scale factor is ________, GH = ________, EH = ________, and AG = ________.

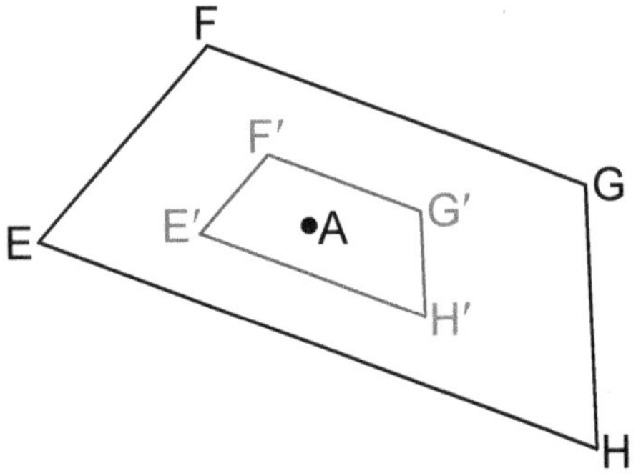

26. The figure at the right shows a dilation of parallelogram IKLM with center J. If IJ = 9, JM = 15, I′M′ = 40, JM′ = 20, I′K′ = 36, and m∠L′ = 114°, then I′J = ________, M′L′ = ________, IK = ________, m∠I = ________, m∠K = ________, and the scale factor is ________.

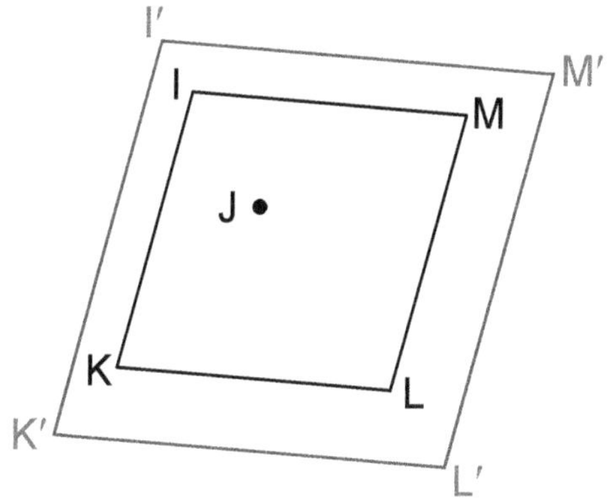

27. The figure at the right shows a dilation of ΔNOP with center Q and scale factor $\frac{2}{3}$. If O′Q = 12, QP′ = 21, ON = 36, and N′P′ = 40, then m∠P = ________, m∠O′ = ________, QP = ________, and O′N′ = ________.

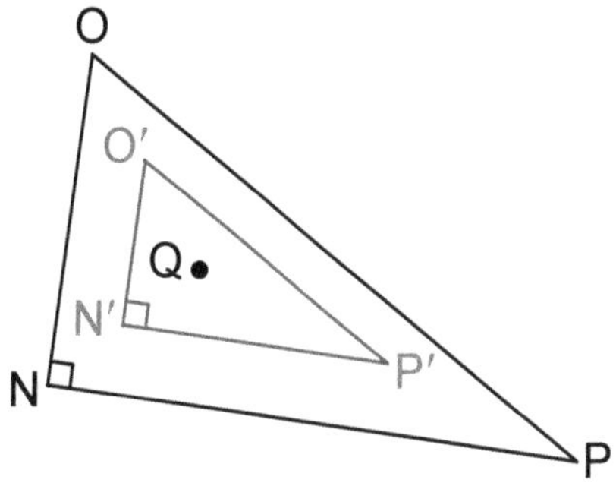

28. The figure at the right shows a dilation of ΔRST with center R. If RT = 10, TS = 9, m∠T = 55°, RS = 8.8, and RT′ = 6, then T′S′ = ________, m∠RT′S′ = ________, and S′S = ________.

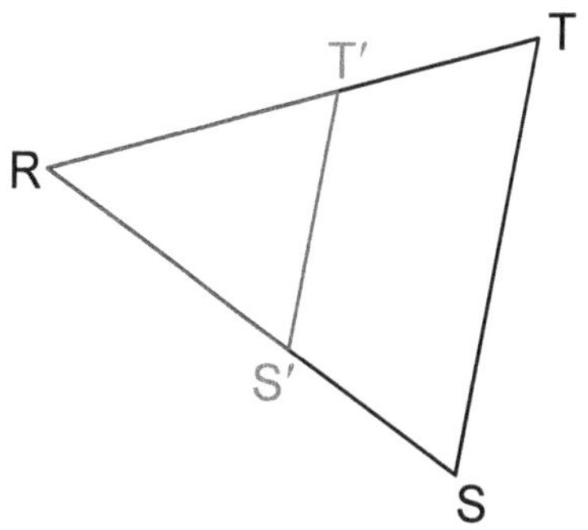

29. The figure at the right shows a dilation of trapezoid TUVW with center X. If XT′ = 8, XU′ = 11.2, T′W′ = 12, WV = 16, TW = 7.5, and m∠T = 87°, then XT = ________, the scale factor is ________, W′V′ = ________, m∠T′ = ________, and m∠U′ = ________.

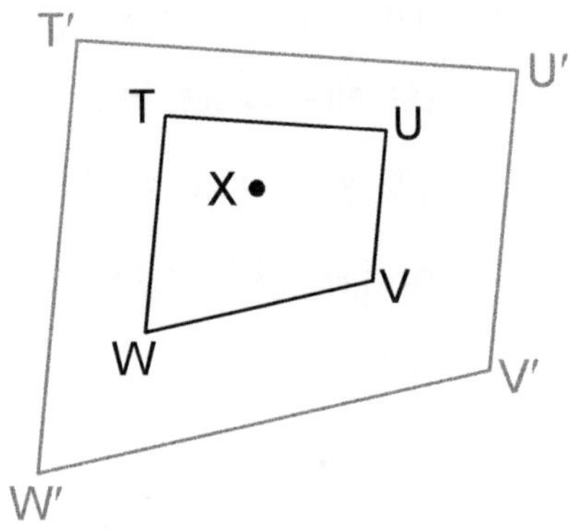

30. The figure at the right shows a dilation of ΔYZH with center O and scale factor $1\frac{1}{2}$. If OY′ = 6, OH = 10, H′Z′ = 25.5, and YH = 15, then OY = ________, YZ = ________, m∠Z = ________, and m∠H′ = ________.

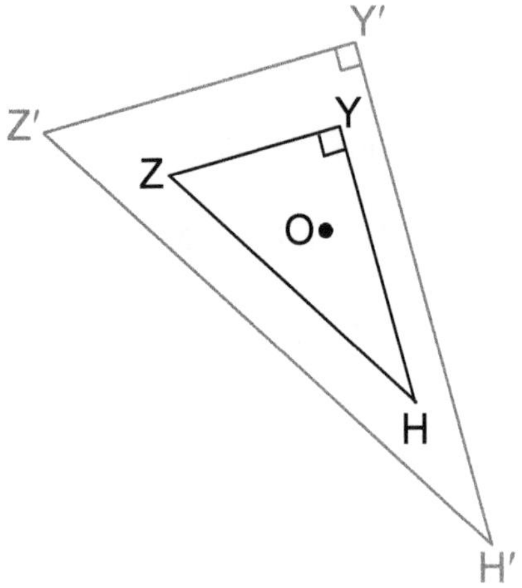

31. The figure at the right shows a dilation of parallelogram ACPE with center C and scale factor $\frac{1}{4}$. If m∠P = 63°, CA = 26, and A′E′ = 5, then m∠A = ________, m∠E′ = ________, CP = ________, and CA′ = ________.

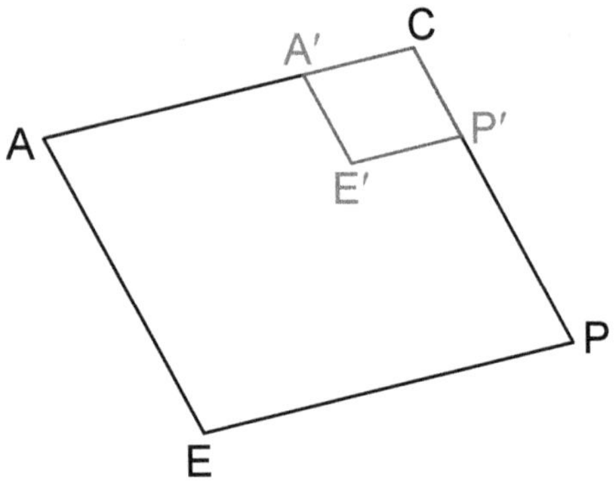

32. The figure at the right shows a dilation of $\triangle GNB$ with center T. If $m\angle B' = 95°$, $NG = 25$, $BN = 18$, $B'G' = 6.96$, and $N'G' = 10$, then $m\angle B =$ ________, $BG =$ ________, and $B'N' =$ ________.

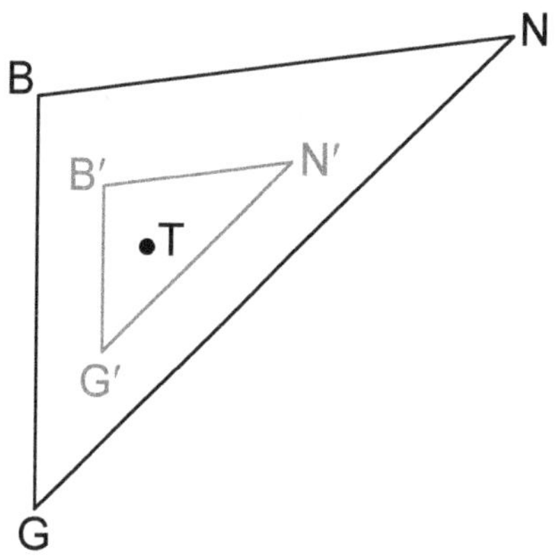

33-34. Slide projectors and movie projectors use the concept of dilations to display their images. A preimage is displayed in front of a light source (which acts as the center of dilation), and then the larger image is projected on a screen. Suppose that, for a certain movie projector, the preimage is displayed 6 inches from the light source, and the preimage is 2.7 inches high and 4.8 inches wide.

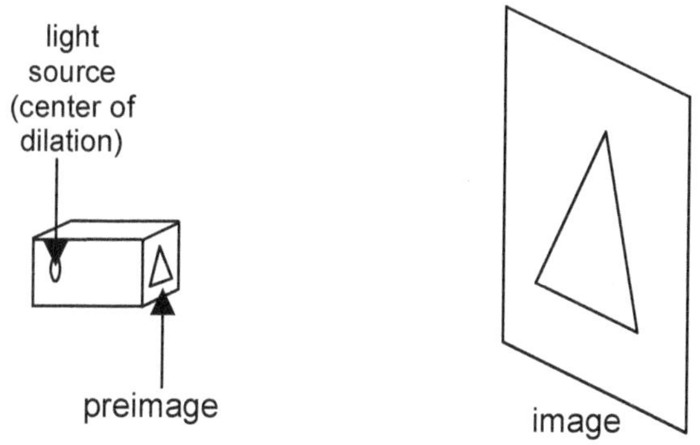

33. If the screen is placed 96 inches (8 feet) from the light source, how tall will the image be? ___________ How wide will the image be? ___________

34. If a person wants to display an image that is 3 feet (36 inches) tall, how far away from the light source should the screen be placed? ___________ If the screen is placed at this distance, how wide will the image be? ___________

35-36. Some older models of cameras use a material called *film*. A person can make a photograph from a roll of film by holding a negative (a small piece of the film that contains a very small version of the picture) a given distance from a light source. The image is then projected on special photographic paper, and a photograph is produced.

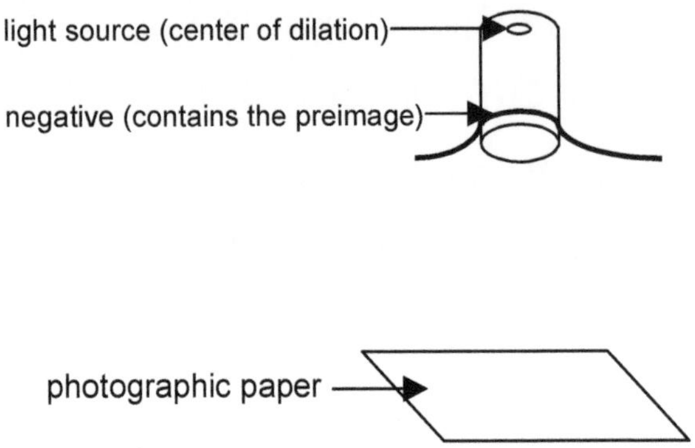

35. A person wants to produce a picture that is 147 mm wide from a negative that is 25 mm tall and 35 mm wide by placing the negative 40 mm from a light source. How far from the light source should the photographic paper be placed? ___________ If the photographic paper is placed at this distance, how tall will the image be? ___________

36. To make a larger print, you could either (a) move the negative (choose one: closer to or farther away from) the light source, or (b) move the photographic paper (choose one: closer to or farther away from) the negative.

37. State whether the following statement is *true* or *false*. If you decide that is *false*, draw a counterexample.

    If ΔABC is a dilation of ΔDEF, then $\Delta ABC \sim \Delta DEF$.

38. State whether the following statement is *true* or *false*. If you decide that is *false*, draw a counterexample.

    If $\Delta ABC \sim \Delta DEF$, then one of the triangles is a dilation of the other.

39. Prove the following theorem: If a dilation with a scale factor of k maps A to A′ and B to B′, then $k = \frac{A'B'}{AB}$.

Given: $\overline{AB} \rightarrow \overline{A'B'}$ by a dilation with center C and scale factor k. (You might notice that this version of the proof assumes that the dilation is an enlargement. If it is a reduction instead, only the picture will change; the rest of the proof will remain the same.)

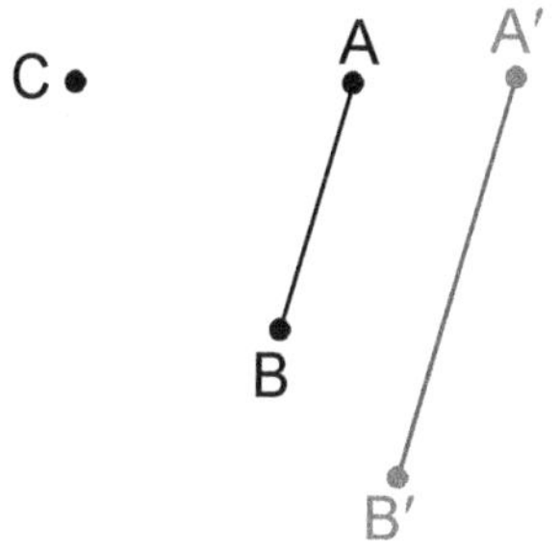

Prove: $k = \frac{A'B'}{AB}$

Statements	Reasons
1.	1.
2. Draw $\overrightarrow{CA'}$ and $\overrightarrow{CB'}$.	2. Through any two points, there is exactly one line.
3. CA′ = k(CA) and CB′ = k(CB)	3. Definition of a dilation with center C and scale factor k
4.	4.
5.	5.
6.	6.
7.	7. SAS Similarity Theorem
8.	8.
9.	9.

Part VI – Compositions of Transformations

In this section, we will discuss what happens when a transformation is performed on a preimage, and then another transformation is performed on the resulting image. When two or more successive transformations are combined to produce a single image, we call this a <u>composition</u> of the transformations.

Example 1: Quadrilateral ABCD has vertices at A(5, 2), B(1, 4), C(2, 7), and D(6, 4). Draw a reflection of quadrilateral ABCD in the x-axis, and then translate the result by the vector $\langle -8, 6 \rangle$.

We will begin by drawing quadrilateral ABCD.

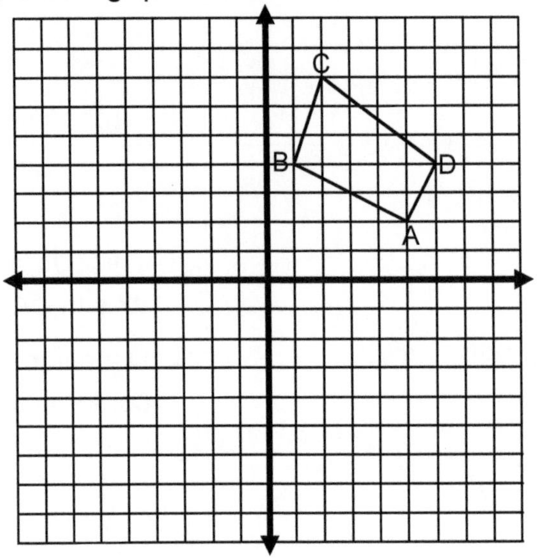

Next, we will draw a reflection of quadrilateral ABCD in the x-axis.

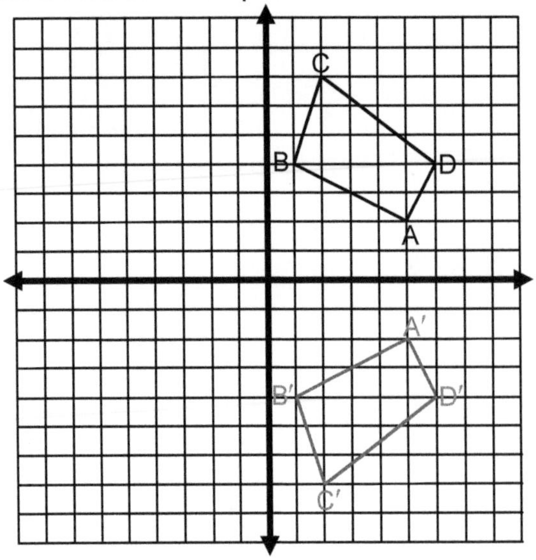

Now, we will take quadrilateral A′B′C′D′ and translate it by the vector $\langle -8, 6 \rangle$. This gives us the picture shown on the next page.

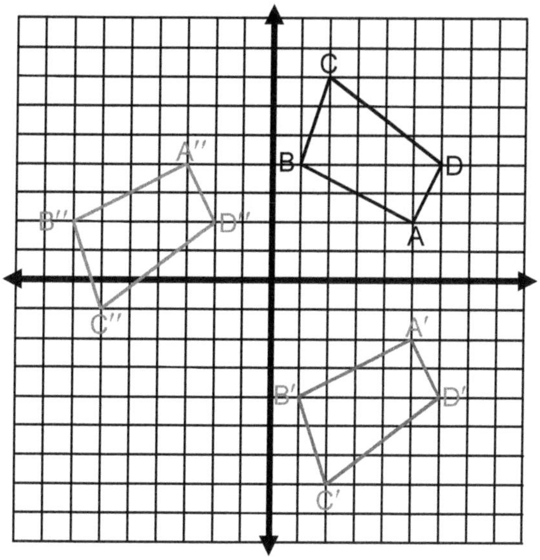

You should notice that we labeled the vertices of the triangle from the last step with "A′′," "B′′," "C′′," and "D′′." We read this as "A double prime," "B double prime," "C double prime," and "D double prime." We use the double prime notation is to avoid confusion with the points we already labeled A′, B′, C′, and D′.

Example 2: Triangle JKL has vertices at J(–1, 4), K(1, 3), and L(–3, 2). Perform the following transformations on ΔJKL in the order they are given: (i) a dilation with center (0, 0) and scale factor 2, (ii) a 90° clockwise rotation about the origin, and (iii) a translation by the vector $\langle -12, -4\rangle$.

We will begin by drawing ΔJKL.

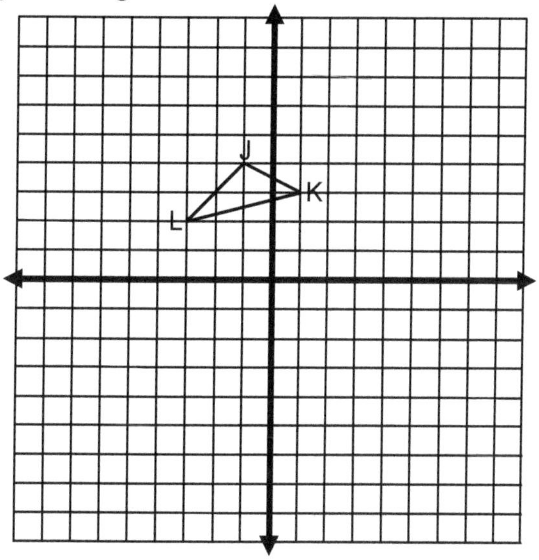

Next, we will perform a dilation of ΔJKL with center (0, 0) and scale factor 2, as shown on the next page.

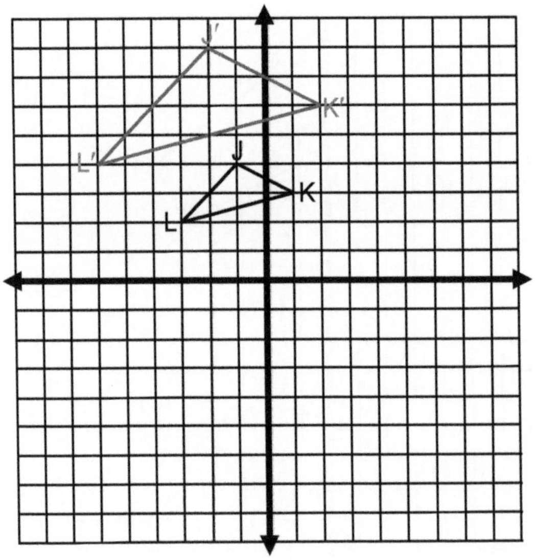

For our second transformation, we will draw a 90º clockwise rotation of $\Delta J'K'L'$ about the origin.

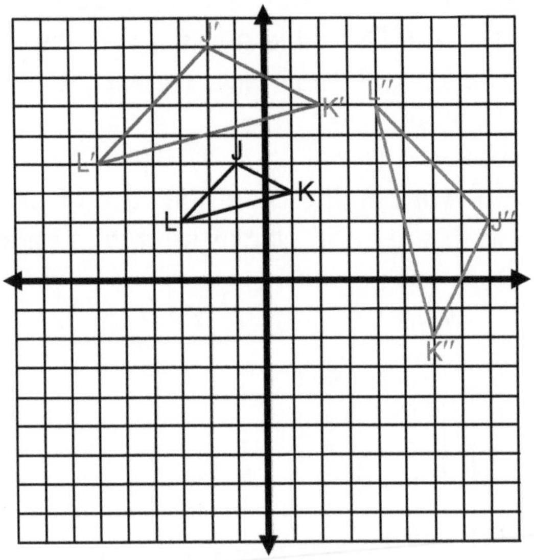

For our final transformation, we must translate $\Delta J''K''L''$ by the vector $\langle -12, -4 \rangle$.

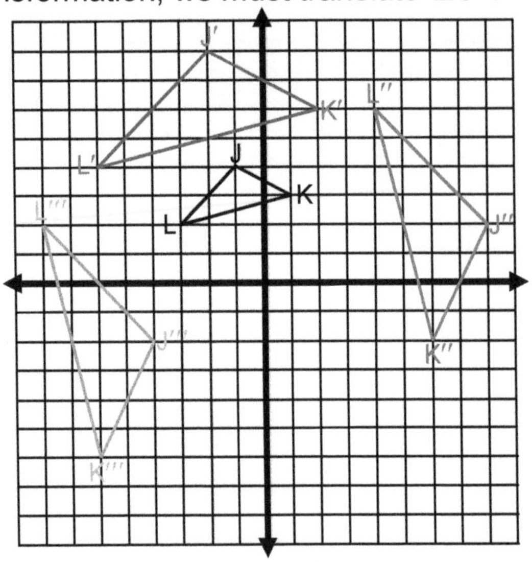

Notice that we used the triple prime notation to distinguish the vertices of this last triangle from the vertices of the other triangles.

Now, we need two theorems.

> If lines ℓ and m intersect at a point P, then a reflection in line ℓ followed by a reflection in line m is identical to a rotation about P, and the measure of the angle of rotation is equal to the measure of the acute angle formed by the intersection of the two lines.

> If lines ℓ and m are parallel to each other, then a reflection in line ℓ followed by a reflection in line m is identical to a translation, and the distance between a point and its final image is equal to twice the distance between line ℓ and line m.

Example 3: The figure at the right shows a reflection of ΔQRS in line ℓ, and then the resulting image is reflected in line m. These two reflections result in a 134° clockwise rotation of ΔQRS about point T. Find the value of x.

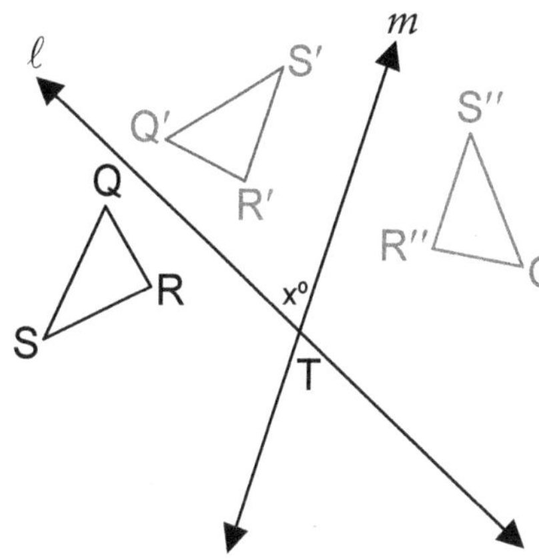

Since lines ℓ and m are not parallel, we will use the first theorem above. The question told us that the angle of rotation is 134°, and we can look at the picture and tell that x° represents the measure of the *acute* angle formed by the intersection of lines ℓ and m. Therefore, we can use the first theorem above to say that 134° = 2x°, and so x must equal 67. (By the way, you can use a ruler and a protractor to check the various statements we have made in this example. To find the angle of rotation, draw a segment connecting T and any of the vertices of ΔQRS. Next, draw a segment connecting T and the corresponding vertex of ΔQ″R″S″, and then measure the angle formed. However, you will not be able to use a ruler and a protractor to answer the questions like this in the exercises for this section. In the exercises, the pictures can and will be deceiving, but you will be able to assume that all angles that appear to be acute are actually acute.)

Also, you might be wondering what would happen if we reflected ΔQRS in line m, and then reflected the resulting image in line ℓ. If we reversed the order of the reflections like this, the final image would still be a 134° rotation of ΔQRS about point T, but it would be a 134° *counterclockwise* rotation about T.

Example 4: The figure at the right shows a reflection of trapezoid WXYZ in line n, and then the resulting image has been reflected in line p. Line n is parallel to line p, and the two lines are 1.25 inches apart.* Find the distance between W and W″.

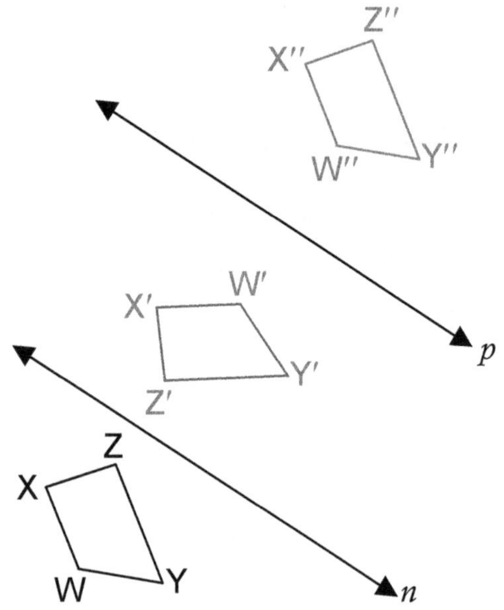

We can use the second theorem on the previous page to say that the distance between W and W″ is equal to 2 • 1.25, or 2.5, inches.

Like we said in the last example, you can use a ruler to check the accuracy of the various statements that we made in working this example, but you will not be able to use a ruler to work the exercises like this problem.

Finally, we will note that, if we reverse the order of the reflections (i.e., reflect trapezoid WXYZ in line p first and then reflect the resulting image in line n), the final result is still a translation of trapezoid WXYZ. The final vertices are still 2.5 inches from their corresponding preimages, but the final image is to the left and below trapezoid WXYZ.

Problems:

1-5. Triangle ABC has vertices at A(−4, 4), B(−6, 0), and C(−2, −2). For each of the following problems, perform the following transformations *in the order they are given*, and give the coordinates of the vertices of the final image.

1. First transformation: Reflection in the y-axis

   Second transformation: Translation by the vector ⟨2, 3⟩

   A″: (______, ______),

   B″: (______, ______),

   C″: (______, ______)

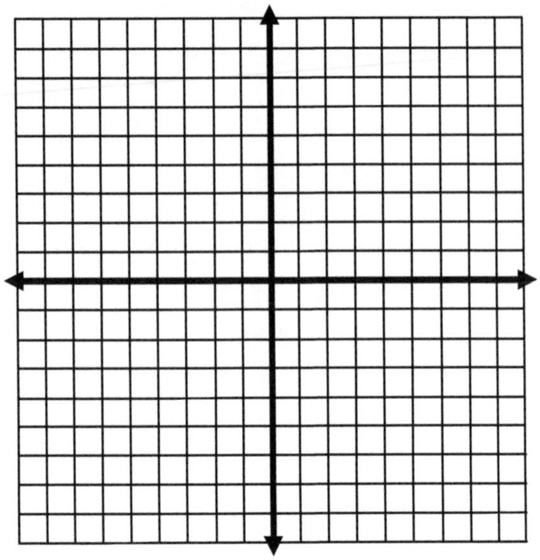

*Recall that we define the distance between two parallel lines as the length of a segment that is perpendicular to both lines.

2. First transformation: Translation by the vector $\langle 8, -6 \rangle$

Second transformation: Dilation with center (0, 0) and a scale factor of $\frac{1}{2}$

A″: (______, ______),

B″: (______, ______),

C″: (______, ______)

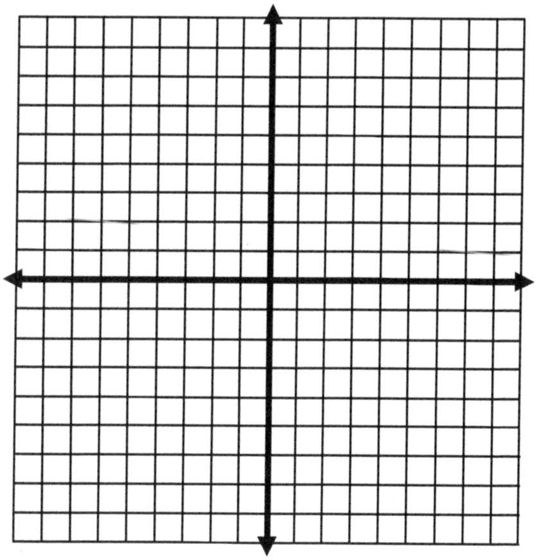

3. First transformation: Translation $(x, y) \rightarrow (x + 7, y)$

Second transformation: 90° clockwise rotation about the origin

A″: (______, ______),

B″: (______, ______),

C″: (______, ______)

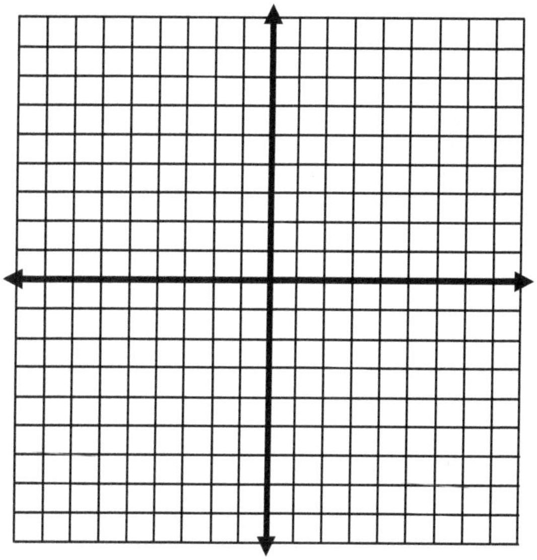

4. First transformation: Counterclockwise rotation of 180° about (–2, –2)

Second transformation: Translation by the vector $\langle 5, 0 \rangle$

Third transformation: Counterclockwise rotation of 90° about the origin

A‴: (______, ______),

B‴: (______, ______),

C‴: (______, ______)

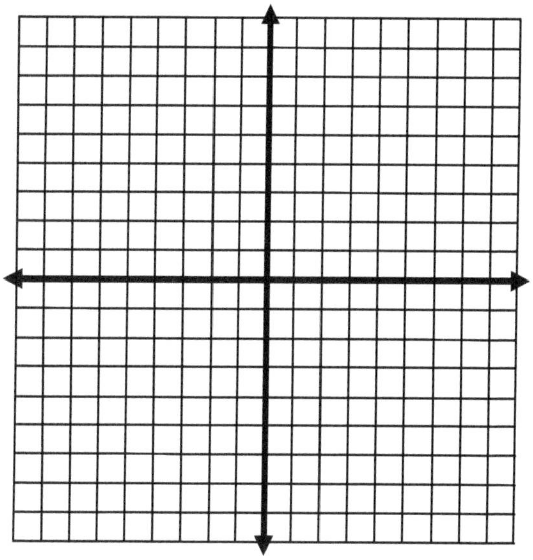

5. First transformation: Reflection in the x-axis

Second transformation: Translation by the vector ⟨6, 2⟩

Third transformation: Dilation with center (0, 0) and scale factor $1\frac{1}{2}$

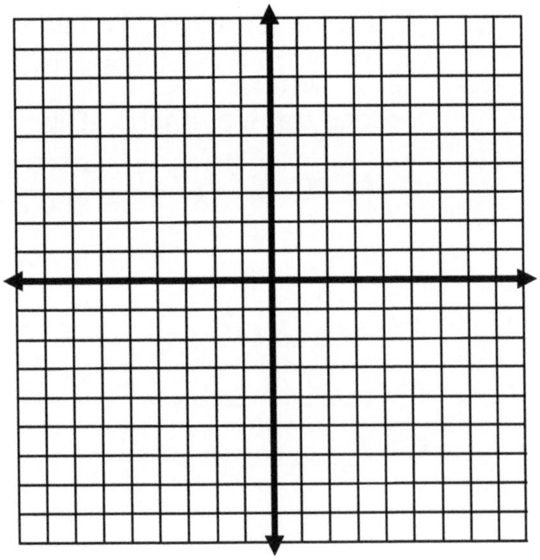

A‴: (_____, _____),

B‴: (_____, _____),

C‴: (_____, _____)

6-10. Quadrilateral DEFG has vertices at D(−4, 4), E(−3, 2), F(−5, 1), and G(−7, 2). For each of the following problems, perform the following transformations *in the order they are given*, and give the coordinates of the vertices of the final image.

6. First transformation: Translation by the vector ⟨5, −3⟩

Second transformation: Dilation with center (0, 0) and scale factor 4

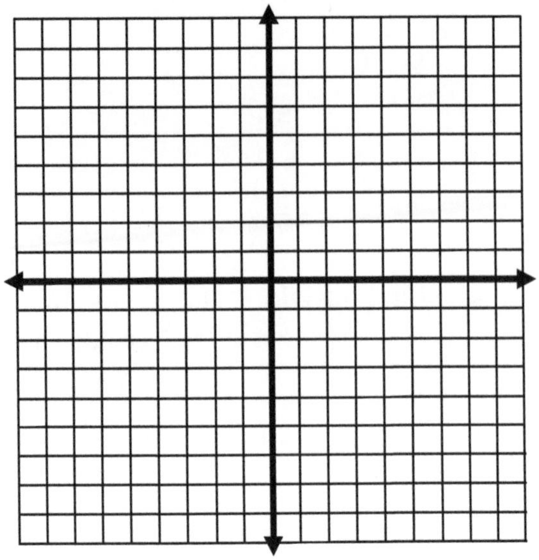

D″: (_____, _____),

E″: (_____, _____),

F″: (_____, _____),

G″: (_____, _____)

7. First transformation: Reflection in the line y = 1

Second transformation: Counter-clockwise rotation of 90° about (0, 3)

D″: (______, ______),

E″: (______, ______),

F″: (______, ______),

G″: (______, ______)

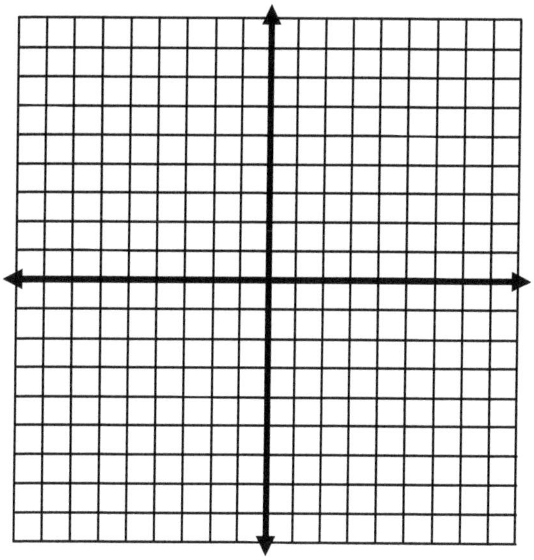

8. First transformation: Reflection in the line x = –4

Second transformation: Reflection in the line x = 1

D″: (______, ______),

E″: (______, ______),

F″: (______, ______),

G″: (______, ______)

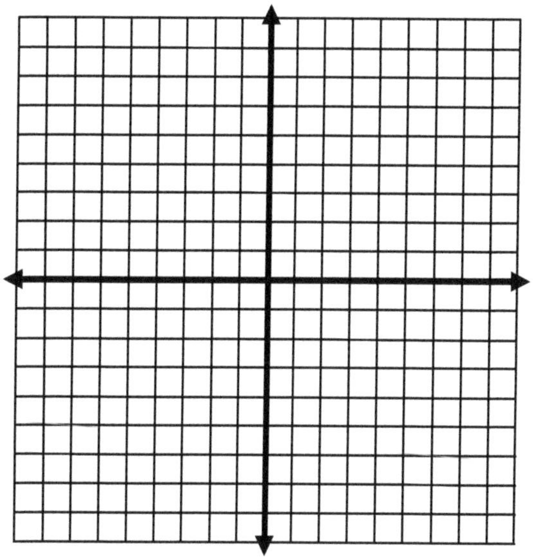

9. First transformation: Translation $(x, y) \rightarrow (x - 1, y - 8)$

Second transformation: Clockwise rotation of 90° about (2, –5)

Third transformation: Reflection in the line y = 4

D‴: (______, ______),

E‴: (______, ______),

F‴: (______, ______),

G‴: (______, ______)

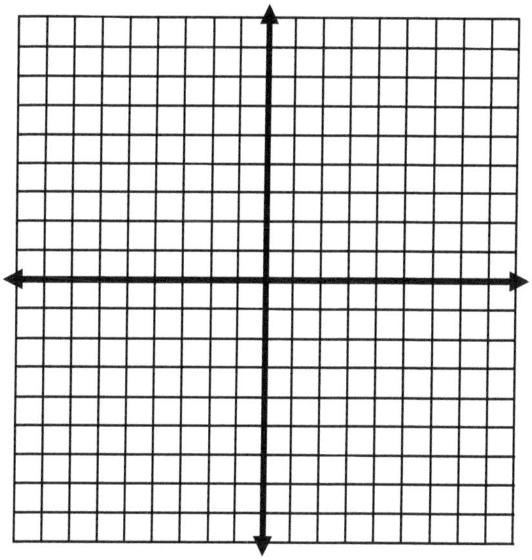

10. First transformation: Reflection in the y-axis

Second transformation: Reflection in the line y = 1

Third transformation: Clockwise rotation of 180° about (0, –3)

D‴: (______, ______),

E‴: (______, ______),

F‴: (______, ______),

G‴: (______, ______)

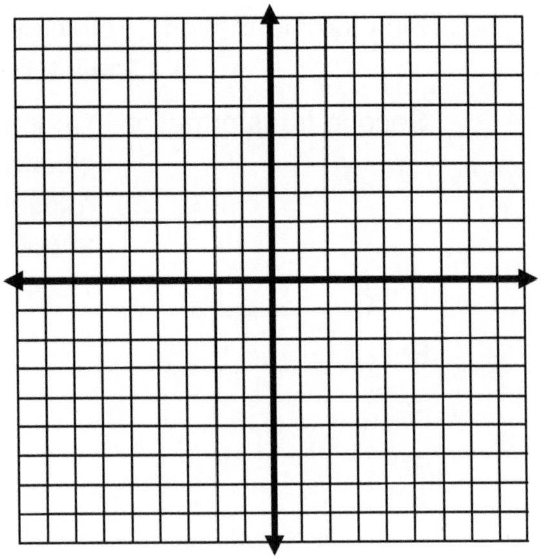

11-14. Triangle RST has vertices at R(–8, –3), S(–5, 6), and T(4, 0). For each of the following problems, perform the following transformations *in the order they are given*, and give the coordinates of the vertices of the final image.

11. First transformation: Reflection in the line x = –1

Second transformation: Dilation with center (0, 0) and scale factor $\frac{2}{3}$

R″: (______, ______),

S″: (______, ______),

T″: (______, ______)

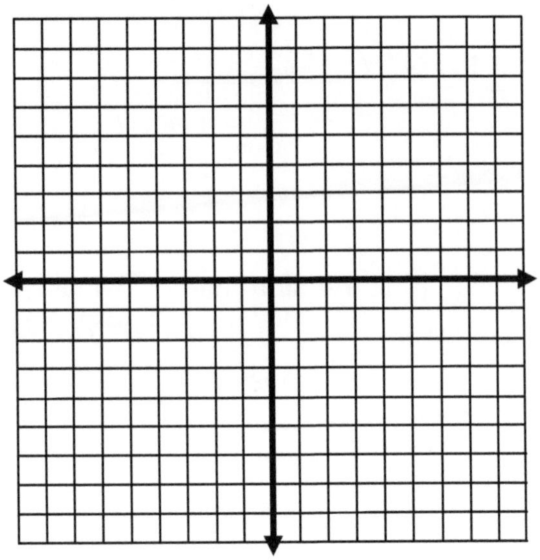

12. First transformation: Translation by the vector ⟨4, 2⟩

Second transformation: Clockwise rotation of 90° about the point (1, 3)

R″: (______, ______),

S″: (______, ______),

T″: (______, ______)

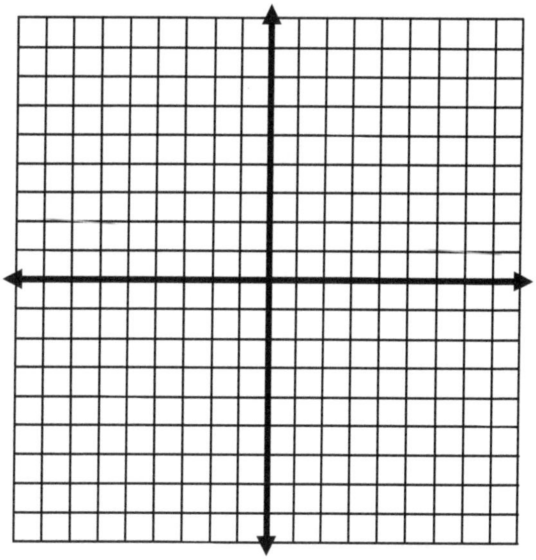

13. First transformation: Reflection in the line y = 1

Second transformation: Clockwise rotation of 90° about the point (–1, –2)

Third transformation: Translation by the vector ⟨–2, 0⟩

R‴: (______, ______),

S‴: (______, ______),

T‴: (______, ______)

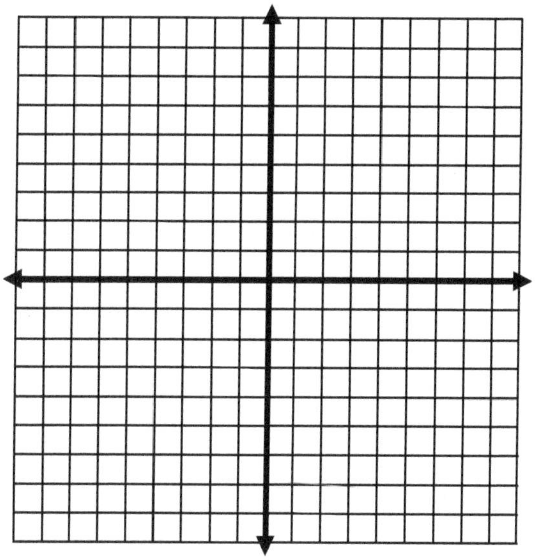

14. First transformation: Clockwise rotation of 90° about the origin

Second transformation: Counter-clockwise rotation of 90° about (4, –1)

R″: (______, ______),

S″: (______, ______),

T″: (______, ______)

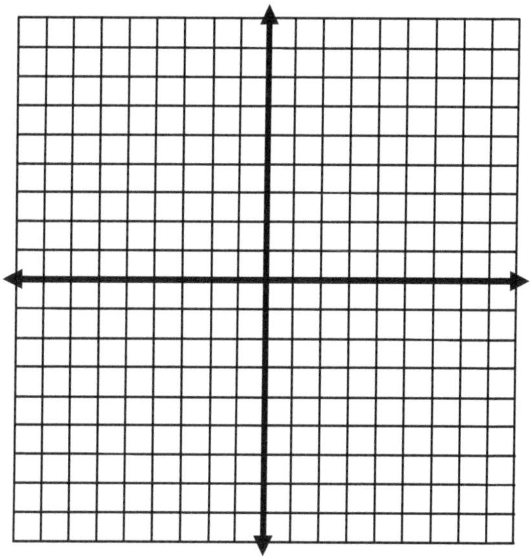

15. The figure at the right shows a reflection of $\overline{AB}$ in line k, and then the resulting image has been reflected in line m. Line k is parallel to line m, and line m is 8 cm from line k. Then the distance between A and A″ = ______________, and the distance between B and B″ = ______________.

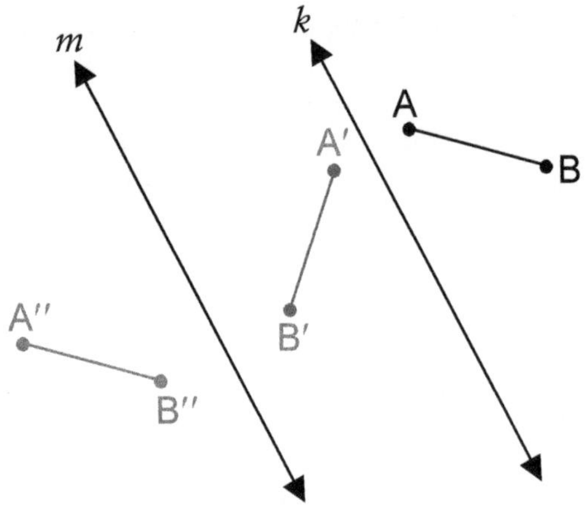

16. The figure at the right shows a reflection of $\triangle$CDE in line ℓ, and then the resulting image has been reflected in line n. Line ℓ is parallel to line n, and the distance between C and C″ is 15 feet. How far apart are lines ℓ and n? ______________

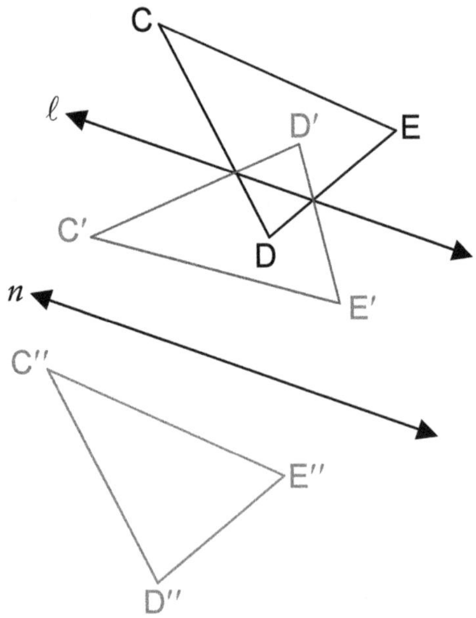

17. The figure at the right shows a reflection of parallelogram GHIJ in line s, and then the resulting image has been reflected in line t. Then m$\angle$G″ZG = ______________

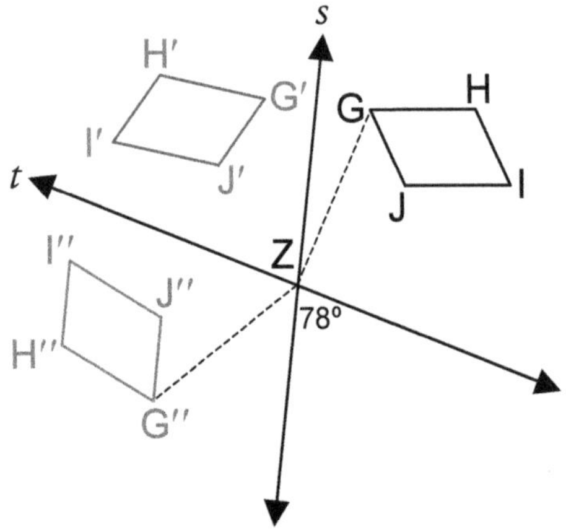

18. The figure at the right shows a reflection of ΔPQR in line u, and then the resulting image has been reflected in line v. Line u is parallel to line v, and the two lines are 4 meters apart. Find the distance between R and R″. ______________

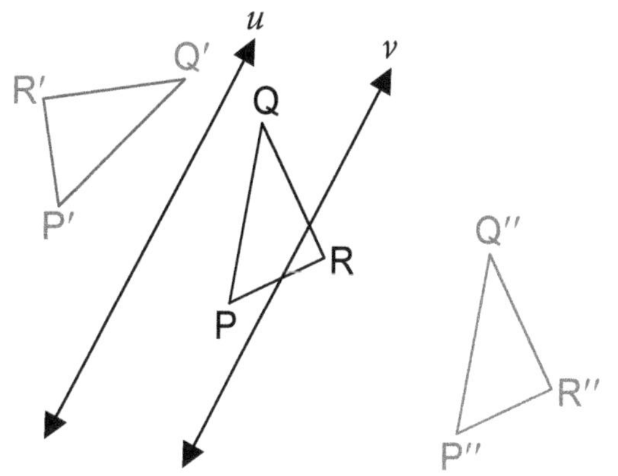

19. The figure at the right shows a reflection of ΔEFG in line m, and then the resulting image has been reflected in line n. The final image is a 124° clockwise rotation of ΔEFG about point O. Then x = ____________ and y = ____________.

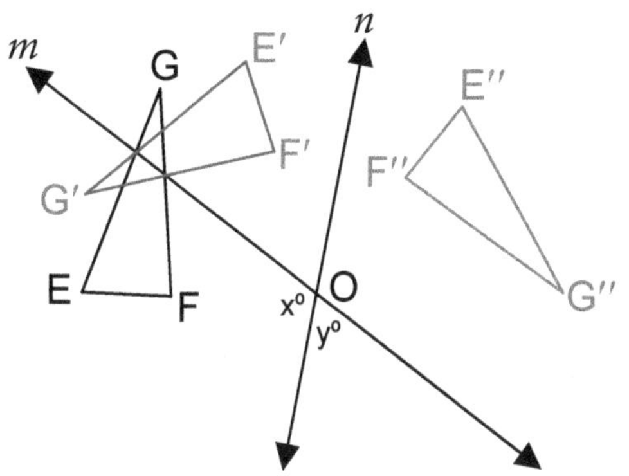

20. The figure at the right shows a reflection of ΔABC in line ℓ, and then the resulting image has been reflected in line t. The final image is a 76° counterclockwise rotation of ΔABC about point J. Find the value of x. ____________

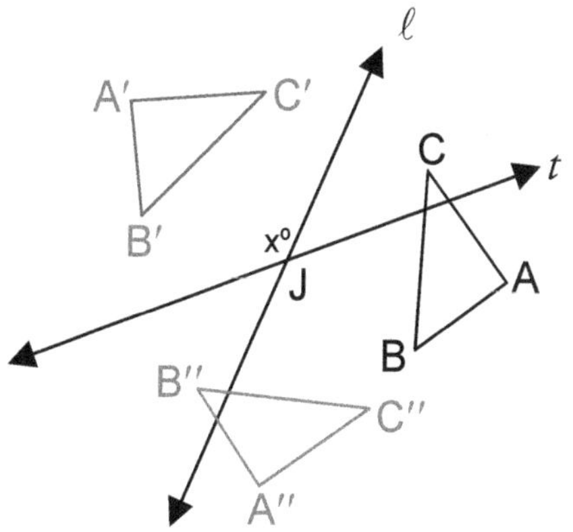

21. The figure at the right shows a reflection of $\overline{DE}$ in line r, and then the resulting image has been reflected in line s. Find the measure of the angle of rotation.

____

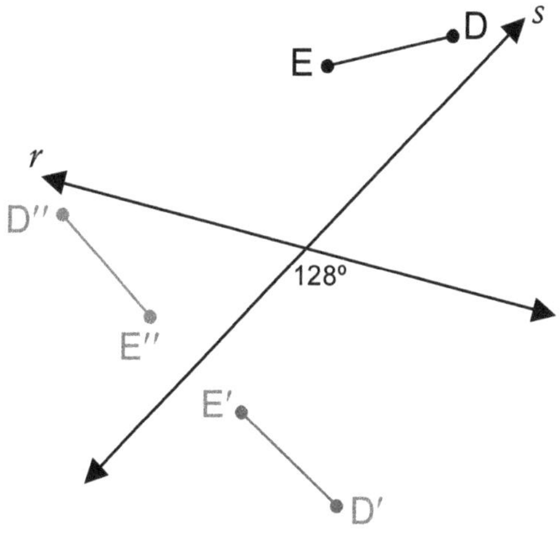

Part VII – Mixed Review

1-4. For each set of figures below, the preimage is the black figure, and the gray figure is the image. Classify each transformation as a *reflection*, *rotation*, *translation*, or *dilation*. Also tell whether or not each transformation appears to be an isometry.

1.

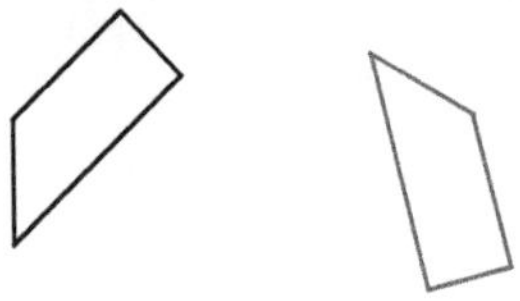

Is this transformation a *rotation*, *reflection*, *translation*, or *dilation*?

____

Is this an isometry? ____________

2.

Is this transformation a *rotation*, *reflection*, *translation*, or *dilation*?

____

Is this an isometry? ____________

3.

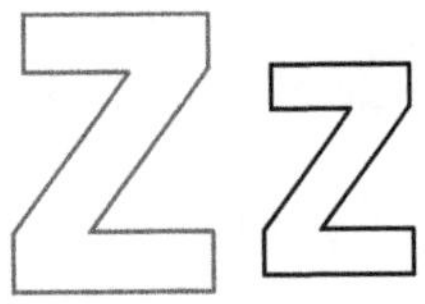

Is this transformation a *rotation*, *reflection*, *translation*, or *dilation*?

____

Is this an isometry? ____________

4.

Is this transformation a *rotation*, *reflection*, *translation*, or *dilation*?

____

Is this an isometry? ____________

5-6. Consider the figure at the right.

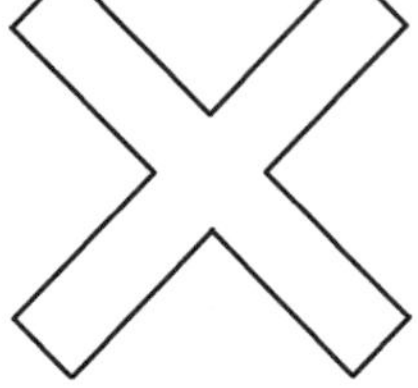

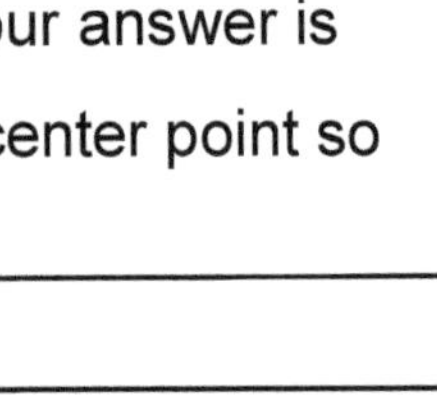

5. Does this figure have line symmetry? ____________ If your answer is *yes*, draw all the lines of symmetry in the figure.

6. Does this figure have rotational symmetry? ____________ If your answer is *yes*, name the angles that the figure can be rotated about the center point so that the resulting image looks exactly like the preimage. ____________________

____

7. Draw a 71° counterclockwise rotation of ΔABC about point D.

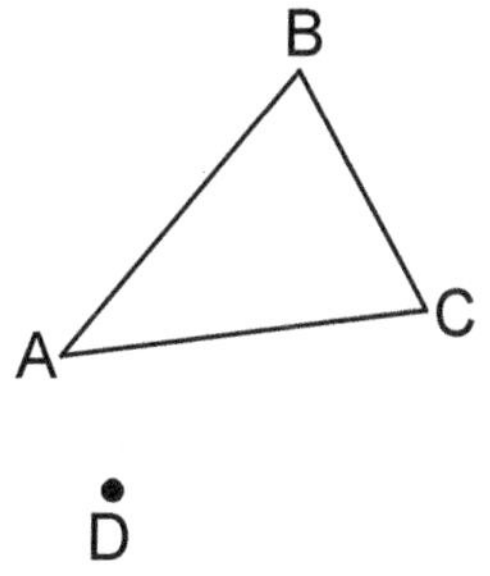

8. Draw a reflection of quadrilateral EFGH in line ℓ.

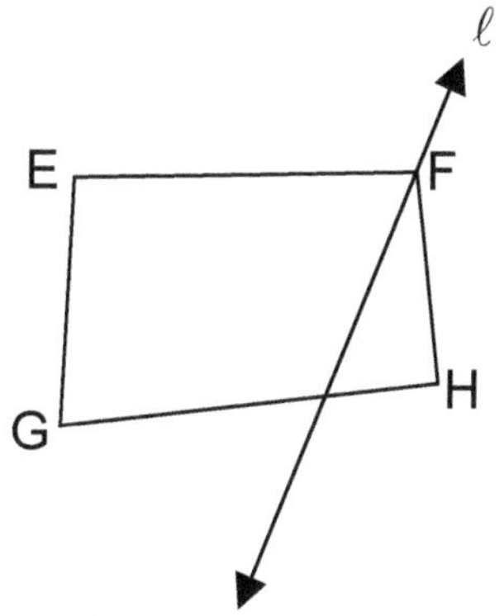

9. Draw a dilation of quadrilateral JKLM with center N and scale factor $1\frac{1}{2}$.

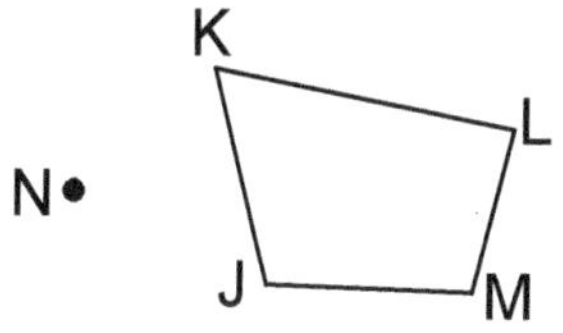

10. The figure below shows a counterclockwise rotation of ΔPQR about point O. Use a protractor to find the angle of rotation. _______________

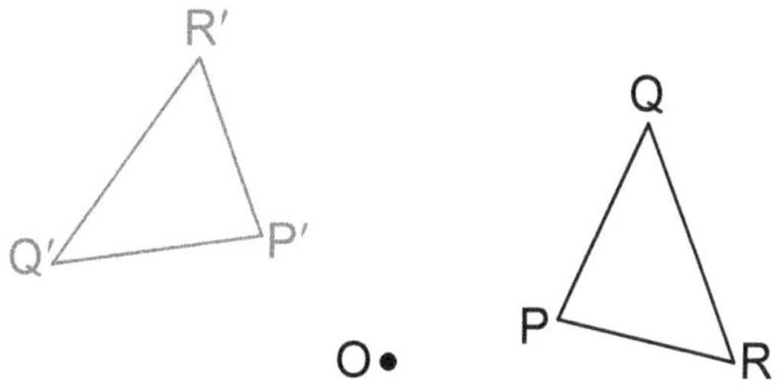

11-16. In the figure at the right, all of the triangles are isosceles right triangles.

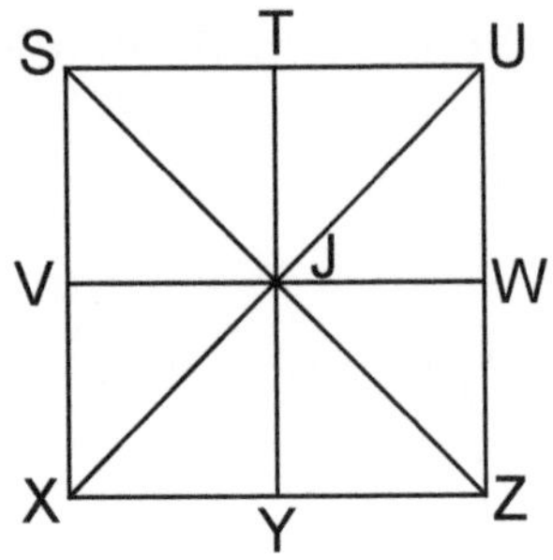

11. Name the image of $\overline{VJ}$ after a reflection in $\overline{UX}$.

____

12. Name the image of ΔSJU after a reflection in $\overline{SZ}$.

____

13. Name the image of ΔSZU after a 90° clockwise rotation about point J.

____

14. Name the image of $\overline{VJ}$ after a 90° clockwise rotation about point V.

____

15. Name the image of ΔUWJ after a 90° counterclockwise rotation about point W.

____

16. Name the image of ΔJZY after a 180° counterclockwise rotation about point J.

____

17-20. Triangle BNH has vertices at B(−4, 0), N(4, −4), and H(6, 4). Perform the following transformations, and give the coordinates of the vertices of the image.

17. Translation by the vector ⟨−1, 2⟩

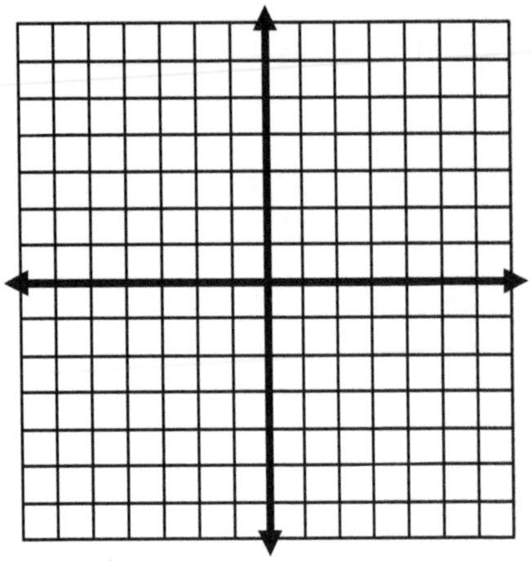

B′: (______, ______),

N′: (______, ______),

H′: (______, ______)

18. Reflection in the line y = 1

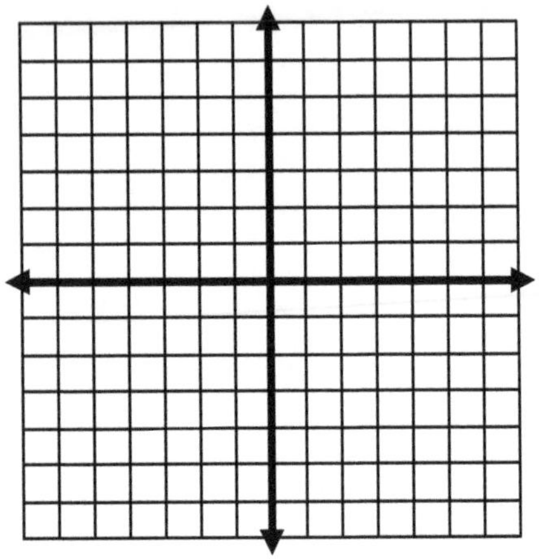

B′: (______, ______),

N′: (______, ______),

H′: (______, ______)

19. 90° counterclockwise rotation about the point (2, 0)

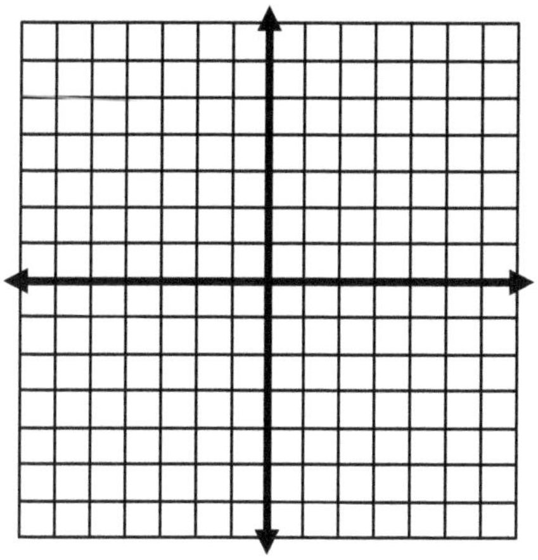

B′: (______, ______),

N′: (______, ______),

H′: (______, ______)

20. Dilation with center (0, 0) and scale factor $\frac{1}{4}$

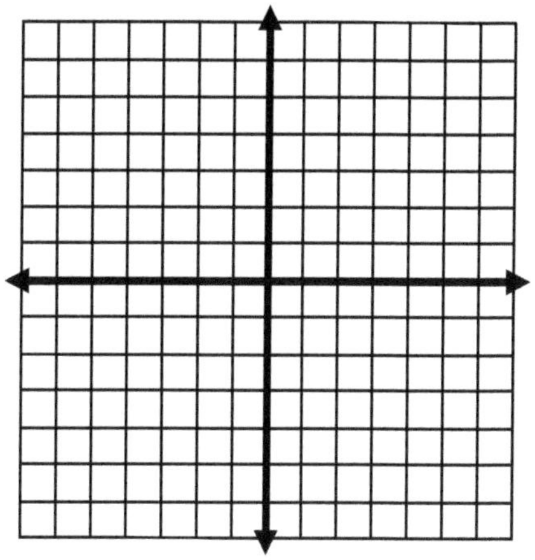

B′: (______, ______),

N′: (______, ______),

H′: (______, ______)

21-22. Quadrilateral ADVY has vertices at A(–7, 4), D(1, 6), V(3, 0), and Y(–5, – 4). Perform the following transformations *in the order they are given*, and give the coordinates of the vertices of the final image.

21. First transformation: Reflection in the line x = –2

Second transformation: 90° clockwise rotation about (–3, –1)

Third transformation: Translation by the vector ⟨3, 0⟩

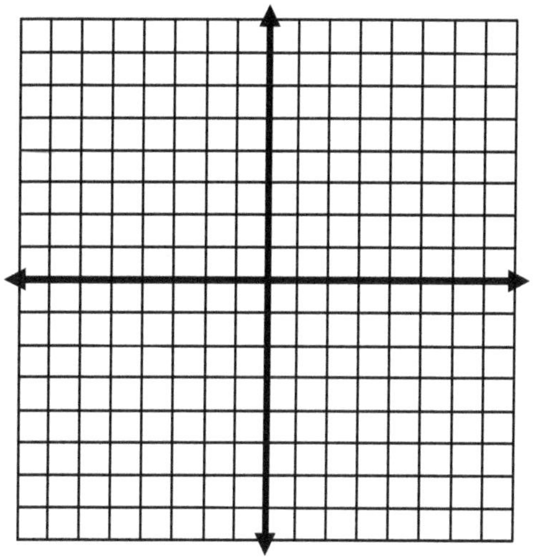

A‴: (______, ______),

D‴: (______, ______),

V‴: (______, ______),

Y‴: (______, ______)

22. First transformation: Translation
$(x, y) \to (x + 3, y)$

Second transformation: Dilation with center (0, 0) and scale factor $\frac{3}{4}$

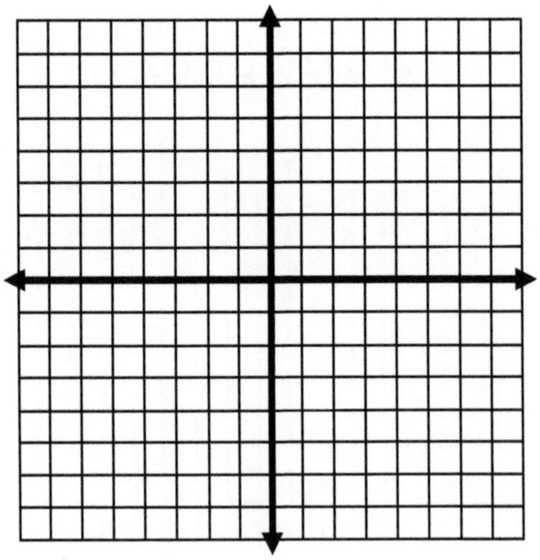

A″: (______, ______),

D″: (______, ______),

V″: (______, ______),

Y″: (______, ______)

23. The figure at the right shows a reflection of ΔCEG in line n, and then the resulting image has been reflected in line ℓ. The final image is a 114° clockwise rotation of ΔCEG about point P. Then x = ____________ and y = ____________.

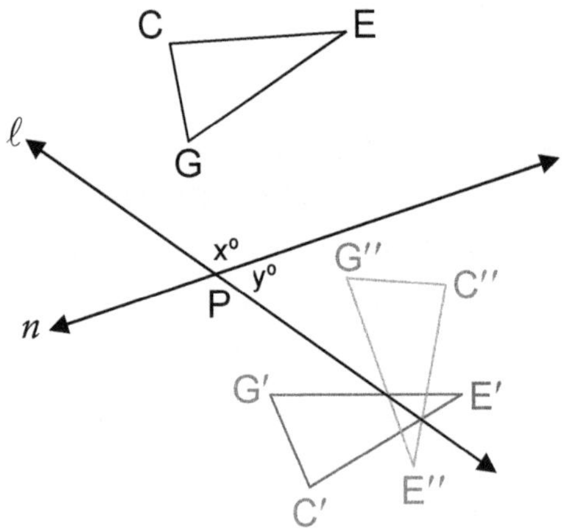

24. The figure at the right shows a reflection of trapezoid TUVW in line p, and then the resulting image has been reflected in line q. Line p is parallel to line q, and the two lines are 12 yards apart. Find the distance between W and W″.

____

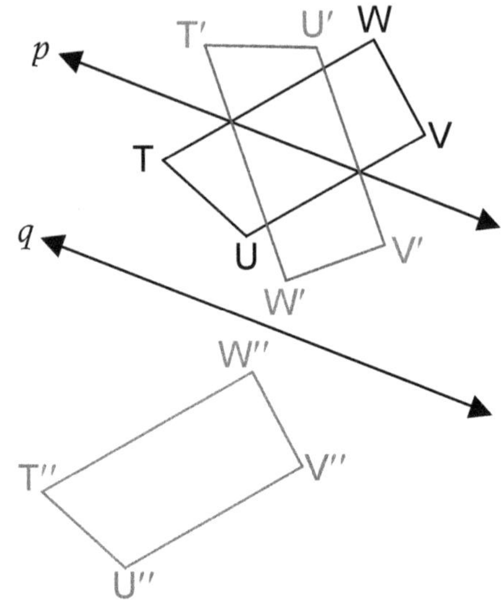

25. The figure at the right shows a dilation of parallelogram HMJL with center Z. If HL = 20, ZH = 30, M′J′ = 32, H′M′ = 12, and m∠J′ = 63°, then the scale factor is ____________, m∠M = ____________, MJ = ____________, ZH′ = ____________, and HH′ = ____________.

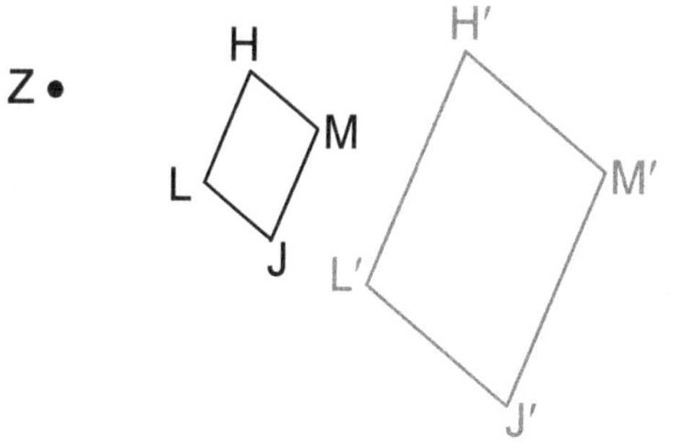

26. State whether each of the following statements is *true* or *false*.

All rotations are isometries. ______________

All reflections are isometries. ______________

All translations are isometries. ______________

All dilations are isometries. ______________

27. In the figure at the right, m∠PQR > m∠QRS and $\overline{PQ} \cong \overline{RS}$. Prove that PR > QS.

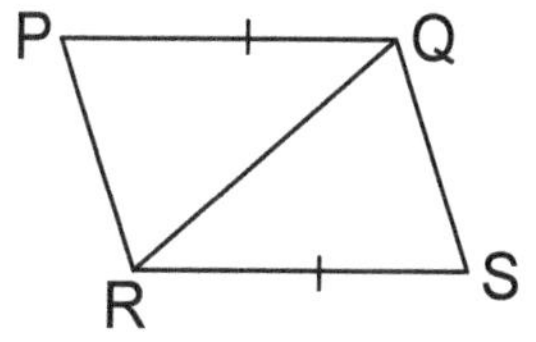

28. The figures below show two different views of a six-sided cube. How many sides are not shown? (At least one of the sides of the cube is blank, but none of the sides have the same pattern.) ______________

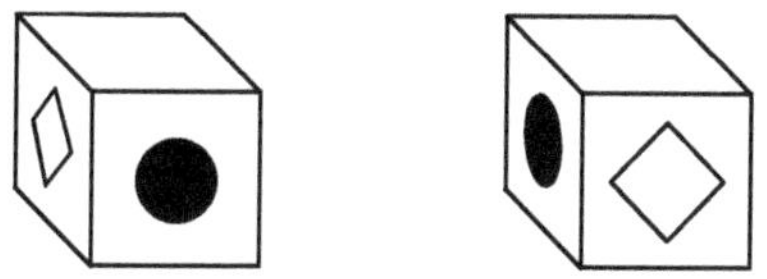

29-31. Use the Pythagorean Theorem and right triangle trigonometry to answer these questions about the triangle drawn at the right.

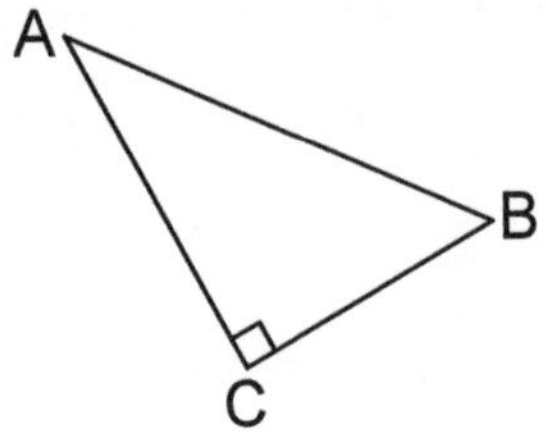

29. If AB = 17 and BC = 9, then $m\angle A$ = ____________

    and AC = ____________.

30. If $m\angle A = 31°$ and BC = 23, then AB = ____________ and AC = ____________.

31. If $m\angle B = 65°$ and AB = 16, then AC = ____________ and BC = ____________.

32-33. In ⊙C at the right, $m\overset{\frown}{AD} = 38°$, $m\overset{\frown}{BE} = 18°$, BD = 11, BF = 5, and EF = 4.

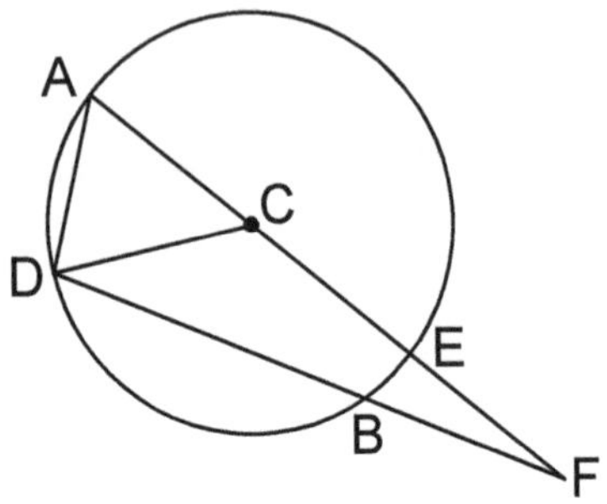

32. $m\angle A$ = ________, $m\angle DCA$ = ________,

    $m\angle F$ = ________, and $m\overset{\frown}{DAE}$ = ________

33. AE = ________ and CD = ________

34. A car's gas tank holds 16 gallons of gasoline. If the car can travel 230 miles on 7 gallons of gasoline, how far can it travel with a full tank of gasoline? Round your answer to the nearest tenth of a mile. ____________

Chapter 12 – Perimeter and Area

Part I – Finding the Perimeter of a Polygon

We will begin this section with a definition.

The perimeter of a polygon is equal to the distance around the outside of the polygon.

Example 1: Find the perimeter of the trapezoid at the right.

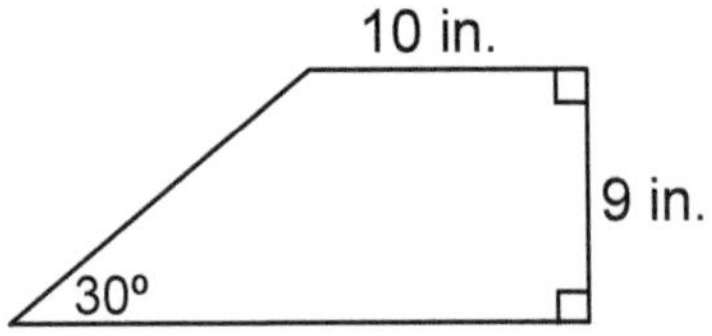

To find the perimeter of this trapezoid, we must begin by finding the lengths of the other sides of the trapezoid. To do this, we will draw the picture below.

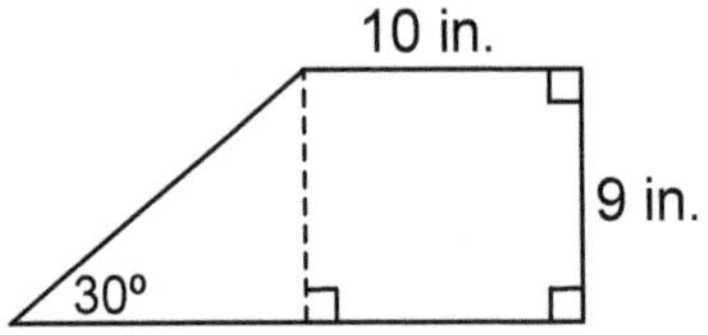

Now, we can label the lengths of different parts of this figure as shown below. (You should notice that, when we drew the dotted line above, we formed a rectangle and a 30°-60°-90° triangle.)

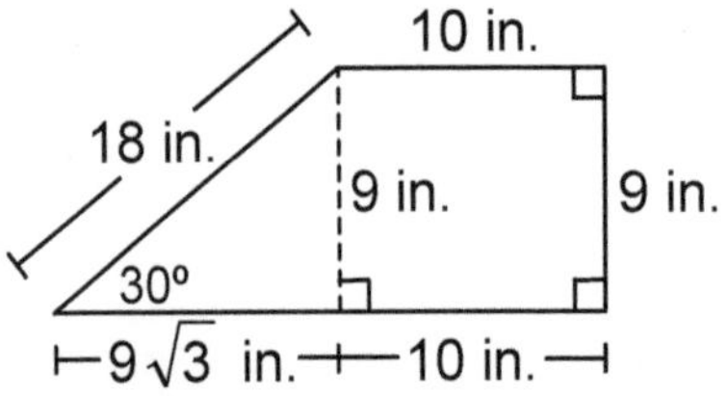

So, now, to find the perimeter of the trapezoid, all we have to do is add up all the lengths of the sides of the trapezoid. This tells us that the perimeter is equal to $(10 + 9 + 10 + 9\sqrt{3} + 18)$ inches, or $(47 + 9\sqrt{3})$ inches.

Example 2: Find the perimeter of the rectangle at the right. Assume that all the angles are right angles.

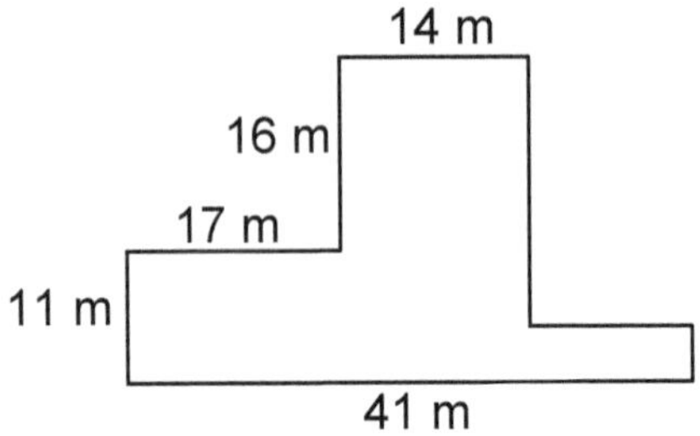

We will begin by drawing the dotted segments shown in the figure on the next page. You should notice that these segments give us three rectangles. (We could also draw horizontal segments to split this polygon into other rectangles, but the thought process we will use here is the easiest way to solve this problem.)

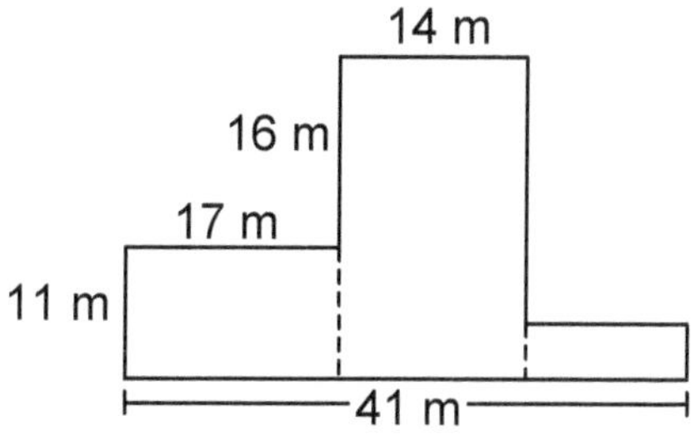

Now, to talk about the lengths of the unlabeled sides, we will label the vertices of this figure as shown below.

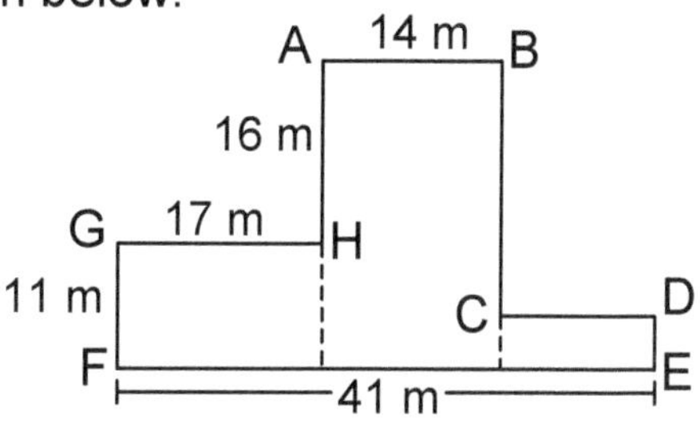

Next, we will note that $\overline{CD}$ must have a length of 10 meters, and BC + DE must equal 27 m. (The figure below illustrates why we can say this.)

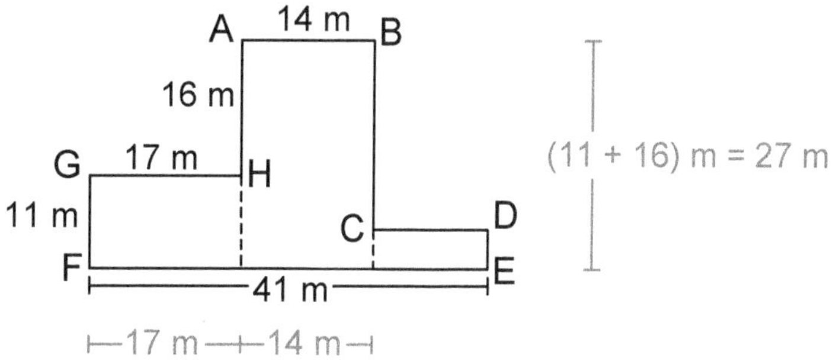

You might notice that we did not find the actual length of either $\overline{BC}$ or $\overline{DE}$. We don't have enough information to do this, but we don't *need* that information. We just need to know the *sum* of the lengths of all the sides. This turns out to be 136 m, and so we can say that the perimeter of this figure is 136 meters.

Now, we need a formula and a definition.

The distance around the outside of a circle is called the circumference of the circle, and it is equal to the product of 2, the number π*, and the radius of the circle. In symbols, we write $C = 2\pi r$.

*You should recall that π is pronounced "pi," and that it is approximately equal to 3.14. You have probably used either 3.14 or $\frac{22}{7}$ as the *actual* value for π in the past, but we will not do that here because these values are only *approximately* equal to π. In reality, π is an irrational number, and so it cannot be written as a fraction, and it cannot be written as a decimal that either stops or repeats.

Example 3: Find the perimeter of the figure at the right. Assume that all the angles that appear to be right angles are actually right angles.

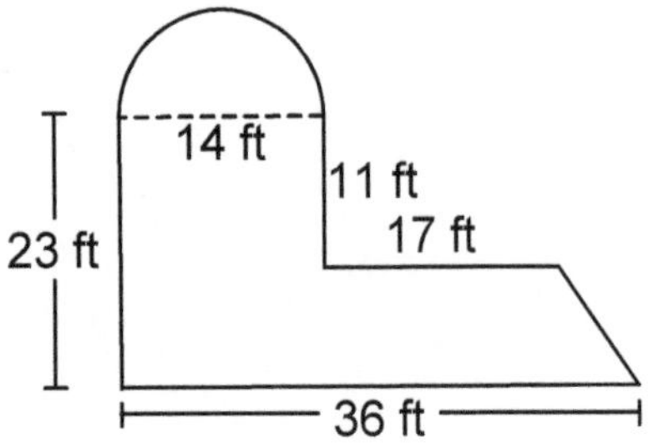

We will begin by splitting this figure up into rectangles, a triangle, and a semicircle, as shown below. We can also label the lengths of parts of this figure as shown below.

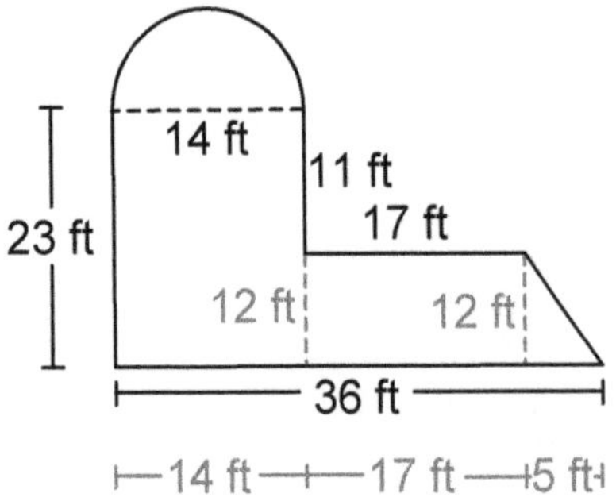

Now, we can use the Pythagorean Theorem to say that the length of the third side of the triangle is 13 feet, and we can use the formula on the previous page to say that the length of the curved path is 7π feet. (To see why the length of the curved path is 7π feet, you need to realize that the curved path is half of a circle that has a radius of 7 feet. Therefore, the circumference of the full circle is 14π feet, but we divide this by 2 because we only want to talk about the distance around the outside of half the circle.) This tells us that the perimeter of this figure is equal to $(23 + 7\pi + 11 + 17 + 13 + 36)$ feet, or $(100 + 7\pi)$ feet.

Now, we need one more formula. This formula talks about the *length* of an arc. Notice that this is different from the *measure* of an arc. When we talk about the *length* of an arc, we are talking about the distance around the outside of that part of the circle. You can measure arc *lengths* in units such as meters and inches, whereas the *measure* of an arc is expressed in degrees. (Later on in your studies of math, you will learn that arcs can also be measured in other units too, but, for now, all measures of arcs will be given to you in degrees.)

The length of an arc is given by the formula

$$\text{Arc length} = \frac{\theta}{360^\circ} \cdot 2\pi r,$$

where θ is a Greek letter that represents the measure of the arc and r represents the length of the radius of the circle.

Example 4: Find the length of $\overset{\frown}{AB}$ in the figure at the right. (Assume that the point C is the center of the circle.)

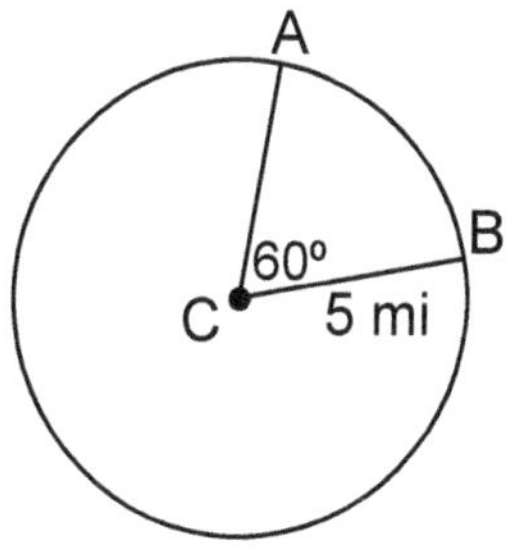

We can use the formula on the previous page to work this problem as shown below.

$$\text{length of } \overset{\frown}{AB} = \frac{60°}{360°} \cdot 2\pi(5 \text{ mi})$$
$$= \frac{1}{6} \cdot 10\pi \text{ mi}$$
$$= \frac{10\pi}{6} \text{ mi}$$
$$= \frac{5\pi}{3} \text{ mi}$$

Now, let's talk about why this formula works.

Since there are 360° in a full circle, we can conclude that an arc that has a measure of 60° makes up $\frac{1}{6}$ of the circle. Therefore, to find the length of $\overset{\frown}{AB}$ in the figure above, we must multiply the circumference of the entire circle by $\frac{1}{6}$, and that is exactly what we did when we multiplied $\frac{60°}{360°}$ by 10π miles.

Example 5: A certain bicycle tire has a diameter of 27 inches. If a person is riding this bicycle, how many revolutions must this tire make in order for the bicycle to travel forward 1 mile? (There are 5280 feet in 1 mile, and there are 12 inches in 1 foot.)

We will begin by noting that, when the tire goes through one revolution, the distance that the bicycle travels is equal to the circumference of the tire. Therefore, when the tire makes one revolution, the tire must travel a distance of 27π inches. (Note that the fact that the tire has a diameter of 27 inches tells us that it has a radius of 13.5 inches, and so the circumference of the tire must equal $2\pi \cdot 13.5$ inches.)

Next, we will note that there are 5280 • 12, or 63,360, inches in one mile.

Now, to find the number of revolutions that the tire must make in order to travel forward one mile, we must take this 63,360 inches and split it up into pieces of 27π inches. Thus, we can say that the tire must make $\frac{63{,}360}{27\pi}$, or $\frac{7040}{3\pi}$, revolutions in order to travel forward one mile.

Problems – Do not forget to include the units in your answers!

1. Find the circumference of the circle at the right. (Assume that the point C is the center of the circle.) ________________

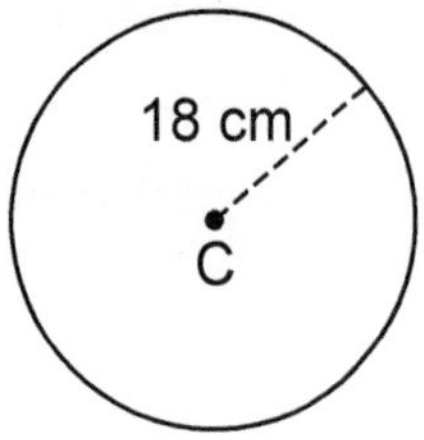

2. Find the circumference of the circle at the right. (Assume that the point O is the center of the circle.) ________________

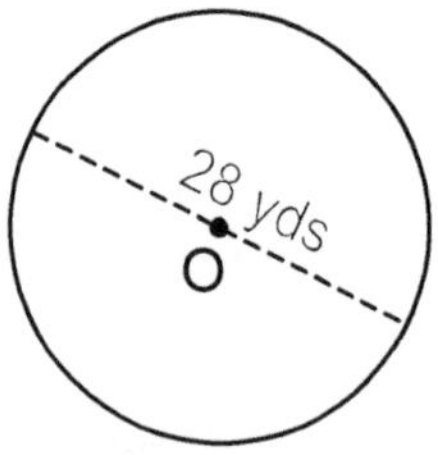

3. Find the perimeter of the rectangle at the right.

____

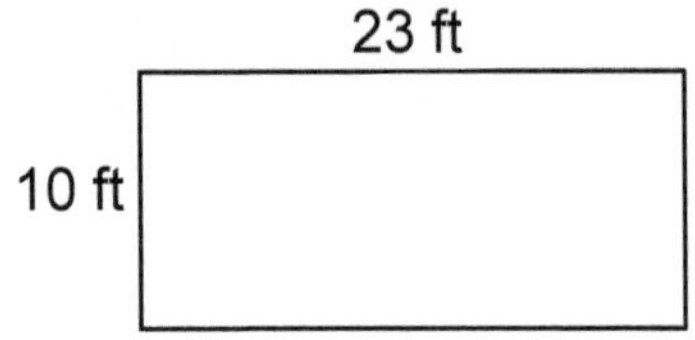

4. Find the perimeter of the parallelogram at the right.

____

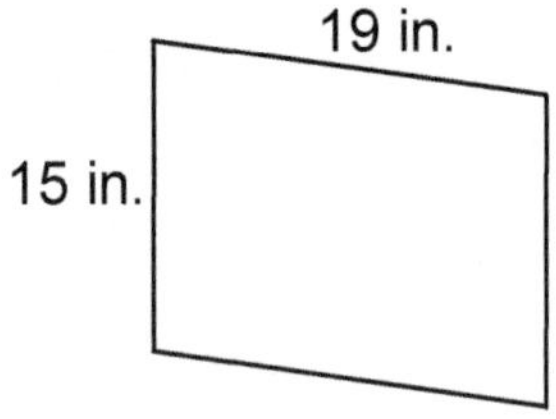

5. Find the perimeter of the triangle at the right.

____

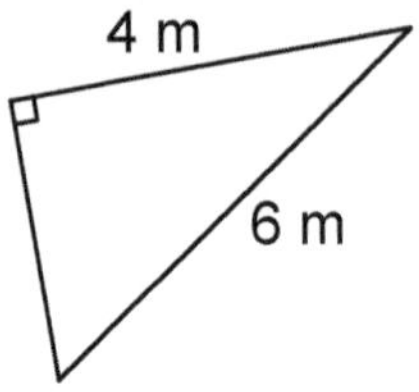

6. Find the perimeter of the square at the right.

____

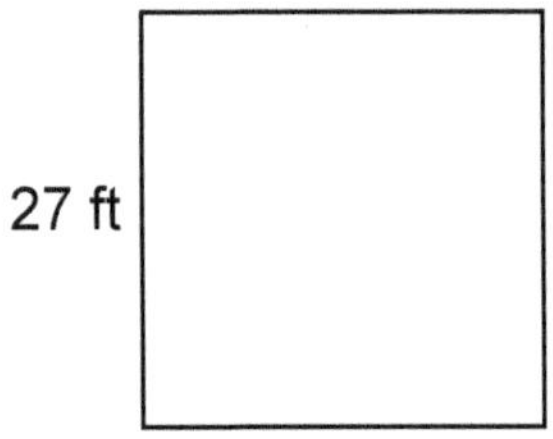

7. Find the perimeter of the trapezoid at the right.

____

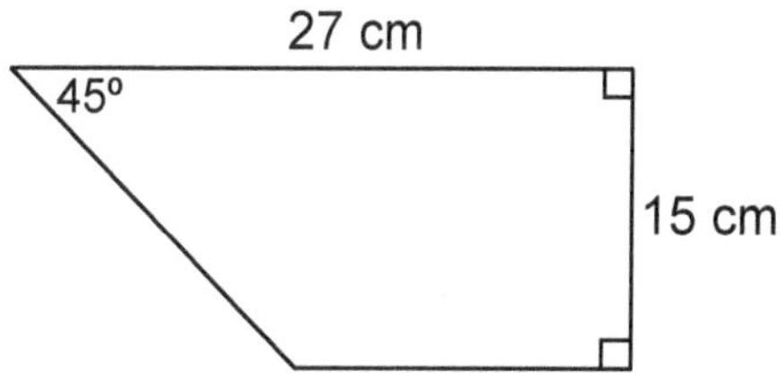

8. Find the perimeter of the trapezoid at the right.

____

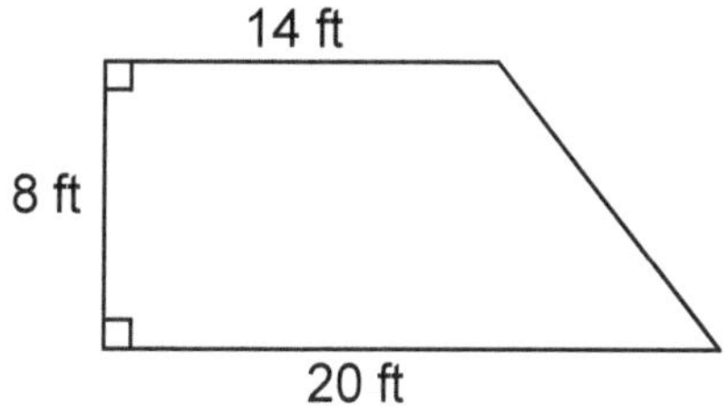

9. Find the perimeter of the regular hexagon at the right.

____

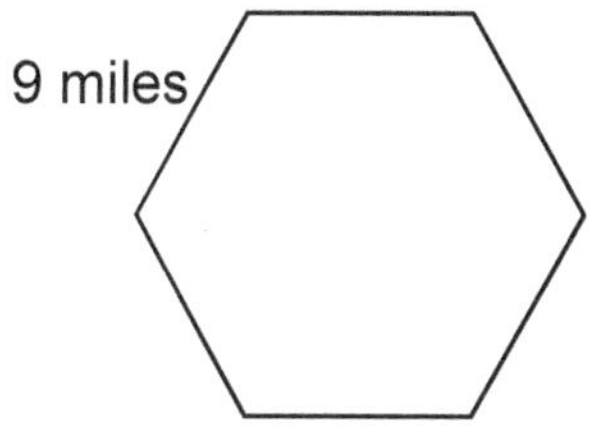

10. Find the length of $\overparen{PQ}$ in the figure at the right. (Assume that the point M is the center of the circle.) _______________

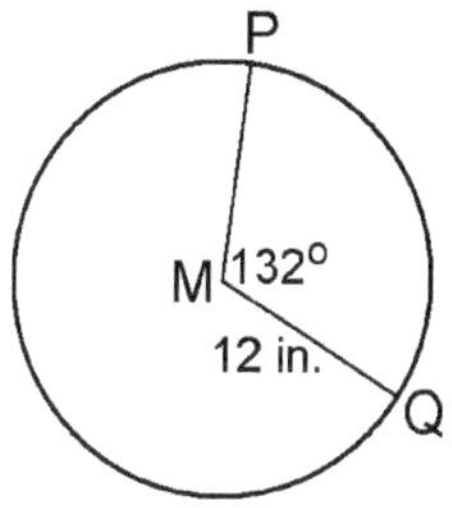

11. Find the length of $\overparen{RST}$ in the figure at the right. (Assume that the point N is the center of the circle.) _______________

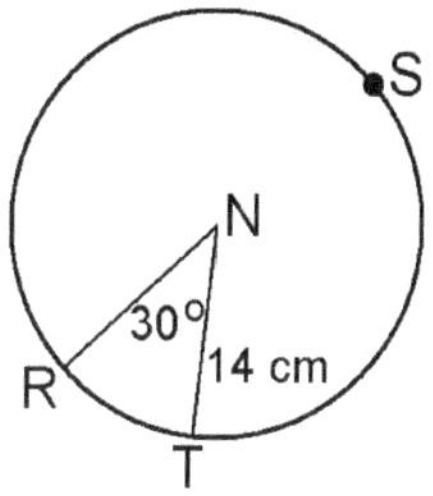

12-23. Assume that all the angles that appear to be right angles are actually right angles unless otherwise stated, and assume that all curved paths are arcs of circles.

12. Find the perimeter of the figure at the right.

____

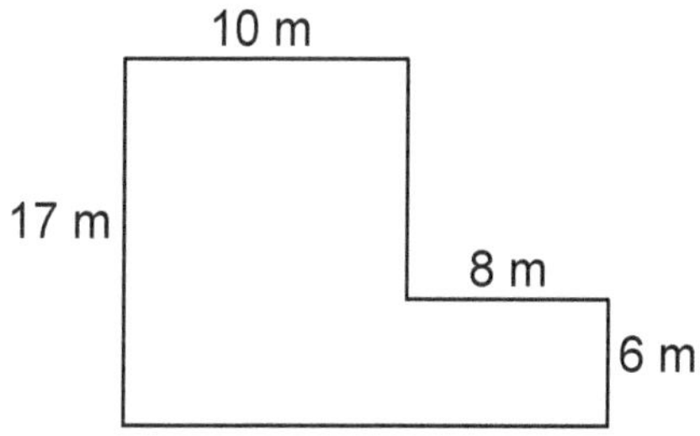

13. Find the perimeter of the figure at the right.

____

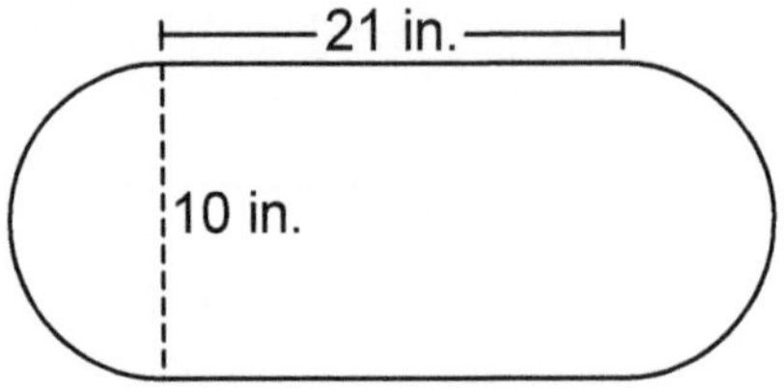

14. Find the perimeter of the figure at the right.

____

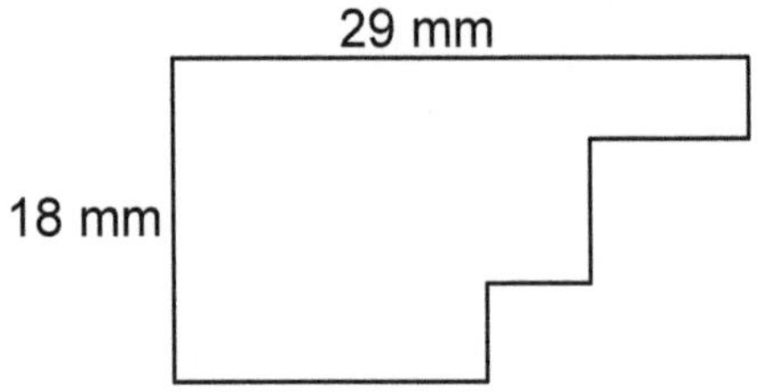

15. Find the perimeter of the figure at the right.

____

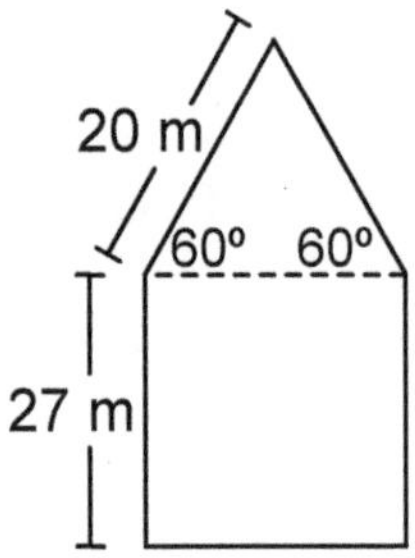

16. Find the perimeter of the figure at the right.

____

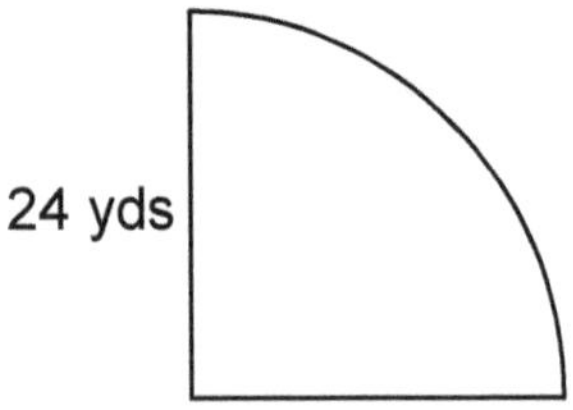

17. Find the perimeter of the figure at the right.

____

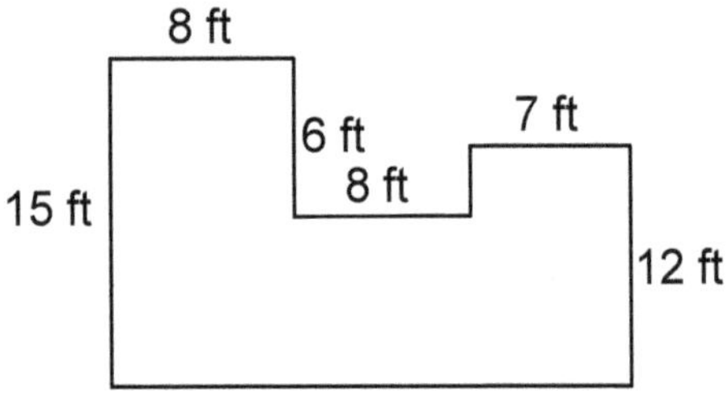

18. Find the perimeter of the figure at the right.

____

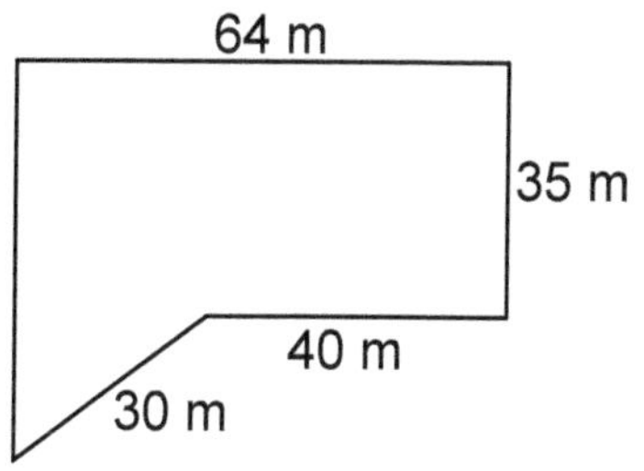

19. Find the perimeter of the figure at the right.

____

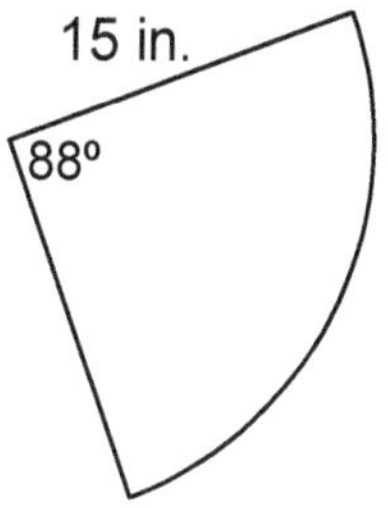

20. Find the perimeter of the figure at the right.

____

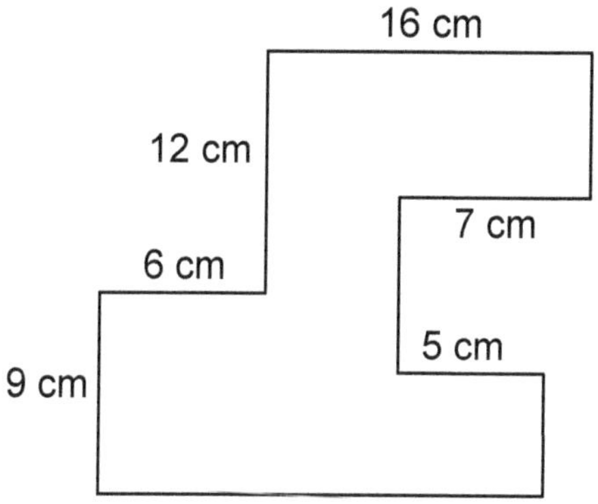

21. Find the perimeter of the figure at the right.

____

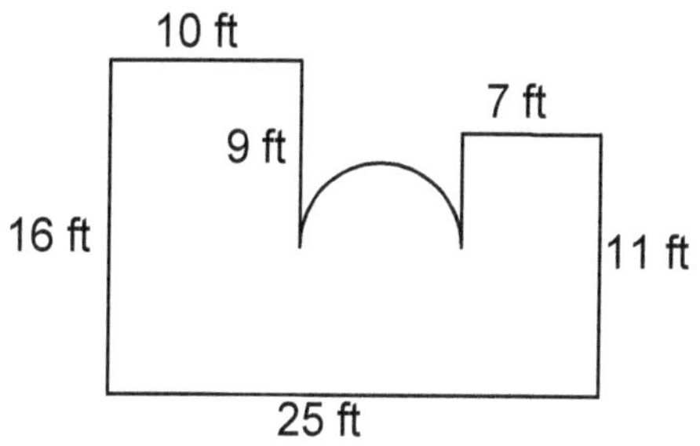

22. Find the perimeter of the figure at the right.

____

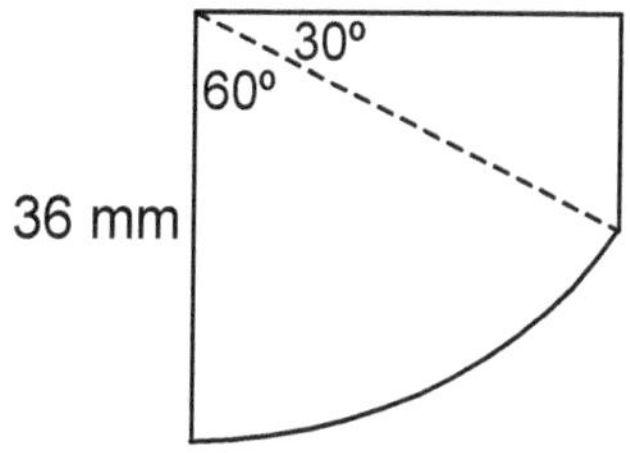

23. Find the perimeter of the figure at the right.

____

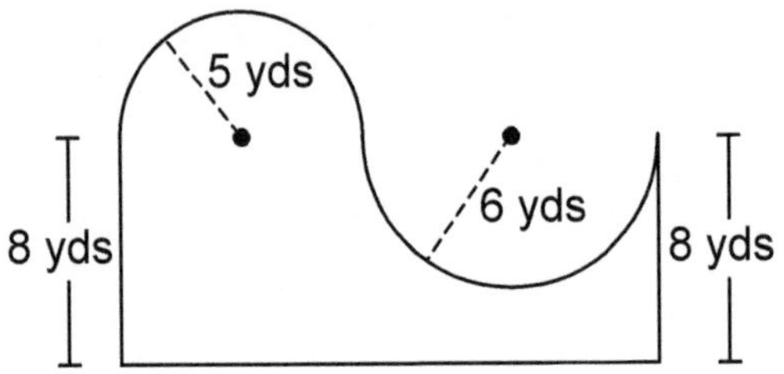

24. The rectangle at the right has a perimeter of 82 cm.

Then x = _______________.

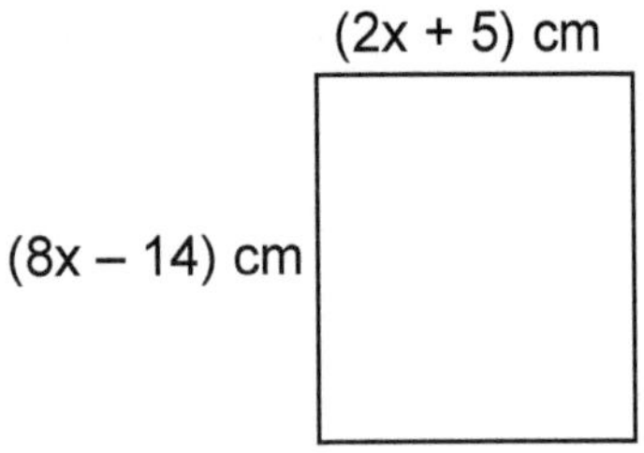

25. A rectangle has a perimeter of 74 inches. The length is 5 inches less than twice the width. What are the dimensions of the rectangle? (Hint: Start by drawing the figure shown at the right.)

Length _______________

Width _______________

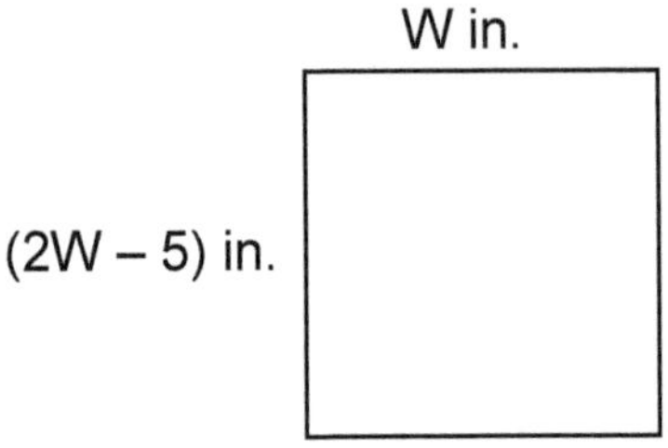

26. A rectangle has a perimeter of 96 yards. The width is 3 yards more than four times the length. What are the dimensions of the rectangle?

Length _______________

Width _______________

27. An isosceles triangle has a perimeter of 34 meters, and the two congruent sides are each 7 meters longer than half the length of the third side. Then the two congruent sides are each _______________ meters long, and the length of the third side is _______________ meters.

28. Tammy is building a rectangular fence for her dogs. If the fence will have a length of 100 feet and a width of 45 feet, and if the fencing material costs $12 per foot, what will the cost of the fence be? ________________

29. If a car tire has a diameter of 26 inches, how far can the car travel when the tire makes 100 revolutions? ________________

30. In the figure at the right, B is the center of the large circle. What is the difference between the circumference of the large circle and the length of the gray curved path from A to C?

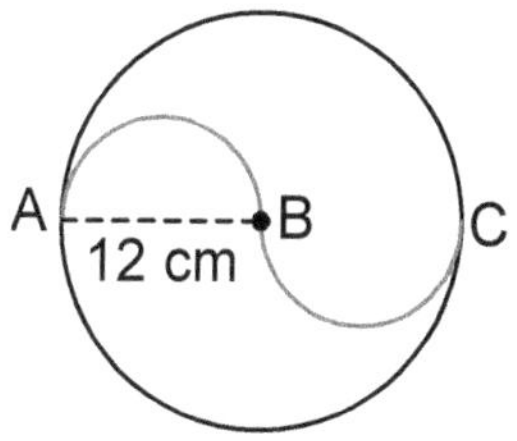

____

31. If a circle has a circumference of 36π feet, then the length of the diameter of the circle is ________________, and the length of the radius of the circle is ________________.

32. In $\odot D$ at the right, $\overset{\frown}{EF}$ has a length of 12 inches. Then DE = ________________.

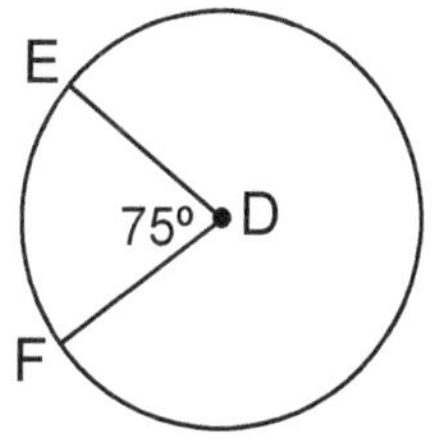

Part II – Finding the Areas of Parallelograms, Triangles, and Circles

We will begin this section with a definition.

> In a plane, the area of a figure is defined to be the amount of space enclosed by the figure.

Notice that the area of a figure is different from its perimeter because the perimeter of the figure talks about the distance around the *outside* of the figure, whereas the area of a figure talks about the space *inside* the figure. The area of a figure is usually measured in terms of a square unit, such as square meters, square inches, or square feet.

To understand what these units are, look at the figures below. The figure on the left shows 1 square centimeter, and the figure on the right shows 1 square inch.

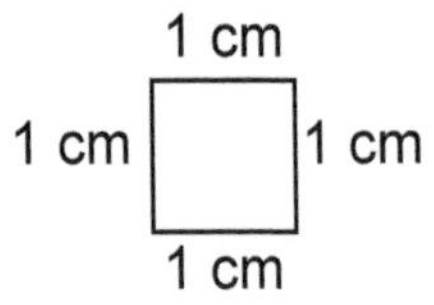

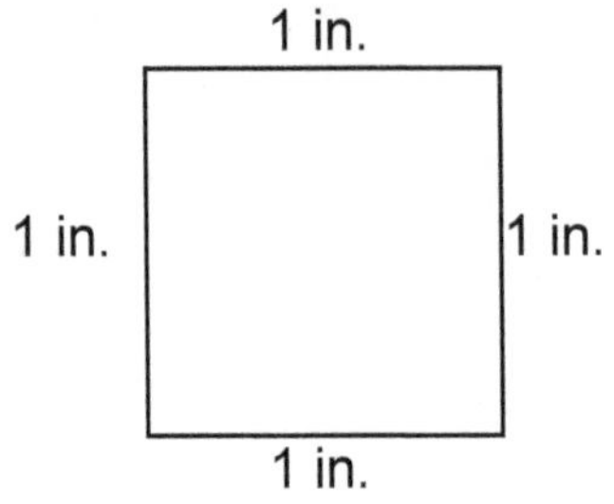

Similarly, 1 square foot (which, by the way, can be abbreviated as 1 sq ft or as 1 ft^2) is defined as the area enclosed by a square that has a length of 1 foot one each side, and 1 square meter (which can be abbreviated as 1 sq m or as 1 m^2) is defined as the area enclosed by a square that has a length of 1 meter one each side.

Example 1: In the figure below, the light vertical and horizontal lines are exactly 1 inch apart. What is the area of the outlined figure?

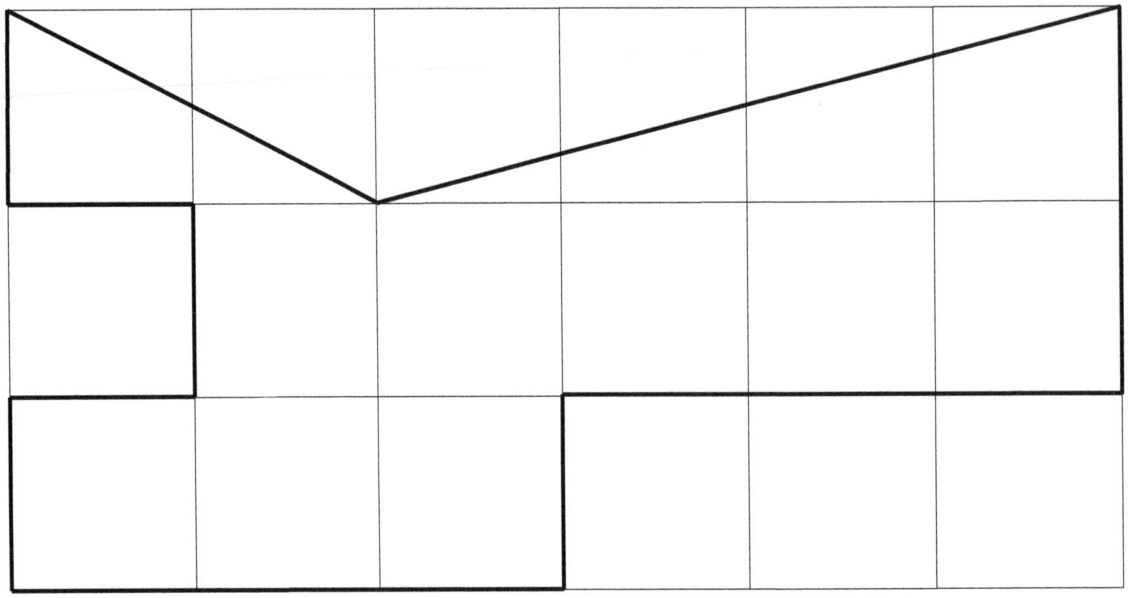

To work this problem, we will begin by labeling the different regions that make up this figure as shown below.

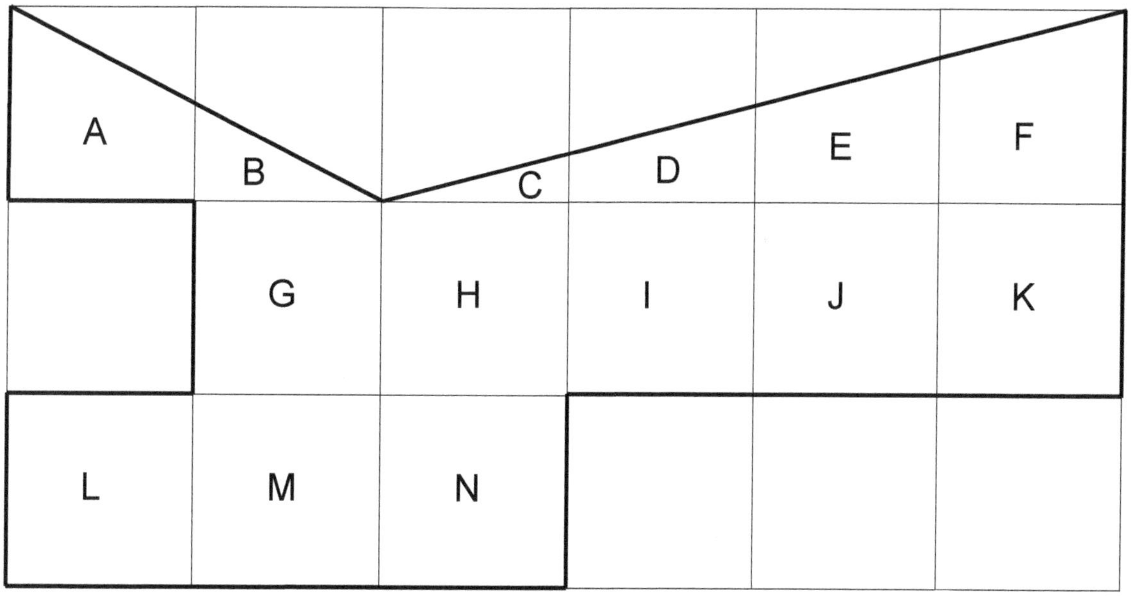

Now, we will note that the squares that are labeled G through N each have an area of 1 square inch. This tells us that the area of these squares is 8 square inches.

Next, let's look at the regions labeled A and B. Together, these two regions have area of 1 square inch. (To see why, note that the region labeled B can be rotated 180° so that, together, regions A and B make a square with a length of 1 inch on each side.)

Similarly, the regions labeled C and F together have an area of 1 square inch, and the regions labeled D and E together have an area of 1 square inch.

Therefore, the total area of this figure is equal to 11 square inches.

Next, we will state some formulas that we use to find the areas of rectangles, parallelograms, triangles, and circles.

Area of a rectangle = (length)(width), or, equivalently, Area of a rectangle = (base)(height)
Area of a parallelogram = (base)(height), where the base and height form 90° angles
Area of a triangle = $\frac{1}{2}$(base)(height), where the base and height form 90° angles
Area of a circle = π(radius)^2

Example 2: Find the area of the rectangle at the right.

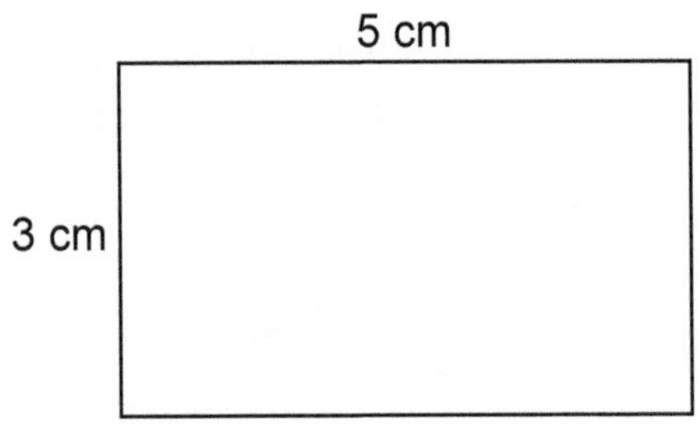

We will begin by noting that the formula for the area of a rectangle that we stated on the previous page tells us that the area of this rectangle is equal to (3 cm)(5 cm), or 15 cm^2. (Note that $3 \cdot 5 = 15$, and $cm \cdot cm = cm^2$.)

Now, to see *why* this formula works, we will draw horizontal and vertical lines every centimeter so that we can count the number of square centimeters inside this rectangle. (You can use a ruler to verify the statements that we make in this example, but you will not be able to use a ruler to verify the statements that we will make in any of the rest of the examples in the rest of this section. Also, you will not be able to use a ruler to work any of the practice problems unless the question specifically says so.)

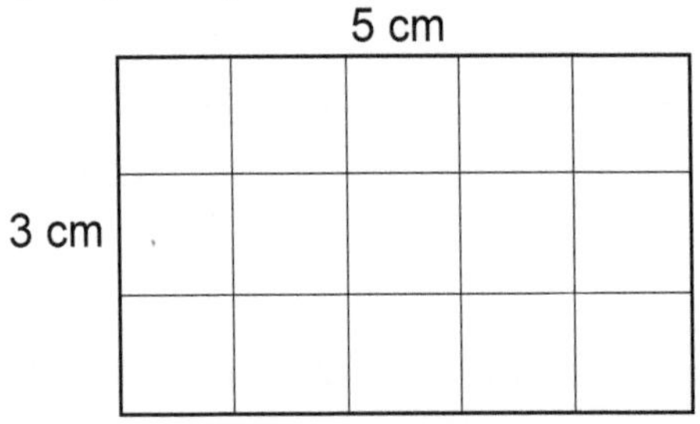

Now, you should be able to see that you can find the area of this rectangle by multiplying the 3 cm and the 5 cm together because the figure above contains 3 rows of 5 square centimeters each (or, if you prefer, you can say that we have 5 columns that each contain 3 square centimeters).

Example 3: Find the area of the parallelogram at the right.

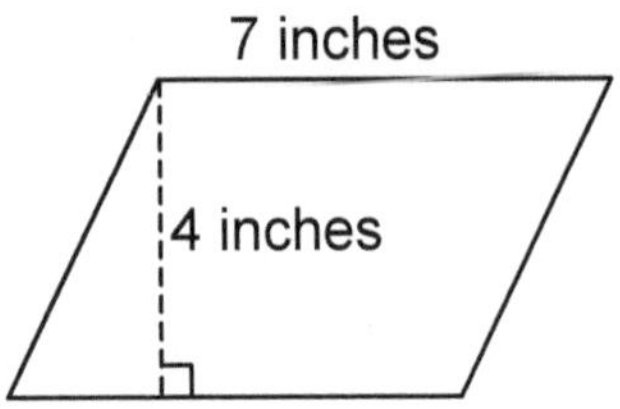

We will begin by noting that the formula for the area of a parallelogram that we stated on the previous page tells us that the area of this parallelogram is equal to (7 inches)(4 inches), or 28 square inches.

Now, to see *why* this formula works, we will begin by noting that the triangle on the left side of the parallelogram can be translated to the right side of the parallelogram to give us a new rectangle, as shown below.

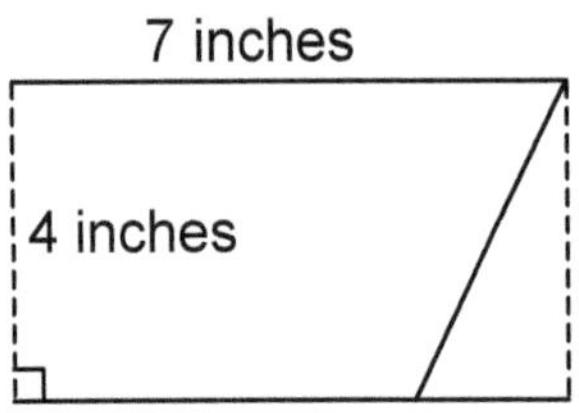

Note that the area of this new rectangle is equal to the area of the original parallelogram, and also note that the area of this new rectangle is equal to 28 square inches.

Example 4: Find the area of the triangle at the right.

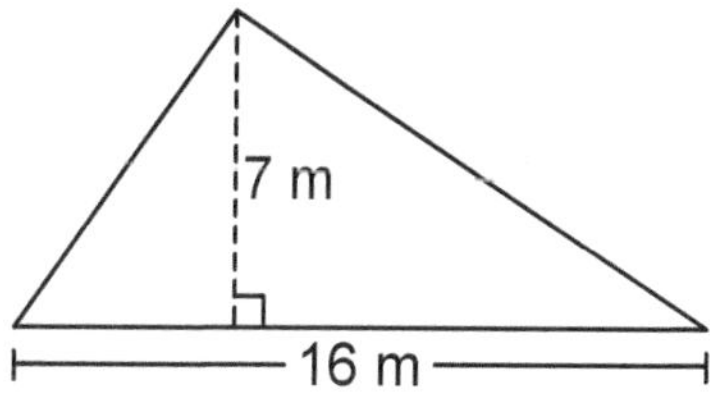

We will begin by noting that the formula for the area of a triangle that we stated on page 580 tells us that the area of this triangle is equal to $\frac{1}{2}$(16 m)(7 m), or 56 m^2. (Note that $\frac{1}{2} \cdot 16 \cdot 7 = 56$ and that $m \cdot m = m^2$.)

Now, to talk about why this formula works, we will draw the following picture.

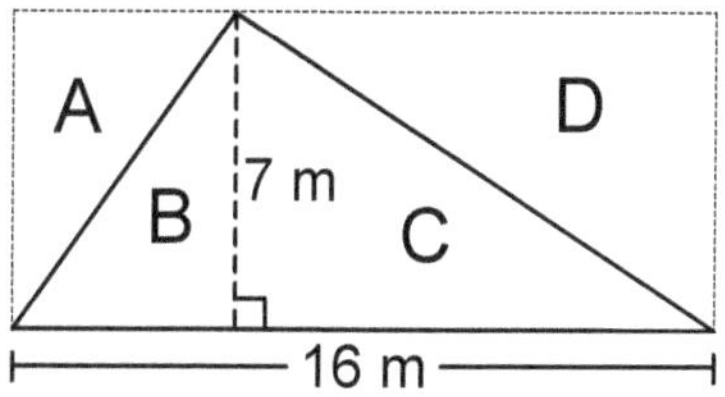

Note that the area of the big rectangle formed here is equal to 112 square meters, the area of the region we labeled A is equal to the area of the region we labeled B, and the area of the region we labeled C is equal to the area of the region we labeled D. Thus, the area of the original triangle must be equal to $\frac{1}{2}$(112 m^2), or 56 m^2.

Example 5: Find the area of ΔABC at the right.

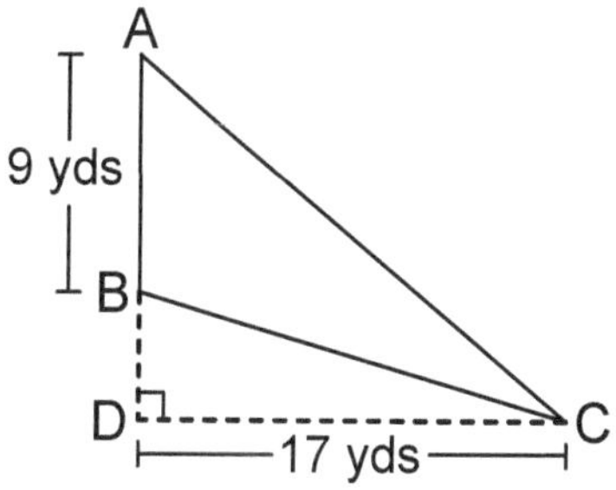

We will begin by noting that the formula for the area of a triangle that we stated on page 580 tells us that the area of this triangle is equal to $\frac{1}{2}$(9 yds)(17 yds), or 76.5 yds^2. (Notice that you can rotate the triangle counterclockwise 90° so that we can say that the length of the base is equal to 9 yards and the height is equal to 17 yards.)

To see why this formula works for this problem, we will label the distance between B and D as x yards, as shown below.

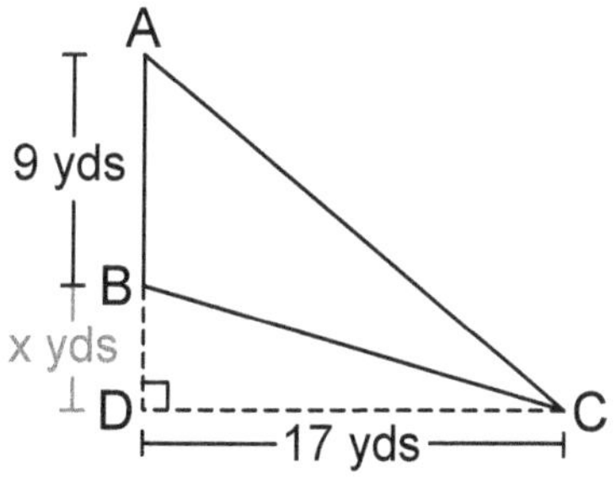

Now, we will note that we can use the concepts we discussed in Example 4 to say that the area of ΔACD is equal to $\frac{1}{2}$[(9 + x) yds](17 yds), which simplifies to (76.5 + 8.5x) square yards.

However, this (76.5 + 8.5x) yds^2 includes the area of ΔBCD, which we do not want to include in our calculation of the area of ΔABC. Since the area of ΔBCD is equal to 8.5x yds^2, we can say that the area of ΔABC must equal 76.5 yds^2.

Example 6: Find the area of the figure at the right. Assume that all angles that appear to be right angles are actually right angles unless otherwise stated, and assume that all curved paths are arcs of circles.

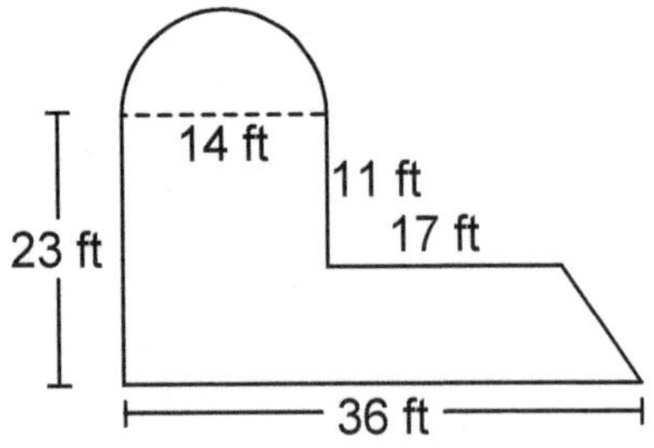

We will begin by noting that this is exactly the same figure that we discussed in Example 3 in the last section, and many of the figures that you will see in the practice problems for this section will be identical to the figures you saw in the last section.

Like we did in the last section, we will begin by splitting this figure up into rectangles, a triangle, and a semicircle, as shown below. We will also label the regions so that we can talk about the areas of these regions.

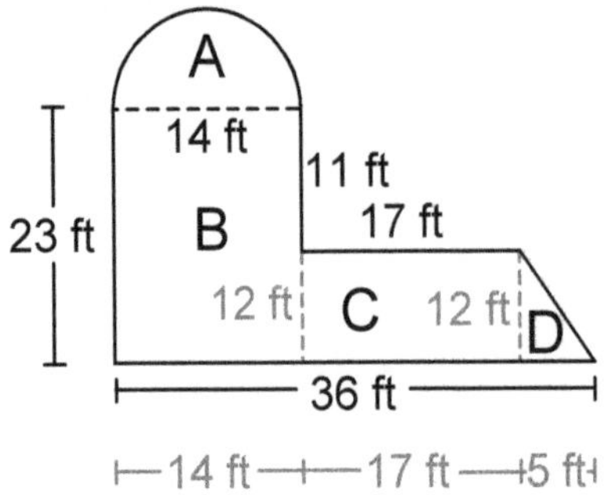

Now, we can find the areas of these regions as follows.

Region A is a semicircle that has a radius with a length of 7 feet. The area of a full circle that has a radius with a length of 7 feet is 49π ft^2. However, since region A is only a semicircle, we will divide this area by 2. Therefore, the area of region A must be equal to 24.5π ft^2.

Region B is a rectangle with a length of 23 feet and a width of 14 feet, and so the area of region B is equal to 322 ft^2.

Region C is a rectangle with a length of 12 feet and a width of 17 feet, and so the area of region C is equal to 204 ft^2.

Region D is a triangle that has a height of 12 feet and a base that has a length of 5 feet, and so the area of region D is equal to 30 ft^2.

Thus, the area of the entire figure must equal (556 + 24.5π) yds^2.

Now, we need one more definition and a formula to go with it. The formula is very similar to the formula we discussed in the last section that we used to find the length of an arc, and the reasoning behind this formula is exactly the same as the reasoning behind the formula for finding the length of an arc.

A sector of a circle is a region of the circle bounded by a central angle and its corresponding arc.

The area of a sector of a circle is equal to $\frac{\theta}{360^\circ} \cdot \pi r^2$, where θ represents the measure of the central angle and r represents the radius of the circle.

Example 7: Find the area of the shaded region in the figure at the right. Assume that the point P is the center of the circle.

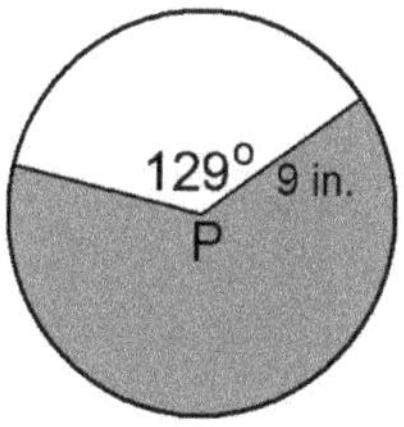

We can use the formula above to work this problem, as shown below.

$$A = \frac{\theta}{360^\circ} \cdot \pi r^2$$

$$A = \frac{231^\circ}{360^\circ} \cdot \pi(9 \text{ in.})^2$$

Note that, for this problem, $\theta = 231^\circ$ (because $360^\circ - 129^\circ = 231^\circ$) and r = 9 inches.

$$A = \frac{77}{120} \cdot \pi(81 \text{ in.}^2)$$

$$A = \frac{2079}{40}\pi \text{ in.}^2$$

Example 8: A room is 15 feet wide and 12 feet long. If carpet costs \$10 per square yard, how much will it cost to carpet the room?

We will begin by noting that the area of the room is 180 square feet. However, since the question tells us the price of the carpet is \$10 per square *yard*, we need to find the area in square yards.

To find out how many square yards this is, consider the picture below.

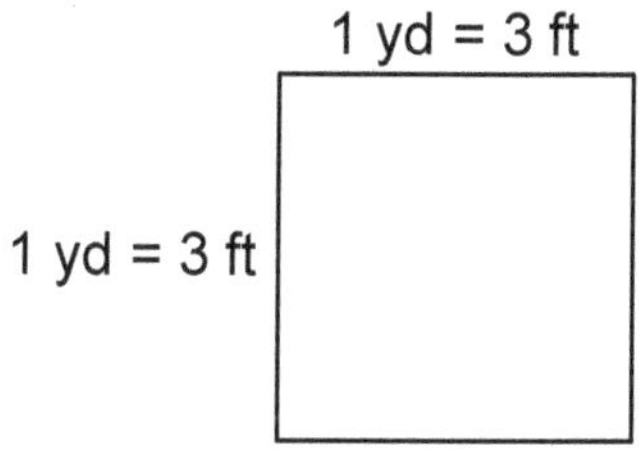

This is a picture of one square yard. We can also find the area of this square by multiplying the length of 3 feet by the width of 3 feet. Thus, 1 square yard must be equal to 9 square feet. So, to find the area of the room in square yards, we will split the 180 square feet up into groups of 9 square feet – in other words, we will divide 180 by 9. This tells us that the area of the room is 20 square yards. (By the way, you could have also worked this part of the problem by noting that 15 feet = 5 yards and 12 feet = 4 yards, and so the area of the room must equal 20 square yards.)

Since the cost of the carpet is $10 per square yard (in other words, the carpet costs $10 for every square yard), the total cost of the carpet must be $200.

Problems – Do not forget to include units in your answers!

1. In the figure below, the light horizontal and vertical lines are all 1 centimeter apart.

   What is the area of the outlined figure? ________________

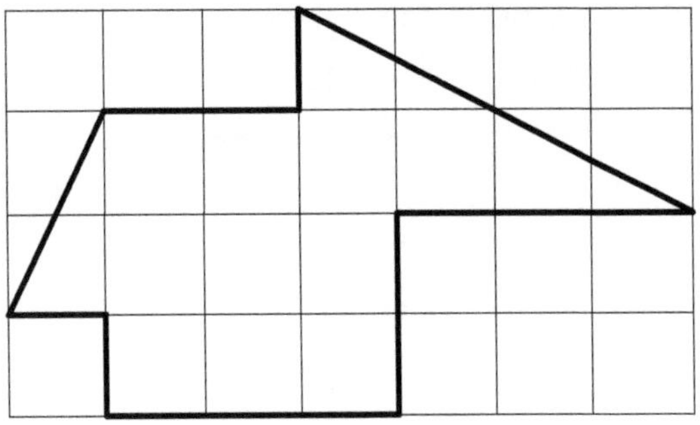

2. The figure below shows a map of a city park, and the light horizontal and vertical lines are all ½ an inch apart. In this figure, ½ an inch on the map represents 100 yards in real life. What is the area of the park in real life? ________________

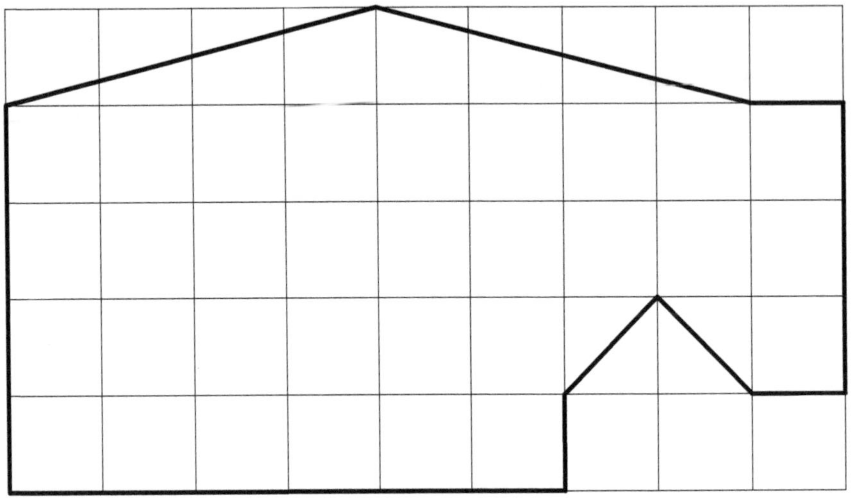

3. The figure below shows a map of a pond, and of the light horizontal and vertical lines are all 1 centimeter apart. In this figure, 1 centimeter on the map represents 10 meters in real life. Estimate the approximate area of the pond in real life.

____

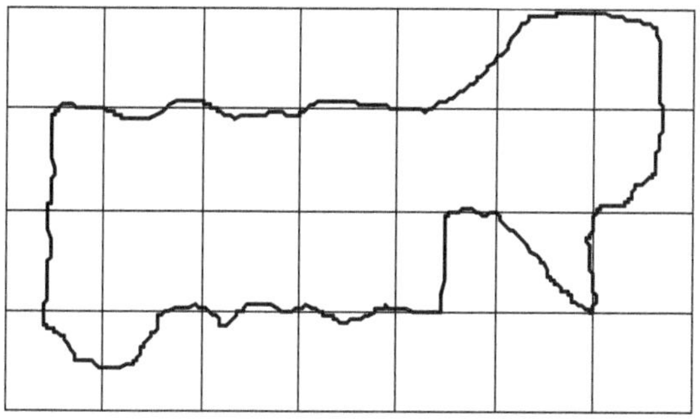

4. 1 yd^2 = __________________ ft^2

5. 1 ft^2 = __________________ in^2

6. 1 m^2 = __________________ cm^2

(Recall that 1 m = 100 cm.)

7-29. Assume that all angles that appear to be right angles are actually right angles unless otherwise stated, and assume that all curved paths are arcs of circles.

7. Find the area of the circle at the right. (Assume that the point C is the center of the circle.)__________________

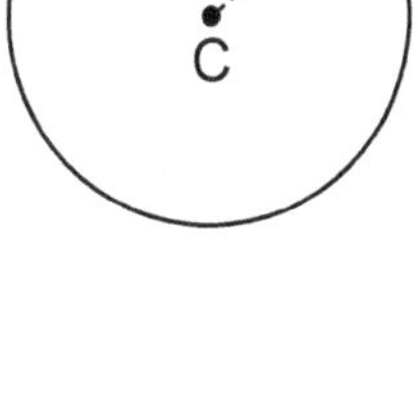

8. Find the area of the circle at the right. (Assume that the point O is the center of the circle.) ________________

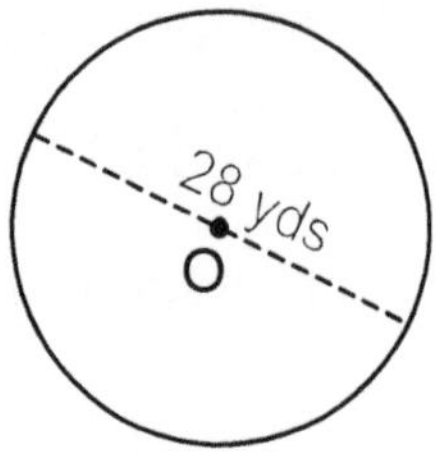

9. Find the area of the rectangle at the right.

____

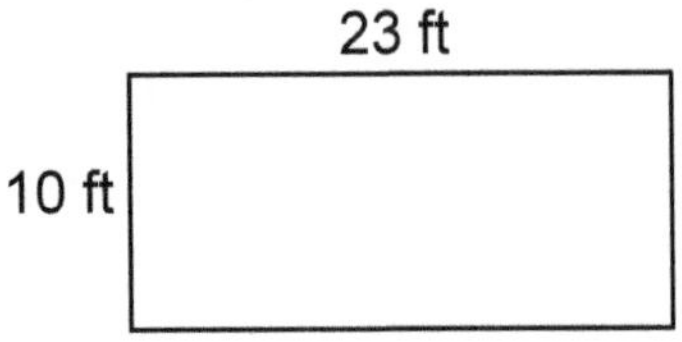

10. Find the area of the parallelogram at the right.

________________ Hint: You will need to use right triangle trigonometry to work this problem.

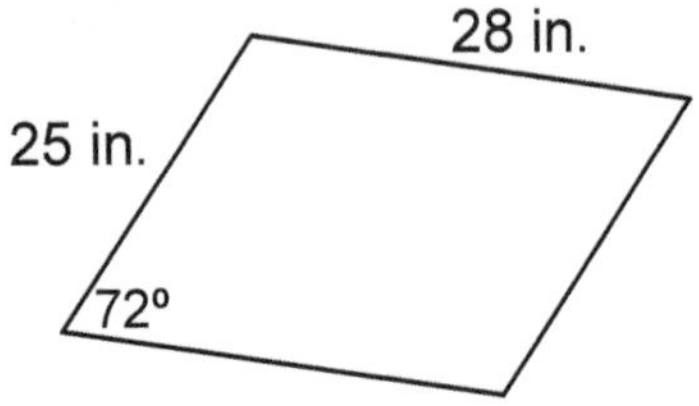

11. Find the area of the triangle at the right.

____

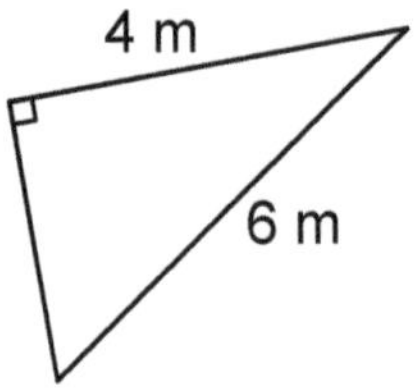

12. Find the area of the square at the right.

____

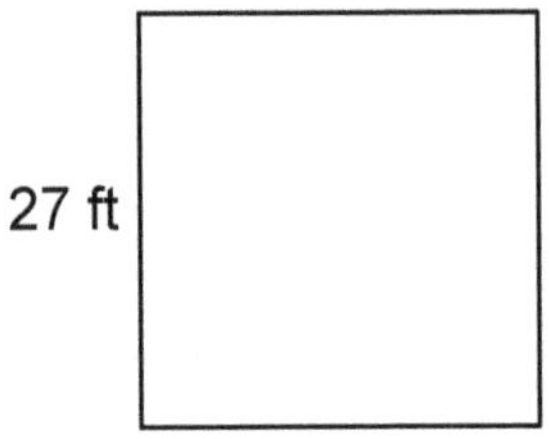

13. Find the area of the trapezoid at the right.

____

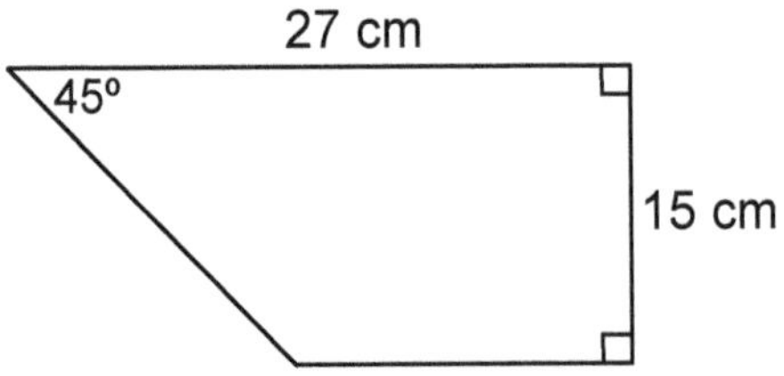

14. Find the area of the trapezoid at the right.

____

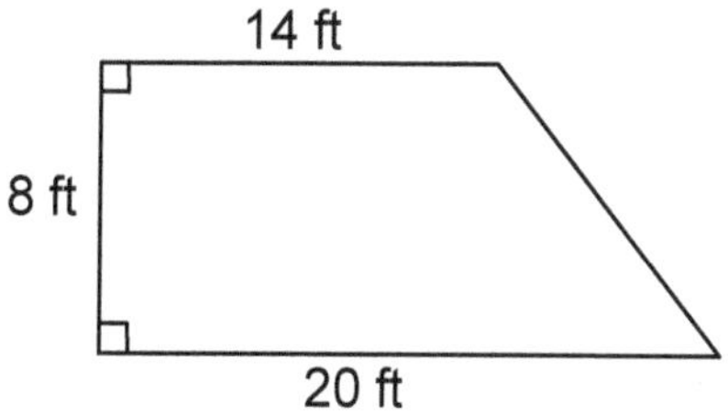

15. Find the area of the equilateral triangle at the right.

_______________ Hint: You will need to draw an altitude.

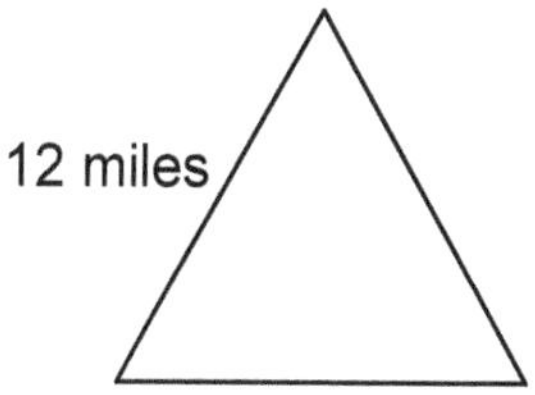

16. Find the area of the shaded region in the figure at the right. (Assume that the point M is the center of the circle.) _______________

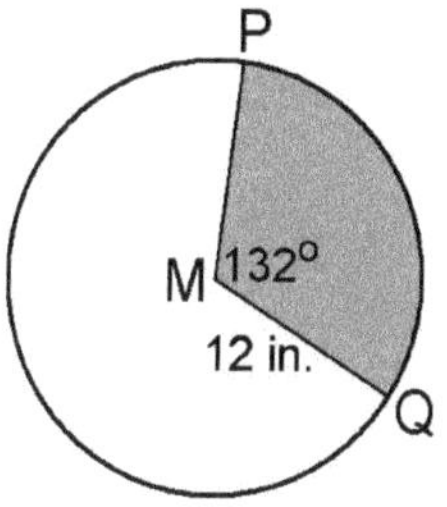

17. Find the area of the shaded region in the figure at the right. (Assume that the point N is the center of the circle.) _______________

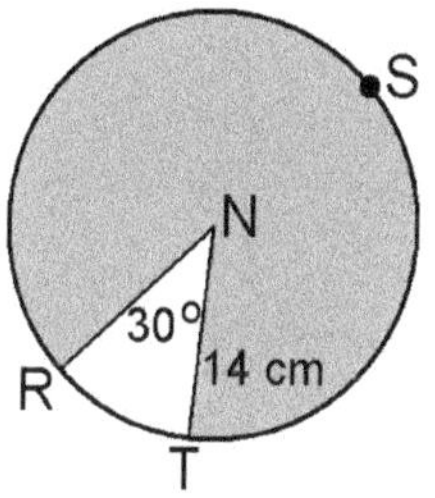

18. Find the area of the figure at the right.

____

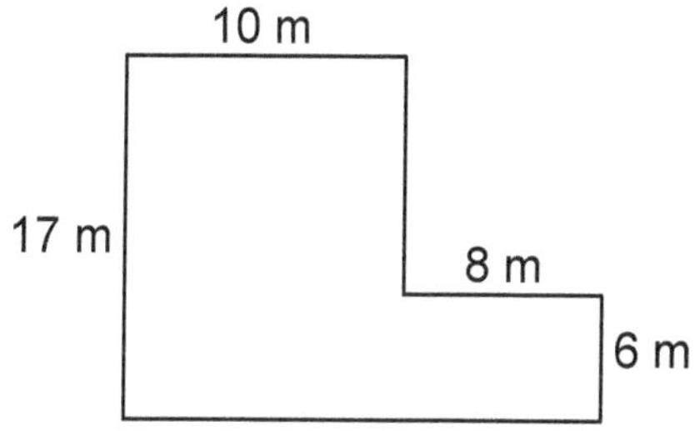

19. Find the area of the figure at the right.

____

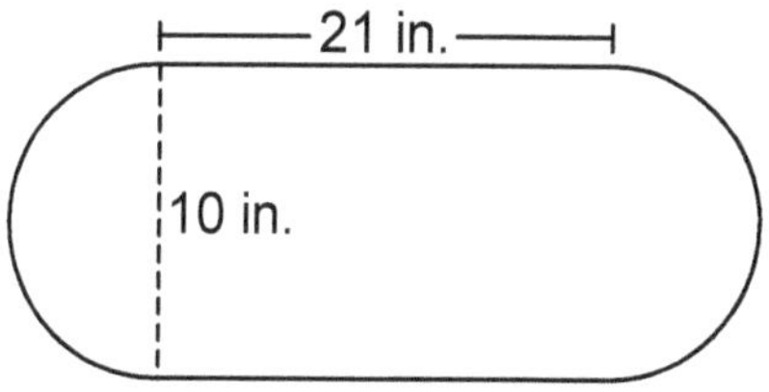

20. Find the area of the figure at the right.

____

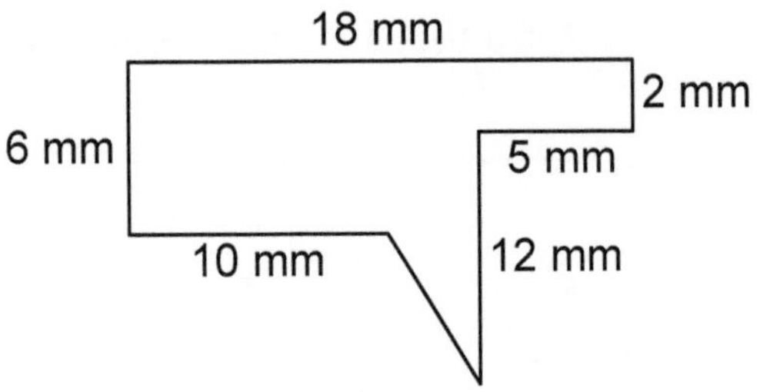

21. Find the area of the figure at the right.

____

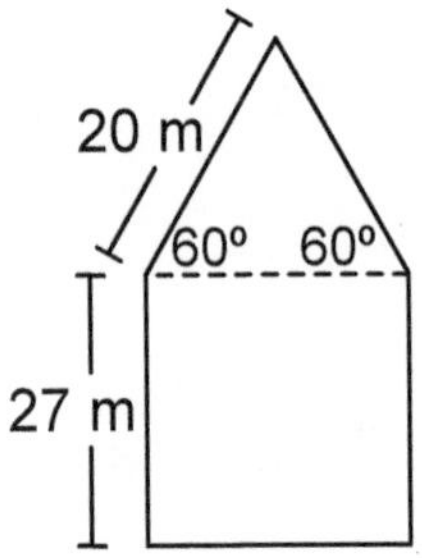

22. Find the area of the figure at the right.

____

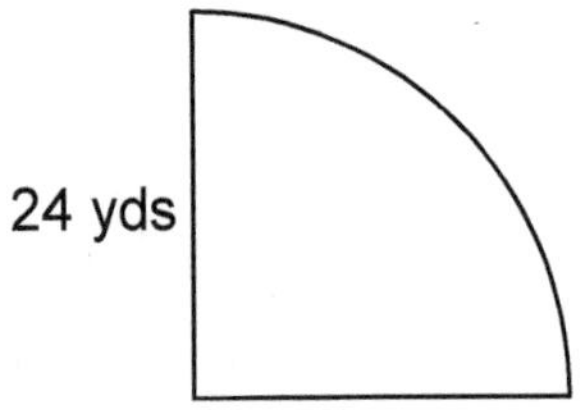

23. Find the area of the figure at the right.

____

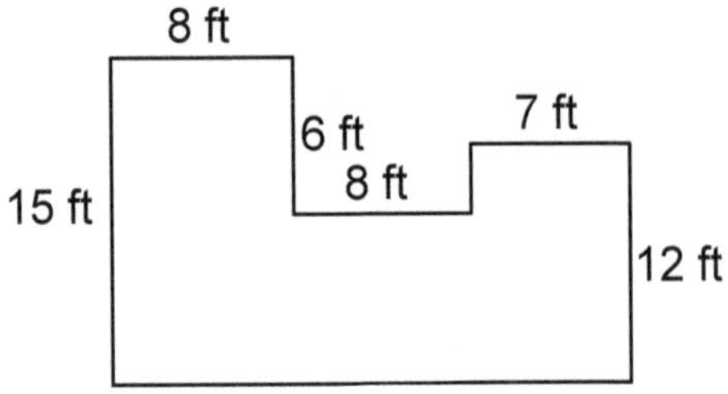

24. Find the area of the figure at the right.

____

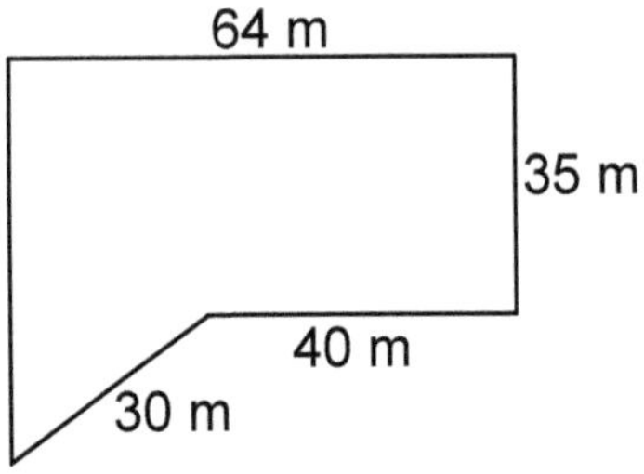

25. Find the area of the figure at the right.

____

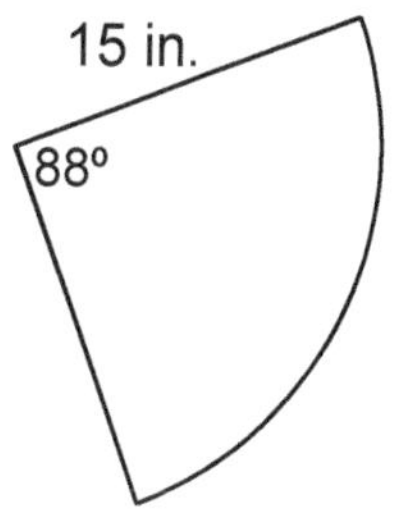

26. Find the area of the figure at the right.

____

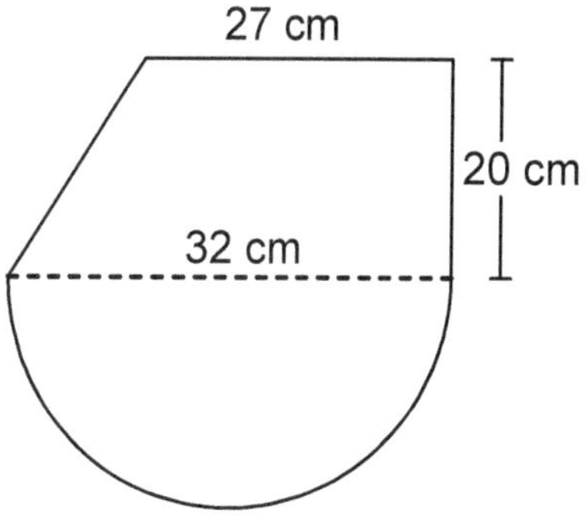

27. Find the area of the figure at the right.

____

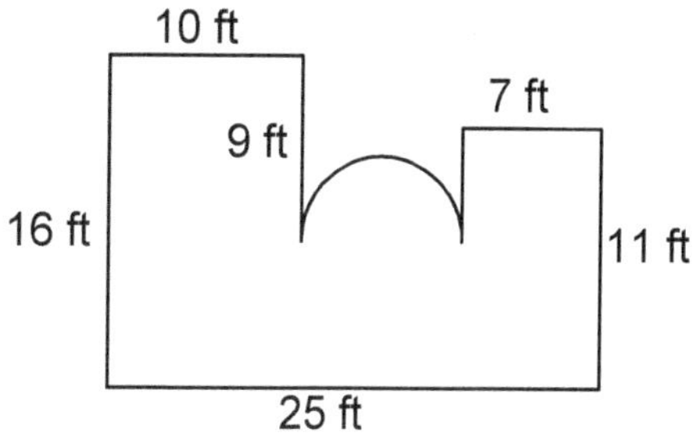

28. Find the area of the figure at the right.

____

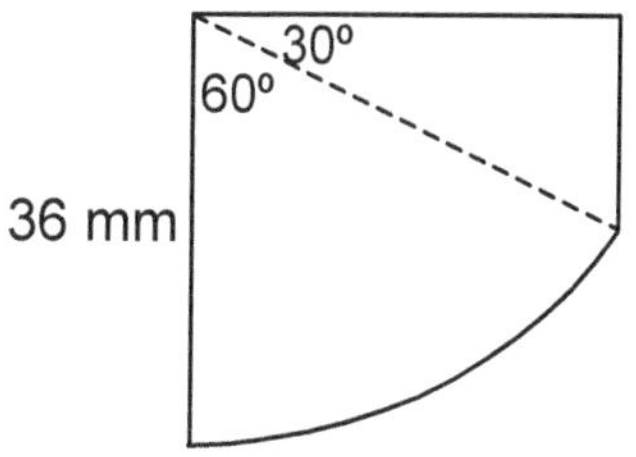

29. Find the area of the figure at the right.

____

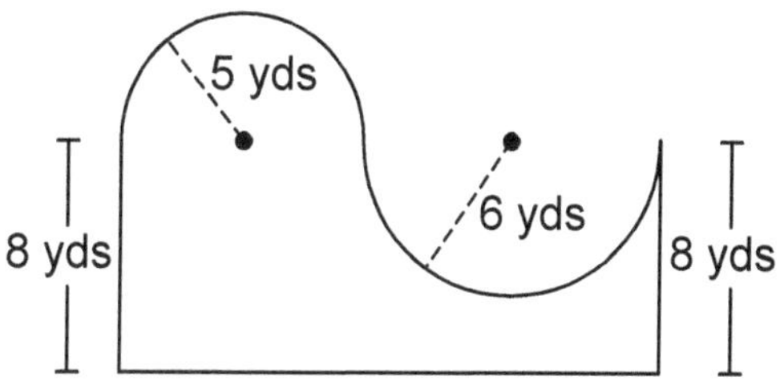

30. In the figure at the right, what is the ratio of the area of ΔTQR to the area of rectangle PQRS? ___________

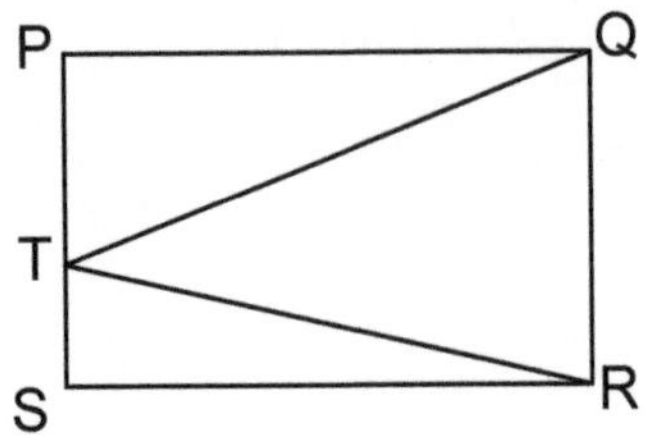

31. What is the area of a circle that has a circumference of 12π inches? ___________

32. Joel is going to stain his deck, which is 45 feet long and 20 feet wide. If one gallon of stain will cover 400 square feet, how many cans of stain does he need to buy? (Assume that he can only buy whole gallons.) ___________

33. Jose is going to build a fence for his goats. He is considering two arrangements. One is a circular fence that has a diameter of 32 feet, and the other is a rectangular fence that measures 20 feet by 34 feet (ie, it has a length of 20 feet and a width of 34 feet). Which arrangement would require more fencing material? ____________ _______________ Which would require him to sow more grass seed? _________ ___________________

34. If the area of the rectangle at the right is 384 square inches, then x = ________.

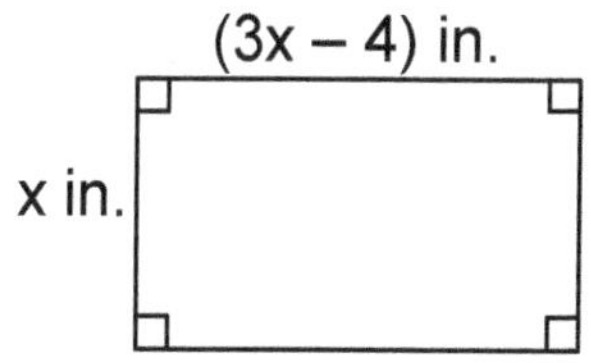

35. Mary is going to build a rectangular fence for her horses. She has 200 feet of fencing material. Make a list of some of the different dimensions she can use for her fence, and decide what dimensions she should use in order to give her horses the most room to roam.

The length should be ___________, and the width should be ___________.

36. Refer back to #35. If she decides to make a circular fence instead, what would the radius of the circle be? (Round your answer to two decimal places.) ___________

Compared to the fence with the dimensions you found in #35, would this give her horses more or less room to roam? ___________

37. The area of the rectangle at the right is 29 square yards. What would the area of the rectangle that has a length of 3x yards and 5y yards be? ___________

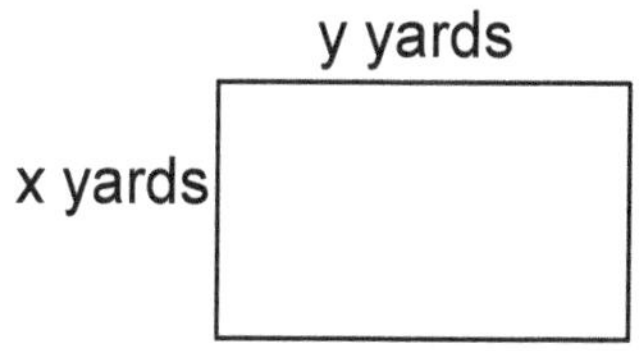

Part III – More on Area

We will begin this section with two formulas.

Area of a trapezoid = $\frac{1}{2}(h)(b_1 + b_2)$,

where h = the height of the trapezoid, b_1 = the length of the one of the bases, and b_2 = the length of the other base

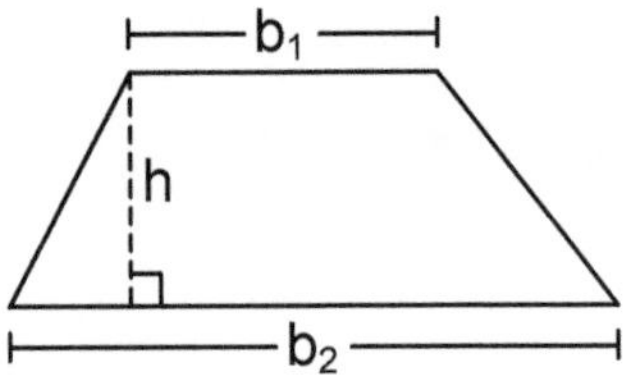

The height of a trapezoid must form a right angle with each of the bases. (Note that this is similar to the terminology we used in the last section.)

Area of a rhombus or kite = $\frac{1}{2}(d_1)(d_2)$,

where d_1 = the length of the one of the diagonals and d_2 = the length of the other diagonal

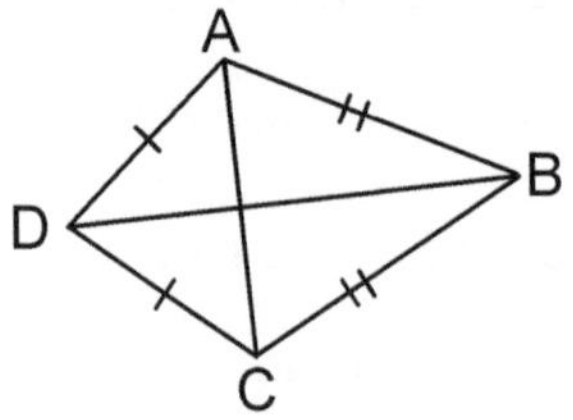

Area of kite ABCD = $\frac{1}{2}(AC)(BD)$

To see why we can use the first formula above to find the area of a trapezoid, you first need to recall that the Midsegment of a Trapezoid Theorem tells us that the length of the midsegment of a trapezoid is equal to the average of the lengths of the two bases. Now, look at the figure below. The gray rectangle has a width of $\frac{1}{2}(b_1 + b_2)$ and a length of h, and its area is equal to the area of the original trapezoid.

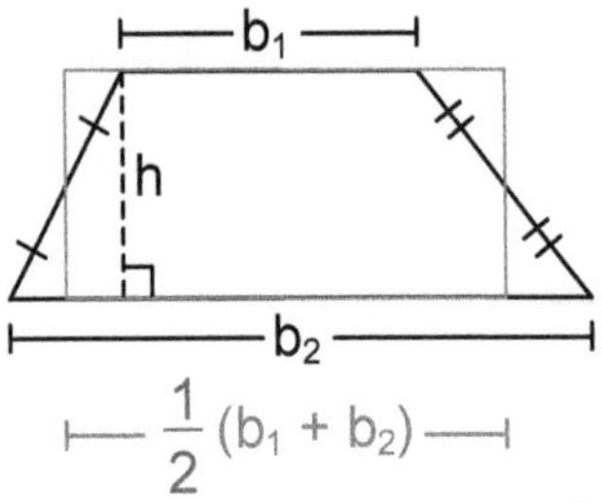

The area of the gray rectangle is equal to $\frac{1}{2}(h)(b_1 + b_2)$, and so, since the area of the gray rectangle is equal to the area of the original trapezoid, the area of the original trapezoid must equal $\frac{1}{2}(h)(b_1 + b_2)$.

To see why we can use the second formula above to find the area of a rhombus or a kite, you first need to recall that the diagonals of kites and rhombi are perpendicular to each other. Now, look at the figure on the next page. The area of kite ABCD is equal to the sum of the areas of ΔDAB and ΔDCB, and so we can find the area of kite ABCD as shown on the next page.

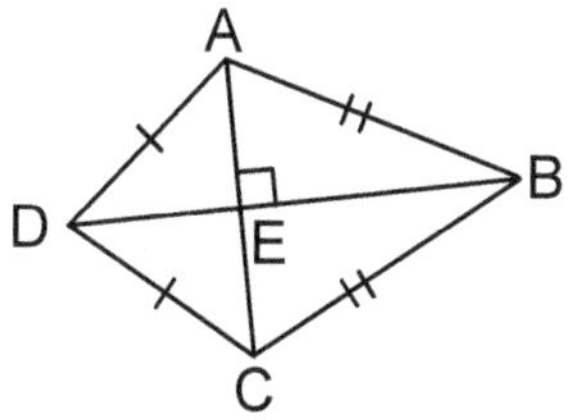

area of kite ABCD = the area of ΔDAB + the area of ΔDCB

area of kite ABCD = $\frac{1}{2}(DB)(EA) + \frac{1}{2}(DB)(EC)$

area of kite ABCD = $\frac{1}{2}(DB)(EA + EC)$ (using the Distributive Property)

area of kite ABCD = $\frac{1}{2}(DB)(AC)$ (Note that the Segment Addition Postulate tells us that AC = EA + EC.)

We can use this same formula to find the area of a rhombus because a rhombus is just like a kite – the only difference is that all the sides are congruent to each other.

Example 1: Find the area of the trapezoid at the right.

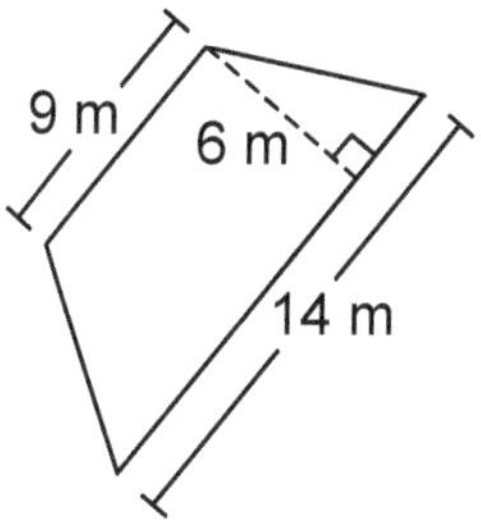

We can work this problem as shown below.

Area = $\frac{1}{2}(h)(b_1 + b_2)$

Area = $\frac{1}{2}(6\text{ m})(9\text{ m} + 14\text{ m})$

Area = $(3\text{ m})\ (23\text{ m})$

Area = 69 m^2

Example 2: If the trapezoid shown at the right has an area of 370 square feet, what is the length of $\overline{UV}$?

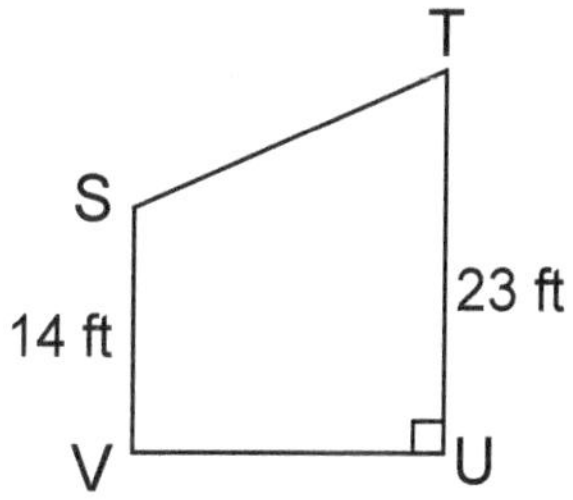

We could work this problem by splitting the trapezoid up into a rectangle and a right triangle (like we did in the last section), but the problem is much simpler if we use the formula for finding the area of a trapezoid instead.

Area of STUV = $\frac{1}{2}(h)(b_1 + b_2)$

Area of STUV = $\frac{1}{2}(UV)(SV + TU)$

$370\text{ ft}^2 = \frac{1}{2}(UV)(14\text{ ft} + 23\text{ ft})$

$370\text{ ft}^2 = \frac{1}{2}(UV)\ (37\text{ ft})$

$370\text{ ft}^2 = (UV)\ (18.5\text{ ft})$

$20\text{ ft} = UV$ (by dividing both sides by 18.5 ft)

Example 3: In the figure at the right, quadrilateral LMNO is a kite, and MN = 12 inches. Find the area of kite LMNO.

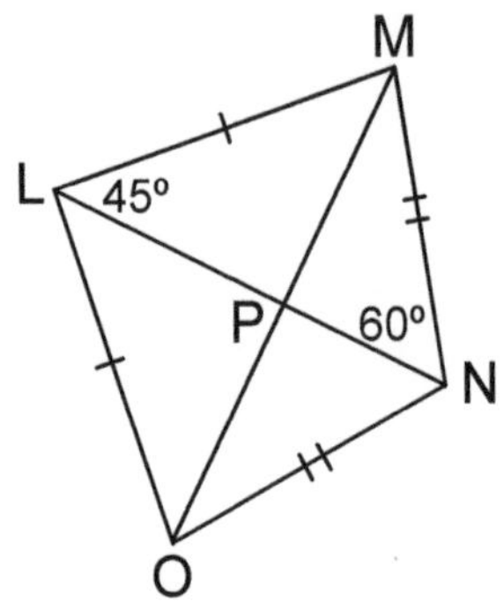

Since we know that quadrilateral LMNO is a kite, we can say that $\overline{LN} \perp \overline{OM}$. This tells us that ΔLPM and ΔLPO are both 45°-45°-90° triangles, and ΔMPN and ΔNPO are both 30°-60°-90° triangles.

Since the length of the hypotenuse in a 30°-60°-90° triangle is equal to twice the length of the shorter leg, this tells us that NP = 6 inches. The length of the longer leg in a 30°-60°-90° triangle is equal to the length of the shorter leg multiplied by $\sqrt{3}$, and so MP must equal $6\sqrt{3}$ inches. Since $\overline{MP} \cong \overline{OP}$, we can say that OM = $12\sqrt{3}$ inches.

Since the legs of a 45°-45°-90° triangle are congruent to each other, LP = $6\sqrt{3}$ inches, and so we can say that LN = $(6\sqrt{3} + 6)$ inches.

Now, we can use the formula for finding the area of a rhombus that we stated on page 593.

$$\text{Area of a rhombus} = \frac{1}{2}(d_1)(d_2)$$

$$\text{Area of rhombus LMNO} = \frac{1}{2}(OM)(LN)$$

$$\text{Area of rhombus LMNO} = \frac{1}{2}(12\sqrt{3}\text{ inches})[(6\sqrt{3} + 6)\text{ inches}]$$

$$\text{Area of rhombus LMNO} = (6\sqrt{3}\text{ inches})\ [(6\sqrt{3} + 6)\text{ inches}]$$

$$\text{Area of rhombus LMNO} = (36\sqrt{9} + 36\sqrt{3})\text{ square inches}$$

$$\text{Area of rhombus LMNO} = (108 + 36\sqrt{3})\text{ square inches}$$

Example 4: In the figure at the right, the circle is tangent to the bases of the trapezoid and has a radius with a length of 10 cm. Find the area of the shaded region.

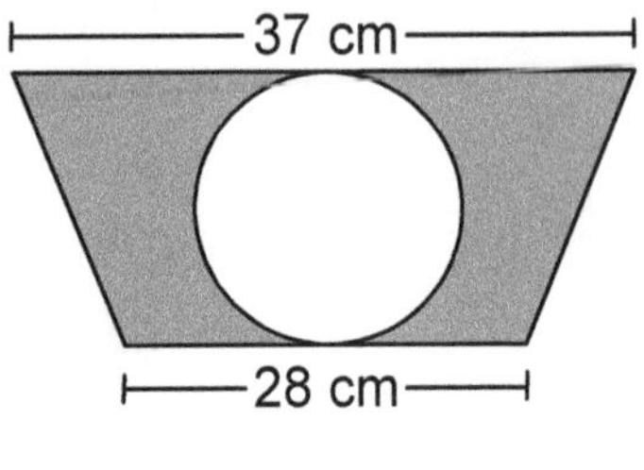

We will begin by noting that, since the radius the circle has a length of 10 cm, the height of the trapezoid must equal 20 cm. Thus, we can find the area of the trapezoid (including the area of the circle) as shown below.

$$\text{Area of the trapezoid} = \frac{1}{2}(20\text{ cm})(37\text{ cm} + 28\text{ cm})$$

$$\text{Area of the trapezoid} = 650\text{ square centimeters}$$

Now, to find the area of *only* the shaded region, we must subtract the area of the circle.

The area of the circle is equal to $\pi(10\text{ cm})^2$, or $100\pi\text{ cm}^2$, and so the area of the shaded region must equal $(650 - 100\pi)$ square centimeters.

Problems – Do not forget to include units in your answers!

1. In the figure at the right, $\overline{AB} \parallel \overline{CD}$. Find the area of quadrilateral ABCD. ________________

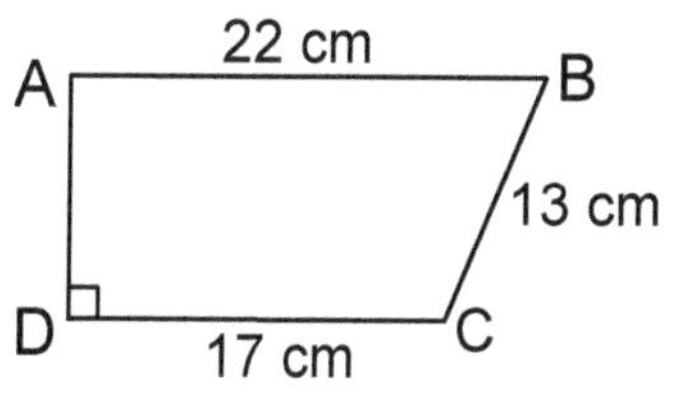

2. In the figure at the right, $\overline{EG}$, $\overline{GI}$, $\overline{HI}$, and $\overline{EH}$ are all congruent to each other. If EF = 12 m and EG = 20 m, what is the area of quadrilateral EGIH?

____

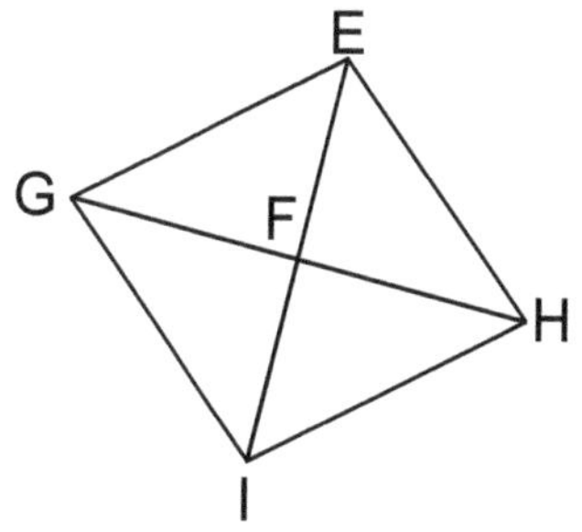

3. In the figure at the right, $\overline{JK} \cong \overline{KL}$, $\overline{JM} \cong \overline{ML}$, JN = 8 ft, and KM = 15 ft. Find the area of quadrilateral JKLM.

____

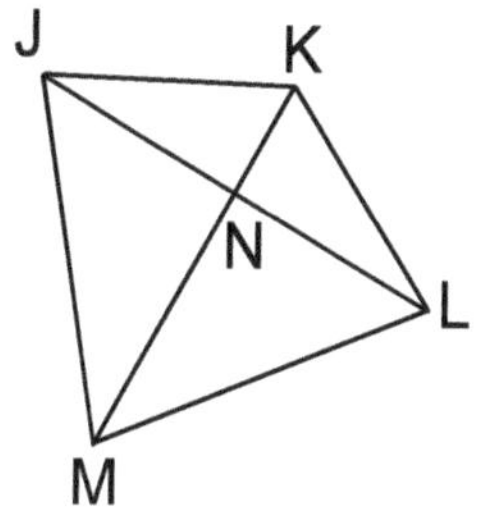

4. In the figure at the right, PR = 24 cm, $\overline{QP} \cong \overline{SP}$, and $\overline{QR} \cong \overline{SR}$. Find the area of quadrilateral PQRS.

____

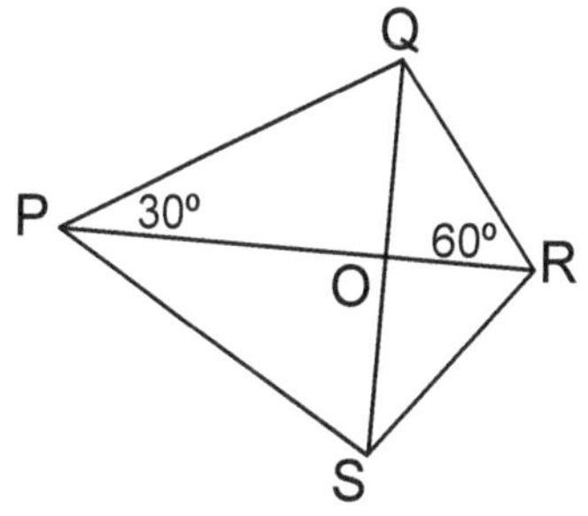

5. In the figure at the right, $\overline{TU}$, $\overline{UW}$, $\overline{WV}$, and $\overline{TV}$ are all congruent to each other. If TX = 9 yards, what is the area of quadrilateral TUVW? ________________ (Hint: You will need to use right triangle trigonometry. You may round your final answer to the nearest tenth of a square yard.)

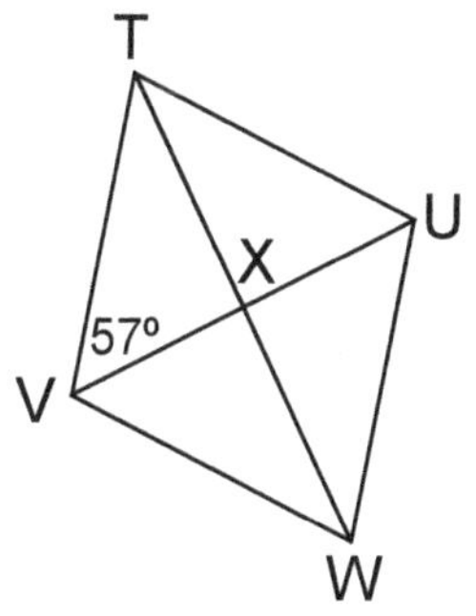

6. In the figure at the right, $\overline{YZ} \parallel \overline{AN}$. Find the area of quadrilateral YZNA. _______________ (Hint: You will need to use right triangle trigonometry. You may round your final answer to the nearest tenth of a square inch.)

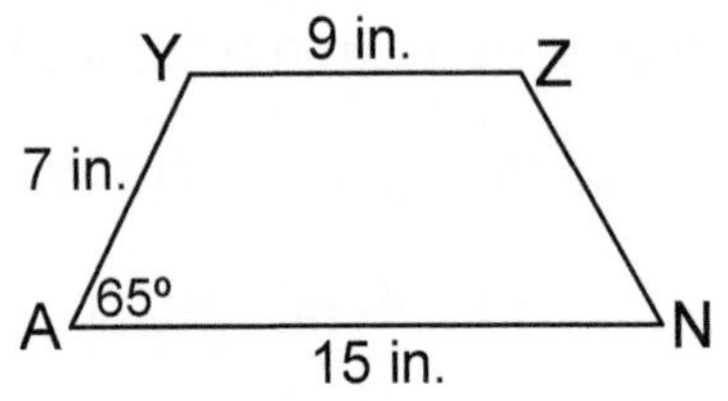

7. What is the area of the figure at the right? Assume that all angles that appear to be right angles are actually right angles. _______________

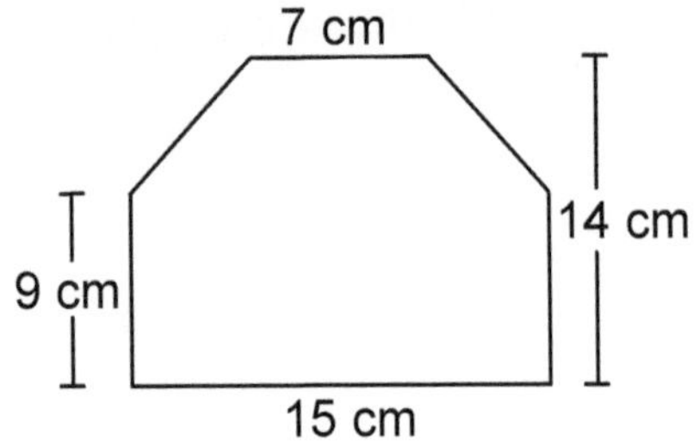

8. What is the area of the figure at the right? Assume that all angles that appear to be right angles are actually right angles. _______________

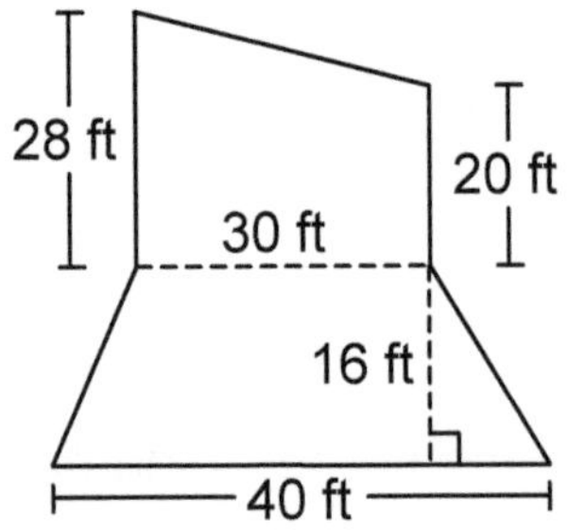

9. The trapezoid at the right has an area of 70 square yards. What is the value of x? _______________

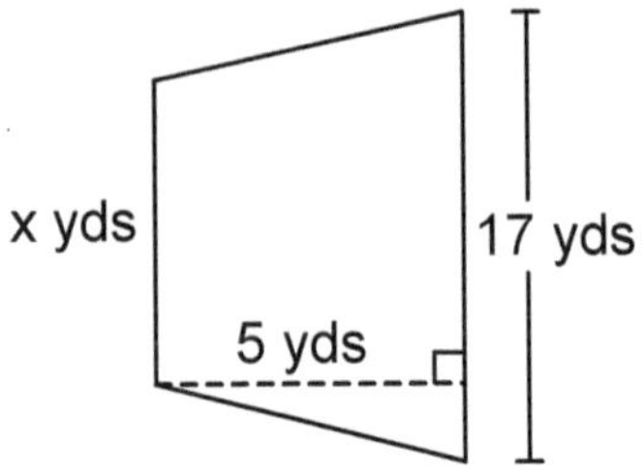

10. The trapezoid at the right has an area of 54 square miles. What is the value of y? _______________

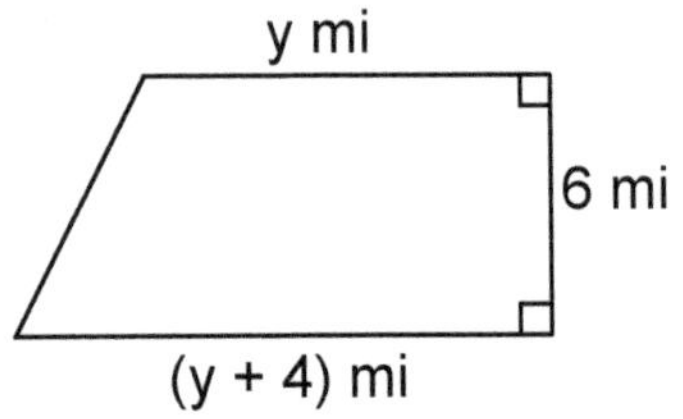

11. If the rhombus drawn at the right has an area of $32\sqrt{3}$ square inches, then the lengths of the diagonals are ________________ and ________________ Hint: Start by saying that the shorter diagonal has a length of 2y inches.

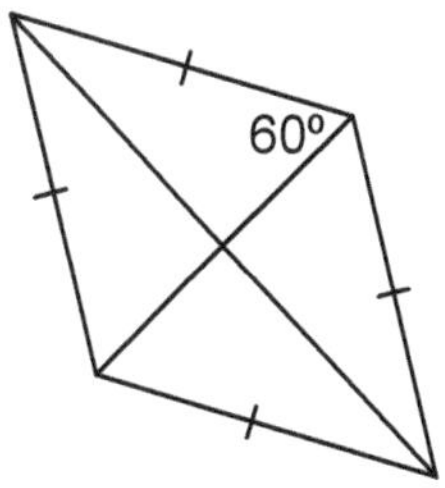

12. One of the diagonals of a certain rhombus has a length of 24 cm. If the area of the rhombus is 96 cm^2, how long is each side of the rhombus? ________________

13. One of the diagonals of a kite is 6 meters longer than twice the length of the other diagonal. If the area of the kite is 40 m^2, then the lengths of the diagonals are ________________ and ________________.

14. The length of the longer base of a trapezoid is 8 feet shorter than three times the length of the shorter base. The height of the trapezoid is 2 feet longer than the length of the shorter base, and the area of the trapezoid is equal to 64 square feet. What is the height of the trapezoid? ________________

15. What is the area of the shaded region in the figure at the right? ________________

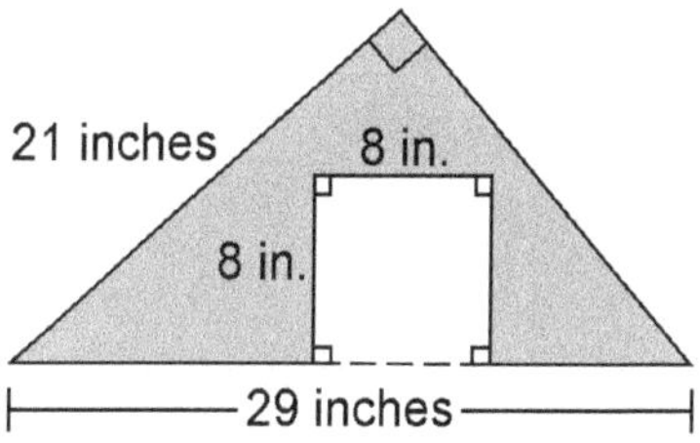

16. In the figure at the right, the longer base of the trapezoid is a diameter of the circle, and the bases of the trapezoid have lengths of 14 mm and 22 mm. _______________

Hint: You can use what you know about circles and isosceles triangles to find that the height of the trapezoid is $6\sqrt{2}$ mm.

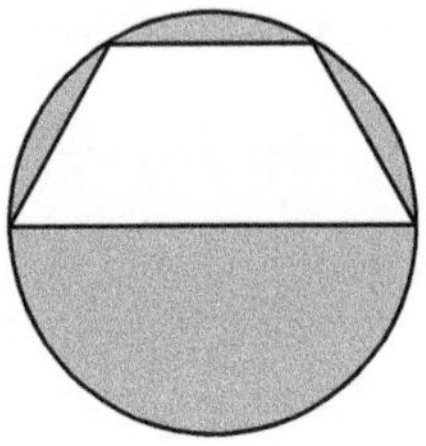

17. What is the area of the shaded region in the figure at the right? _______________

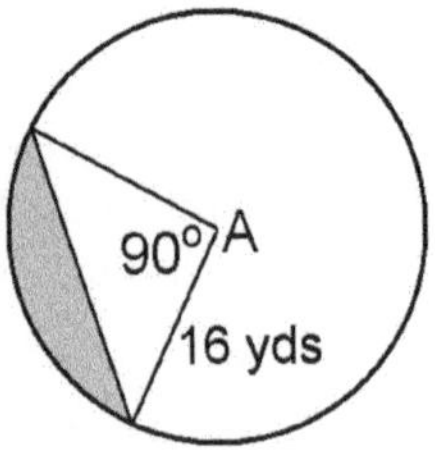

18. In the figure at the right, each of the circles is tangent to two circles and two sides of the square. If each circle has a diameter with a length of 18 yards, what is the total area of the shaded regions? _________________

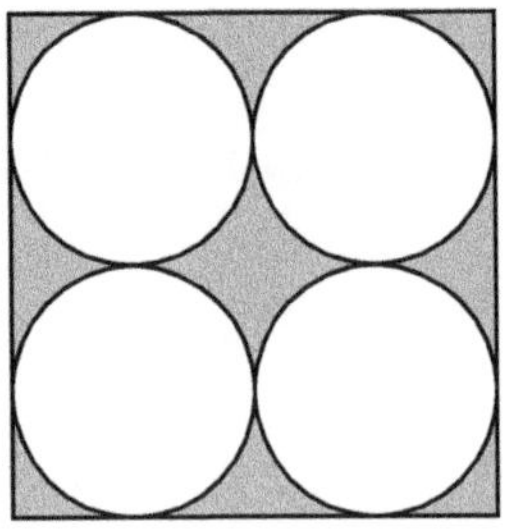

19. What is the area of the shaded region in the figure at the right? _________________

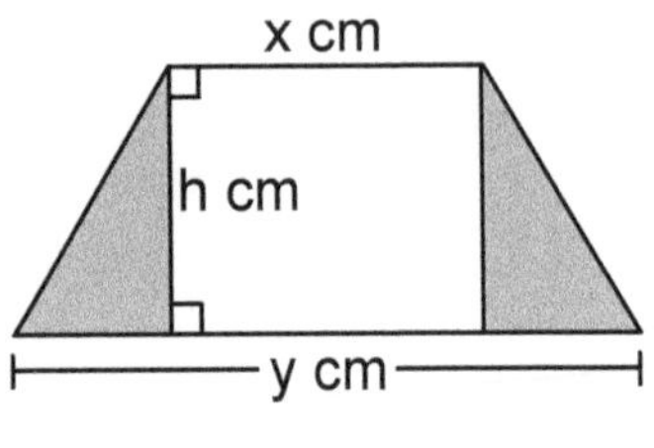

20. What is the area of the shaded region in the figure at the right? _________________

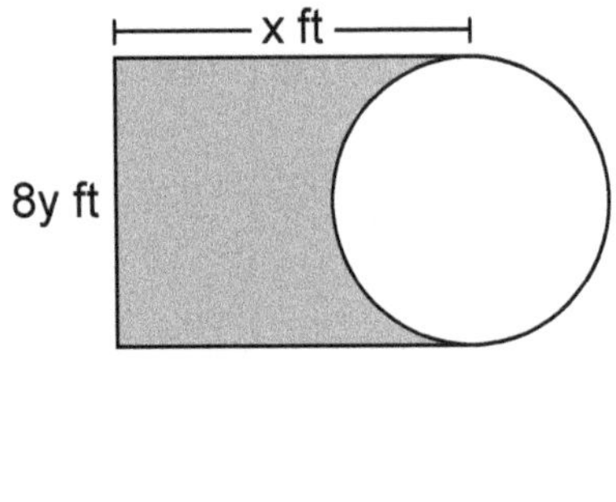

21. In the figure at the right, HF = 16 inches, EF = EH = 17 inches, and FG = GH = 10 inches. If $\overline{EG}$ is a diameter of the circle, then the area of the shaded region is ________________.

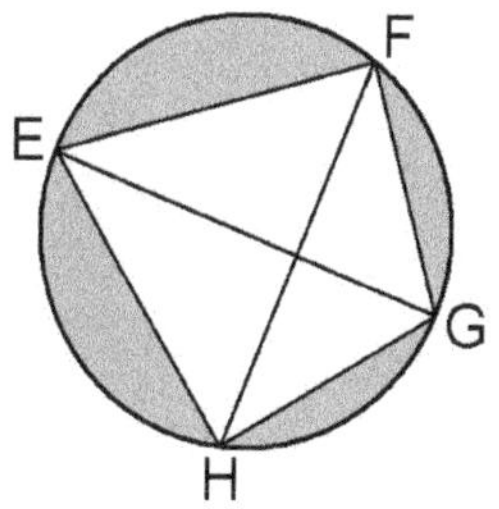

22. In the figure at the right, RS = 3 ft, ST = 15 ft, and the area of the shaded region is 11π ft^2. What is the area of the unshaded region? ________________

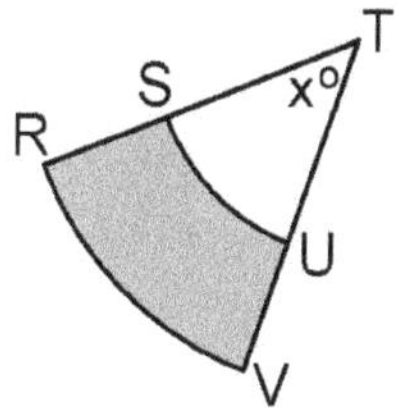

23. In the figure at the right, the area of the shaded region is 16π mm^2, and the radius of the larger circle has a length of 5 mm. What is the area of the smaller circle? ________________ What is the length of the radius of the smaller circle? ________________

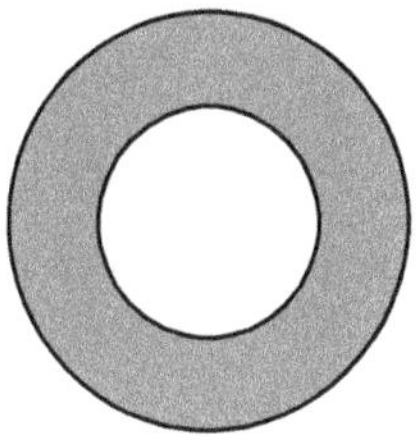

24. In the figure at the right, the area of the shaded region is 816 square inches. What is the perimeter of the square? ________________

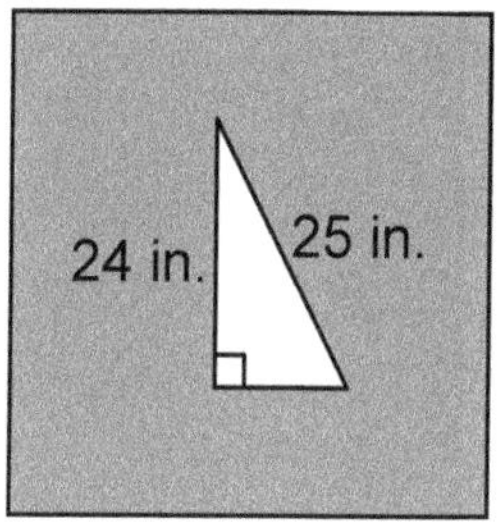

25. In the figure at the right, both quadrilaterals ACEG and BDFH are squares, and BD = 25 meters. If the area of the shaded region is 275 square meters, what is the length of $\overline{AC}$? ________________

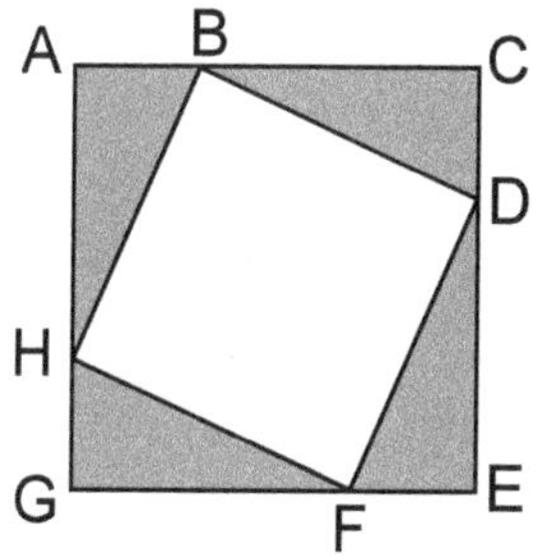

Part IV – Finding the Area of a Regular Polygon

In this section, we will discuss how we can find the area of a regular polygon. (Recall that a polygon is called a regular polygon if and only if it is both equilateral and equiangular.) We will begin with three definitions.

A point is the center of a regular polygon if and only if it is equidistant from each of the vertices. The center of a regular polygon is also the center of the circle that can be circumscribed around the outside of the polygon.

A segment is a called a radius of a regular polygon if and only if one of its endpoints is the center of the polygon and the other endpoint is a vertex of the polygon. The length of such a segment is also called the radius of the polygon.

The apothem of a regular polygon is the defined as the length of the segment that connects the center of the polygon to the midpoint of a side of the polygon. (This segment will also be perpendicular to the side of the polygon.)

Example 1: If each side of a regular hexagon has a length of 14 inches, what is the area of the hexagon?

We will begin by drawing a regular hexagon that has sides that are 14 inches long, and we will also draw all of the radii of the hexagon.

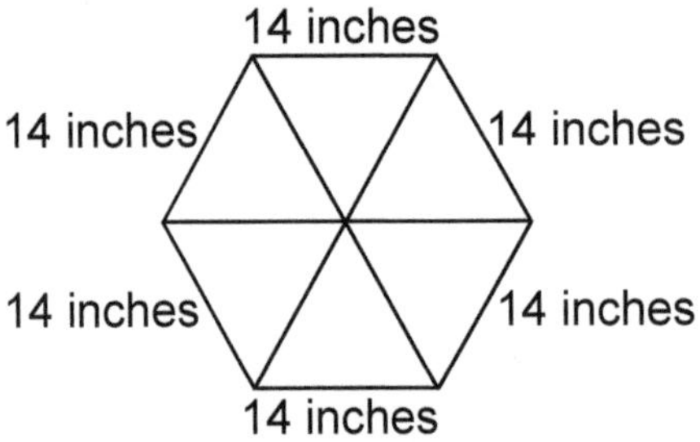

Next, we will find the measures of each of the central angles. Recall that there are 360° in a full circle, and note that, since the hexagon is a *regular* hexagon, each of the central angles must congruent to each other. Therefore, each of the central angles must have a measure of 360° ÷ 6, or 60°.

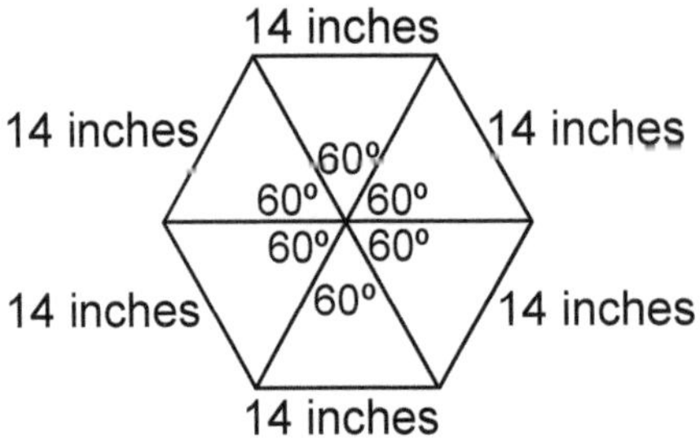

Now, let's look at one of these triangles. If we draw a segment that starts at the center of the hexagon and ends at the midpoint of one of the sides, it will be perpendicular to one of the sides of this hexagon, and it will split the corresponding central angle into two congruent angles that measure 30° each. This gives us two 30°-60°-90° triangles, as shown below.*

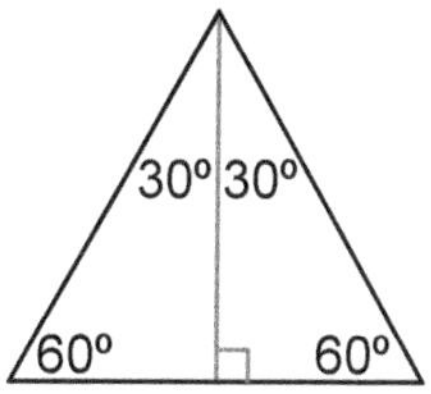

Next, we will note that the apothem (illustrated by the gray segment in the figure above) must equal $7\sqrt{3}$ inches. Thus, the area of this triangle must equal $\frac{1}{2}$(14 inches)($7\sqrt{3}$ inches), or $49\sqrt{3}$ square inches.

Since the hexagon is made up of 6 of these triangles, the area of the entire hexagon must equal $6 \cdot 49\sqrt{3}$ square inches, or $294\sqrt{3}$ square inches.

The thought process that we used to find the area of this hexagon gives rise to the following formula.

> The area of a regular polygon is equal to $\frac{1}{2}$(a)(s)(n), or, equivalently, $\frac{1}{2}$(a)(P), where
>
> a = apothem,
> s = length of a side of the polygon,
> n = number of sides of the polygon, and
> P = perimeter of the polygon

Example 2: A regular pentagon has a radius of 8 feet. What is the area of the pentagon?

We will begin by drawing a picture.

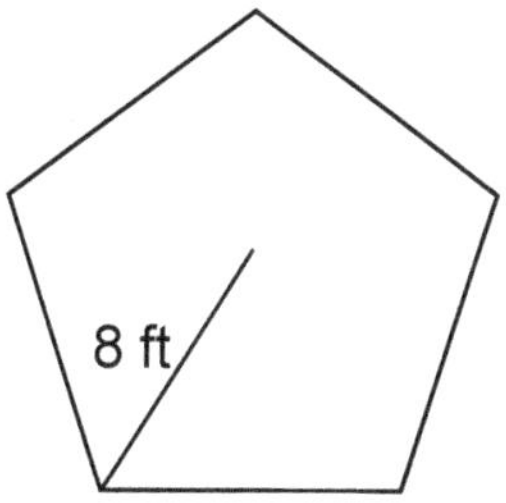

Now, just like we did in the last example, we will draw all the radii of the pentagon. We will also note that each of the central angles must have measures of 360° ÷ 5, or 72°.

*Alternatively, we could have used the following thought process to find the measures of the angles in one of these triangles. As we discussed in Chapter 6, the sum of the measures of the interior angles of a regular polygon is equal to 180°(n – 2), where n represents the number of sides of the polygon. Thus, each interior angle of the hexagon must have a measure of 720° ÷ 6, or 120°. Since each triangle splits each interior angle of the hexagon into two congruent angles, the angles that we said had measures of 60° in the figure at the top of the page must, in fact, have measures of 60°.

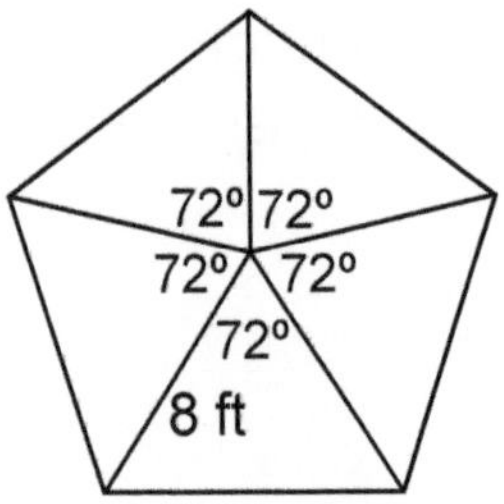

Now, let's look at one of these triangles. We can label the angles of one of these triangles as shown below.

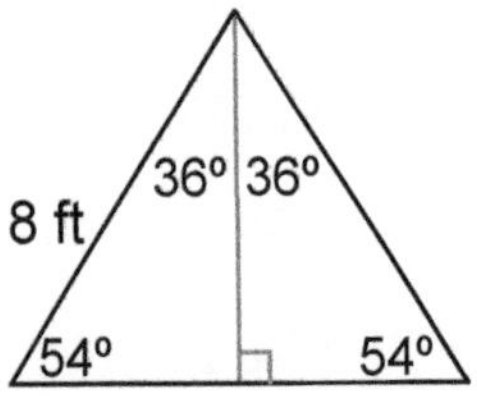

Now, we can use right triangle trigonometry to say that the apothem (illustrated by the gray segment in the triangle above) is equal to approximately 6.4721 feet, and each side of the pentagon must have a length of approximately 9.4046 feet. (To see why each side of the pentagon must have a length of approximately 9.4046 feet, note that each half of the base in the triangle above has a length of approximately 4.7023 feet, and, to find the length of a side of the pentagon, we must multiply this answer by 2.)

Now, we can use either of the formulas for the area of a regular polygon that we stated on the previous page.

$$\text{Area of this pentagon} \approx \frac{1}{2}(6.4721 \text{ ft})(5)(9.4046 \text{ ft})$$

$$\text{Area of this pentagon} \approx 152.2 \text{ ft}^2$$

(Like we said in the sections involving trigonometry in Chapter 8, the answers you get may vary slightly from the answers we get because of rounding differences, but your answers should not vary by more than a few tenths.)

Problems:

1-6. For these problems, leave your answers in simplified radical form where necessary.

1. What is the area of a regular hexagon that has a radius of 18 meters?

____

2. What is the area of a square that has a radius of 10 inches?

____

3. What is the area of an equilateral triangle that has an apothem equal to 16 yards? ____________________

4. What is the area of a regular hexagon that has an apothem equal to $5\sqrt{3}$ cm?

____

5. If a regular hexagon has a perimeter of $48\sqrt{3}$ millimeters, what is the area of the hexagon? ____________________

6. If each side of an equilateral triangle has a length of $4\sqrt{6}$ feet on each side, what is the area of the triangle? ____________________

7-18. For these problems, you may round your final answers to the nearest tenth.

7. What is the area of a regular octagon that has a radius of 2 kilometers?

____

8. What is the area of a regular decagon that has a radius of 7 feet?

____

9. What is the area of a regular nonagon that has a radius of 5 inches?

____

10. What is the area of a regular dodecagon that has an apothem equal to 8 centimeters? ____________________

11. What is the area of a regular pentagon that has an apothem equal to 6 yards?

____

12. What is the area of a regular decagon that has an apothem equal to 16 meters?

____

13. What is the area of a regular pentagon that has a length of 3 miles on each side? ____________________

14. What is the area of a regular octagon that has a length of 14 feet on each side?

____

15. What is the area of a regular nonagon that has a perimeter of 72 inches?

____

16. What is the area of a regular pentagon that has a perimeter of 100 millimeters?

____

17. What is the area of a regular dodecagon that has a perimeter of 192 yards?

____

18. What is the area of a regular 15-gon that has a perimeter of 150 meters?

____

19-22. For these problems, leave your answers in simplified radical form where necessary.

19. In the figure at the right, the quadrilateral is a square, and the hexagon is a regular hexagon. What is the area of the shaded region? ____________________

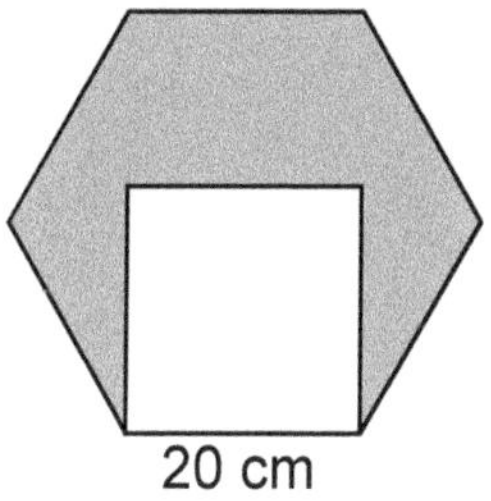

20. The figure at the right shows a regular hexagon inscribed inside another regular hexagon, and the vertices of the smaller hexagon are the midpoints of the sides of the larger hexagon. What is the total area of the shaded regions? (Note that the apothem of the larger hexagon is equal to the length of the radius of the smaller hexagon.) ____________________

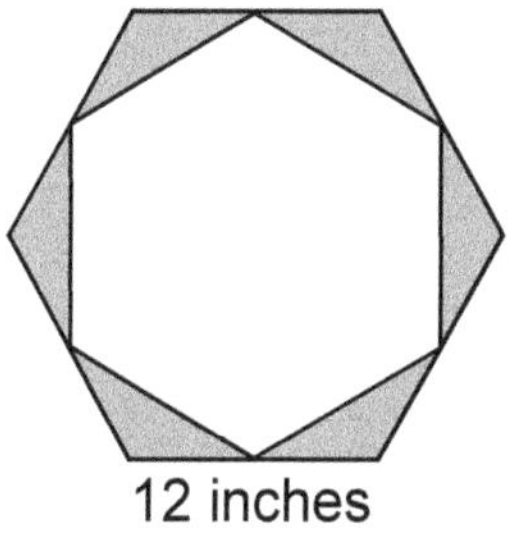

21. In the figure at the right, the hexagon is a regular hexagon. What is the total area of the shaded regions?

____

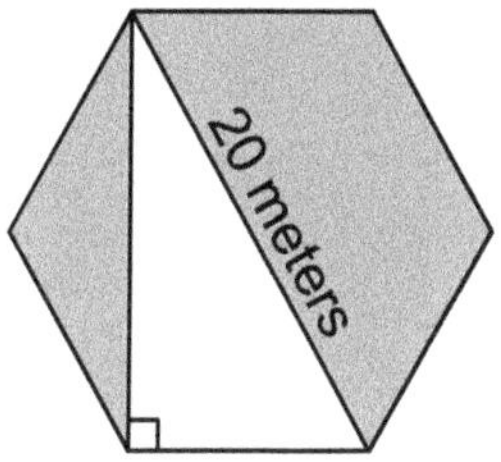

22. The figure at the right shows a regular hexagon inscribed inside a circle. If the radius of the circle is 16 feet, what is the total area of the shaded regions? ____________________

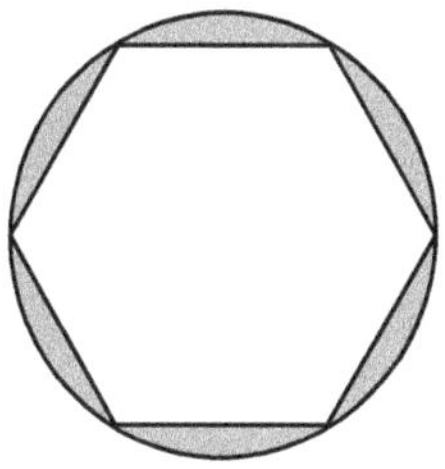

23-26. For these questions, round your final answers to the nearest tenth.

23. In the figure at the right, the sides of the octagon are tangent to the circle. If the radius of the circle is 4 meters, what is the total area of the shaded regions?

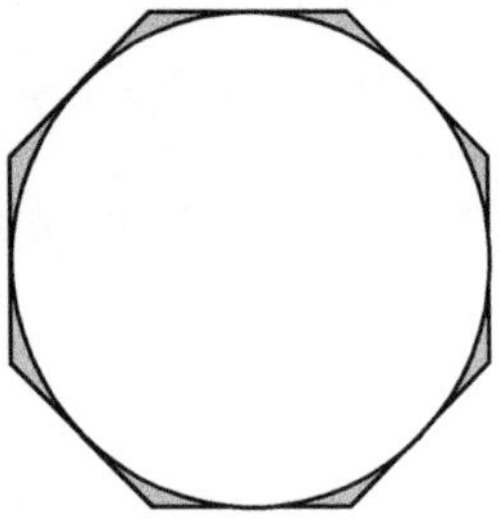

____

24. In the figure at the right, the quadrilateral is a square, and the octagon is a regular octagon. If each side of the square has a length of $5\sqrt{2}$ feet, what is the total area of the shaded regions? ____________________

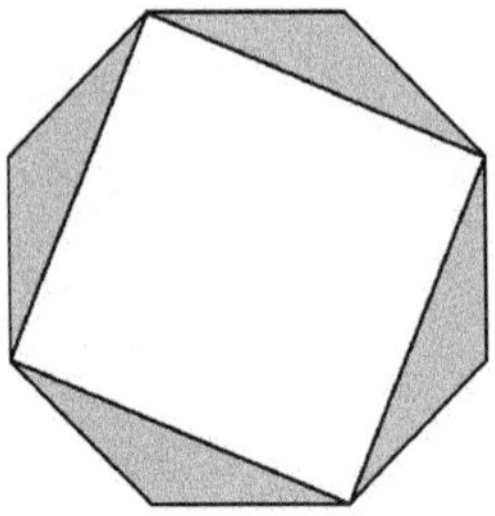

25. In the figure at the right, the triangle is an equilateral triangle, and the pentagon is a regular pentagon. What is the area of the shaded region? ____________________

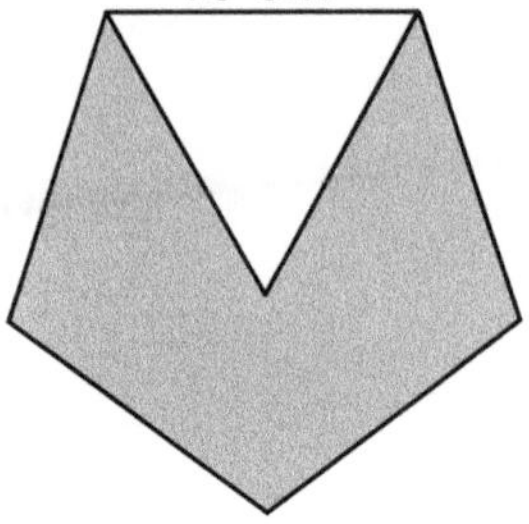

26. In the figure at the right, the pentagon is a regular pentagon, and the triangles are all isosceles triangles. What is the total area of the shaded regions?

____

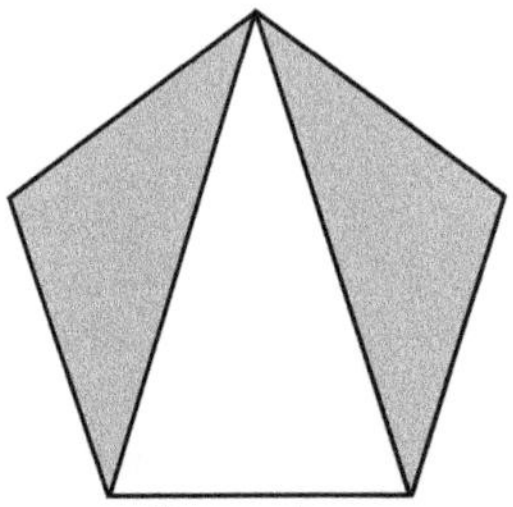

Part V – Finding the Areas and Perimeters of Congruent and Similar Figures

We will begin this section with two theorems.

If two polygons are congruent, then their perimeters are equal, and their areas are also equal.

If two polygons are similar and two corresponding sides have a ratio of $a:b$, then their perimeters also have a ratio of $a:b$, and their areas have a ratio of $a^2:b^2$.

It is not hard to see why, if two polygons are congruent, then their perimeters and areas are equal. After all, if two polygons are congruent, then their corresponding sides and angles are congruent, and so we would have to use the same methods to calculate the areas and perimeters of the figures.

Now, let's talk about why, if two polygons are similar and two corresponding sides have a ratio of $a:b$, then their perimeters also have a ratio of $a:b$, and their areas have a ratio of $a^2:b^2$.

Example 1: Prove that, If two polygons are similar and two corresponding sides have a ratio of $a:b$, then their perimeters also have a ratio of $a:b$.

We will begin by drawing a picture that describes the part of this theorem that follows the "if." (We will draw two similar pentagons; if the figures are triangles, quadrilaterals, or any other polygons, then the proof is very similar.)

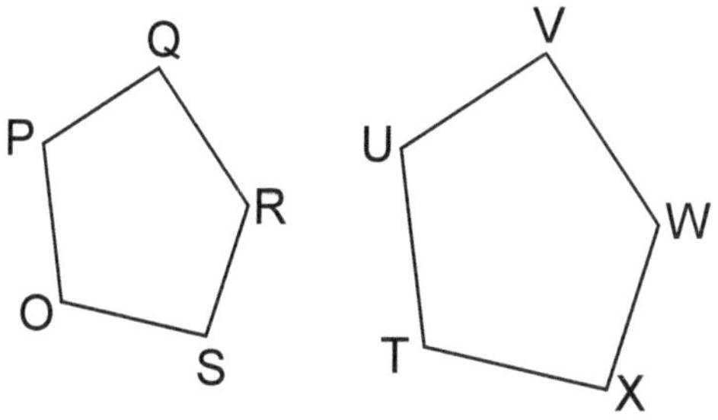

Now, we can say that we are given that pentagon OPQRS ~ pentagon TUVWX, and we want to prove that $\frac{\text{perimeter of OPQRS}}{\text{perimeter of TUVWX}} = \frac{OP}{TU} = \frac{PQ}{UV} = \frac{QR}{VW} = \frac{RS}{WX} = \frac{SO}{XT}$.

The definition of similar polygons tells us that $\frac{OP}{TU} = \frac{PQ}{UV} = \frac{QR}{VW} = \frac{RS}{WX} = \frac{SO}{XT}$.

We will let k equal each of these ratios (i.e., $k = \frac{OP}{TU}$, $k = \frac{PQ}{UV}$, and so on). Then, by the Multiplication Property of Equality, k(TU) = OP, k(UV) = PQ, k(VW) = QR, k(WX) = RS, and k(XT) = SO.

Next, we will note that the definition of the perimeter of a polygon tells us that the perimeter of pentagon TUVWX = TU + UV + VW + WX + XT and that the perimeter of pentagon OPQRS = OP + PQ + QR + RS + SO. Then, by the

Substitution Property of Equality, we can say that the perimeter of pentagon OPQRS = k(TU) + k(UV) + k(VW) + k(WX) + k(XT). Then, by the distributive Property, the perimeter of pentagon OPQRS = k(TU + UV + VW + WX + XT).

Now, we can use the Substitution Property of Equality again to say that $\frac{\text{perimeter of OPQRS}}{\text{perimeter of TUVWX}} = \frac{k(TU+UV+VW+WX+XT)}{TU+UV+VW+WX+XT}$. Since we can reduce the fraction $\frac{k(TU+UV+VW+WX+XT)}{TU+UV+VW+WX+XT}$ to k by dividing both the numerator and denominator by (TU + UV + VW + WX + XT), the Substitution Property of Equality tells us that $\frac{\text{perimeter of OPQRS}}{\text{perimeter of TUVWX}} = k$.

Finally, we will use the Substitution Property of Equality one more time to say that $\frac{\text{perimeter of OPQRS}}{\text{perimeter of TUVWX}} = \frac{OP}{TU} = \frac{PQ}{UV} = \frac{QR}{VW} = \frac{RS}{WX} = \frac{SO}{XT}$.

Example 2: Prove that, if two rectangles are similar and two corresponding sides have a ratio of $a:b$, then their areas have a ratio of $a^2:b^2$.

As usual, we will begin by drawing a picture that describes the part of the theorem that follows the "if."

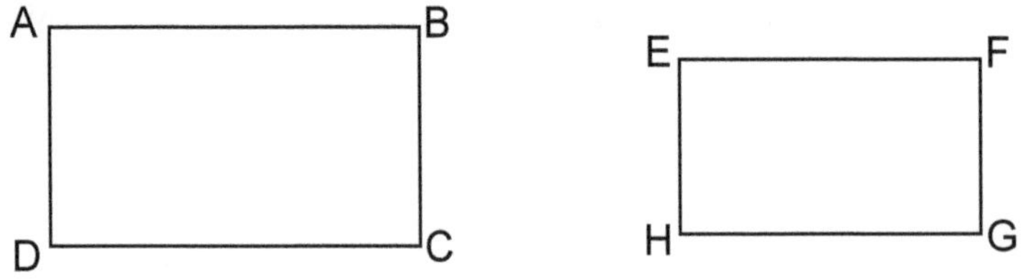

Now, we can say that we are given that rectangle ABCD ~ rectangle EFGH, and we want to prove that $\frac{\text{area of ABCD}}{\text{area of EFGH}} = \frac{(AB)^2}{(EF)^2} = \frac{(BC)^2}{(FG)^2} = \frac{(CD)^2}{(GH)^2} = \frac{(DA)^2}{(HE)^2}$.

The definition of similar polygons tells us that $\frac{AB}{EF} = \frac{BC}{FG} = \frac{CD}{GH} = \frac{DA}{HE}$. We will let n equal each of these ratios (i.e., $n = \frac{AB}{EF}$, $n = \frac{BC}{FG}$, and so on). Then, by the Multiplication Property of Equality, n(EF) = AB and n(FG) = BC.

Next, we will note that the definition of the area of a rectangle us that the area of rectangle ABCD = (AB)(AD) and also that the area of rectangle EFGH = (EF)(EH). Then, by the Substitution Property of Equality, we can say that the area of rectangle ABCD = n(EF) • n(EH), or n^2(EF)(EH).

Now, we can use the Substitution Property of Equality again to say that $\frac{\text{area of ABCD}}{\text{area of EFGH}} = \frac{n^2(EF)(GH)}{(EF)(GH)}$. Since we can reduce the fraction $\frac{n^2(EF)(GH)}{(EF)(GH)}$ to

n^2 by dividing both the numerator and denominator by (EF)(GH), the Substitution Property of Equality tells us that $\frac{\text{area of ABCD}}{\text{area of EFGH}} = n^2$.

Since we said earlier that $n = \frac{AB}{EF} = \frac{BC}{FG} = \frac{CD}{GH} = \frac{DA}{HE}$, we can use the Multiplication Property of Equality to say that $n^2 = \frac{AB}{EF}(n) = \frac{BC}{FG}(n) = \frac{CD}{GH}(n) = \frac{DA}{HE}(n)$. Then, by the Substitution Property, $\frac{\text{area of ABCD}}{\text{area of EFGH}} = \frac{(AB)^2}{(EF)^2} = \frac{(BC)^2}{(FG)^2} = \frac{(CD)^2}{(GH)^2} = \frac{(DA)^2}{(HE)^2}$.

Technically, of course, this example only proves this part of the theorem for rectangles. However, the proof of this part of the theorem gets significantly more complicated when we try to prove this theorem part of the theorem for *all* types of polygons, and so we will not prove this part of the theorem for all types of polygons here.

Now, let's look at some examples that illustrate how we can use these theorems.

Example 3: In the figure at the right, $\Delta YOJ \sim \Delta VZL$, and ΔYOJ has an area of 31 cm^2 and a perimeter of 24 cm. Find the area and the perimeter of ΔVZL. Round the answers to the nearest tenth of a centimeter or square centimeter where necessary.

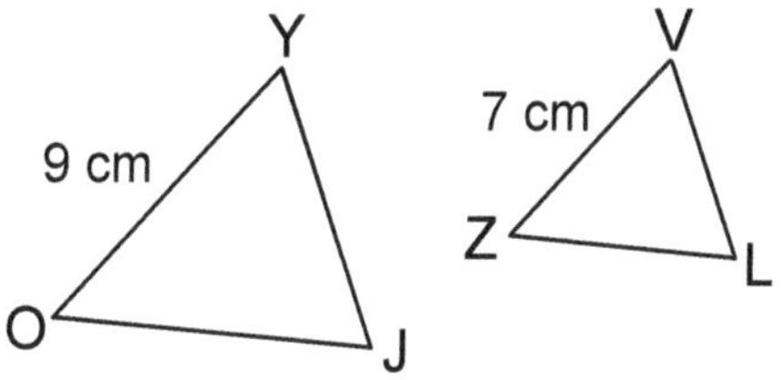

We will use the second theorem on page 610 to work this problem as shown below.

$$\frac{\text{perimeter of } \Delta YOJ}{\text{perimeter of } \Delta VZL} = \frac{YO}{VZ}$$

$$\frac{24 \text{ cm}}{\text{perimeter of } \Delta VZL} = \frac{9 \text{ cm}}{7 \text{ cm}}$$

$$168 \text{ cm}^2 = (9 \text{ cm})(\text{perimeter of } \Delta YOJ)$$

$$18.7 \text{ cm} \approx \text{perimeter of } \Delta YOJ$$

(by dividing both sides by 9 cm)

$$\frac{\text{area of } \Delta YOJ}{\text{area of } \Delta VZL} = \frac{(YO)^2}{(VZ)^2}$$

$$\frac{31 \text{ cm}^2}{\text{area of } \Delta VZL} = \frac{(9 \text{ cm})^2}{(7 \text{ cm})^2}$$

$$\frac{31 \text{ cm}^2}{\text{area of } \Delta VZL} = \frac{81 \text{ cm}^2}{49 \text{ cm}^2}$$

$$1519 \text{ cm}^4 = 81 \text{ cm}^2(\text{area of } \Delta VZL)$$

(using the Cross Products Property of Proportions)

$$18.8 \text{ cm}^2 \approx \text{area of } \Delta VZL$$

(by dividing both sides by 81 cm^2)

Example 4: In the figure at the right, rectangle KPMR is congruent to rectangle USWA. Find the perimeter and area of both rectangles.

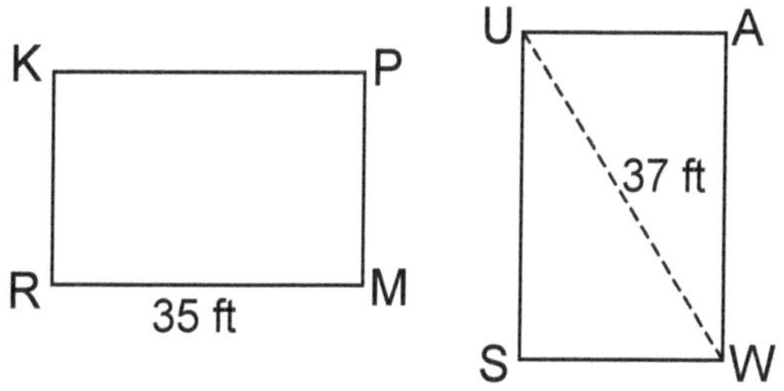

We will begin by noting that, since the question told us that rectangle KPMR is congruent to rectangle USWA, we can say that WA = 35 inches. Now, we can use the Pythagorean Theorem to find the length of $\overline{UA}$ as shown below.

$$(UA)^2 + (AW)^2 = (UW)^2$$
$$(UA)^2 + (35\ ft)^2 = (37\ ft)^2$$
$$(UA)^2 + 1225\ ft^2 = 1369\ ft^2$$
$$(UA)^2 = 144\ ft^2$$
$$UA = 12\ ft$$

This tells us that the perimeter of each rectangle is equal to 94 feet, and the area of each rectangle is equal to 420 square feet.

Problems:

1-6. In these problems, first find the corresponding dimensions of the second figure, and then use these dimensions to find the area and the perimeter of the second figure.

1. $\Delta ABC \sim \Delta DEF$

   DE = ____________ and FE = ____________

   Perimeter of ΔDFE = ______________

   Area of ΔDFE = ______________

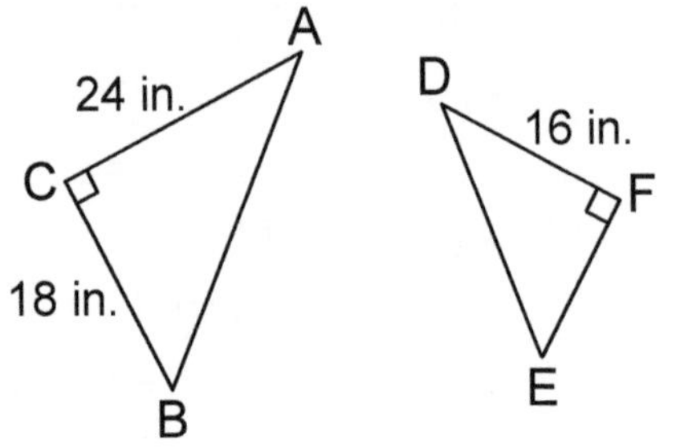

2. $\Delta GJI \sim \Delta NML$

   GI = ____________, MN = ____________,

   NL = ____________, and LM = ____________

   Perimeter of ΔNML = ______________

   Area of ΔNML = ______________

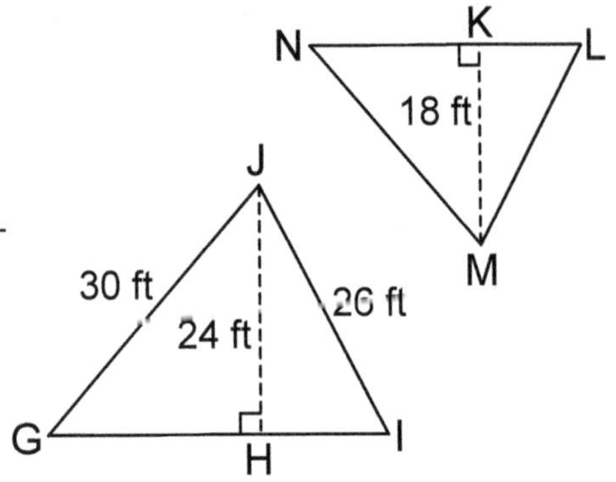

3. rectangle OPRQ ~ rectangle TUVS

SV = ____________

Perimeter of rectangle TUVS = ____________

Area of rectangle TUVS = ____________

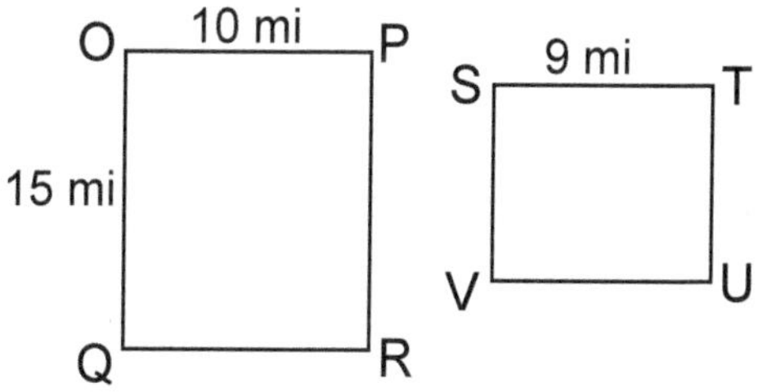

4. trapezoid WXZY ~ trapezoid AQEG

YZ = ____________, GA = ____________,

GE = ____________, AQ = ____________,

and EQ = ____________

Perimeter of trapezoid AQEG = ____________

Area of trapezoid AQEG = ____________

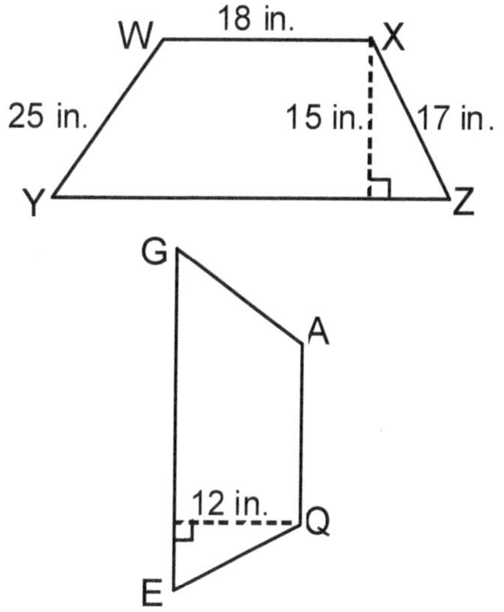

5. Hexagon MCDFBH and hexagon IKLJNO are both regular hexagons.

Apothem of hexagon IKLJNO = ____________

Perimeter of hexagon IKLJNO = ____________

Area of hexagon IKLJNO = ____________

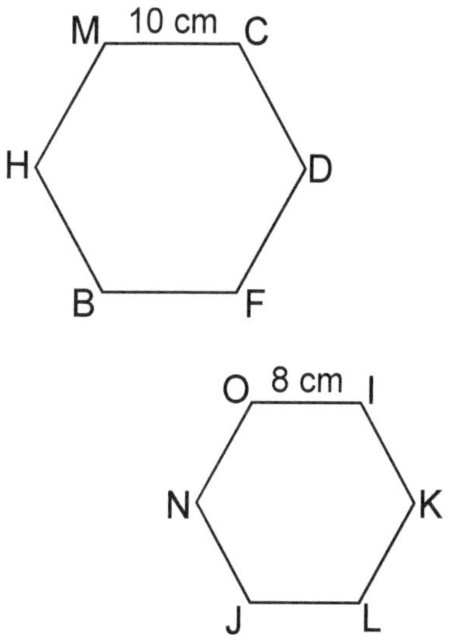

6. Octagon ZAGLEBVY and octagon QSRUWTXP are both regular octagons, the radius of octagon ZAGLEBVY is 7 feet, and the radius of octagon QSRUWTXP is 6 feet. (You may round your final answers to the nearest tenth.)

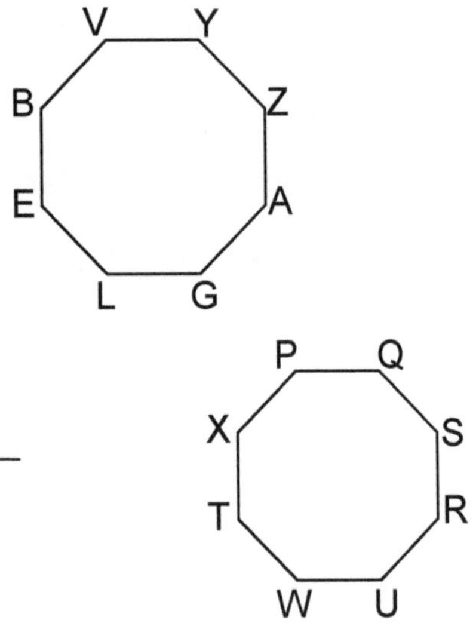

PQ = ___________

Perimeter of octagon QSRUWTXP = ___________

Area of octagon QSRUWTXP = ___________

7-12. In these problems, first find the area and perimeter of the first figure, and then use the second theorem on page 610 to find the area and the perimeter of the second figure. (Note that your answers to these problems should agree with the answers you found to Problems 1-6.)

7. $\Delta ABC \sim \Delta DEF$

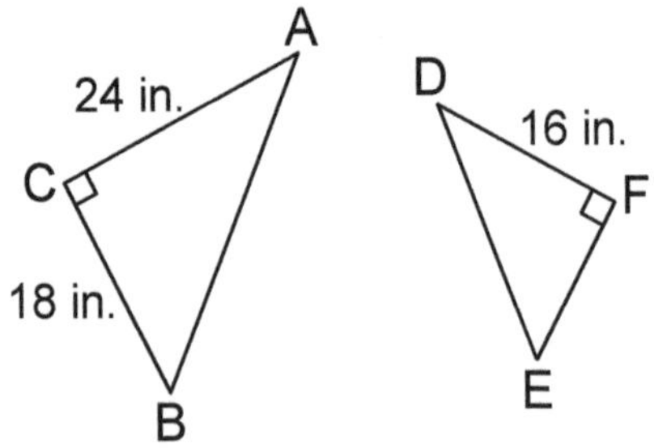

Perimeter of ΔABC = ___________

Area of ΔABC = ___________

Perimeter of ΔDFE = ___________

Area of ΔDFE = ___________

8. $\Delta GJI \sim \Delta NML$

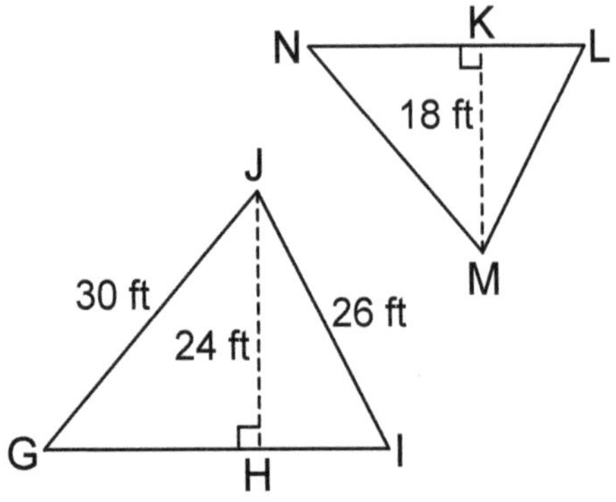

Perimeter of ΔGJI = ___________

Area of ΔGJI = ___________

Perimeter of ΔNML = ___________

Area of ΔNML = ___________

9. rectangle OPRQ ~ rectangle TUVS

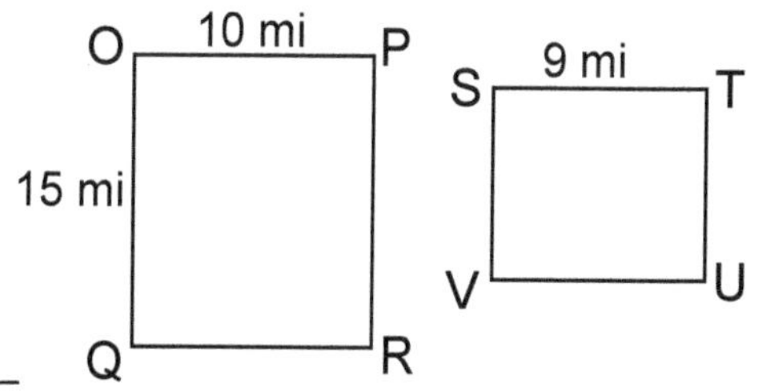

Perimeter of rectangle OPRQ = __________

Area of rectangle OPRQ = __________

Perimeter of rectangle TUVS = __________

Area of rectangle TUVS = __________

10. trapezoid WXZY ~ trapezoid AQEG

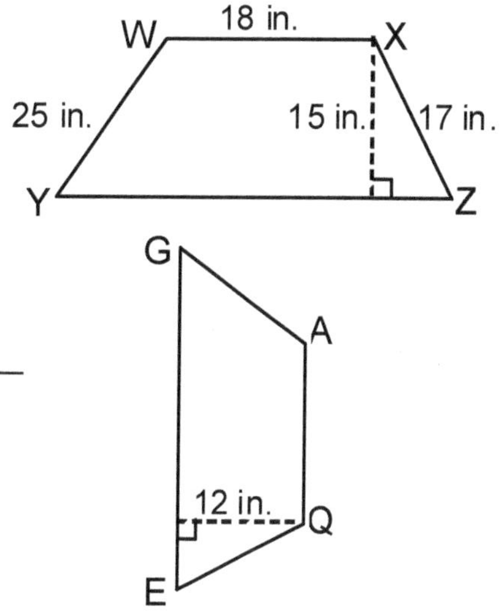

Perimeter of trapezoid WXZY =

____

Area of trapezoid WXZY = __________

Perimeter of trapezoid AQEG = __________

Area of trapezoid AQEG = __________

11. Hexagon MCDFBH and hexagon IKLJNO are both regular hexagons.

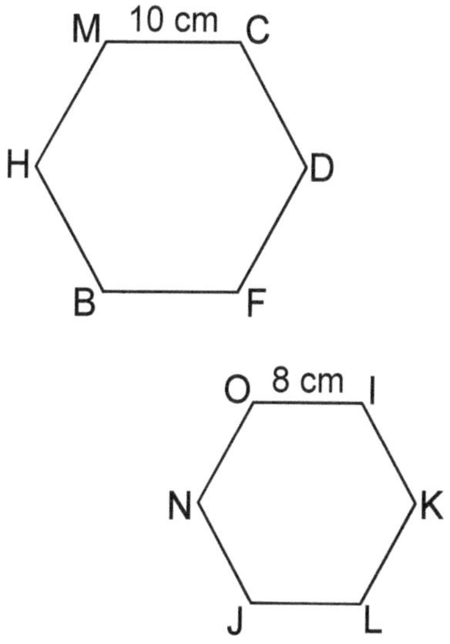

Perimeter of hexagon MCDFBH = __________

Area of hexagon MCDFBH = __________

Perimeter of hexagon IKLJNO = __________

Area of hexagon IKLJNO = __________

12. Octagon ZAGLEBVY and octagon QSRUWTXP are both regular octagons, the radius of octagon ZAGLEBVY is 7 feet, and the radius of octagon QSRUWTXP is 6 feet. (You may round your final answers to the nearest tenth.)

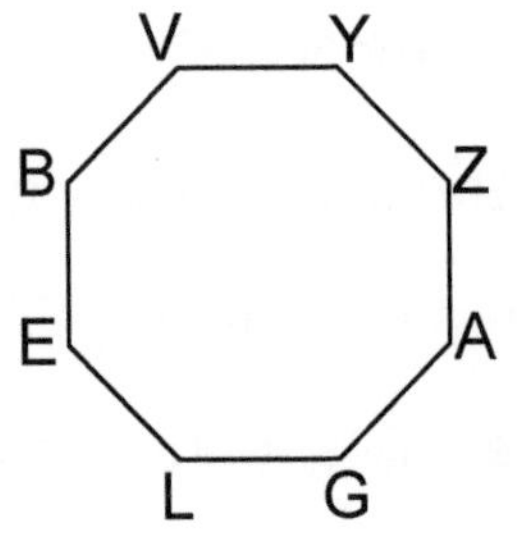

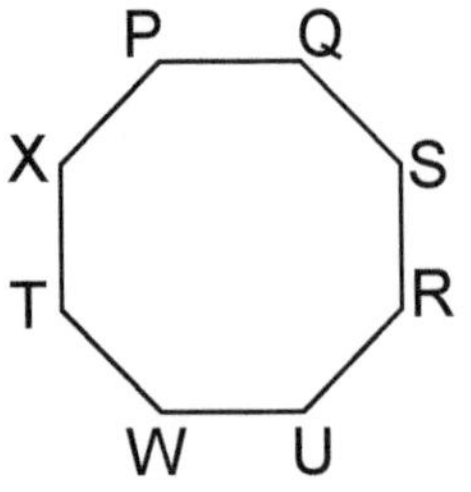

Perimeter of octagon ZAGLEBVY = ____________

Area of octagon ZAGLEBVY = ____________

Perimeter of octagon QSRUWTXP = ____________

Area of octagon QSRUWTXP = ____________

13. In the figure at the right, $\Delta CDF \sim \Delta HIJ$. If the perimeter of ΔHIJ is 15 meters, then the perimeter of ΔCDF is ____________.

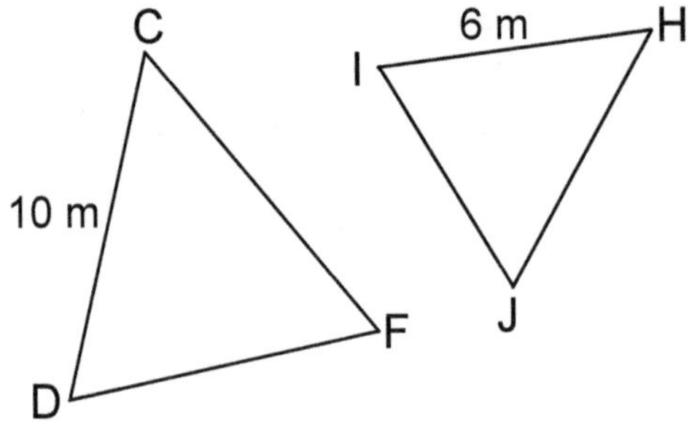

14. In the figure at the right, $\Delta KMR \sim \Delta NOL$. If the area of ΔKMR is 64 square feet, then the area of ΔNOL is ____________.

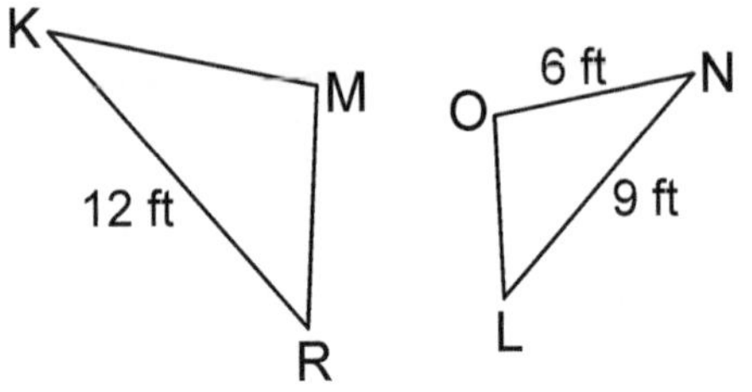

15. In the figure at the right, quadrilateral TEGP is congruent to quadrilateral UXVW. If the perimeter of quadrilateral TEGP is 23 m, then the perimeter of quadrilateral UXVW is ____________.

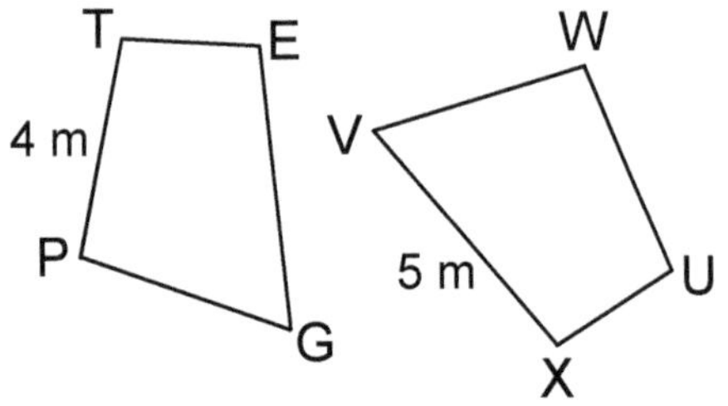

16. Each of the angles of ΔQSB (not shown) is congruent to one of the angles of ΔYZO (shown at the right). If one of the sides of ΔQSB has a length of 30 mm, what is one possible value for the perimeter of ΔQSB? ___________

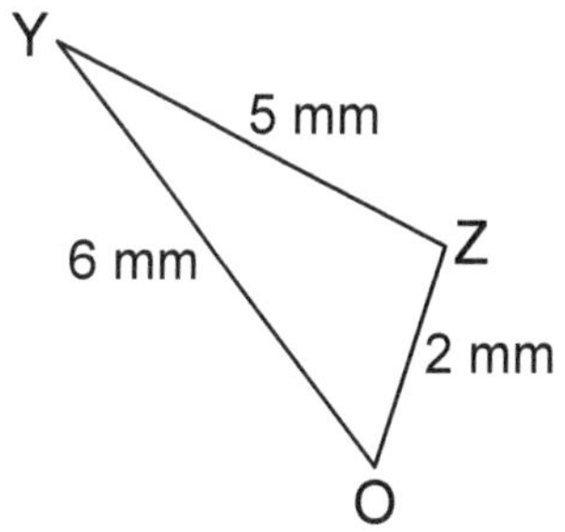

17. In the figure at the right, $\Delta LMN \sim \Delta TUV$. If the area of ΔTUV is 10 square inches, then the area of ΔLMN is ___________.

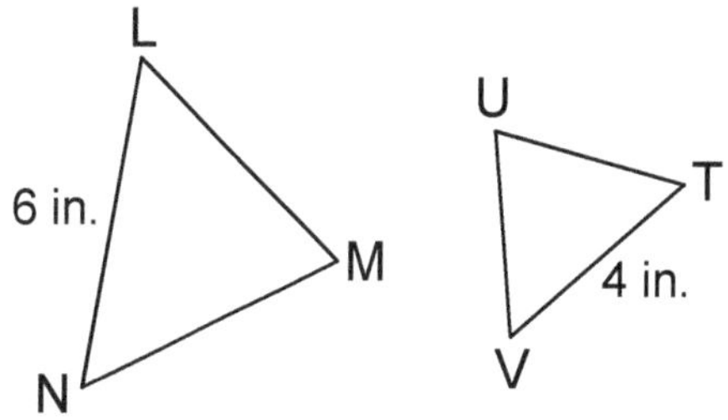

18. In the figure at the right, pentagon OKTYL is similar to pentagon APGRE. If the area of pentagon OKTYL is 50 cm^2, then the area of pentagon APGRE is ___________.

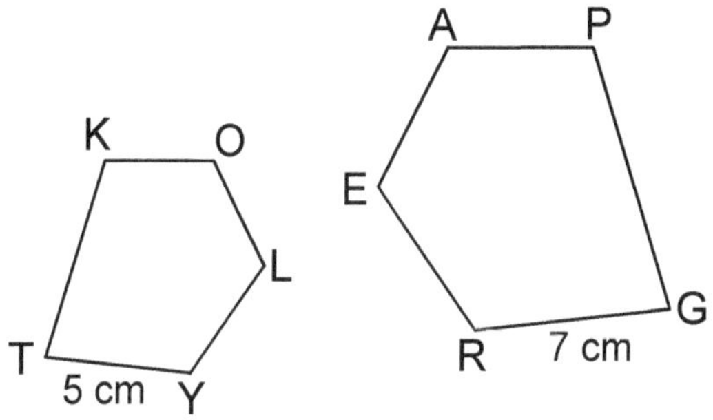

19. Each of the angles of ΔTSM (not shown) is congruent to one of the angles of ΔBYH (shown at the right). If ΔTSM has a perimeter of 48 km, then the lengths of the sides of ΔTSM are ___________, ___________, and ___________.

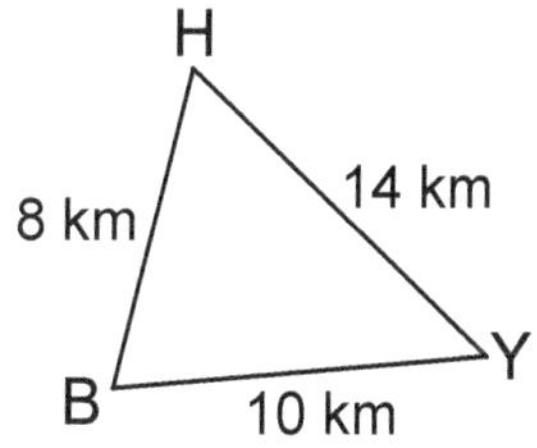

20. In the figure at the right, $\Delta ACW \cong \Delta HIJ$. If the area of ΔACW is 22 square yards, then the area of ΔHCJ is ____________.

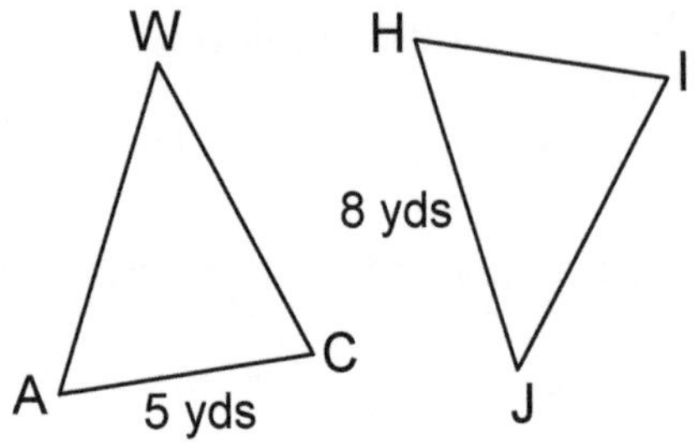

21. In the figure at the right, $\Delta PQR \sim \Delta BDE$. If the perimeter of ΔBDE is 42 inches, then the perimeter of ΔPQR is ____________.

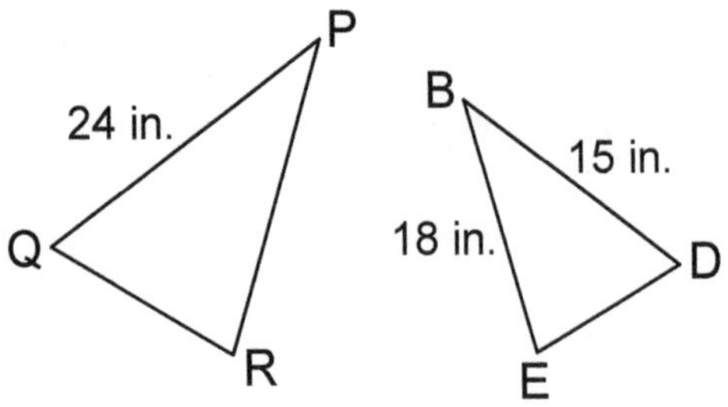

22. Triangle GKO (not shown) is similar to ΔFLS (shown at the right). If ΔGKO has an area of 24 mi^2, then the lengths of the sides of ΔGKO are ___________, ___________, and ___________.

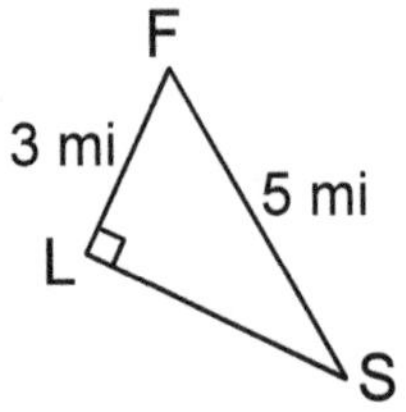

23. Trapezoid TVAB (not shown) is congruent to trapezoid HMGI (shown at the right). What is the area of trapezoid TVAB? ____________

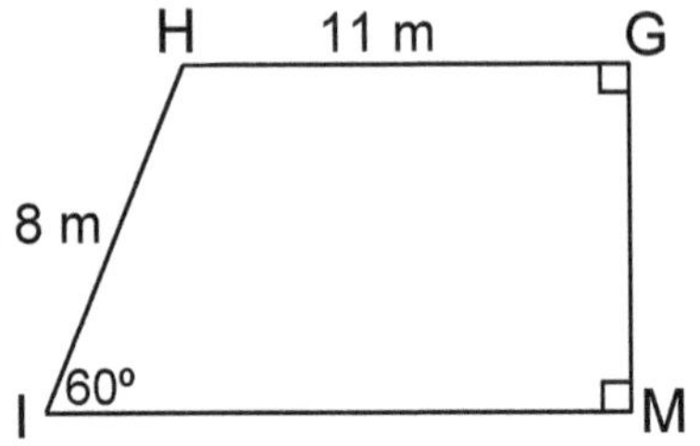

24. Suppose that quadrilateral RLUW is similar to quadrilateral KVEQ. If the area of quadrilateral RLUW is 64 square inches and the area of quadrilateral KVEQ is 16 square inches, then $\frac{\text{perimeter of quadrilateral RLUW}}{\text{perimeter of quadrilateral KVEQ}}$ = ____________ and

$\frac{RL}{KV}$ = ____________.

25. In the figure at the right, $\Delta CFG \sim \Delta OJN$. Then

$\frac{\text{perimeter of } \Delta OJN}{\text{perimeter of } \Delta CFG}$ = ____________ and

$\frac{\text{area of } \Delta OJN}{\text{area of } \Delta CFG}$ = ____________.

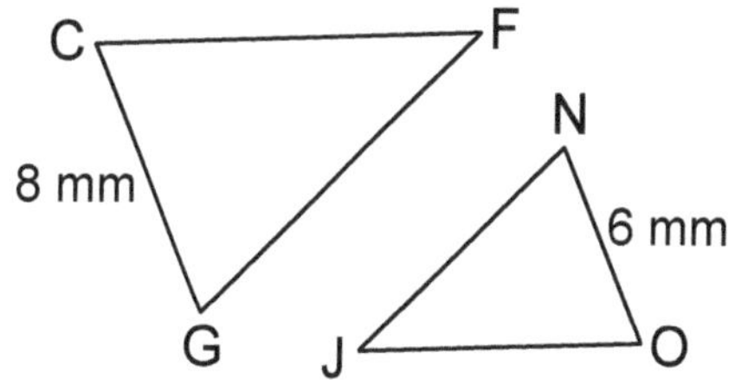

26. The ratio of the circumferences of two circles is 5 : 7. Then the ratio of the lengths of their radii is ____________, and the ratio of their areas is ____________.

27. Suppose that $\Delta SYB \sim \Delta XAZ$. If the perimeter of ΔSYB is 9 meters and the perimeter of ΔXAZ is 4 meters, then $\frac{\text{area of } \Delta SYB}{\text{area of } \Delta XAZ}$ = ____________ and

$\frac{SY}{XA}$ = ____________.

28. If rectangle DHTL is similar to rectangle ZEIJ and $\frac{\text{perimeter of rectangle ZEIJ}}{\text{perimeter of rectangle DHTL}} = \frac{5}{3}$,

then $\frac{HT}{EI}$ = ____________ and $\frac{\text{area of rectangle ZEIJ}}{\text{area of rectangle DHTL}}$ = ____________.

29. If $\Delta YLA \sim \Delta TNC$ and $\frac{NC}{LA} = 7$, then $\frac{\text{area of } \Delta YLA}{\text{area of } \Delta TNC}$ = ____________ and

$\frac{\text{perimeter of } \Delta YLA}{\text{perimeter of } \Delta TNC}$ = ____________.

30. On a map, the area of a pond is 9 square centimeters, and the perimeter of the pond is 15 centimeters. If the map's legend says that 1 centimeter on the map represents 10 feet in real life, then the area of the pond in real life is ____________, and the perimeter of the pond in real life is ____________.

31. On a blueprint of a house, the area of a room is 9 square inches, and the perimeter of the room is 16 inches. If the area of the room in real life is 225 square feet, then 1 inch on the blueprint represents ____________ feet in real life, and the perimeter of the room in real life is ____________ feet.

Part VI – Geometric Probability

We will begin this section with a review of basic probability, and then we will discuss how this concept relates to Geometry. (Example 1 has nothing to do with Geometry; it is only an example that illustrates the basic concept of probability.)

Example 1: A bucket contains 7 white marbles, 9 blue marbles, and 4 red marbles, and all the marbles are the same size. If a person reaches in the bucket and pulls out a marble at random, what is the probability that the marble will be white? What is the probability that the marble will not be blue?

One definition for probability is probability = $\frac{\text{part}}{\text{total}}$. Therefore, if a person reaches in the bucket and pulls out a marble at random, the probability that the marble will be white is $\frac{7}{20}$ (because there are 7 white marbles and a total of 20 marbles). If a person reaches in the bucket and pulls out a marble at random, the probability that the marble will not be blue is $\frac{11}{20}$ (because there are 11 marbles that are not blue and a total of 20 marbles).*

Now, let's look at how this concept relates to Geometry.

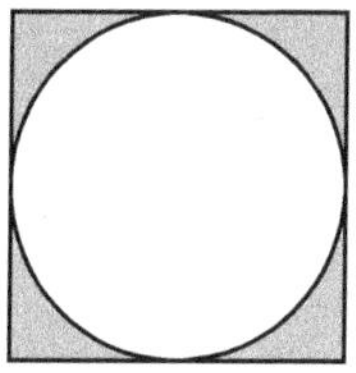

Example 2: In the figure at the right, the sides of the square are tangent to the circle, and the area of the square is 36 ft^2. If a point is picked at random from inside the square, what is the probability that it will lie in one of the shaded regions?

We will begin by noting that, since the area of the square is 36 ft^2, each side of the square must have a length of 6 feet. Thus, the radius of the circle must be 3 feet long, and so the area of the circle must equal 9π ft^2. Hence, the total area of the shaded regions must equal $(36 - 9\pi)$ ft^2. Now, when we use the formula probability = $\frac{\text{part}}{\text{total}}$, we find that, if a point is picked at random from inside the square, the probability that it will lie in one of the shaded regions is $\frac{(36-9\pi)\ \text{ft}^2}{36\ \text{ft}^2}$, or $\frac{36-9\pi}{36}$. We can reduce this fraction further by dividing each of the terms by 9, and so our final answer to this question is $\frac{4-\pi}{4}$.

(Many students will try to reduce this further by cancelling the 4's, but you **<u>cannot</u>** do this because you must divide *each* of the terms by 4. You could, however, think about your rules for adding and subtracting fractions and rewrite this as $\frac{4}{4} - \frac{\pi}{4}$, or, equivalently, $1 - \frac{\pi}{4}$.)

*These probabilities tell us that, for every 20 times that a person reaches in the bucket and pulls out a marble at random, the person will, on average, pull out 7 white marbles. Similarly, for every 20 times that a person reaches in the bucket and pulls out a marble at random, the person will, on average, pull out 11 marbles that are not blue.

Example 3: In the figure at the right, the circles have radii with lengths of 4 meters, 7 meters, 10 meters, and 13 meters. If a point is picked at random from inside the largest circle, what is the probability that the point will lie inside one of the shaded regions?

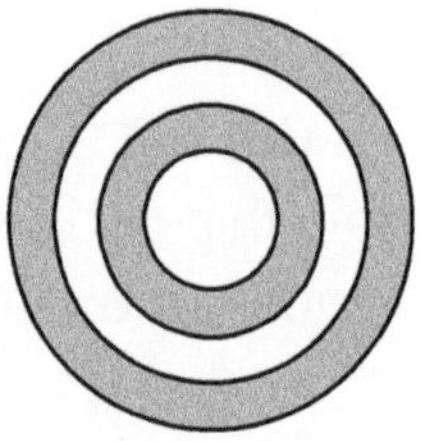

We will begin by noting that the total area of the entire figure is 169π square meters. The area of the larger shaded region is $(169\pi - 100\pi)$ m^2 (because the larger shaded region is a circle with a smaller circle taken out of it), or 69π m^2. The area of the smaller shaded region is $(49\pi - 16\pi)$ m^2, or 33π m^2. Thus, the area of the two shaded regions must equal 102π m^2. Hence, if a point is picked at random from inside the largest circle, the probability that the point will lie inside one of the shaded regions is $\frac{102\pi \text{ m}^2}{169\pi \text{ m}^2}$, or $\frac{102}{169}$.

Example 4: If a person picks a point at random from inside the large triangle at the right, what is the probability that it will lie in the unshaded region? What is the probability that it will lie in the one of the shaded regions?

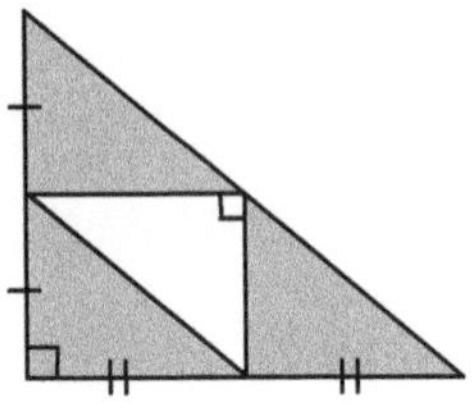

We will begin by labeling the base and height of the large triangle as shown below.

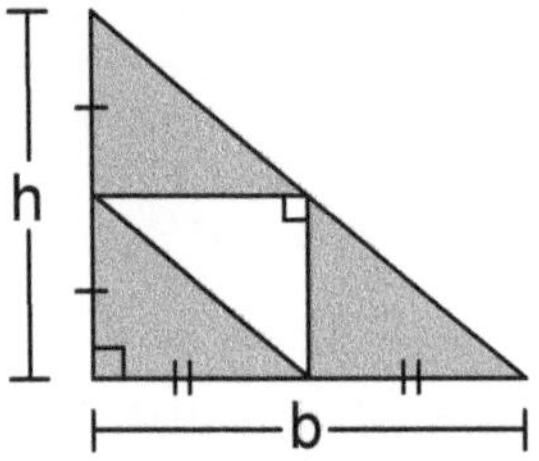

This tells us that the area of the large triangle is equal to $\frac{1}{2}$bh. It also tells us that the base and height of the unshaded triangle must equal $\frac{1}{2}$b and $\frac{1}{2}$h, and so the area of the unshaded triangle must equal $\frac{1}{2}\left(\frac{1}{2}b\right)\left(\frac{1}{2}h\right)$, or $\frac{1}{8}$bh.

Now, we can find the probability that a point picked at random from the large triangle will lie in the unshaded region as shown below.

$$\text{probability that the point will lie in the unshaded region} = \frac{\frac{1}{8}bh}{\frac{1}{2}bh}$$

$$= \frac{\frac{1}{8}}{\frac{1}{2}}$$

Notice that we can reduce the fraction above by dividing both the top and bottom by bh.

We can simplify this further by noting that $\frac{1}{8} \div \frac{1}{2} = \frac{1}{8} \bullet \frac{2}{1} = \frac{1}{4}$, and so we can conclude that, if a person picks a point at random from inside the large triangle, the probability that it will lie in the unshaded region is $\frac{1}{4}$.

Now, to find the probability that the point will lie in one of the shaded regions, let's think about what this $\frac{1}{4}$ means. It tells that, for every 4 points picked at random from inside the large triangle, on average, one of them will lie in the unshaded region and the other three will lie in one of the shaded regions. Hence, if a point is picked at random from inside the large triangle, the probability that it will lie in one of the shaded regions must equal $\frac{3}{4}$.

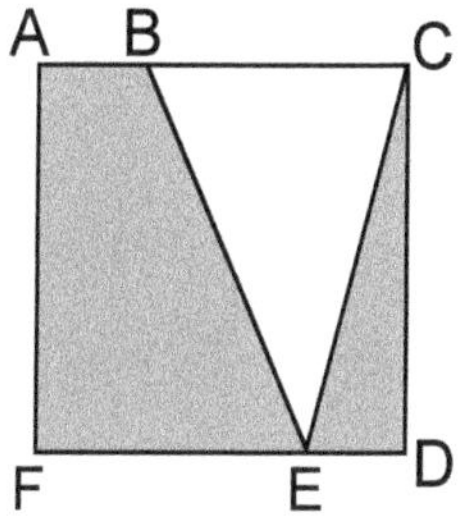

Example 5: In the figure at the right, the quadrilateral ACDF is a square with a length of 6 cm on each side. If a point will be picked at random from inside square ACDF, what must the length of $\overline{BC}$ be in order for the probability of landing in one of the shaded regions to equal $\frac{2}{3}$?

We will begin by letting x cm represent the distance between B and C. Then the area of ΔBCE must equal $\frac{1}{2}$(x cm)(6 cm), or 3x cm^2.

Next, we will note that the area of square ACDF is 36 cm^2, and so the area of the shaded region must equal (36 – 3x) cm^2. This means that, if a point is picked at random from inside square ACDF, the probability that it will lie in one of the shaded regions is $\frac{36-3x}{36}$. Since the problem told us that this must equal $\frac{2}{3}$, we can finish solving this problem as shown below.

$$\frac{36-3x}{36} = \frac{2}{3}$$

$$3(36 - 3x) = 2(36)$$ Use the Cross Products Property of Proportions.

$$108 - 9x = 72$$

$$x = 4$$

Since we decided to let x cm represent the distance between B and C, this tells us that the length of $\overline{BC}$ must be 4 cm.

(By the way, you may find it interesting to note that it does not matter where the point E lies on $\overline{DF}$; the answer to this question will always be the same.)

Problems:

1-10. These problems are very similar to some of the problems that you saw in Parts III and IV of this chapter. Feel free to use your work from the problems you have already worked!

1. If a point will be picked at random from inside the triangle at the right, what is the probability that it will lie in the shaded region? ____________

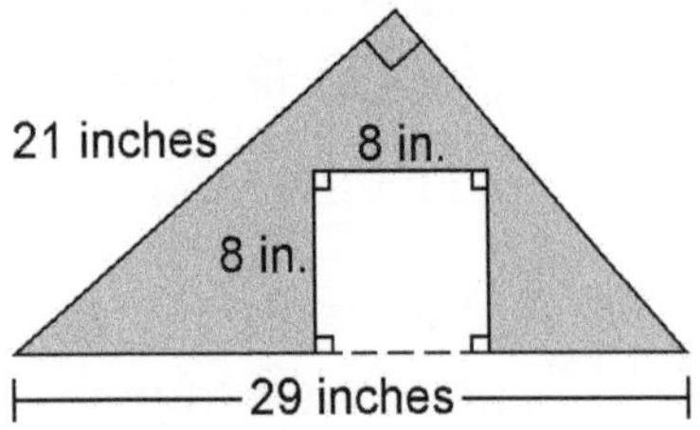

2. In the figure at the right, the longer base of the trapezoid is a diameter of the circle, the bases of the trapezoid have lengths of 14 mm and 22 mm, and the height of the trapezoid is $6\sqrt{2}$ mm. If a point will be picked at random from inside the circle, what is the probability that it will lie in one of the shaded regions? ______________

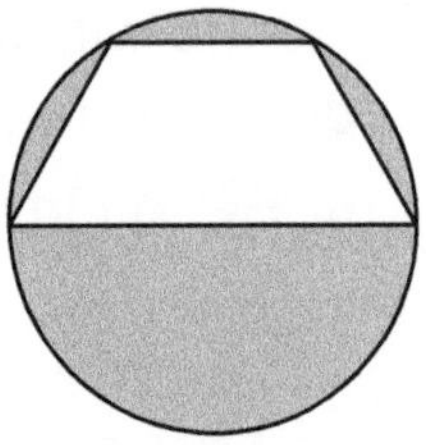

3. If a point will be picked at random from inside the circle at the right, what is the probability that it will lie in the shaded region? ______________

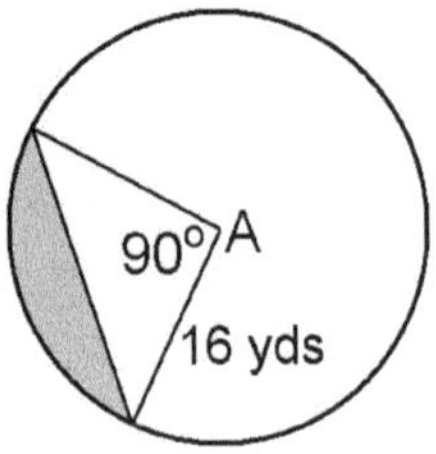

4. If a point will be picked at random from inside the figure at the right, what is the probability that it will lie in the shaded region? ________________

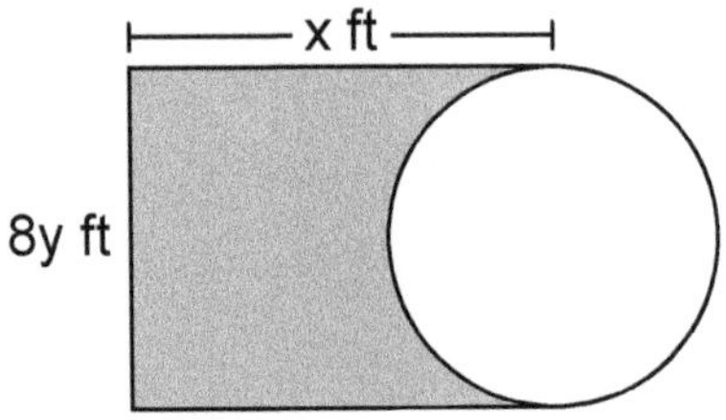

5. In the figure at the right, the area of the shaded region is 16π mm^2, and the radius of the larger circle has a length of 5 mm. If a point will be picked at random from inside the larger circle, then the probability that it will lie in the *smaller* circle is ________________.

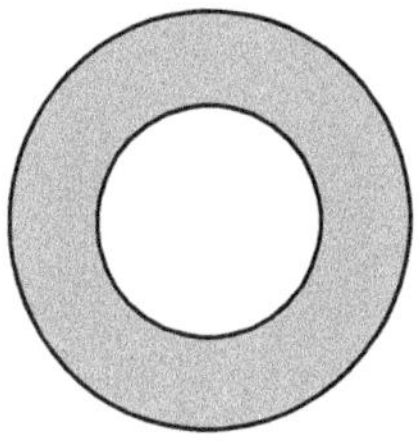

6. In the figure at the right, the quadrilateral is a square, and the area of the shaded region is 816 square inches. If a point will be picked at random from inside the square, then the probability that it will lie inside the triangle is ________________.

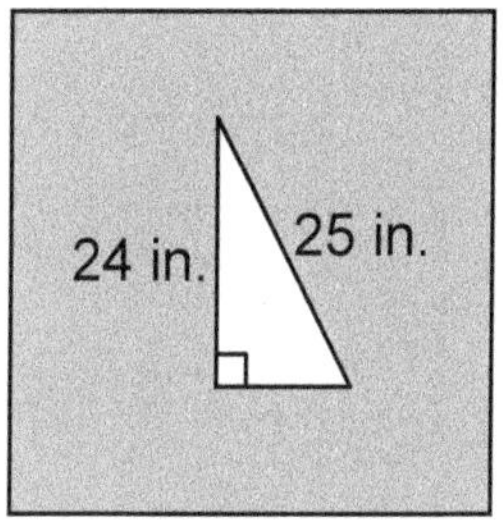

7. In the figure at the right, the quadrilateral is a square, and the hexagon is a regular hexagon. If a point will be picked at random from inside the hexagon, then the probability that it will lie in the square is ________________.

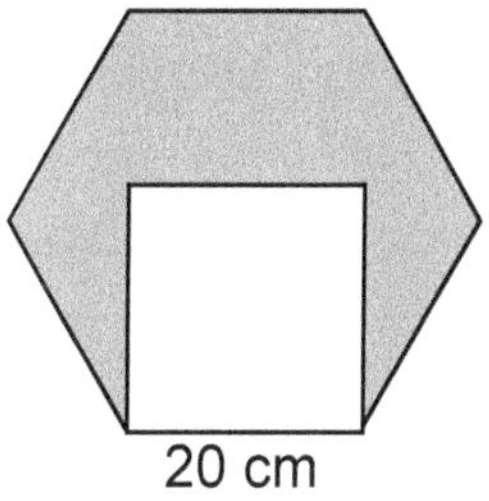

8. The figure at the right shows a regular hexagon inscribed inside another regular hexagon, and the vertices of the smaller hexagon are the midpoints of the sides of the larger hexagon. If a point will be picked at random from inside the larger hexagon, then the probability that it will lie in one of the shaded regions is ________________. (Note that the apothem of the larger hexagon is equal to the length of the radius of the smaller hexagon.)

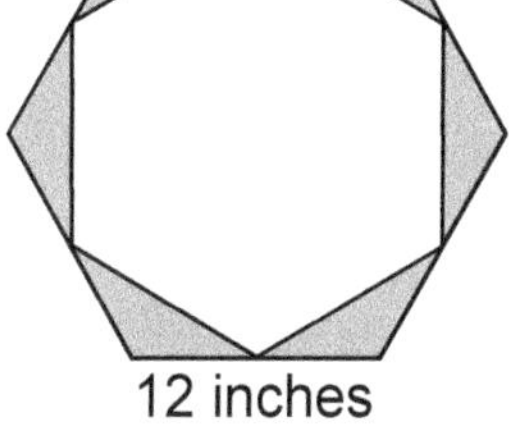

9. In the figure at the right, the hexagon is a regular hexagon. If a point will be picked at random from inside the hexagon, then the probability that it will lie in one of the shaded regions is ________________.

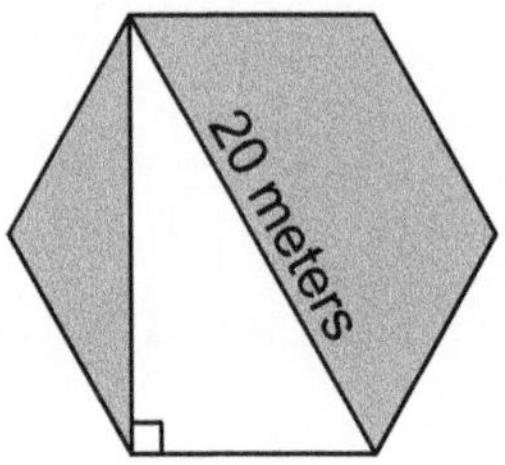

10. The figure at the right shows a regular hexagon inscribed inside a circle. If a point will be picked at random from inside the circle, then the probability that it will lie in one of the shaded regions is ________________.

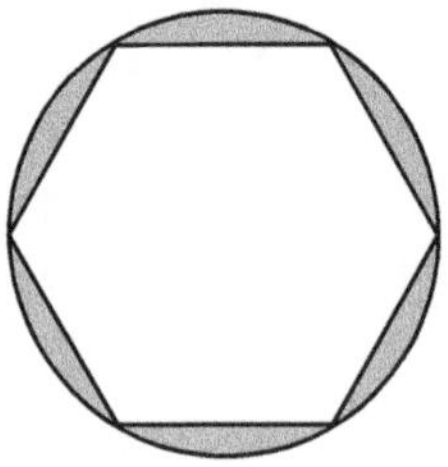

11-13. A dartboard is shown at the right. The central angles are congruent to each other, and the lengths of the radii of the circles are as follows: 32 mm, 99 mm, 107 mm, 162 mm, and 170 mm. Assume that a person will throw a dart at the dartboard and that the dart will hit the dartboard. Also assume that the results of the throw are due to pure chance (in other words, assume that there is no skill involved).

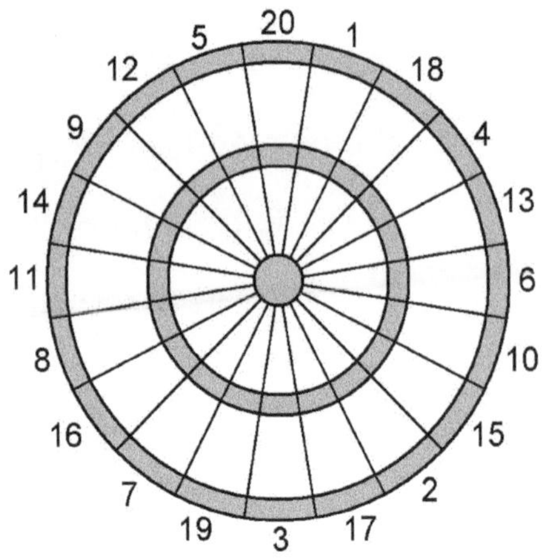

11. What is the probability that the person will hit the gray circle in the center? ___________

12. A person can triple his or her score on a throw if he or she can hit the gray middle ring. What is the probability that the person will hit this ring?

____

13. What is the probability that the person will hit the outer white space labeled 20?

____

14. If a point will be picked at random from inside the rectangle shown at the right, what is the probability that it will lie in one of the shaded regions? ____________

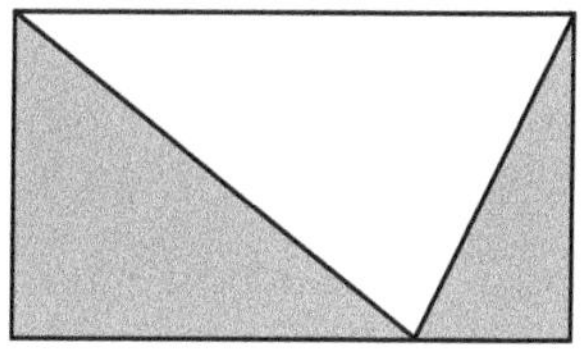

15. In the figure at the right, W is the midpoint of $\overline{QN}$. If a point will be picked at random from inside the rectangle, what is the probability that it will lie in one of the shaded regions? ____________ What is the probability that it will lie in the triangle? ____________

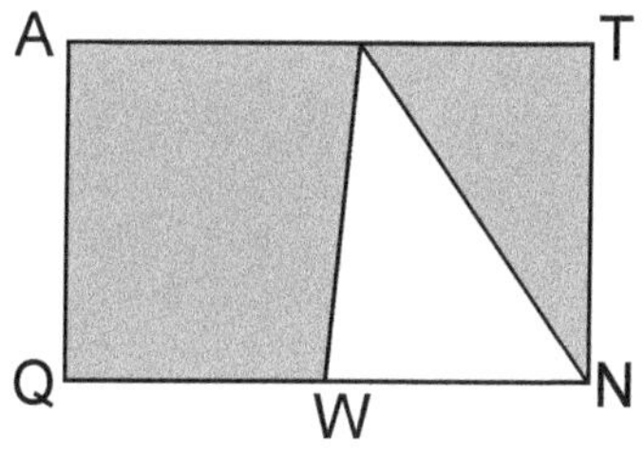

16. The figure at the right shows a circle inside of a rectangle, and the top and bottom of the rectangle are both tangent to the circle. If a point is picked at random from inside the rectangle, what is the probability that the point will lie inside the circle? ____________ What is the probability that the point will NOT lie inside the circle? ____________

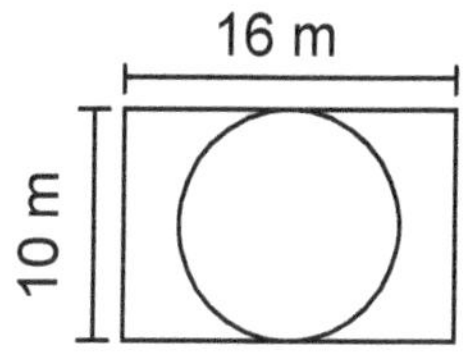

17. In the figure at the right, $\overline{RL}$ is a diameter of the circle. If a point will be picked at random from inside the circle, what is the probability that it will lie in one of the shaded regions? ____________

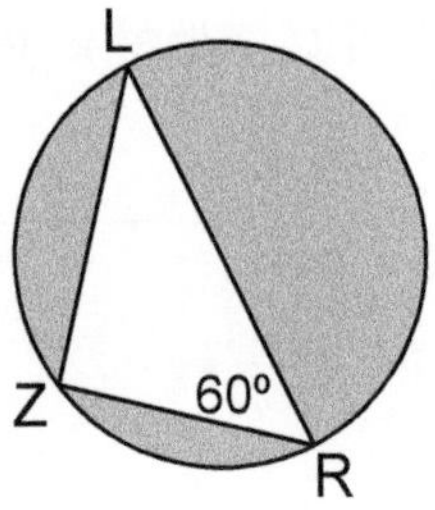

18. The figure at the right shows a circle inscribed inside a hexagon. If a point will be picked at random from inside the hexagon, what is the probability that it will lie inside the circle? ____________

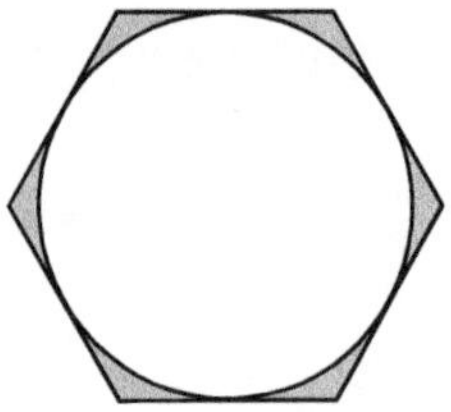

19. In the figure at the right, each of the circles is tangent to two circles and two sides of the rectangle. If a point will be picked at random from inside the square, what is the probability that it will lie in one of the shaded regions?

____

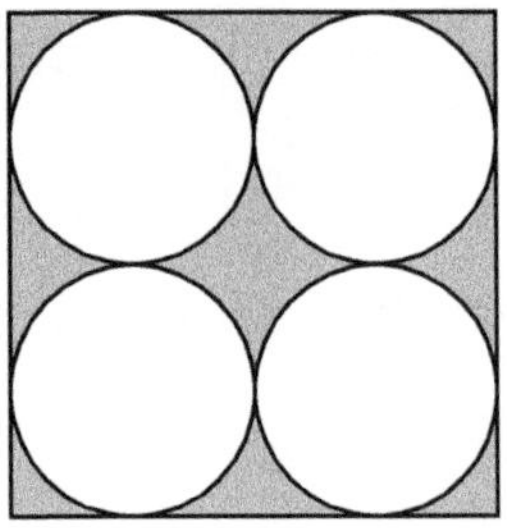

20. If a point is picked at random from inside the larger circle shown at the right, the probability that it will lie in the shaded region is $\frac{3}{4}$. If the radius of the larger circle is 8 m, then the length of the radius of the smaller circle is ____________.

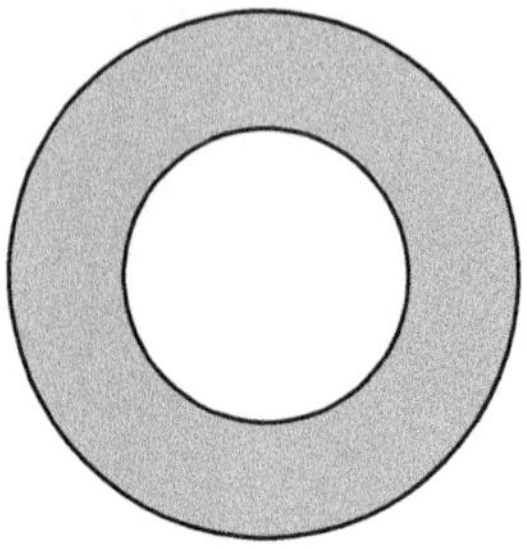

21. If a point is picked at random from inside the circle shown at the right, the probability that it will lie in the shaded region is $\frac{3}{5}$. What is the value of n? ____________

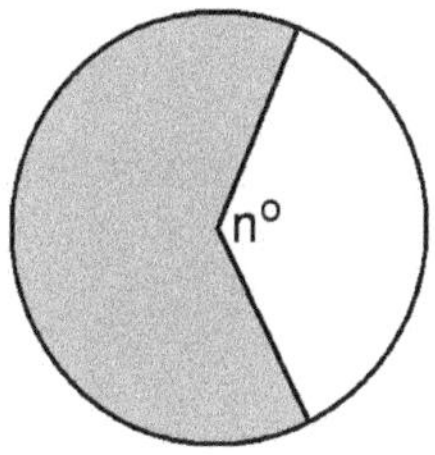

22. If a point will be picked at random from inside the trapezoid at the right, the probability that it will lie in one of the shaded regions is $\frac{4}{7}$. What is the value of y?

____

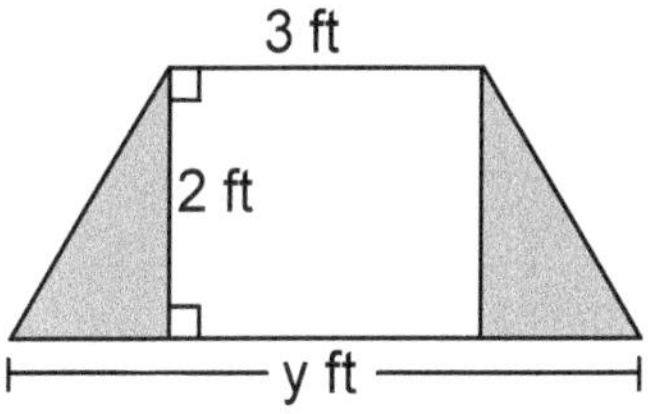

23. In the figure at the right, BY = YG, BC = CG, and CE = 8 m. If a point is picked at random from inside kite BCGY, the probability that it will lie in the shaded region is $\frac{2}{5}$. Then EY = __________ and CY = __________.

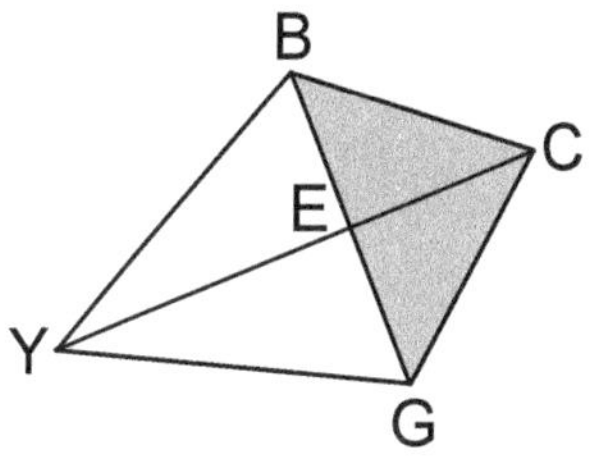

24. If a point is picked at random from inside the figure at the right, the probability that it will lie inside the semicircle is $\frac{1}{4}$. What is the value of w? ____________

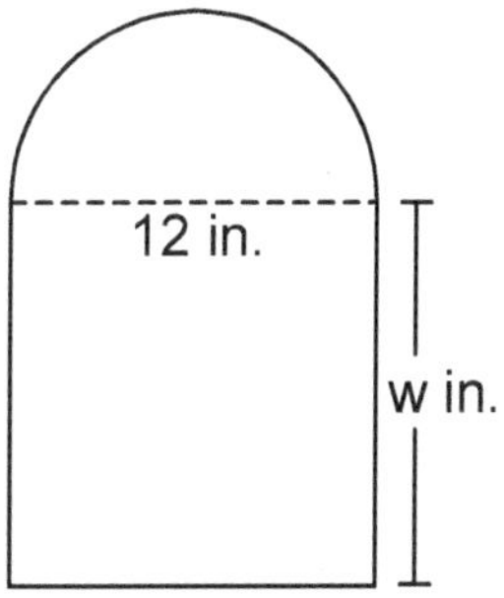

Part VII – Mixed Review

1. The perimeter of a hexagon is 48 meters. If the length of each side is decreased by 3 meters, then the perimeter of the new hexagon is __________ meters.

2. The perimeter of a regular octagon is 160 inches. If the length of each side is increased by 20%, then the perimeter of the new octagon is __________ inches.

3. A rectangular room is x feet long and y feet wide. What is the area of the room in square *yards*? __________

4. Refer back to #3. If carpet costs $12 per square yard, how much would it cost to carpet this room? __________

5. Suppose that ΔJKL has an area of x square yards, $\overline{JM}$ is an altitude of ΔJKL and has a length of y yards, and the length of $\overline{KL}$ is equal to twice the length of $\overline{JM}$. Then, in terms of x, y = ___________. (Hint: When a question says *in terms of* x, that means that there will probably be an x in your answer.)

6. In ΔABC, the length of $\overline{BC}$ is equal to $\frac{3}{4}$ of the length of $\overline{AD}$, and $\overline{AD}$ is an altitude of ΔABC. If AD = h feet, then, in terms of h, the area of ΔABC is ___________ ft^2. (Hint: Begin by drawing a picture!)

7. Find the area and perimeter of the triangle at the right.

Area = ________________

Perimeter = ____________

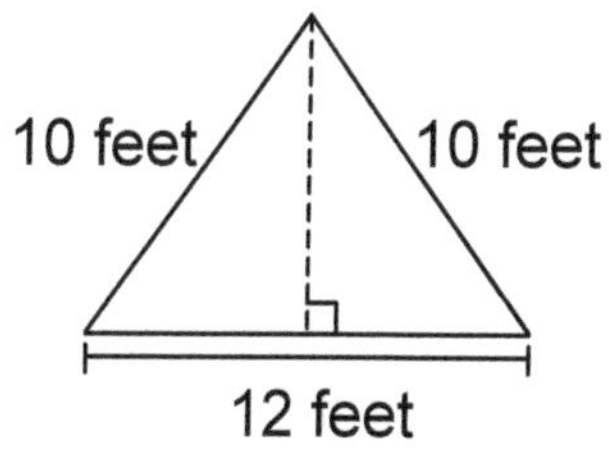

8-9. Assume that all angles that appear to be right angles are actually right angles, and assume that all curved paths are arcs of circles.

8. The area of the figure at the right is ________________, and the perimeter is ________________.

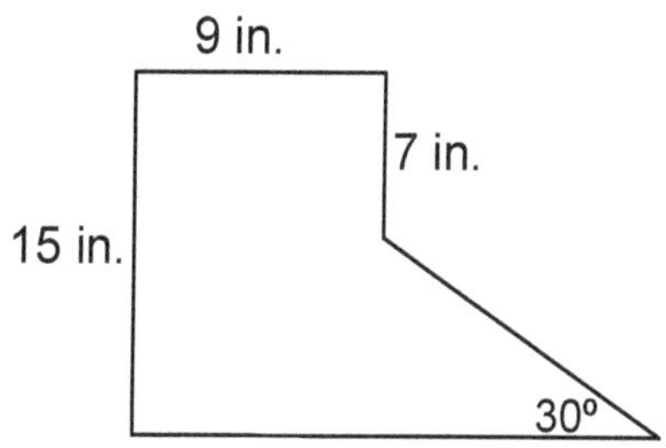

9. What is the perimeter of the figure shown at the right? ____________

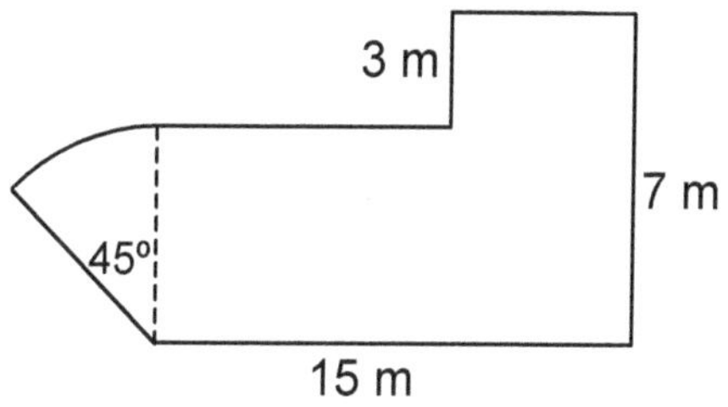

10. In ⊙ J at the right, $\overline{LH}$ has a length of 60 centimeters. What is the area of the shaded region? ______________

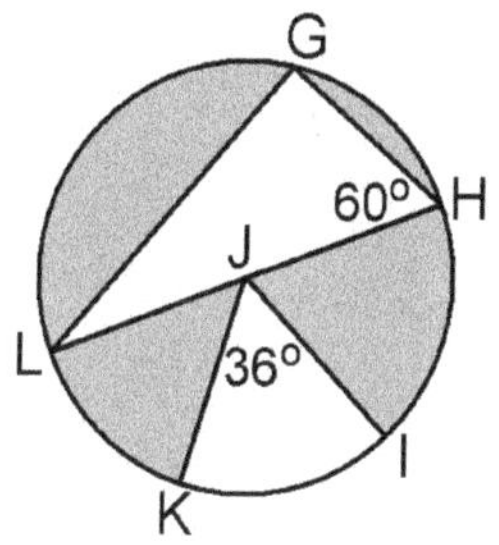

11. Refer back to #10. If a point will picked at random from inside the circle, what is the probability that it will lie in one of the shaded regions? ______________ What is the probability that it will lie in one of the unshaded regions? ______________

12. The figure at the right shows a circle is inscribed inside an equilateral triangle. If a point will picked at random from inside this triangle, what is the probability that it will lie in one of the shaded regions? _______________

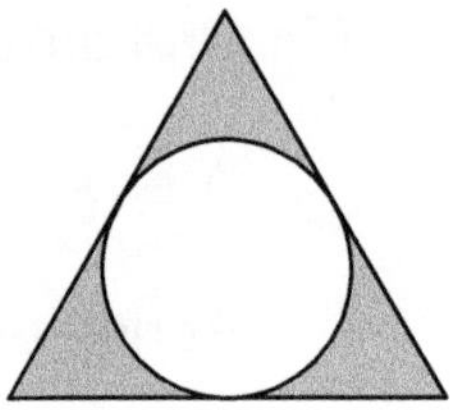

13. A quadrilateral has vertices at (–5, 2), (–3, 6), (5, 2), and (1, –1). What is the area of this quadrilateral? _______________ What is the perimeter of this quadrilateral? _______________

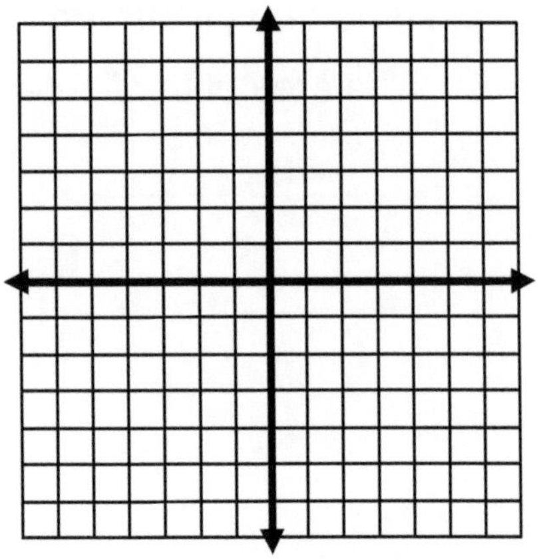

14. In the figure at the right, quadrilateral DEFG is similar to quadrilateral QRST. The perimeter of quadrilateral DEFG is 76 ft, and the area of quadrilateral QRST is 54 ft^2. Then the perimeter of quadrilateral QRST is _____________, and the area of quadrilateral DEFG is _____________.

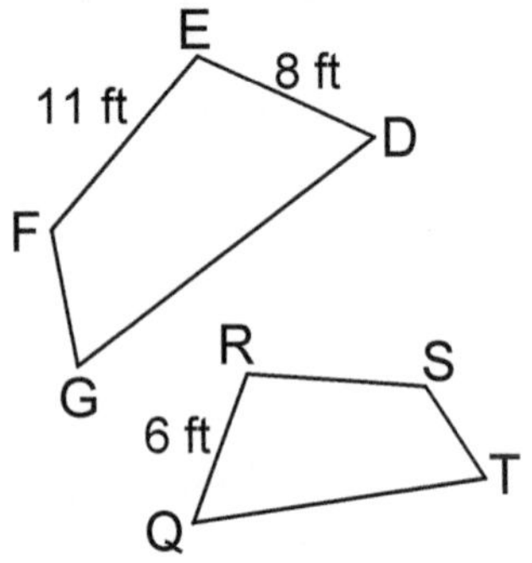

15. If the radius of a circle gets doubled, what happens to its circumference? _______________ What happens to its area? _______________

16. Draw a 114° counterclockwise rotation of the triangle at the right about the point M.

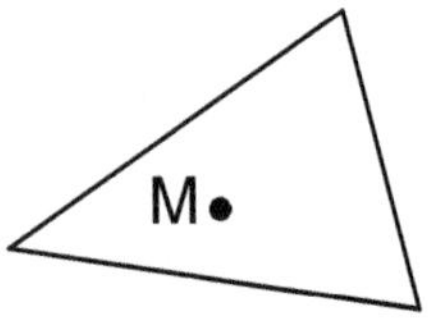

17. Draw a dilation of the quadrilateral shown at the right with center C and scale factor $1\frac{1}{2}$.

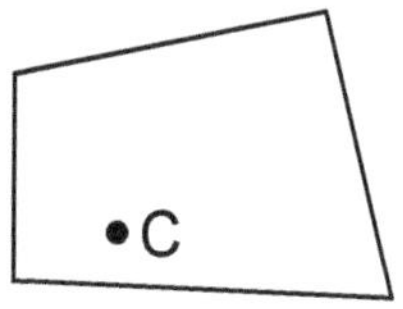

18. Triangle TUV has vertices at T(1, 1), U(4, –5), and V(6, –3). Perform the following transformations *in the order they are given*, and give the coordinates of the vertices of the final image.

First transformation: Reflection in the line y-axis

Second transformation: 90° clockwise rotation about the point (–2, –2)

T″: (____, ____), U″: (____, ____), V″: (____, ____)

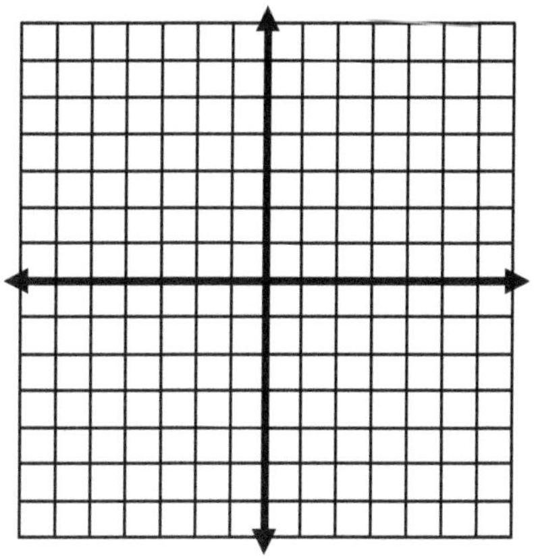

19-24. In the figure at the right, $\overline{OW}$ and $\overline{UW}$ are both tangent to the circle, LW = 4, UW = 6, m∠OWY = 23°, m∠YLU = 78°, and m$\overset{\frown}{YO}$ = 107°.

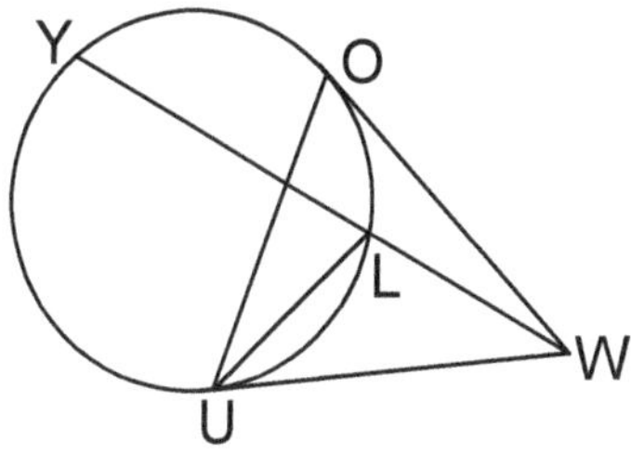

19. m$\overset{\frown}{UY}$ = ___________

20. If the radius of the circle is 3 cm, what is the length of $\overset{\frown}{UY}$? ___________

21. m$\overset{\frown}{OL}$ = ___________

22. m$\overset{\frown}{LUY}$ = ___________

23. m∠YWU = ___________

24. m∠UOW = ___________

25. LY = ___________

26. WO = ___________

27. If two sides of a triangle have lengths of 12 feet and 15 feet, then the perimeter of the triangle must be greater than ______________ and less than ______________. (Hint: Use the Triangle Inequality Theorem.)

Chapter 13 – Surface Area and Volume

Part I – Surface Areas of Prisms and Cylinders

We will begin this section with some definitions.

A solid is a set of boundaries that enclose three-dimensional space. (Three-dimensional space is called that because there are three dimensions: length, width, and height.)

If the boundaries of a solid are polygons, the polygons are called faces of the solid.

A prism is a solid that has the following characteristics.

1. Two faces, called bases, are formed by congruent polygons in parallel planes.
2. The faces that are not bases are called lateral faces and are formed by parallelograms. (If the parallelograms are rectangles, the prism is called a right prism; if the parallelograms are not rectangles, then the prism is called an oblique prism.

Prisms are often named by the shapes of their bases.

A cylinder is a solid that is formed by two congruent circles (called the bases of the cylinder) in parallel planes joined by a smooth continuous closed surface. If the smooth continuous closed surface is always perpendicular to the circles, the cylinder is called a right cylinder; if not, the cylinder is called an oblique cylinder.

Example 1: Classify the solids drawn below according to the definitions above.

(a) 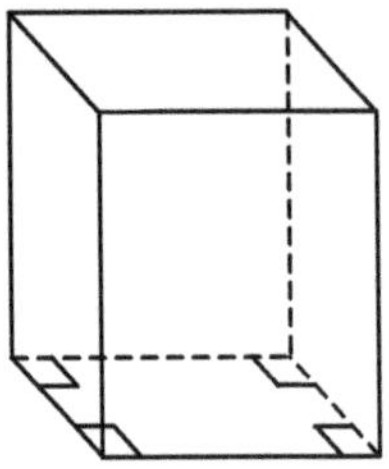

(b) 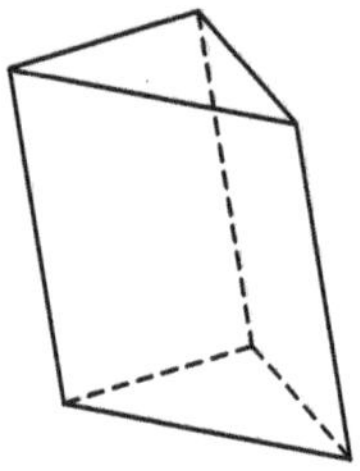

(c) 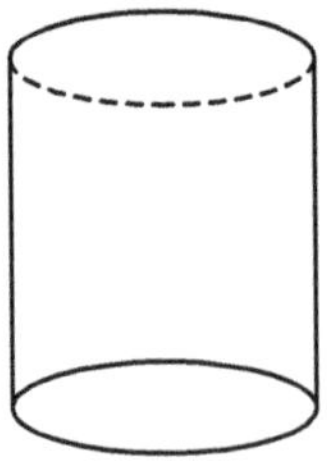

(d) 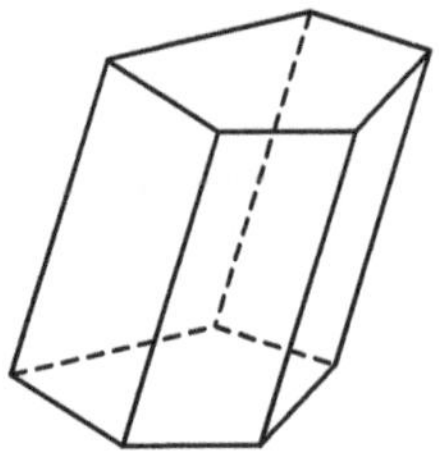

(e) 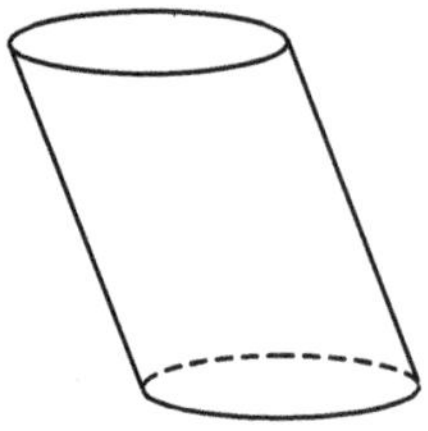

(f) 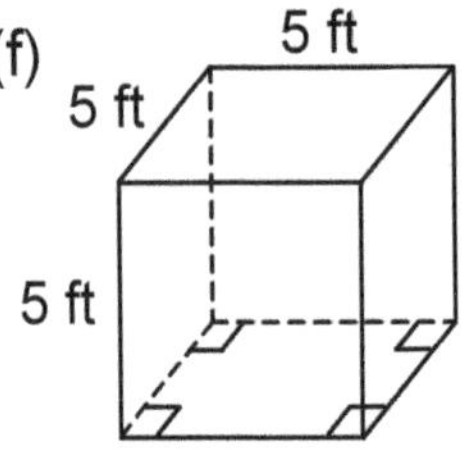

(g) 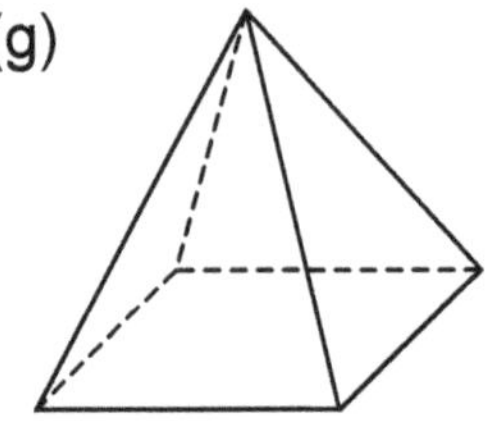

(h) 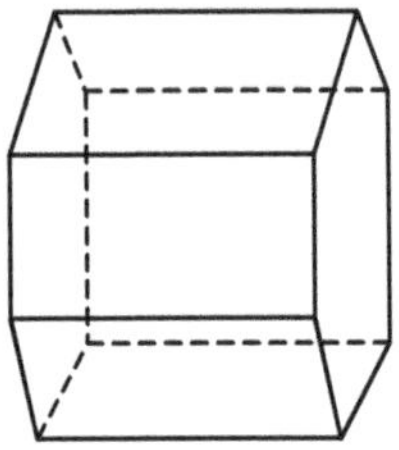

(a) We will begin by noting that the dashed segments represent the edges of the solid that you can't see. If you have trouble seeing what this picture is showing you, get a rectangular box and move it around so that you can see the top, front, and left sides of the box. Notice that you cannot see the edges of the box that we represented with dotted lines, and also notice that the top of the box appears to look more like a parallelogram that is not a rectangle. If you still have trouble seeing this, move the box around slightly and look at it from slightly different viewpoints. You might also try moving it closer to your eyes.

Now, we can say that this is a *right rectangular prism*. It is a prism because it has two congruent parallel bases, and it is a rectangular prism because the bases are rectangles. It is a *right* rectangular prism because the lateral faces of the prism form right angles with the bases. (Technically, of course, we are not allowed to assume that an angle is a right angle just because it appears to be. However, for this chapter, you may assume that all angles that appear to be right angles are actually right angles.)

(b) This is an *oblique triangular prism*. It has two bases that are in the shapes of triangles, and the lateral faces do not appear to form right angles with the bases.

(c) This is an example of a *right cylinder*. The bases are congruent circles in parallel planes, and the smooth continuous surface connecting the bases appears to form a right angle with the bases. (By the way, you may notice that we drew part of the top circle as dotted. As you may be able to guess, this means that this cylinder is drawn as if we are looking at the bottom and side of the cylinder.)

(d) This is an example of an *oblique pentagonal prism*. It has two bases that appear to be congruent pentagons in parallel planes, and the lateral faces do not appear to be rectangles.

(e) This is an example of an *oblique cylinder*. The bases appear to be congruent circles in parallel planes, and the smooth continuous surface connecting the bases does not appears to form a right angle with the bases.

(f) This solid can be called a *right rectangular prism*, a *right square prism*, or a *cube*. A <u>cube</u> is a right rectangular prism that has all its edges congruent to each other (or, in other words, the bases and all its lateral faces are squares).

(g) This solid is neither a prism nor a cylinder because it does not have two congruent surfaces that we can call bases. It is an example of a *pyramid*, and pyramids will be discussed in the next section.

(h) This is an example of a *right hexagonal prism*. It is turned on its side, but the only shapes that we can call "bases" are the hexagons. Also, we can call it a *right* hexagonal prism because the lateral faces appear to be rectangles.

In the remainder of this chapter, you may assume that all the prisms are right prisms and that all the cylinders are right cylinders.

Now, we need two more definitions.

> The <u>total surface area</u> of a solid is the sum of the areas of all the outer surfaces.

> The <u>lateral area</u> of a solid is the sum of the areas of all the *lateral* surfaces.

To understand these definitions, look at the rectangular prism and the cylinder drawn below.

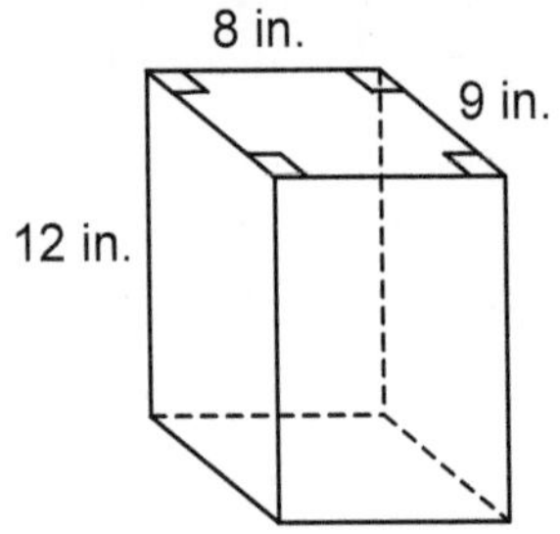

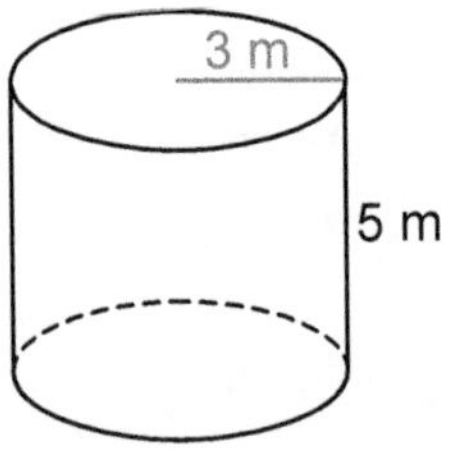

Now, imagine what would happen if we "unfolded" these solids. We would get something like what you see in the pictures below. (If you have trouble seeing this, feel free to make models for yourself. You might choose to "unfold" yours slightly differently, but you should get something very similar to what you see in the pictures below.)

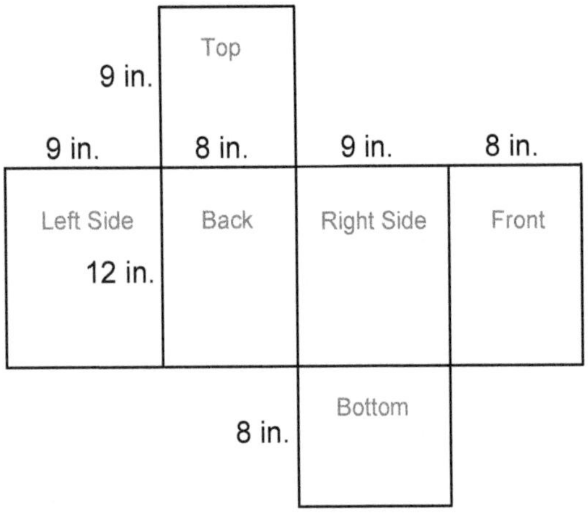

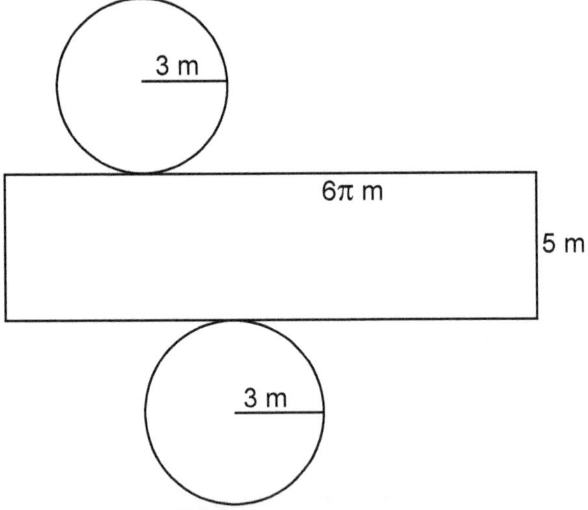

To see why we said that the rectangle we get from unfolding the cylinder has a width of 6π m, imagine putting the cylinder back together and note that the width of this rectangle is equal to the circumference of the base of the cylinder.

Now, we can talk about the total surface area and the lateral area of the rectangular prism and the cylinder drawn above.

The lateral faces of the rectangular prism are the rectangles that we labeled "left side," "back," "right side," and "front." The total area of these surfaces is equal to (12 in.)(9 in. + 8 in. + 9 in. + 8 in.), or 408 square inches. Therefore, the lateral area of the rectangular prism drawn above must equal 408 square inches.

The total surface area of the rectangular prism is equal to sum of the lateral area and the areas of the two bases (the rectangles labeled "top" and "bottom" in the picture above). Since the bases have an area of 72 square inches each, the total surface area of the rectangular prism must equal 552 square inches.

The only lateral surface of the cylinder is the rectangle we drew on the previous page that had a length of 5 m and a width of 6π m. Since this rectangle has an area of 30π m^2, the lateral area of the cylinder must equal 30π square meters.

The total surface area of the cylinder is equal to sum of the lateral area and the areas of the two bases. Since the bases are circles that each have an area of 9π m^2, the total surface area of the rectangular prism must equal 48π square meters.

These two examples give rise to the following theorems.

> The lateral area of a prism or cylinder is given by the formula
> $$L.A. = PH,$$
> where L.A. represents the lateral area of the prism or cylinder, P represents the perimeter or circumference of a base, and H represents the height of the prism or cylinder.

> The total surface area of a prism or cylinder is given by the formula
> $$T.S.A. = L.A. + 2B,$$
> where T.S.A. represents the total surface area of the prism or cylinder, L.A. represents the lateral area of the prism or cylinder, and B represents the area of a base of the prism or cylinder.

Now, let's look at some examples that use these theorems.

Example 2: Find the lateral area and the total surface area of the prism drawn at the right.

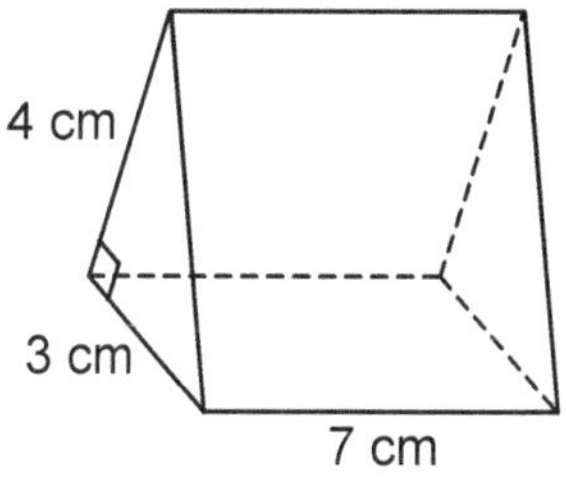

We will begin by noting that the only surfaces that we can call "bases" of this solid are the triangles. Hence, this must be a triangular prism that is lying on its side. So, to use the formulas above, we must imagine the prism turned so that the bases are found on the top and bottom, as shown below.

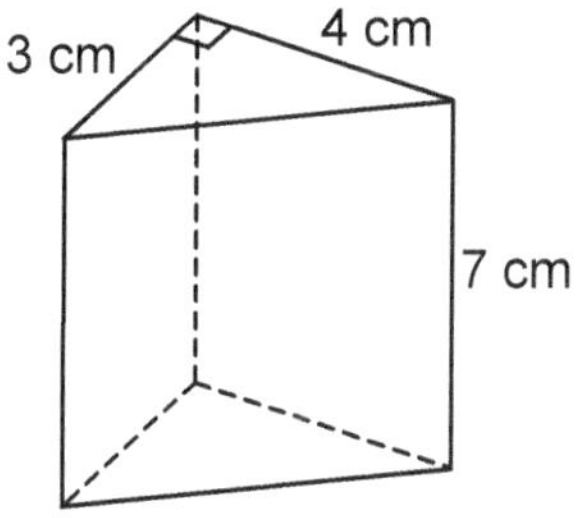

Next, we will note that the Pythagorean Theorem tells us that the third sides of the triangles must each have a length of 5 cm, and so the perimeter of a base must equal (3 + 4 + 5) cm, or 12 cm.

Now, we can use the formulas discussed on the previous page to find the lateral area and the total surface area of this prism.

$L.A. = PH$

$L.A. = (12\text{ cm})(7\text{ cm})$ — The perimeter of a base is 12 cm, and the height of the prism is 7 cm.

$L.A. = 84\text{ cm}^2$

$T.S.A. = L.A. + 2B$

$T.S.A. = 84\text{ cm}^2 + 2(6\text{ cm}^2)$ — Note that each base must have an area of $\frac{1}{2}(3\text{ cm})(4\text{ cm})$, or 6 cm^2, and we just said that the lateral area of this prism is 84 cm^2.

$T.S.A. = 96\text{ cm}^2$

Example 3: The base of a cylinder has a diameter of 30 inches, and the height of the cylinder is 18 inches. Find the lateral area and the total surface area of the cylinder.

We can work this problem using the formulas on the previous page, as shown below.

$L.A. = PH$

$L.A. = (30\pi\text{ in.})(18\text{ in.})$ — If the diameter of a base is 30 inches, then the radius must have a length of 15 inches. Therefore, the circumference of a base must equal $2\pi(15\text{ in.})$, or 30π in. Also note that the question told us that the height of the cylinder is 18 inches.

$L.A. = 540\pi\text{ in.}^2$

$T.S.A. = L.A. + 2B$

$T.S.A. = 540\pi\text{ in.}^2 + 2(225\pi\text{ in.}^2)$ — Each base of this cylinder must have an area of $\pi(15\text{ in.})^2$, or $225\pi\text{ in.}^2$, and we just said that the lateral area of this cylinder is 540π square inches.

$T.S.A. = 990\pi\text{ in.}^2$

Example 4: The total surface area of a prism with a square base is 126 square yards. If the height of the prism is equal to 3 times the length of a side of the base, what are the dimensions of the prism?

We will begin by drawing a picture to describe the rectangular prism described above.

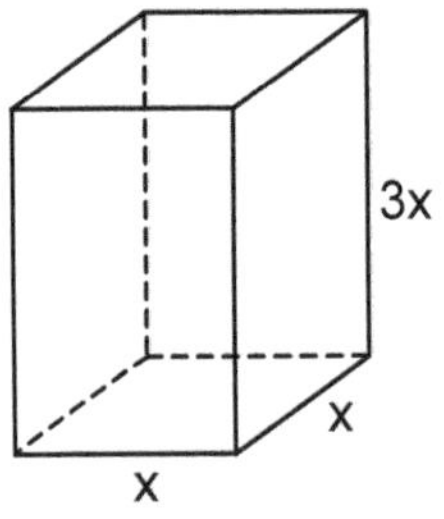

Now, we can use the formulas for lateral area and total surface area that we discussed earlier to finish working this problem.

$$T.S.A. = L.A. + 2B$$

$$T.S.A. = PH + 2B$$

$$126 \text{ yds}^2 = (4x)(3x) + 2(x^2)$$

Note that the perimeter of a base of the prism is equal to x + x + x + x, or 4x. Also note that the area of a base is equal to x • x, or x^2.

$$126 \text{ yds}^2 = 12x^2 + 2x^2$$

$$126 \text{ yds}^2 = 14x^2$$

$$9 \text{ yds}^2 = x^2$$

$$3 \text{ yds} = x$$

Take the square of both sides. (Technically, this should say x = ±3 yds. However, since x represents the length of a side of the box, x cannot be negative.)

This tells us that the length and width of the box are both 3 yards, and the height of the box is 9 yards.

Example 5: You want to stain a wooden rectangular box with no top. The bottom of the box is a square that measures 1½ feet on each side, and the sides of the box are all 2 feet tall. If you want to stain the sides and the bottom of the box, how much stain do you need? Assume that you only want to stain the outside of the box.

We will use the formula for total surface area of a prism, but we will add 1B (and not 2B) because the box has no top.

$$T.S.A. = L.A. + 1B$$

$$T.S.A. = PH + 1B$$

$$T.S.A. = (6 \text{ ft})(2 \text{ ft}) + 1(2.25 \text{ ft}^2)$$

Note that the perimeter of the base is equal to 4 • 1.5 ft, or 6 ft, and that the area of the base is equal to 1.5 ft • 1.5 ft, or 2.25 ft^2.

$$T.S.A. = 12 \text{ ft}^2 + 2.25 \text{ ft}^2$$

$$T.S.A. = 14.25 \text{ ft}^2$$

This tells us that you need a stain that covers at least 14.25 square feet.

Problems:

1-13. Find the lateral area and the total surface area of each of the solids drawn below.

1. Lateral area: _______________

   Total surface area: _______________

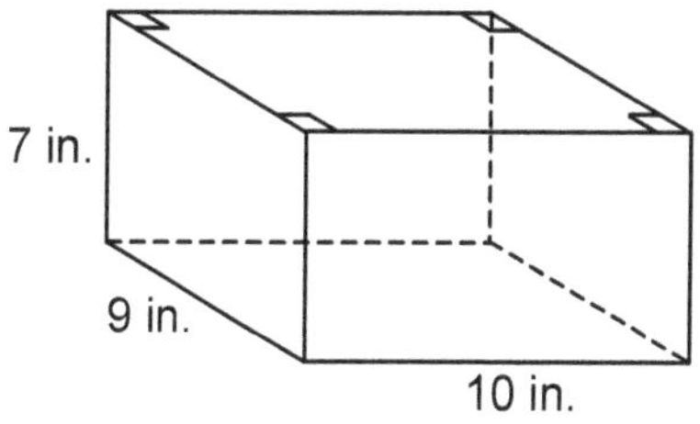

2. Lateral area: ________________

Total surface area: ________________

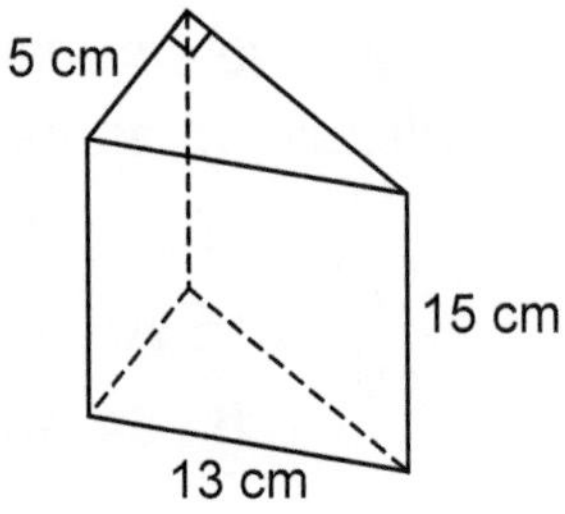

3. Lateral area: ________________

Total surface area: ________________

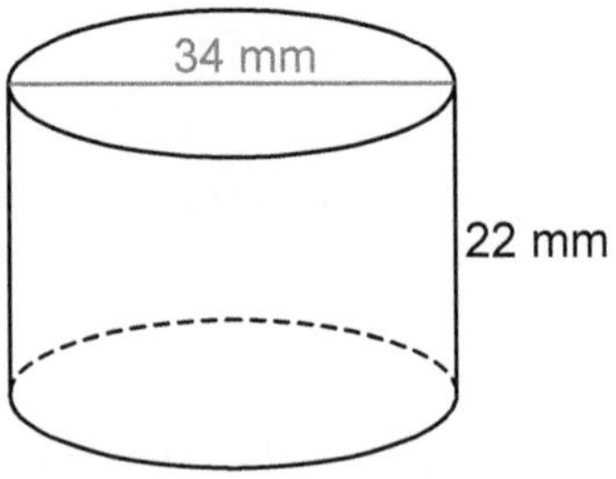

4. Lateral area: ________________

Total surface area: ________________

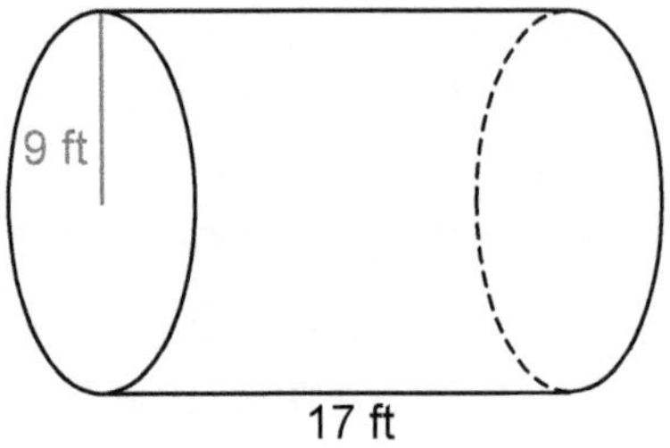

5. Lateral area: ________________

Total surface area: ________________

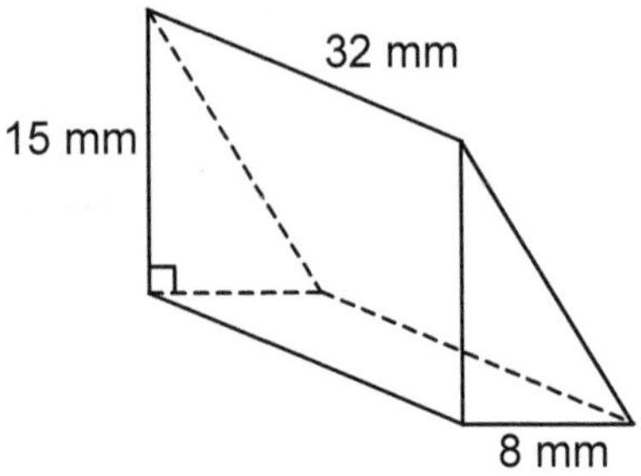

6. Lateral area: ________________

Total surface area: ________________

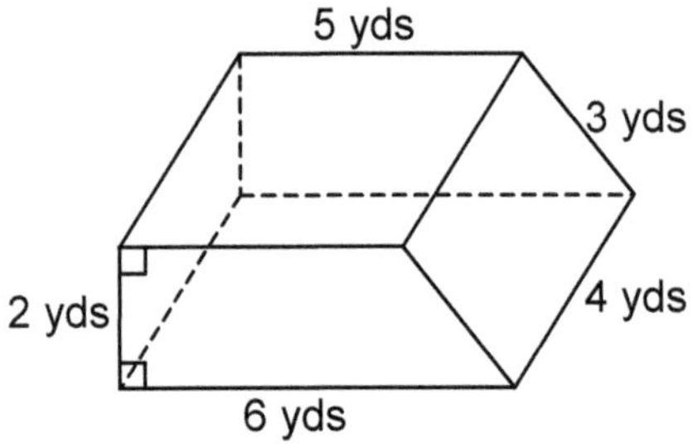

7. Lateral area: _______________

Total surface area: _______________

(Assume that the pentagons are *regular* pentagons. Also, you may find it helpful to review Part IV of Chapter 12 before you try to find the total surface area.)

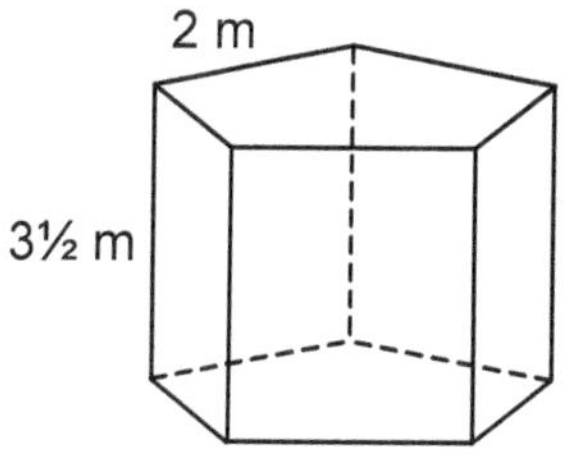

8. Lateral area: _______________

Total surface area: _______________

(Assume that the hexagons are regular hexagons.)

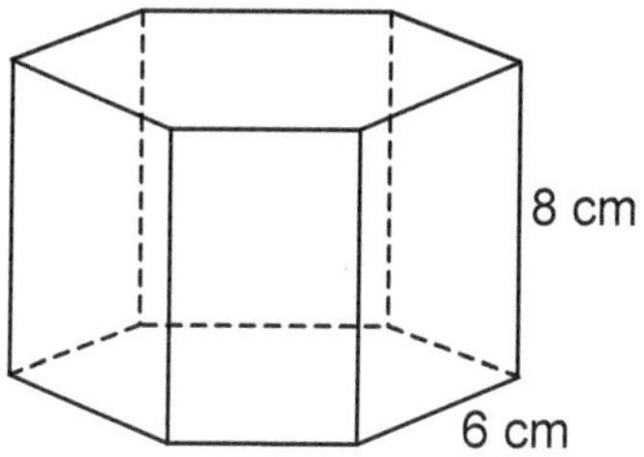

9. Lateral area: _______________

Total surface area: _______________

(Assume that the triangles are equilateral triangles.)

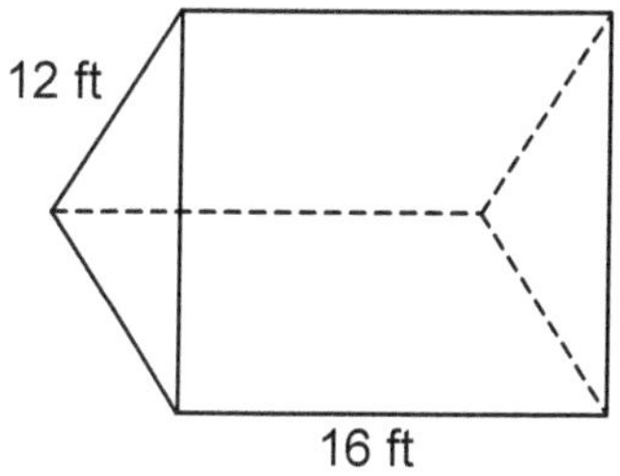

10. Lateral area: _______________

Total surface area: _______________

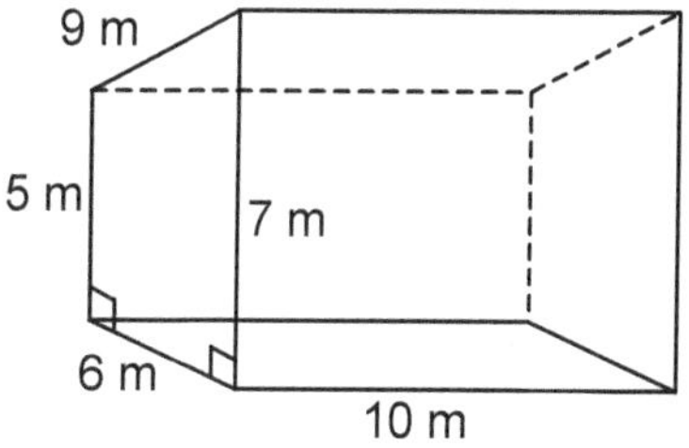

11. Lateral area: _______________

Total surface area: _______________

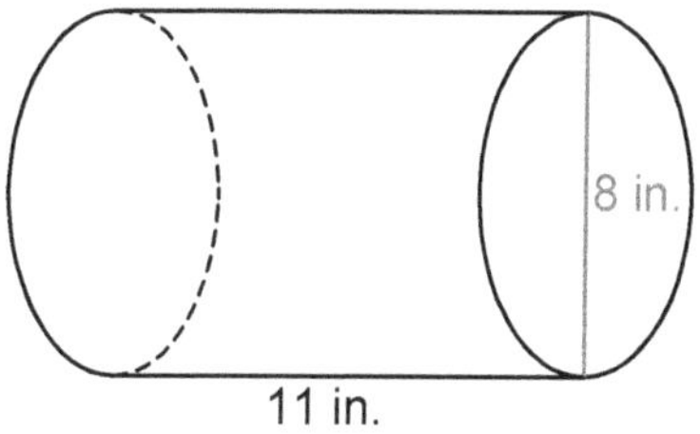

12. Lateral area: _______________

Total surface area: _______________

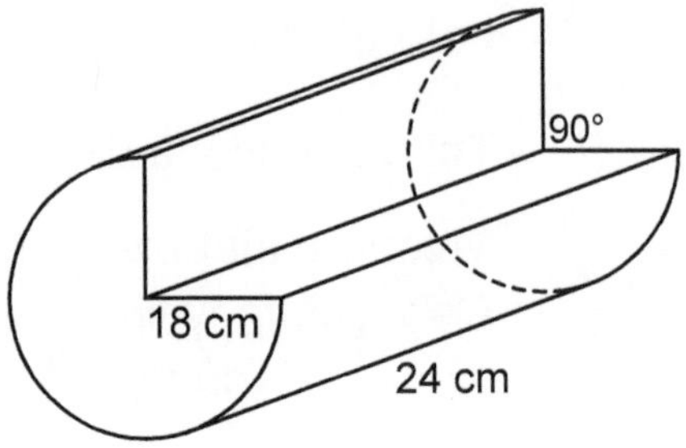

13. Lateral area: _______________

Total surface area: _______________

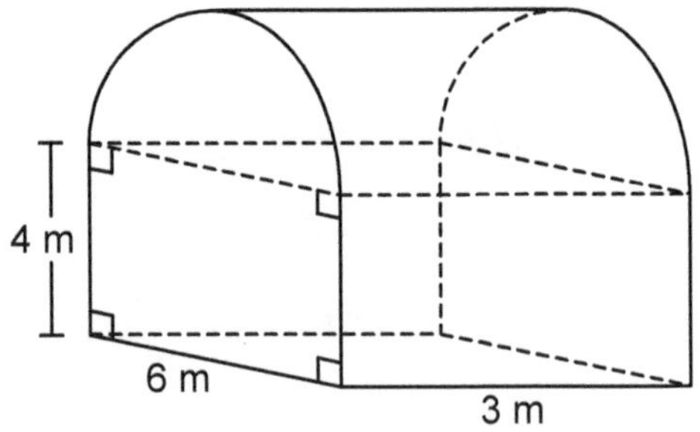

14-20. Find the lateral area and the total surface area of each of the solids described below.

14. The length of each side of a cube is 23 millimeters. Then the lateral area of the cube is _______________, and the total surface area of the cube is _______________.

15. A prism has a base that is a regular hexagon. The prism is 19 inches tall, and each side of the hexagon has a length of 8 inches. Then the lateral area of the prism is _______________, and the total surface area of the prism is _______________.

16. A prism has a base that is a regular octagon. The prism is 20 centimeters tall, and each side of the octagon has a length of 12 centimeters. Then the lateral area of the prism is ______________, and the total surface area of the prism is ______________.

17. A cylinder that has a height of 16 feet, and the bases each have a diameter of 10 feet. Then the lateral area of the cylinder is ______________, and the total surface area of the cylinder is ______________.

18. A base of a prism is shown at the right. If the height of the prism is 5 yards, then the lateral area of the prism is ______________, and the total surface area of the prism is ______________.

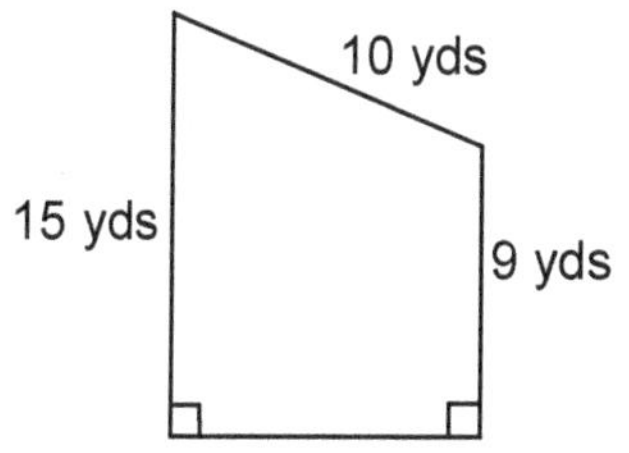

19. A base of a prism is shown at the right. If the prism has a height of 33 millimeters, then the lateral area of the prism is ______________, and the total surface area of the prism is ______________.

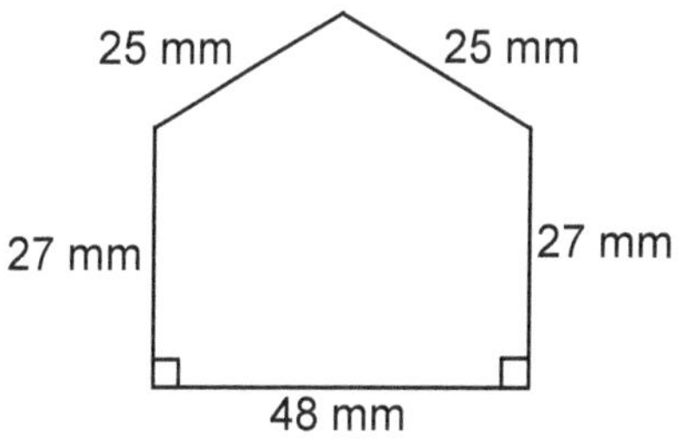

20. A base of a prism is shown at the right. If the prism has a height of 5 feet, then the lateral area of the prism is _______________, and the total surface area of the prism is _______________. (Assume that all the angles are right angles.)

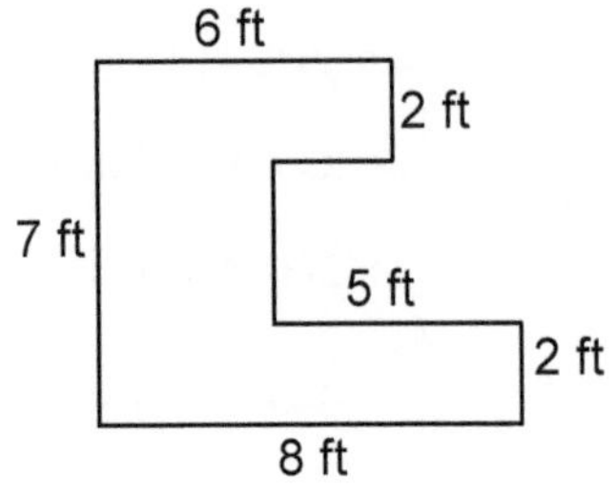

21. The base of a prism is shown at the right. If the prism has a height of 8 inches, then the lateral area of the prism is _______________, and the total surface area of the prism is _______________.

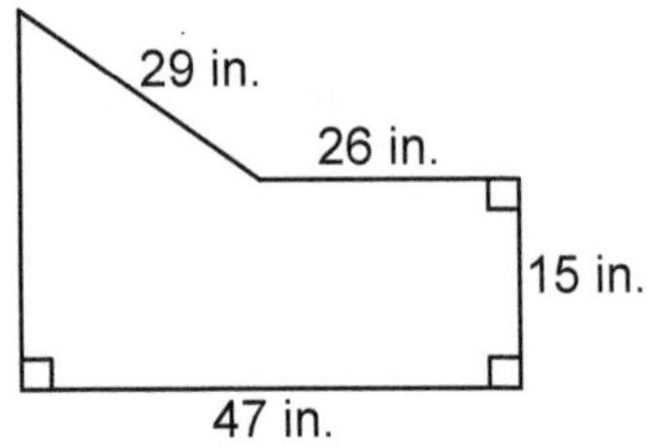

22. The lateral area of a prism that has a regular octagon as its base is 280 square feet. If the height of the prism is 7 feet, then a side of the octagon has a length of _______________.

23. If a cube has a lateral surface area of 28 square yards, then the total surface area of the cube is _______________.

24. A rectangular prism has a height of 2 meters, and the width of the prism is 3 meters more than its length. If the total surface area of the prism is 208 m^2, then the length of the prism is _______________, and the width of the prism is _______________.

25. A cylinder has a total surface area of 288π mm^2. If the radius of a base has a length of 9 inches, then the height of the cylinder is _____________.

26. If a cylinder has a lateral area of 90π square inches and a height of 9 inches, then the total surface area of the cylinder is _____________.

27. A prism has a lateral area of 360 cm^2. If the height of the prism is 15 cm, and if each base of the prism is a regular hexagon, then the area of a base is _____________.

28. Simon wants to paint the walls and the ceiling of a rectangular room that is 12 feet long, 14 feet wide, and 9 feet high. If one quart of paint covers 100 ft^2, how many quarts of paint does he need? Assume that he can only buy whole quarts.

____

29. A packaging company needs to make some rectangular cardboard boxes that are all 14 inches wide, 25 inches long, and 8 inches tall. If the company wants to make 100 of these boxes, then they will need at least ___________ square feet of cardboard. (Assume that the boxes will each have bottom and a top.)

30. The sides of a can of biscuits will be made of cardboard. The bases of the cans will each have a diameter of 2 inches, and the cans will be 5 inches tall. How much cardboard will be needed to make 30 of these cans? _____________.

31. A tent manufacturer wants to make a tent with the shown at the right. If the manufacturer of the tent will cover the front, back, bottom, and sides of the tent with fabric, how many square feet of fabric will be needed to make 10 of these tents? Assume that the triangles are isosceles triangles.______________

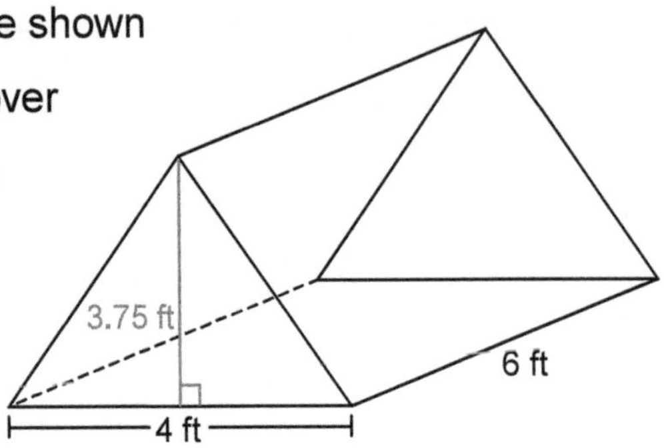

32. The tent manufacturer mentioned in #31 is also considering making the tent shown at the right. Then the manufacturer will need at least ____________ square feet of fabric to make 15 of these tents. (Assume that the two unlabeled sides of the pentagons are congruent to each other and that the manufacturer will still cover the front, back, bottom, and sides of the tent with fabric.)

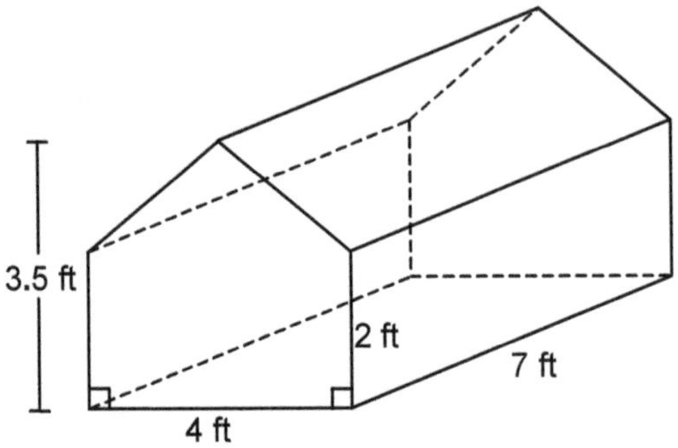

33. Refer back to #31 and #32. If the fabric costs $7 per square foot, then the cost of the fabric for the 10 tents in #31 will be ______________, and the cost of the fabric for the 15 tents in #32 will be ______________.

34. The sides and the bottom of a rectangular swimming pool will be lined with vinyl. If the swimming pool is in the shape of a rectangular prism with a length of 20 yards, a width of 18 yards, and a depth of 2 yards, how many square yards of vinyl will be needed? ______________

Part II – Volume of Prisms and Cylinders

We will begin this section with a definition.

The volume of a solid is the amount of three-dimensional space enclosed by the solid.

Now, let's look at two cubes: one that measures 1 centimeter on each side, and one that measures 1 centimeter on each side.

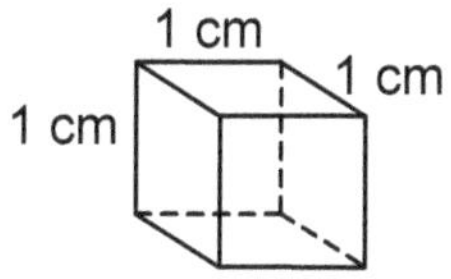

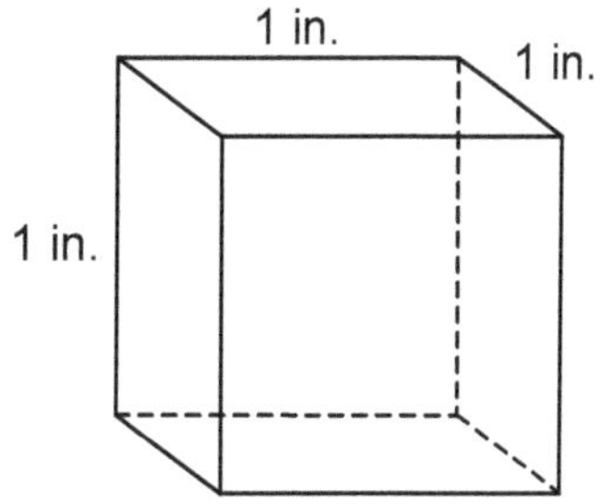

If we want to talk about the amount of space inside these cubes, we can say that the volume of the cube on the left is 1 cubic centimeter (which we can abbreviate as 1 cm^3), and the volume of the cube on the right is 1 cubic inch (which we can abbreviate as 1 $in.^3$). Similarly, 1 m^3 is defined as the amount of space enclosed by a cube that measures 1 meter on each side, and 1 cubic foot is defined as the amount of space enclosed by a cube that measures 1 foot on each side.

You can also measure volume using units like liters, gallons, and pints, but we will confine our discussion in this book to problems that involve cubic units (such as cubic inches or cubic centimeters).

In Examples 1-3, we will find the volume of three of the solids that we looked at in Part I of this chapter.

Example 1: Find the volume of the rectangular prism shown at the right.

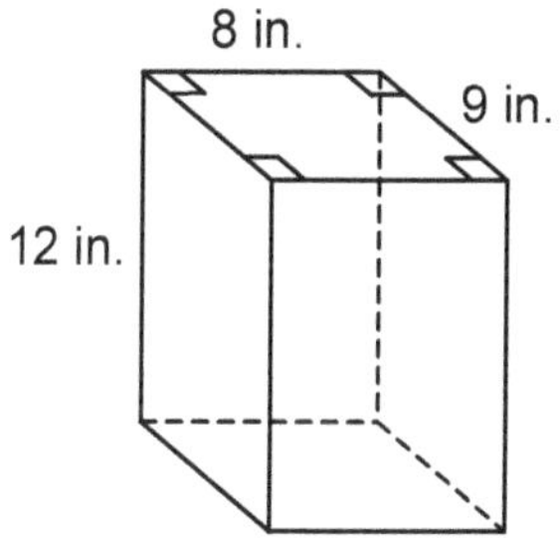

We will begin by noting that the base of this prism has an area of 72 square inches. So, imagine a set of 72 cubes that all measure 1 inch on each side covering the bottom of the prism, as shown below.

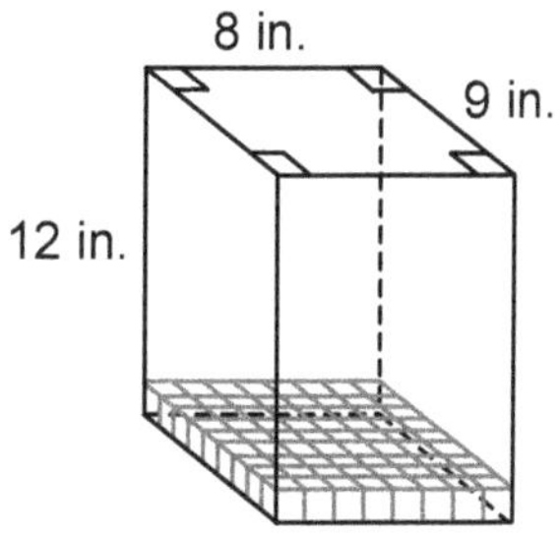

Now, since the height of the prism is 12 inches, you should notice that we can fill up the entire space inside this rectangular prism by adding 11 more rows (for a total of 12 rows) of these cubes. This tells us that, in order to find the volume of this prism, we can add 72 in.^{3} to itself 12 times. Or, in other words, we could find the volume by multiplying 72 in.^{2} by 12 inches. Either way, you should find that the volume of this prism is 864 cubic inches.

Example 2: Find the volume of the cylinder shown at the right.

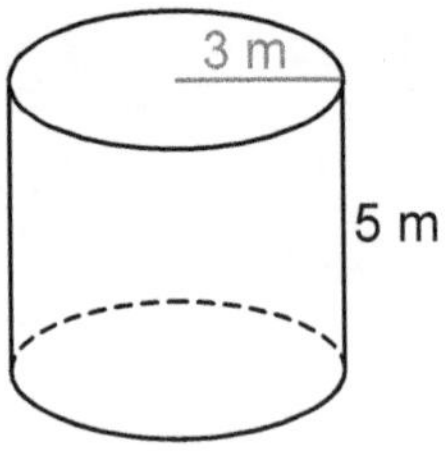

Notice that the area of a base of this cylinder is 9π m^2. We can't really draw cubes on the base of the cylinder like we did in Example 1, but, if you use the same thought process, you should realize that the volume of this cylinder is equal to (9π m^2)(5 m), or 45π m^3.

These two examples and the thought process behind them give rise to the following formula.

> The volume of a prism or cylinder is given by the formula
>
> $$V = BH,$$
>
> where V represents the volume of the prism or cylinder, B represents the area of a base, and H represents the height of the prism or cylinder.

Now, let's look at some examples that use this formula.

Example 3: Find the volume of the triangular prism shown at the right.

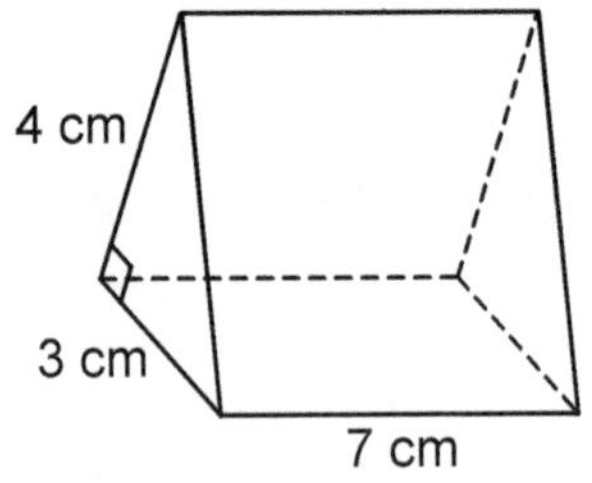

As we said in Part I of this chapter, the only surfaces that we can call "bases" of this solid are the triangles. So, to use the formula above, we must imagine the prism turned so that the bases are found on the top and bottom.

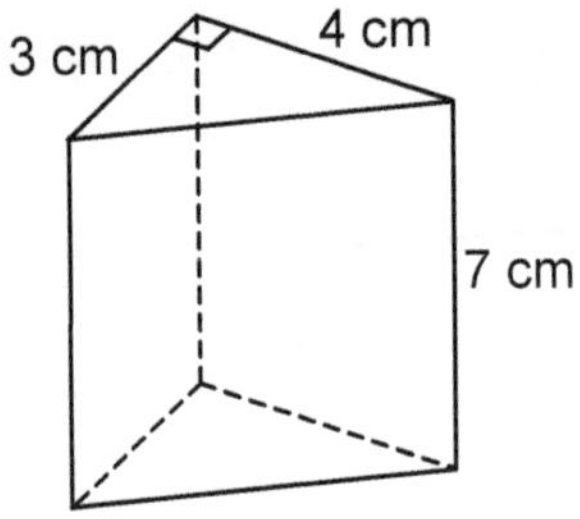

As we said in Part I, the bases of this prism are triangles that each have an area of 6 cm^2, and so the volume of this prism must be equal to (6 cm^2)(7 cm), or 42 cm^3.

Example 4: The volume of a cylinder is equal to 275π cubic feet. If the height of the cylinder is 11 feet, what is the length of a diameter of a base?

We can use the formula V = BH to solve this problem, as shown on the next page.

$V = BH$	
$275\pi \text{ ft}^3 = B(11 \text{ ft})$	We were told that the volume of the cylinder is $275\pi \text{ ft}^3$ and that the height of the cylinder is 11 feet.
$25\pi \text{ ft}^2 = B$	Divide both sides by 11 feet.
$25\pi \text{ ft}^2 = \pi r^2$	Since the solid is a cylinder, we can represent the area of a base by writing πr^2.
$25 \text{ ft}^2 = r^2$	Divide both sides by π.
$5 \text{ ft} = r$	Take the square root of both sides.

Now, since the length of a diameter of a circle is equal to twice the length of its radius, we can say that the diameter of a base must have a length of 10 feet.

Example 5: Matthew wants to put in a set of concrete steps to the front door of a house he is building. The drawing at the right shows the dimensions of the set of steps. The steps will be made of concrete, and the concrete will cost $25 per cubic foot (installed). How much money should Matthew have to spend on these steps?

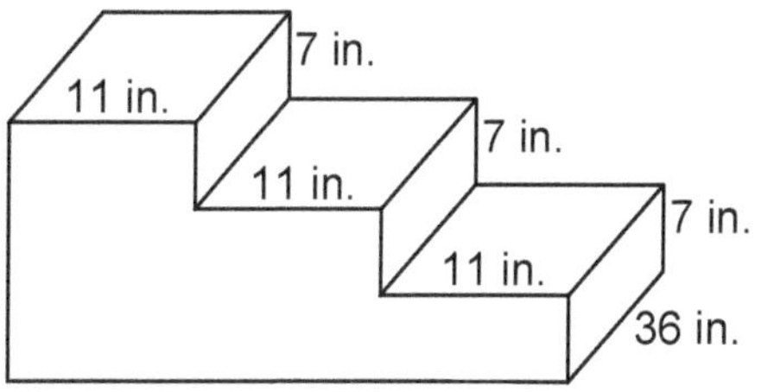

We will begin by noting that the steps have the shape of a prism, but the "bases" of the prism are actually the *sides* of the steps.* So, we must begin by finding the area of one of these sides. We will do this by splitting this shape up into rectangles and then finding the area of each rectangle, like we discussed in Part II of Chapter 12.

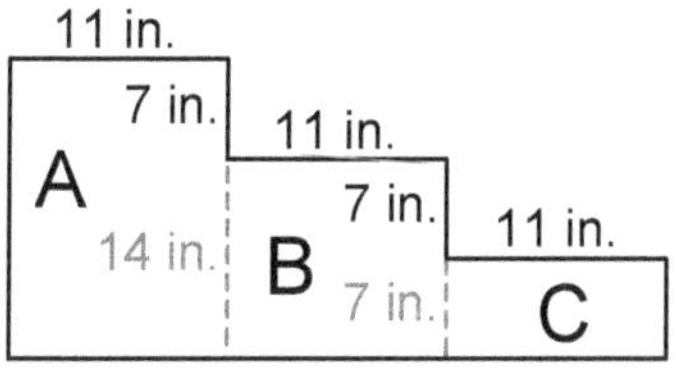

The area of region A in the figure above is 231 square inches, the area of region B in the figure above is 154 square inches, and the area of region C in the figure above is 77 square inches. This tells us that the total area of one of the sides of the steps is 462 square inches. When we multiply this by the height of the prism (the 36 inches), we find that the total volume of the steps is 16,632 cubic inches.

*We could also look at this at three separate rectangular prisms, as shown below. If you choose to look at this problem like this, you would not have to imaging the steps turned on their side, but you should still find that the total volume of the concrete 16,632 cubic inches.

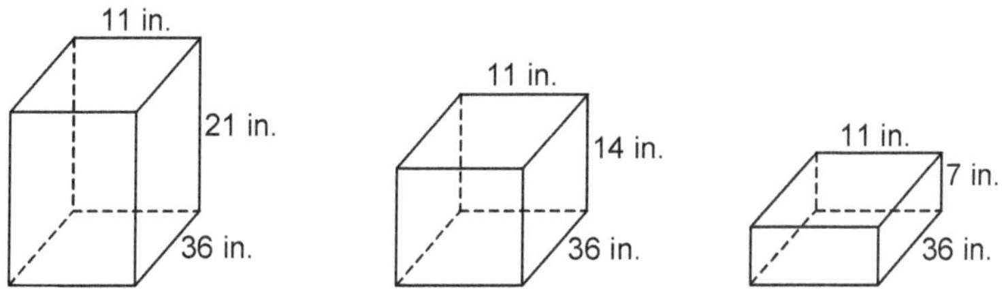

Now, we need to find out how much this amount of concrete should cost.

The question tells us that the concrete costs $25 for each cubic *foot*, and so we must divide the 16,632 cubic inches by 12^3, or 1728, to find out how many cubic feet this is. (To see why we need to do this, look back at Example 8 from Part II of Chapter 12. The reasoning here is very similar to why we divided by 9 in that example.) This tells us that these steps will have a volume of 9.625 cubic feet. Now, when we multiply this by the cost of 1 cubic foot, we find that the cost of the concrete should be $240.63.

Problems:

1-13. Find the volume of each of the solids drawn below. Assume that the prisms are right prisms and that the cylinders are right cylinders. (Notice that these solids are identical to the ones you saw in the problems in Part I, but now you need to find the volume instead of the lateral area and total surface area.)

1. Volume: _______________

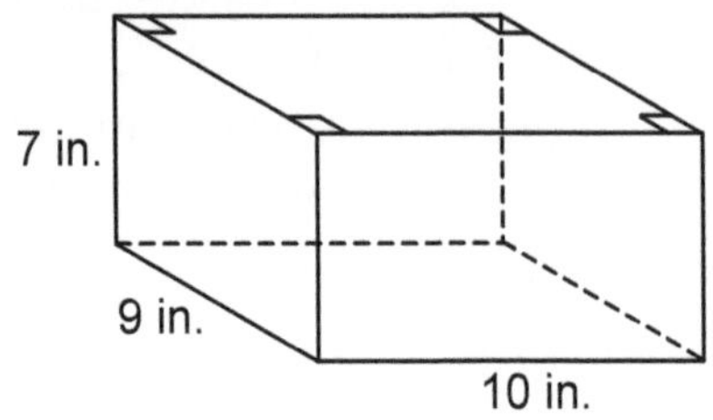

2. Volume: _______________

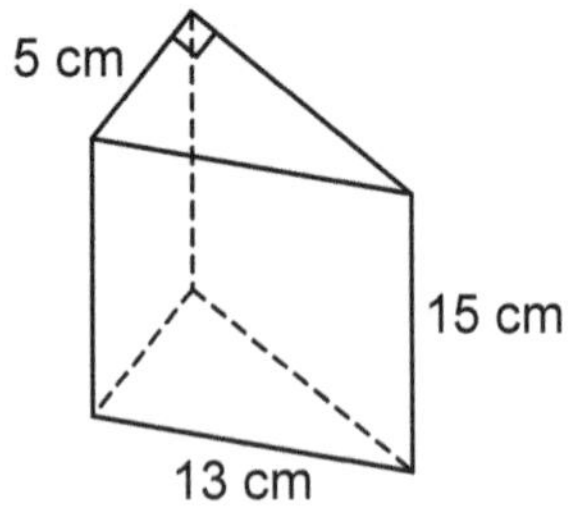

3. Volume: _______________

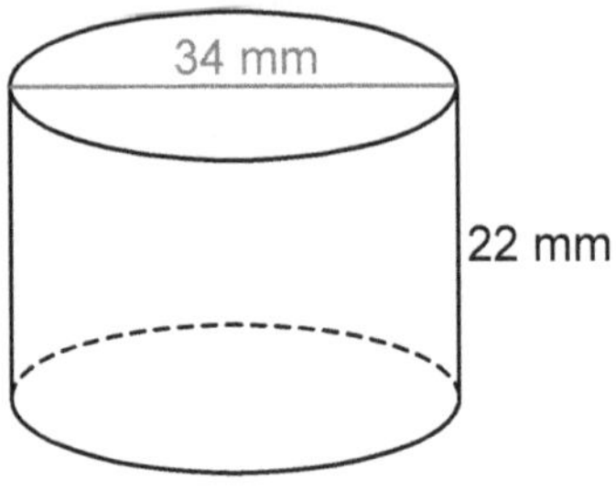

4. Volume: _______________

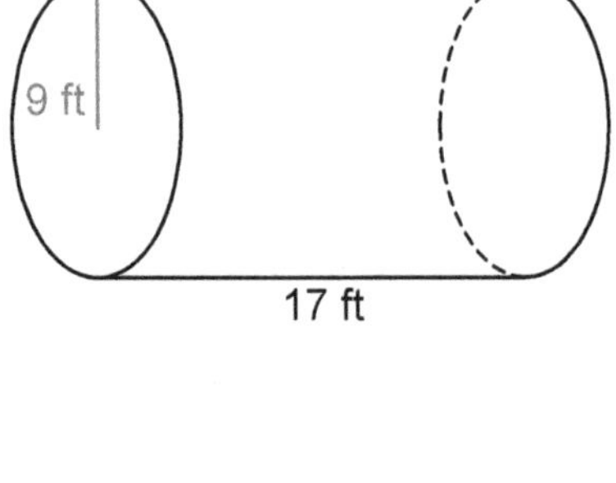

5. Volume: _______________

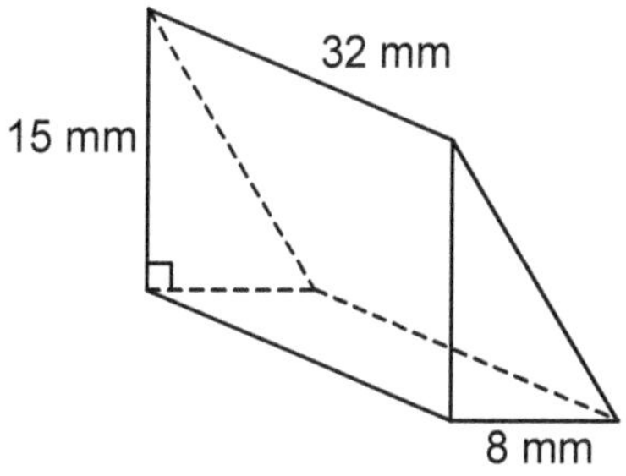

6. Volume: _______________

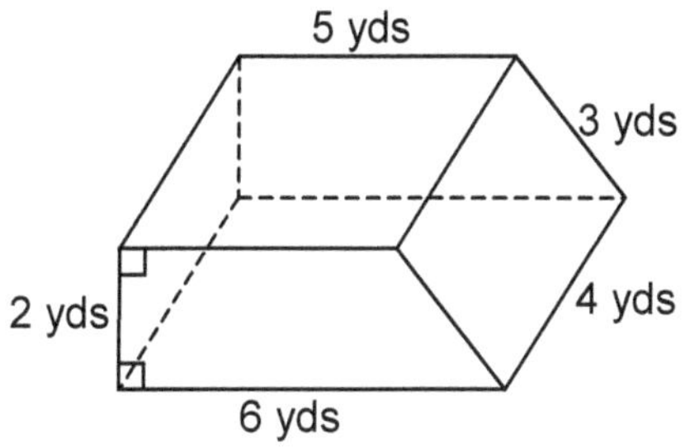

7. Volume: _______________
(Assume that the pentagons are regular pentagons.)

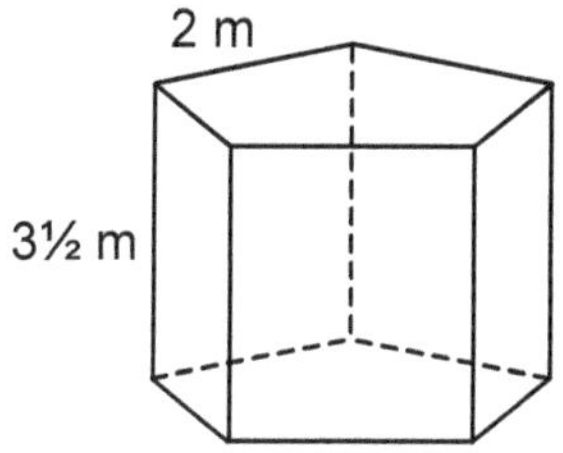

8. Volume: _______________
(Assume that the hexagons are regular hexagons.)

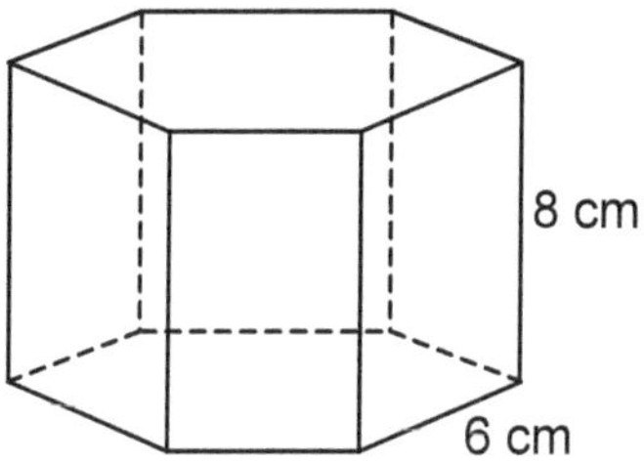

9. Volume: _______________
(Assume that the triangles are equilateral triangles.)

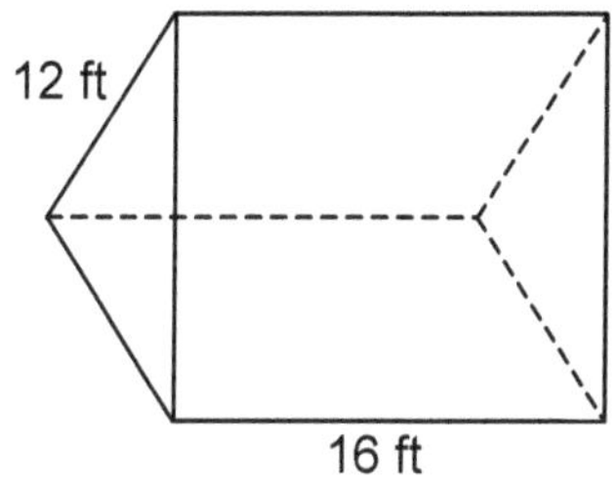

10. Volume: _______________

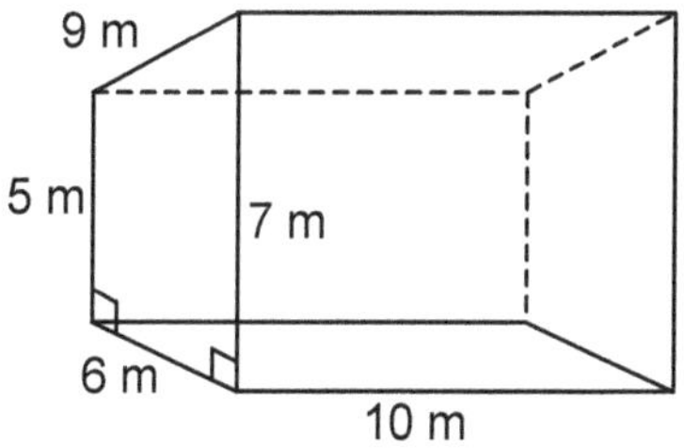

11. Volume: _______________

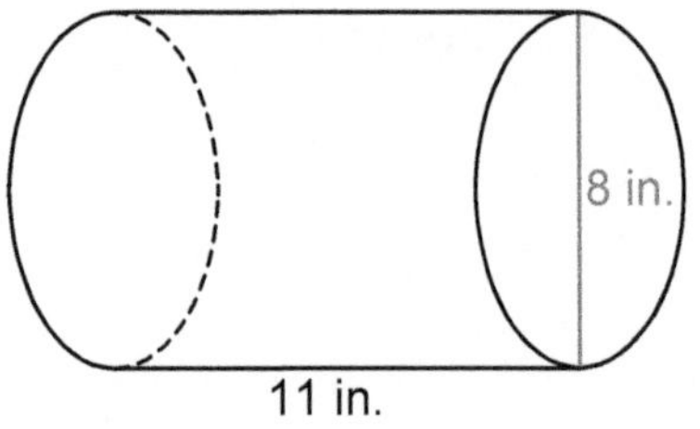

12. Volume: _______________

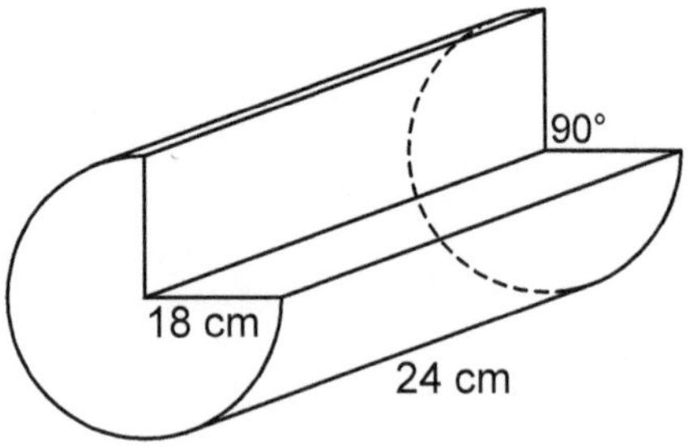

13. Volume: _______________

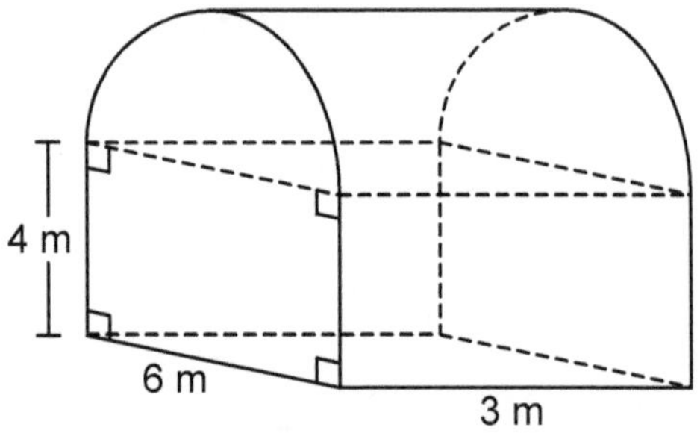

14-20. Find the lateral area and the total surface area of each of the solids described below. Assume that the prisms are right prisms and that the cylinders are right cylinders. (Notice that these solids are also identical to the ones you saw in the problems in Part I.)

14. The length of each side of a cube is 23 millimeters. Then the volume of the cube is _______________.

15. A prism has a base that is a regular hexagon. The prism is 19 inches tall, and each side of the hexagon has a length of 8 inches. Then the volume of the prism is _______________.

16. A prism has a base that is a regular octagon. The prism is 20 centimeters tall, and each side of the octagon has a length of 12 centimeters. Then the volume of the prism is _______________.

17. A cylinder has a height of 16 feet, and the bases each have a diameter of 10 feet. Then the volume of the cylinder is _______________.

18. A base of a prism is shown at the right. If the height of the prism is 5 yards, then the volume of the prism is _______________.

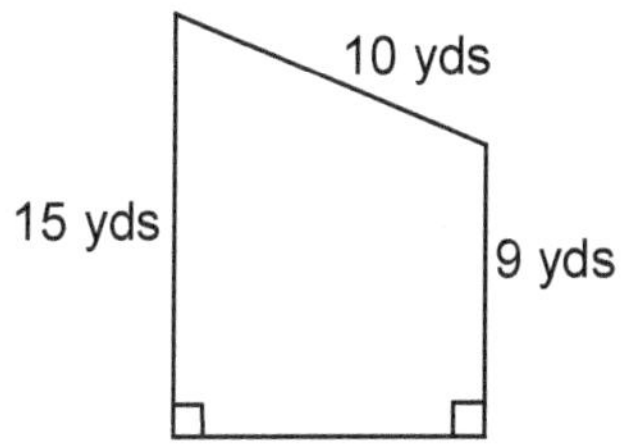

19. A base of a prism is shown at the right. If the prism has a height of 33 millimeters, then the volume of the prism is _______________.

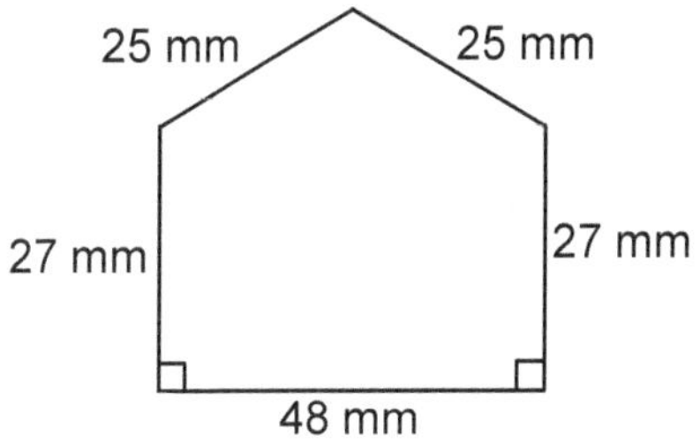

20. A base of a prism is shown at the right. If the prism has a height of 5 feet, then the volume of the prism is _______________. (Assume that all the angles are right angles.)

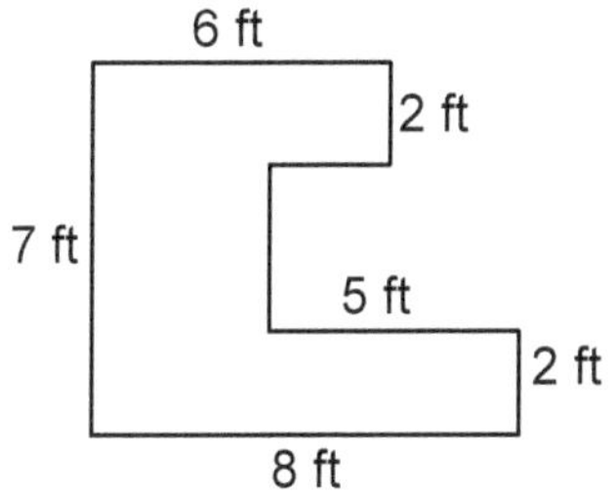

21. A base of a prism is shown at the right. If the prism has a height of 8 inches, then the volume of the prism is _______________.

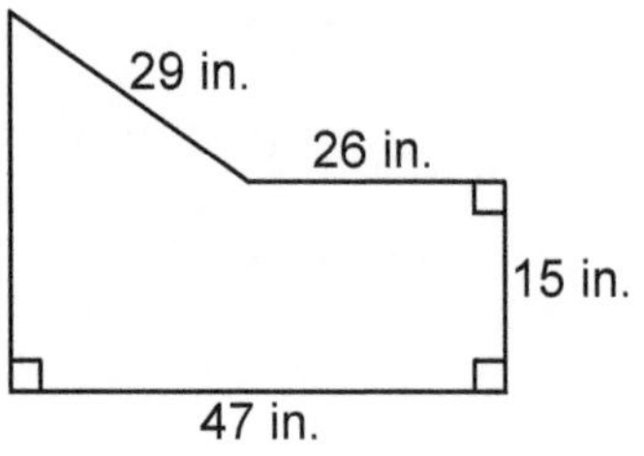

22. The volume of a rectangular prism is 4760 m^3. The height of the prism is 7 m, and the length of the prism is 6 m more than twice its width. Then the length of the prism is _______________, and the width of the prism is _______________.

23. A prism has a height of 25 cm and a lateral area of 2100 cm^2. If the bases of the prism are equilateral triangles, then the volume of the prism is _______________.

24. A cylinder has a volume of 144π in^3. If the height of the cylinder is 9 inches, then the total surface area of the cylinder is _______________.

25. The height of a prism with a square base is 8 ft. If the volume of the prism is 1152 cubic feet, then the total surface area of the prism is _______________.

26. If the volume of a cube is 8 cubic yards, then the then the lateral area of the prism is _______________, and the total surface area of the prism is _______________.

27. A cylinder has a total surface area of 152π mm^2. If the radius of the base is 4 mm, then the volume of the cylinder is _____________.

28. A swimming pool has the shape of a trapezoidal prism, and its dimensions are shown at the right. If a drain in the bottom of the pool can make the water drain at a rate of 2 cubic feet per minute, how long will it take to empty the pool if it starts out completely filled with water?

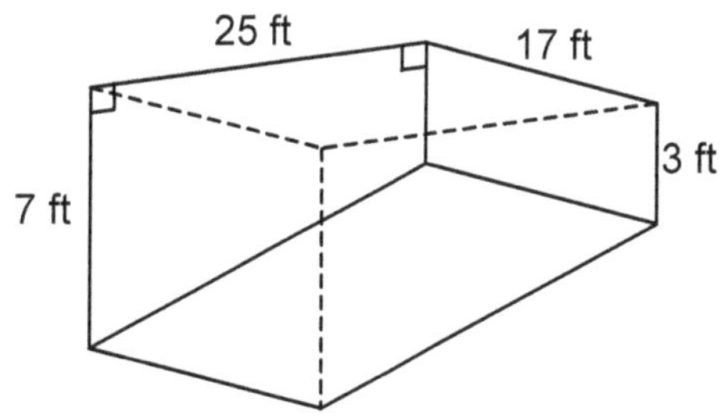

____

29. The dimensions of the inside of a gasoline tanker truck are shown at the right. If Ryan owns a gasoline station and has calculated that the average person gets about 2 cubic feet of gasoline at a time, about how many customers will Ryan be able to serve with the gasoline that this tanker truck can hold? _____________

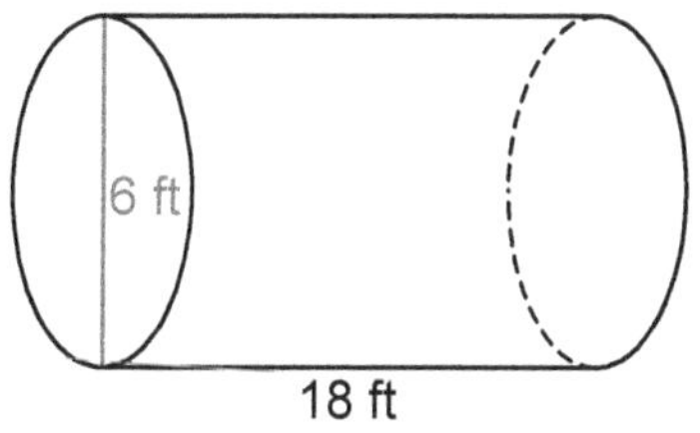

30. Henry has calculated that the floor of an office building has 5062 square feet, and the ceilings are all 8 feet high. If a manufacturer of a certain air conditioner recommends that 1 air conditioner should be installed for every 13,500 cubic feet of air, how many of these air conditioners does Henry need to install for this office building? _____________

31. How much dirt would be needed to fill a sinkhole that has the dimensions shown at the right? _______________

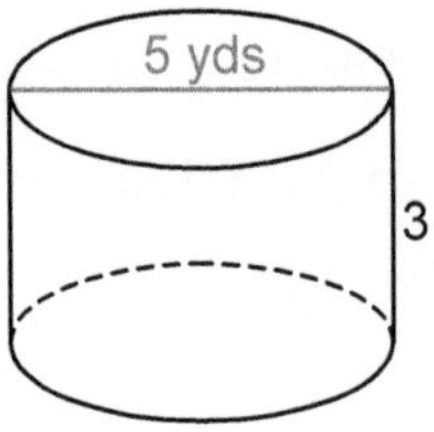

32. The diameter of the base of a can of soup is 7 centimeters, and the height of the can is 10 centimeters. If the soup has a density of 1.5 grams per cubic centimeter, about how many grams of soup will fit in this can? _______________

33. A certain cereal box is 2 inches wide, 10 inches long, and 12 inches high. What is the volume of the cereal box? _______________

34. Dustin is going to put mulch in his yard. He wants to cover an area of 250 square feet with a layer of mulch that is 3 inches (¼ foot) thick. If the mulch comes in bags that cover 2 cubic feet each, how many bags does he need to buy? Assume that he can only buy whole bags. _______________

35. You may have noticed a note on the packages of cereal boxes or other boxes of food that says something like this: "This package is sold by weight, not volume. Some settling may occur during shipment." Explain what this statement means.

____

____

Part III – Surface Area of Pyramids, Cones, and Spheres

We will begin this section with some definitions.

A <u>pyramid</u> is a solid that has a single polygonal base and triangular lateral faces that all intersect at a single point, called the <u>vertex</u> or <u>apex</u> of the pyramid. Pyramids are named according to the shapes of their bases.

A <u>cone</u> is a solid that tapers smoothly from a flat circular base to a single point, called the <u>vertex</u> or <u>apex</u> of the cone.

The <u>altitude</u> of a pyramid or cone is the segment that has one endpoint at the apex of the pyramid or cone and the other at the base and is perpendicular to the base. The length of this segment is also called the <u>height</u> of the pyramid or cone.

A <u>right</u> pyramid or cone is a pyramid or cone in which one of the endpoints of the altitude is the center of the base or cone. An <u>oblique</u> pyramid or cone is a pyramid or cone in which the segment joining the vertex and the center of the base is not perpendicular to the base of the pyramid or cone.

A <u>sphere</u> is a solid that consists of all the points that are a given distance from a certain point. The given distance is called the <u>radius</u> of the sphere, and the certain point is called the <u>center</u> of the sphere.

Example 1: Classify each of the following solids using the terms above.

(a)

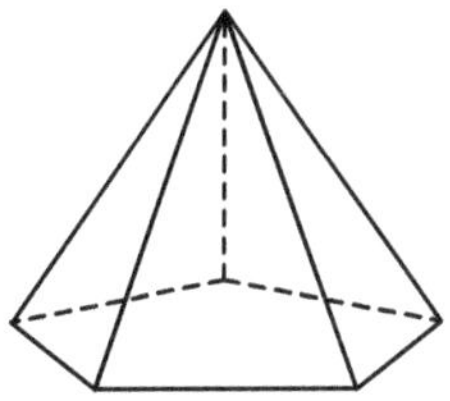

(b)

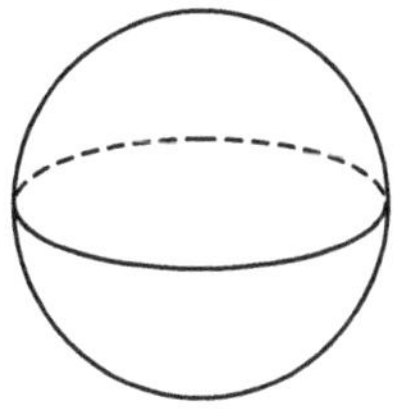

(c)

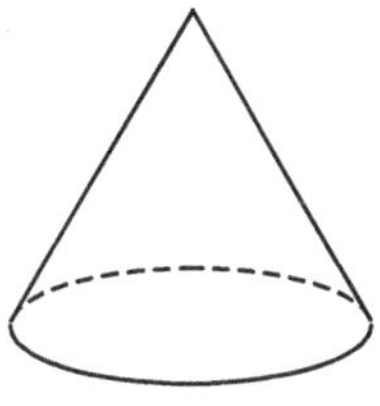

(d)

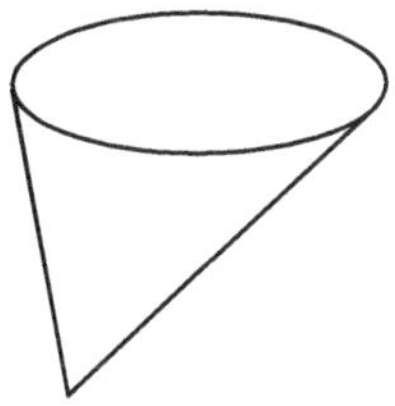

(e)

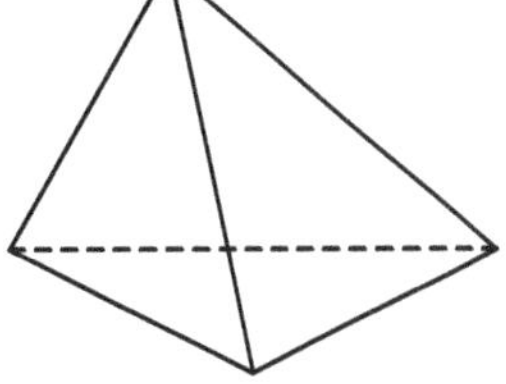

(f)

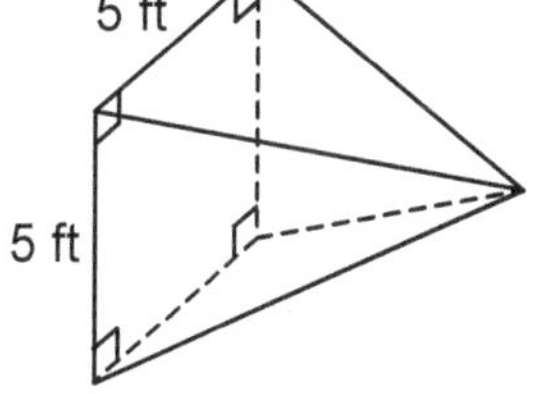

(a) This is an example of a *right pentagonal pyramid*. It is a pentagonal pyramid because it has a single base that is in the shape of a pentagon and triangles for lateral faces, and it is a *right* pentagonal pyramid because the segment that joins the apex and the center of the base appears to be perpendicular to the base of the pyramid.

(b) This is an example of a *sphere*. (There are no edges to a sphere, so the arcs you see in the middle of the sphere are not really edges, but we have to draw them so that anyone who looks at this picture will know that the picture is one of is a three-dimensional figure, and not a flat circle.)

(c) This is an example of a *right cone*. It has a single circular base, and the segment that joins the apex and the center of the base appears to be perpendicular to the base.

(d) This is an example of an *oblique cone*. It has a single circular base, and the segment that joins the apex and the center of the base does not appear to be perpendicular to the base.

(e) This is an example of an *oblique triangular pyramid*. It has a single base that is in the shape of a triangle, and the segment that joins the apex and the center of the base does not appear to be perpendicular to the base.

(f) This is an example of a *right square pyramid*. It is turned sideways, but we can still say that it has a single base that is in the shape of a square and that the segment that joins the apex and the center of the base appears to be perpendicular to this base.

In the remainder of this chapter, you may assume that all the pyramids and cones are *right* pyramids and cones unless you are told otherwise, and you may also assume that all the bases of the pyramids are regular polygons unless you are told otherwise.

Before we can look at how we can find the lateral area and the total surface area of pyramids and cones, we need two more definitions.

The slant height of a pyramid is equal to the height of a lateral face of the pyramid.

The slant height of a cone is equal to the length of a segment that has one endpoint at the apex of the cone and the other endpoint at a point where the lateral face intersects the base of the cone.

We usually denote the slant height with a lowercase script L (ℓ), and the pictures below illustrate these definitions.

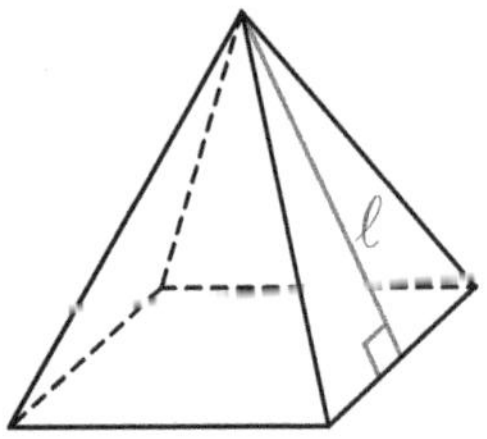

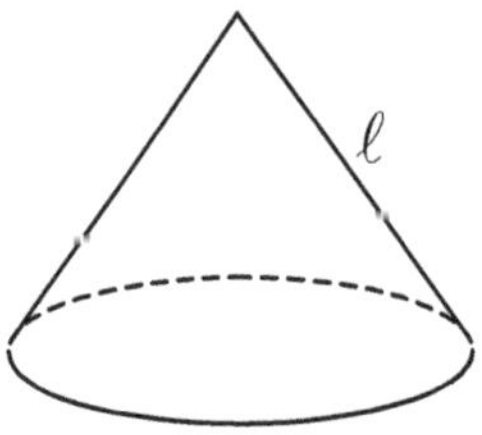

Example 2: Each side of the base of a square pyramid has a length of 10 feet, and the slant height of the pyramid is 13 feet. Find the lateral area and the total surface area of this pyramid.

We will begin by drawing a picture of this pyramid, as shown on the next page.

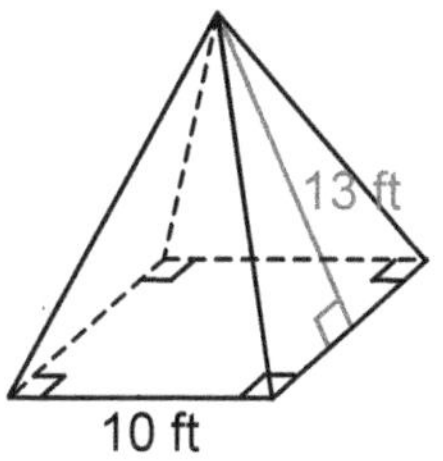

If we "unfold" this pyramid, we get something like what you see below.

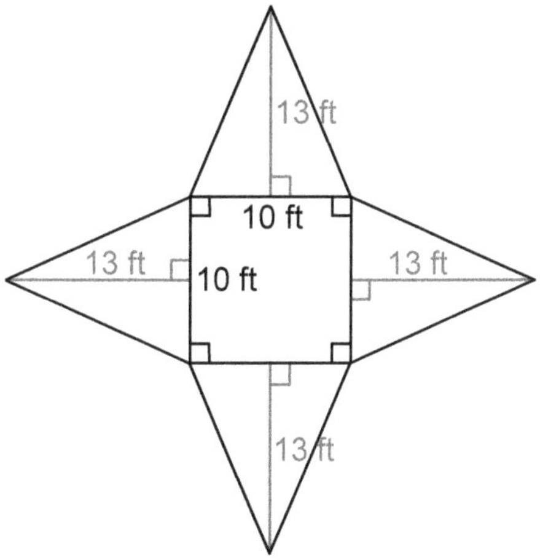

Now, we can find the lateral area of the pyramid by noting that the triangles are the lateral faces of the pyramid, and the total area of these triangles is equal to $\frac{1}{2}$(10 ft)(13 ft)(4), or 260 ft^2. Thus, the lateral area of this pyramid must be 260 ft^2.

Since the area of the base is 100 ft^2, the total surface area of this pyramid must equal (260 + 100) ft^2, or 360 ft^2.

This example gives rise to the following formulas.

> If the base of a right pyramid is a regular polygon, then the lateral area and total surface area of the pyramid are given by the formulas
>
> $$\text{L.A.} = \frac{1}{2}P\ell \text{ and } \text{T.S.A.} = \frac{1}{2}P\ell + B,$$
>
> where L.A. represents the lateral area of the pyramid, P represents the perimeter of the base of the pyramid, ℓ represents the slant height of the pyramid, T.S.A. represents the total surface area of the pyramid, and B represents the area of the base of the pyramid.

We can extend this thought process to talk about the lateral area and the total surface area of a cone. The "perimeter" and the area of the base of a cone are given by the formulas $C = 2\pi r$ and $A = \pi r^2$, and so we can substitute $2\pi r$ for P and πr^2 for B in the formulas above to find formulas for the lateral area and total surface area of a cone. When we do this and simplify the result, we get the following formulas.

The lateral area and total surface area of a right cone are given by the formulas

$$\text{L.A.} = \pi r\ell \text{ and } \text{T.S.A.} = \pi r\ell + \pi r^2,$$

where L.A. represents the lateral area of the cone, r represents the radius of the base of the cone, and ℓ represents the slant height of the pyramid.

Example 3: A cone has a height of 15 inches, and the radius of the base is 8 inches. Find the lateral area and the total surface area of this cone.

We will begin by drawing a picture of this cone.

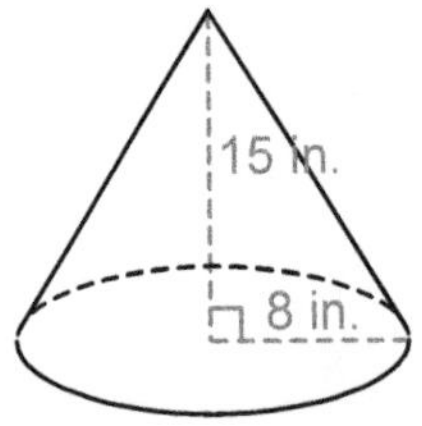

To use the formulas above, we first need to find the slant height of this cone. We can do this by drawing the following picture.

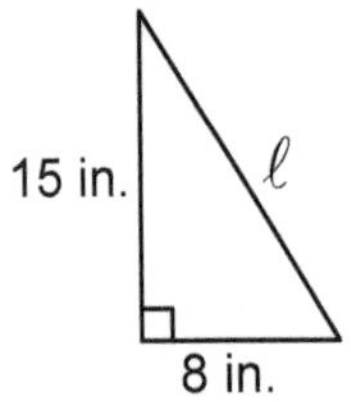

Now, we can use the Pythagorean Theorem to find the slant height.

$$(15 \text{ in.})^2 + (8 \text{ in.})^2 = \ell^2$$
$$225 \text{ in.}^2 + 64 \text{ in.}^2 = \ell^2$$
$$289 \text{ in.}^2 = \ell^2$$
$$17 \text{ in.} = \ell$$

Now, we can use the formulas shown above to find the lateral area and total surface area of the sphere.

$\text{L.A.} = \pi r\ell$	and	$\text{T.S.A.} = \pi r\ell + \pi r^2$
$\text{L.A.} = \pi(8 \text{ in.})(17 \text{ in.})$	and	$\text{T.S.A.} = \pi(8 \text{ in.})(17 \text{ in.}) + \pi(8 \text{ in.})^2$
$\text{L.A.} = 136\pi \text{ in.}^2$	and	$\text{T.S.A.} = 200\pi \text{ in.}^2$

In the next example, we will talk about the surface area of a sphere. You should notice that, since a sphere does not really have any lateral faces, it does not make sense to talk about the lateral area of a sphere, but we can still talk about the total surface area of a sphere. The reasoning behind the formula below is quite complicated, and so we will not discuss it here.

The total surface area of a sphere is given by the formula

$$\text{T.S.A.} = 4\pi r^2,$$

where T.S.A. represents the total surface area of the sphere and r represents the radius of the sphere.

Example 4: Find the total surface area of a sphere that has a diameter of 7 meters.

We have not actually stated a definition of a diameter of a sphere yet, but you can probably figure out what it is. A diameter of a sphere is a segment that passes through the center of the sphere and has both endpoints on the surface of the sphere. The length of such a segment is also called the diameter of the sphere, and it is equal to twice the radius of the sphere. Therefore, if the diameter of a sphere is 7 meters, the radius of the sphere must equal 3.5 meters. This tells us that the total surface area of a sphere that has a diameter of 7 meters is equal to $4\pi(3.5 \text{ m})^2$, or $49\pi \text{ m}^2$.

Example 5: Find the total surface area of the solid shown at the right.

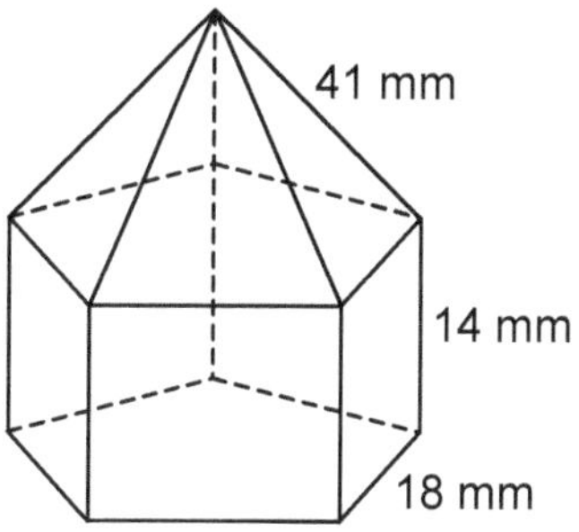

We will begin by noting that we said earlier in this section that you can assume that the bases of all pyramids are regular polygons unless you are told otherwise. Therefore, we will assume that the base of the pyramid (and, therefore, the base of the prism also) is a *regular* pentagon.

Next, we will note that this solid consists of the lateral faces of the pyramid, the lateral faces of the prism, and one of the bases of the prism. We will find the area of each of these sets of surfaces, and then we will add the results together.

To find the lateral area of the pentagonal pyramid:

We must begin by finding the slant height of the prism. To do this, we will begin by redrawing a lateral face of the pyramid.

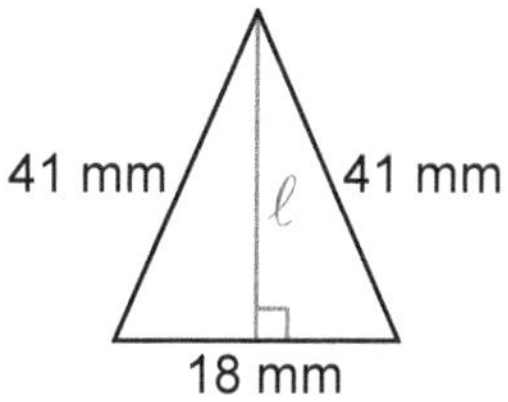

Now, you proved in the Mixed Review of Chapter 5 that the altitude from the vertex angle of an isosceles triangle is also a median, a perpendicular bisector, and an angle bisector. Hence, we can use the Pythagorean Theorem to find the slant height as shown below.

$$(9 \text{ mm})^2 + \ell^2 = (41 \text{ mm})^2$$
$$81 \text{ mm}^2 + \ell^2 = 1681 \text{ mm}^2$$
$$\ell^2 = 1600 \text{ mm}^2$$
$$\ell = 40 \text{ mm}$$

Now, we can find the lateral area of this pyramid using the formula L.A. = $\frac{1}{2}P\ell$, as shown on the next page.

$$\text{L.A.} = \frac{1}{2}P\ell$$

$$\text{L.A.} = \frac{1}{2}(90\text{ mm})(40\text{ mm})$$

$$\text{L.A.} = 1800\text{ mm}^2$$

To find the lateral area of the pentagonal prism:

$$\text{L.A.} = PH$$

$$\text{L.A.} = (90\text{ mm})(14\text{ mm})$$

$$\text{L.A.} = 1260\text{ mm}^2$$

To find the area of the base:

We can use the thought process we used in Part IV of Chapter 12 to say that the area of this pentagon is approximately 557.4 mm^2 (although your answer may be slightly different due to rounding differences).

This tells us that the total surface area of this solid is approximately 3617.4 mm^2.

Example 6: A toy manufacturer will be making some vinyl beach balls. If the radius of each ball will be 1 foot, how much vinyl will be needed to make 50 of these balls?

Since we want to know how much space is on the surface of a sphere, we can use the formula for total surface area of a sphere to answer this question, as shown below.

$$\text{T.S.A.} = 4\pi r^2$$

$$\text{T.S.A.} = 4\pi(1\text{ foot})^2$$

$$\text{T.S.A.} = 4\pi(1\text{ ft}^2)$$

$$\text{T.S.A.} = 4\pi\text{ ft}^2$$

This tells us that the toy manufacturer will need $50(4\pi\text{ ft}^2)$, or $200\pi\text{ ft}^2$, of vinyl to make 50 of these beach balls

Problems:

1-21. Find the lateral area (where applicable) and the total surface area of each of the solids drawn or described below.

1. Lateral area: ______________

   Total surface area: ______________

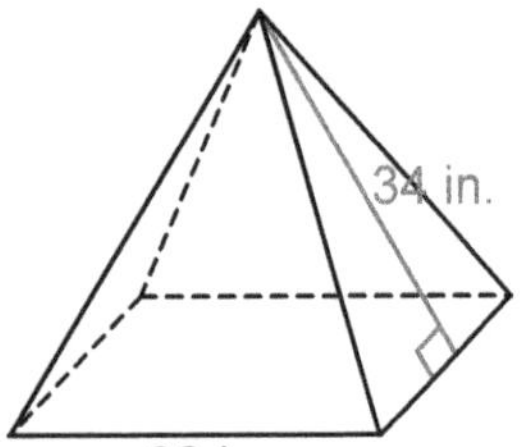

2. Each side of the base of a square pyramid has a length of 6 yards, and the height of the pyramid is 4 yards. Then the lateral area of the pyramid is ______________, and the total surface area of the pyramid is ______________.

3. Lateral area: ______________

   Total surface area: ______________

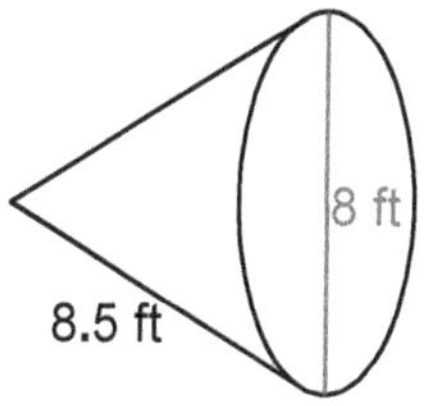

4. Lateral area: ______________

   Total surface area: ______________

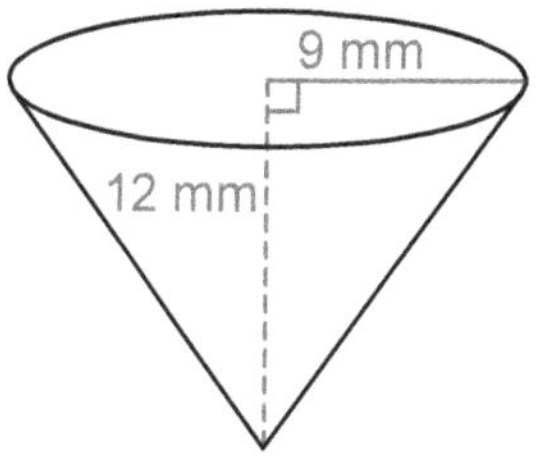

5. Each side of the base of a hexagonal pyramid has a length of 10 meters, and the height of the pyramid is 11 meters. Then the lateral area of the pyramid is ______________, and the total surface area of the pyramid is ______________. Hint: You will need to find the apothem of the hexagon, and then you can use this to find the slant height of the pyramid.

6. The slant height of a square pyramid is 29 inches, and the height of the pyramid is 21 inches. Then the lateral area of the pyramid is ______________, and the total surface area of the pyramid is ______________.

7. The slant height of a cone is 26 centimeters, and the height of the cone is 24 centimeters. Then the lateral area of the cone is ______________, and the total surface area of the cone is ______________.

8. Lateral area: _______________

Total surface area: _______________

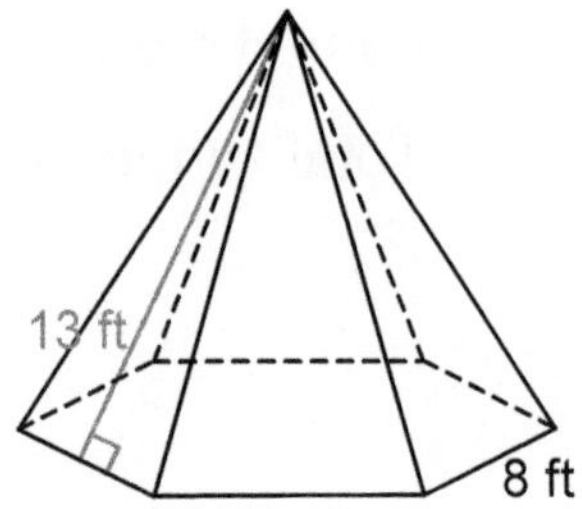

9. Total surface area: _______________

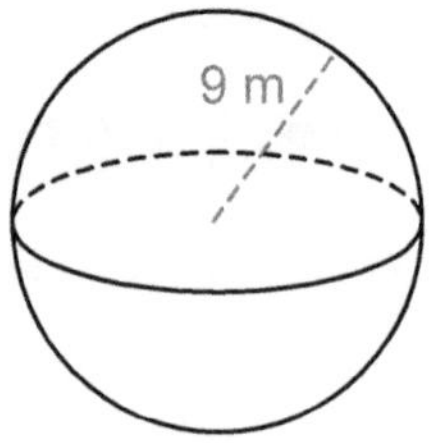

10. Total surface area: _______________

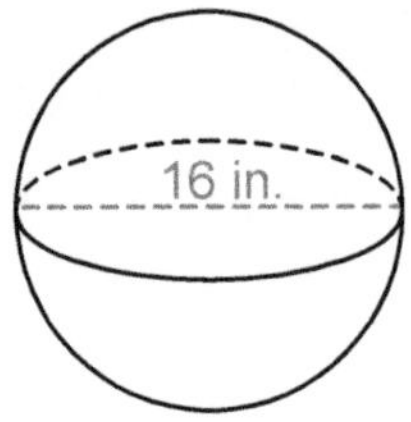

11. Each side of the base of a pentagonal pyramid has a length of 16 mm, and the height of the pyramid is 23 mm. Then the lateral area of the pyramid is _______________, and the total surface area of the pyramid is _______________.

12. Lateral area: _______________

Total surface area: _______________

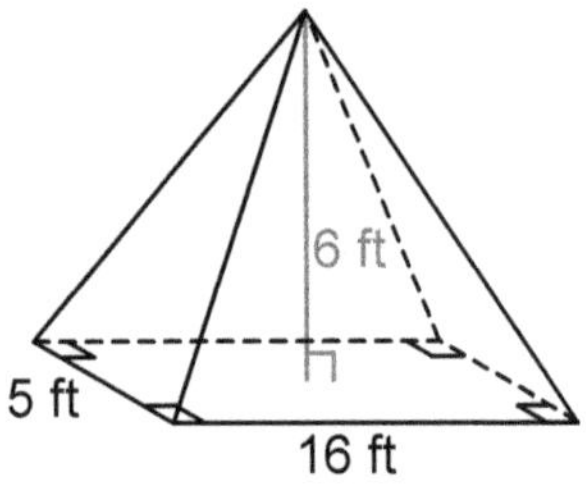

Hint: Note that, because the base of this pyramid is not a regular polygon, the slant heights will not all be the same. Therefore, you cannot use the formulas for lateral area and total surface area that we discussed in this section to work this problem. Instead, you must "unfold" the pyramid and find the areas of each of the surfaces.

13. Lateral area: _______________

Total surface area: _______________

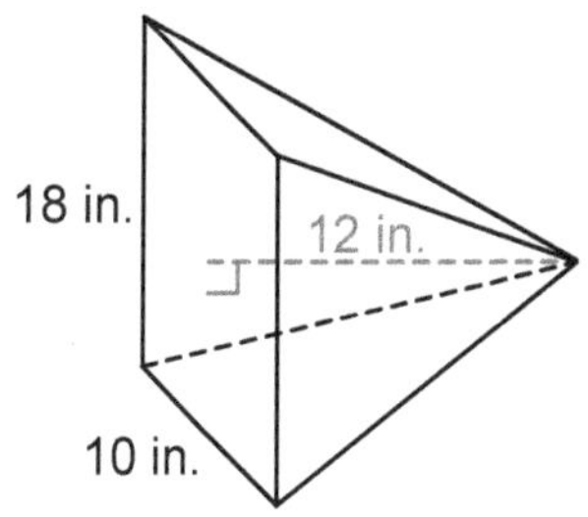

14. In the figure at the right, $\overline{AC}$, $\overline{BC}$, and $\overline{CD}$ are all perpendicular to each other. If AC = 7 cm, BC = 3 cm, CD = 4 cm, and the area of $\triangle ABD$ is 18.5 cm^2, then the lateral area of the pyramid is _______________, and the total surface area of the pyramid is _______________. (Assume that the base of the pyramid is $\triangle BCD$.)

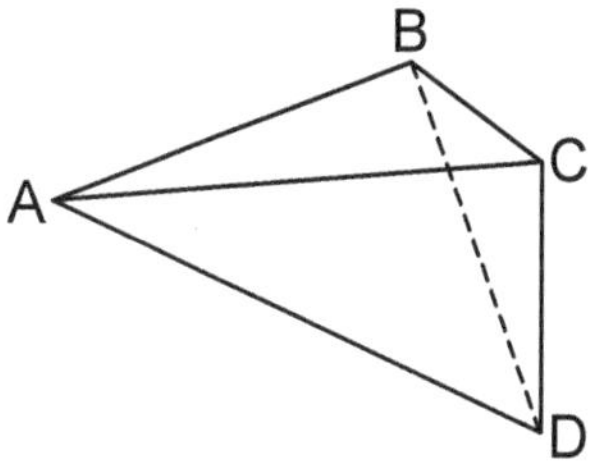

15. If the diameter of a sphere is 12 mm, then the total surface area of the sphere is _______________.

16. Lateral area: _______________

Total surface area: _______________

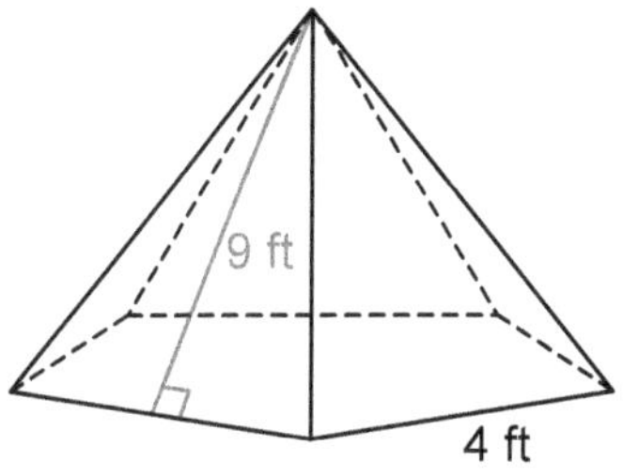

17. Lateral area: _______________

Total surface area: _______________

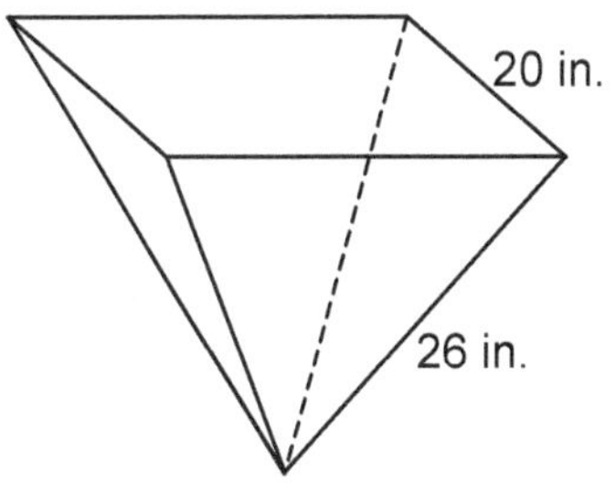

18. The altitude of a cone has a length of 12 millimeters, and the diameter of the base is 32 millimeters. Then the lateral area of the cone is _______________, and the total surface area of the cone is _______________.

19. The lateral faces and the base of a pyramid are all equilateral triangles. If each side of each triangle has a length of 18 feet, then the lateral area of the pyramid is _______________, and the total surface area of the pyramid is _______________.

20. Lateral area: _______________

Total surface area: _______________

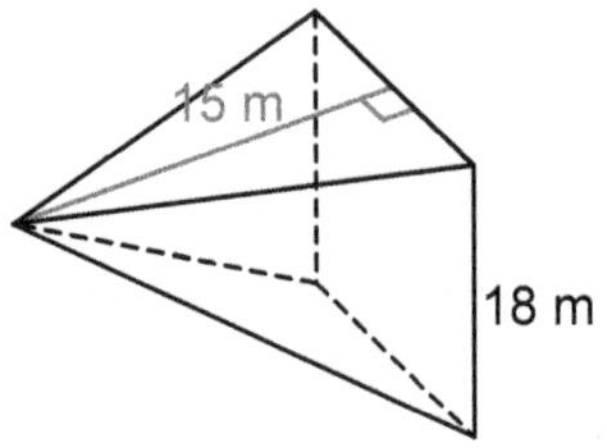

21. If the radius of a sphere is 21 centimeters, then the total surface area of the sphere is _______________.

22-27. Find the total surface area of each of the following solids.

22. The figure at the right shows a hemisphere (or half of a sphere). The total surface area of this solid is _______________. Hint: Don't forget the bottom!

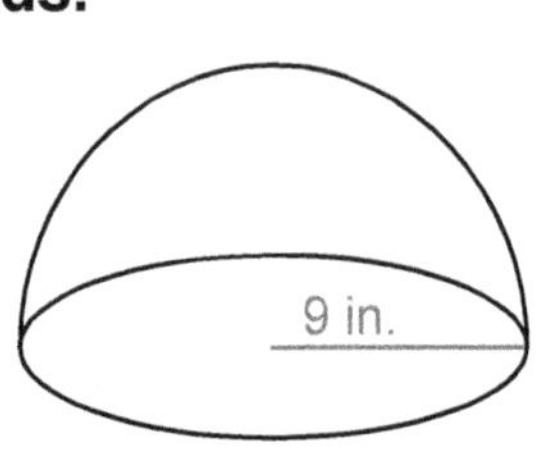

23. Total surface area: _______________

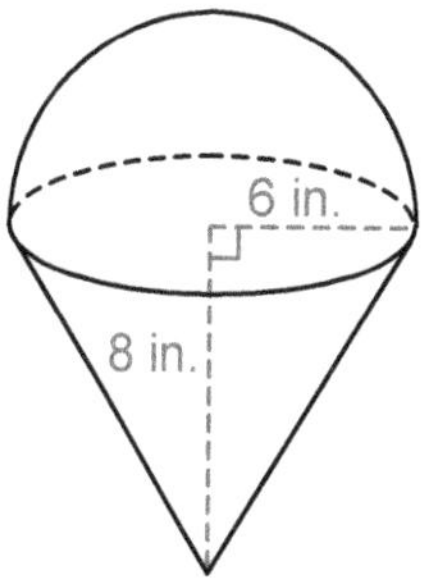

24. Total surface area: _______________

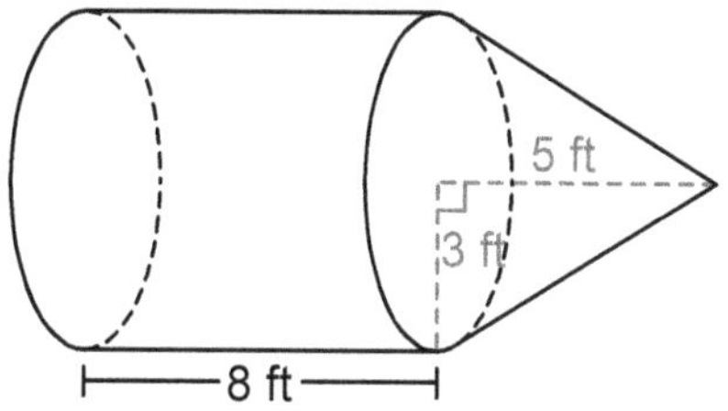

25. Total surface area: _______________

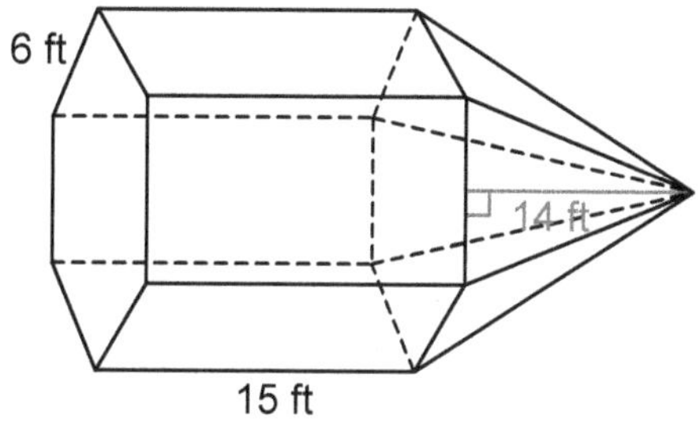

26. Total surface area: _______________

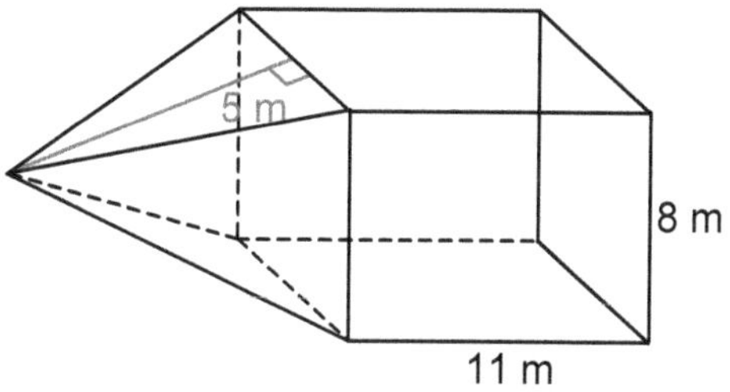

27. The figure at the right shows two square pyramids glued together. If each pyramid has a height of 15 inches and a slant height of 17 inches, then the total surface area of the solid is _______________.

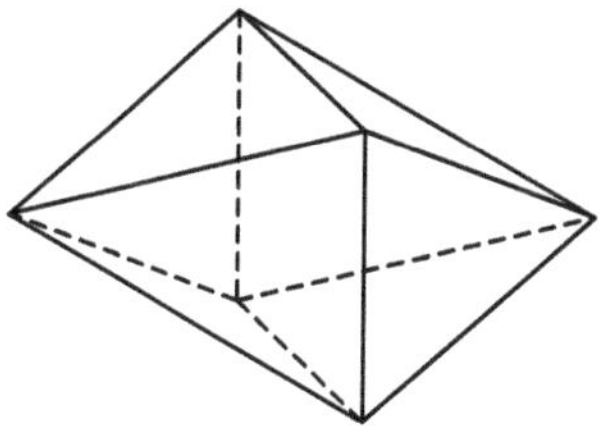

28. How many square centimeters of paint would be needed to cover 40 wooden balls if each ball has a radius of 7 centimeters? _______________

29. The Great Pyramid of Giza is a square pyramid. It is the oldest of the Seven Wonders of the Ancient World, and it is the only one that remains largely intact today. It is estimated that, when the pyramid was originally built, the sides of the base were about 756 feet long and that the pyramid had a height of about 481 feet. (The pyramid is actually a slight bit smaller today due to erosion and the absence of its capstone.) Based on these measurements, what would the approximate original lateral area of the Great Pyramid of Giza have been? _______________

30. What would be the minimum square inches of paper required to cover an ice cream cone if the cone has a slant height of 3 inches and the "base" has a radius of 1 inch? _______________

31. What is the surface area of the Earth if its radius is approximately 3960 miles?

____

32. A company is considering manufacturing a portable gazebo with the dimensions shown at the right. How much material would be needed to cover the sides of the gazebo? _____________ How much material would be needed to cover the roof of the gazebo? _____________

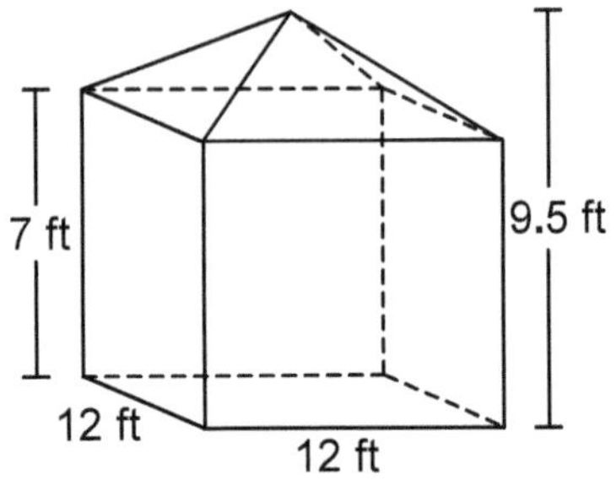

Part IV – Volume of Pyramids, Cones, and Spheres

In this section, we will discuss how we can find the volume of pyramids, cones, and spheres. Like we did with Parts I and II of this chapter, we will use many of the same solids that you saw in Part III, but we will talk about the volume of these solids instead of the lateral area and the total surface area.

We will begin with two formulas. The proofs of these formulas are quite complicated, and so we will not discuss them here.

> The volume of a pyramid or cone is given by the formula
> $$V = \frac{1}{3}BH,$$
> where V represents the volume of the pyramid or cone, B represents the area of the base of the pyramid or cone, and H represents the height of the pyramid or cone.

> The volume of a sphere is given by the formula
> $$V = \frac{4}{3}\pi r^3,$$
> where V represents the volume of the sphere and r represents the radius of the sphere.

Example 1: Each side of the base of a square pyramid has a length of 10 feet, and the slant height of the pyramid is 13 feet. Find the volume of this pyramid.

We will begin by drawing a picture of this pyramid.

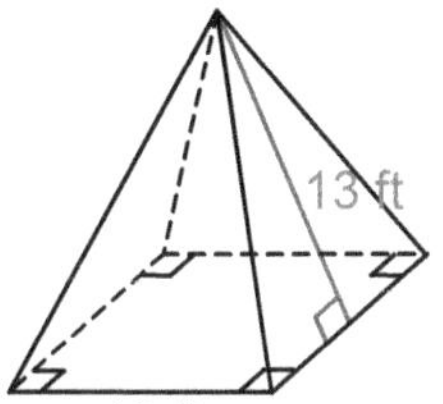

Now, before we can use the formula above, we must find the height of the pyramid. We can do this by drawing the right triangle shown in the figure below and then using the Pythagorean Theorem.

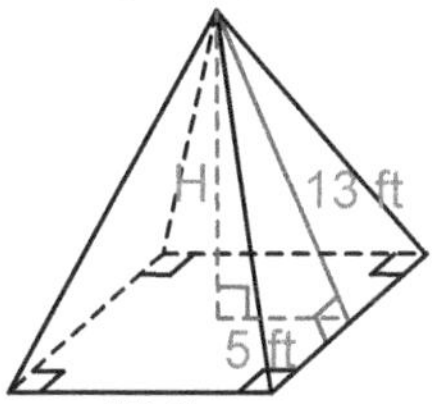

Now, we can use the Pythagorean Theorem as shown below.

$$(5\text{ ft})^2 + H^2 = (13\text{ ft})^2$$
$$25\text{ ft}^2 + H^2 = 169\text{ ft}^2$$
$$H^2 = 144\text{ ft}^2$$
$$H = 12\text{ ft}$$

Now, we can use the formula for finding the volume of a pyramid that we stated on the previous page.

$V = \frac{1}{3}BH$

$V = \frac{1}{3}(100\ ft^2)(12\ ft)$ — Note that the base of this pyramid is a square with an area of $100\ ft^2$.

$V = 400\ ft^3$

Example 2: A cone has a height of 15 inches, and the radius of the base is 8 inches. Find the volume of this cone.

To work this problem, we just need to use the finding the volume of a cone that we stated on the previous page.

$V = \frac{1}{3}BH$

$V = \frac{1}{3}(64\pi\ in.^2)(15\ in.)$ — Note that the base of this cone is a circle with an area of 64π square inches.

$V = 320\pi\ in.^3$

Example 3: Find the volume of a sphere that has a diameter of 7 meters.

We can work this problem using the formula for finding the volume of a sphere that we stated on the previous page, as shown below.

$V = \frac{4}{3}\pi r^3$

$V = \frac{4}{3}\pi(3.5\ m)^3$ — As we stated in the last section, a sphere that has a diameter of 7 meters must have a radius of 3.5 meters.

$V = \frac{343}{6}\pi\ m^3$

Example 4: Find the volume of the solid shown at the right.

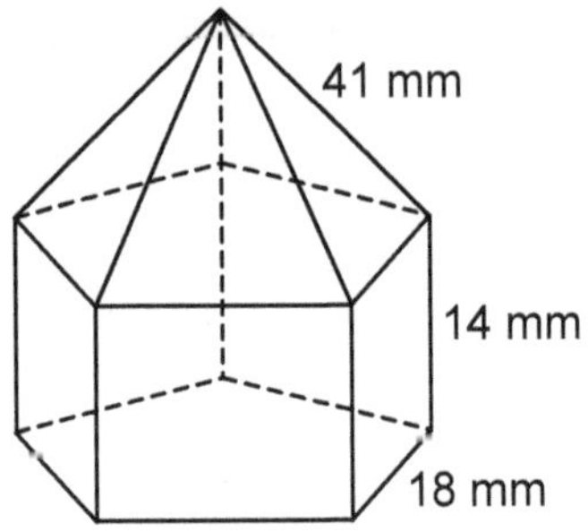

We will begin by noting that the volume of this solid is equal to the sum of the volumes of the pyramid and the prism. Also, we stated in the last section that you may assume that the bases of all pyramids are regular polygons unless you are told otherwise, and so we will assume that the base of the pyramid (and, therefore, the base of the prism also) is a *regular* pentagon.

We will also note that the answers you get to the different parts of this problem may vary slightly from the answers we give because of rounding differences. In working the various parts of this problem, we will use the unrounded versions of the numbers, but you may choose to use rounded numbers.

To find the volume of the prism:

As we said in the last section, we can use the thought process we used in Part IV of Chapter 12 to say that the area of base of the this pentagon is approximately 557.4 mm^2. Therefore, the volume of the prism is approximately equal to (557.4 mm^2)(14 mm), or 7804.1 mm^3.

To find the volume of the pyramid:

Before we can use the formula $V = \frac{1}{3}BH$ to find the volume of the pyramid, we must find the height of the pyramid. We can do this by noting that we can form a right triangle with segments representing the apothem of the pentagon, the slant height of the pyramid, and the altitude of the pyramid. This gives us the right triangle shown below. (Note that we found that the slant height of this pyramid is 40 mm in the last section.)

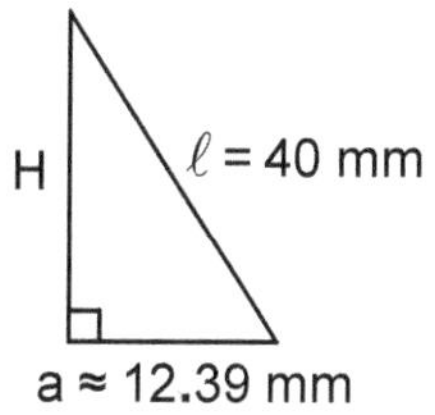

Now, if we use the Pythagorean Theorem, we find that the height of the pyramid is approximately 38.0 mm.

Now, we can use the formula $V = \frac{1}{3}BH$ to find the volume of the pyramid.

$$V = \frac{1}{3}BH$$

$$V \approx \frac{1}{3}(557.4\ mm^2)(38.0\ mm)$$

$$V \approx 7067.1\ mm^3$$

This tells us that the volume of this solid is about 14,871.2 cubic millimeters.

Example 5: Find the volume of the pyramid shown at the right.

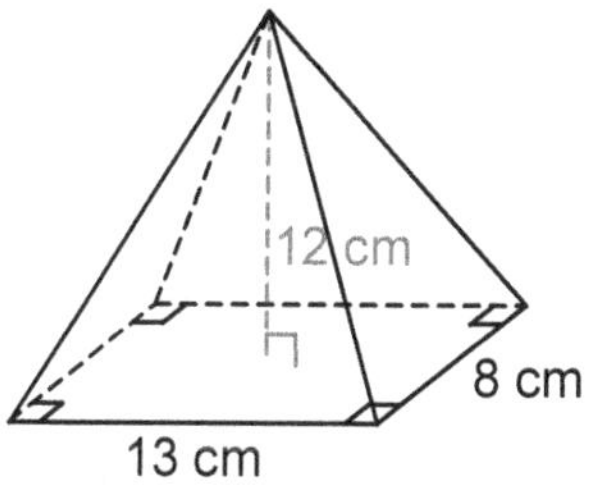

We can use the formula $V = \frac{1}{3}BH$ regardless of whether or not the base is a regular polygon, and so we can work this problem as shown below.

$$V = \frac{1}{3}BH$$

$$V = \frac{1}{3}(104\ cm^2)(12\ cm)$$

$$V = 416\ cm^3$$

Note that the base of this pyramid is a rectangle with an area of 104 cm^2 and that the height of the pyramid is 12 cm.

Problems:

1-27. Find the volume of each of the solids drawn or described below.

1. Volume: _______________

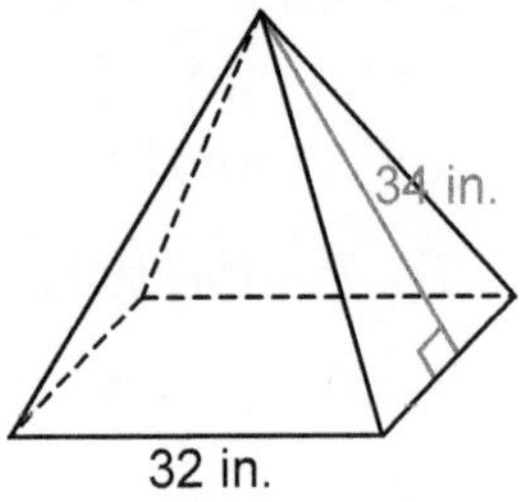

2. Each side of the base of a square pyramid has a length of 6 yards, and the height of the pyramid is 4 yards. Then the volume of the pyramid is _______________.

3. Volume: _______________

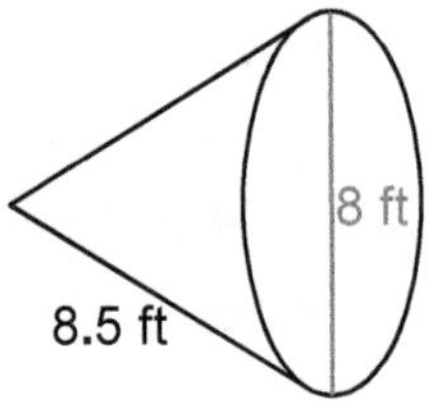

4. Volume: _______________

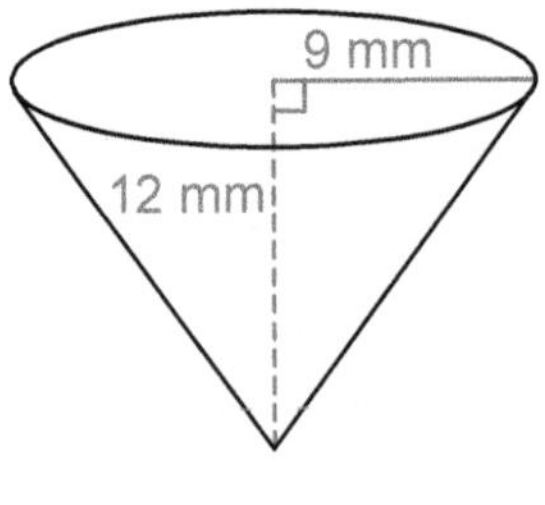

5. Each side of the base of a hexagonal pyramid has a length of 10 meters, and the height of the pyramid is 11 meters. Then the volume of the pyramid is _______________.

6. The slant height of a triangular pyramid is 29 inches, and the height of the pyramid is 21 inches. Then the volume of the pyramid is _______________.

7. The slant height of a cone is 26 centimeters, and the height of the cone is 24 centimeters. Then the volume of the cone is _______________.

8. Volume: _______________

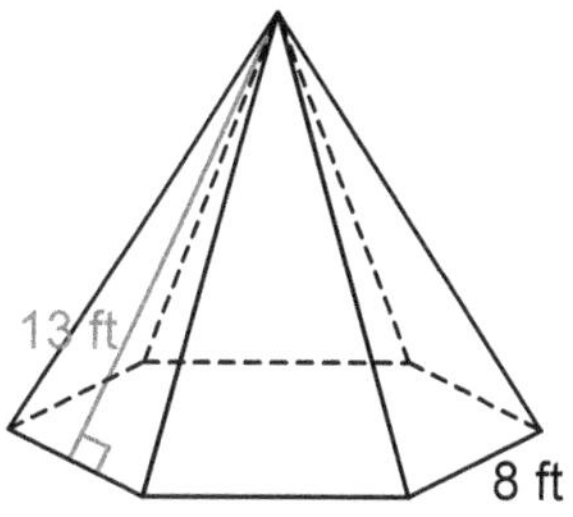

9. Volume: _______________

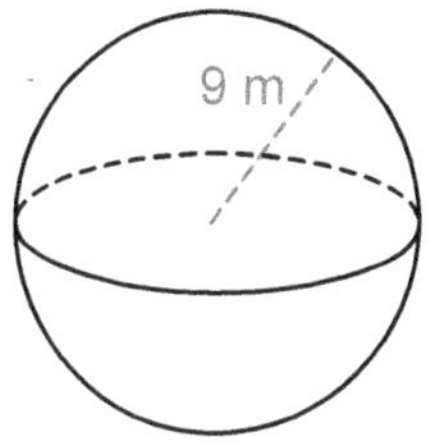

10. Volume: _______________

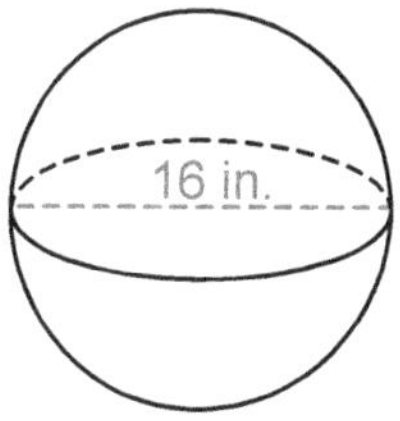

11. Each side of the base of a pentagonal pyramid has a length of 16 mm, and the height of the pyramid is 23 mm. Then the volume of the pyramid is _______________.

12. Volume: _______________

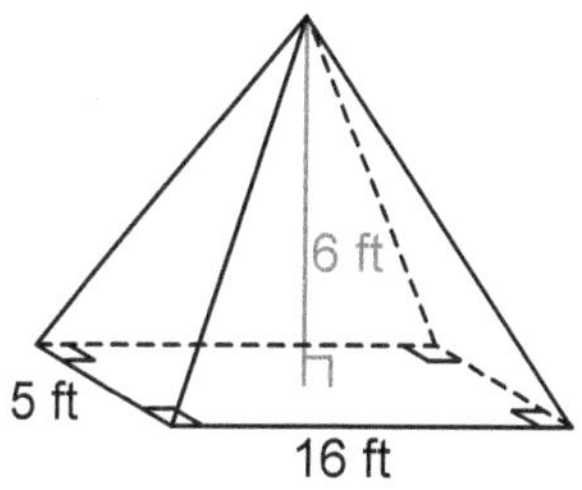

13. Volume: _______________

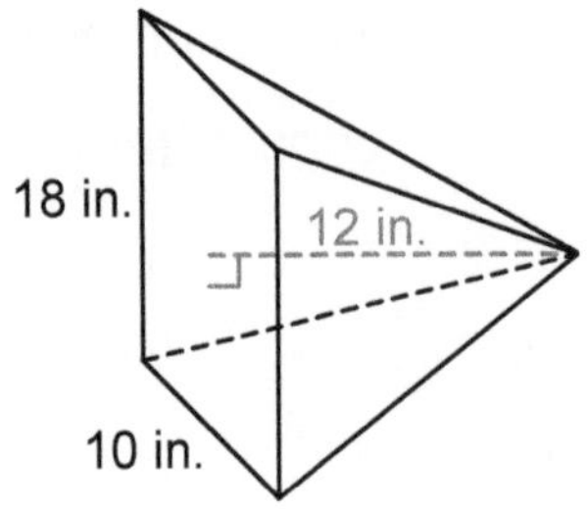

14. In the figure at the right, $\overline{AC}$, $\overline{BC}$, and $\overline{CD}$ are all perpendicular to each other. If AC = 7 cm, BC = 3 cm, and CD = 4 cm, then the volume of the pyramid is _______________.

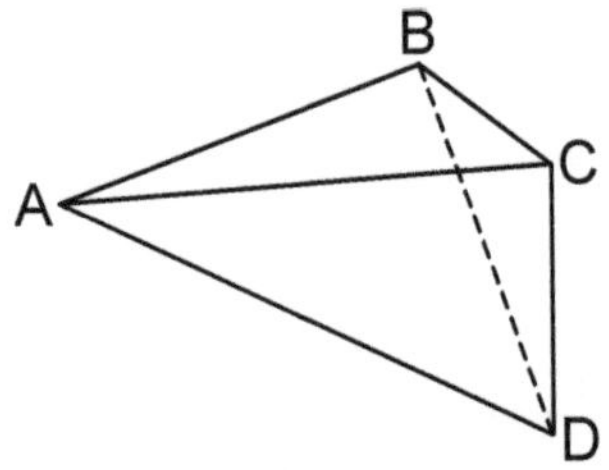

15. If the diameter of a sphere is 12 mm, then the volume of the sphere is _______________.

16. Volume: _______________

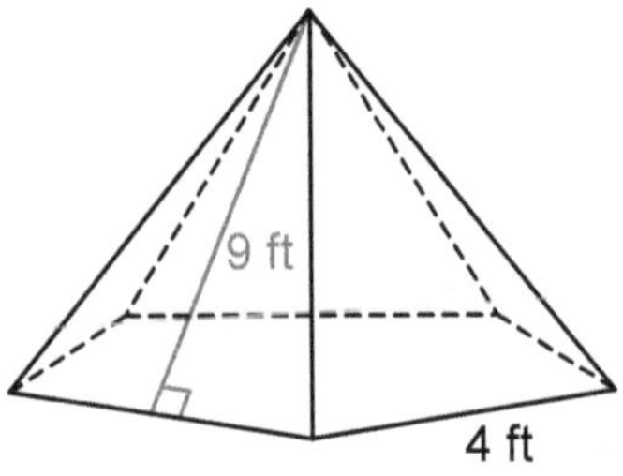

17. Volume: _______________ (You may round your final answer to the nearest tenth of a cubic inch.)

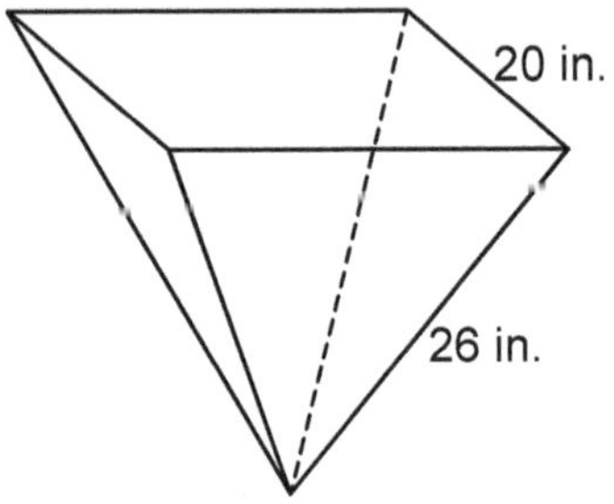

18. The altitude of a cone has a length of 12 millimeters, and the diameter of the base is 32 millimeters. Then the volume of the cone is _______________.

19. The lateral faces and the base of a pyramid are all equilateral triangles. If each side of each triangle has a length of 18 feet, then the volume is ______________.

20. Volume: ________________

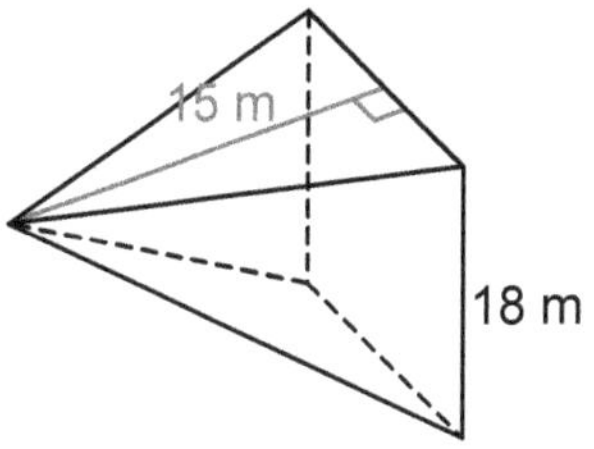

21. If the radius of a sphere is 21 centimeters, then the volume of the sphere is ________________.

22. The figure at the right shows a hemisphere (or half of a sphere). The volume of this solid is ________________.

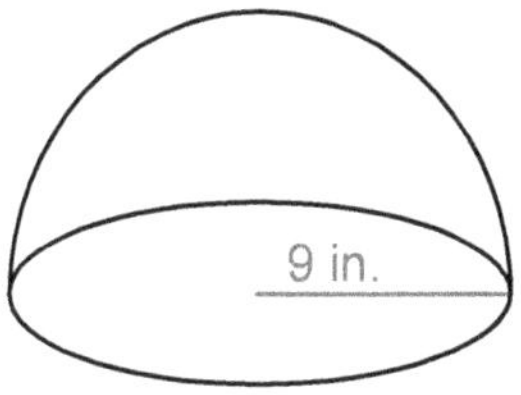

23. Total volume: ________________

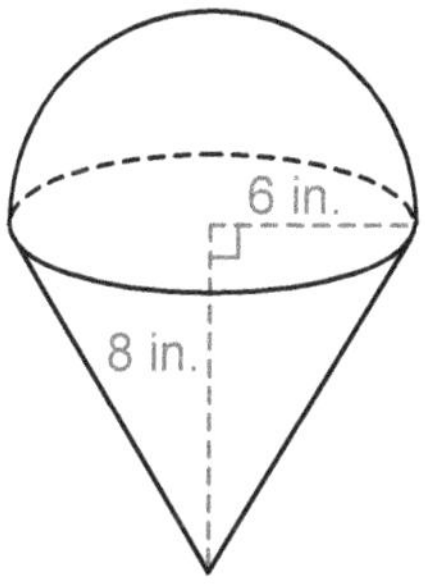

24. Total volume: ________________

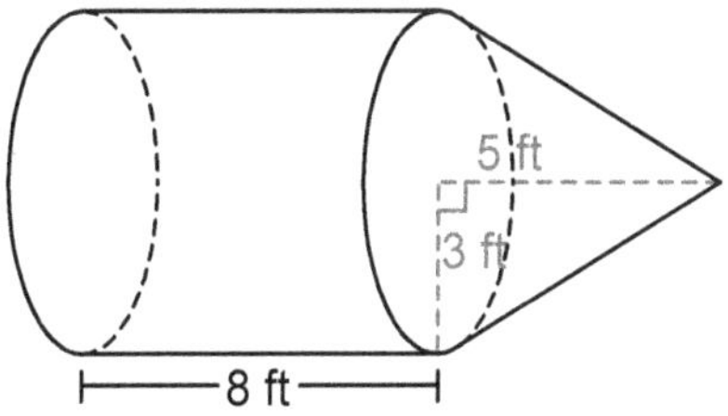

25. Total volume: _______________

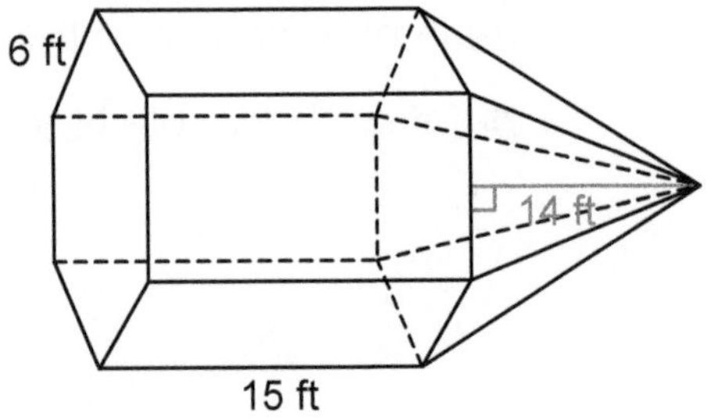

26. Total volume: _______________

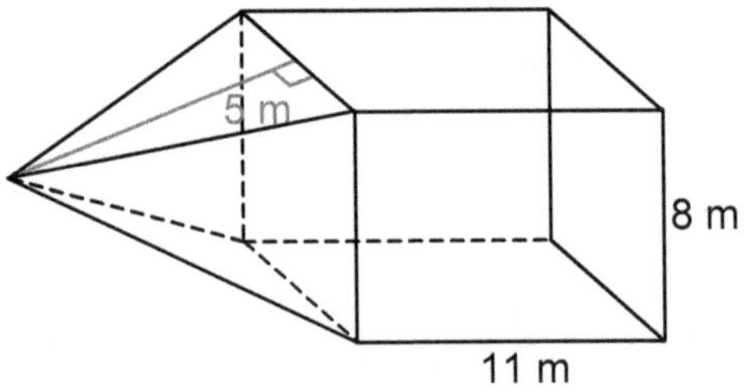

27. The figure at the right shows two square pyramids glued together. If each pyramid has a height of 15 inches and a slant height of 17 inches, then the total volume of the solid is _______________.

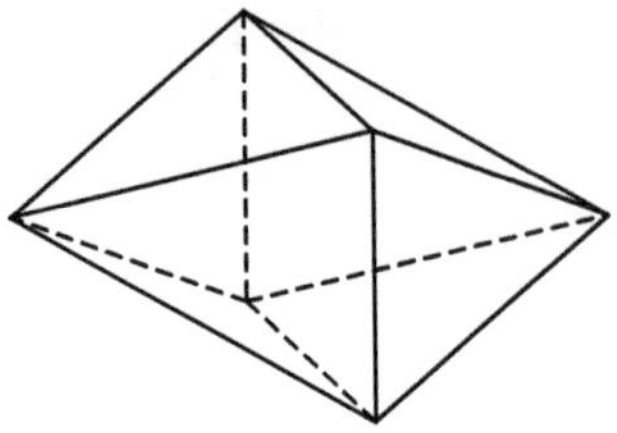

28. If a spherical scoop of ice cream with a radius of 2.5 cm melts into an ice cream cone that has a "base" radius of 2 cm and a slant height of 6 cm, will the cone overflow? _______________

29. The Great Pyramid of Giza is made mostly of limestone bricks. It is estimated that, when the pyramid was originally built, the sides of the base were about 756 feet long and that the pyramid had a height of about 481 feet. What volume of limestone would have been required to build the Great Pyramid of Giza? _______________

Note: Parts of the pyramid have tunnels and chambers in it, but, for the purposes of this problem, you may assume that this pyramid is made of solid bricks and that the tunnels and chambers do not exist.

30. The radius of the Earth is approximately 3960 miles, and, although there is no definite line between outer space and the Earth's atmosphere, most experts agree that the Earth's atmosphere ends about 62 miles above the sea level of the Earth. What is the approximate volume of the Earth? _______________

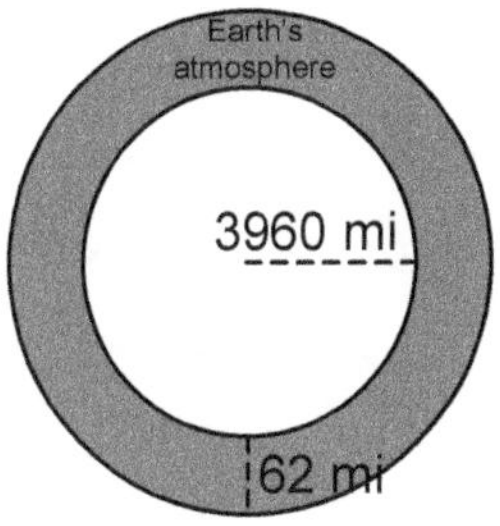

31. Refer back to #30. What volume of air is in the Earth's atmosphere? _____________

32. Most oxygen tanks that will be used for medical purposes are in the shape of a cylinder with a hemisphere (or half of a sphere) on top. If a patient needs about 120 cubic inches of oxygen every hour, about how long should the oxygen tank shown at the right last for this patient? _______________

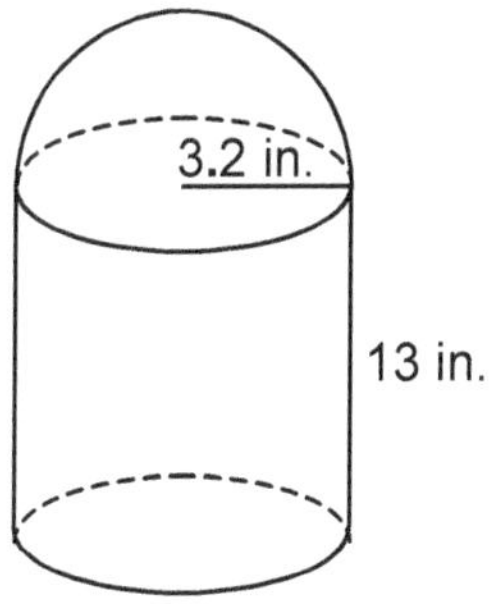

33. The height of a conical pile of dirt is 2.5 yards, and the base of the pile has a radius of 2 yards. Will the dirt fit in a rectangular dump truck that has a length of 3 yards, a width of 2 yards, and a height of 1.5 yards? _______________

34. Michelle wants to pack 3 glass balls (each with diameter of 12 cm) into a rectangular box that has a length of 15 cm, a width of 19 cm, and a height of 45 cm. How much extra space will be inside the box (and will therefore need to be filled with packing material)? _______________

Part V – Mixed Review

1-3. Find the volume, lateral area (where applicable), and total surface area of each of the solids shown below.

1. Lateral area: _______________

   Total surface area: _______________

   Volume: _______________

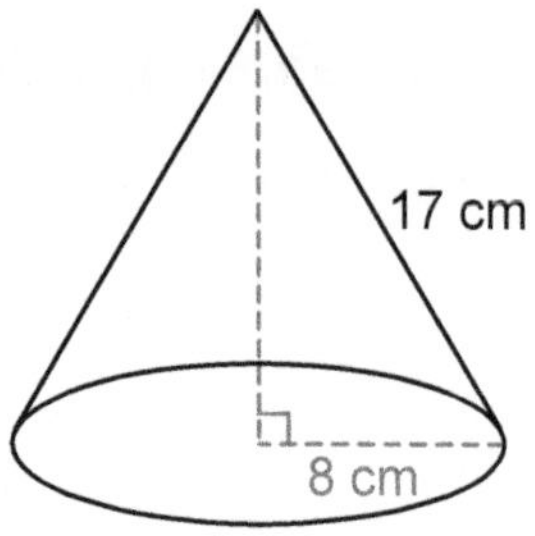

2. Lateral area: _______________

   Total surface area: _______________

   Volume: _______________

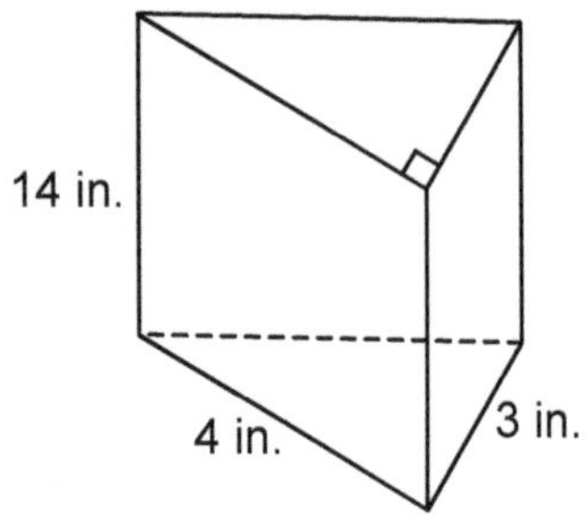

3. Total surface area: _______________

   Volume: _______________

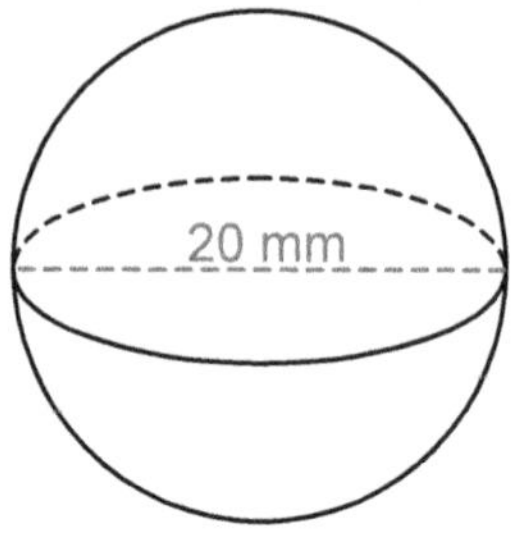

4. If a cube has a volume of 27 cm^3, what is the total surface area of the cube?

   ____

5. If a rectangular box has a volume of 12 ft^3, what is the maximum number of these boxes that you could fit into a storage space that is 9 feet high, 16 feet long, and 11 feet wide? _______________

6. Suppose that a can of mushrooms has a height of 9 cm, and the base has a diameter of 7 cm. Also suppose that one mushroom occupies about 3 cm^3 of space, and the label costs $0.01 for every 20 square centimeters. About how much money will it cost to make the label for the side of the can? _______________
About how many mushrooms will fit in the can? _______________

7. A company is considering making two Easter different baskets. The first is a rectangular basket with a length of 12 inches, a width of 9 inches, and a height of 5 inches. The second basket is a cylindrical basket with a height of 6 inches and a diameter of 11 inches. Which basket would hold more Easter eggs? _______________ Which basket would use more materials (and would therefore cost more money to make)? _______________ (Assume that the company would make the sides and the bottom but not the top.)

8. The figure at the right shows a rectangular prism with a hole cut in it. If the hole has a diameter of 12 mm, what is the volume of the solid? _______________

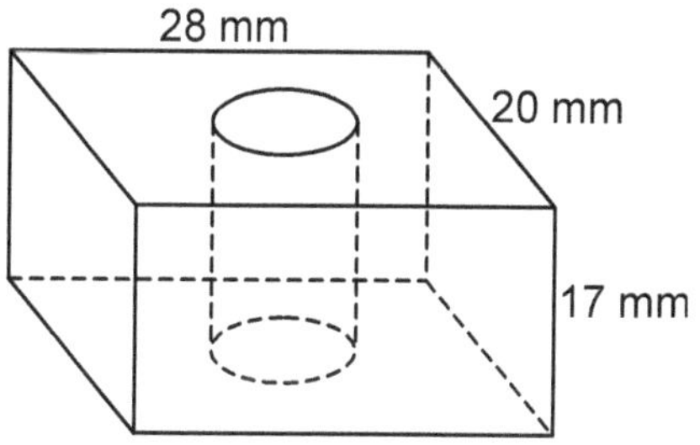

9. If you double the radius of the base of a cone, what happens to the lateral area of the cone? _______________________________________ What happens to the volume of the cone? _______________________________________

10. If you cut the radius of a sphere in half, what happens to the volume of the sphere? ______________________________ What happens to the surface area of the sphere? ______________________________

11. If you double the length of an edge of a cube, what happens to the volume of the cube? ______________________________ What happens to the surface area of the cube? ______________________________

12. The trapezoid at the right has an area of 48 square inches. Then x = ______________, and the perimeter of the trapezoid is ______________.

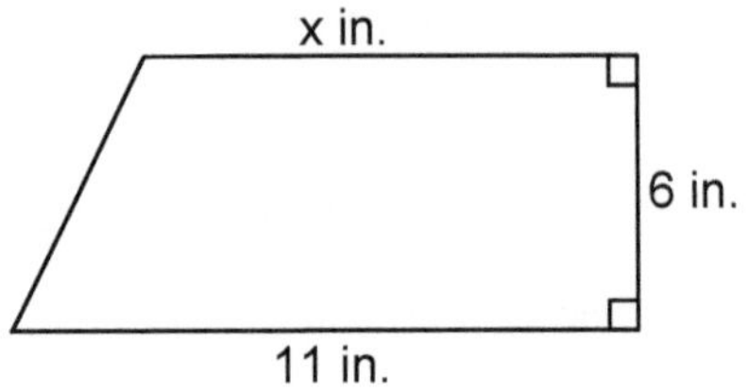

13. The scale on a map says that 2 inches on the map represent 3 miles in real life. If two towns are 42 miles apart in real life, how far apart should they be on the map?

____

14. Refer back to #13. If a city has an area of 144 square miles in real life, how many square inches should it occupy on the map? ______________

15. A regular nonagon has a radius of 12 cm. Then its perimeter is ______________, and its area is ______________.

16. Find the area and the perimeter of the figure drawn at the right. You may assume that all angles that appear to be right angles are actually right angles and that all curved paths are arcs of circles.

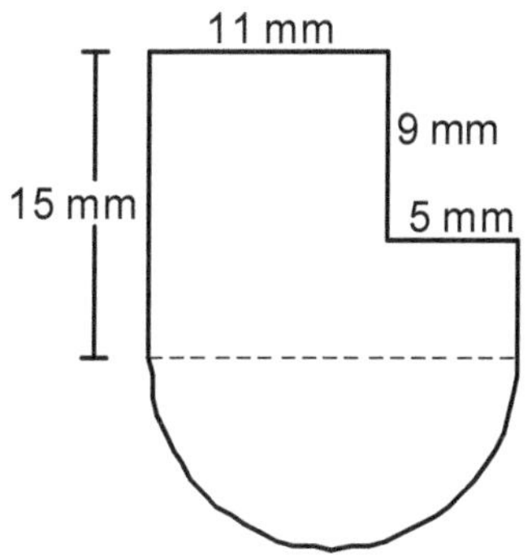

Perimeter: _______________

Area: _______________

17. The height of a solid is 8 mm, and the base of the solid looks like the shape shown in #16. If the sides of the solid form right angles with the base, then the volume of the solid is _______________, and the total surface area of the solid is _______________.

18. If a point will be picked at random from inside ⊙G at the right, what is the probability that it will lie in the shaded region?

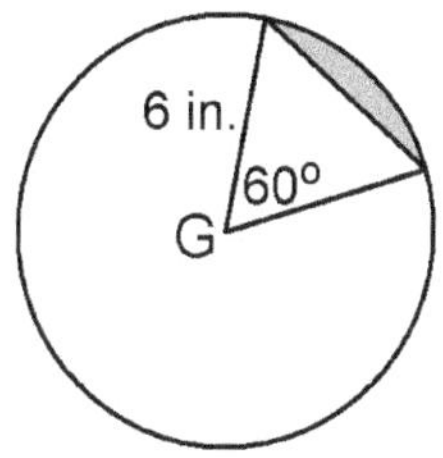

____

19. If a point will be picked at random from inside the circle at the right, what is the probability that it will lie in the shaded region? _____________ Hint: The center of the circle is the circumcenter of the triangle, and you can use what you learned about circumcenters and perpendicular bisectors in Chapter 5 to find that the radius of the circle is $9\sqrt{2}$ m.

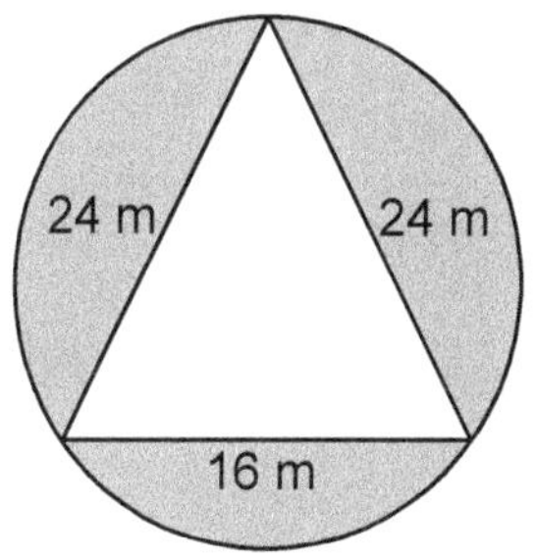

20. In the figure at the right, the diameter of the large circle is 10 feet. If a point will be picked at random from inside the large circle, the probability that it will lie in the shaded region is $\frac{3}{5}$. What is the radius of the smaller circle? _____________

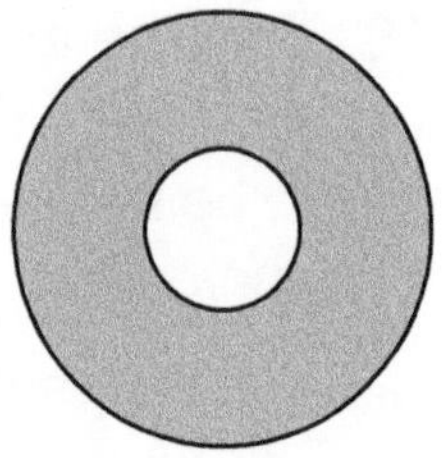

21. In the figure at the right, $\overline{AD}$ is three times as long as $\overline{AB}$ and twice as long as $\overline{AC}$. If a point on $\overline{AD}$ will be picked at random, what is the probability that it will lie on $\overline{AB}$? __________ What is the probability that it will lie on $\overline{AC}$? __________

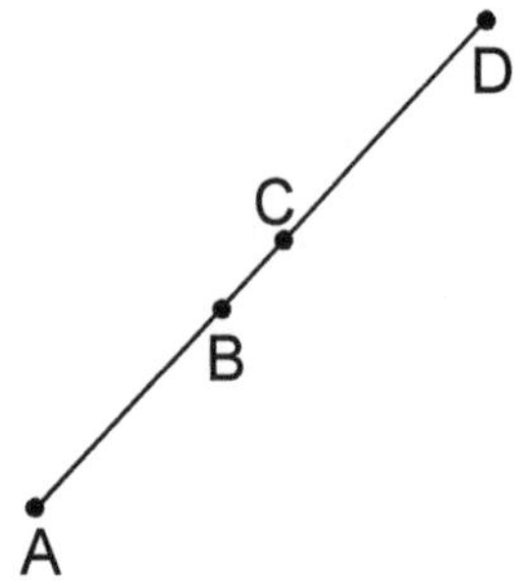

22. Quadrilateral RSTU has its vertices at R(–3, –2), S(–5, 6), T(3, 4), and U(5, –4). Tell which of the following terms apply to quadrilateral RSTU: parallelogram, trapezoid, kite, rectangle, rhombus, square. Name all that apply.

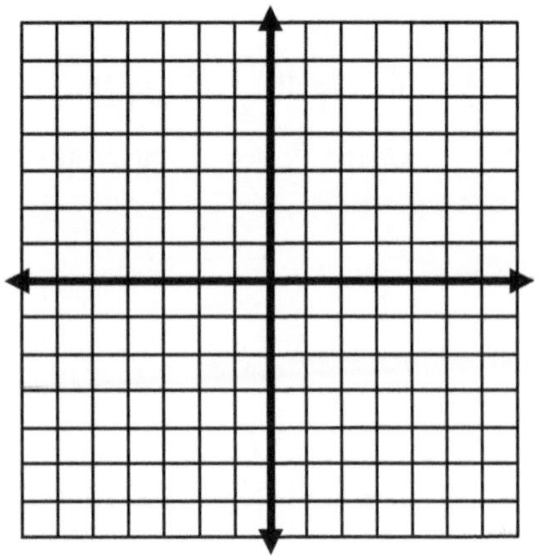

23. Refer back to #22. The area of quadrilateral RSTU is _______________, and the perimeter of quadrilateral RSTU is _______________.

24. What is an equation of the line that is perpendicular to the x-axis and 2 units to the left of the y-axis? _______________

25. If two sides of a triangle has lengths of 5 feet and 2 feet, then the perimeter of the triangle must be less than _______________ and greater than _______________.
Hint: Use the Triangle Inequality Theorem.

26. The figure at the right shows a dilation of ΔLEZ with center P and scale factor $\frac{4}{3}$. If $E'L'$ = 19 mm, then the area of ΔLEZ is _______________, and the perimeter of ΔLEZ is _______________. (You may round your final answers to one decimal place.)

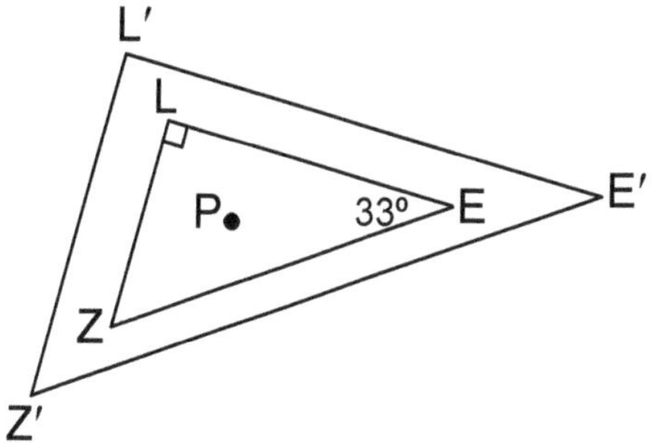

27. In ⊙V at the right, VY = 5 cm and $m\angle XWY = 36°$. Then $m\angle XVY$ = ____________, $m\overset{\frown}{XY}$ = ____________, $m\overset{\frown}{XWY}$ = ____________, and the length of $\overset{\frown}{XWY}$ is ____________.

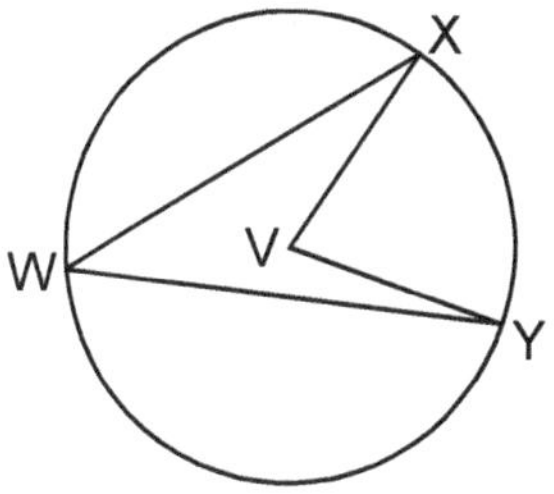

28. If a square pyramid has a height of 9 inches and a volume of 1728 cubic inches, then the lateral area of the pyramid is _______________, and the total surface area of the pyramid is _______________.

Appendix A – Review of Algebraic Concepts

Part I – Solving Linear Equations in One Variable

For the most part, the problems in the first three sections of this Appendix are identical to those in Part V of Chapter 1; it's just that you don't have to state formal reasons for each step.

In this section, we will review how to solve elementary equations. When a question asks you to solve an equation or to find the solutions to an equation, it wants you to find the value(s) of the variable(s) that make the equation true.

We will begin by stating some of the properties that we stated in Part V of Chapter 1.

> Let a, b, and c represent real numbers. Then:
>
> - the Addition Property of Equality says that $a = b$ if and only if $a + c = b + c$
> - the Subtraction Property of Equality says that $a = b$ if and only if $a - c = b - c$
> - the Multiplication Property of Equality says that $a = b$ if and only if $ac = bc$ and $c \neq 0$
> - the Division Property of Equality says that $a = b$ if and only if $\frac{a}{c} = \frac{b}{c}$ and $c \neq 0$

These properties say that you can do almost anything you want to one side of the equation as long as you do exactly the same thing to the other side. Let's look at some examples.

Example 1: Solve for x in the equation $x + 3 = -9$.

We want to rearrange this equation so that the x is by itself on one side of the equation and everything else is on the other side. This means that we need to cancel out the "+ 3" on the left side. We do this by subtracting 3 from both sides, as shown below.

$$\begin{array}{rcl} x + 3 &=& -9 \\ \underline{\quad -3} && \underline{-3} \\ x &=& -12 \end{array}$$

Note that $x + 3 - 3 = x$ and $-9 - 3 = -12$.

This tells us that, when we substitute -12 in for x in the original problem, we should get a true statement. We can check this as shown below.

$$-12 + 3 \stackrel{?}{=} -9$$
$$-9 = -9 \quad \checkmark$$

Since we did get a true statement, we can say that our answer of $x = -12$ must be correct.

Example 2: Solve for y in the equation $-8 = 3y - 1$.

We will begin by noting that this question wants us to rearrange the equation so that y is by itself on one side that everything else is on the other side. This means that we must cancel out both the subtraction of 1 and the multiplication by 3. To decide which one we need to cancel out first, we will look at the order of operations, which is summarized in the following list. (The phrase "Please excuse my dear Aunt Sally" is only a tool to help you remember the order of operations; it has no real relevance to math or to this lesson.)

P	Please	Parentheses
E	Excuse	Exponents
M/D	My Dear	Multiplication and Division in order from left to right
A/S	Aunt Sally	Addition and Subtraction in order from left to right

When we are trying to decide what to cancel out first in an equation, we use the *reverse* order of operations. This means that, in order to solve the equation $-8 = 3y - 1$, we must first cancel out the subtraction of 1. Hence, we can solve this equation as shown below.

$$-8 = 3y - 1$$
$$\underline{+1 \qquad +1}$$
$$-7 = 3y \qquad \text{Note that } -8 + 1 = -7 \text{ and } 3y - 1 + 1 = 3y.$$

$$-\frac{7}{3} = \frac{3y}{3}$$

We can cancel out the multiplication by 3 by dividing both sides by 3.

$$-\frac{7}{3} = y$$

When you multiply a number by 3 and then divide the answer by 3, you get what you started with. Also, when your answer turns out to be an improper fraction in this book, you may leave your answer as an improper fraction. (It is also equally correct to leave your answer as a mixed number, but we will leave our answers as improper fractions.)

We can check this answer as shown below.

$$-8 \stackrel{?}{=} 3\left(-\frac{7}{3}\right) - 1$$
$$-8 \stackrel{?}{=} -7 \quad -1$$
$$-8 = \quad -8 \quad \checkmark$$

This tells us that our answer of $-\frac{7}{3} = y$ (or, equivalently, $y = -\frac{7}{3}$) is correct.

Before we work our next example, we will review a concept called the Distributive Property.

The Distributive Property

Let a, b, and c represent real numbers. Then $a(b + c) = ab + ac$ and $a(b - c) = ab - ac$.

The following examples illustrate this property.

$3(4x - 5y) = 12x - 15y$	To multiply 3 by (4x – 5y), we must multiply 3 by each of the terms, or pieces, in the expression (4x – 5y).
$2x(3x^2 + 4y - z) = 6x^3 + 8xy - 2xz$	To multiply 2x by ($3x^2$ + 4y – z), we must multiply 2x by each of the terms in the expression ($3x^2$ + 4y – z).

Example 3: Solve for k in the equation 5(1 + 2k) + 4 = 29.

There are several ways of solving this equation, and one of them is shown below.

$5(1 + 2k) + 4 = 29$	
$5 + 10k + 4 = 29$	Use the Distributive Property.
$9 + 10k = 29$	Since the 5 and 4 are on the same side, we can go ahead and add them together.
$10k = 20$	We can use the Subtraction Property of Equality to subtract 9 from both sides. (Note that 9 + 10k – 9 = 10k, and also note that 29 – 9 = 20.)
$k = 2$	We can use the Division Property of Equality to divide both sides by 10. (Note that 10k ÷ 10 = k, and also note that 20 ÷ 10 = 2.)

Now, we can check this answer as shown below.

$$5(1 + 2 \bullet 2) + 4 \stackrel{?}{=} 29$$
$$5(1 + 4) + 4 \stackrel{?}{=} 29$$
$$5 (5) + 4 \stackrel{?}{=} 29$$
$$25 + 4 \stackrel{?}{=} 29$$
$$29 = 29 \checkmark$$

Thus, our answer of k = 2 must be correct.

Example 4: Solve for b in the equation 8b – 4 – 2b = 5b.

There are several ways of solving this equation, and one of them is discussed below.

$8b - 4 - 2b = 5b$	
$6b - 4 = 5b$	Since the 8b and the –2b are on the same side, we can go ahead and combine them: 8b – 2b = 6b. (To see why this is true, note that 8b 2b = b(8 2), or b • 6.)
$-4 = -b$	We need both the b's on one side and everything else on the other side, so we can subtract 6b from both sides. Note that 6b – 4 – 6b = –4 and that 5b – 6b = –1b, or –b.
$4 = b$	To cancel out the –1 multiplied by the b, we can divide both sides by –1. Note that –4 ÷ –1 = 4 and –b ÷ –1 = b.

We can check this answer as shown on the next page.

$$8(4) - 4 - 2(4) \stackrel{?}{=} 5(4)$$
$$32 - 4 - 8 \stackrel{?}{=} 20$$
$$20 = 20 \checkmark$$

Hence, our answer of 4 = b (or, equivalently, b = 4) must be correct.

Example 5: Solve for n in the equation $\frac{2}{5}n - 4(n-1) = \frac{3}{4} - n$.

Once again, there are several ways of solving this equation, and one of them is shown below.

$$\frac{2}{5}n - 4(n-1) = \frac{3}{4} - n$$

$$\frac{2}{5}n - 4n + 4 = \frac{3}{4} - n$$

We can begin by distributing the -4.

$$-\frac{18}{5}n + 4 = \frac{3}{4} - n$$

Since the $\frac{2}{5}n$ and the $-4n$ are on the same side, we can go ahead and combine them. Notice that $\frac{2}{5}n - 4n = \frac{2}{5}n - \frac{20}{5}n = -\frac{18}{5}n$.

$$-\frac{13}{5}n + 4 = \frac{3}{4}$$

To get the n's on the same side of the equation, we can add n to both sides of the equation. Note that $-\frac{18}{5}n + 4 + n = -\frac{18}{5}n + 4 + 1n = -\frac{18}{5}n + 4 + \frac{5}{5}n$, or $-\frac{13}{5}n + 4$, and that $\frac{3}{4} - n + n = \frac{3}{4}$.

$$-\frac{13}{5}n = -\frac{13}{4}$$

We can cancel out the addition of 4 by subtracting 4 from both sides. Note that $-\frac{13}{5}n + 4 - 4 = -\frac{13}{5}n$ and that $\frac{3}{4} - 4 = \frac{3}{4} - \frac{16}{4}$, or $-\frac{13}{4}$.

$$n = \frac{5}{4}$$

To cancel out the multiplication by $-\frac{13}{5}$, we can divide both sides by $-\frac{13}{5}$. Note that $-\frac{13}{5}n \div -\frac{13}{5} = n$ and that $-\frac{13}{4} \div -\frac{13}{5} = -\frac{13}{4} \bullet -\frac{5}{13} = \frac{5}{4}$.

We can check this answer as shown below.

$$\frac{2}{5}\left(\frac{5}{4}\right) - 4\left(\frac{5}{4} - 1\right) \stackrel{?}{=} \frac{3}{4} - \frac{5}{4}$$
$$\frac{1}{2} - 4\left(\frac{1}{4}\right) \stackrel{?}{=} -\frac{1}{2}$$
$$\frac{1}{2} - 1 = -\frac{1}{2} \checkmark$$

Thus, our answer of $n = \frac{5}{4}$ must be correct.

Problems – Solve each equation for the indicated variable.

1. $x + 7 = 3$ $x =$ _______

2. $4y = 12$ $y =$ _______

3. $\frac{t}{5} = 3$ $t =$ _______

Hint: To cancel out the division by 5, you can multiply both sides by 5.

4. $\frac{x}{6} + 4 = 7$ $x =$ _______

5. $3(k - 2) = -6$ $k =$ _______

6. $4p + 7 = -17$ $p =$ _______

7. $1 - 5n = 1$ $n =$ _______

8. $6 - 2a = 3a + 1$ $a =$ _______

9. $4r = r + 8$ $r =$ _______

10. $3 - 2d = 5(2d + 5)$ $d =$ _______

11. $2b + 3(b + 4) = b$ $b =$ _______

12. $1 - 5(2w + 3) = -14$ $w =$ _______

13. $5 - 3(4q + 7) = 3q$ $q =$ _______

14. $c + 2(4 - 3c) = 5c$ $c =$ _______

15. $2(x - 4) = 3x + 1$ $x =$ _______

16. $3a + 5 = 7 - a$ $a =$ _______

17. $3(2 - 3u) + 4(5u + 3) = 7$ $u =$ ________

18. $7.2k - 5 = 16.6$ $k =$ ________

19. $5.1y - 3.9 = 11.1y + 44.1$ $y =$ ________

20. $0.73d - d + 5 = -11.2$ $d =$ ________

21. $1.2(n - 3) + 0.6n = 2n$ $n =$ ________

22. $7.5 - (3.4x - 8) = x + 8.9$ $x =$ ________

23. $-4 = 2.25(2a - 5) + 2(3 - a)$ $a =$ ________

24. $7 = 9.1 - 2.5(2 - b)$ $b =$ _______

25. $2(2y + 7) + 3(5 - y) = 4(y + 2)$ $y =$ _______

26. $\frac{2}{3}(3j - 12) = j + 7$ $j =$ _______

27. $3x + 1 = \frac{1}{4}(8x - 5)$ $x =$ _______

28. $7 + \frac{1}{2}(m - 4) = 6$ $m =$ _______

29. $\frac{1}{5}v + 2 = \frac{3}{5}v - 3$ $v =$ _______

30. $\frac{1}{5} + \frac{2}{5}(2 + 3y) = y - 2$ $y =$ _______

31. $\frac{3}{4}g - (2g + 1) = \frac{1}{2}g + \frac{2}{5}$ g = ________

32. $1\frac{3}{4}k + \frac{1}{5} = \frac{3}{5}(k - 1)$ k = ________

33. $\frac{3}{7}(2a + 4) = 2\frac{1}{2}(a + 1)$ a = ________

34. $\frac{7}{10} - \frac{3}{4}\left(2p + \frac{2}{5}\right) = 1 - p$ p = ________

35. $\frac{5}{6}\left(\frac{1}{5}c - 3\right) = \frac{1}{2}c + 2$ c = ________

36. $3(2h - 4) - (h - 5) = h$ h = ________

37. $4(3x + 2) - 0.4(2x - 3) = -2$ x = ________

Part II – Solving Linear Inequalities in One Variable

We state a formal definition of inequality in Chapter 4, but, for now, we will say that an inequality is a lot like an equation; it just has one of the following signs in the middle: $<$, $>$, $\leq$, $\geq$, or $\neq$. Now, we will state some more properties from Part V of Chapter 1.

> Let a, b, and c represent real numbers. Then:
>
> - the Addition Property of Inequality says that $a < b$ if and only if $a + c < b + c$.
> - the Subtraction Property of Inequality says that $a < b$ if and only if $a - c < b - c$.
> - the Multiplication Property of Inequality says that, if $a < b$ and $c > 0$, then $ac < bc$; if $a < b$ and $c < 0$, then $ac > bc$.
> - the Division Property of Inequality says that, if $a < b$ and $c > 0$, then $\frac{a}{c} < \frac{b}{c}$; if $a < b$ and $c < 0$, then $\frac{a}{c} > \frac{b}{c}$.
> - the Symmetric Property of Inequality says that $a < b$ if and only if $b > a$.
> - the Transitive Property of Inequality says that, if $a < b$ and $b < c$, then $a < c$.

The first four properties tell us that, for the most part, we can solve the problems in this section just like we solved the problems in the last section; the only real difference is that, whenever we multiply or divide both sides of the inequality by a negative number, we must flip the inequality symbol.

Example 1: Solve the inequality $4y + 3 < -7$ for y.

We can work this problem as shown below.

$4y + 3 < -7$

$4y < -10$ — We can cancel out the addition of 3 by subtracting 3 from both sides. Note that $4y + 3 - 3 = 4y$ and that $-7 - 3 = -10$.

$y < -\frac{5}{2}$ — We can cancel out the multiplication of 4 by dividing both sides by 4. Since we divided both sides by a positive number, we do not flip the inequality symbol.

To check this answer, we must check both the number and the direction of the inequality symbol.

To check the number, we must substitute the $-\frac{5}{2}$ for y in the original problem, but we must make sure that both sides **equal** each other, as shown below.

$4 \cdot -\frac{5}{2} + 3 \stackrel{?}{=} -7$

$-10 + 3 \stackrel{?}{=} -7$

$-10 + 3 = -7$ ✓

To check the direction of the inequality symbol, we must first pick a number that actually falls in the range of our solution (in this case, we want a number less than $-\frac{5}{2}$). We must then substitute this number into the original inequality for our variable and make sure that we get a true statement. We will pick y = –3, but you could pick any other number that is less than $-\frac{5}{2}$.

$$4 \cdot -3 + 3 \overset{?}{<} -7$$
$$-12 + 3 \overset{?}{<} -7$$
$$-9 < -7 \checkmark$$

Since both the number and the direction of the inequality symbol checked, we can say that our answer of $y < -\frac{5}{2}$ must be correct.

Example 2: Solve the inequality $2n - 6(n + 4) \geq 8$ for n.

There are several sets of steps we can follow to work this problem, and one of them is shown below.

$2n - 6(4 + n) \geq 8$	
$2n - 24 - 6n \geq 8$	We can begin by distributing the -6.
$-24 - 4n \geq 8$	Since the 2n and 6n are on the same side of the inequality symbol, we can combine them: $2n - 6n = -4n$.
$-4n \geq 32$	We can cancel out the subtraction of 24 by adding 24 to both sides. Note that $-4n - 24 + 24 = -4n$ and $8 + 24 = 32$.
$n \leq -8$	We can cancel out the multiplication of -4 by dividing both sides by -4. Notice that we divided both sides by a negative number, and so we must flip the inequality symbol.

To check this answer, we must check both the number and the direction of the inequality symbol.

To check the number:

$$2 \cdot -8 - 6(-8 + 4) \overset{?}{=} 8$$
$$-16 - 6(-4) \overset{?}{=} 8$$
$$-16 + 24 \overset{?}{=} 8$$
$$8 = 8 \checkmark$$

To check the direction of the inequality symbol:

(We picked n = –9.)

$$2 \cdot -9 - 6(-9 + 4) \overset{?}{\geq} 8$$
$$-18 - 6(-5) \overset{?}{\geq} 8$$
$$-18 + 30 \overset{?}{\geq} 8$$
$$12 \geq 8 \checkmark$$

Since both the number and the direction of the inequality symbol checked, we can say that our answer of $n \leq -8$ must be correct.

Example 3: Solve the inequality $5 - 8(3 - 2x) < x - 3$ for x.

Once again, there are several ways of working this problem, and one of them is shown below.

$5 - 8(3 - 2x) < x - 3$

$5 - 24 + 16x < x - 3$ — We can begin by distributing the -8.

$-19 + 16x < x - 3$ — Since the 5 and 24 are on the same side, we can combine them: $5 - 24 = -19$.

$-19 + 15x < -3$ — To get the x's on the same side, we can subtract x from both sides of the inequality. Note that $-19 + 16x - x = -19 + 15x$ and that $x - 3 - x = -3$.

$15x < 16$ — To cancel out the -19, we can add 19 to both sides. Note that $-19 + 15x + 19 = 15x$ and that $-3 + 19 = 16$.

$x < \frac{16}{15}$ — To cancel out the multiplication by 15, we can divide both sides by 15.

Example 4: Solve the inequality $2\frac{1}{2}k - 3\left(k - \frac{1}{4}\right) \le \frac{4}{5}(k - 7)$ for k.

We can work this problem by following the steps shown below.

$2\frac{1}{2}k - 3\left(k - \frac{1}{4}\right) \le \frac{4}{5}(k - 7)$

$\frac{5}{2}k - 3k + \frac{3}{4} \le \frac{4}{5}k - \frac{28}{5}$ — Use the Distributive Property and change the mixed number to an improper fraction.

$-\frac{1}{2}k + \frac{3}{4} \le \frac{4}{5}k - \frac{28}{5}$ — Note that $\frac{5}{2}k - 3k = \frac{5}{2}k - \frac{6}{2}k = -\frac{1}{2}k$.

$\frac{3}{4} \le \frac{13}{10}k - \frac{28}{5}$ — To cancel out the subtraction of $\frac{1}{2}k$ from the left side, we can add $\frac{1}{2}k$ to both sides. (Note that $\frac{4}{5}k + \frac{1}{2}k = \frac{8}{10}k + \frac{5}{10}k$, or $\frac{13}{10}k$.)

$\frac{127}{20} \le \frac{13}{10}k$ — To cancel out the subtraction of $\frac{28}{5}$ from the right side, we can add $\frac{28}{5}$ to both sides (Note that $\frac{3}{4} + \frac{28}{5} = \frac{15}{20} + \frac{112}{20}$, or $\frac{127}{20}$.)

$\frac{127}{26} \le k$,

or, equivalently, $k \ge \frac{127}{26}$ — To cancel out the multiplication by $\frac{13}{10}$, we will divide both sides by $\frac{13}{10}$. (Notice that $\frac{127}{20} \div \frac{13}{10} = \frac{127}{20} \cdot \frac{10}{13} = \frac{127}{26}$.)

Example 5: Solve the inequality $4.4(a - 2.9) + 2(5 - a) \neq 3(2a + 1)$ for a.

As we have said with the other examples in this section, there are several ways of working this problem, and one of them is shown below.

$4.4(a - 2.9) + 2(5 - a) \neq 3(2a + 1)$		
$4.4a - 12.76 + 10 - 2a \neq 6a + 3$		Use the Distributive Property.
$2.4a - 2.76$	$\neq 6a + 3$	Note that $4.4a - 2a = 2.4a$ and that $-12.76 + 10 = -2.76$.
$2.4a$	$\neq 6a + 5.76$	Add 2.76 to both sides.
$-3.6a$	$\neq 5.76$	Subtract 6a from both sides.
a	$\neq -1.6$	Divide both sides by −3.6.

Problems – Do not forget to include the inequality symbol in your answer!

1. Solve for q: $5q + 9 < q - 7$ ______________

2. Solve for w: $9 - 4w \leq -15$ ______________

3. Solve for x: $2x - 5(3x + 1) \geq 5 - 3x$ ______________

4. Solve for n: $3(n - 5) + 2(4 - 2n) > 8$ ______________

5. Solve for a: $6a + 5 \neq 4(2a - 5) - a$ ______________

6. Solve for p: $4p - (3p + 7) < 5p + 2$ ______________

7. Solve for k: $6k < 2(5k - 1) + 3(k + 12)$ ____________

8. Solve for c: $-4 \neq c - 3(2c - 4)$ ____________

9. Solve for v: $5v \geq 4 - (3v - 14)$ ____________

10. Solve for d: $7(d - 2) \geq 5(2d - 9) + 31$ ____________

11. Solve for m: $2 - \frac{3}{4}m > 7$ ____________

12. Solve for y: $-\frac{5}{6} \leq \frac{3}{4} + 2y$ ____________

13. Solve for g: $1\frac{3}{5}g - 5 > 3g - 7$ ____________

14. Solve for h: $\frac{1}{2}(h - 5) \geq \frac{1}{2} - (2h + 1)$ ____________

15. Solve for p: $2\frac{1}{3}(6p + 9) - (8p + 5) \neq \frac{2}{5}$ ____________

16. Solve for j: $\frac{1}{4}(5j - 3\frac{1}{3}) - 2j < \frac{1}{6} - j$ ____________

17. Solve for k: $2\frac{3}{10}(2k - 5) - 5k \leq 1\frac{1}{2}(3 - 2\frac{1}{3}k)$ ____________

18. Solve for n: $\frac{4}{5}(2n - 2\frac{1}{2}) \geq \frac{1}{2}n + \frac{1}{6}$ ____________

19. Solve for y: $\frac{5}{6}(2 - \frac{3}{10}y) + \frac{2}{3}y < -1\frac{1}{4}$ ____________

20. Solve for w: $\frac{3}{4} \leq 1\frac{2}{5}(3w - 5) + \frac{4}{5}w$ ____________

21. Solve for q: $2.4(2q - 5) - 3q > -12$ ____________

22. Solve for x: $6.8 - x < 7.7$ ____________

23. Solve for h: $3.5(1.8 - h) - 3(1 - 2h) \le 2(2h - 3.6)$ ____________

24. Solve for c: $0.6(3c - 5) + c \ne -2.3$ ____________

25. Solve for y: $1.3(3 + 4.1y) + 3.7(1 - 3.9y) < 2.3y + 1.9$ ____________

26. Solve for j: $2 - 2.3(3 - j) \ge j + 0.3$ ____________

27. Solve for b: $0.9(5 - 1.3b) - 3.1 > 0.2(3.1b + 7)$ ____________

28. Solve for v: $3(2.4 - 4v) + 1.7(3.4 + 2.8v) \le v + 6.8$ ____________

29. Solve for m: $5(0.24m + 0.8) - m \ne 2(3.1m + 1.2) - 2$ ____________

30. Solve for a: $3a - 2.6(0.8 - 3.2a) < 0.32a - 3.07$ ____________

31. Solve for d: $\frac{5d-1}{7} \leq 2$ ____________

Hint: Start by canceling out the division of 7 by multiplying both sides by 7.

32. Solve for u: $5.7 + \frac{4}{5}(3u - 1.2) \neq 2(u + 4) - 3.26$ ____________

Hint: Note that $\frac{4}{5} = 4 \div 5$, or 0.8.

33. Solve for x: $\frac{4-6x}{-5} > 8$ ____________

34. Solve for w: $\frac{w+9}{-2} \leq -6$ ____________

35. Solve for n: $\frac{3}{4}(n + 2.4) < \frac{3}{5} - 3n$ ____________

36. Solve for d: $2.4(5 - \frac{9}{10}d) + 4.3(d + 1) \geq \frac{1}{4}$ ____________

Part III – Solving Systems of Equations Using the Substitution Method

In this section and the next section, we will discuss systems of equations, or a set of two or more equations. When a question asks you to *solve* a system of equations, it is asking you to find the value(s) of the variable(s) that will make all the equations true. We will discuss how to do this using a method called substitution in this section, and we will discuss how to do this using a method called elimination in the next section.

To solve a system of equations using the substitution method, we start by rearranging one of the equations so that one of the variables is by itself on one side of the equation and everything else is on the other side. Next, we replace (or substitute) that expression for that variable in one of the other equations.

Let's look at some examples.

Example 1: If $3x + 2y = -14$ and $5x - y = -6$, what values of x and y make both equations true at the same time?

We can work this problem as shown below.

$$5x - y = -6$$
$$-y = -6 - 5x$$
$$y = 6 + 5x$$

We must begin by rearranging one of the equations so that one of the variables is by itself on one side of the equation. For this example, we will rearrange the second equation so that y is by itself on one side. We can do this by subtracting 5x from both sides of the equation and then dividing both sides by –1.

$$3x + 2(6 + 5x) = -14$$

Now, we can look at the other equation and use the Substitution Property of Equality change the y to 6 + 5x (because we just decided in the last step that y must be equal to 6 + 5x).

$$3x + 12 + 10x = -14$$
$$12 + 13x = -14$$
$$13x = -26$$
$$x = -2$$

Now, we can solve this equation using the techniques that we discussed in the first part of this Appendix.

$$y = 6 + 5x$$
$$y = 6 + 5(-2)$$
$$y = -4$$

We are not finished yet because the question asked us to find the values of x *and y* that make both equations true at the same time. To find the correct value for y, we can go back to either of the original equations (or to one of the rearranged versions of these equations) and change the x to –2 and then solve the resulting equation. We chose to use the equation y = 6 + 5x, but we would have gotten exactly the same answer if we had chosen to use one of the other equations instead.

This tells us that both of our original equations are true when $x = -2$ and $y = -4$. (You could check this by following the steps shown below.)

$$3 \cdot -2 + 2 \cdot -4 \stackrel{?}{=} -14$$
$$-6 - 8 \stackrel{?}{=} -14$$
$$-14 = -14 \checkmark$$

$$5 \cdot -2 - (-4) \stackrel{?}{=} -6$$
$$-10 + 4 \stackrel{?}{=} -6$$
$$-6 = -6 \checkmark$$

Example 2: If $7x - 2(x + 3y) = 4x + 17$ and $3x + 2y + 5x - 6 = 180$, what values of x and y make both equations true at the same time?

To work this problem, we will start by using the techniques we discussed in the first part of this Appendix to make the equations nicer to look at and easier to work with.

$$\begin{aligned} 7x - 2(x + 3y) &= 4x + 17 \quad \text{and} \quad 3x + 2y + 5x - 6 = 180 \\ 7x - 2x - 6y &= 4x + 17 \quad \text{and} \quad 8x + 2y - 6 = 180 \\ 5x - 6y &= 4x + 17 \quad \text{and} \quad 8x + 2y = 186 \\ x - 6y &= 17 \end{aligned}$$

Now, we can follow steps similar to the ones we followed in Example 1.

$$\begin{aligned} x - 6y &= 17 \\ x &= 17 + 6y \end{aligned}$$

We must begin by rearranging one of the equations so that one of the variables is by itself on one side of the equation. For this example, we will rearrange the first equation so that x is by itself on one side. We can do this by adding 6y to both sides.

$$8(17 + 6y) + 2y = 186$$

Now, we can look at the other equation, and we can use the Substitution Property of Equality to change the x to 17 + 6y (because we just decided in the last step that x must be equal to 17 + 6y).

$$\begin{aligned} 136 + 48y + 2y &= 186 \\ 136 + 50y &= 186 \\ 50y &= 50 \\ y &= 1 \end{aligned}$$

Now, we can solve this equation using the techniques that we discussed in the first part of this Appendix.

$$\begin{aligned} x &= 17 + 6y \\ x &= 17 + 6(1) \\ x &= 23 \end{aligned}$$

We are not finished yet because the question asked us to find the values of *both* x and y that make both equations true at the same time. To find the correct value for x, we can go back to either of the original equations (or to one of the rearranged versions of these equations) and change the y to 1 and then solve the resulting equation. We chose to use the equation x = 17 + 6y, but we would have gotten exactly the same answer if we had chosen to use one of the other equations instead.

This tells us that both of our original equations are true when x = 23 and y = 1. (You could check this by following the steps shown below.)

$$\begin{aligned} 7 \cdot 23 - 2(23 + 3 \cdot 1) &\stackrel{?}{=} 4 \cdot 23 + 17 \\ 161 - 2(23 + 3) &\stackrel{?}{=} 92 + 17 \\ 161 - 2 \cdot 26 &\stackrel{?}{=} 109 \\ 161 - 52 &\stackrel{?}{=} 109 \\ 109 &= 109 \checkmark \end{aligned}$$

$$\begin{aligned} 3 \cdot 23 + 2 \cdot 1 + 5 \cdot 23 - 6 &\stackrel{?}{=} 180 \\ 69 + 2 + 115 - 6 &\stackrel{?}{=} 180 \\ 180 &= 180 \checkmark \end{aligned}$$

You should note that, when you are checking a solution, you should **not** add, subtract, multiply, or divide both sides by anything. You should work with each side individually and separately and make sure that you end up with the same number on both sides.

Problems – Use the substitution method to find the values of x and y that make both equations true at the same time.

1. If $y = 2x - 7$ and $x = 3y + 1$, then x = __________ and y = __________.

2. If $5y + 18 = x$ and $3x + y = -10$, then x = __________ and y = __________.

3. If $8x + y = -21$ and $x + 2y = -12$, then x = __________ and y = __________.

4. If $4x - y = 15$ and $2y = 24 - x$, then x = __________ and y = __________.

5. If $3x + 7y = -5$ and $5x - y = 17$, then x = __________ and y = __________.

6. If $2x + y = x - 3$ and $4x + 5y = 6 - y$, then $x =$ __________ and $y =$ __________.

7. If $8 - 2x = 6y - x$ and $y = 5 - 2x$, then $x =$ __________ and $y =$ __________.

8. If $5x + 2y = y + 4x$ and $6x - 7y = 3x + 10$, then $x =$ __________ and $y =$ __________.

9. If $x + 4y = 8y - 12$ and $5y + 9 = x - 1$, then $x =$ __________ and $y =$ __________.

10. If $6(x - y) = 9 - y$ and $4x = y - 1$, then $x =$ __________ and $y =$ __________.

11. If $5x + 2(x - y) = 4$ and $x - 5(y + 1) = 5$, then $x =$ __________ and $y =$ __________.

12. If $8 + 3(x + 2y) = y$ and $x - 2(y + 4) = 4$, then x = __________ and y = __________.

13. If $4x - (y + 1) = -1$ and $5x + 3y = 3x - 28$, then x = __________ and y = __________.

14. If $7x - 3(2x - 9) = 4y$ and $2x - 3 = 3y - 2$, then x = __________ and y = __________.

15. If $8y - 3(x - 6) = 23$ and $3x = 1 + 4(x + y)$, then x = __________ and y = __________.

16. If $9 - (x + 6y) = 7$ and $3x + 4(y + 1) = 24$, then x = __________ and y = __________.

17. If $7y - 3(2 - y) = 2x$ and $3x + 2(3y - x) = 8$, then $x =$ __________ and $y =$ __________.

18. If $6y - (3x + 1) = -1$ and $3x + 2(y - 7) = y$, then $x =$ __________ and $y =$ __________.

19. If $4 = x - (8 + 2y)$ and $7x = 3y + (2x - y)$, then $x =$ __________ and $y =$ __________.

20. If $4x + y = 5(x + 7)$ and $3 + (x - 2y) = 6$, then $x =$ __________ and $y =$ __________.

21. If $2x + y = 5(x - 2)$ and $3(x + 1) - 5(y + 1) = 8$, then $x =$ __________ and $y =$ __________.

22. If $3x - 2(x + 3y) = -9$ and $x = 2y - (1 + 4x)$, then x = __________ and y = __________.

23. If $x + 6(y - 2) = 14$ and $5(x - 4) = 6x - 2y$, then x = __________ and y = __________.

24. If $8 - 5(x + 3) = y$ and $7(x + 2) = x + 3y$, then x = __________ and y = __________.

25. If $4(x + 1) = 3(2y - 7)$ and $3x + y = 2y - 6$, then x = __________ and y = __________.

26. If $x + (4y - 1) = -6$ and $4(2x - y) = 3(x + 1)$, then x = __________ and y = __________.

Part IV – Solving Systems of Equations Using the Elimination Method

You will notice that the problems in this section look very similar to the ones you saw in the last section. In this section, we still have a system of equations, and we still want to know the values of the variables that make both equations true at the same time. The only difference is that we will discuss how you can use a process called *elimination* (instead of substitution) to solve these problems.

Example 1: If $4x + 7y = -26$ and $5x - 7y = 62$, use the elimination method to find the values of x and y that make both equations true at the same time.

To work this problem, we will start by adding the equations together, as shown below.

$$\begin{array}{rr} & 4x + 7y = -26 \\ + & \underline{5x - 7y = \;\;62} \\ & 9x \qquad = \;\;36 \end{array}$$

Now, of course, we can divide both sides of this new equation by 9 and find that x must equal 4.

Now, to find the value of y, we can go back to one of the original equations and substitute this value for x. We chose the first equation, but we would have gotten the same answer if we had chosen the second equation instead.

$$\begin{aligned} 4(4) + 7y &= -26 \\ 16 + 7y &= -26 \\ 7y &= -42 \\ y &= -6 \end{aligned}$$

This tells us that both of our original equations are true when $x = 4$ and $y = -6$. (You can check this just like we checked the solutions from the last section.)

For our next example, we will re-work the problem that we worked in Example 2 of the last section.

Example 2: If $7x - 2(x + 3y) = 4x + 17$ and $3x + 2y + 5x - 6 = 180$, use the elimination method to find the values of x and y that make both equations true at the same time.

To work this problem, we will start by using the techniques we discussed in the first part of this Appendix to rearrange both of the equations so that they have the form $Ax + By = C$ (where A, B, and C are constants).

$$\begin{array}{lcl} 7x - 2(x + 3y) = 4x + 17 & \text{and} & 3x + 2y + 5x - 6 = 180 \\ 7x - 2x - 6y = 4x + 17 & \text{and} & 8x + 2y - 6 = 180 \\ 5x - 6y = 4x + 17 & \text{and} & 8x + 2y = 186 \\ x - 6y = 17 & & \end{array}$$

Now, if we try to add these equations together, we do not get a variable to cancel out and go away (like we did in the last example), as shown on the next page.

$$\begin{array}{r} x - 6y = 17 \\ + \quad 8x + 2y = 186 \\ \hline 9x - 4y = 203 \end{array}$$

In order to get a variable to cancel out and go away, we must first multiply both sides of one of the equations by a number. We can either (a) multiply both sides of the first equation by −8, or (b) multiply both sides of the second equation by 3. There are many other ways we could work this problem, but these are the easiest.

Method 1: Multiply both sides of the first equation by −8 and then add the equations together. (Notice that this will make the x's cancel out and go away.)

$$\begin{array}{r} -8x + 48y = -136 \\ + \quad 8x + 2y = 186 \\ \hline 50y = 50 \\ y = 1 \end{array}$$

(by dividing both sides of the last equation by 50)

Now, to find the correct value of x, we can go back to either of the original equations (or to one of the rearranged versions of these equations) and substitute this value for y. We chose to use the equation $x - 6y = 17$, but we would have gotten the same answer if we had chosen one of the other equations instead.

$$x - 6y = 17$$
$$x - 6(1) = 17$$
$$x - 6 = 17$$
$$x = 23$$

Method 2: Multiply both sides of the second equation by 3 and then add the equations together. (Notice that this will make the y's cancel out and go away.)

$$\begin{array}{r} x - 6y = 17 \\ + \quad 24x + 6y = 558 \\ \hline 25x \qquad = 575 \\ x \qquad = 23 \end{array}$$

(by dividing both sides of the last equation by 25)

Now, to find the correct value of y, we can go back to either of the original equations (or to one of the rearranged versions of these equations) and substitute this value for x. We chose to use the equation $x - 6y = 17$, but we would have gotten the same answer if we had chosen one of the other equations instead.

$$x - 6y = 17$$
$$23 - 6y = 17$$
$$-6y = -6$$
$$y = 1$$

Note that, regardless of which method we use, we find that x must equal 23 and y must equal 1. Also note that these are exactly the same values for x and y that we came up with when we worked this problem in the last section.

Example 3: If $5x - 2(y + x) = -10$ and $2(x + 9) + 7y = -2$, use the elimination method to find the values of x and y that make both equations true at the same time.

We will start by rearranging these equations so that they have the form $Ax + By = C$ (where A, B, and C are constants).

$$5x - 2(y + x) = -10 \text{ and } 2(x + 9) + 7y = -2$$
$$5x - 2y - 2x = -10 \text{ and } 2x + 18 + 7y = -2$$
$$3x - 2y = -10 \text{ and } 2x + 7y = -20$$

Now, if we try to add these equations together, we do not get a variable to cancel out and go away, as shown below.

$$\begin{array}{rr} & 3x - 2y = -10 \\ + & 2x + 7y = -20 \\ \hline & 5x + 5y = -30 \end{array}$$

To work this problem, we must multiply both sides of *both* equations by numbers. There are many ways of working this problem, and two of them are shown below.

Method 1: Multiply both sides of the first equation by –2, and multiply both sides of the second equation by 3. (Notice that this will make the x's cancel out and go away.)

$$\begin{array}{rr} & -6x + 4y = 20 \\ + & 6x + 21y = -60 \\ \hline & 25y = -40 \\ & y = -\frac{8}{5} \end{array}$$

Now, to find the correct value of x, we can go back to either of the original equations (or to one of the rearranged versions of these equations) and substitute this value for y. We chose to use the equation $2x + 7y = -20$.

$$2x + 7\left(-\frac{8}{5}\right) = -20$$
$$2x - \frac{56}{5} = -20$$
$$2x = -\frac{44}{5}$$
$$x = -\frac{22}{5}$$

Method 2: Multiply both sides of the first equation by 7, and multiply both sides of the second equation by 2. (Notice that this will make the y's cancel out and go away.)

$$\begin{array}{rr} & 21x - 14y = -70 \\ + & 4x + 14y = -40 \\ \hline & 25x = -110 \\ & x = -\frac{22}{5} \end{array}$$

Now, to find the correct value of x, we can go back to either of the original equations (or to one of the rearranged versions of these equations) and substitute this value for x. We chose to use the equation $2x + 7y = -20$.

$$2\left(-\frac{22}{5}\right) + 7y = -20$$
$$-\frac{44}{5} + 7y = -20$$
$$7y = -\frac{56}{5}$$
$$y = -\frac{8}{5}$$

Notice that both methods tell us that x must equal $-\frac{22}{5}$ and y must equal $-\frac{8}{5}$.

Problems – Use the elimination method to find the values of x and y that make both equations true at the same time.

1. If $x + 2y = -1$ and $3x - 2y = 21$, then x = __________ and y = __________.

2. If $4x - 5y = 3$ and $-4x + 9y = 17$, then x = __________ and y = __________.

3. If $3x + 4y = 5$ and $x - 2y = 15$, then x = __________ and y = __________.

4. If $2x + y = 7$ and $6x + 5y = -1$, then x = __________ and y = __________.

5. If $5x + 3y = -9$ and $2x - 9y = -24$, then x = __________ and y = __________.

6. If $10x + 3y = 9$ and $5x - 6y = -18$, then x = __________ and y = __________.

7. If $3x - 2(x - y) = -9$ and $3x + 5y = 7 + y$, then x = __________ and y = __________.

8. If $7x - 4y = 8$ and $2x - 5y = 37$, then x = __________ and y = __________.

9. If $2x + 4(x - 3) = 7 - 5y$ and $3x + 3y - x = 5$, then x = __________ and y = __________.

10. If $5y - 2(x + 1) = 10$ and $4x - (3y + 5) = 13$, then x = __________ and y = __________.

11. If $3x + 4y = 26$ and $5x - 3y = 24$, then x = __________ and y = __________.

12. If $3 + 5(x - 8) = 4y$ and $2x + 7(y + 5) = 24$, then x = __________ and y = __________.

13. If $12x + 2y = -12$ and $8x + 3y = 32$, then x = __________ and y = __________.

14. If $7x + 6y = 10$ and $4y - 5x = -32$, then x = __________ and y = __________.

15. If $5x - 2(y + 8) = 16$ and $6x + (y - 6) = 4y$, then x = __________ and y = __________.

16. If $6x + 2(y + 1) = x - 10y$ and $10 = 4(x + y) + 2(2x + y)$, then x = __________ and y = __________.

17. If $4(x - 7) + 9(y + 3) = 5$ and $3x + 4y = 2(y - 13) - 7x$, then x = __________ and y = __________.

18. If $10y - 3(x + 9) = 3$ and $50 + 2(3x - y) = x - 5y$, then x = __________ and y = __________.

19. If $3x - 3(y + 7) = 9 - 10y$ and $4y - 9(x - 1) = -6$, then x = __________ and y = __________.

20. If $3(x - 4y) + (x + y) = 9$ and $2x - 1 = 4 + 5(2 - y)$, then x = __________ and y = __________.

21. If $5(x + y) = 16 + 3y$ and $3x - 2(y - 3) = -3$, then x = __________ and y = __________.

22. If $x + 5y = 4 - 6(x - 2)$ and $4(x + 3) - y = 7$, then $x =$ __________ and $y =$ __________.

23. If $14 = 2(x + y) - (x - y)$ and $9 + 3(2x + y) = 5 - 4y$, then $x =$ __________ and $y =$ __________.

24. If $5x + (x + 4y) = -11$ and $7y - 3x = 2(y - 6)$, then $x =$ __________ and $y =$ __________.

25. If $2(x + 5y) - 6(1 + y) = -15$ and $8 - x = 4(7 + y)$, then $x =$ __________ and $y =$ __________.

26. If $3(x + y) + 9 = 8 - 4(x + y)$ and $2(x + y - 5) = y - 9$, then $x =$ __________ and $y =$ __________.

Part V – Simplifying Square Roots

In this section, we will review a concept called *square roots*. In general, when you want to find the square root of a number, you need to ask yourself, "What multiplied by itself gives me this number?" Also, we use the symbol "$\sqrt{\ }$" to talk about square roots.

Example 1: Simplify $\sqrt{36}$.

This question wants us to find the square root of 36, and so we must ask ourselves the question, "What multiplied by itself gives me 36?" Since the answer is 6, we can say that $\sqrt{36} = 6$.*

Example 2: Simplify $7\sqrt{25} - 4\sqrt{9}$.

We can work this problem as shown below.

$7\sqrt{25} - 4\sqrt{9} = 7 \cdot \sqrt{25} - 4 \cdot \sqrt{9}$ Since there is not a sign that tells us whether to add, subtract, multiply, or divide between the 7 and the $\sqrt{25}$, we must assume multiplication. Similarly, there is not a sign that tells us whether to add, subtract, multiply, or divide between the 4 and the $\sqrt{9}$, and so we must assume multiplication again.

$= 7 \cdot 5 - 4 \cdot 3$ Note that $\sqrt{25} = 5$ (because $5 \cdot 5 = 25$) and $\sqrt{9} = 3$ (because $3 \cdot 3 = 9$).

$= 35 - 12$ Remember that the order of operations tells us that we must multiply and divide before we can add or subtract.

$= 23$

To work the rest of the examples in this section, we will use the following theorem.

> If $a \geq 0$ and $b \geq 0$, then $\sqrt{a} \cdot \sqrt{b} = \sqrt{ab}$ and $\dfrac{\sqrt{a}}{\sqrt{b}} = \sqrt{\dfrac{a}{b}}$.

Example 3: Simplify $8\sqrt{\dfrac{9}{16}}$.

We can work this problem as shown below and continued on the next page.

$8\sqrt{\dfrac{9}{16}} = 8 \cdot \sqrt{\dfrac{9}{16}}$ Since there is not a sign that tells us whether to add, subtract, multiply, or divide between the 8 and the $\sqrt{\dfrac{9}{16}}$, we must assume multiplication.

$= 8 \cdot \dfrac{\sqrt{9}}{\sqrt{16}}$ Use the theorem above.

*While it is also true that $-6 \cdot -6 = 36$, we only want the positive answer when we use the $\sqrt{\ }$ symbol.

$= 8 \cdot \frac{3}{4}$ — Note that $\sqrt{9} = 3$ (because $3 \cdot 3 = 9$) and $\sqrt{16} = 4$ (because $4 \cdot 4 = 16$).

$= 6$ — Note that $8 \cdot \frac{3}{4} = 6$.

Example 4: Simplify $\frac{5\sqrt{42}}{7\sqrt{6}}$.

The easiest way to work this problem is to start by reducing the fraction. We can do this by dividing both the top and bottom by $\sqrt{6}$. This tells us that $\frac{5\sqrt{42}}{7\sqrt{6}}$ simplifies to $\frac{5\sqrt{7}}{7}$. We **cannot** reduce this fraction further by dividing both the top and bottom by 7 because the 7 on the top is under a square root symbol but the 7 on the bottom of the fraction is not. Next, we will note that we can use a calculator and find that $\sqrt{7}$ is approximately 2.646, and so $\frac{5\sqrt{7}}{7} \approx \frac{5 \cdot 2.646}{7}$, or about 1.89. However, since this is only *approximately* equal to the original problem, we will leave our final answer as $\frac{5\sqrt{7}}{7}$. (Incidentally, we will discuss a more complicated way of working this type of problem in Examples 8 and 9. If we had chosen to work this problem like the problems in Examples 8 and 9, we would have made our life more difficult, but we would have gotten this same answer in the end.)

Example 5: Simplify $\sqrt{72}$.

We will begin by noting that we can use a calculator and find that $\sqrt{72}$ is approximately 8.485. However, this is an approximation, and not *exactly* equal to $\sqrt{72}$. Therefore, we must simplify it using a different method. The easiest way to simplify $\sqrt{72}$ is shown below.

$\sqrt{72} = \sqrt{36} \cdot \sqrt{2}$ — Notice that $36 \cdot 2 = 72$. We chose these particular factors of 72 because we can easily take the square root of 36. We would not, for instance, have wanted to choose 12 and 6 because we cannot take the square root of either 12 or 6. However, as we will discuss on the next page, we could have chosen 9 and 8. (Note that you can easily take the square root of 9.) As you will see, we get the same final answer either way.

$= 6 \cdot \sqrt{2}$, or $6\sqrt{2}$ — Note that $\sqrt{36} = 6$.

Now, let's suppose that you didn't realize that $36 \cdot 2 = 72$. You could have worked this problem using the steps shown below.

$\sqrt{72} = \sqrt{9} \cdot \sqrt{8}$ — Notice that $9 \cdot 8 = 72$ and that you can easily take the square root of 9. (Like we said earlier in this example, we want to be able to easily take the square root of one of the factors we choose.)

$= 3 \cdot \sqrt{8}$ — Note that $\sqrt{9} = 3$.

$= 3 \cdot \sqrt{4} \cdot \sqrt{2}$ — Now, we must simplify $\sqrt{8}$. Once again, we want to find two numbers that will multiply together to give us 8 and one of which we can easily take the square root of.

$= 3 \cdot 2 \cdot \sqrt{2}$ — Note that $\sqrt{4} = 2$.

$= 6 \cdot \sqrt{2}$,

or $6\sqrt{2}$

By the way, you also could have gotten this same final answer by starting with $\sqrt{72} = \sqrt{4} \cdot \sqrt{18}$ as your first step.

Example 6: Simplify $\sqrt{5} - \sqrt{45} + 3\sqrt{20}$.

We will start by noting that we can simplify $\sqrt{45}$ and $3\sqrt{20}$ using the same thought process as the one we used in Example 5, as shown below.

$\sqrt{45} = \sqrt{9} \cdot \sqrt{5}$ and $3\sqrt{20} = 3 \cdot \sqrt{4} \cdot \sqrt{5}$

$\sqrt{45} = 3 \cdot \sqrt{5}$ and $3\sqrt{20} = 3 \cdot 2 \cdot \sqrt{5}$

$\sqrt{45} = 3\sqrt{5}$ and $3\sqrt{20} = 6\sqrt{5}$

This tells us that our original problem simplifies to $\sqrt{5} - 3\sqrt{5} + 6\sqrt{5}$, which simplifies further to $4\sqrt{5}$. (To see why, note that the expression $\sqrt{5} - 3\sqrt{5} + 6\sqrt{5}$ is very similar to $x - 3x + 6x$, which simplifies to $4x$. Also note, however, that the original problem is similar to $x - y + 3z$, which, of course, cannot be simplified further. Thus, when you want to add or subtract square roots, you must worry about like terms just like you must worry about like terms when you want to add or subtract variables.) This cannot be simplified further, and so the final answer to this question is $4\sqrt{5}$.

Example 7: Simplify $(2\sqrt{18})^3$.

There are several ways to work this problem, and one of them is shown below.

$(2\sqrt{18})^3 = (2 \cdot 3\sqrt{2})^3$ — We will start by simplifying $\sqrt{18}$. Notice that $\sqrt{18} = \sqrt{9} \cdot \sqrt{2}$, or $3\sqrt{2}$.

$= (6\sqrt{2})^3$

$= (6\sqrt{2})(6\sqrt{2})(6\sqrt{2})$ — Recall that, when you want to raise an expression to the third power, you must multiply it by itself three times.

$= \quad 216\sqrt{8}$ Note that $6 \cdot 6 \cdot 6 = 216$ and $\sqrt{2} \cdot \sqrt{2} \cdot \sqrt{2} = \sqrt{8}$.

$= \quad 216 \cdot 2\sqrt{2}$ We can simplify $\sqrt{8}$ by noting that $\sqrt{8} = \sqrt{4} \cdot \sqrt{2}$, or $2\sqrt{2}$.

$= \quad 432\sqrt{2}$ Note that $216 \cdot 2 = 432$.

The last two examples in this section talk about a technique for simplifying square roots called rationalizing the denominator. Whenever you have a problem involving square roots, you never want to leave a square root symbol in the denominator.

Example 8: Simplify $\dfrac{24}{\sqrt{6}}$.

To work this problem, we can follow the steps shown below.

$\dfrac{24}{\sqrt{6}} = \dfrac{24}{\sqrt{6}} \cdot \dfrac{\sqrt{6}}{\sqrt{6}}$ To get the square root out of the denominator, we will multiply both the numerator and denominator by $\sqrt{6}$. (To see why we decided to multiply by $\sqrt{6}$ instead of some other number, note that this will give us $\sqrt{36}$ on the bottom and that we can easily take the square root of 36.)

$= \dfrac{24\sqrt{6}}{\sqrt{36}}$

$= \dfrac{24\sqrt{6}}{6}$

$= 4\sqrt{6}$ Since the 24 in the numerator and the 6 in the denominator are both outside the square roots symbols now, we can reduce the fraction by dividing both of them by 6.

Example 9: Simplify $\dfrac{5\sqrt{12}}{\sqrt{7}}$.

We can work this problem by following the steps shown below.

$\dfrac{5\sqrt{12}}{\sqrt{7}} = \dfrac{10\sqrt{3}}{\sqrt{7}}$ We will start by simplifying $5\sqrt{12}$. Note that $\sqrt{12} = \sqrt{4} \cdot \sqrt{3}$, or $2\sqrt{3}$. Therefore, $5\sqrt{12} = 5 \cdot 2\sqrt{3}$, or $10\sqrt{3}$.

$= \dfrac{10\sqrt{3}}{\sqrt{7}} \cdot \dfrac{\sqrt{7}}{\sqrt{7}}$ Now, to get the square root out of the denominator, we will multiply both the numerator and denominator by $\sqrt{7}$. (To see why picked $\sqrt{7}$ instead of some other number, note that this will give us $\sqrt{49}$ on the bottom and that we can easily take the square root of 49.)

$= \dfrac{10\sqrt{21}}{\sqrt{49}}$

$= \dfrac{10\sqrt{21}}{7}$ Note that $\sqrt{49} = 7$. Also, you can break $\sqrt{21}$ down to $\sqrt{7} \cdot \sqrt{3}$, but, since neither $\sqrt{7}$ nor $\sqrt{3}$ is a nice, pretty number, we will write $\sqrt{21}$ instead of $\sqrt{7} \cdot \sqrt{3}$.

Problems – Simplify each of the following.

1. $\sqrt{45}$ = ______________

8. $\dfrac{3\sqrt{6}}{\sqrt{54}}$ = ______________

2. $\sqrt{100}$ = ______________

9. $\dfrac{\sqrt{40}}{3\sqrt{10}}$ = ______________

3. $\sqrt{25}$ = ______________

10. $\dfrac{9\sqrt{84}}{\sqrt{7}}$ = ______________

4. $\sqrt{108}$ = ______________

11. $\dfrac{3\sqrt{160}}{5\sqrt{20}}$ = ______________

5. $\dfrac{5}{\sqrt{36}}$ = ______________

12. $\dfrac{5\sqrt{18}}{\sqrt{2}}$ = ______________

6. $\sqrt{\dfrac{9}{4}}$ = ______________

13. $\dfrac{4\sqrt{2}}{\sqrt{5}}$ = ______________

7. $\dfrac{4\sqrt{60}}{\sqrt{5}}$ = ______________

14. $\dfrac{\sqrt{10}}{2\sqrt{3}}$ = ______________

15. $\dfrac{5\sqrt{12}}{6\sqrt{5}} =$ ____________________

16. $\dfrac{4}{\sqrt{5}} =$ ____________________

17. $\dfrac{3}{\sqrt{24}} =$ ____________________

18. $\dfrac{3}{7\sqrt{45}} =$ ____________________

19. $\dfrac{9}{\sqrt{3}} =$ ____________________

20. $\dfrac{4}{3\sqrt{28}} =$ ____________________

21. $\dfrac{12}{6\sqrt{2}} =$ ____________________

22. $\dfrac{5\sqrt{3}}{12\sqrt{5}} =$ ____________________

23. $\dfrac{4\sqrt{3}}{5\sqrt{2}} =$ ____________________

24. $\dfrac{7\sqrt{27}}{6\sqrt{8}} =$ ____________________

25. $\dfrac{9\sqrt{5}}{4\sqrt{15}} =$ ____________________

26. $\dfrac{\sqrt{7}}{\sqrt{14}} =$ ____________________

27. $\sqrt{\dfrac{7}{10}} =$ ____________________

Hint: $\sqrt{\dfrac{7}{10}} = \dfrac{\sqrt{7}}{\sqrt{10}}$

28. $\sqrt{\dfrac{25}{2}} =$ ____________________

29. $\sqrt{18} + \sqrt{50} =$ ______________

30. $5\sqrt{54} - 3\sqrt{24} =$ ______________

31. $3\sqrt{7} - \sqrt{63} =$ ______________

32. $\sqrt{\frac{32}{9}} + \sqrt{\frac{8}{25}} =$ ______________

33. $\sqrt{\frac{75}{4}} + \sqrt{\frac{27}{64}} =$ ______________

34. $(5\sqrt{2})(3\sqrt{6}) =$ ______________

35. $(4\sqrt{3})(\sqrt{3}) =$ ______________

36. $(6\sqrt{2})^2 =$ ______________

37. $(7\sqrt{2})(3\sqrt{5}) =$ ______________

38. $\sqrt{48}(\sqrt{3} + 2) =$ ______________
Hint: Use the Distributive Property.

39. $\sqrt{10}(4 - 6\sqrt{5}) =$ ______________

Part VI – Solving Quadratic Equations

We will begin this section with a definition.

An equation is a <u>quadratic equation</u> if and only if it can be written in the form $ax^2 + bx + c = 0$ (where a, b, and c are constants).

In this section, we will discuss how we can solve quadratic equations. We will discuss three methods of doing this: the *square root method*, *factoring*, and *the quadratic formula*. All quadratic equations can be solved using the quadratic formula, and many of them can be solved using any of the three methods.

Method 1: The Square Root Method

Before we look at any complicated examples that involve using the square root method, let's talk about the equation $m^2 = 49$. When they look at this equation, most people realize that m can equal 7 (because $7^2 = 49$). However, you should also realize that m can also equal –7 (because $(-7)^2$ also equals 49).

To solve a quadratic equation using the square root method, we start by rearranging the equation so that the quantity being squared is by itself on one side of the equation and the only thing on the other side is a number. Then we take the square root of both sides, and we put a "±" sign in front of the side with the number. (The sign "±" says that the number can be either positive or negative, and it is read, "plus or minus".) This tells us that we can solve the equation $m^2 = 49$ using the square root method by following the steps shown below.

$$m^2 = 49$$

$$\sqrt{m^2} = \pm\sqrt{49}$$

Since the quantity being squared is already by itself on one side of the equation with only a number on the other side, we can take the square root of both sides, but we must remember to put a "±" sign in front of the side with the number.

$$m = \pm 7$$

Note that $\sqrt{m^2} = m$ and that $\sqrt{49} = 7$.

Now, let's look at how to solve some more complicated equations using the square root method.

Example 1: Solve the equation $7 - (2x - 5)^2 = -2$ for x.

We can work this problem as shown below.

$$7 - (2x - 5)^2 = -2$$

$$-(2x - 5)^2 = -9$$

$$(2x - 5)^2 = 9$$

To solve a quadratic equation using the square root method, we must start by rearranging the equation so that the quantity being squared is by itself. For this example, we can do this by subtracting 7 from both sides and then dividing both sides by –1.

$$2x - 5 = \pm 3$$

$$2x - 5 = 3 \text{ or } 2x - 5 = -3$$

Now, we can take the square root of both sides, but we must remember to put a "±" sign in front of the side with the number.

$$x = 4 \quad \text{or} \quad x = 1$$

Add 5 to both sides of each equation and then divide both sides by 2.

Example 2: Solve the equation $25y^2 = 12$ for y.

We can work this problem by following the steps shown below.

$25y^2 = 12$

$y^2 = \frac{12}{25}$ — To solve a quadratic equation using the square root method, we must start by rearranging the equation so that the quantity being squared is by itself. For this example, we can do this by dividing both sides by 25.

$y = \pm\frac{2\sqrt{3}}{5}$ — Now, we can take the square root of both sides, but we must remember to put a "±" sign in front of the side with the number. (Note that $\sqrt{\frac{12}{25}} = \frac{\sqrt{12}}{\sqrt{25}} = \frac{2\sqrt{3}}{5}$.)

We could write our final answer as $y = \frac{2\sqrt{3}}{5}$ or $y = -\frac{2\sqrt{3}}{5}$, or we could just write $y = \pm\frac{2\sqrt{3}}{5}$.

Method 2: Factoring

To solve a quadratic equation by factoring, you must first rearrange the equation so that it has the form $ax^2 + bx + c = 0$. Next, factor the trinomial, and then use the Zero Product Principle stated below.

The Zero Product Principle
If mn = 0, then one of the following statements must be true: m = 0, n = 0, or both m and n equal zero.

Example 3: Solve the equation $7 - (2x - 5)^2 = -2$ for x.

We can work this problem as shown below.

$7 - (2x - 5)^2 = -2$

$7 - (2x - 5)(2x - 5) = -2$
$7 - (4x^2 - 20x + 25) = -2$
$7 - 4x^2 + 20x - 25 = -2$
$-4x^2 + 20x - 18 = -2$
$-4x^2 + 20x - 16 = 0$

To solve this equation using factoring, we must start by rearranging it so that it has the form $ax^2 + bx + c = 0$.

$-4(x^2 - 5x + 4) = 0$
$-4(x - 1)(x - 4) = 0$

Now, we can factor. We must look for a greatest common factor first, and we must make sure that our factored expression multiplies back out to give us what we started with.

$-4 = 0$, $x - 1 = 0$, or $x - 4 = 0$ — Now, we can use the Zero Product Principle stated above.

$x = 1$ or $x = 4$ — Finally, we can solve for x. Note that −4 will never equal zero, and so we can forget about that part of the answer.

Example 4: Solve the equation $4k^2 = 8k$ for k using factoring.

We will begin by noting that we cannot use the square root method to solve this equation because we cannot easily rearrange this equation so that we have a quantity being squared on one side of the equation and only a number on the other side.

We can, however, solve this equation using factoring, as shown below.

$4k^2 = 8k$

$4k^2 - 8k = 0$ — To solve this equation using factoring, we must start by rearranging it so that it has the form $ak^2 + bk + c = 0$.

$4k(k - 2) = 0$ — Now, we can factor. We must look for a greatest common factor first, and we must make sure that our factored expression multiplies back out to give us what we started with.

$4k = 0$ or $k - 2 = 0$ — Next, we can use the Zero Product Principle stated on the previous page.

$k = 0$ or $k = 2$ — Finally, we can solve for k.

Finally, we will note that we could not solve the equation from Example 2 using factoring because we cannot factor $25y^2 - 12$ using integers. (In other words, if you try to factor $25y^2 - 12$ using only integers, you will not be able to get an expression that multiplies out to give you what you started with.)

Method 3: The Quadratic Formula

We will begin by stating a formula called the quadratic formula.

If $ax^2 + bx + c = 0$, then $x = \dfrac{-b \pm \sqrt{b^2 - 4ac}}{2a}$.

Now, let's look at some examples that use this formula.

Example 5: Solve the equation $7 - (2x - 5)^2 = -2$ for x.

We can work this problem as shown below.

$7 - (2x - 5)^2 = -2$

$$\begin{aligned} 7 - (2x - 5)(2x - 5) &= -2 \\ 7 - (4x^2 - 20x + 25) &= -2 \\ 7 - 4x^2 + 20x - 25 &= -2 \\ -4x^2 + 20x - 18 &= -2 \\ -4x^2 + 20x - 16 &= 0 \end{aligned}$$

To solve a quadratic equation using the quadratic formula, we must start by rearranging it so that it has the form $ax^2 + bx + c = 0$.

$$x = \frac{-20 \pm \sqrt{20^2 - 4(-4)(-16)}}{2(-4)}$$

Now, we can substitute values for a, b, and c into the quadratic formula. (Note that, for this example, $a = -4$, $b = 20$, and $c = -16$.)

$$x = \frac{-20 \pm \sqrt{400 - 256}}{-8}$$ Simplify the result.

$$x = \frac{-20 \pm \sqrt{144}}{-8}$$

$$x = \frac{-20 \pm 12}{-8}$$

$$x = \frac{-20 + 12}{-8} \quad \text{or} \quad x = \frac{-20 - 12}{-8}$$

$$x = 1 \quad \text{or} \quad x = 4$$

Example 6: Solve the equation $25y^2 = 12$ for y.

We can work this problem as shown below.

$$25y^2 = 12$$

$$25y^2 - 12 = 0$$

To solve this equation using the quadratic formula, we must start by rearranging it so that it has the form $ay^2 + by + c = 0$.

$$y = \frac{0 \pm \sqrt{0^2 - 4(25)(-12)}}{2(25)}$$

Now, we can substitute values for a, b, and c into the quadratic formula. (Note that, for this example, a = 25, b = 0, and c = –12.)

$$y = \frac{0 \pm \sqrt{1200}}{50}$$

Simplify the result.

$$y = \frac{0 \pm \sqrt{1200}}{50}$$

$$y = \frac{0 \pm 20\sqrt{3}}{50}$$

$$y = \frac{0 + 20\sqrt{3}}{50} \quad \text{or} \quad y = \frac{0 - 20\sqrt{3}}{50}$$

$$y = \frac{20\sqrt{3}}{50} \quad \text{or} \quad y = \frac{-20\sqrt{3}}{50}$$

$$y = \frac{2\sqrt{3}}{5} \quad \text{or} \quad y = \frac{-2\sqrt{3}}{5}$$

Example 7: Solve the equation $4k^2 = 8k$ for k.

We can work this problem as shown below.

$$4k^2 = 8k$$

$$4k^2 - 8k = 0$$

To solve this equation using the quadratic formula, we must start by rearranging it so that it has the form $ak^2 + bk + c = 0$.

$$k = \frac{-(-8) \pm \sqrt{(-8)^2 - 4(4)(0)}}{2(4)}$$

Now, we can substitute values for a, b, and c into the quadratic formula. (Note that, for this example, $a = 4$, $b = -8$, and $c = 0$.)

$$k = \frac{8 \pm \sqrt{64 - 0}}{8}$$

Simplify the result.

$$k = \frac{8 \pm \sqrt{64}}{8}$$

$$k = \frac{8 \pm 8}{8}$$

$$k = \frac{8+8}{8} \text{ or } k = \frac{8-8}{8}$$

$$k = 2 \quad \text{or} \quad k = 0$$

Problems – Solve each of the following equations using the method of your choice.

1. $x^2 = 5$ x = ___________

2. $n^2 - 5 = 4n$ n = ___________

3. $4 - 2y^2 = y$ y = ___________

4. $3q^2 + 5 = q + 5$ q = ___________

5. $3n^2 + 2n = 1$ n = ___________

6. $(2x + 1)^2 = 9$ x = ___________

7. $4(k^2 - 1) = 6k$ $k =$ ___________

8. $5 - 2w^2 = 4w$ $w =$ ___________

9. $5(u - 1)^2 + 2 = 47$ $u =$ ___________

10. $3y^2 + 2 = 5(y + 2)$ $y =$ ___________

11. $2p^2 = 4(p + 1) + 3(p - 3)$ $p =$ ___________

12. $4(x - 5)^2 = 32$ $x =$ ___________

13. $7(v^2 + 2) = 3v + 14$ $v =$ ___________

14. $4n(n + 5) = 20n + 27$ $n =$ ___________

15. $3(r - 2)^2 = 2r$ $r =$ ___________

16. $7(k + 1) - 2k(k + 1) = 7$ $k =$ ___________

17. $3(c + 5) = 2c^2 + 1$ $c =$ ___________

18. $(j - 5)(j + 1) = 1 - 2j^2$ $j =$ ___________

19. $(3h + 2)(h - 5) = 15 - 13h$ $h =$ ___________

20. $(1 - 2b)^2 = 2b$ $b =$ ___________

21. $5(3m - 2)^2 + 1 = 51$ $m =$ ___________

22. $1 = 10 - (y + 1)^2$ $y =$ ___________

23. $(d - 2)(d - 8) = -2d$ $d =$ ___________

24. $x(9x - 1) - 5(x + 1) = -6$ $x =$ ___________

25. $3a(a - 5) = 9a$ $a =$ ___________

26. $8(p + 1)^2 - 1 = 1$ $p =$ ___________

Appendix B – Answers to the Odd-Numbered Questions

Chapter 1, Part I (pages 2-5)

1. deductive reasoning
3. inductive reasoning
5. deductive reasoning
7. deductive reasoning
9. inductive reasoning
11. The next two numbers of the sequence are 54 and 61.
13. The sum of an odd number and an even number is an odd number.
15. The cafeteria at the college Adam is attending will serve hamburgers today.
17. Pat Green will win the next election for the mayor of your town.
19. Simon's favorite football team will lose their game tonight.
21. even

Chapter 1, Part II (pages 9-13)

1. true
3. true
5. true
7. true
9. false
11. true
13. true
15. true
17. true
19. true
21. 2 is a prime number but is not odd
23. Example: 0.5 is a real number, but 0.5 is not greater than $\frac{1}{0.5}$
25. Example: 7.3 is a rational number but not a whole number

Chapter 1, Part II (pages 9-13) continued

27. Example: The figure below has 4 sides and is a square. (The little squares in the corners say that those angles are right angles.)

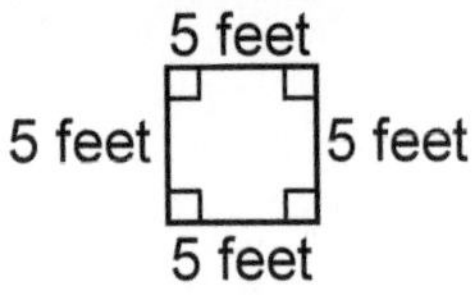

29. Example: The number 18 is divisible by 6 but not by 12.
31. No conclusion is possible.
33. If a figure is a square, then it is a quadrilateral.
35. The number 3 is a rational number.
37. If it is before 9 p.m., then Helen will get her medicine.
39. No conclusion is possible.
41. No conclusion is possible.

Chapter 1, Part III (pages 17-23)

1. (a), (c)
3. (b)
5. (a)
7. (d), (e)
9. (d)
11. The original statement is true.
    The converse is, "If $x^2 - 7 \neq 9$, then $x = 8$," and it is false.
    The inverse is, "If $x \neq 8$, then $x^2 - 7 = 9$," and it is false.
    The contrapositive is, "If $x^2 - 7 = 9$, then $x \neq 8$," and it is true.

Chapter 1, Part III (pages 17-23) continued

13. The original statement is false.

    The converse is, "If a number is a natural number, then it is a positive number," and it is true.

    The inverse is, "If a number is not a positive number, then it is not a natural number," and it is true.

    The contrapositive is, "If a number is not a natural number, then it is not a positive number," and it is false.

15. The original statement is true.

    The converse is, "If 2x = 14, then x = 7," and it is true.

    The inverse is, "If x ≠ 7, then 2x ≠ 14," and it is true.

    The contrapositive is, "If 2x ≠ 14, then x ≠ 7," and it is true.

17. The original statement is false.

    The converse is, "If a figure has 12 sides, then it is a triangle," and it is false.

    The inverse is, "If a figure is not a triangle, then it does not have 12 sides," and it is false.

    The contrapositive is, "If a figure does not have 12 sides, then it is not a triangle," and it is false.

19. The converse is, "If you call me at 1-800-555-1234, then you are interested in buying a house."

    The inverse is, "If you are not interested in buying a house, then don't call me at 1-800-555-1234."

    The contrapositive is, "If don't call me at 1-800-555-1234, then you are not interested in buying a house."

21. (a), (c), and (g)

23. (b)

Chapter 1, Part III (pages 17-23) continued

25. (b) and (c)

27. is

29. may

Chapter 1, Part IV (pages 25-28)

1. false

3. false

5. true

7. true

9. false

11. false

13. (d), (e), (f), and (g)

15. (a), (b), (c), and (e)

17. (a), (c), (d), (e), (g), and (h)

Chapter 1, Part V (pages 32-40)

1.

Statements	Reasons
1. 5x = 3x – 14	1. Given
2. 2x = –14	2. Subtraction Property of Equality
3. x = –7	3. Division Property of Equality

3.

Statements	Reasons
1. 5y + 4 = 2 – 3y	1. Given
2. 8y + 4 = 2	2. Addition Property of Equality
3. 8y = –2	3. Subtraction Property of Equality
4. $y = -\frac{1}{4}$	4. Division Property of Equality

5.

Statements	Reasons
1. $5 - \frac{3w}{4} = 15$	1. Given
2. $-\frac{3w}{4} = 10$	2. Subtraction Property of Equality
3. $-3w = 40$	3. Multiplication Property of Equality
4. $w = -\frac{40}{3}$	4. Division Property of Equality

7.

Statements	Reasons
1. $2n - 5 = 3 - (n + 4)$	1. Given
2. $2n - 5 = 3 - n - 4$	2. Distributive Property
3. $2n - 5 = -n - 1$	3. Substitution Property of Equality
4. $3n - 5 = -1$	4. Addition Property of Equality
5. $3n = 4$	5. Addition Property of Equality
6. $n = \frac{4}{3}$	6. Division Property of Equality

9.

Statements	Reasons
1. $3q + 4 \le 5$	1. Given
2. $3q \le 1$	2. Subtraction Property of Inequality
3. $q \le \frac{1}{3}$	3. Division Property of Inequality

Chapter 1, Part V (pages 32-40) continued

11.

Statements	Reasons
1. $x + 4(2x - 1) < 5$	1. Given
2. $x + 8x - 4 < 5$	2. Distributive Property
3. $9x - 4 < 5$	3. Distributive Property
4. $9x < 9$	4. Addition Property of Inequality
5. $x < 1$	5. Division Property of Inequality

13.

Statements	Reasons
1. $3 - \frac{5y}{12} < \frac{1}{4}$	1. Given
2. $-\frac{5y}{12} < -\frac{11}{4}$	2. Subtraction Property of Inequality
3. $-5y < -33$	3. Multiplication Property of Inequality
4. $y > \frac{33}{5}$	4. Division Property of Inequality

15.

Statements	Reasons
1. $5x + y = 36$ and $x - 5y = 2$	1. Given
2. $y = 36 - 5x$	2. Subtraction Property of Equality
3. $x - 5(36 - 5x) = 2$	3. Substitution Property of Equality
4. $x - 180 + 25x = 2$	4. Distributive Property
5. $26x - 180 = 2$	5. Distributive Property
6. $26x = 182$	6. Addition Property of Equality
7. $x = 7$	7. Division Property of Equality
8. $y = 36 - 5(7)$	8. Substitution Property of Equality
9. $y = 1$	9. Substitution Property of Equality

17.

Statements	Reasons
1. $2x + y = -4$ and $3x - y = -11$	1. Given
2. $y = -4 - 2x$	2. Subtraction Property of Equality
3. $3x - (-4 - 2x) = -11$	3. Substitution Property of Equality
4. $3x + 4 + 2x = -11$	4. Distributive Property
5. $5x + 4 = -11$	5. Distributive Property
6. $5x = -15$	6. Subtraction Property of Equality

Chapter 1, Part V (pages 32-40) continued

(#17 continued)

Statements continued	Reasons continued
7. $x = -3$	7. Division Property of Equality
8. $y = -4 - 2(-3)$	8. Substitution Property of Equality
9. $y = 2$	9. Substitution Property of Equality

19.

Statements	Reasons
1. $5a - 4 = 31$	1. Given
2. Assume that $a \neq 7$.	2. Assumption
3. $5a \neq 35$	3. Multiplication Property of Inequality
4. $5a - 4 \neq 31$	4. Subtraction Property of Inequality
5. $a = 7$	5. Contradiction

21.

Statements	Reasons
1. $\frac{5c}{8} + 1 = -9$	1. Given
2. Assume that $c \neq -16$.	2. Assumption
3. $5c \neq -80$	3. Multiplication Property of Inequality
4. $\frac{5c}{8} \neq -10$	4. Division Property of Inequality
5. $\frac{5c}{8} + 1 \neq -9$	5. Addition Property of Inequality
6. $c = -16$	6. Contradiction

Chapter 1, Part V (pages 32-40) continued

23.

Statements	Reasons
1. $2 = 3 + 7y$	1. Given
2. $3 + 7y = 2$	2. Symmetric Property of Equality
3. Assume that $y \neq -\frac{1}{7}$.	3. Assumption
4. $7y \neq -1$	4. Multiplication Property of Inequality
5. $3 + 7y \neq 2$	5. Addition Property of Inequality
6. $y = -\frac{1}{7}$	6. Contradiction

25.

Statements	Reasons
1. $3 - 2n \geq 5$	1. Given
2. Assume that $n > -1$.	2. Assumption
3. $-2n < 2$	3. Multiplication Property of Inequality
4. $3 - 2n < 5$	4. Addition Property of Inequality
5. $n \leq -1$	5. Contradiction

Chapter 2, Part I (pages 44-46)

1. (i), (j), (k), (l)
3. (c)
5. (a) and (b)
7. (f) and (g)
9. (e)
11. plane JKQ, plane JQK, plane KJQ, plane KQJ, plane QKJ, plane QJK, plane $\mathcal{T}$

Chapter 2, Part I (pages 44-46) continued

13. $\overrightarrow{UV}$, $\overrightarrow{UT}$
15. $\overleftrightarrow{SR}$, $\overleftrightarrow{RS}$, line k
17. false
19. false
21. true
23. true
25. false
27. Example:

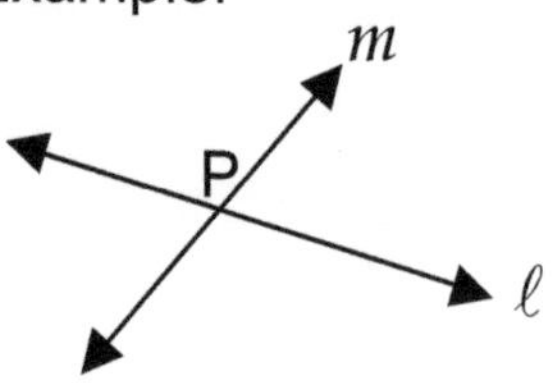

29. Example:

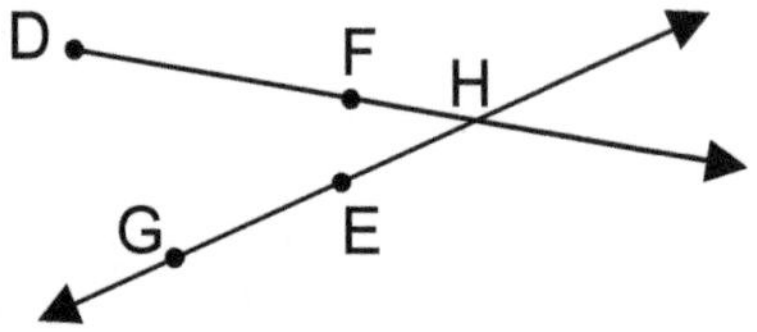

31. Example:

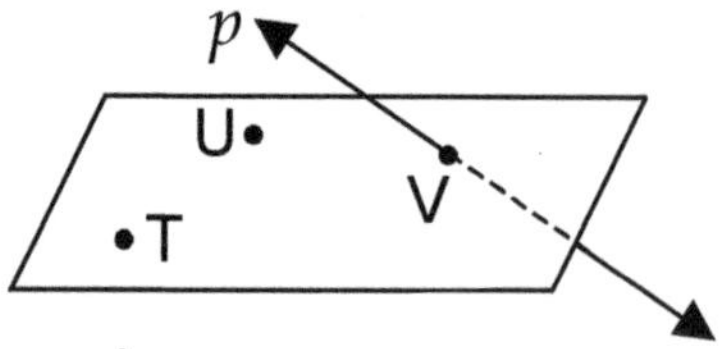

33. Example:

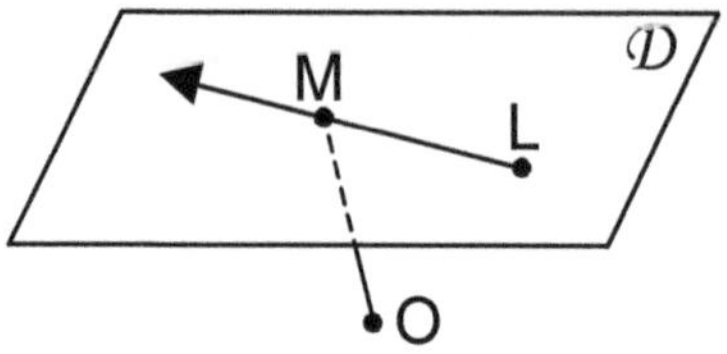

35. Example:

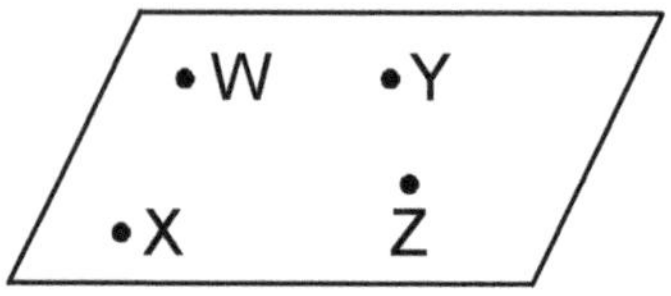

37. Example:

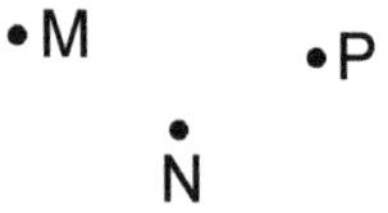

Chapter 2, Part I (pages 44-46) continued

39. Example:

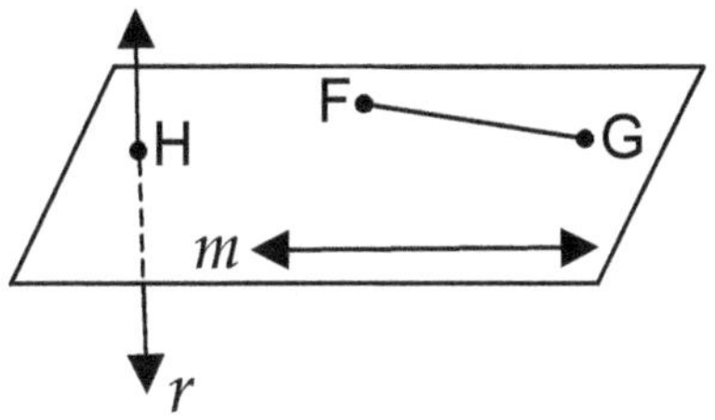

Chapter 2, Part II (pages 50-54)

1. yes
3. yes
5. no
7. yes
9. none
11. one
13. Through any two points there is exactly one line and definition of collinear points
15. definition of coplanar points
17. $\overleftrightarrow{BC}$
19. point D
21. If the points are collinear, then there would be an infinite number of planes through those points. If we named only two points, then there would be an infinite number of planes through those two points. We do not need to name four points because this is excessive (since there is exactly one plane through any three noncollinear points).
23. A line contains at least two points.
25. line n contains at least two points
27. Conclusion: There is not a line that contains points L, M, and N.
29. Conclusion: Points C, G, and U are collinear.
31. Conclusion: At least one of the points D and F does not lie in plane $\mathcal{Y}$.

Chapter 2, Part II (pages 50-54) continued

33. Given: Lines u and v are two distinct lines that intersect each other.

    Definition, postulate, or theorem used: If two distinct lines intersect, then they intersect in exactly one point.
35. Given: There is not a plane that contains all of points R, L, G, and I.
37. Given: Points D and E both lie in plane $\mathcal{H}$.

    Definition, postulate, or theorem used: If two points lie in a plane, then the entire line containing those points lies in the plane.

Chapter 2, Part III (pages 57-59)

1. true
3. false
5. true
7. never
9. 10
11. 4
13. 1.5
15. false
17. true
19. $1\frac{3}{8}$ inches; 3.5 centimeters
21. 39
23. $\frac{7}{8}$
25. true
27. false

Chapter 2, Part IV (pages 62-66)

1. 6
3. 11
5. 4
7. 12
9. x = 6 and EF = 10

Chapter 2, Part IV (pages 62-66) continued

11. LM = 14 and KM = 28
13. QR = 10 and QS = 19
15. AM = 8.5 and AB = 17
17. x = 5, y = –1, and GK = 25
19.

Given: B is the midpoint of $\overline{AC}$

Prove: AB = BC

Statements	Reasons
1. B is the midpoint of $\overline{AC}$	1. Given
2. AB = BC	2. Definition of midpoint
3. $\overline{AB} \cong \overline{BC}$	3. Definition of congruent segments

21.

Statements	Reasons
1. $\overline{AB} \cong \overline{CD}$	1. Given
2. AB = CD	2. Definition of congruent segments
3. AB + BC = BC + CD	3. Addition Property of Equality
4. AB + BC = AC and BC + CD = BD	4. Segment Addition Postulate
5. AC = BD	5. Substitution Property of Equality
6. $\overline{AC} \cong \overline{BD}$	6. Definition of congruent segments

Chapter 2, Part V (pages 70-75)

1. Vertex: A

   Sides: $\overrightarrow{AC}$ and $\overrightarrow{AB}$

   Name the angle in four different ways: $\angle$BAC, $\angle$CAB, $\angle$A, $\angle$2

Chapter 2, Part V (pages 70-75) continued

3. Vertex: H

   Sides: $\overrightarrow{HY}$ and $\overrightarrow{HP}$

   Name the angle in four different ways: $\angle$HYP, $\angle$YHP, $\angle$H, $\angle$4

5. Vertex: N

   Sides: $\overrightarrow{NW}$ (or, equivalently, $\overrightarrow{NG}$) and $\overrightarrow{NV}$

   Name the angle in six different ways: $\angle$GNV, $\angle$WNV, $\angle$VNG, $\angle$VNW, $\angle$N, $\angle$3

7. Vertex: Z

   Sides: $\overrightarrow{ZK}$ (or, equivalently, $\overrightarrow{ZN}$) and $\overrightarrow{ZB}$ (or, equivalently, $\overrightarrow{ZX}$)

   Name the angle in ten different ways: $\angle$9, $\angle$Z, $\angle$KZX, $\angle$KZB, $\angle$NZX, $\angle$NZB, $\angle$XZK, $\angle$BZK, $\angle$XZN, $\angle$BZN

9. $\angle$JVA (or, equivalently, $\angle$AVJ), $\angle$AVM (or, equivalently, $\angle$MVA), and $\angle$MVJ (or, equivalently, $\angle$JVM)
11. m$\angle$ACE = 142°; this is an obtuse angle
13. m$\angle$ACD = 90°; this is a right angle
15. m$\angle$1 = 34°; this is an acute angle
17. m$\angle$3 = 27°; this is an acute angle
19. m$\angle$GKL = 180°; this is a straight angle
21. true
23. true
25. true
27. Example:

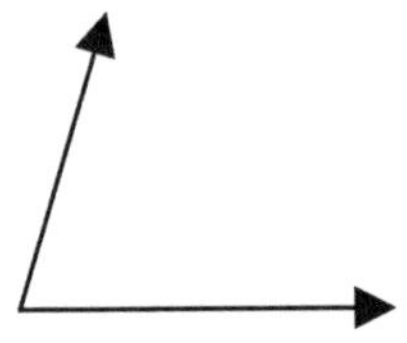

29. Example:

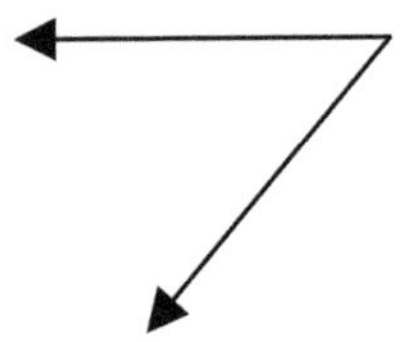

Chapter 2, Part V (pages 70-75) continued

31. Example:

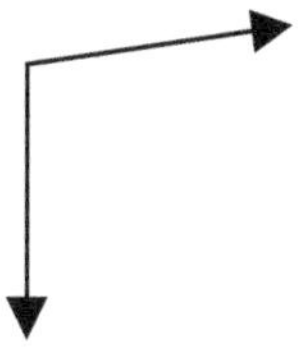

33. LMO (or, equivalently, OML)

35. 93°

37. $m\angle LMN = 63^\circ$ and $m\angle NMO = 63^\circ$

Chapter 2, Part VI (pages 80-87)

1. 90°

3. 37°

5. 142°

7. false

9. $\angle ABD$ (or, equivalently, $\angle DBA$)

11. Example: $\angle CBD$ and $\angle DBG$

13. $\angle GBE$ (or, equivalently, $\angle GBE$)

15. $\angle CBA$, $\angle GBA$, $\angle GBE$, and $\angle CBE$

17. $x = 22$ and $m\angle 5 = 135^\circ$

19. $x = 19$ and $m\angle LOM = 32^\circ$

21. $x = 17$ and $m\angle RSQ = 117^\circ$

23. $x = 12$, $y = 5$, $m\angle 2 = 139^\circ$

25. $x = 11$, $m\angle FIG = 28^\circ$, and $m\angle FIH = 56^\circ$

27.

Statements	Reasons
1. $\angle ABC \cong \angle DEF$	1. Given
2. $m\angle ABC = m\angle DEF$	2. Definition of congruent angles
3. $m\angle DEF = m\angle ABC$	3. Symmetric Property of Equality
4. $\angle DEF \cong \angle ABC$	4. Definition of congruent angles

Chapter 2, Part VI (pages 80-87) continued

29.

Statements	Reasons
1. $\angle 1$ is supplementary to $\angle 2$ and $\angle 1$ is supplementary to $\angle 3$	1. Given
2. $m\angle 1 + m\angle 2 = 180^\circ$ and $m\angle 1 + m\angle 3 = 180^\circ$	2. Definition of supplementary angles
3. $m\angle 1 + m\angle 2 = m\angle 1 + m\angle 3$	3. Substitution Property of Equality
4. $m\angle 2 = m\angle 3$	4. Subtraction Property of Equality
5. $\angle 2 \cong \angle 3$	5. Definition of congruent angles

31.

Statements	Reasons
1. $\angle 1$ and $\angle 2$ form a linear pair	1. Given
2. $\angle 1$ and $\angle 2$ are supplementary	2. Linear Pair Postulate
3. $m\angle 1 + m\angle 2 = 180^\circ$	3. Definition of supplementary angles
4. $\angle 1 \cong \angle 2$	4. Given
5. $m\angle 1 = m\angle 2$	5. Definition of congruent angles
6. $m\angle 2 + m\angle 2 = 180^\circ$	6. Substitution Property of Equality
7. $2(m\angle 2) = 180^\circ$	7. Distributive Property
8. $m\angle 2 = 90^\circ$	8. Division Property of Equality
9. $m\angle 1 = 90^\circ$	9. Substitution Property of Equality
10. $\angle 1$ and $\angle 2$ are both right angles	10. Definition of a right angle

33.

Statements	Reasons
1. $\ell \perp m$, making $\angle 1$ a right angle	1. Given
2. $m\angle 1 = 90°$	2. Definition of a right angle
3. $\angle 1$ and $\angle 2$ form a linear pair; $\angle 1$ and $\angle 3$ form a linear pair	3. Definition of a linear pair
4. $\angle 1$ and $\angle 2$ are supplementary; $\angle 1$ and $\angle 3$ are supplementary	4. Linear Pair Postulate
5. $m\angle 1 + m\angle 2 = 180°$ and $m\angle 1 + m\angle 3 = 180°$	5. Definition of supplementary angles
6. $90° + m\angle 2 = 180°$ and $90° + m\angle 3 = 180°$	6. Substitution Property of Equality
7. $m\angle 2 = 90°$ and $m\angle 3 = 90°$	7. Subtraction Property of Equality
8. $\angle 2$ is a right angle and $\angle 3$ is a right angle	8. Definition of a right angle
9. $\angle 1 \cong \angle 4$	9. Vertical Angles Theorem
10. $m\angle 1 = m\angle 4$	10. Definition of congruent angles
11. $90° = m\angle 4$	11. Substitution Property of Equality
12. $\angle 4$ is a right angle	12. Definition of a right angle

Chapter 2, Part VI (pages 80-87) continued

35.

Statements	Reasons
1. $\angle 1$ and $\angle 2$ are right angles	1. Given
2. $m\angle 1 = 90°$ and $m\angle 2 = 90°$	2. Definition of a right angle
3. $m\angle 1 = m\angle 2$	3. Substitution Property of Equality
4. $\angle 1 \cong \angle 2$	4. Definition of congruent angles

Chapter 2, Part VII (pages 88-92)

1. inductive reasoning

3. The original statement is false.
   The converse is, "If an angle has a measure of 133°, then it is obtuse," and it is true
   The inverse is, "If an angle is not obtuse, then its measure is not 133°," and it is true.
   The contrapositive is, "If an angle does not have a measure of 133°, then it is not obtuse," and it is false.

5.

Statements	Reasons
1. $2x - 8 = 11x - 35$	1. Given
2. $2x = 11x - 27$	2. Addition Property of Equality
3. $-9x = -27$	3. Subtraction Property of Equality
4. $x = 3$	4. Division Property of Equality

Chapter 2, Part VII (pages 88-92) continued

7.

Statements	Reasons
1. 3k – 10 = 11	1. Given
2. Assume that k ≠ 7.	2. Assumption
3. 3k ≠ 21	3. Multiplication Property of Inequality
4. 3k – 10 ≠ 11	4. Subtraction Property of Inequality
5. k = 7	5. Contradiction

9. (A), (B), (D), and (F)
11. no
13. 97°
15. 83°
17. no because m ∠MAR = 32° and m∠RAC = 51°, and thus ∠MAR is not congruent to ∠RAC
19. AR = 11 and AM = 8
21. x = 23, y = 69.5, m∠1 = 41°, and m∠2 = 139°
23. b = –2 and SW = 44
25. Example:

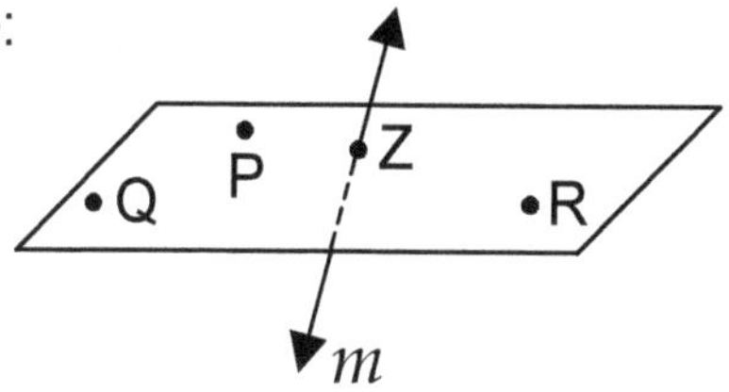

27. Example:

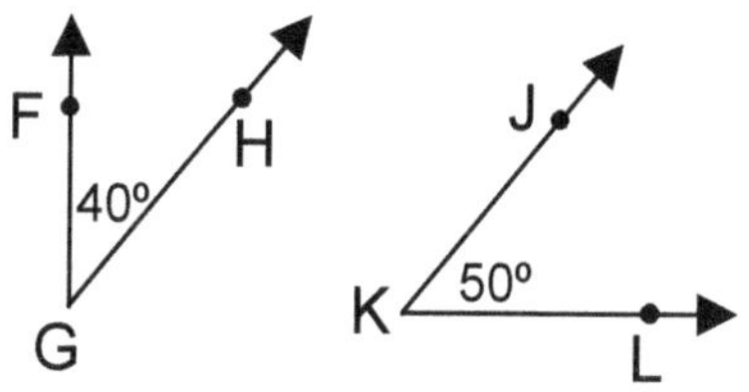

29. Through any three noncollinear points there is exactly one plane.
31. Line p contains at least two points.
33. $\overrightarrow{EO}$ and $\overrightarrow{EY}$

Chapter 3, Part I (pages 95-97)

1. parallel planes
3. parallel lines
5. parallel lines, skew lines
7. skew
9. intersecting
11. parallel
13. parallel
15. plane ACD, plane DFE, plane ACE, and plane BEF
17. $\overleftrightarrow{GH}$, $\overleftrightarrow{KJ}$, and $\overleftrightarrow{QP}$
19. $\overleftrightarrow{GM}$, $\overleftrightarrow{HN}$, $\overleftrightarrow{NO}$, $\overleftrightarrow{MR}$, $\overleftrightarrow{QR}$, and $\overleftrightarrow{OP}$
21. $\overleftrightarrow{KJ}$, $\overleftrightarrow{QP}$, $\overleftrightarrow{GH}$, $\overleftrightarrow{MN}$, $\overleftrightarrow{OP}$, $\overleftrightarrow{NO}$, $\overleftrightarrow{HI}$, and $\overleftrightarrow{IJ}$
23. $\overleftrightarrow{RQ}$, $\overleftrightarrow{LK}$, and $\overleftrightarrow{HI}$
25. plane PQK
27. plane MRL, plane RQL, plane NOI, plane OPJ, plane RQN, and plane GLI
29. always
31. always
33. never
35. sometimes
37. never

Chapter 3, Part II (pages 103-112)

1. 84°
3. 96°
5. 120°
7. 52°
9. 64°
11. 52°
13. 64°
15. 64°
17. 52°

19. w = 59, x = 67, y = 59, and z = 54

21. x = 52 and y = 8

23. $x = \frac{21}{2}$ and y = 41

25. $x = \frac{96}{5}$ and $y = \frac{149}{5}$

27. x = 18 and $y = \frac{27}{2}$

29. $x = \frac{45}{2}$ and y = 9

31. This is only one of several versions of this proof.

Statements	Reasons
1. $\ell \parallel m$, and the transversal t intersects both line ℓ and line m	1. Given
2. $\angle 2 \cong \angle 6$ and $\angle 4 \cong \angle 8$	2. Corresponding Angles Postulate
3. $m\angle 2 = m\angle 6$ and $m\angle 4 = m\angle 8$	3. Definition of congruent angles
4. $\angle 5$ and $\angle 6$ are a linear pair, and $\angle 7$ and $\angle 8$ are a linear pair	4. Definition of a linear pair
5. $\angle 5$ and $\angle 6$ are supplementary, and $\angle 7$ and $\angle 8$ are supplementary	5. Linear Pair Postulate
6. $m\angle 5 + m\angle 6 = 180°$ and $m\angle 7 + m\angle 8 = 180°$	6. Definition of supplementary angles
7. $m\angle 5 + m\angle 2 = 180°$ and $m\angle 7 + m\angle 4 = 180°$	7. Substitution Property of Equality
8. $\angle 2$ is supplementary to $\angle 5$, and $\angle 4$ is supplementary to $\angle 7$	8. Definition of supplementary angles

33. This is only one of several versions of this proof.

Statements	Reasons
1. $\ell \parallel m$ and $\ell \perp t$	1. Given
2. $\angle 2$ is a right angle	2. If two lines are perpendicular, then they form four right angles.
3. $m\angle 2 = 90°$	3. Definition of a right angle
4. $\angle 2 \cong \angle 6$	4. Corresponding Angles Postulate
5. $m\angle 2 = m\angle 6$	5. Definition of congruent angles
6. $90° = m\angle 6$	6. Substitution Property of Equality
7. $\angle 6$ is a right angle	7. Definition of a right angle
8. $m \perp t$	8. Definition of perpendicular lines

35.

Statements	Reasons
1. $\overline{IJ} \parallel \overline{KL}$	1. Given
2. $m\angle IJL + m\angle 3 = 180°$	2. Same-Side Interior Angles Theorem
3. $m\angle IJL = m\angle 1 + m\angle 2$	3. Angle Addition Postulate
4. $m\angle 1 + m\angle 2 + m\angle 3 = 180°$	4. Substitution Property of Equality

37.

Statements	Reasons
1. $\overleftrightarrow{EF} \parallel \overleftrightarrow{GH}$ and $\angle EFH \cong \angle GHF$	1. Given
2. $m\angle EFH = m\angle GHF$	2. Definition of congruent angles
3. $\angle EFH$ is supplementary to $\angle GHF$	3. Same-Side Interior Angles Theorem
4. $m\angle EFH + m\angle GHF = 180^\circ$	4. Definition of supplementary angles
5. $m\angle EFH + m\angle EFH = 180^\circ$	5. Substitution Property of Equality
6. $2(m\angle EFH) = 180^\circ$	6. Distributive Property
7. $m\angle EFH = 90^\circ$	7. Division Property of Equality
8. $\angle EFH$ is a right angle	8. Definition of right angle
9. $\overleftrightarrow{EF} \perp \overleftrightarrow{FH}$	9. Definition of perpendicular lines
10. $\overleftrightarrow{GH} \perp \overleftrightarrow{FH}$	10. Perpendicular Transversal Theorem

Chapter 3, Part III (pages 118-126)

1. $\overline{AC} \parallel \overline{BD}$
3. no conclusion is possible
5. no conclusion is possible
7. $\overline{EG} \parallel \overrightarrow{HF}$ by the Alternate Interior Angles Converse Theorem
9. $\overleftrightarrow{NO} \parallel \overleftrightarrow{OQ}$ by the Corresponding Angles Converse Postulate
11. no conclusion is possible

13. $\overline{FG} \parallel \overline{HJ}$ by either the Same-Side Interior Angles Converse Theorem or the theorem *In a plane, if two different lines are perpendicular to a third line, then the first two lines are parallel*
15. $\overleftrightarrow{QR} \parallel \overleftrightarrow{UV}$ by the Alternate Interior Angles Converse Theorem
17. $x = 102$ and $y = 78$
19. $x = 95$ and $y = 95$
21. $x = 15.5$ and $y = 18.4$
23. $x = 31$ and $y = 11$
25. $x = 75$ and $y = 22$
27. This is only one of several possible proofs.

Statements	Reasons
1. ℓ, m, and t are coplanar, and $\angle 2 \cong \angle 7$	1. Given
2. $\angle 7 \cong \angle 4$	2. Vertical Angles Theorem
3. $\angle 2 \cong \angle 4$	3. Transitive Property of Angle Congruence
4. $\ell \parallel m$	4. Corresponding Angles Converse Postulate

29. This is only one of several possible proofs.

Statements	Reasons
1. ℓ, m, and t are coplanar, and $\angle 1$ is supplementary to $\angle 4$	1. Given
2. $\angle 1$ and $\angle 2$ are a linear pair	2. Definition of a linear pair
3. $\angle 1$ and $\angle 2$ are supplementary	3. Linear Pair Postulate
4. $\angle 4 \cong \angle 2$	4. Congruent Supplements Theorem
5. $\ell \parallel m$	5. Corresponding Angles Converse Postulate

Chapter 3, Part III (pages 118-126) continued

31. This is only one of several possible proofs.

Statements	Reasons
1. $\angle 2$ is supplementary to $\angle 8$	1. Given
2. $\ell \parallel m$	2. Same-Side Exterior Angles Converse Theorem
3. $\angle 8 \cong \angle 9$	3. Given
3. $m \parallel n$	4. Alternate Interior Angles Converse Theorem
4. $\ell \parallel n$	5. Transitive Property of Parallel Lines
5. $\angle 2 \cong \angle 11$	6. Alternate Exterior Angles Theorem

33.

Statements	Reasons
1. line ℓ is not parallel to line m	1. Given
2. Assume that $\angle 1 \cong \angle 2$.	2. Assumption
3. $\ell \parallel m$	3. Corresponding Angles Converse Postulate
4. $\angle 1$ is not congruent to $\angle 2$	4. Contradiction

Chapter 3, Part IV (pages 127-130)

1. true
3. may be
5. may be
7. Example:

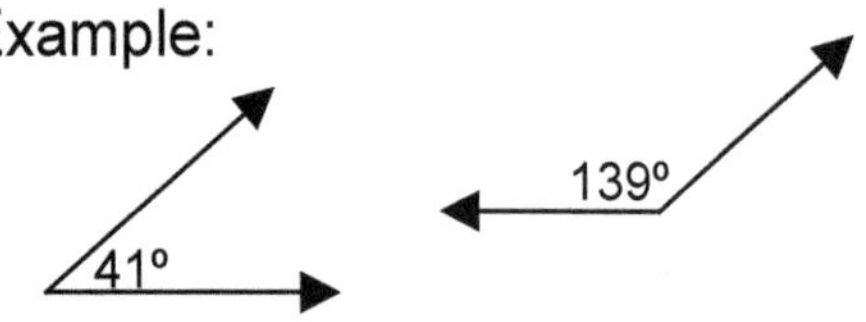

Chapter 3, Part IV (pages 127-130) continued

9. 41°
11. 131°
13. alternate exterior angles
15. vertical angles
17. none of these
19. alternate interior angles
21. y = 21, m$\angle 2$ = 64°, and m$\angle 3$ = 116°
23. 109°
25. 82°
27. 82°
29. $\overleftrightarrow{AE} \parallel \overleftrightarrow{BF}$ by the Alternate Exterior Angles Converse Theorem
    $\overleftrightarrow{AB} \parallel \overleftrightarrow{EF}$ by the Corresponding Angles Converse Postulate
31. $\overline{GT} \parallel \overline{HB}$ by the Same-Side Interior Angles Converse Theorem

33.

Statements	Reasons
1. $\overleftrightarrow{WX} \perp \overleftrightarrow{XY}$ and $\overleftrightarrow{XY} \perp \overleftrightarrow{ZY}$	1. Given
2. $\overleftrightarrow{WX} \parallel \overleftrightarrow{ZY}$	2. In a plane, if two different lines are perpendicular to a third line, then the first two lines are parallel.
3. $\angle WXZ \cong \angle YZX$	3. Alternate Interior Angles Theorem

Chapter 4, Part I (pages 136-146)

1. 50
3. 110°
5. w = 43, x = 51, y = 86, and z = 94
7. w = 70, x = 84, y = 61, and z = 80
9. 360°
11. x = 26 and m$\angle 1$ = 64°

13. $x = 28$ and $m\angle 1 = 23°$

15. $x = -12$ and $m\angle 3 = 72°$

17. $w = 31$, $m\angle 1 = 146°$, $m\angle 2 = 34°$, $m\angle 5 = 130°$, and $x = 20$

19. $x = 30$, $y = 15$, and $m\angle 1 = 45°$

21.

Statements	Reasons
1. We have $\triangle ABC$ with $\angle BCD$ as an exterior angle.	1. Given
2. $\angle BCA$ and $\angle BCD$ are a linear pair	2. Definition of a linear pair
3. $\angle BCA$ and $\angle BCD$ are supplementary	3. Linear Pair Postulate
4. $m\angle BCA + m\angle BCD = 180°$	4. Definition of supplementary angles
5. $m\angle BCA + m\angle B + m\angle A = 180°$	5. Sum of Measures of the Angles in a Triangle Theorem
6. $m\angle BCA + m\angle BCD = m\angle BCA + m\angle B + m\angle A$	6. Substitution Property of Equality
7. $m\angle BCD = m\angle B + m\angle A$	7. Subtraction Property of Equality

23.

Statements	Reasons
1. We have quadrilateral HIJK.	1. Given
2. Draw $\overline{IK}$.	2. Through any two points there is exactly one line.
3. $m\angle J + m\angle KIJ + m\angle JKI = 180°$ and $m\angle H + m\angle IKH + m\angle HIK = 180°$	3. Sum of the Measures of the Angles in a Triangle Theorem

Chapter 4, Part I (pages 136-146) continued

(#23 continued)

Statements continued	Reasons cont'd
4. $m\angle J + m\angle KIJ + m\angle JKI + 180° = 360°$	4. Addition Property of Equality
5. $m\angle J + m\angle KIJ + m\angle JKI + m\angle H + m\angle IKH + m\angle HIK = 360°$	5. Substitution Property of Equality
6. $m\angle HIK + m\angle KIJ = m\angle HIJ$ and $m\angle JKI + m\angle IKH = m\angle JKH$	6. Angle Addition Postulate
7. $m\angle J + m\angle HIJ + m\angle H + m\angle JKH = 360°$	7. Substitution Property of Equality

25.

Statements	Reasons
1. $\angle L \cong \angle O$ and $\angle M \cong \angle P$	1. Given
2. $m\angle L = m\angle O$ and $m\angle M = m\angle P$	2. Definition of congruent angles
3. $m\angle L + m\angle M + m\angle N = 180°$ and $m\angle O + m\angle P + m\angle Q = 180°$	3. Sum of the Measures of the Angles in a Triangle Theorem
4. $m\angle L + m\angle M + m\angle N = m\angle O + m\angle P + m\angle Q$	4. Substitution Property of Equality
5. $m\angle L + m\angle M + m\angle N = m\angle L + m\angle M + m\angle Q$	5. Substitution Property of Equality
6. $m\angle N = m\angle Q$	6. Subtraction Property of Equality
7. $\angle N \cong \angle Q$	7. Definition of congruent angles

Chapter 4, Part I (pages 136-146) continued

31.

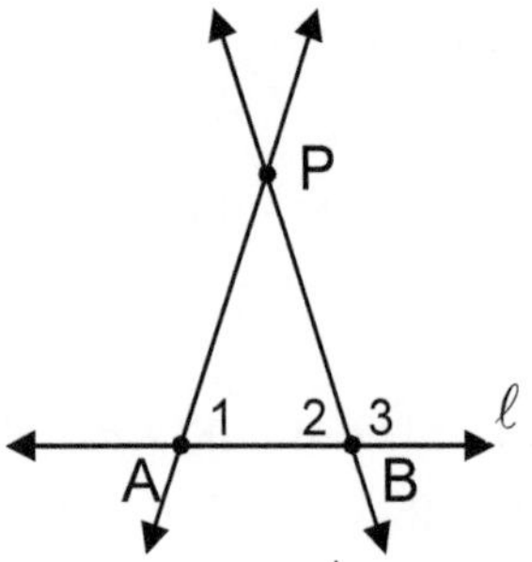

Statements	Reasons
1. We have line ℓ and point P not on line ℓ.	1. Given
2. Assume that you can draw two lines that pass through P and are perpendicular to line ℓ. Draw these lines, and call the points of intersection A and B as shown in the figure above. Also label ∠1, ∠2, and ∠3 as shown in the figure above.	2. Assumption
3. ∠1 and ∠2 are right angles	3. If two lines are perpendicular, then they form four right angles.
4. m∠1 = 90° and m∠2 = 90°	4. Definition of a right angle
5. m∠1 + m∠2 + m∠APB = 180°	5. Sum of the Measures of the Angles in a Triangle Theorem
6. 90° + 90° + m∠APB = 180°	6. Substitution Property of Equality
7. m∠APB = 0°	7. Subtraction Property of Equality
8. You cannot draw more than one line through P that is perpendicular to ℓ.	8. Contradiction

Chapter 4, Part II (pages 148-152)

1. scalene, acute
3. isosceles, obtuse
5. scalene, obtuse
7. isosceles, right
9. equilateral, isosceles, acute, equiangular
11. scalene, right
13. isosceles, acute
15. equilateral, isosceles, acute, equiangular
17. Example:

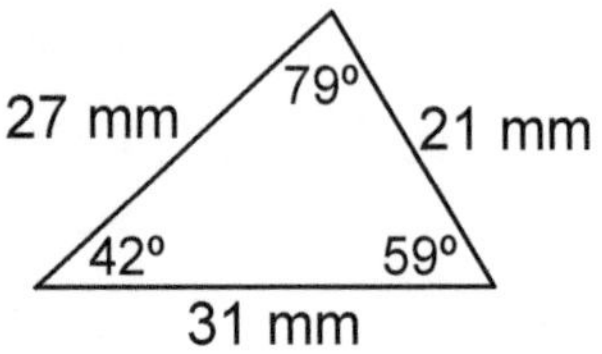

19. Example:

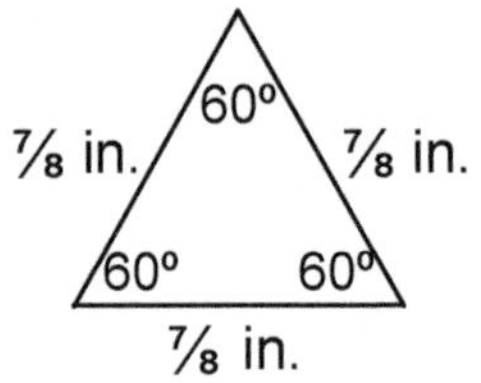

21. not possible
23. Example:

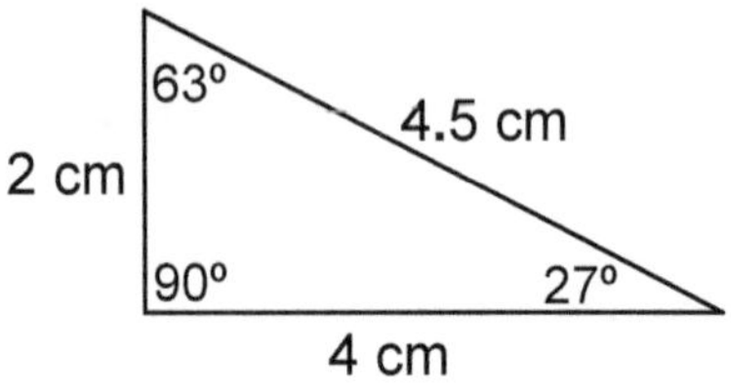

25. Example:

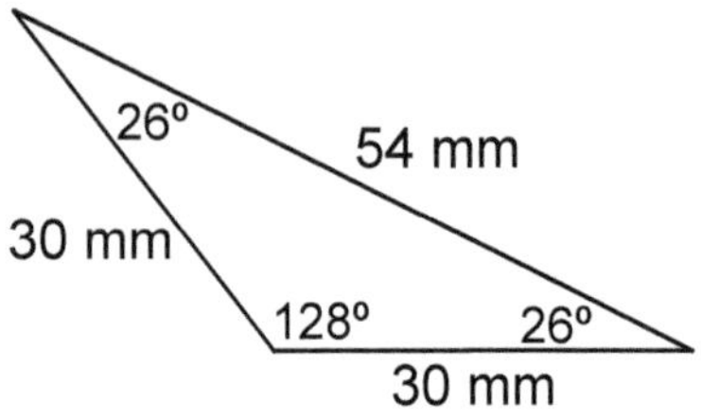

Chapter 4, Part II (pages 148-152) continued

27.

Statements	Reasons
1. We have right ΔEFG with $\angle F$ as the right angle	1. Given
2. $m\angle F = 90^\circ$	2. Definition of a right angle
3. $m\angle F + m\angle E + m\angle G = 180^\circ$	3. Sum of the Measures of the Angles in a Triangle Theorem
4. $90^\circ + m\angle E + m\angle G = 180^\circ$	4. Substitution Property of Equality
5. $m\angle E + m\angle G = 90^\circ$	5. Subtraction Property of Equality
6. $\angle E$ and $\angle G$ are complementary	6. Definition of complementary angles

29.

Statements	Reasons
1. $m\angle R = 30^\circ$ and $m\angle T = 41^\circ$	1. Given
2. $m\angle R + m\angle T + m\angle S = 180^\circ$	2. Sum of the Measures of the Angles in a Triangle Theorem
3. $30^\circ + 41^\circ + m\angle S = 180^\circ$	3. Substitution Property of Equality
4. $m\angle S = 109^\circ$	4. Subtraction Property of Equality
5. $\angle S$ is an obtuse angle	5. Definition of an obtuse angle
6. ΔRST is an obtuse triangle	6. Definition of an obtuse triangle

Chapter 4, Part III (pages 158-167)

1. false
3. false
5. true
7. false
9. w = 54, x = 96, and y = –2
11. x = 0.5 and y = 4

13a. yes
b. $\Delta GIH \cong \Delta KJL$ by the SAS Congruence Postulate

15a. no
b. N/A

17a. yes
b. $\Delta ZYG \cong \Delta HGY$ by the SSS Congruence Postulate

19a. yes
b. $\Delta QRS \cong \Delta QTS$ by the HL Congruence Postulate

21a. yes
b. $\Delta ADC \cong \Delta ABC$ by the AAS Congruence Theorem

23a. yes
b. $\Delta JKL \cong \Delta IML$ by the AAS Congruence Theorem

25a. yes
b. $\Delta QRP \cong \Delta ORN$ by the ASA Congruence Postulate

27.

Statements	Reasons
1. $\overline{MO} \cong \overline{PQ}$, $\angle M \cong \angle P$, and $\angle N \cong \angle R$	1. Given
2. $\angle O \cong \angle Q$	2. If two angles of a triangle are congruent to two angles of another triangle, then the third angles are also congruent.
3. $\Delta MON \cong \Delta PQR$	3. ASA Congruence Postulate

Chapter 4, Part III (pages 158-167) continued

29.

Statements	Reasons
1. $\overline{GH} \cong \overline{IJ}$ and $\overline{GJ} \cong \overline{HI}$	1. Given
2. $\overline{HJ} \cong \overline{HJ}$	2. Reflexive Property of Segment Congruence
3. $\triangle GHJ \cong \triangle IJH$	3. SSS Congruence Postulate

31.

Statements	Reasons
1. $\overline{KL} \cong \overline{KN}$ and $\overline{KM}$ bisects $\angle LKN$	1. Given
2. $\angle LKM \cong \angle NKM$	2. Definition of an angle bisector
3. $\overline{KM} \cong \overline{KM}$	3. Reflexive Property of Segment Congruence
4. $\triangle KLM \cong \triangle KNM$	4. SAS Congruence Postulate

33. This is only one of several possible proofs.

Statements	Reasons
1. $\overline{OP} \parallel \overline{SR}$	1. Given
2. $\angle O \cong \angle S$ and $\angle P \cong \angle R$	2. Alternate Interior Angles Theorem
3. Q is the midpoint of $\overline{OS}$	3. Given
4. $\overline{OQ} \cong \overline{SQ}$	4. Midpoint Theorem
5. $\triangle OPQ \cong \triangle SRQ$	5. AAS Congruence Theorem

35.

Statements	Reasons
1. $\overline{TX} \cong \overline{TU}$ and $\overline{TV} \perp \overline{XU}$	1. Given
2. $\angle TVX$ and $\angle TVU$ are right angles	2. If two lines are perpendicular, then they form four right angles.
3. $\overline{TV} \cong \overline{TV}$	3. Reflexive Property of Segment Congruence
4. $\triangle VXT \cong \triangle VUT$	4. HL Congruence Postulate

Chapter 4, Part III (pages 158-167) continued

37.

Statements	Reasons
1. $\angle DBE \cong \angle DAE$, $\overline{AD} \perp \overline{DE}$, and $\overline{BE} \perp \overline{DE}$	1. Given
2. $\angle ADE$ and $\angle BED$ are right angles	2. If two lines are perpendicular, then they form four right angles *OR* definition of perpendicular lines
3. $\angle ADE \cong \angle BED$	3. If two angles are right angles, then they are congruent.
4. $\overline{DE} \cong \overline{DE}$	4. Reflexive Property of Segment Congruence
5. $\triangle ADE \cong \triangle BED$	5. AAS Congruence Theorem

Chapter 4, Part IV (pages 170-182)

Note: The proofs given here show only one version of each proof.

1.

Statements	Reasons
1. We have $\triangle ABC$.	1. Given
2. $\overline{AB} \cong \overline{AB}$, $\overline{BC} \cong \overline{BC}$, and $\overline{AC} \cong \overline{AC}$	2. Reflexive Property of Segment Congruence
3. $\triangle ABC \cong \triangle ABC$	3. SSS Congruence Postulate

3.

Statements	Reasons
1. $\triangle JKL \cong \triangle MNO$ and $\triangle MNO \cong \triangle PQR$	1. Given
2. $\overline{JK} \cong \overline{MN}$ and $\overline{MN} \cong \overline{PQ}$, $\overline{JL} \cong \overline{MO}$ and $\overline{MO} \cong \overline{PR}$, and $\overline{KL} \cong \overline{NO}$ and $\overline{NO} \cong \overline{QR}$	2. CPCTC
3. $\overline{JK} \cong \overline{PQ}$, $\overline{JL} \cong \overline{PR}$, and $\overline{KL} \cong \overline{QR}$	3. Transitive Property of Segment Congruence
4. $\triangle JKL \cong \triangle PQR$	4. SSS Congruence Postulate

5.

Statements	Reasons
1. $\overline{GH} \cong \overline{JL}$, $\angle G \cong \angle L$, and $\angle H \cong \angle J$	1. Given
2. $\Delta GHI \cong \Delta LJK$	2. ASA Congruence Postulate
3. $\overline{GI} \cong \overline{LK}$	3. CPCTC

7.

Statements	Reasons
1. $\overline{SW} \cong \overline{UV}$ and $\overline{SW} \parallel \overline{UV}$	1. Given
2. $\angle VSW \cong \angle SVU$ and $\angle UWS \cong \angle WUV$	2. Alternate Interior Angles Theorem
3. $\Delta STW \cong \Delta VTU$	3. ASA Congruence Postulate
4. $\overline{ST} \cong \overline{VT}$	4. CPCTC

9.

Statements	Reasons
1. $\overline{SW} \cong \overline{SU}$ and $\overline{ST}$ bisects $\angle USW$	1. Given
2. $\angle UST \cong \angle WST$	2. Definition of an angle bisector
3. $\overline{ST} \cong \overline{ST}$	3. Reflexive Property of Segment Congruence
4. $\Delta STW \cong \Delta STU$	4. SAS Congruence Postulate
5. $\angle SWT \cong \angle SUT$	5. CPCTC

11.

Statements	Reasons
1. $\Delta ABE \cong \Delta ADE$	1. Given
2. $\angle BAC \cong \angle DAC$ and $\overline{AB} \cong \overline{AD}$	2. CPCTC
3. $\overline{AC} \cong \overline{AC}$	3. Reflexive Property of Segment Congruence
4. $\Delta ABC \cong \Delta ADC$	4. SAS Congruence Postulate
5. $\overline{BC} \cong \overline{CD}$	5. CPCTC

13.

Statements	Reasons
1. $\overline{FH} \cong \overline{GI}$, $\overline{HI} \cong \overline{IJ}$, and $\overline{FH} \parallel \overline{GI}$	1. Given
2. $\angle FHI \cong \angle GIJ$	2. Corresponding Angles Postulate
3. $\Delta FHI \cong \Delta GIJ$	3. SAS Congruence Postulate
4. $\angle FIH \cong \angle GJI$	4. CPCTC
5. $\overline{FI} \parallel \overline{GJ}$	5. Corresponding Angles Converse Postulate

15.

Statements	Reasons
1. $\angle L \cong \angle O$, $\overline{LM} \cong \overline{NO}$, and $\angle LKM \cong \angle OKN$	1. Given
2. $\Delta LKM \cong \Delta OKN$	2. AAS Congruence Theorem
3. $\overline{KM} \cong \overline{KN}$	3. CPCTC
4. ΔMKN is an isosceles triangle	4. Definition of an isosceles triangle

17.

Statements	Reasons
1. $\Delta SQU \cong \Delta TRU$	1. Given
2. $\overline{QS} \cong \overline{RT}$, $\overline{SU} \cong \overline{TU}$, and $\overline{UQ} \cong \overline{UR}$	2. CPCTC
3. SU = TU and UQ = UR	3. Definition of congruent segments
4. SR = SU + UR and TQ = TU + UQ	4. Segment Addition Postulate
5. TQ = SU + UR	5. Substitution Property of Equality
6. TQ = SR	6. Substitution Property of Equality
7. $\overline{TQ} \cong \overline{SR}$	7. Definition of congruent segments
8. $\overline{ST} \cong \overline{ST}$	8. Reflexive Property of Segment Congruence
9. $\Delta QTS \cong \Delta RST$	9. SSS Congruence Postulate

19.

Statements	Reasons
1. $\overline{AB} \cong \overline{AF}$, $\angle EBA$ is a right angle, and $\angle CFA$ is a right angle	1. Given
2. $\angle EBA \cong \angle CFA$	2. If two angles are right angles, then they are congruent.
3. $\angle A \cong \angle A$	3. Reflexive Property of Angle Congruence
4. $\Delta ABE \cong \Delta AFC$	4. ASA Congruence Postulate
5. $\angle E \cong \angle C$	5. CPCTC

21.

Statements	Reasons
1. $\angle 1 \cong \angle 2$ and $\overline{LN}$ is not congruent to $\overline{ON}$	1. Given
2. Assume that $\overline{LM} \cong \overline{OM}$.	2. Assumption
3. $\overline{MN} \cong \overline{MN}$	3. Reflexive Property of Segment Congruence
4. $\Delta LMN \cong \Delta OMN$	4. SAS Congruence Postulate
5. $\overline{LN} \cong \overline{ON}$	5. CPCTC
6. $\overline{LM}$ is not congruent to $\overline{OM}$	6. Contradiction

23.

Statements	Reasons
1. $\overline{GI}$ is not parallel to $\overline{HJ}$	1. Given
2. Assume that $\Delta GKH \cong \Delta JKI$.	2. Assumption
3. $\overline{GK} \cong \overline{JK}$ and $\overline{HK} \cong \overline{IK}$	3. CPCTC
4. $\angle GKI \cong \angle JKH$	4. Vertical Angles Theorem

(#23 continued)

Statements continued	Reasons continued
5. $\Delta IKG \cong \Delta HKJ$	5. SAS Congruence Postulate
6. $\angle IGK \cong \angle HJK$	6. CPCTC
7. $\overline{GI} \parallel \overline{HJ}$	7. Alternate Interior Angles Converse Theorem
8. ΔGKH is not congruent to ΔJKI.	8. Contradiction

Chapter 4, Part V (pages 185-192)

1. x = 50 and y = 65
3. x = 52 and y = 76
5. x = 67.5 and y = 67.5
7. w = 8 and x = 106
9. w = 69, x = 3.5 and y = 42
11. w = 5, x = 72, and y = 6
13. x = 8 and perimeter = 26
15. x = 17 and perimeter = 59

17.

Statements	Reasons
1. ΔABC is an isosceles triangle with $\overline{AB} \cong \overline{BC}$	1. Given
2. Let M be the midpoint of $\overline{AC}$.	2. A segment has exactly one midpoint.
3. Draw $\overline{BM}$.	3. Through any two points there is exactly one line.
4. $\overline{AM} \cong \overline{CM}$	4. Midpoint Theorem
5. $\overline{BM} \cong \overline{BM}$	5. Reflexive Property of Segment Congruence
6. $\Delta ABM \cong \Delta CBM$	6. SSS Congruence Postulate
7. $\angle A \cong \angle C$	7. CPCTC

19.

Statements	Reasons
1. ΔGHI is an equilateral triangle	1. Given
2. $\overline{GH} \cong \overline{HI} \cong \overline{GI}$	2. Definition of an equilateral triangle
3. $\angle G \cong \angle H$ and $\angle G \cong \angle I$	3. Isosceles Triangle Theorem
4. $\angle G \cong \angle H \cong \angle I$	4. Transitive Property of Angle Congruence
5. ΔGHI is an equiangular triangle	5. Definition of an equiangular triangle
6. $m\angle G = 60°$, $m\angle H = 60°$, and $m\angle I = 60°$	6. If a triangle is equiangular, then each angle of the triangle measures 60°.

21. This is only one of several versions of this proof.

Statements	Reasons
1. $\angle 1 \cong \angle 4$	1. Given
2. $m\angle 1 = m\angle 4$	2. Definition of congruent angles
3. $\angle 1$ and $\angle 2$ form a linear pair, and $\angle 3$ and $\angle 4$ form a linear pair	3. Definition of a linear pair
4. $\angle 1$ and $\angle 2$ are supplementary, and $\angle 3$ and $\angle 4$ are supplementary	4. Linear Pair Postulate
5. $m\angle 3 + m\angle 4 = 180°$	5. Definition of supplementary angles
6. $m\angle 3 + m\angle 1 = 180°$	6. Substitution Property of Equality
7. $\angle 3$ and $\angle 1$ are supplementary	7. Definition of supplementary angles
8. $\angle 2 \cong \angle 3$	8. Congruent Supplements Theorem
9. $\overline{AB} \cong \overline{BC}$	9. Isosceles Triangle Converse Theorem

Chapter 4, Part V (pages 185-192) continued

23. This is one of several possible proofs.

Statements	Reasons
1. $\overline{JK} \cong \overline{ML}$	1. Given
2. JK = ML	2. Definition of congruent segments
3. JK + KL = ML + KL	3. Addition Property of Equality
4. JL = JK + KL and MK = ML + KL	4. Segment Addition Postulate
5. JL = MK	5. Substitution Property of Equality
6. $\overline{JL} \cong \overline{MK}$	6. Definition of congruent segments
7. $\angle LKO \cong \angle KLO$	7. Given
8. $\overline{LO} \cong \overline{KO}$	8. Isosceles Triangle Converse Theorem
9. $\Delta JLO \cong \Delta MKO$	9. SAS Congruence Postulate
10. $\overline{JO} \cong \overline{MO}$	10. CPCTC
11. ΔJOM is an isosceles triangle	11. Definition of an isosceles triangle

Chapter 4, Part VI (pages 193-198)

1. $(180 - x)°$
3. 37°, 39°, and 104°
5. true
7. true
9. true
11. x = 17, $m\angle MKL = 98°$, and $m\angle LKJ = 82°$
13. (I), (II), (V), (VI)
15. w = 9, x = 59, and y = 59

17a. yes

b. $\Delta DEF \cong \Delta EDG$ by the SAS Congruence Postulate

Chapter 4, Part VI (pages 193-198) continued

19a. yes

b. $\Delta NOP \cong \Delta RQP$ by the AAS Congruence Postulate

21. This is only one of several possible proofs.

Statements	Reasons
1. $\overline{ST} \cong \overline{SV}$ and U is the midpoint of $\overline{TV}$	1. Given
2. $\overline{UT} \cong \overline{UV}$	2. Midpoint Theorem
3. $\overline{SU} \cong \overline{SU}$	3. Reflexive Property of Segment Congruence
4. $\Delta STU \cong \Delta SVU$	4. SSS Congruence Theorem
5. $\angle SUT \cong \angle SUV$	5. CPCTC
6. $\angle SUT$ and $\angle SUV$ form a linear pair	6. Definition of a linear pair
7. $\angle SUT$ and $\angle SUV$ are right angles	7. If two congruent angles form a linear pair, then the angles are right angles.
8. $\overline{TV} \perp \overline{SU}$	8. Definition of perpendicular lines

23. 104°

25. yes

27. right angle

29. yes; Alternate Interior Angles Converse Theorem

31. x = 93 and y = 31

33. Example:

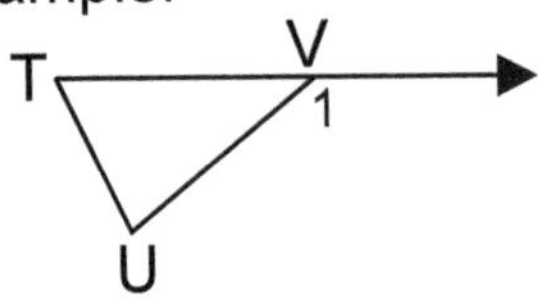

35. Example:

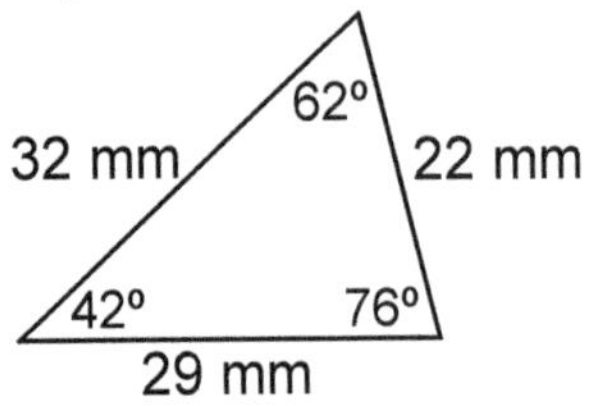

Chapter 5, Part I (pages 205-214)

1. $\angle C, \angle B, \angle A$

3. $\angle G, \angle I, \angle H$

5. $\overline{NP}$, $\overline{PO}$, $\overline{NO}$

7. $m\angle T < m\angle U$ by the Opposite Angles of a Triangle Theorem

9. $m\angle ABD = m\angle CBD$ by the Reflexive Property of Segment Congruence, SSS Congruence Postulate, CPCTC, and the definition of congruent angles

11. HI < GJ by the Reflexive Property of Segment Congruence and the SAS Inequality Theorem

13. $m\angle Q + m\angle P = m\angle NOP$ by the Exterior Angle of a Triangle Theorem

15. XY > WZ by the Reflexive Property of Segment Congruence and the SAS Inequality Theorem

17. EF + EG > FG by the Triangle Inequality Theorem

19. no

21. yes

23. no

25. $\frac{31}{5} < x < 10$

27. $\frac{17}{6} < x < \frac{9}{2}$ and y > 7

29. the third side must have a length greater than <u>5</u> inches and less than <u>11</u> inches

31. 24

33. Case 1: JL = KL

Then, by the Isosceles Triangle Theorem, $\angle J \cong \angle K$, which contradicts what we were given. Therefore, this is impossible.

Case 2: JL < KL

Then $m\angle K < m\angle J$ because of the Opposite Angles of a Triangle Theorem. This contradicts what we were given, and so this is also impossible.

Hence, JK must be larger than KL.

35. We are given that ΔGHI is a right triangle with $\angle H$ is its right angle. Then, using the definition of a right angle, we can say that $m\angle H = 90°$. We proved in the last chapter that the acute angles of a right triangle are complementary, and so we can say that $\angle G$ and $\angle I$ are complementary. Then, by the definition of complementary angles, we can say that $m\angle G + m\angle I = 90°$. Now, we can use the Substitution Property of Equality to say that $m\angle H = m\angle G + m\angle I$. Then, by the definition of inequality, $m\angle H > m\angle G$ and $m\angle H > m\angle I$. Then, by the Opposite Sides of a Triangle Theorem, GI > HI and GI > GH.

37. We are given that $m\angle TUV < m\angle TVU$. Then, by the Opposite Sides of a Triangle Theorem, TV < TU. We are also given that $\overline{TU} \cong \overline{VW}$ and that $\overline{TV} \cong \overline{UW}$. By the definition of congruent segments, this means that TU = VW and TV = UW. So, by the Substitution Property of Equality, UW < VW.

Chapter 5, Part I (pages 205-214) continued

39. We are given that $\angle FIH \cong \angle FHI$. Then, by the Isosceles Triangle Theorem, we can say that $\overline{FI} \cong \overline{FH}$. We are also given that $\overline{EF} \cong \overline{FG}$ and that EI > GH. Then, by the SSS Inequality Theorem, $m\angle EFI > m\angle GFH$.

41. We are given that $\overline{NP} \cong \overline{PQ}$. Then, by the definition of congruent segments, we can say that NP = PQ. The Triangle Inequality Theorem tells us that OP + NP > ON. Then, by the Substitution Property of Equality, we can say that OP + PQ > ON. The Segment Addition Postulate tells us that OP + PQ = OQ, and so now we can use the Substitution Property of Equality to say that OQ > ON. Thus, $m\angle ONQ > m\angle Q$ by the Opposite Angles of a Triangle Theorem.

Chapter 5, Part II (pages 219-226)

1. $3\sqrt{5}$
3. 12
5. 10
7. 12
9. $\sqrt{3}$
11. $\sqrt{7}$
13. $\sqrt{2}$
15. right triangle
17. acute triangle
19. obtuse triangle
21. no triangle
23. obtuse triangle
25. approximately 13.9 inches

27a. approximately 6.2 feet

b. approximately 6.2 feet

Chapter 5, Part II (pages 219-226) continued

29. 11 meters
31. 6, 8, and 10
33. no
35. approximately 22.9 feet
37. 870 kilometers
39. 10:00 p.m.
41a. 30 miles
 b. Carl must travel at 17 miles per hour to catch up with Al at 4:00 p.m. or about 13.5 miles per hour to catch up with him at 6:00 p.m.
43. about 31 laps from A to C or about 24 laps from A to D
45. $x = 5\sqrt{2}$ and $y = 45$

Chapter 5, Part III (pages 230-233)

1. The perpendicular bisectors of this triangle are shown in gray below.

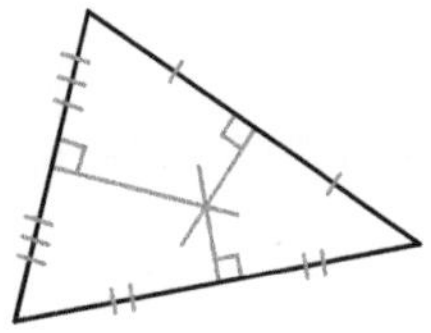

3. The perpendicular bisectors of this triangle are shown in gray below.

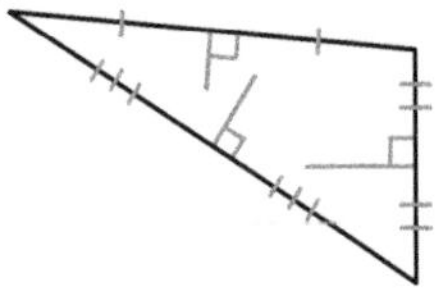

5. The angle bisectors of this triangle are shown in gray below.

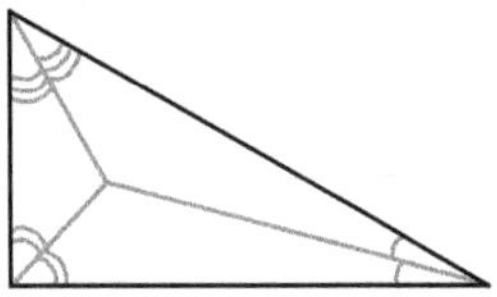

7. $\overline{AD}$
9. $\overline{BD}$
11. $\overline{ED}$
13. sometimes

Chapter 5, Part III (pages 230-233) continued

15. always
17. always
19. sometimes
21. always
23. always
25. 90°
27. AB = 38 inches and JB = 19 inches
29. BD = 15 feet and DC = 15 feet
31. $m\angle RPS = 15°$ and $m\angle SPQ = 15°$
33. $x = 15$ and $m\angle PQR = 114°$
35. 8
37. This is one of several possible proofs.

We are given that the point J is the incenter of ΔKOM. Then $\overline{JO}$, $\overline{JM}$, and $\overline{JK}$ must be angle bisectors of ΔKOM by the definition of an incenter of a triangle. So, by the definition of an angle bisector of a triangle, we can say that $\angle POJ \cong \angle JON$ and $\angle PKJ \cong \angle JKL$.

We are also given that $\overline{JP} \perp \overline{KO}$, $\overline{JL} \perp \overline{KM}$, and $\overline{JN} \perp \overline{OM}$. Since perpendicular lines intersect to form four right angles, this tells us that $\angle ONJ$, $\angle OPJ$, $\angle JPK$, and $\angle JLK$ are all right angles.

The Reflexive Property of Segment Congruence tells that $\overline{JO} \cong \overline{JO}$ and $\overline{KJ} \cong \overline{KJ}$.

We can now use the HL Congruence Postulate to say that $\Delta JNO \cong \Delta JPO$ and $\Delta JPK \cong \Delta JLK$. Then $\overline{JN} \cong \overline{JP}$ and $\overline{JP} \cong \overline{JL}$ by CPCTC. So, by the Transitive Property of Segment Congruence, we can say that $\overline{JN} \cong \overline{JP} \cong \overline{JL}$. By the definition of congruent segments, we now conclude that $JN = JP = JL$.

Chapter 5, Part IV (pages 240-242)

1. The medians of this triangle are shown in gray below.

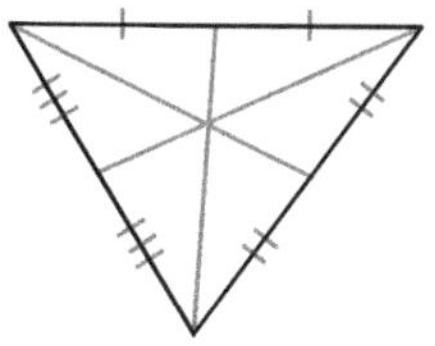

3. The medians of this triangle are shown in gray below.

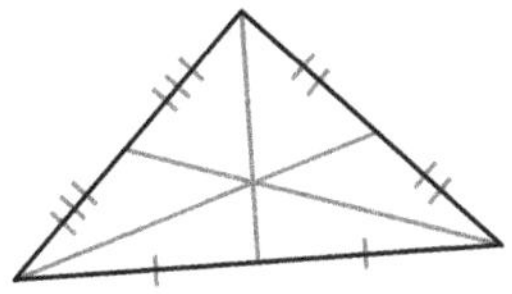

5. The altitudes of this triangle are shown in gray below.

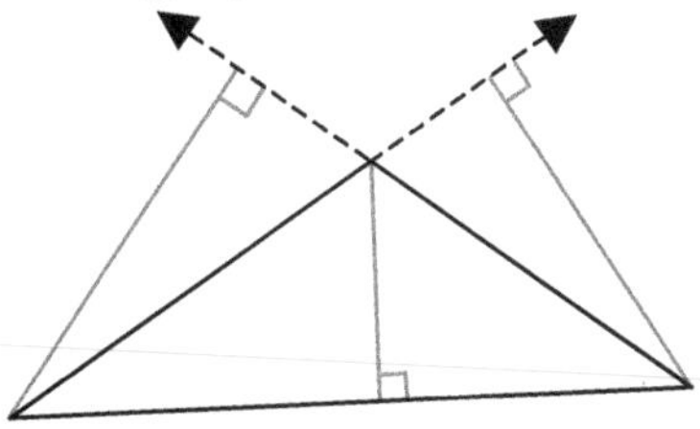

7. The midsegments of this triangle are shown in gray below.

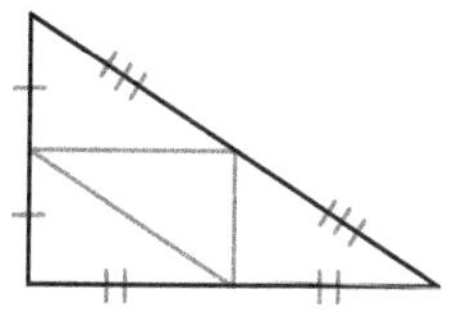

9. The midsegments of this triangle are shown in gray below.

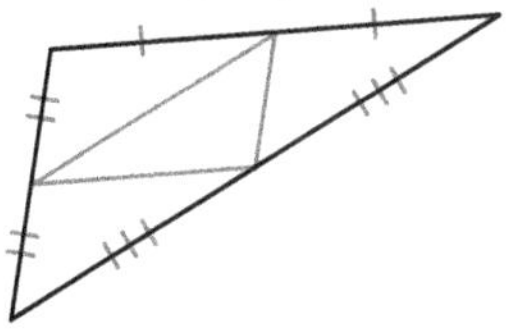

11. CP = 36 and CF = 54
13. w = 5 and BE = 33
15. y = 19 and DE = 69
17. 21
19. 67°
21. JN = 24, JO = 12, and ON = 12
23. w = 4 and LN = 56

Chapter 5, Part IV (pages 240-242) continued

25. LM = 29 and LN = 58
27. 77

Chapter 5, Part V (pages 243-248)

1. w = 14 and m$\angle$RLT = 44°
3. EJ = 2y centimeters and EH = 3y centimeters
5. altitude of $\triangle$QRT, median of $\triangle$QRT, perpendicular bisector of $\triangle$QRT, angle bisector of $\triangle$QRT
   (To see why $\overline{QS}$ is an angle bisector of $\triangle$QRT, note that $\triangle QRS \cong \triangle QTS$ by the SAS Congruence Postulate, and so $\angle RQS \cong \angle TQS$ by CPCTC.)
7. Example:

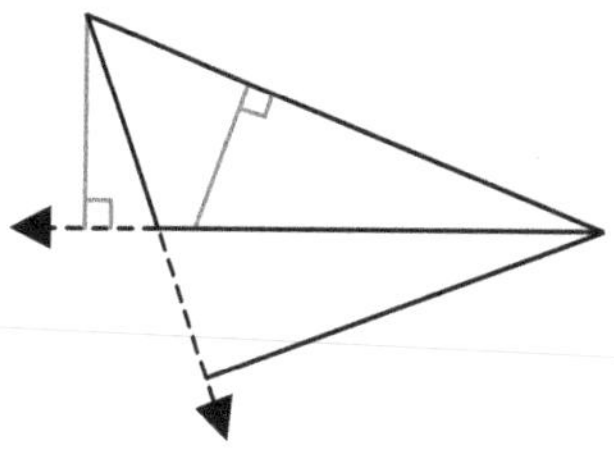

9. Example:

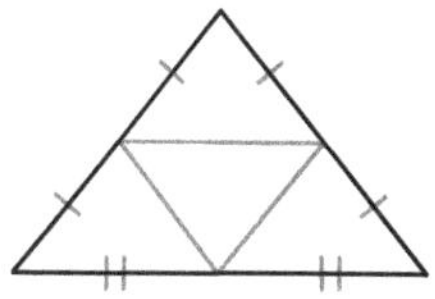

11. Example:

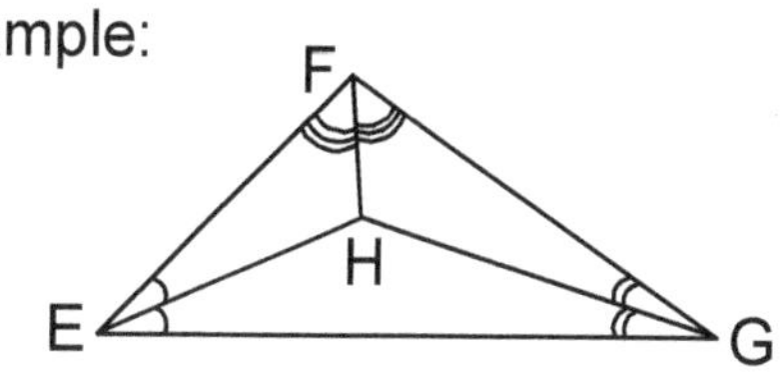

13. $2\sqrt{5}$
15. m$\angle$MZP > m$\angle$M by the Opposite Angles of a Triangle Theorem
17. MP + PZ > MZ by the Triangle Inequality Theorem
19. $\overline{XK} \parallel \overline{WB}$ by the Alternate Interior Angles Converse Theorem
    $\overline{XW} \parallel \overline{KB}$ by the Same-Side Interior Angles Converse Theorem
21. 8 feet, 15 feet, and 17 feet

Chapter 5, Part V (pages 243-248) continued

23. $\angle 6$, $\angle 13$, and $\angle 14$
25. 3 cm
27. 6 cm
29. approximately 127.28 feet
31. approximately 3.33 seconds
33. (D)
35. Given: ΔWXY is an isosceles triangle with $\angle WXY$ as its vertex angle, and $\overline{XZ}$ is an altitude of ΔWXY

Prove: $\overline{XZ}$ is also a perpendicular bisector, a median, and an angle bisector of ΔWXY

Proof: (We will use a paragraph proof here, but you may use the two-column format if you wish.)

We are given that ΔWXY is an isosceles triangle with $\angle WXY$ as its vertex angle. The definition of an isosceles triangle tells us that $\overline{WX} \cong \overline{XY}$, and the Isosceles Triangle Theorem tells us $\angle W \cong \angle Y$. We are also given that $\overline{XZ}$ is an altitude of ΔWXY. Using the definition of an altitude of a triangle, this tells us $\overline{XZ} \perp \overline{WY}$. The theorem *If two lines are perpendicular, then they intersect to form four right angles* tells us that $\angle WZX$ and $\angle YZX$ must be right angles. The theorem *If two angles are right angles, then they are congruent* tells us that $\angle WZX \cong \angle YZX$. The Reflexive Property of Segment Congruence tells us that $\overline{XZ} \cong \overline{XZ}$. This means that $\Delta WZX \cong \Delta YZX$ by the AAS Congruence Theorem. Now, we can say that $\angle WXZ \cong \angle YXZ$ by CPCTC. Then, by the definition of an angle bisector, $\overline{XZ}$ must be an angle bisector of ΔWXY. We can also use CPCTC to say that $\overline{WZ} \cong \overline{YZ}$. By the definition of congruent segments and the definition of a midpoint, Z must be the midpoint of $\overline{WY}$. Then, by the definition of a median of a triangle and the definition of a perpendicular bisector of a triangle, $\overline{XZ}$ must also be a median and a perpendicular bisector of ΔWXY.

Chapter 6, Part I (pages 253-257)

1. (b) and (d)
3. (a) and (d)
5. Example: octagon STVXZYWU (There are may other ways you can name this figure, but octagon STUVWXYZ would NOT be acceptable.)
7. It has 24 congruent sides and 24 congruent angles (and the angles will all have measures of 165°).
9. 900°
11. 16
13. c = 11, d = 88
15. 160°
17. 135°
19. 45°
21. 72°
23. $\dfrac{360^\circ}{n}$
25. 9
27. 40
29. 180
31. 6
33. $\dfrac{360^\circ}{y^\circ}$
35. The measures of the exterior angles decrease.

Chapter 6, Part II (pages 261-264)

1. OT = 35 and UT = 70
3. UV = 8 and TV = 6
5. $m\angle SUV = 114^\circ$ and $m\angle UVT = 66^\circ$
7. $m\angle UVT = 76^\circ$, $m\angle VSU = 44^\circ$, and $m\angle UST = 76^\circ$
9. OU = 7.5 and OT = 7.5
11. $\Delta OUS \cong \Delta OTV$
13. n = 14 and $m\angle REZ = 103^\circ$

Chapter 6, Part II (pages 261-264) continued

15. $a = -1$ and $EG = 7$

17. $p = 51$ and $m\angle ERL = 86^\circ$

19. $w = 7$, $m\angle LER = 48^\circ$, and $m\angle ZER = 91^\circ$

21. $d = 33$ and $EL = 38$

Note for #23 and #25: We will prove these statements using the two-column format, but you may use a paragraph proof if you wish. Also, the both of the proofs given here show only one of several possible proofs.

23.

Statements	Reasons
1. Quadrilateral EFGH is a parallelogram	1. Given
2. $\overline{EH} \parallel \overline{FG}$	2. Definition of a parallelogram
3. $\angle HEZ \cong \angle FGZ$ and $\angle EHZ \cong \angle GFZ$	3. Alternate Interior Angles Theorem
4. $\overline{EH} \cong \overline{GF}$	4. Opposite Sides of Parallelogram Theorem
5. $\Delta HEZ \cong \Delta FGZ$	5. ASA Congruence Postulate
6. $\overline{EZ} \cong \overline{ZG}$ and $\overline{FZ} \cong \overline{ZH}$	6. CPCTC
7. $\overline{EG}$ bisects $\overline{HF}$ and $\overline{HF}$ bisects $\overline{EG}$	7. Definition of a segment bisector

25.

Statements	Reasons
1. Quadrilaterals NOQR and NOPQ are both parallelograms	1. Given
2. $\overline{NR} \parallel \overline{OQ}$ and $\overline{NQ} \parallel \overline{OP}$	2. Definition of a parallelogram
3. $\angle NRQ \cong \angle OQP$ and $\angle NQR \cong \angle OPQ$	3. Corresponding Angles Postulate
4. $\overline{NR} \cong \overline{OQ}$	4. Opposite Sides of a Parallelogram Theorem
5. $\Delta RNQ \cong \Delta QOP$	5. AAS Congruence Theorem

Chapter 6, Part III (pages 269-275)

1a. no
b. N/A

3a. yes
b. Opposite Sides of a Parallelogram Converse Theorem

5a. no
b. N/A

7a. no
b. N/A

9a. yes
b. Consecutive Angles of a Parallelogram Converse Theorem

11. $x = 57$ and $y = 123$

13. $x = 4.5$ and $y = 4$

15. $x = 37$ and $y = 8$

17. $x = 14$ and $y = 51$

19. $x = 31$ and $y = 11$

21. This is one of two versions of this proof.

Given: $\overline{AD} \cong \overline{BC}$ and $\overline{AB} \cong \overline{DC}$
Prove: Quadrilateral ABCD is a parallelogram

Statements	Reasons
1. $\overline{AD} \cong \overline{BC}$ and $\overline{AB} \cong \overline{DC}$	1. Given
2. Draw $\overline{AC}$.	2. Through any two points there is exactly one line.
3. $\overline{AC} \cong \overline{AC}$	3. Reflexive Property of Segment Congruence
4. $\Delta ABC \cong \Delta CDA$	4. SSS Congruence Postulate
5. $\angle ACB \cong \angle CAD$ and $\angle CAB \cong \angle ACD$	5. CPCTC
6. $\overline{AD} \parallel \overline{BC}$ and $\overline{AB} \parallel \overline{DC}$	6. Alternate Interior Angles Converse Theorem
7. Quadrilateral ABCD is a parallelogram	7. Definition of a parallelogram

23. This is one of several possible proofs.

Given: $\overline{JM} \cong \overline{KL}$ and $\overline{JM} \parallel \overline{KL}$

Prove: Quadrilateral JKLM is a parallelogram

Statements	Reasons
1. $\overline{JM} \cong \overline{KL}$ and $\overline{JM} \parallel \overline{KL}$	1. Given
2. Draw $\overline{JL}$.	2. Through any two points there is exactly one line.
3. $\angle MJL \cong \angle KLJ$	3. Alternate Interior Angles Theorem
4. $\overline{JL} \cong \overline{JL}$	4. Reflexive Property of Segment Congruence
5. $\Delta MJL \cong \Delta KLJ$	5. SAS Congruence Postulate
6. $\overline{JK} \cong \overline{ML}$	6. CPCTC
7. Quadrilateral JKLM is a parallelogram	7. Opposite Sides of a Parallelogram Converse Theorem (Note that we can use this theorem in this proof because we proved it earlier in #21.)

25. This is one of several possible proofs.

We are given that $\overline{GH}$ bisects both $\angle FGI$ and $\angle FHI$. The definition of an angle bisector tells us that $\angle FGH \cong \angle HGI$ and $\angle FHG \cong \angle GHI$.

By the Reflexive Property of Segment Congruence, $\overline{GH} \cong \overline{GH}$. The ASA Congruence Postulate tells us that this means that $\Delta FGH \cong \Delta IGH$. This means that we can say that $\angle F \cong \angle I$ by CPCTC.

Since we were given that $\angle FGI \cong \angle FHI$, we can now use the Opposite Angles of a Parallelogram Converse Theorem to say that quadrilateral FGIH must be a parallelogram.

Chapter 6, Part III (pages 269-275) continued

27. This is one of several possible proofs.

We are given that quadrilaterals RSVU, STWV, UVYX, and VWZY are all parallelograms.

Then, by the Opposite Angles of a Parallelogram Theorem, $\angle R \cong \angle SVU$, $\angle WVY \cong \angle Z$, $\angle T \cong \angle SVW$, and $\angle X \cong \angle UVY$.

The Vertical Angles Theorem tells us that $\angle SVU \cong \angle VWY$ and $\angle SVW \cong \angle UVY$.

Then, by the Transitive Property of Angle Congruence, $\angle R \cong \angle Z$ and $\angle T \cong \angle X$.

We can now say that the Opposite Angles of a Parallelogram Converse Theorem tells us that quadrilateral RTZX must be a parallelogram.

Chapter 6, Part IV (pages 278-287)

1. AC = 4, AD = 8, and BD = 5
3. x = 14, $m\angle BDE = 70°$, and $m\angle BDA = 35°$
5. $m\angle HFI = 36°$ and $m\angle GHF = 36°$
7. n = 3 and GI = 22
9. $m\angle NOK = 90°$, $m\angle MNK = 90°$, and $m\angle NMK = 45°$
11. w = 7 and MK = 82
13. must be
15. might be
17. might be
19. might be
21. might be
23. cannot be
25. must be
27. Quadrilateral EFGH <u>must be</u> a parallelogram, <u>cannot be</u> a rhombus, <u>might be</u> a rectangle, and <u>cannot be</u> a square.
29. cannot be

31. Given: Quadrilateral EFGH is a rhombus

Prove: Quadrilateral EFGH is a parallelogram

Statements	Reasons
1. Quadrilateral EFGH is a rhombus	1. Given
2. $\overline{FE} \cong \overline{EH} \cong \overline{HG} \cong \overline{GF}$	2. Definition of a rhombus
3. Quadrilateral EFGH is a parallelogram	3. Opposite Sides of a Parallelogram Converse Theorem

33. This is one of several versions of the proof of this theorem.

Given: Quadrilateral NORQ is a rectangle

Prove: $\overline{NR} \cong \overline{OQ}$

Statements	Reasons
1. Quadrilateral NORQ is a rectangle	1. Given
2. $\angle ONQ$ and $\angle NOR$ are both right angles	2. Definition of a rectangle
3. $\angle ONQ \cong \angle NOR$	3. If two angles are right angles, then they are congruent.
4. $\overline{NO} \cong \overline{NO}$	4. Reflexive Property of Segment Congruence
5. Quadrilateral NORQ is a parallelogram	5. If a quadrilateral is a rectangle, then it is a parallelogram.
6. $\overline{NQ} \cong \overline{OR}$	6. Opposite Sides of a Parallelogram Theorem
7. $\Delta NOQ \cong \Delta ONR$	7. SAS Congruence Postulate
8. $\overline{NR} \cong \overline{OQ}$	8. CPCTC

Chapter 6, Part IV (pages 278-287) continued

35. This is one of several versions of the proof of this theorem.

Given: Quadrilateral LAXQ is a rhombus

Prove: $\overline{LX}$ bisects both $\angle ALQ$ and $\angle AXQ$, and $\overline{QA}$ bisects both $\angle LQX$ and $\angle LAX$

Statements	Reasons
1. Quadrilateral LAXQ is a rhombus	1. Given
2. $\overline{LQ} \cong \overline{LA}$ and $\overline{QX} \cong \overline{AX}$; $\overline{LQ} \cong \overline{XQ}$ and $\overline{LA} \cong \overline{XA}$	2. Definition of a rhombus
3. $\overline{LX} \cong \overline{LX}$ and $\overline{QA} \cong \overline{QA}$	3. Reflexive Property of Segment Congruence
4. $\Delta LQX \cong \Delta LAX$ and $\Delta QAL \cong \Delta QAX$	4. SSS Congruence Postulate
5. $\angle QLX \cong \angle ALX$ and $\angle LXQ \cong \angle LXA$; $\angle LQA \cong \angle XQA$ and $\angle LAQ \cong \angle XAQ$	5. CPCTC
6. $\overline{LX}$ bisects both $\angle ALQ$ and $\angle AXQ$; $\overline{QA}$ bisects both $\angle LQX$ and $\angle LAX$	6. Definition of an angle bisector

Chapter 6, Part IV (pages 278-287) continued

37. This is only one of several possible proofs for this theorem.

Given: Quadrilateral ZWBK is a parallelogram and $\overline{WK}$ bisects $\angle ZWB$

Prove: Quadrilateral ZWBK is a rhombus

Statements	Reasons
1. Quadrilateral ZWBK is a parallelogram	1. Given
2. $\overline{ZW} \parallel \overline{KB}$ and $\overline{ZK} \parallel \overline{WB}$	2. Definition of a parallelogram
3. $\angle BKW \cong \angle ZWK$ and $\angle BWK \cong \angle ZKW$	3. Alternate Interior Angles Theorem
4. $\overline{WK}$ bisects $\angle ZWB$	4. Given
5. $\angle ZWK \cong \angle BWK$	5. Definition of an angle bisector
6. $\angle BKW \cong \angle BWK$ and $\angle ZWK \cong \angle ZKW$	6. Transitive Property of Angle Congruence
7. $\overline{BW} \cong \overline{BK}$ and $\overline{ZK} \cong \overline{ZW}$	7. Isosceles Triangle Converse Theorem
8. $\overline{ZW} \cong \overline{BK}$ and $\overline{ZK} \cong \overline{BW}$	8. Opposite Sides of a Parallelogram Theorem
9. $\overline{ZW} \cong \overline{ZK} \cong \overline{WB} \cong \overline{BK}$	9. Transitive Property of Segment Congruence
10. Quadrilateral ZWBK is a rhombus	10. Definition of a rhombus

39. This is only one of several possible proofs.

Statements	Reasons
1. Quadrilateral RSTU is a rhombus	1. Given
2. $\overline{TS} \cong \overline{TU}$	2. Definition of a rhombus
3. $\angle TSU \cong \angle TUS$	3. Isosceles Triangle Theorem

Chapter 6, Part IV (pages 278-287) continued

41.

Statements	Reasons
1. Quadrilateral EAKR is a rectangle	1. Given
2. $\overline{RA} \cong \overline{EK}$	2. If a quadrilateral is a rectangle, then its diagonals are congruent.
3. RA = EK	3. Definition of congruent segments
4. Quadrilateral EAKR is a parallelogram	4. If a quadrilateral is a rectangle, then it is a parallelogram.
5. $\overline{RA}$ bisects $\overline{EK}$, and $\overline{EK}$ bisects $\overline{RA}$	5. Diagonals of a Parallelogram Theorem
6. N is the midpoint of both $\overline{EK}$ and $\overline{RA}$	6. Definition of a segment bisector
7. $\overline{RN} \cong \overline{NA}$ and $\overline{KN} \cong \overline{NE}$	7. Definition of a midpoint
8. RN = NA and KN = NE	8. Definition of congruent segments
9. RA = RN + NA and EK = KN + NE	9. Segment Addition Postulate
10. RN + NA = KN + NE	10. Substitution Property of Equality
11. RN + RN = KN + KN	11. Substitution Property of Equality
12. 2(RN) = 2(KN)	12. Distributive Property
13. RN = KN	13. Division Property of Equality
14. $\overline{RN} \cong \overline{KN}$	14. Definition of congruent segments

Chapter 6, Part V (pages 291-298)

1. $\overline{MN}$ is parallel to $\overline{TP}$ and $\overline{RA}$ by the Midsegment of a Trapezoid Theorem
3. 27
5. 4
7. AD = 4 and JK = 7
9. 68°
11. $m\angle HFG = 42°$ and $m\angle FHE = 42°$
13. $m\angle STW = 71°$ by the Base Angles of an Isosceles Trapezoid Theorem
15. TW = 5 by the definition of an isosceles trapezoid
17. y = −0.5 and TW = 4.5
19. 90°
21. $m\angle LRT = 59°$, $m\angle RLS = 31°$, and $m\angle RSL = 31°$
23. LR = $\sqrt{34}$ and RS = $\sqrt{34}$
25. 5

27. Given: Quadrilateral GHJK is an isosceles trapezoid with bases $\overline{GH}$ and $\overline{KJ}$

Prove: $\overline{HK} \cong \overline{GJ}$

Statements	Reasons
1. Quadrilateral GHJK is an isosceles trapezoid with bases $\overline{GH}$ and $\overline{KJ}$	1. Given
2. $\overline{GK} \cong \overline{HJ}$	2. Definition of an isosceles trapezoid
3. $\angle HGK \cong \angle GHJ$	3. Base Angles of an Isosceles Trapezoid Theorem
4. $\overline{GH} \cong \overline{GH}$	4. Reflexive Property of Segment Congruence
5. $\Delta GHK \cong \Delta HGJ$	5. SAS Congruence Postulate
6. $\overline{HK} \cong \overline{GJ}$	6. CPCTC

Chapter 6, Part V (pages 291-298) continued

29. Given: Quadrilateral STUV is a trapezoid with $\overline{ST}$ and $\overline{UV}$ as its bases and $\overline{SU} \cong \overline{TV}$

Prove: Quadrilateral STUV is an isosceles trapezoid

Statements	Reasons
1. Quadrilateral STUV is a trapezoid with $\overline{ST}$ and $\overline{UV}$ as its bases	1. Given
2. $\overline{ST} \parallel \overline{VU}$	2. Definition of a trapezoid
3. Draw $\overline{VY}$ so that Y is on $\overleftrightarrow{ST}$ and $\overline{VY} \perp \overleftrightarrow{ST}$. Also draw $\overline{UZ}$ so that Z is on $\overleftrightarrow{ST}$ and $\overline{UZ} \perp \overleftrightarrow{ST}$.	3. Through any point not on a line, there is exactly one line that passes through the point and is perpendicular to the given line.
4. VY = UZ	4. If two lines are parallel, then they are everywhere equidistant.
5. $\overline{VY} \cong \overline{UZ}$	5. Definition of congruent segments
6. $\angle TYV$ and $\angle SZU$ are right angles	5. If two lines are perpendicular, then they intersect to form four right angles.
6. $\Delta TVY \cong \Delta SUZ$	6. HL Congruence Postulate
7. $\angle USZ \cong \angle VTY$	7. CPCTC
8. $\overline{ST} \cong \overline{ST}$	8. Reflexive Property of Segment Congruence
9. $\Delta TVS \cong \Delta SUT$	9. SAS Congruence Postulate
10. $\overline{SV} \cong \overline{TU}$	10. CPCTC
11. Quadrilateral STUV is an isosceles trapezoid	11. Definition of an isosceles trapezoid

Chapter 6, Part V (pages 291-298) continued

31.

Statements	Reasons
1. $\angle CBD \cong \angle ADB$ and $\overline{AB}$ is not parallel to $\overline{CD}$	1. Given
2. $\overline{AD} \parallel \overline{BC}$	2. Alternate Interior Angles Converse Theorem
3. Quadrilateral ABCD is a trapezoid	3. Definition of a trapezoid

33. This is only one of several possible proofs.

Statements	Reasons
1. $\Delta KNJ \cong \Delta MNJ$ and $\overline{KJ}$ is not congruent to $\overline{KL}$	1. Given
2. $\overline{KJ} \cong \overline{JM}$ and $\angle KJL \cong \angle MJL$	2. CPCTC
3. $\overline{JL} \cong \overline{JL}$	3. Reflexive Property of Segment Congruence
4. $\Delta KJL \cong \Delta MJL$	4. SAS Congruence Postulate
5. $\overline{KL} \cong \overline{ML}$	5. CPCTC
6. Quadrilateral JMLK is a kite	6. Definition of a kite

Chapter 6, Part VI (pages 299-304)

1. $m\angle B = 102^\circ$, $m\angle C = 78^\circ$, and $m\angle D = 102^\circ$
3. $\overline{ZV}$, $\overline{TM}$, and $\overline{LN}$
5. 20
7. true
9. true

Chapter 6, Part VI (pages 299-304) continued

11. Example: The figure below is both a rhombus and a rectangle.

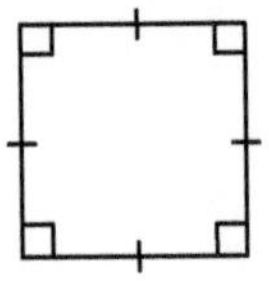

13. 4
15. 6
17. x = 83 and y = 48
19. MP = 10, MN = 12, and LM = 16
21. 90°
23. x = 9 and $m\angle URS = 126^\circ$
25. 11
27. parallelogram and rectangle
29. trapezoid
31. 126
33. x = 25 and y = 56
35.

Statements	Reasons
1. $\overline{QR} \cong \overline{YR}$, $QR \neq QW$, and $\overline{RP} \perp \overline{QY}$	1. Given
2. $\angle QPR$ and $\angle YPR$ are right angles	2. If two lines are perpendicular, then they intersect to form four right angles.
3. $\overline{RP} \cong \overline{RP}$	3. Reflexive Property of Segment Congruence
4. $\Delta RPQ \cong \Delta RPY$	4. HL Congruence Postulate
5. $\angle QRP \cong \angle YRP$	5. CPCTC
6. $\overline{RW} \cong \overline{RW}$	6. Reflexive Property of Segment Congruence
7. $\Delta RQW \cong \Delta RYW$	7. SAS Congruence Postulate
8. $\overline{QW} \cong \overline{YW}$	8. CPCTC
9. Quadrilateral QRYW is a kite	9. Definition of a kite

Chapter 7, Part I (pages 308-312)

1. 6
3. 15.5
5. 2
7. $\frac{23}{9}$
9. –2
11. 6 or –2
13. 1 or $-\frac{2}{5}$
15. 10.8 centimeters
17. approximately 7.14 inches
19. 240 feet long, 30 feet wide, and 12 feet tall
21. 30
23. 8 : 10 : 9
25. 4 : 3
27. 15
29. 42 feet, 24 feet, and 30 feet
31. a = 126 and c = 18
33. JK = 36 yards and LM = 18 yards

Chapter 7, Part II (pages 317-322)

1a. yes

b. hexagon DVSOZF is congruent to hexagon EMSOTH
(It is also correct to say that hexagon DVSOZF is congruent to hexagon HTOSME.)

Chapter 7, Part II (pages 317-322) continued

3a. yes (Note that the Opposite Sides of a Parallelogram Converse Theorem tells us that both quadrilaterals are parallelograms, and you can use this to prove that that there are four sets of congruent corresponding angles.)

b. quadrilateral GJUX is congruent to quadrilateral GPIA
(It is also correct to say that quadrilateral GJUX is congruent to quadrilateral IAGP.)

5a. no

b. N/A

7. The two figures from #6 are similar to each other, and the scale factor of heptagon PQRSYZA to heptagon STUVWXY is 1 : 1.

9a. no

b. N/A

11a. yes

b. $\Delta CYV \sim \Delta RYA$

13a. yes

b. octagon QSMRPNGJ is similar to octagon EBCDYTOH
(It is equally correct to name the vertices of octagon EBCDYTOH in any other order as long as consecutive vertices are named next to each other.)

15. 30
17. 39°
19. the perimeter of ΔCNT = 160 inches and the perimeter of ΔGNQ = 120 inches
21. 40 m
23. 113°
25. $\frac{2}{5}$

Chapter 7, Part II (pages 317-322) continued

27. 2 : 5
29. must be
31. must be
33. cannot be

Chapter 7, Part III (pages 326-340)

1a. yes
b. ΔSPO ~ ΔLCO by the SAS Similarity Theorem
3a. yes
b. ΔGXR ~ ΔAUQ by the SSS Similarity Theorem
5a. yes
b. ΔKWC ~ ΔIWY by either the AA Similarity Theorem or the AAA Similarity Postulate

(Note that $\angle$KWC $\cong$ $\angle$IWY by the Reflexive Property of Angle Congruence and that $\angle$C $\cong$ $\angle$IYW by the Corresponding Angles Converse Postulate.)
7a. no
b. N/A

(Note that there is no SSA Similarity Postulate or Theorem.)
9a. yes
b. ΔZWD ~ ΔMQT by the SAS Similarity Theorem **or** ΔZWD ~ ΔTQM by the SAS Similarity Theorem
11a. no
b. N/A
13a. no
b. N/A
15. 18 m
17. BC = 12 m, EG = 6.4 m, and EH = 3.2 m
19. 10.5 ft

Chapter 7, Part III (pages 326-340) continued

21.

We are given that ΔIJK ~ ΔONM. Then, by the definition of similar triangles, $\angle$K $\cong$ $\angle$M and $\angle$IJK $\cong$ $\angle$ONM. The definition of congruent angles tells us that this means that m$\angle$IJK = m$\angle$ONM. Next, we will use the Angle Addition Postulate to say that m$\angle$IJK = m$\angle$IJL + m$\angle$KJL and that m$\angle$MNO = m$\angle$MNP + m$\angle$ONP. Then, by the Substitution Property of Equality, m$\angle$IJL + m$\angle$KJL = m$\angle$MNP + m$\angle$ONP. We were also given that $\overline{NP}$ is an angle bisector of ΔONM and $\overline{JL}$ is an angle bisector of ΔIJK. Then, by the definition of an angle bisector, $\angle$MNP $\cong$ $\angle$ONP and $\angle$IJL $\cong$ $\angle$KJL. The definition of congruent angles tells us that this means that m$\angle$MNP = m$\angle$ONP and m$\angle$IJL = m$\angle$KJL. Now, the Substitution Property of Equality tells us m$\angle$KJL + m$\angle$KJL = m$\angle$MNP + m$\angle$MNP. The Distributive Property tells us that this means that 2(m$\angle$KJL) = 2(m$\angle$MNP). So m$\angle$KJL = m$\angle$MNP by the Division Property of Equality. By the definition of congruent angles, $\angle$KJL $\cong$ $\angle$MNP. Since we already said that $\angle$K $\cong$ $\angle$M, we can now use the AA Similarity Theorem to say that ΔLJK ~ ΔPNM.

23. m$\angle$U = 28° and m$\angle$W = 53°
25. 13.6 yards
27. 21 yards
29. ΔABF ~ ΔACD by either the AAA Similarity Postulate or the AA Similarity Theorem (Note that $\angle$CAD $\cong$ $\angle$BAF and that the theorem *In a plane, if two different lines are perpendicular to a third line, then the first two lines are parallel* tells us that $\overline{BF} \parallel \overline{CD}$, and so $\angle$ABF $\cong$ $\angle$ACD); BF = $\frac{8}{3}$ ft
31. approximately 20.8 m

33. 102 inches

35. approximately 97.1 feet

37.

We are given that $\frac{ON}{RQ} = \frac{OP}{RS}$ and that $\angle O \cong \angle R$. We will assume that the lengths of the sides of ΔNOP are longer than those of ΔQRS. If this is not the case, then the proof will essentially stay the same; only the next picture will change. We will begin by using the Ruler Postulate to label point T on $\overrightarrow{ON}$ so that OT = RQ. Then, by the definition of congruent segments, $\overline{OT} \cong \overline{RQ}$. Next, we will use the Parallel Postulate to draw $\overline{TU}$ so that $\overline{TU} \parallel \overline{NP}$ and U is on $\overrightarrow{OP}$.

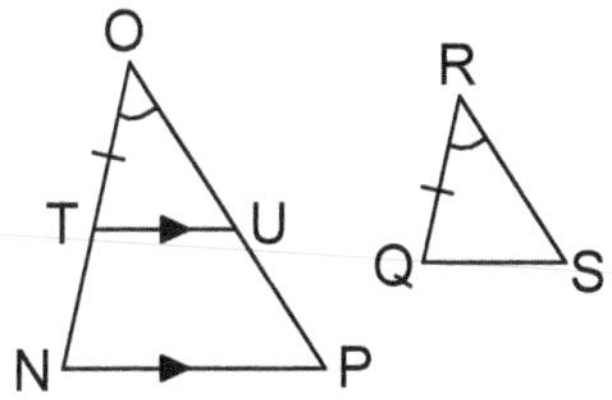

Then, by the Corresponding Angles Postulate, $\angle N \cong \angle OTU$. By the Reflexive Property of Angle Congruence, $\angle O \cong \angle O$. Then, by the AA Similarity Theorem, $\Delta TOU \sim \Delta NOP$. By the definition of similar triangles, $\frac{ON}{OT} = \frac{OP}{OU}$. By the Substitution Property of Equality, $\frac{ON}{RQ} = \frac{OP}{OU}$. By the Substitution Property of Equality, $\frac{OP}{RS} = \frac{OP}{OU}$. By the Cross Products Property of Proportions and the Division Property of Equality, RS = OU. By the definition of congruent segments, $\overline{OU} \cong \overline{RS}$. Since we were given that $\angle O \cong \angle R$, we can now use the SAS Congruence Postulate to say that $\Delta TOU \cong \Delta QRS$. Then $\angle OTU \cong \angle Q$ by CPCTC. Since we already said that $\angle N \cong \angle OTU$, we can use the Transitive Property of Angle Congruence to say that $\angle N \cong \angle Q$. Therefore, $\Delta NOP \sim \Delta QRS$ by the AA Similarity Theorem.

Chapter 7, Part III (pages 326-340) continued

Note for #39-#47: The proofs given here show only one version of each proof. Other versions are possible.

39.

Statements	Reasons
1. We are given ΔDEF.	1. Given
2. $\angle D \cong \angle D$ and $\angle E \cong \angle E$	2. Congruence of angles is reflexive.
3. $\Delta DEF \sim \Delta DEF$	3. AA Similarity Theorem

41.

Statements	Reasons
1. $\Delta MNO \sim \Delta PQR$ and $\Delta PQR \sim \Delta STU$	1. Given
2. $\angle M \cong \angle P$, $\angle N \cong \angle Q$, $\angle P \cong \angle S$, and $\angle Q \cong \angle T$	2. Definition of similar triangles
3. $\angle M \cong \angle S$ and $\angle N \cong \angle T$	3. Transitive Property of Angle Congruence
4. $\Delta MNO \sim \Delta STU$	4. AA Similarity Theorem

43.

We are given that quadrilateral WXYZ is a trapezoid with bases $\overline{WZ}$ and $\overline{XY}$. Then, by the definition of a trapezoid, $\overline{WZ} \parallel \overline{XY}$. We are also given that $\overline{MN}$ is a midsegment of trapezoid WXYZ. Then, by the definition of a midsegment of a trapezoid, M is the midpoint of $\overline{WX}$ and N is the midpoint of $\overline{ZY}$. By the Midpoint Theorem, $\overline{ZN} \cong \overline{NY}$. Now, we can use the postulate Through any two points there is exactly one line to draw $\overrightarrow{XY}$ and $\overrightarrow{WN}$, and we will call the point where they intersect V.

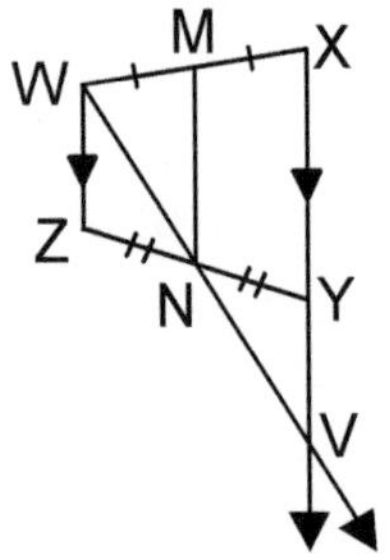

The Alternate Interior Angles Theorem tells us that $\angle ZWN \cong \angle NVY$ and $\angle WZN \cong \angle VYN$. Then $\Delta WZN \cong \Delta VYN$ by the AAS Congruence Theorem. Therefore, $\overline{WN} \cong \overline{NV}$ and $\overline{WZ} \cong \overline{YV}$ by CPCTC. Since $\overline{WN} \cong \overline{NV}$, the definition of midpoint and the definition of congruent segments tell us that N is the midpoint of $\overline{WV}$, and so we can use the definition of a midsegment of a triangle to say that $\overline{MN}$ is a midsegment of ΔWXV. The Midsegment of a Triangle Theorem tells us that $\overline{MN} \parallel \overline{XY}$. Then, by the Transitive Property of Parallel Lines, $\overline{MN} \parallel \overline{WZ}$. The Midsegment of a Triangle Theorem also tells us that $MN = \frac{XV}{2}$. The Segment Addition Postulate tells us that $XY + YV = XV$, and so we can use the Substitution Property of Equality to say that $MN = \frac{XY+YV}{2}$. We already said that $\overline{WZ} \cong \overline{YV}$, and so we can use the definition of congruent segments to say that WZ = YV. Then, by the Substitution Property of Equality, $MN = \frac{WZ+XY}{2}$.

45.

Given: $\Delta XYH \sim \Delta CMP$, $\overline{KY}$ is a median of ΔXYH, and $\overline{EM}$ is a median of ΔCMP

Prove: $\frac{KY}{EM} = \frac{XY}{CM} = \frac{XH}{CP} = \frac{HY}{PM}$

Statements	Reasons
1. $\Delta XYH \sim \Delta CMP$	1. Given
2. $\frac{XY}{CM} = \frac{XH}{CP} = \frac{HY}{PM}$ and $\angle X \cong \angle C$	2. Definition of similar triangles
3. $\overline{KY}$ is a median of ΔXYH, and $\overline{EM}$ is a median of ΔCMP	3. Given
4. K is the midpoint of $\overline{XH}$, and E is the midpoint of $\overline{CP}$	4. Definition of a median
5. XK = KH and CE = EP	5. Definition of a midpoint
6. XK + KH = XH and CE + EP = CP	6. Segment Addition Postulate
7. XK + XK = XH and CE + CE = CP	7. Substitution Property of Equality
8. 2(XK) = XH and 2(CE) = CP	8. Distributive Property
9. $\frac{XY}{CM} = \frac{2(XK)}{2(CE)}$	9. Substitution Property of Equality
10. $\frac{XY}{CM} = \frac{XK}{CE}$	10. Substitution Property of Equality
11. $\Delta XYK \sim \Delta CME$	11. SAS Similarity Theorem
12. $\frac{XY}{CM} = \frac{KY}{EM}$	12. Definition of similar triangles
13. $\frac{XY}{CM} = \frac{XH}{CP} = \frac{HY}{PM} = \frac{KY}{EM}$	13. Transitive Property of Equality

47. Given: $\Delta XWP \sim \Delta BGH$, $\overline{MI}$ is a midsegment of ΔXWP, and $\overline{DS}$ is a midsegment of ΔBGH

Prove: $\frac{XW}{BG} = \frac{XP}{BH} = \frac{PW}{HG} = \frac{MI}{DS}$

Statements	Reasons
1. $\Delta XUP \sim \Delta BGH$	1. Given
2. $\frac{XW}{BG} = \frac{XP}{BH} = \frac{PW}{HG}$	2. Definition of similar triangles
3. $\overline{MI}$ is a midsegment of ΔXWP, and $\overline{DS}$ is a midsegment of ΔBGH	3. Given
4. 2(MI) = XP and 2(DS) = BH	4. Midsegment of a Triangle Theorem
5. $\frac{XW}{BG} = \frac{2(MI)}{2(DS)}$	5. Substitution Property of Equality
6. $\frac{XW}{BG} = \frac{MI}{DS}$	6. Substitution Property of Equality
7. $\frac{XW}{BG} = \frac{XP}{BH} = \frac{PW}{HG} = \frac{MI}{DS}$	7. Transitive Property of Equality

Chapter 7, Part IV (pages 347-350)

1. $\frac{20}{3}$
3. 4 or 12
5. x = 20, y = 14.4
7. 7
9. 7.6
11. 6
13. none
15. $\overline{JS} \parallel \overline{NO}$
17. $\overline{XY} \parallel \overline{MU}$
19. 22.4
21. 6

23. 12
25. 6
27. Given: $\frac{WX}{XY} = \frac{VZ}{ZY}$

Prove: $\overline{WV} \parallel \overline{XZ}$

We are given that $\frac{WX}{XY} = \frac{VZ}{ZY}$, and so we can use the Addition Property of Equality to say that $\frac{WX}{XY} + 1 = \frac{VZ}{ZY} + 1$. Since $\frac{WX+XY}{XY} = \frac{WX}{XY} + \frac{XY}{XY} = \frac{WX}{XY} + 1$, and since $\frac{VZ+ZY}{ZY} = \frac{VZ}{ZY} + \frac{ZY}{ZY} = \frac{VZ}{ZY} + 1$, we can use the Substitution Property of Equality to say that $\frac{WX+XY}{XY} = \frac{VZ+ZY}{ZY}$.

The Segment Addition Postulate tells us that WY = WX + XY and that VY = VZ + ZY, and so we can use the Substitution Property of Equality again to say that $\frac{WY}{XY} = \frac{VY}{ZY}$.

The Reflexive Property of Angle Congruence tells us that $\angle Y \cong \angle Y$, and so we can use the SAS Similarity Theorem to say that $\Delta WYV \sim \Delta XYZ$. Then, by the definition of similar triangles, $\angle YXZ \cong \angle W$. By the Corresponding Angles Converse Postulate, $\overline{WV} \parallel \overline{XZ}$.

Chapter 7, Part V (pages 351-356)

1. 2 or $-\frac{7}{5}$
3. 300 miles
5. 7 hours
7. 60 inches (or, equivalently, 5 feet)

9a. yes

b. $\Delta CEU \sim \Delta NSU$ by the SAS Similarity Theorem

11. x = 19, y = 16, and m$\angle$OPR = 76°
13. (C) and (E)

Chapter 7, Part V (pages 351-356) continued

15. $w = 76$, $x = 28$, and $y = 104$

17. $x = 47$, $y = 28$, $m\angle LGW = 94°$, and $m\angle TGW = 133°$

19. $x = 4$, $CU = 5$, $BC = 18$, and $BN = 36$

21. This is only one of several possible proofs.

We are given that quadrilateral JKLM is a trapezoid. Then, by the definition of a trapezoid, $\overline{KL} \parallel \overline{JM}$. By the Alternate Interior Angles Theorem, $\angle LKZ \cong \angle JMZ$ and $\angle ZJM \cong \angle ZLK$. So, we can use the AA Similarity Theorem to say that $\Delta KLZ \sim \Delta MJZ$. Then, by the definition of similar triangles, $\frac{KZ}{MZ} = \frac{LZ}{JZ}$.

23. (D) and (J)

25. $\frac{3}{4}$

27. 20

29. $16 < x < 48$ and $9 < y < 40$

31. The statement is false. If $x = 0$, then $(x + 3)^2$ does equal $x^2 + 9$.

Chapter 8, Part I (pages 361-365)

1. 8

3. $3\sqrt{5}$

5. $5\sqrt{6}$

7. $\Delta GKA \sim \Delta \underline{AKE} \sim \Delta \underline{GAE}$, and so $\frac{GA}{GE} = \frac{GK}{\underline{GA}}$.

9. $\Delta MBZ \sim \Delta \underline{MIB} \sim \Delta \underline{BIZ}$, and so $\frac{BM}{\underline{IB}} = \frac{BZ}{\underline{IZ}}$.

11. $\Delta LYW \sim \Delta \underline{OYL} \sim \Delta \underline{OLW}$, and so $\frac{YL}{LO} = \frac{\underline{LW}}{OW}$.

13. $x = 8$ and $y = \frac{225}{17}$

Chapter 8, Part I (pages 361-365) continued

15. $x = 4\sqrt{5}$ and $y = 8$

17. $x = 2\sqrt{5}$ and $y = 9$

19. $x = 2$ and $y = \sqrt{117}$

21. $x = 12$ and $y = 9$

23. $x = 5$ and $y = 18\sqrt{2}$

25. $x = 20$ and $y = 40$

27. $x = \frac{2\sqrt{10}}{3}$ and $y = 2$

29. $x = 3$ and $y = 6\sqrt{3}$

(Note that, if $x = 6$, then $UE = QE = 6$. Since UE must be *greater* than QE, $x \neq 6$.)

31. Given: ΔMPO is a right triangle with $\angle MPO$ as its right angle and $\overline{PN}$ is an altitude of ΔMPO

Prove: $\frac{MO}{MP} = \frac{MP}{MN}$ and $\frac{MO}{PO} = \frac{PO}{NO}$

Statements	Reasons
1. ΔMPO is a right triangle with $\angle MPO$ as its right angle; $\overline{PN}$ is an altitude of ΔMPO	1. Given
2. $\overline{MO} \perp \overline{PN}$	2. Definition of an altitude of a triangle
3. $\angle MNP$ and $\angle ONP$ are right angles	3. If two lines are perpendicular, then they intersect to form four right angles.
4. $\angle MNP \cong \angle MPO$ and $\angle ONP \cong \angle MPO$	4. If two angles are right angles, then they are congruent.
5. $\angle M \cong \angle M$ and $\angle O \cong \angle O$	5. Reflexive Property of Angle Congruence
6. $\Delta MNP \sim \Delta MPO$ and $\Delta PNO \sim \Delta MPO$	6. AA Similarity Theorem
7. $\frac{MO}{MP} = \frac{MP}{MN}$ and $\frac{MO}{PO} = \frac{PO}{NO}$	7. Definition of similar triangles

Chapter 8, Part II (pages 369-374)

1. $b = 4\sqrt{3}$ and $c = 8$
3. $k = 16$ and $w = 8$
5. $q = 9$ and $v = 9$
7. $c = 9\sqrt{2}$ and $d = 9\sqrt{2}$
9. $p = 16\sqrt{3}$ and $r = 8\sqrt{3}$
11. $b = \frac{7\sqrt{15}}{3}$ and $k = \frac{14\sqrt{15}}{3}$
13. $x = 5\sqrt{5}$ and $y = 5\sqrt{5}$
15. $a = 4$ and $b = 4\sqrt{3} + 4$
17. $b = 9\sqrt{3}$ and $w = 18\sqrt{3}$
19. $5\sqrt{2}$ inches
21. 36 meters
23. $12\sqrt{3}$ ft^2
25. $243\sqrt{3}$ in.^{2}
27. $\sqrt{3}$ cm^2
29. $6\sqrt{2}$ feet
31. $m\sqrt{2}$
33. 54 meters

Chapter 8, Part III (pages 381-383)

1. $\sin A = \frac{4}{5}$, $\cos A = \frac{3}{5}$, $\tan A = \frac{4}{3}$,
   $\sin B = \frac{3}{5}$, $\cos B = \frac{4}{5}$, $\tan B = \frac{3}{4}$
3. $\sin G = \frac{\sqrt{2}}{2}$, $\cos G = \frac{\sqrt{2}}{2}$, $\tan G = 1$,
   $\sin H = \frac{\sqrt{2}}{2}$, $\cos H = \frac{\sqrt{2}}{2}$, $\tan H = 1$
5. $\sin N = \frac{\sqrt{3}}{3}$, $\cos N = \frac{\sqrt{6}}{3}$, $\tan N = \frac{\sqrt{2}}{2}$,
   $\sin O = \frac{\sqrt{6}}{3}$, $\cos O = \frac{\sqrt{3}}{3}$, $\tan O = \sqrt{2}$
7. $\sin U = \frac{1}{2}$, $\cos U = \frac{\sqrt{3}}{2}$, $\tan U = \frac{\sqrt{3}}{3}$,
   $\sin T = \frac{\sqrt{3}}{2}$, $\cos T = \frac{1}{2}$, $\tan T = \sqrt{3}$

Chapter 8, Part III (pages 381-383) continued

9. $w \approx 15.13$, $x = 19$, and $y \approx 5.21$
11. $w = 52$, $x \approx 8.96$, and $y \approx 11.37$
13. $w \approx 23.91$, $x \approx 7.31$, and $y = 17$
15. $w \approx 9.60$, $x = 32$, and $y \approx 11.32$
17. $w \approx 43.95$, $x \approx 25.21$, and $y = 35$
19. $w = 72$, $x \approx 15.39$, and $y \approx 16.18$
21. $w = 50$, $x \approx 36.55$, and $y \approx 23.49$

Chapter 8, Part IV (pages 387-393)

1. $w \approx 48.59$, $x \approx 41.41$, and $y \approx 5.29$
3. $w \approx 5.81$, $x \approx 9.89$, and $y = 36$
5. $w \approx 66.19$, $x \approx 23.81$, and $y \approx 3.72$
7. $w \approx 46.23$, $x \approx 51.15$, and $y \approx 38.85$
9. $w = 60$, $x = 30$, and $y \approx 38.11$
11. $w \approx 8.09$, $x = 18$, and $y \approx 7.69$
13. $w \approx 4.96$, $x \approx 42.19$, and $y \approx 47.81$
15. $w \approx 2.33$, $x \approx 3.09$, and $y = 37$
17. $w \approx 51.34$, $x = 4$, and $y \approx 38.66$
19. $w = 45$, $x = 45$, and $y \approx 7.07$
21. $w \approx 43.60$, $x \approx 46.40$, and $y = 29$
23. approximately 16.08 meters
25. approximately 1.96°
27a. approximately 4.59°
  b. approximately 99.39 feet
29. approximately 16.04°
31. approximately 91.89 feet
33. approximately 80.94 meters
35. approximately 53.47°

Chapter 8, Part V (pages 394-400)

1. $a = 30$, $b = 4\sqrt{2}$, and $c = 8\sqrt{2}$
3. $w = 5\sqrt{5}$, $x = 4\sqrt{5}$, and $y = 2\sqrt{5}$
5. $m\angle B = 40°$, $BC \approx 9.75$, and $AC \approx 8.18$
7. approximately 72.69 feet

9. approximately 0.95 second
11. approximately 35.43 yards
13. The measure of one interior angle of a regular decagon is <u>144º</u>, and the measure of one exterior angle of a regular decagon is <u>36º</u>.

15. This is just one of several possible proofs of this statement.

Statements	Reasons
1. $\overline{SG} \cong \overline{SW}$ and $\overline{SE} \perp \overline{GW}$	1. Given
2. $\angle SEG$ and $\angle SEW$ are right angles	2. If two lines are perpendicular, then they intersect to form four right angles.
3. $\angle SEG \cong \angle SEW$	3. If two angles are right angles, then they are congruent.
4. $\overline{SE} \cong \overline{SE}$	4. Reflexive Property of Segment Congruence
5. $\triangle SEG \cong \triangle SEW$	5. HL Congruence Postulate
6. $\overline{GE} \cong \overline{WE}$	6. CPCTC

17. 30º
19. x = 27 and y = 18
21. DC > DB by the theorem *A triangle cannot have more than one right or obtuse angle, and it cannot have both a right angle and an obtuse angle* and the Opposite Sides of a Triangle Theorem
23. isosceles and acute

25a. yes

b. $\triangle DCQ \sim \triangle NCM$ by the Vertical Angles Theorem and the SAS Similarity Theorem

27. x = 4 and BH = 58
29. This means that the distances in the picture are not representative of the distances in real life. (For example, in real life, the sun is about 395 times farther away from the earth than the moon, but the picture is drawn as if it is only about 3 times as far away.)

Chapter 9, Part I (pages 403-405)

1. $\overline{EC}$, $\overline{EG}$, and $\overline{EF}$
3. $\overline{CF}$ and $\overline{FM}$
5. There are no rays tangent to ⊙E drawn.
7. $\overline{HL}$ and $\overline{IJ}$
9. $\overline{EJ}$
11. no; N/A
13. 11
15. A
17. true
19. false
21. true
23. $\overline{UT}$, $\overline{QT}$, and $\overline{TV}$
25. OM = 5 and NO = 10
27. MN = 14, NQ = 9, and PQ = 46
29. yes; point Q

Chapter 9, Part II (pages 410-416)

1. 41º
3. 52º
5. $m\overset{\frown}{EF} = 41°$; this is a minor arc
7. $m\overset{\frown}{CFD} = 308°$; this is a major arc
9. $m\overset{\frown}{EFB} = 180°$; this is a semicircle
11. $m\overset{\frown}{KL} = 28°$; this is a minor arc
13. $m\overset{\frown}{OM} = 56°$; this is a minor arc

15. $m\overset{\frown}{LOK} = 332°$; this is a major arc

17. TV = 15, UT = 15, and UV = 30

19. $m\angle HLQ = 55°$, $m\angle OMH = 55°$, and $m\overset{\frown}{MO} = 70°$

21a. yes

b. definition of congruent circles and definition of congruent arcs

23a. no

b. N/A

25a. no

b. N/A

27a. yes

b. If a radius of a circle is perpendicular to a chord of the circle, then it bisects the chord and its arc; definition of a segment bisector; the Midpoint Theorem

29.

Statements	Reasons
1. In $\odot C$, $\overset{\frown}{AB} \cong \overset{\frown}{DE}$	1. Given
2. $m\overset{\frown}{AB} = m\overset{\frown}{DE}$	2. Definition of congruent arcs
3. Draw $\overline{AC}$, $\overline{BC}$, $\overline{DC}$, and $\overline{EC}$	3. Through any two points there is exactly one line.
4. $\overline{AC} \cong \overline{BC} \cong \overline{DC} \cong \overline{EC}$	4. Definition of a circle
5. $m\overset{\frown}{AB} = m\angle ACB$ and $m\overset{\frown}{DE} = m\angle DCE$	5. Definition of the measure of an arc
6. $m\angle ACB = m\angle DCE$	6. Substitution Property of Equality
7. $\angle ACB \cong \angle DCE$	7. Definition of congruent angles
8. $\Delta ACB \cong \Delta DCE$	8. SAS Congruence Postulate
9. $\overline{AB} \cong \overline{DE}$	9. CPCTC

Chapter 9, Part II (pages 410-416) continued

31.

Statements	Reasons
1. In $\odot U$, $\overline{RS} \cong \overline{WX}$	1. Given
2. RS = WX	2. Definition of congruent segments
3. $\overline{UT}$ bisects $\overline{RS}$, and $\overline{UV}$ bisects $\overline{WX}$	3. If a radius of a circle is perpendicular to a chord of the circle, then it bisects the chord and its arc.
4. T is the midpoint of $\overline{RS}$, and V is the midpoint of $\overline{WX}$.	4. Definition of a segment bisector
5. RT = TS and WV = VX	5. Definition of midpoint
6. RT + TS = RS and WV + VX = WX	6. Segment Addition Postulate
7. TS + TS = RS and VX + VX = WX	7. Substitution Property of Equality
8. 2(TS) = RS and 2(VX) = WX	8. Distributive Property
9. 2(TS) = 2(VX)	9. Substitution Property of Equality
10. TS = VX	10. Division Property of Equality
11. $\overline{TS} \cong \overline{VX}$	11. Definition of congruent segments
12. Draw $\overline{US}$ and $\overline{UX}$.	12. Through any two points there is exactly one line.
13. $\overline{US} \cong \overline{UX}$	13. Definition of a circle
14. $\overline{RS} \perp \overline{TU}$ and $\overline{WX} \perp \overline{UV}$	14. Given
15. $\angle UTS$ and $\angle UVX$ are right angles	15. If two lines are perpendicular, then they intersect to form four right angles.
16. $\Delta TUS \cong \Delta VUX$	16. HL Congruence Postulate
17. $\overline{UT} \cong \overline{UV}$	17. CPCTC

Chapter 9, Part III (pages 421-427)

1. $m\widehat{AD} = 116°$ and $m\widehat{DC} = 64°$
3. $m\angle AED = 116°$ and $m\angle CED = 64°$
5. $m\angle ABC = 90°$ and $m\angle CAB = 58°$
7. $m\widehat{ADC} = 180°$ and $m\widehat{ACD} = 244°$
9. $m\widehat{ST} = 95°$ and $m\widehat{QT} = 141°$
11. $m\angle QRS = 118°$ and $m\angle QTS = 62°$
13. $m\widehat{TQS} = 265°$ and $m\widehat{QTS} = 236°$
15. 9
17. $m\angle MLO = 74°$ and $m\angle ONM = 106°$
19. $m\widehat{MLO} = 212°$, $m\widehat{LO} = 102°$, and $m\widehat{ML} = 110°$

21.

Statements	Reasons
1. In $\odot F$, $\angle HJG$ and $\angle GIH$ intercept the same arc	1. Given
2. $m\angle HJG = \frac{1}{2}m\widehat{HG}$ and $m\angle GIH = \frac{1}{2}m\widehat{HG}$	2. Measure of an Inscribed Angle Theorem
3. $m\angle HJG = m\angle GIH$	3. Substitution Property of Equality
4. $\angle HJG \cong \angle GIH$	4. Definition of congruent angles

23.

Statements	Reasons
1. $\angle RST$ is inscribed in the semicircle $\widehat{RVT}$	1. Given
2. $m\angle RST = \frac{1}{2}m\widehat{RVT}$	2. Measure of an Inscribed Angle Theorem
3. $m\widehat{RVT} = 180°$	3. Definition of a semicircle
4. $m\angle RST = \frac{1}{2}(180°)$	4. Substitution Property of Equality
5. $m\angle RST = 90°$	5. Substitution Property of Equality
6. $\angle RST$ is a right angle	6. Definition of a right angle

Chapter 9, Part III (pages 421-427) continued

25. $\widehat{QN}$ <u>must be</u> congruent to $\widehat{SY}$, and $\widehat{QS}$ <u>must be</u> congruent to $\widehat{NY}$
27. might be
29. must be

Chapter 9, Part IV (pages 433-439)

1. 218°
3. 24.5°
5. 46.5°
7. 94°
9. 29°
11. 65°
13. 47°
15. 34°
17. 93°
19. 121°
21. 152°
23. 75°
25. 66.5°
27. 113.5°
29. 135°
31. 90°
33. 10
35. 68°
37. $x = 30$ and $y = -12$
39. no

41.

Given: $\overrightarrow{ZA}$ and $\overrightarrow{ZN}$ are two secants of $\odot F$ that intersect outside $\odot F$

Prove: $m\angle Z = \frac{1}{2}(m\overset{\frown}{AN} - m\overset{\frown}{HV})$

We are given that $\overrightarrow{ZA}$ and $\overrightarrow{ZN}$ are two secants of $\odot F$ that intersect outside $\odot F$. We can use the postulate Through any two points there is exactly one line to draw $\overline{VA}$, as shown at the right.

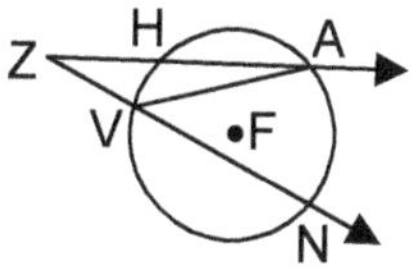

We can use the Exterior Angle of a Triangle Theorem, the Subtraction Property of Equality, and the Symmetric Property of Equality to say that $m\angle Z = m\angle AVN - m\angle ZAV$. The Measure of an Inscribed Angle Theorem tells us that $m\angle AVN = \frac{1}{2}m\overset{\frown}{AN}$ and $m\angle ZAV = \frac{1}{2}m\overset{\frown}{HV}$. Then, by the Substitution Property of Equality, $m\angle Z = \frac{1}{2}m\overset{\frown}{AN} - \frac{1}{2}m\overset{\frown}{HV}$. By the Distributive Property, $m\angle Z = \frac{1}{2}(m\overset{\frown}{AN} - m\overset{\frown}{HV})$.

43. This is only one of several possible proofs of this theorem.

We are given that $\overrightarrow{QX}$ is tangent to $\odot L$ at X and that $\overrightarrow{QI}$ is a secant of $\odot L$. We can use the postulate *Through any two points there is exactly one line* to draw $\overline{XI}$. Then, by the Exterior Angle of a Triangle Theorem, $m\angle MXI = m\angle Q + m\angle QIX$. The Subtraction Property of Equality and the Symmetric Property of Equality tell us that this means that $m\angle Q = m\angle MXI - m\angle QIX$. By the Measure of an Inscribed Angle Theorem, $m\angle QIX = \frac{1}{2}m\overset{\frown}{XR}$. By the theorem *If an angle is formed by a chord that intersects a line tangent to a circle at the point of tangency, then the measure of each angle formed is equal to half the measure of the corresponding arc*, $m\angle MXI = \frac{1}{2}m\overset{\frown}{IBX}$. By the Substitution Property of Equality, $m\angle Q = \frac{1}{2}m\overset{\frown}{IBX} - \frac{1}{2}m\overset{\frown}{XR}$. Then, by the Distributive Property, $m\angle Q = \frac{1}{2}(m\overset{\frown}{IBX} - m\overset{\frown}{XR})$.

Chapter 9, Part V (pages 443-448)

1. JM = 20 and QJ = 13
3. LM = 12 and LG = 15
5. QJ = 13 and QS = 4
7. 5 and –5
9. 12
11. FH = 28.4 cm and AF = 11.6 cm
13. x = 20 and AC = 27
15. q = 1.5 and AB = 8
17. 16 and 25
19. JL = 10 and JM = 20
21. u = 2 and OK = 32
23. 17
25. x = 4 and y = 10
27. x = 50 and y = –5
29. Given: $\overline{AB}$ and $\overline{AC}$ are tangent to $\odot D$ at points B and C

Prove: $\overline{AB} \cong \overline{AC}$

Statements	Reasons
1. $\overline{AB}$ and $\overline{AC}$ are tangent to $\odot D$ at points B and C	1. Given
2. Draw $\overline{BD}$, $\overline{CD}$, and $\overline{DA}$.	2. Through any two points there is exactly one line.
3. $\overline{BD} \cong \overline{CD}$	3. Definition of a circle
4. $\overline{AD} \cong \overline{AD}$	4. Reflexive Property of Segment Congruence
5. $\overline{AB} \perp \overline{BD}$ and $\overline{AC} \perp \overline{CD}$	5. If a line is tangent to a circle, then it is perpendicular to the radius drawn to the point of tangency.
6. $\angle ABD$ and $\angle ACD$ are right angles	6. Definition of perpendicular lines
7. $\triangle ABD \cong \triangle ACD$	7. HL Congruence Postulate
8. $\overline{AB} \cong \overline{AC}$	8. CPCTC

Chapter 9, Part V (pages 443-448) continued

31.

Given: $\overline{AF}$ and $\overline{CF}$ are secant segments of ⊙E that intersect outside ⊙E at point F

Prove: (BF)(CF) = (DF)(AF)

Statements	Reasons
1. $\overline{AF}$ and $\overline{CF}$ are secant segments of ⊙E that intersect outside ⊙E at point F.	1. Given
2. Draw $\overline{AB}$ and $\overline{DC}$.	2. Through any two points there is exactly one line.
3. $\angle DAB \cong \angle BCD$	3. In a circle or in congruent circles, if two inscribed angles intercept the same arc or congruent arcs, then the inscribed angles are congruent to each other.
4. $\angle F \cong \angle F$	4. Reflexive Property of Angle Congruence
5. $\Delta ABF \sim \Delta CDF$	5. AA Similarity Theorem
6. $\frac{BF}{DF} = \frac{AF}{CF}$	6. Definition of similar triangles
7. (BF)(CF) = (DF)(AF)	7. Cross Products Property of Proportions

Chapter 9, Part VI (pages 449-454)

1. $m\angle A = 53.5°$ and $m\angle C = 53.5°$
3. (D), (E), (G), and (H)
5. 24
7. radius
9. $\overline{HF}$
11. yes because they both have radii that have lengths of 8 feet
13. x = 16, $m\overset{\frown}{CM} = 49°$, and $m\overset{\frown}{CRM} = 311°$
15. $m\overset{\frown}{KP} = 108°$; this is a minor arc

Chapter 9, Part VI (pages 449-454) continued

17. $m\overset{\frown}{KQ} = 62°$; this is a minor arc
19. 18°
21. 36°
23. 82°
25. 24
27. We don't have enough information to decide whether or not $\overset{\frown}{ZD} \cong \overset{\frown}{PF}$.
29. x = 9 and TG = 16
31. 9 and 1
33. $m\angle J \approx 50.8°$ and $m\angle H \approx 39.2°$
35. $m\angle URV = 32°$, $m\angle TUR = 32°$, and $m\angle TSU = 116°$
37. (A), (B), (C), (D), (E), (F)

Chapter 10, Part I (pages 457-460)

1. 7
3. 11
5. $4\sqrt{2}$
7. $\sqrt{13}$
9. 10
11. $3\sqrt{2}$
13. 5
15. $5\sqrt{2}$
17. $\sqrt{19}$
19. 6
21. isosceles triangle
23. scalene triangle
25. equilateral triangle and isosceles triangle
27. scalene triangle

Chapter 10, Part II (pages 463-466)

1. (6, −1)
3. (3, −4)

Chapter 10, Part II (pages 463-466) continued

5. $\left(\frac{1}{2}, -2\right)$

7. $\left(\frac{1}{2}, -\frac{3}{2}\right)$

9. $\left(-\frac{21}{2}, -\frac{1}{2}\right)$

11. $\left(-16, \frac{3}{2}\right)$

13. $(4, 0)$

15. $(9, -1)$

17. $\left(3, \frac{3\sqrt{7}}{2}\right)$

19. $(3\sqrt{5}, -4)$

21. $\left(-\sqrt{2}, \frac{15\sqrt{2}}{2}\right)$

23. $(2, -12)$

25. $(1, 13)$

27. $(-11, -14)$

29. $(1, -3\sqrt{3})$

Chapter 10, Part III (pages 472-481)

1. parallelogram
3. parallelogram, rhombus
5. trapezoid
7.

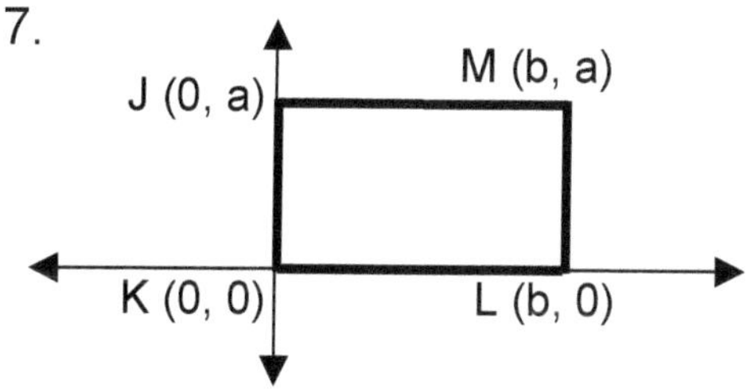

9.

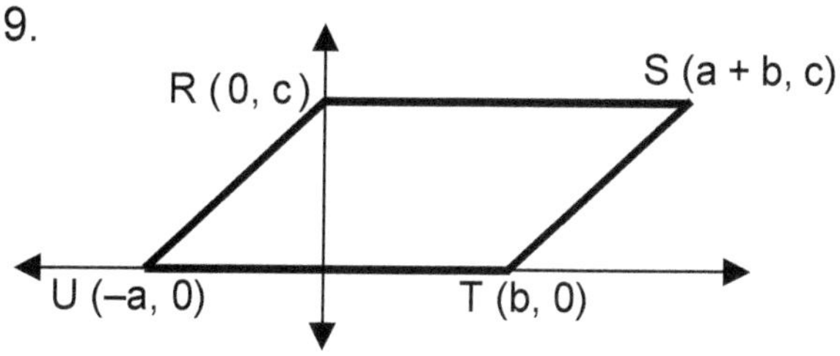

Chapter 10, Part III (pages 472-481) continued

11. Example:

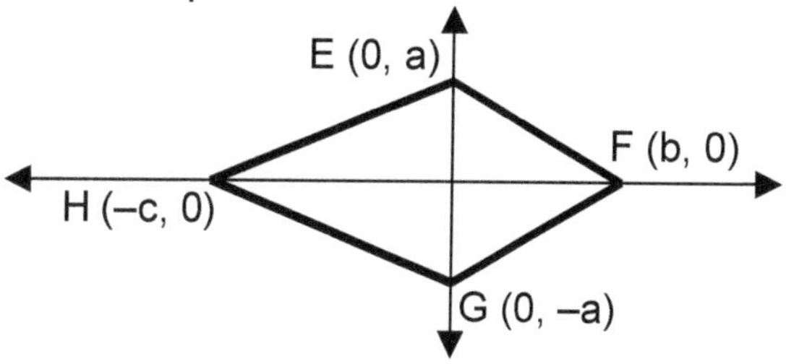

13. Example:

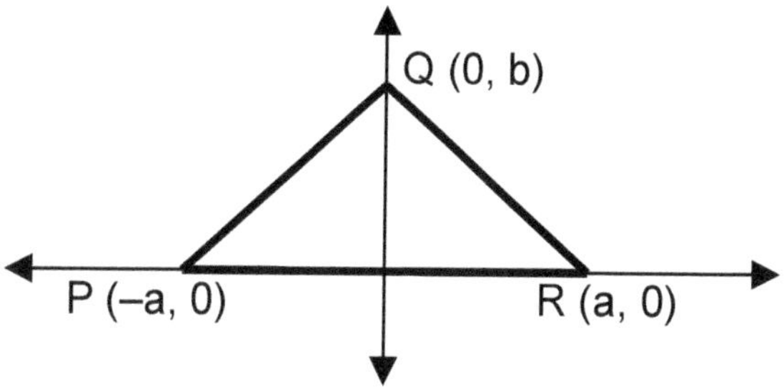

15. Example:

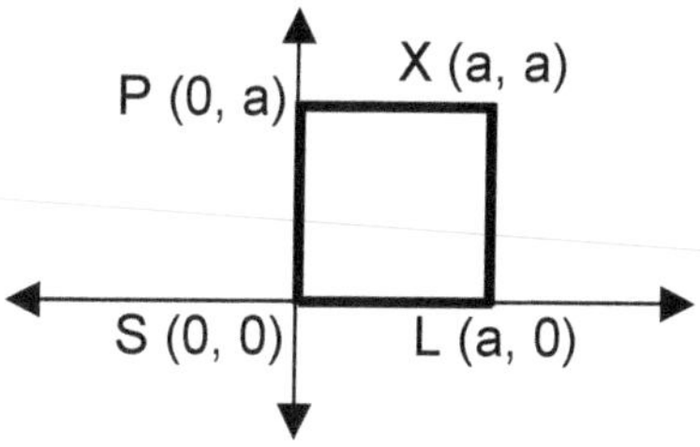

17. This is only one of several versions of the proof of this statement.

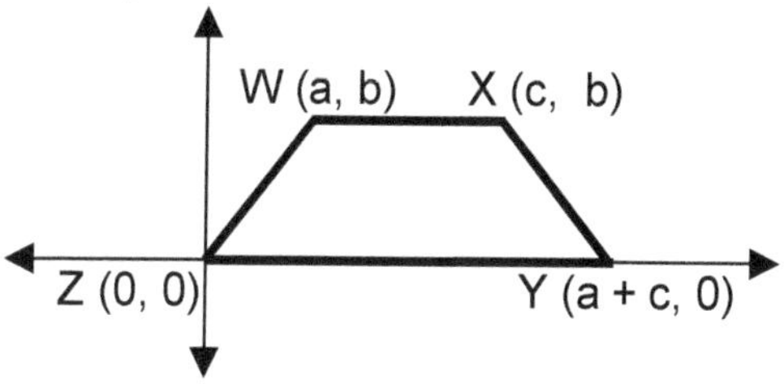

Given: Quadrilateral WXYZ is an isosceles trapezoid

Prove: $\overline{WY} \cong \overline{XZ}$

Using the distance formula, we can say the following.

$$WY = \sqrt{(a + c - a)^2 + (0 - b)^2}\text{, or }\sqrt{c^2 + b^2}$$

$$XZ = \sqrt{(0 - c)^2 + (0 - b)^2}\text{, or }\sqrt{c^2 + b^2}$$

Using the Substitution Property of Equality, this tells us that WY = XZ. By the definition of congruent segments, this means that $\overline{WY} \cong \overline{XZ}$.

19. This is only one of several versions of the proof of this statement.

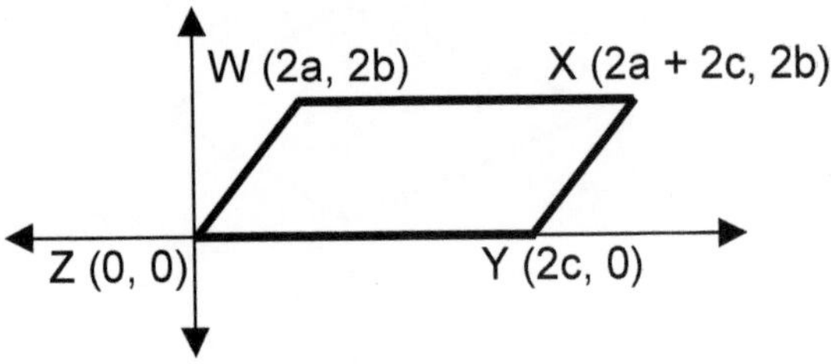

Given: Quadrilateral WXYZ is a parallelogram

Prove: $\overline{WY}$ bisects $\overline{XZ}$ and $\overline{XZ}$ bisects $\overline{WY}$

We can use the midpoint formula to say that the midpoint of $\overline{WY}$ is at the point (a + c, b). We will call this point M. Then, by the Midpoint Theorem, $\overline{WM} \cong \overline{MY}$.

We can use the midpoint formula again to say that the midpoint of $\overline{XZ}$ is also at the point M (a + c, b). Then, by the Midpoint Theorem, $\overline{ZM} \cong \overline{XM}$.

Since M is on both $\overline{WY}$ and $\overline{XZ}$, we can now use the definition of the bisector of a segment to say that $\overline{WY}$ bisects $\overline{XZ}$ and $\overline{XZ}$ bisects $\overline{WY}$.

21. This is only one of several versions of the proof of this statement.

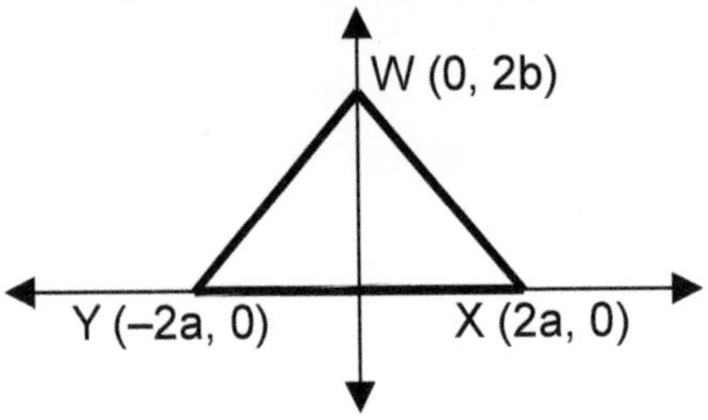

Given: ΔWXY is an isosceles triangle

Prove: The medians to the legs of ΔWXY are congruent

We will begin by noting that we can use the midpoint formula to say that the midpoint of $\overline{WY}$ is at (–a, b). We will call this point P. We can also use the midpoint formula to say that the midpoint of $\overline{WX}$ is at (a, b). We will call this point Q. Since there is one, and only one, line between any two given points, we can draw $\overline{XP}$ and $\overline{YQ}$. This gives us the following picture.

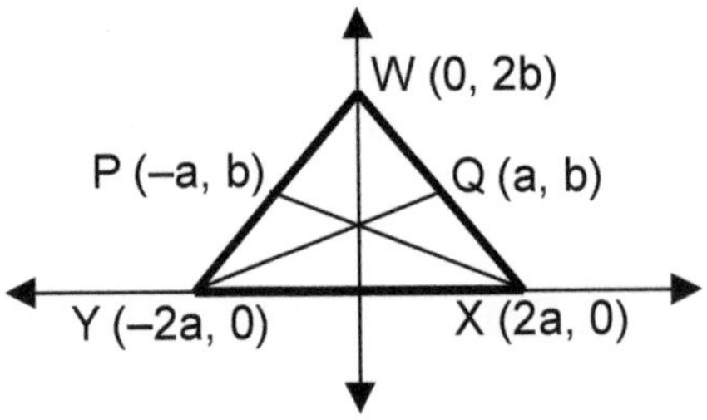

Using the definition of a median of a triangle, we can say that $\overline{XP}$ and $\overline{YQ}$ are the medians to the legs of ΔWXY, and this means that we need to prove that $\overline{XP} \cong \overline{YQ}$.

Now, we can use the distance formula to say the following.

$$XP = \sqrt{(-a-2a)^2 + (b-0)^2} = \sqrt{9a^2 + b^2}$$

$$YQ = \sqrt{(a-(-2a))^2 + (b-0)^2} = \sqrt{9a^2 + b^2}$$

We can now us the Substitution Property of Equality to say that XP = YQ. Therefore, by the definition of congruent segments, $\overline{XP}$ must be congruent to $\overline{YQ}$.

23. This proof is only one of several versions of the proof of this statement.

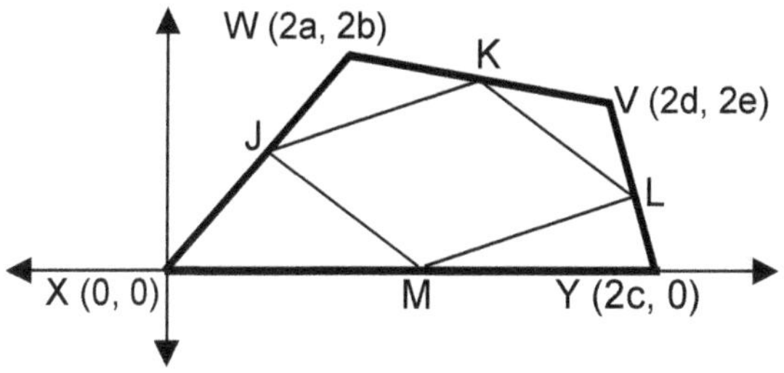

Given: J, K, L, and M are the midpoints of the sides of quadrilateral VWXY

Prove: Quadrilateral JKLM is a parallelogram

We will begin by noting that we can use the midpoint formula to label the coordinates of J, K, L, and M as shown below.

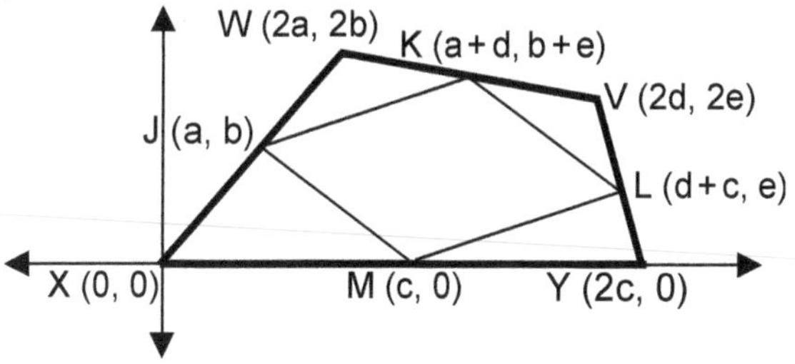

Now, we will prove that quadrilateral JKLM is a parallelogram by showing that the slopes of the opposite sides are equal.

$$\text{slope of } \overline{JK} = \frac{b+e-b}{a+d-a} = \frac{e}{d}$$

$$\text{slope of } \overline{ML} = \frac{e-0}{d+c-c} = \frac{e}{d}$$

$$\text{slope of } \overline{LK} = \frac{b+e-e}{a+d-(d+c)} = \frac{b}{a-c}$$

$$\text{slope of } \overline{MJ} = \frac{b-0}{a-c} = \frac{b}{a-c}$$

Now, we can use the Substitution Property of Equality to say that the slopes of $\overline{JK}$ and $\overline{ML}$ are equal, and so $\overline{JK} \parallel \overline{ML}$. Similarly, we can use the Substitution Property of Equality to say that the slopes of $\overline{LK}$ and $\overline{MJ}$ are equal, and so $\overline{LK} \parallel \overline{MJ}$.

We can now use the definition of a parallelogram to say that quadrilateral JKLM is a parallelogram.

25. This proof is only one of several versions of the proof of this statement.

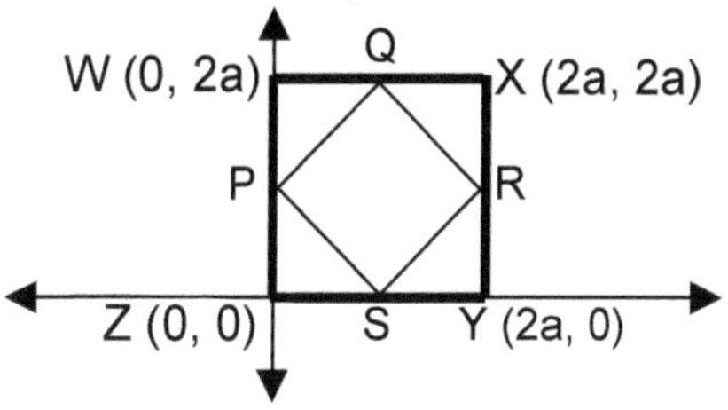

Given: P, Q, R, and S are the midpoints of the sides of square WXYZ

Prove: Quadrilateral PQRS is a square

We will begin by noting that we can use the midpoint formula to label the coordinates of P, Q, R, and S as shown below.

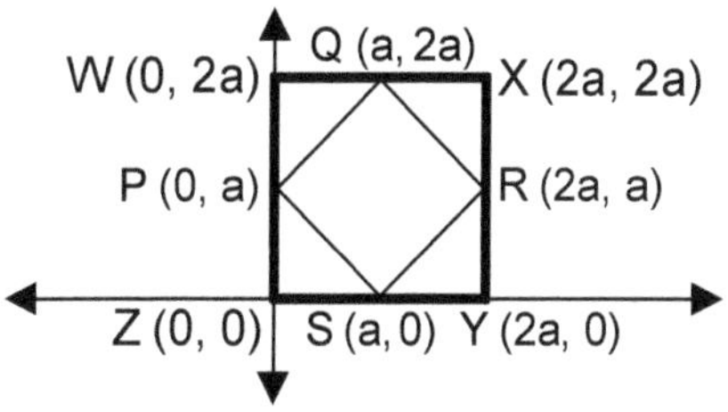

Next, we will use the distance formula to show that all the sides of quadrilateral PQRS are congruent to each other.

$$PQ = \sqrt{(a-0)^2 + (2a-a)^2} = \sqrt{2a^2}\text{, or } a\sqrt{2}$$

$$QR = \sqrt{(2a-a)^2 + (a-2a)^2} = \sqrt{2a^2}\text{, or } a\sqrt{2}$$

$$RS = \sqrt{(a-2a)^2 + (0-a)^2} = \sqrt{2a^2}\text{, or } a\sqrt{2}$$

$$SP = \sqrt{(0-a)^2 + (a-0)^2} = \sqrt{2a^2}\text{, or } a\sqrt{2}$$

We can now say use the Substitution Property of Equality and the definition of congruent segments to say that $\overline{PQ} \cong \overline{QR} \cong \overline{RS} \cong \overline{SP}$. Then, by the definition of a rhombus, quadrilateral PQRS must be a rhombus. This means that it must also be a parallelogram.

Now, we will use the distance formula to show that the diagonals of quadrilateral PQRS are congruent.

$$PR = \sqrt{(2a-0)^2 + (a-a)^2} = 2a$$

$$QS = \sqrt{(a-a)^2 + (0-2a)^2} = 2a$$

We can now say that $\overline{PR} \cong \overline{QS}$. Since we said earlier that quadrilateral PQRS is a parallelogram, we can say that the fact that the diagonals are congruent tells us that it is also a rectangle.

We can now use the definition of a square to say that quadrilateral PQRS must be a square.

27. This proof is only one of several versions of the proof of this statement.

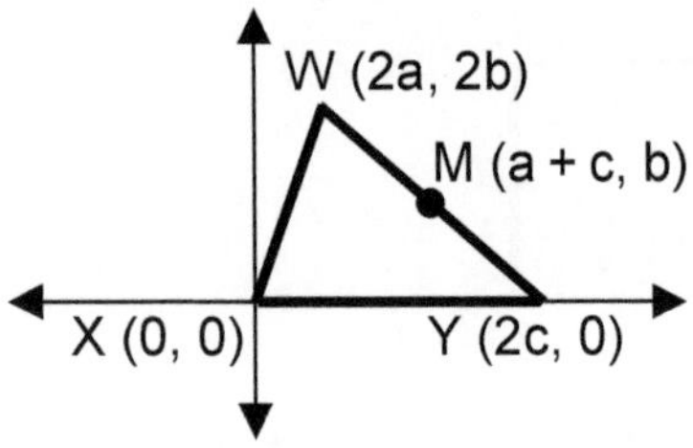

Given: WM = XM = YM

Prove: ΔWXY is a right triangle

We will begin by noting that we can use the midpoint formula to say that the coordinates of M are (a + c, b).

Now, we will use the distance formula to note the following.

$$XM = \sqrt{(a+c-0)^2+(b-0)^2}$$
$$= \sqrt{(a+c)^2+b^2}$$
$$YM = \sqrt{(a+c-2c)^2+(b-0)^2}$$
$$= \sqrt{(a-c)^2+b^2}$$

Now, since we were given that XM = YM, we can use the Substitution Property of Equality to say that $\sqrt{(a+c)^2+b^2} = \sqrt{(a-c)^2+b^2}$. This allows us to say the following.

$$(a+c)^2+b^2 = (a-c)^2+b^2$$
(by squaring both sides)
$$(a+c)^2 = (a-c)^2$$
(by subtracting b^2 from both sides)
$$a+c = \pm(a-c)$$
(by taking the square root of both sides)
$$a+c = a-c \quad \text{or} \quad a+c = -a+c$$
$$c = 0 \quad \text{or} \quad a = 0$$

If c = 0, then ΔWXY is not actually a triangle. Thus, a must equal zero. This means that $\overline{WX}$ must lie on the y-axis. Since $\overline{WX}$ lies on the x-axis, and since the x-axis is perpendicular to the y-axis, we can say that $\overline{WX} \perp \overline{XY}$. This means that $\angle WXY$ must be a right angle, and so, by the definition of a right triangle, ΔWXY must be a right triangle.

29. This proof is only one of several versions of the proof of this statement.

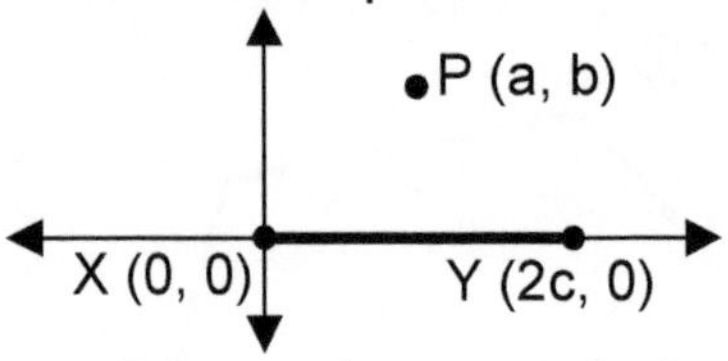

Given: P lies on the perpendicular bisector of $\overline{XY}$

Prove: PX = PY

We will begin by noting that the midpoint of $\overline{XY}$ is at the point (c, 0).

Now, since $\overline{XY}$ lies on the x-axis, the perpendicular bisector of $\overline{XY}$ should be a vertical line, and so we can rewrite the coordinates of point P as (c, b). To show that PX = PY, we will use the distance formula.

$$PX = \sqrt{(0-c)^2+(0-b)^2} = \sqrt{c^2+b^2}$$
$$PY = \sqrt{(2c-c)^2+(0-b)^2} = \sqrt{c^2+b^2}$$

We can now use the Substitution Property of Equality to say that PX = PY.

Chapter 10, Part IV (pages 482-486)

1. (B), (C), (D), (F)
3. 15
5. (A), (D), (E)
7. $2\sqrt{2}$
9. 4 pounds
11.

Statements	Reasons
1. P is the midpoint of both $\overline{BA}$ and $\overline{NK}$	1. Given
2. $\overline{BP} \cong \overline{PA}$ and $\overline{NP} \cong \overline{KP}$	2. Midpoint Theorem
3. $\angle BPN \cong \angle APK$	3. Vertical Angles Theorem
4. $\Delta PBN \cong \Delta PAK$	4. SAS Congruence Postulate
5. $\angle B \cong \angle A$	5. CPCTC
6. $\overline{BN} \parallel \overline{KA}$	6. Alternate Interior Angles Converse Theorem

Chapter 10, Part IV
(pages 482-486) continued

13. obtuse triangle
15. kite
17. (19, –16)
19. 9
21. 118°
23. 107°
25. k ≈ 17.8, m ≈ 21.5, and m∠L = 34°
27. IA = 7 and QW = 4
29. The measure of one interior angle of a regular pentagon is 108°, and the measure of one exterior angle of a regular pentagon is 72°.

Chapter 11, Part I
(pages 490-494)

1. dilation; no, it is not an isometry
3. rotation; yes, it is an isometry
5. translation; yes, it is an isometry
7. rotation; yes, it is an isometry
9. reflection; yes, it is an isometry
11. reflection; yes, it is an isometry
13. translation; yes, it is an isometry
15. reflection; yes, it is an isometry

Chapter 11, Part I
(pages 490-494) continued

17. rotation; yes, it is an isometry
19. dilation; no, it is not an isometry
21. rotation, translation, reflection
23. reflection, translation
25. rotation
27. ΔLMN → ΔTSR; this is a reflection
29. rotation

Chapter 11, Part II
(pages 502-509)

1.
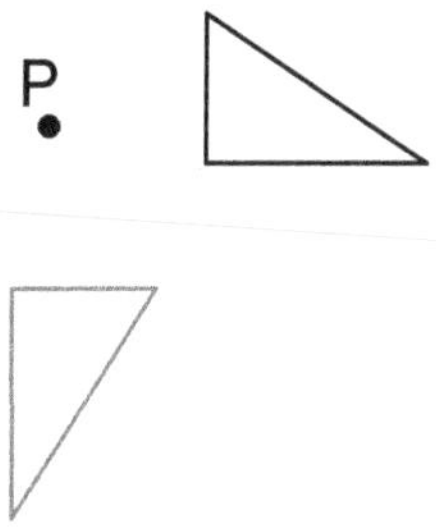

3.
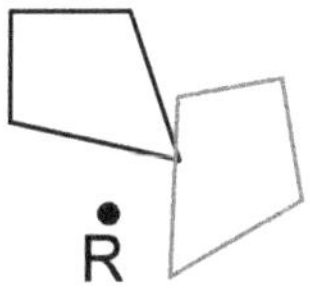

5.
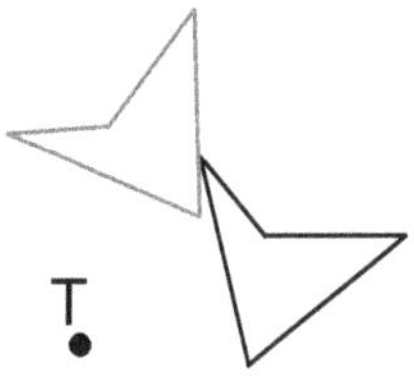

7.
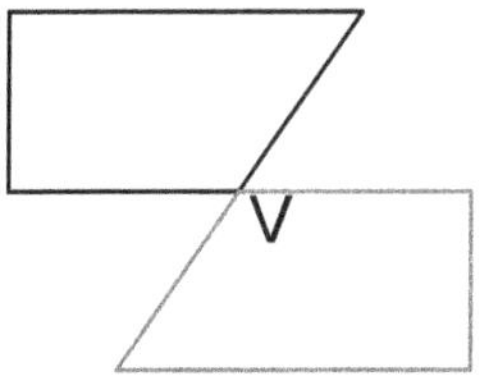

Chapter 11, Part II
(pages 502-509) continued

9.
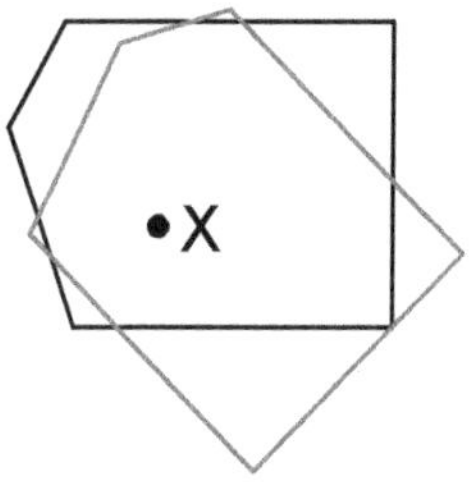

11.
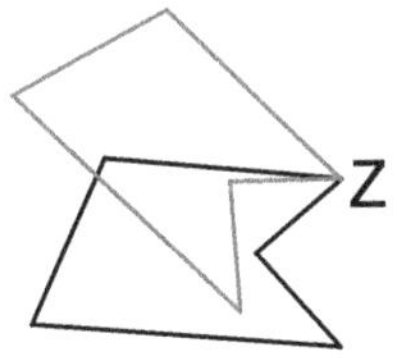

13.
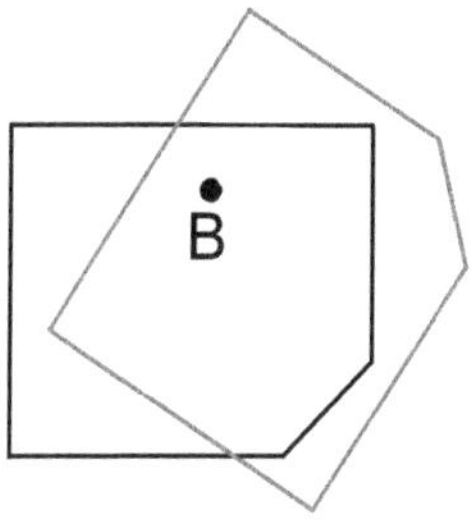

15.
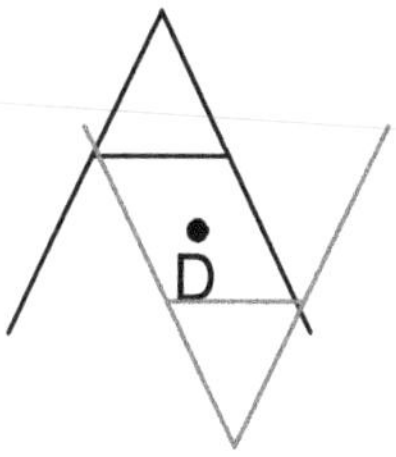

17. M
19. I
21. $\overline{GF}$
23. $\overline{KF}$
25. ΔFLG
27. ΔJNI
29.
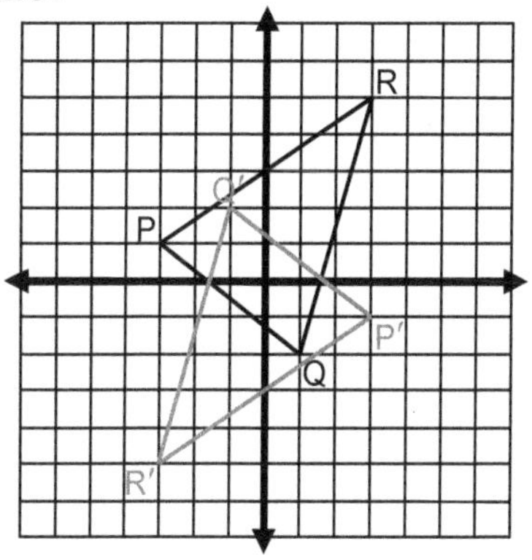

Chapter 11, Part II (pages 502-509) continued

31.

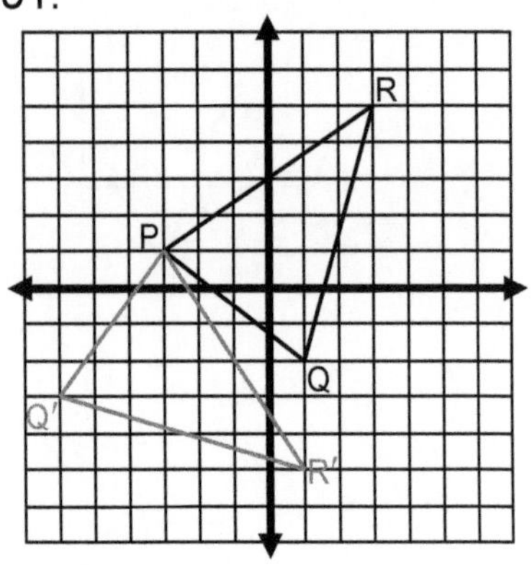

33.

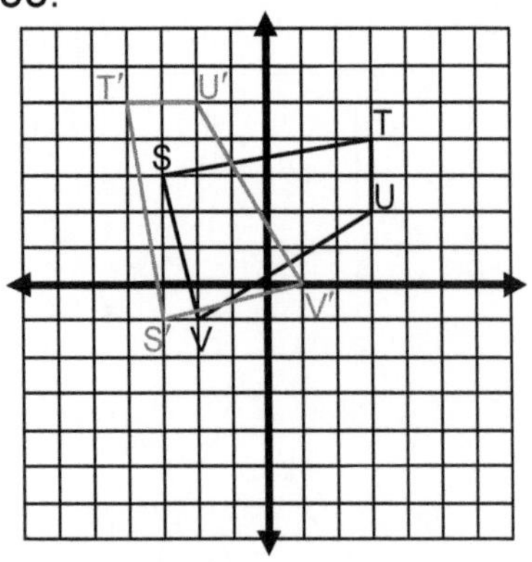

35. yes; 90° clockwise, 90° counterclockwise, 180° clockwise, 180° counterclockwise
37. no; N/A
39. yes; 120° clockwise, 120° counterclockwise
41. no; N/A
43. yes; 180° clockwise, 180° counterclockwise
45. yes; 180° clockwise, 180° counterclockwise

Chapter 11, Part III (pages 517-521)

1.

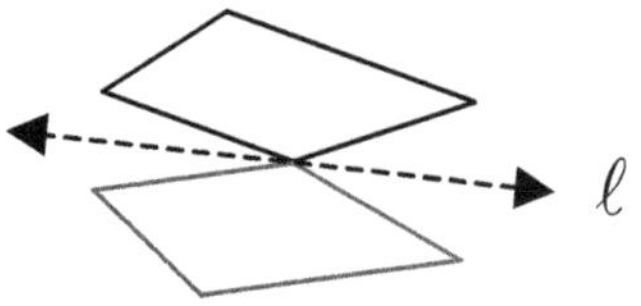

Chapter 11, Part III (pages 517-521) continued

3.

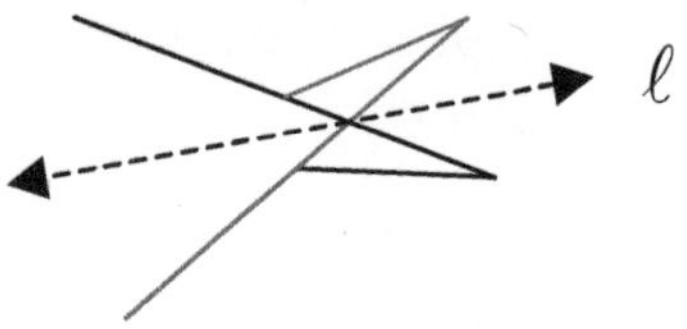

5.

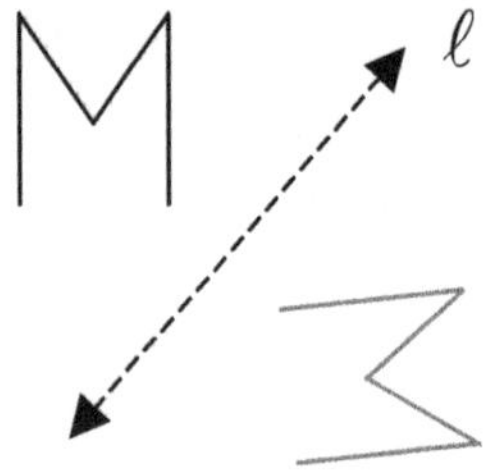

7.

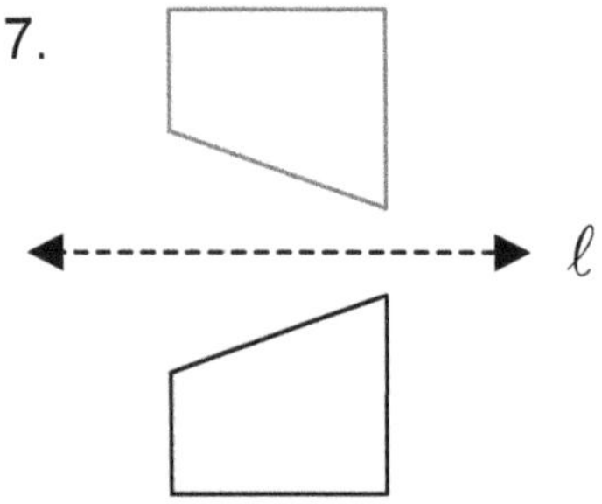

9.

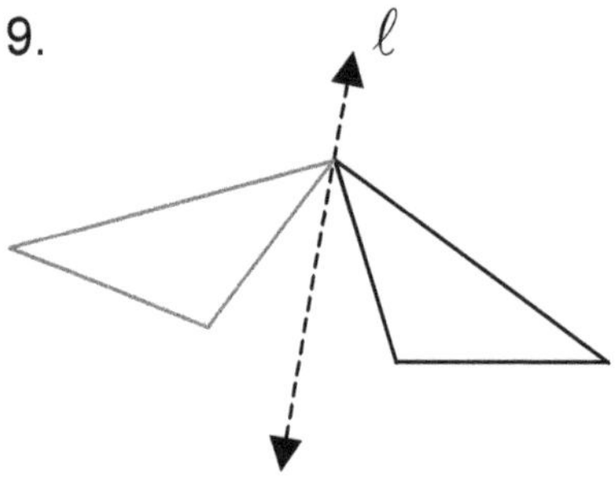

11.

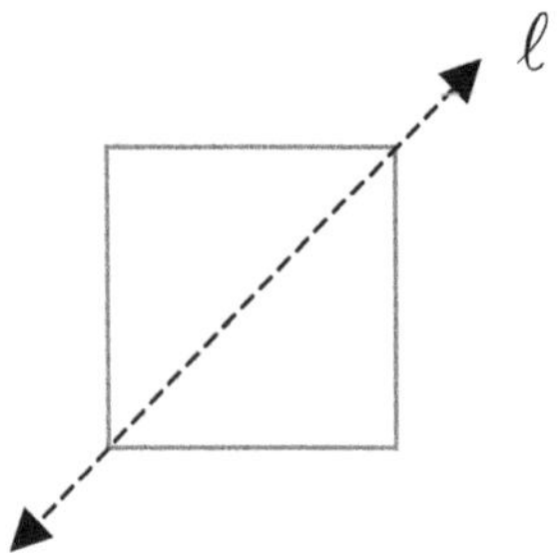

(The image is exactly the same as the preimage.)

Chapter 11, Part III (pages 517-521) continued

13.

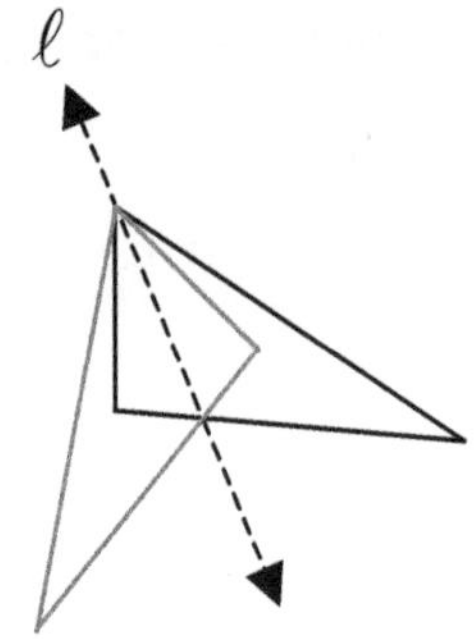

15.

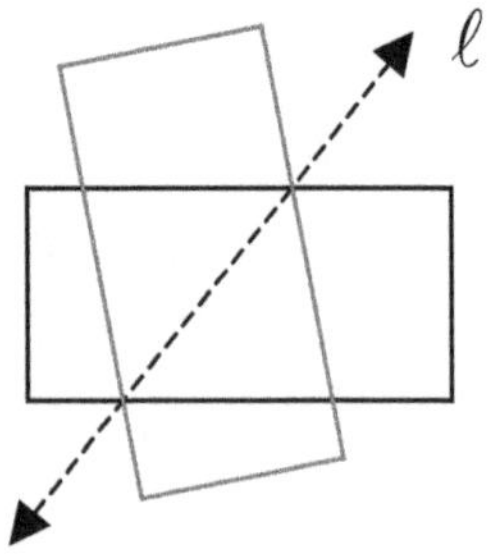

17.

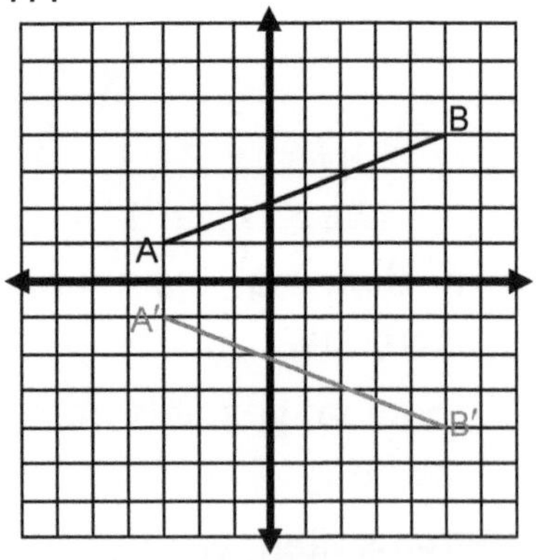

19.

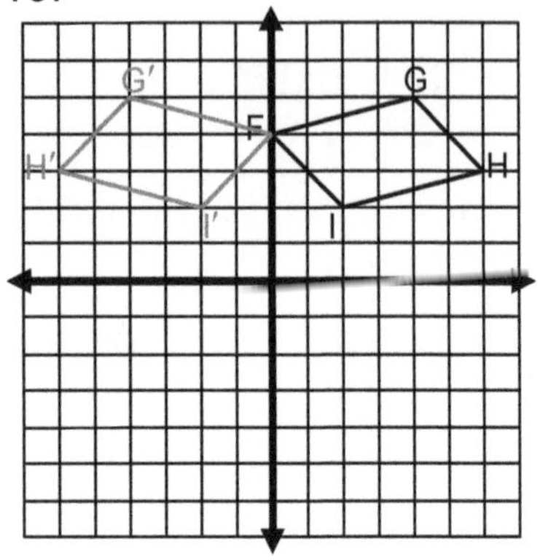

Chapter 11, Part III
(pages 517-521) continued

21.

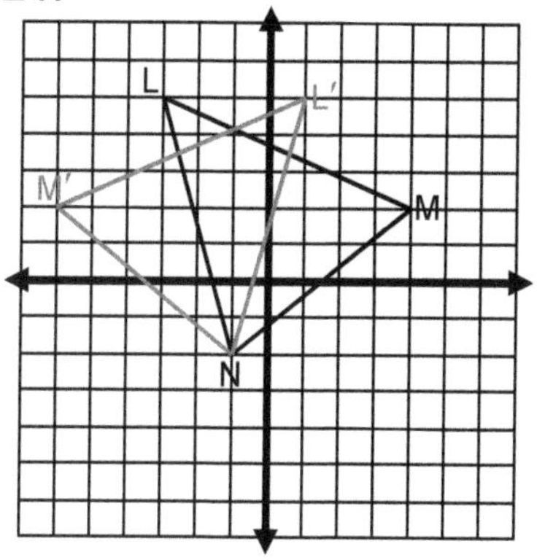

23.

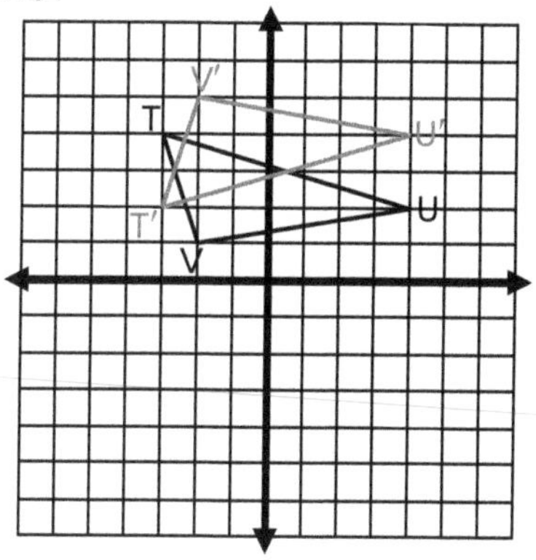

25. $\overline{GH}$

27. $\triangle$CBF

29. square BADE

31. yes, the figure does have line symmetry

33. yes, the figure does have line symmetry

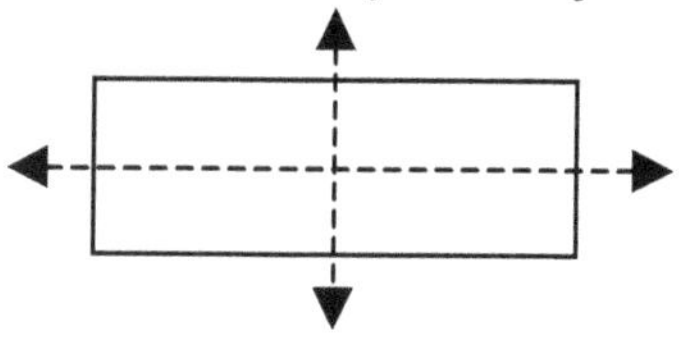

Chapter 11, Part III
(pages 517-521) continued

35. yes, the figure does have line symmetry

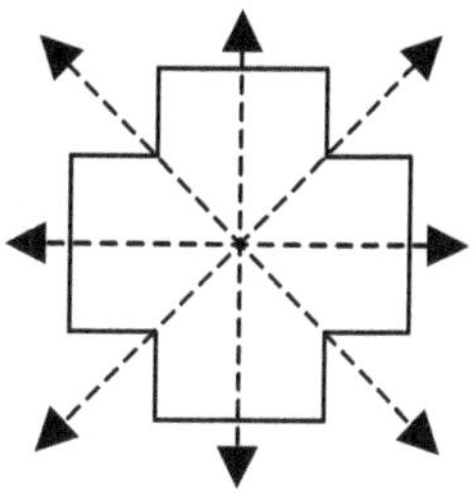

37. yes, the figure does have line symmetry

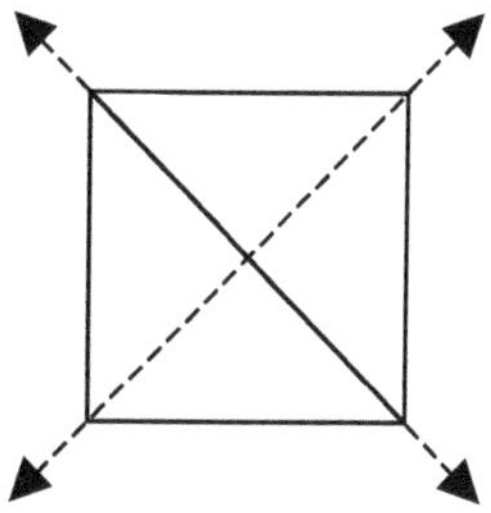

Chapter 11, Part IV
(pages 525-531)

1a.

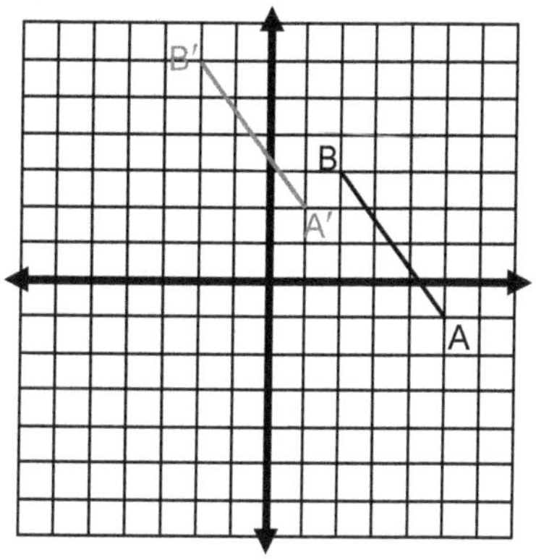

b. A′: (1, 2), B′: (–2, 6)

c. (x, y) → (x – 4, y + 3)

Chapter 11, Part IV
(pages 525-531) continued

3a.

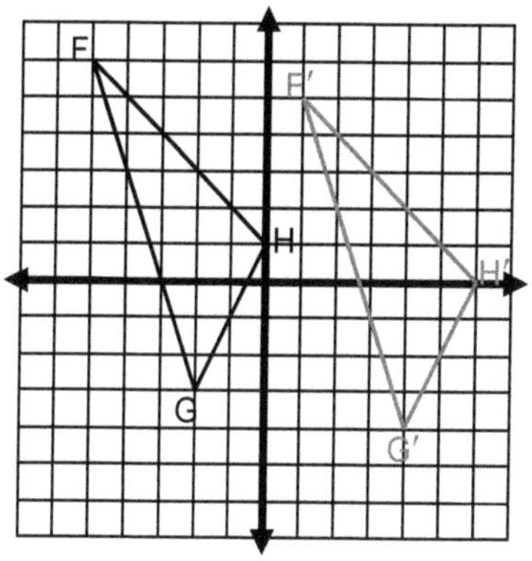

b. F′: (1, 5), G′: (4, –4), H′: (6, 0)

c. (x, y) → (x + 6, y – 1)

5a.

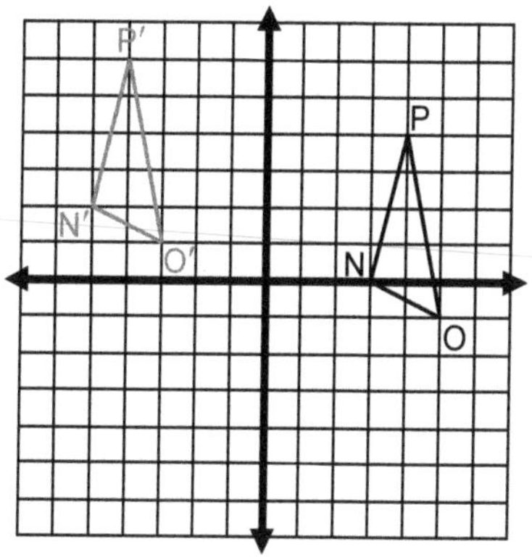

b. O′: (–3, 1), P′: (–4, 6)

c. (x, y) → (x – 8, y + 2)

7a.

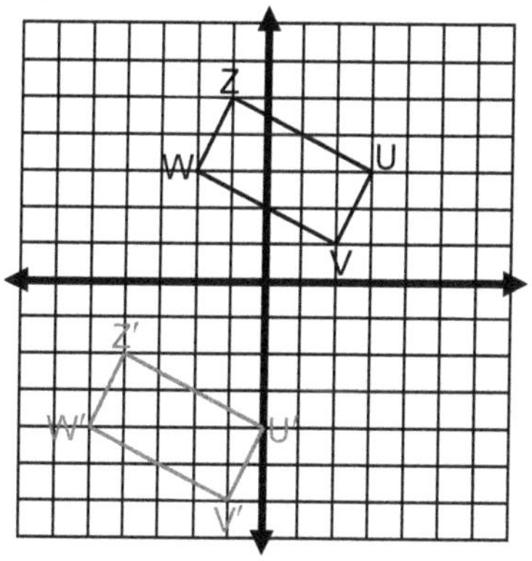

b. U′: (0, –4), V′: (–1, –6), Z′: (–4, –2)

c. (x, y) → (x – 3, y – 7)

9. $\overrightarrow{PQ}$; $\langle 0, -5\rangle$

11. Examples:

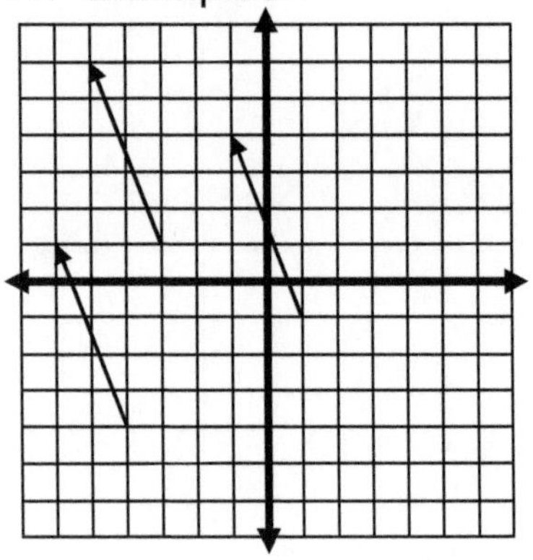

13a.

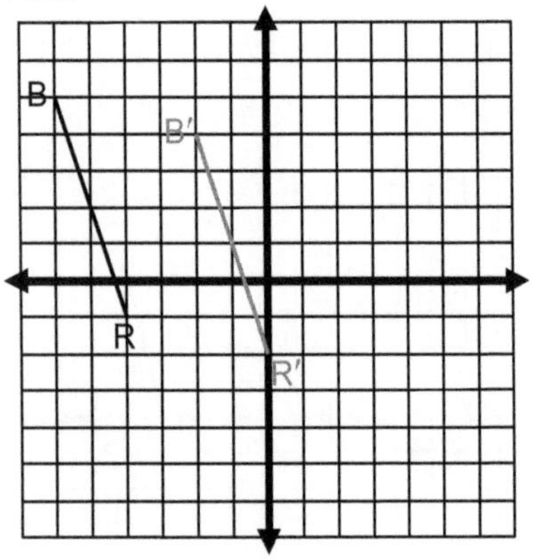

b. R′: (0, –2), B′: (–2, 4)

c. $\langle 4, -1\rangle$

15a.

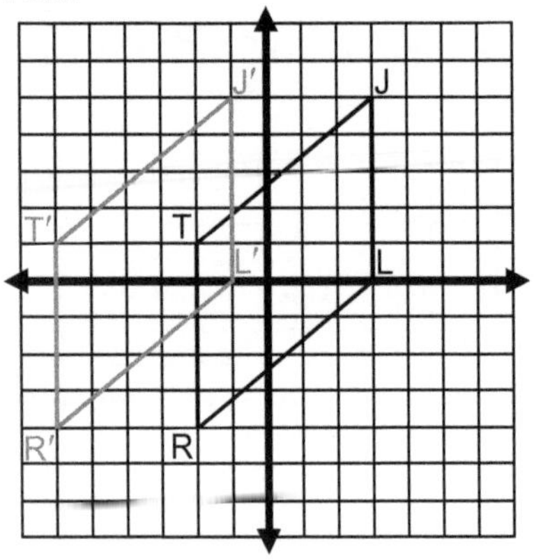

b. T′: (–6, 1), J′: (–1, 5), L′: (–1, 0), R′: (–6, –4)

c. $\langle -4, 0\rangle$

Chapter 11, Part IV (pages 525-531) continued

17a.

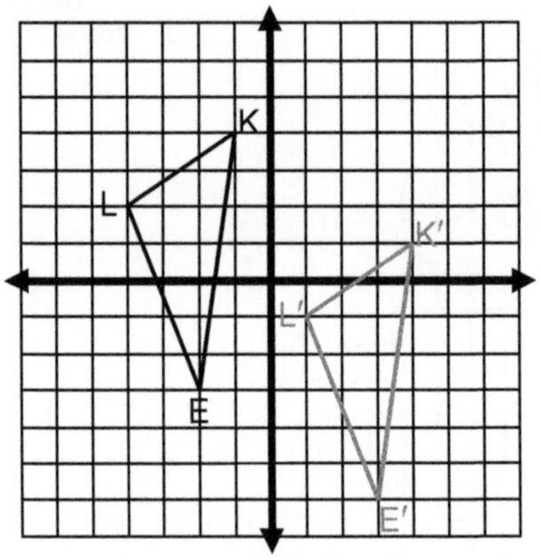

b. E′: (3, –6), K′: (4, 1), L′: (1, –1)

c. $(x, y) \rightarrow (x + 5, y - 3)$

19a.

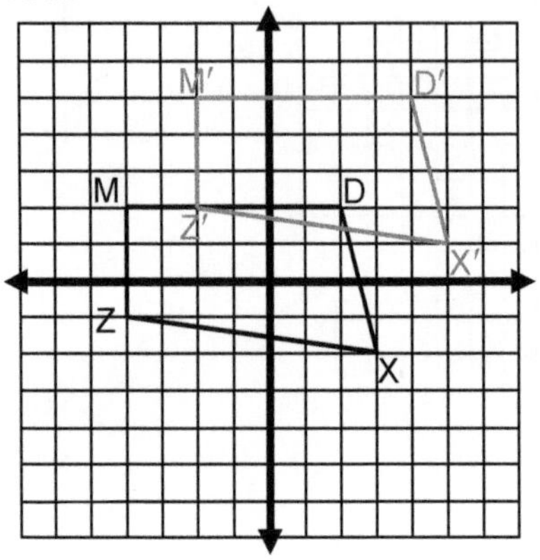

b. M′: (–2, 5), D′: (4, 5), X′: (5, 1)

c. $\langle 2, 3\rangle$

21a.

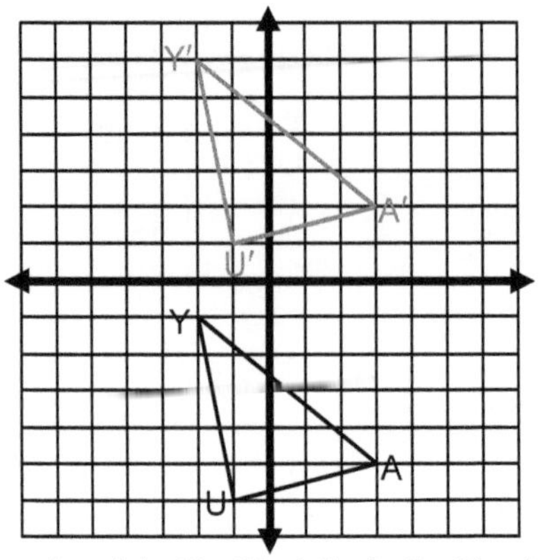

b. A′: (3, 2), Y′: (–2, 6), U′: (–1, 1)

c. $(x, y) \rightarrow (x, y + 7)$

Chapter 11, Part V (pages 536-548)

1.

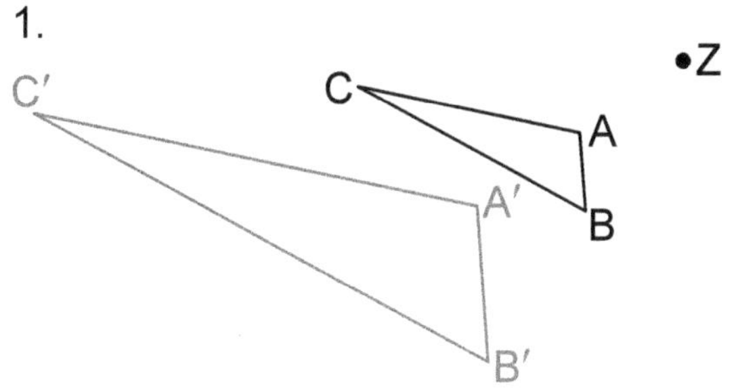

3.

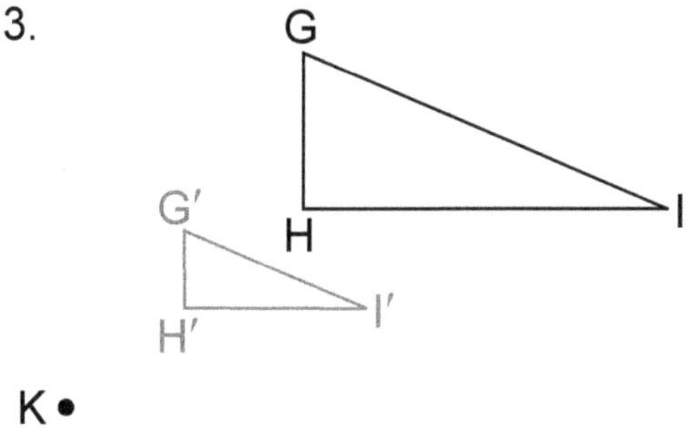

5.

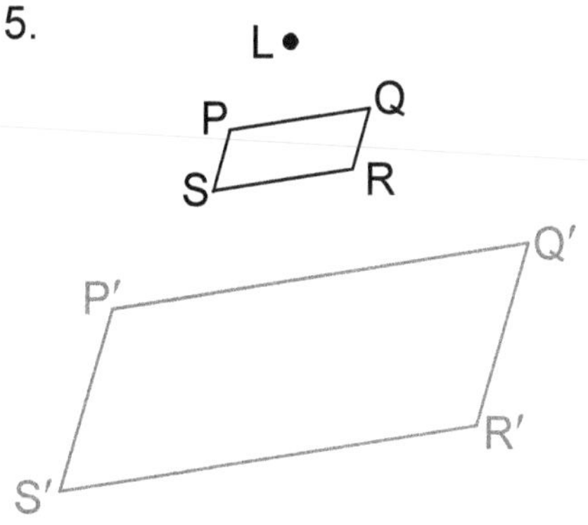

7.

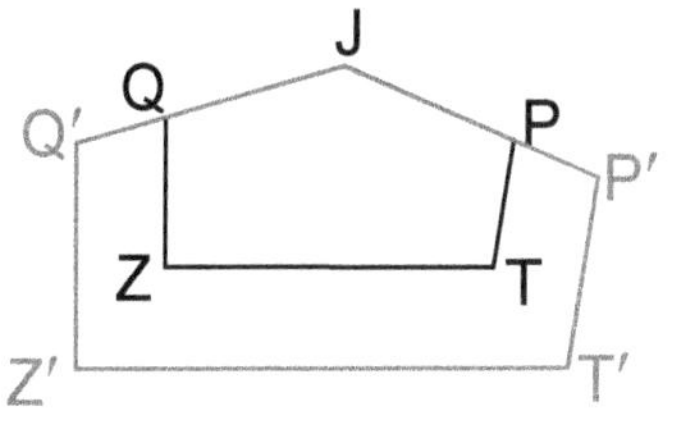

9.

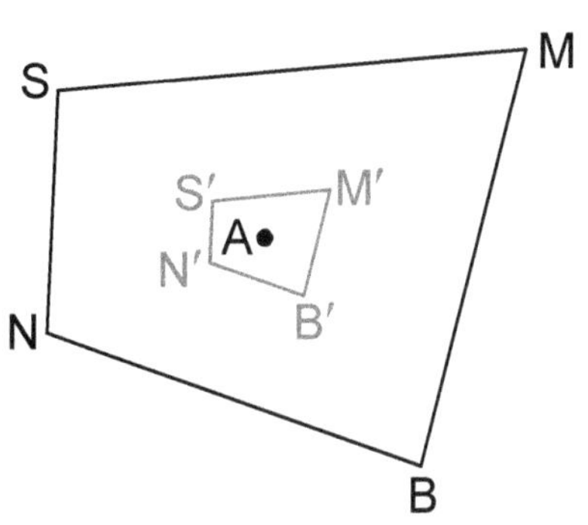

Chapter 11, Part V (pages 536-548) continued

11a.

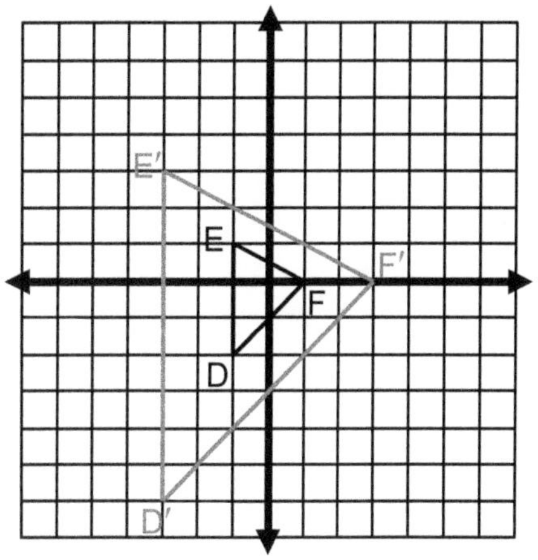

b. D′: (–3, –6), E′: (–3, 3); F′: (3, 0)

13a.

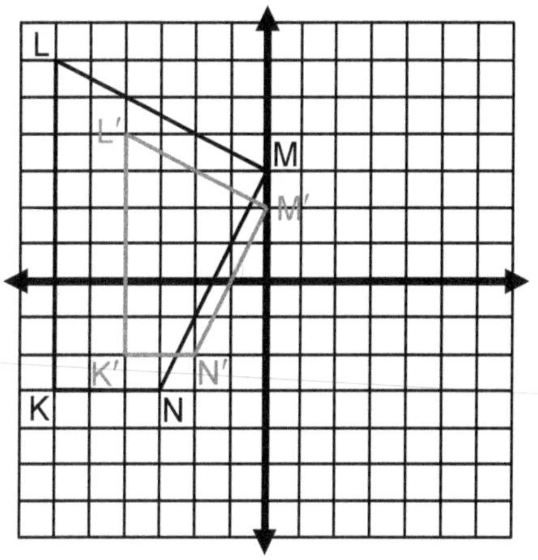

b. K′: (–4, –2), L′: (–4, 4), M′: (0, 2), N′: (–2, –2)

15a.

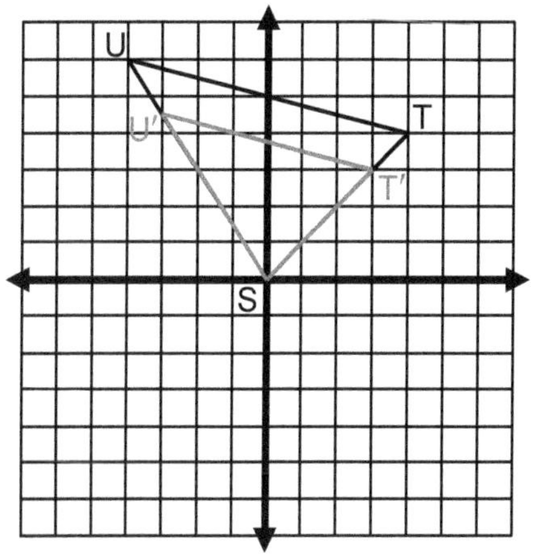

b. S′: (0, 0), T′: (3, 3), U′: (–3, 4½)

17a. $\frac{2}{3}$

b. reduction

Chapter 11, Part V (pages 536-548) continued

19a. 2

b. enlargement

21. $A'J' = 6$, $RU = 40$, and the scale factor is $\frac{3}{5}$

23. $X'O' = 33$, $GP = 30$, $I'P' = 33$, and the scale factor is $\frac{3}{2}$

25. $AF' = 14$, the scale factor is $\frac{1}{2}$, $GH = 20$, $EH = 46$, and $AG = 36$

27. $m\angle P \approx 31.0°$, $m\angle O' \approx 59.0°$, $QP = 31.5$, and $O'N' = 24$

29. $XT = 5$, the scale factor is $\frac{8}{5}$, $W'V' = 25.6$, $m\angle T' = 87°$, and $m\angle U' = 93°$

31. $m\angle A = 63°$, $m\angle E' = 117°$, $CP = 20$, and $CA' = 6.5$

33. The image will be 43.2 inches tall and 76.8 inches wide.

35. The photographic paper should be placed 168 mm from the light source, and the photograph will be 105 mm tall.

37. true

Chapter 11, Part V (pages 536-548) continued

39.

Statements	Reasons
1. $\overline{AB} \rightarrow \overline{A'B'}$ by a dilation with center C and scale factor k.	1. Given
2. Draw $\overrightarrow{CA'}$ and $\overrightarrow{CB'}$.	2. Through any two points, there is exactly one line.
3. $CA' = k(CA)$ and $CB' = k(CB)$	3. Definition of a dilation with center C and scale factor k
4. $\frac{CA'}{CA} = k$ and $\frac{CB'}{CB} = k$	4. Division Property of Equality
5. $\frac{CA'}{CA} = \frac{CB'}{CB}$	5. Substitution Property of Equality
6. $\angle C \cong \angle C$	6. Reflexive Property of Angle Congruence
7. $\triangle BCA \sim \triangle B'CA'$	7. SAS Similarity Theorem
8. $\frac{CA'}{CA} = \frac{CB'}{CB} = \frac{A'B'}{AB}$	8. Definition of similar triangles
9. $k = \frac{A'B'}{AB}$	9. Substitution Property of Equality

Chapter 11, Part VI (pages 553-560)

1. A″: (6, 7), B″: (8, 3), C″: (4, 1)

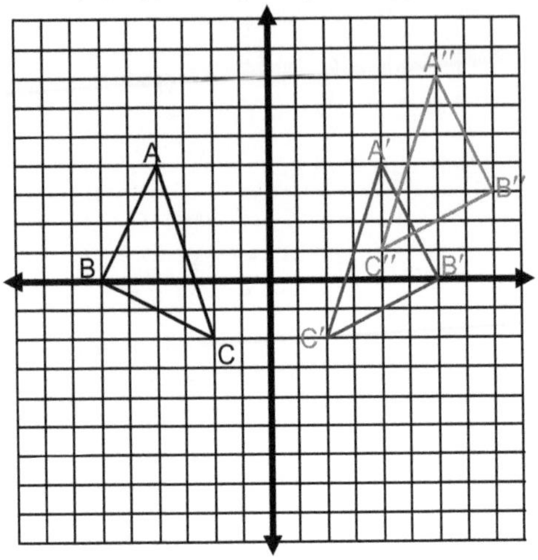

3. A″: (4, –3), B″: (0, –1), C″: (–2, –5)

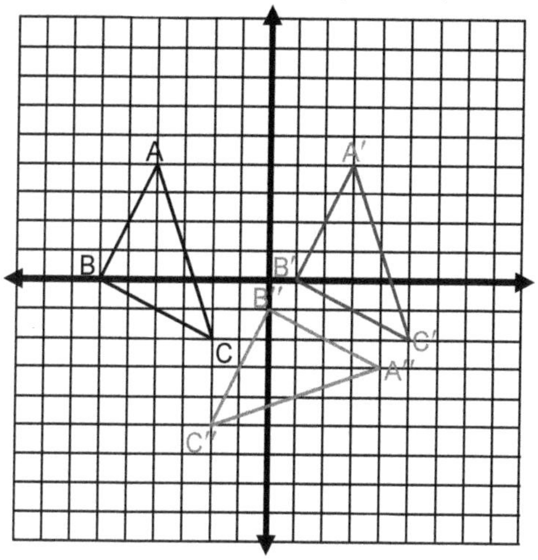

5. A‴: (3, –3), B‴: (0, 3), C‴: (6, 6)

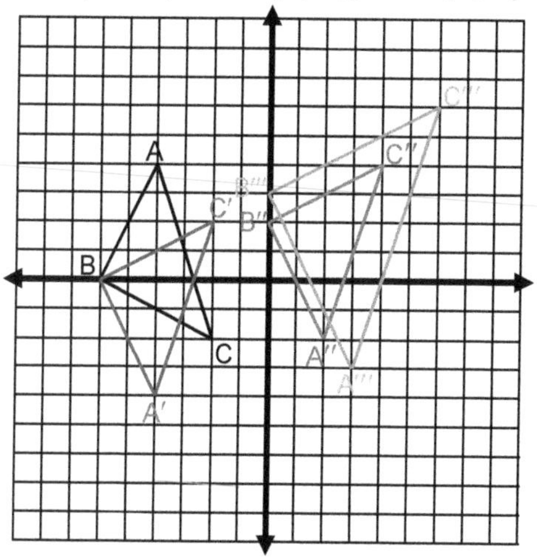

7. D″: (5, –1), E″: (3, 0), F″: (2, –2), G″: (3, –4)

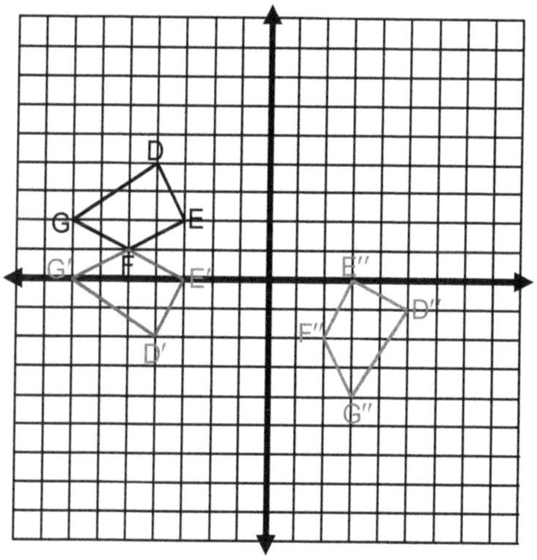

Chapter 11, Part VI (pages 553-560) continued

9. D‴: (3, 6), E‴: (1, 7), F‴: (0, 5), G‴: (1, 3)

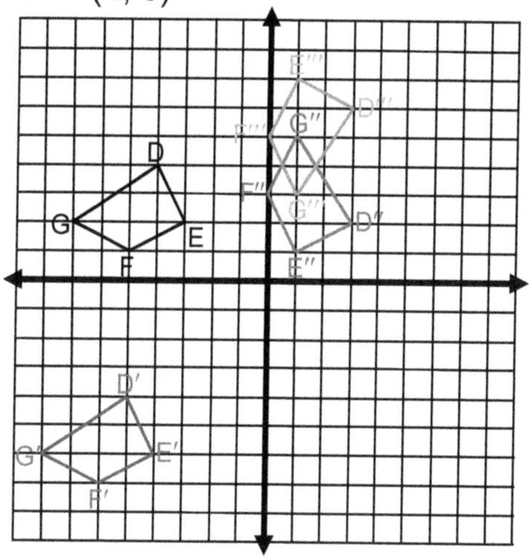

11. R″: (4, –2), S″: (2, 4), T″: (–4, 0)

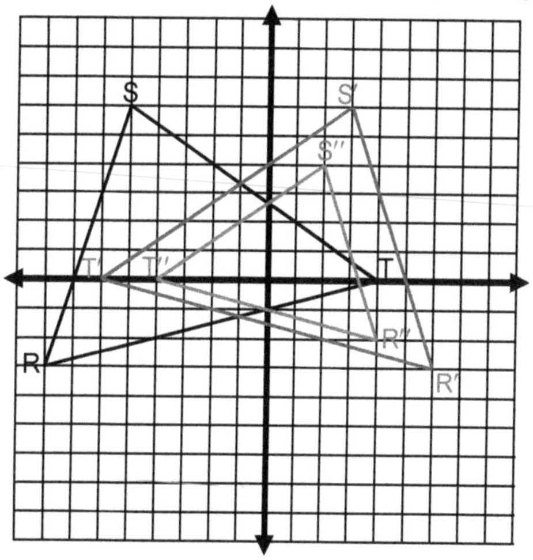

13. R‴: (4, 5), S‴: (–5, 2), T‴: (1, –7)

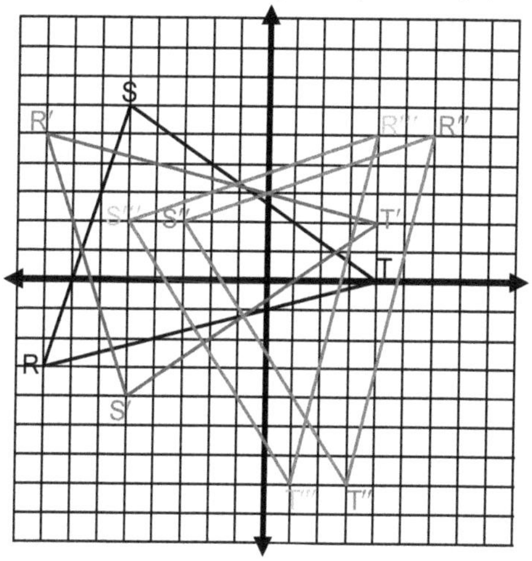

Chapter 11, Part VI
(pages 553-560) continued

15. The distance between A and A″ is 16 cm, and the distance between B and B″ is also 16 cm.
17. 156°
19. x = 118 and y = 62
21. 104° counterclockwise

Chapter 11, Part VII
(pages 561-568)

1. rotation; yes, it is an isometry
3. dilation; no, it is not an isometry
5. yes, the figure does have line symmetry

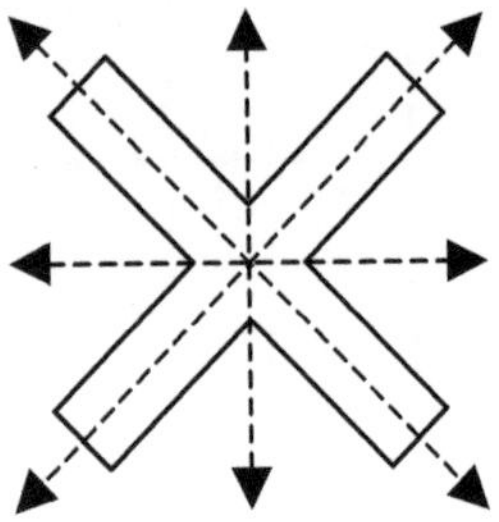

7.

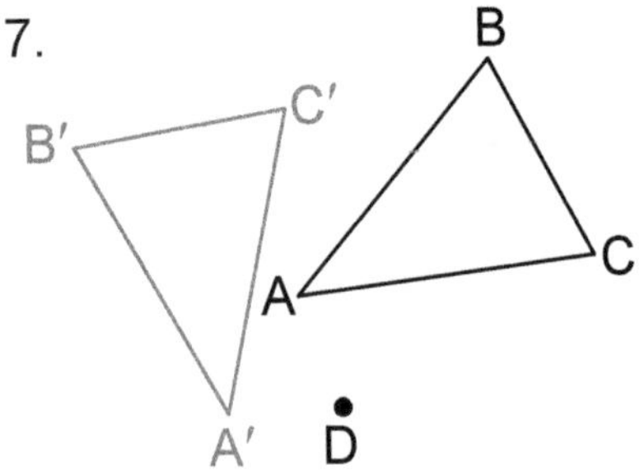

9.

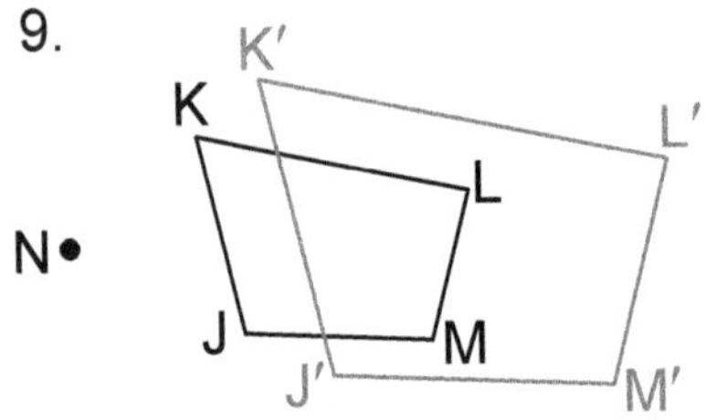

Chapter 11, Part VII
(pages 561-568) continued

11. $\overline{YJ}$
13. ΔUXZ
15. ΔJWZ
17. B′: (–5, 2), N′: (3, –2), H′: (5, 6)

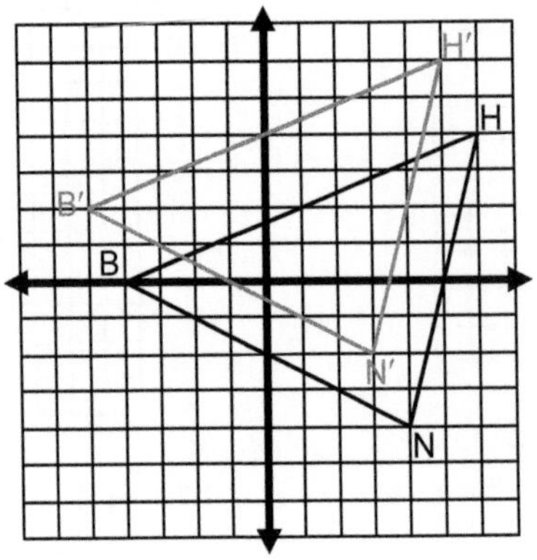

19. B′: (2, –6), N′: (6, 2), H′: (–2, 4)

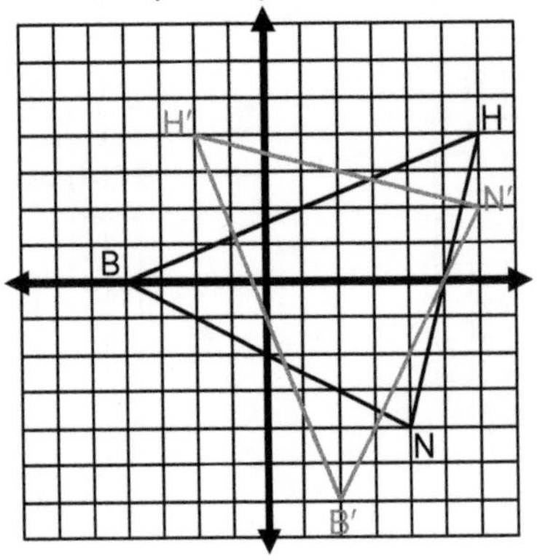

21. A‴: (5, –7), D‴: (7, 1), V‴: (1, 3), Y‴: (–3, –5)

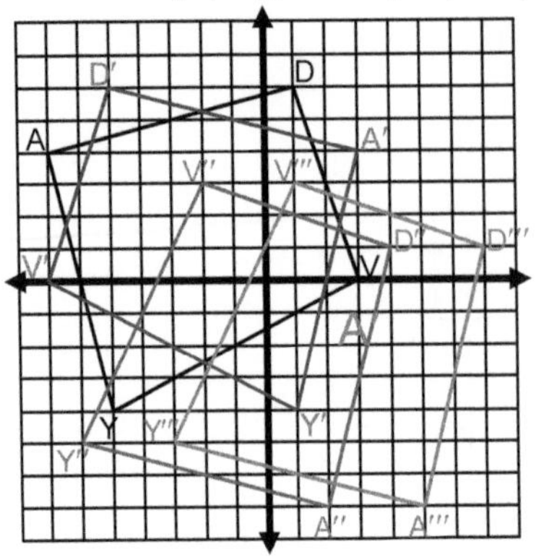

23. x = 123 and y = 57

Chapter 11, Part VII
(pages 561-568) continued

25. the scale factor is $\frac{8}{5}$, $m\angle M = 117°$, MJ = 20, ZH′ = 48, and HH′ = 18
27.

We are given that $m\angle PQR > m\angle QRS$ and that $\overline{PQ} \cong \overline{RS}$. By the Reflexive Property of Segment Congruence, $\overline{QR} \cong \overline{RQ}$. Then PR > QS by the SAS Inequality Theorem.

29. $m\angle A \approx 32.0°$ and $AC = 4\sqrt{13}$
31. $AC \approx 14.5$ and $BC \approx 6.8$
33. AE = 16 and CD = 8

Chapter 12, Part I
(pages 573-578)

1. 36π cm
3. 66 ft
5. $(10 + 2\sqrt{5})$ m
7. $(54 + 15\sqrt{2})$ cm
9. 54 miles
11. $\frac{77}{3}\pi$ cm
13. $(42 + 10\pi)$ in.
15. 114 m
17. 82 ft
19. $(30 + \frac{22}{3}\pi)$ in.
21. $(82 + 4\pi)$ ft
23. $(38 + 11\pi)$ yds
25. The length is 23 inches, and the width is 14 inches.

Chapter 12, Part I
(pages 573-578) continued

27. The two congruent sides are each 12 meters long, and the length of the third side is 10 meters.

29. 2600π inches (or approximately 680.7 ft)

31. The length of the diameter of the circle is 36 feet, and the length of the radius of the circle is 18 feet.

Chapter 12, Part II
(pages 585-592)

1. 13 cm^2
3. approximately 1250 square meters
5. 144
7. $324\pi \text{ cm}^2$
9. 230 ft^2
11. $4\sqrt{5} \text{ m}^2$
13. 292.5 cm^2
15. $36\sqrt{3} \text{ mi}^2$
17. $\frac{539}{3}\pi \text{ cm}^2$
19. $(210 + 25\pi) \text{ in.}^2$
21. $(540 + 100\sqrt{3}) \text{ m}^2$
23. 276 ft^2
25. $55\pi \text{ in.}^2$
27. $(293 + 8\pi) \text{ ft}^2$
29. $(176 - \frac{11}{2}\pi) \text{ yds}^2$
31. $36\pi \text{ in.}^2$

Chapter 12, Part II
(pages 585-592) continued

33. The rectangular arrangement will require more fencing material, and the circular arrangement will require him to sow more grass seed.

35. The length should be 50 feet, and the width should be 50 feet.

37. 435 yd^2

Chapter 12, Part III
(pages 596-600)

1. 234 cm^2
3. 120 ft^2
5. approximately 105.2 yd^2
7. 190 cm^2
9. 11
11. 8 inches and $8\sqrt{3}$ inches
13. 5 meters and 16 meters
15. 146 in.^2
17. $(64\pi - 128) \text{ yds}^2$
19. $\left(\frac{1}{2}hy - \frac{1}{2}hx\right) \text{ cm}^2$
21. $(110.25\pi - 168) \text{ in.}^2$
23. The area of the smaller circle is $9\pi \text{ mm}^2$, and the radius of the smaller circle is 3 mm.
25. 30 meters

Chapter 12, Part IV
(pages 603-609)

1. $486\sqrt{3} \text{ m}^2$
3. $768\sqrt{3} \text{ yds}^2$
5. $288\sqrt{3} \text{ mm}^2$
7. 11.3 km^2
9. 72.3 in.^2
11. 130.8 yds^2
13. 15.5 mi^2
15. 395.6 in.^2
17. 2866.2 yds^2
19. $(600\sqrt{3} - 400) \text{ cm}^2$
21. $100\sqrt{3} \text{ m}^2$
23. 2.8 m^2
25. 417.1 cm^2

Chapter 12, Part V
(pages 613-621)

1. DE = 20 in. and FE = 12 in.
   Perimeter of ΔDFE = 48 in.
   Area of ΔDFE = 96 in.^2

3. SV = 6 miles
   Perimeter of rectangle TUVS = 30 miles
   Area of rectangle TUVS = 54 mi^2

5. Apothem of hexagon IKLJNO = $4\sqrt{3}$ cm
   Perimeter of hexagon IKLJNO = 48 cm
   Area of hexagon IKLJNO = $96\sqrt{3} \text{ cm}^2$

Chapter 12, Part V
(pages 613-621) continued

7. Perimeter of
$\Delta ABC = 72$ in.
Area of $\Delta ABC = 216$ in.^{2}
Perimeter of
$\Delta DFE = 48$ in.
Area of $\Delta DFE = 96$ in.^{2}

9. Perimeter of rectangle
OPRQ = 50 mi
Area of rectangle
OPRQ = 150 mi^2
Perimeter of rectangle
TUVS = 30 mi
Area of rectangle
TUVS = 54 mi^2

11. Perimeter of hexagon
MCDFBH = 60 cm
Area of hexagon
MCDFBH = $150\sqrt{3}$ cm^2
Perimeter of hexagon
IKLJNO = 48 cm
Area of hexagon
IKLJNO = $96\sqrt{3}$ cm^2

13. 25 m

15. 23 m

17. 22.5 in.^{2}

19. 12 km, 21 km, and 15 km

21. 67.2 in.^{2}

23. $52\sqrt{3}$ m^2

25. $\dfrac{\text{perimeter of } \Delta OJN}{\text{perimeter of } \Delta CFG} = \dfrac{3}{4}$
and $\dfrac{\text{area of } \Delta OJN}{\text{area of } \Delta CFG} = \dfrac{9}{16}$

Chapter 12, Part V
(pages 613-621) continued

27. $\dfrac{\text{area of } \Delta SYB}{\text{area of } \Delta XAZ} = \dfrac{81}{16}$
and $\dfrac{SY}{XA} = \dfrac{9}{4}$

29. $\dfrac{\text{area of } \Delta YLA}{\text{area of } \Delta TNC} = \dfrac{1}{49}$ and
$\dfrac{\text{perimeter of } \Delta YLA}{\text{perimeter of } \Delta TNC} = \dfrac{1}{7}$

31. 1 inch on the blueprint represents <u>5</u> feet in real life, and the perimeter of the room in real life is <u>80</u> feet.

Chapter 12, Part VI
(pages 625-630)

1. $\dfrac{73}{105}$

3. $\dfrac{\pi-2}{4\pi}$, or, equivalently,
$\dfrac{1}{4}-\dfrac{1}{2\pi}$

5. $\dfrac{9}{25}$

7. $\dfrac{2\sqrt{3}}{9}$
(Recall that you should never leave a radical in the denominator!)

9. $\dfrac{2}{3}$

11. $\dfrac{256}{7225}$

13. $\dfrac{739.75}{28{,}900}$ or,
equivalently, $\dfrac{2{,}959}{115{,}600}$

Chapter 12, Part VI
(pages 625-630) continued

15. The probability that the point will lie in the shaded region is $\dfrac{3}{4}$, and the probability that the point will lie in the triangle is $\dfrac{1}{4}$.

17. $\dfrac{\pi-0.5\sqrt{3}}{\pi}$, or,
equivalently, $\dfrac{2\pi-\sqrt{3}}{2\pi}$

19. $\dfrac{4-\pi}{4}$

21. 144

23. EY = 12 and CY = 20

Chapter 12, Part VII
(pages 631-634)

1. 30

3. $\dfrac{xy}{9}$

5. $\sqrt{x}$

7. Area = 48 square feet
Perimeter = 32 feet

9. $(44 + \pi)$ m

11. The probability that it will lie in one of the shaded regions is $\dfrac{9\pi-5\sqrt{3}}{10\pi}$, and the probability that it will lie in one of the unshaded regions is $\dfrac{\pi+5\sqrt{3}}{10\pi}$.

Chapter 12, Part VII
(pages 631-634) continued

13. The area is 35 square units, and the perimeter is $(9\sqrt{5} + 5)$ units.

15. The circumference gets doubled, and the area gets quadrupled.

17.

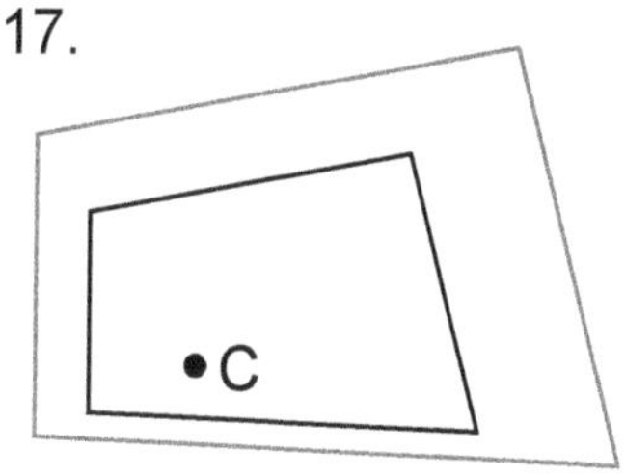

19. 156°

21. 61°

23. 60°

25. 5

27. The perimeter of the triangle must be greater than 30 feet and less than 54 feet.

Chapter 13, Part I
(pages 640-647)

1. L.A.: 266 in.^{2}
   T.S.A.: 446 in.^{2}

3. L.A.: 748π mm^2
   T.S.A.: 1326π mm^2

5. L.A.: 1280 mm^2
   T.S.A.: 1400 mm^2

7. L.A.: 35 m^2
   T.S.A.: ≈ 48.8 m^2

9. L.A.: 576 cm^2
   T.S.A.: $(576 + 72\sqrt{3})$ ft^2

11. L.A.: 88π in.^{2}
    T.S.A.: 120π in.^{2}

Chapter 13, Part I
(pages 640-647) continued

13. L.A.: $(42 + 9\pi)$ m^2
    T.S.A.: $(90 + 18\pi)$ m^2

15. L.A.: 912 in.^{2}
    T.S.A.: $(912 + 192\sqrt{3})$ in.^{2}

17. L.A.: 160π ft^2
    T.S.A.: 210π ft^2

19. L.A.: 5016 mm^2
    T.S.A.: 7944 mm^2

21. L.A.: 1216 in.^{2}
    T.S.A.: 3046 in.^{2}

23. 42 yds^2

25. 7 mm

27. $24\sqrt{3}$ cm^2

29. 132,400 in.^{2}

31. 900 ft^2

33. The cost of the fabric for the 10 tents in #31 will be $6300, and the cost of the fabric for the 15 tents in #32 will be $11,865.

Chapter 13, Part II
(pages 651-657)

1. 630 in.^{3}

3. 6358 mm^3

5. 1920 mm^3

7. ≈ 24.1 m^3

9. $576\sqrt{3}$ ft^3

11. 176π in.^{3}

13. $(72 + 13.5\pi)$ m^3

15. $1824\sqrt{3}$ in.^{3}

17. 400π ft^3

Chapter 13, Part II
(pages 651-657) continued

19. 48,312 mm^3

21. 7320 in.^{3}

23. $4900\sqrt{3}$ cm^3

25. 672 ft^2

27. 240π mm^3

29. 254

31. 18.75π yd^3

33. 240 in.^{3}

35. This note is saying that you should not worry that you got less cereal than you were supposed to if the box does not seem to be as full as it should be. (In reality, however, you may want to check their measurements of the mass of the cereal.)

Chapter 13, Part III
(pages 663-669)

1. L.A.: 2176 in.^{2}
   T.S.A.: 3200 in.^{2}

3. L.A.: 34π ft^2
   T.S.A.: 50π ft^2

5. L.A.: 420 m^2
   T.S.A.: $(420 + 150\sqrt{3})$ m^2

7. L.A.: 260π cm^2
   T.S.A.: 360π cm^2

9. T.S.A.: 324π m^2

11. L.A.: ≈ 1020.0 mm^2
    T.S.A.: ≈ 1460.4 mm^2

Chapter 13, Part III
(pages 663-669) continued

13. L.A.: 384 in.^2
T.S.A.: 564 in.^2

15. T.S.A.: 144π mm^2

17. L.A.: 960 in.^2
T.S.A.: 1360 in.^2

19. L.A.: $243\sqrt{3}$ ft^2
T.S.A.: $324\sqrt{3}$ ft^2

21. T.S.A.: 1764π cm^2

23. 132π in.^2

25. $(792 + 54\sqrt{3})$ ft^2

27. 1088 in.^2

29. 924,974.6 ft^2

31. $62{,}726{,}400\pi$ mi^2
(or approximately 197,060,797.4 mi^2)

Chapter 13, Part IV
(pages 673-678)

1. 10,240 in.^3

3. 40π ft^3

5. $550\sqrt{3}$ m^3

7. 800π cm^3

9. 972π m^3

11. ≈ 3376.7 mm^3

13. 720 in.^3

15. 288π mm^3

17. ≈ 2909.0 in.^3

19. $486\sqrt{2}$ ft^3

21. $12{,}348\pi$ cm^3

23. 240π in.^3

25. $1044\sqrt{3}$ ft^3

27. 2560 in.^3

Chapter 13, Part IV
(pages 673-678) continued

29. 91,636,272 ft^3

31. $3{,}950{,}243{,}531\pi$ mi^3
(If your calculator told you something like $3.9502\pi\text{E}9$ mi^3, this means $3.9502\pi \times 10^9$ mi^3, and it is telling you to move the decimal to the right 9 places.)

33. no

Chapter 13, Part V
(pages 679-684)

1. L.A.: 136π cm^2
T.S.A.: 200π cm^2
V: 320π cm^3

3. T.S.A.: 400π mm^2
V: $\frac{4000}{3}\pi$ mm^3

5. 132

7. The cylindrical basket would hold more Easter eggs, and the rectangular basket would use more materials.

9. The lateral area doubles, and the volume quadruples.

11. The volume gets multiplied by 8, and the surface area quadruples.

13. 28 inches

15. Perimeter: ≈ 73.9 cm
Area: ≈ 416.5 cm^2

17. V: $(1560 + 256\pi)$ mm^3
T.S.A.: $(758 + 128\pi)$ mm^2

Chapter 13, Part V
(pages 679-684) continued

19. $\frac{81\pi - 64\sqrt{2}}{81\pi}$

21. The probability that it will lie on $\overline{AB}$ is $\frac{1}{3}$, and the probability that it will lie on $\overline{AC}$ is $\frac{1}{2}$.

23. Area: 60 square units
Perimeter: $8\sqrt{17}$ units

25. The perimeter must be less than <u>14 feet</u> and greater than <u>10 feet</u>.

27. $m\angle XVY = 72°$,
$m\overset{\frown}{XY} = 72°$,
$m\overset{\frown}{XWY} = 288°$, and
the length of $\overset{\frown}{XWY}$ is 8π cm

Appendix A, Part I
(pages 689-692)

1. −4

3. 15

5. 0

7. 0

9. $\frac{8}{3}$

11. −3

13. $-\frac{16}{15}$

15. −9

17. −1

19. −8

21. −18

23. 0.5

25. 7

Appendix A, Part I
(pages 687-690) continued

27. $-\frac{9}{4}$

29. $\frac{25}{2}$

31. $-\frac{4}{5}$

33. $-\frac{11}{23}$

35. $-\frac{27}{2}$

37. -1

Appendix A, Part II
(pages 696-700)

1. $q < -4$
3. $x \leq -1$
5. $a \neq 25$
7. $k > -\frac{34}{7}$
9. $v \geq \frac{9}{4}$
11. $m < -\frac{20}{3}$
13. $g < \frac{10}{7}$
15. $p \neq -\frac{13}{5}$
17. $k \leq \frac{160}{31}$
19. $y < -7$
21. $q > 0$
23. $h \geq 7$
25. $y > 0.5$
27. $b < 0$
29. $m \neq 0.6$
31. $d \leq 3$

Appendix A, Part II
(pages 696-700) continued

33. $x > \frac{22}{3}$
35. $n < -0.32$

Appendix A, Part III
(pages 703-707)

1. $x = 4$ and $y = 1$
3. $x = -2$ and $y = -5$
5. $x = 3$ and $y = -2$
7. $x = 2$ and $y = 1$
9. $x = -100$ and $y = -22$
11. $x = 0$ and $y = -2$
13. $x = -2$ and $y = -8$
15. $x = -\frac{7}{5}$ and $y = \frac{1}{10}$
17. $x = 2$ and $y = 1$
19. $x = -3$ and $y = -\frac{15}{2}$
21. $x = \frac{10}{3}$ and $y = 0$
23. $x = -\frac{17}{2}$ and $y = \frac{23}{4}$
25. $x = -\frac{11}{14}$ and $y = \frac{51}{14}$

Appendix A, Part IV
(pages 711-715)

1. $x = 5$ and $y = -3$
3. $x = 7$ and $y = -4$
5. $x = -3$ and $y = 2$
7. $x = 25$ and $y = -17$
9. $x = 4$ and $y = -1$
11. $x = 6$ and $y = 2$
13. $x = -5$ and $y = 24$
15. $x = 28$ and $y = 54$
17. $x = -3$ and $y = 2$

Appendix A, Part IV
(pages 711-715) continued

19. $x = 3$ and $y = 3$
21. $x = \frac{7}{8}$ and $y = \frac{93}{16}$
23. $x = -10$ and $y = 8$
25. $x = 11$ and $y = -\frac{31}{4}$

Appendix A, Part V
(pages 720-722)

1. $3\sqrt{5}$
3. 5
5. $\frac{5}{6}$
7. $8\sqrt{3}$
9. $\frac{2}{3}$
11. $\frac{6\sqrt{2}}{5}$
13. $\frac{4\sqrt{10}}{5}$
15. $\frac{\sqrt{15}}{3}$
17. $\frac{\sqrt{6}}{4}$
19. $3\sqrt{3}$
21. $\sqrt{2}$
23. $\frac{2\sqrt{6}}{5}$
25. $\frac{3\sqrt{3}}{4}$
27. $\frac{\sqrt{70}}{10}$
29. $8\sqrt{2}$
31. 0

Appendix A, Part V
(pages 718-720) continued

33. $\frac{23\sqrt{3}}{8}$

35. 12

37. $21\sqrt{10}$

39. $4\sqrt{10} - 30\sqrt{2}$

Appendix A, Part VI
(pages 727-730)

1. $\pm\sqrt{5}$

3. $\frac{1 \pm \sqrt{33}}{-4}$ (or, equivalently, $\frac{-1 \pm \sqrt{33}}{4}$)

5. -1 or $\frac{1}{3}$

7. $-\frac{1}{2}$ or 2

9. -2 or 4

11. $\frac{5}{2}$ or 1

13. 0 or $\frac{3}{7}$

15. $\frac{7 \pm \sqrt{13}}{3}$; $\frac{14 \pm 2\sqrt{13}}{6}$ is also acceptable

17. -2 or $\frac{7}{2}$

19. $\pm\frac{5\sqrt{3}}{3}$

Appendix A, Part VI
(pages 727-730) continued

21. $\frac{2 \pm \sqrt{10}}{3}$; $\frac{60 \pm 30\sqrt{10}}{90}$ is also acceptable

23. 4

25. 8 or 0